Lecture Notes in Computer Science 2906

Edited by G. Goos, J. Hartmanis, and J. van Leeuwen

Springer
Berlin
Heidelberg
New York
Hong Kong
London
Milan
Paris
Tokyo

Toshihide Ibaraki   Naoki Katoh
Hirotaka Ono (Eds.)

Algorithms
and Computation

14th International Symposium, ISAAC 2003
Kyoto, Japan, December 15-17, 2003
Proceedings

 Springer

Series Editors

Gerhard Goos, Karlsruhe University, Germany
Juris Hartmanis, Cornell University, NY, USA
Jan van Leeuwen, Utrecht University, The Netherlands

Volume Editors

Toshihide Ibaraki
Kyoto University, Graduate School of Informatics
Department of Applied Mathematics and Physics
Yoshida-Honmachi, Sakyo-ku, Kyoto 606-8501, Japan
E-mail: ibaraki@i.kyoto-u.ac.jp

Naoki Katoh
Kyoto University, Graduate School of Engineering
Department of Architecture and Architectural Systems
Yoshida-Honmachi, Sakyo-ku, Kyoto 606-8501, Japan
E-mail: naoki@archi.kyoto-u.ac.jp

Hirotaka Ono
Kyushu University
Graduate School of Information Science and Electrical Engineering
Department of Computer Science and Communication Engineering
6-10-1, Hakozaki, Fukuoka, 812-8581, Japan
E-mail: ono@csce.kyushu-u.ac.jp

Cataloging-in-Publication Data applied for

A catalog record for this book is available from the Library of Congress.

Bibliographic information published by Die Deutsche Bibliothek
Die Deutsche Bibliothek lists this publication in the Deutsche Nationalbibliografie;
detailed bibliographic data is available in the Internet at <http://dnb.ddb.de>.

CR Subject Classification (1998): F.2, C.2, G.2-3, I.3.5, F.1

ISSN 0302-9743
ISBN 3-540-20695-7 Springer-Verlag Berlin Heidelberg New York

Springer-Verlag is a part of Springer Science+Business Media

springeronline.com

© Springer-Verlag Berlin Heidelberg 2003
Printed in Germany

Typesetting: Camera-ready by author, data conversion by PTP-Berlin, Protago-TeX-Production GmbH
Printed on acid-free paper   SPIN: 10975527   06/3142   5 4 3 2 1 0

Preface

This volume contains the proceedings of the 14th Annual International Symposium on Algorithms and Computation (ISAAC 2003), held in Kyoto, Japan, 15–17 December 2003. In the past, it was held in Tokyo (1990), Taipei (1991), Nagoya (1992), Hong Kong (1993), Beijing (1994), Cairns (1995), Osaka (1996), Singapore (1997), Taejon (1998), Chennai (1999), Taipei (2000), Christchurch (2001), and Vancouver (2002).

ISAAC is an annual international symposium that covers the very wide range of topics in algorithms and computation. The main purpose of the symposium is to provide a forum for researchers working in algorithms and the theory of computation where they can exchange ideas in this active research community.

In response to our call for papers, we received unexpectedly many submissions, 207 papers. The task of selecting the papers in this volume was done by our program committee and referees. After a thorough review process, the committee selected 73 papers. The selection was done on the basis of originality and relevance to the field of algorithms and computation. We hope all accepted papers will eventually appear in scientific journals in more polished forms.

The best paper award was given for "On the Geometric Dilation of Finite Point Sets" to Annette Ebbers-Baumann, Ansgar Grüne and Rolf Klein. Two eminent invited speakers, Prof. Andrew Chi-Chih Yao of Princeton University and Prof. Takao Nishizeki of Tohoku University, contributed to this proceedings.

It is impossible to organize such a successful program without the help of many individuals. I would like to express my appreciation to the authors of the submitted papers, and to the program committee members and external referees for their excellent work. We would also like to thank the members of the organizing committee, Kazuo Iwama, Hiro Ito, Takashi Horiyama, Hiroyoshi Miwa, and Shuichi Miyazaki, for their tremendous work in making ISAAC 2003 a successful conference. Finally, we thank our sponsors for their assistance and support.

August 2003

Toshihide Ibaraki
Naoki Katoh
Hirotaka Ono

Organization

Conference Chair

Toshihide Ibaraki (Kyoto University, Japan)

Program Committee

Naoki Katoh, Program Chair (Kyoto University, Japan)
Tatsuya Akutsu (Kyoto University, Japan)
Susanne Albers (University of Freiburg, Germany)
Franz Aurenhammer (Graz University of Technology, Austria)
Prosenjit Bose (Carleton University, Canada)
Danny Chen (University of Notre Dame, USA)
Otfried Cheong (Eindhoven University of Technology, Netherlands)
Rudolf Fleischer (Hong Kong University of Science and Technology, Hong Kong)
Naveen Garg (Indian Institute of Technology, Delhi, India)
Satoru Iwata (University of Tokyo, Japan)
Tao Jiang (University of California, Riverside, USA)
Tibor Jordan (Eötvös Loránd University, Hungary)
Xuemin Lin (University of New South Wales, Australia)
Kazuhisa Makino (Osaka University, Japan)
Kunsoo Park (Seoul National University, Korea)
Günter Rote Freie Universität Berlin, Germany)
Mario Szegedy (Rutgers University, USA)
Paul Vitanyi (CWI and University of Amsterdam, Netherlands)

Organizing Committee

Kazuo Iwama, Co-chair (Kyoto University, Japan)
Hiro Ito, Co-chair (Kyoto University, Japan)
Hiroyoshi Miwa (Kwansei Gakuin University, Japan)
Shuichi Miyazaki (Kyoto University, Japan)
Takashi Horiyama (Kyoto University, Japan)
Hirotaka Ono (Kyushu University, Japan)

Sponsors

Telecommunications Advancement Foundation
International Communications Foundation
Kansai Research Foundation for Technology Promotion
Casio Science Promotion Foundation
Kansai Chapter of the Information Processing Society of Japan
21st Century COE Program: Information Research Center for Development of
Knowledge Society Infrastructure

Referees

Scott Aaronson
Eric Allender
Noga Alon
Takao Asano
Tetsuo Asano
Yasuhito Asano
Hideo Bannai
Marc Benkert
Britta Broser
Kevin Buchin
Adam Buchsbaum
Sergio Cabello
Leizhen Cai
Maw-Shang Chang
Xiaomin Chen
Zhi-Zhong Chen
Jurek Czyzowicz
Ovidiu Daescu
Mark de Berg
Erik Demaine
Luc Devroye
Darko Dimitrov
Vida Dujmovic
Peter Eades
Vladimir Estivill-Castro
Uriel Feige
Tamas Fleiner
Satoshi Fujita
Hiroshi Furutani
Joachim von zur Gathen
Panos Giannopoulos
Joachim Gudmundsson
Masahiro Hachimori
Magnus M. Halldorsson
Yijie Han
Xin He
Frank Hoffmann
Tsan-sheng Hsu
John Iacono
Hiroshi Imai
Russell Impagliazzo
Toshimasa Ishii
Kazuo Iwama
Ravi Janardan

Karin Johnsgard
Haim Kaplan
Menelaos Karavelas
Takumi Kasai
Leonid Khachiyan
Rohit Khandekar
Shuji Kijima
Dong Kyue Kim
Sung-Ryul Kim
Gunnar Klau
Oliver Klein
Christian Knauer
Janos Komlos
Klaus Kriegel
Danny Krizanc
Keshav Kunal
Kaoru Kurosawa
Tak-Wah Lam
Stefan Langerman
Mun-Kyu Lee
Tobias Lenz
Qing Liu
Hsueh-I Lu
Yi Luo
Hiroyoshi Miwa
Anil Maheshwari
Masahiro Mambo
Jiri Matousek
Hideo Matsuda
Yasuko Matsui
Shuichi Miyazaki
Pat Morin
Hiroshi Nagamochi
Naomi Nishimura
Yoshio Okamoto
Rene van Oostrum
Evanthia Papadopoulou
Heejin Park
C.K. Poon
Oded Regev
Ares Ribó
Udi Rotics
Tim Roughgarden
Kunihiko Sadakane

Koichi Sakurai
Maiko Shigeno
Akiyoshi Shioura
Jeong Seop Sim
Michiel Smid
Joel Spencer
Astrid Sturm
Benny Sudakov
Masayuki Takeda
Yasuhiko Takenaga
Akihisa Tamura
Xuehou Tan
Anusch Taraz
Seinosuke Toda
Takeshi Tokuyama
Etsuji Tomita
Gerhard Trippen
Tatsuhiro Tsuchiya
Ryuhei Uehara
Shunji Umetani

Takeaki Uno
Yushi Uno
Marc van Kreveld
Kasturi Varadarajan
Antoine Vigneron
Caoan Wang
Chao Wang
Lei Wang
John Watrous
Steve Wismath
David Wood
Xiaodong Wu
Jinhui Xu
Atsuko Yamaguchi
Koichi Yamazaki
Yidong Yuan
Guochuan Zhang
Zhou Zhen
Binhai Zhu

Table of Contents

2B Graph and Combinatorial Algorithms II

3A Quantum Computation

3B Graph and Combinatorial Algorithms III

4A Computational Geometry II

4B Combinatorial Optimization I

5A Scheduling

5B Computational Biology

6A Computational Geometry III

6B Graph and Combinatorial Algorithms IV

7A Distributed and Parallel Algorithms

7B Graph and Combinatorial Algorithms V

8A Data Structure

8B Graph and Combinatorial Algorithms VI

9A Combinatorial and Network Optimization

9B Computational Complexity and Cryptography

10A Game Theory and Randomized Algorithm

10B Algebraic and Arithmetic Computation

Interactive Proofs for Quantum Computation

Andrew Chi-Chih Yao

Computer Science Department
Princeton University
Princeton, NJ 08544, USA
yao@cs.princeton.edu

Abstract. It is by now well established that quantum machines can solve certain computational problems much faster than the best algorithms known in the standard Turing machine model. The complexity question of which problems can be feasibly computed by quantum machines has also been extensively investigated in recent years, both in the context of one machine models (quantum polynomial classes) and various flavors of multi-machine models (single and multiple prover quantum interactive proofs). In this talk we examine the more general (but less theoretically investigated) question of which quantum states can be feasibly computed. Specifically, we will focus on the question of what quantum states can be generated by quantum interactive proofs. We will show that several classical interactive proof theorems have analogs in such models. For example, we show that any quantum state computable in quantum polynomial space has a 2-prover quantum interactive proof. Open questions will be discussed.

T. Ibaraki, N. Katoh, and H. Ono (Eds.): ISAAC 2003, LNCS 2906, p. 1, 2003.
© Springer-Verlag Berlin Heidelberg 2003

Drawing Plane Graphs

Takao Nishizeki

Graduate School of Information Sciences, Tohoku University
Aoba-yama 05, Sendai 980-8579, Japan
nishi@ecei.tohoku.ac.jp

Automatic aesthetic drawing of plane graphs has recently created intense interest due to its broad applications, and as a consequence, a number of drawing methods, such as the straight line drawing, convex drawing, orthogonal drawing, rectangular drawing and box-rectangular drawing, have come out [8,9,3,4,5,6,7, 10,11,14,16,23,29,33]. In this talk we survey the recent results on these drawings of plane graphs.

The most typical method is a *straight line drawing* in which all edges of a plane graph are drawn as straight line segments without any edge-intersection, as illustrated in Fig. 1(a). Every plane graph has a straight line drawing [10, 31,34]. A straight line drawing of a plane graph G is called a *grid drawing* of G if the vertices of G are put on grid points of integer coordinates. The *integer grid* of size $W \times H$ consists of $W + 1$ vertical segments and $H + 1$ horizontal segments, and has a rectangular contour. It is known that every plane graph of $n \geq 3$ vertices has a grid drawing on an $(n - 2) \times (n - 2)$ grid, and that such a grid drawing can be found in linear time [5,7,11,29]. It is also shown that, for each $n \geq 3$, there exists a plane graph which needs a grid of size at least $\lfloor 2(n - 1)/3 \rfloor \times \lfloor 2(n - 1)/3 \rfloor$ for any grid drawing [6,11]. It has been conjectured that every plane graph has a grid drawing on a $\lceil 2n/3 \rceil \times \lceil 2n/3 \rceil$ grid, but the conjecture is still remained as an open problem. On the other hand, a restricted class of plane graphs has a more compact grid drawing [14,21]. Miura *et al.* [21] recently give a very simple algorithm which finds a grid drawing of any given 4-connected plane graph G on a $W \times H$ grid such that $W = \lceil n/2 \rceil - 1$ and $H = \lceil n/2 \rceil$ in linear time if G has four or more vertices on the outer face. Since $W = \lceil n/2 \rceil - 1$ and $H = \lceil n/2 \rceil$, $W + H \leq n$.

Another typical method which often produces an aesthetic straight line drawing is a *convex drawing*, in which every face boundary is drawn as a convex polygon as illustrated in Fig. 1(b). Not every plane graph has a convex drawing, but every 3-connected plane graph has a convex drawing [33]. Thomassen obtained a necessary and sufficient condition for a plane graph to have a convex drawing [32]. Chiba *et al.* gave a linear algorithm to examine the condition and find a convex drawing [3,4]. A convex drawing is called a *convex grid drawing* if it is a grid drawing. Every 3-connected plane graph has a convex grid drawing on an $(n - 2) \times (n - 2)$ grid, and such a grid drawing can be found in linear time [5,30]. Miura *et al.* [22] recently give an algorithm which finds in linear time a convex grid drawing of any given 4-connected plane graph G on an integer grid such that $W + H \leq n - 1$ if G has four or more vertices on the outer face boundary. Since $W + H \leq n - 1$, $W \times H \leq \lceil (n - 1)/2 \rceil \cdot \lfloor (n - 1)/2 \rfloor$.

T. Ibaraki, N. Katoh, and H. Ono (Eds.): ISAAC 2003, LNCS 2906, pp. 2–5, 2003.
© Springer-Verlag Berlin Heidelberg 2003

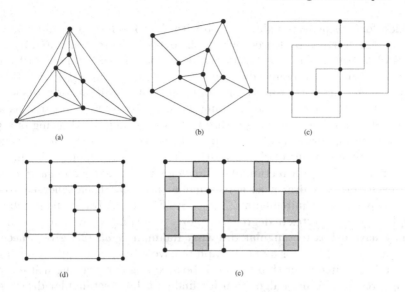

Fig. 1. (a) Straight line drawing, (b) convex drawing, (c) orthogonal drawing, (d) rectangular drawing, and (e) box-rectangular drawing.

In the last few years, substantial researches on graph drawings have been devoted to "orthogonal drawings" for their numerous applications in circuit schematics, entity relationship diagrams, data flow diagrams etc. [9]. An *orthogonal drawing* of a plane graph G is a drawing of G with the given embedding in which each vertex is mapped to a point, each edge is drawn as a sequence of alternate horizontal and vertical line segments, and any two edges do not cross except at their common end, as illustrated in Fig. 1(c). Orthogonal drawings have applications in circuit schematics, and it is desired to find an orthogonal drawing with a small number of bends, because a bend corresponds to a "via" or "throughhole," and increases the fabrication cost of VLSI [19]. It is a challenging problem to find a *bend-minimum* orthogonal drawing, that is, an orthogonal drawing with the minimum number of bends [2,16]. Garg and Tamassia [12] presented an $O(n^{7/4}\sqrt{\log n})$ time algorithm to find a bend-minimum orthogonal drawing of any plane graph of the maximum degree Δ at most four; if a plane graph has a vertex of degree 5 or more, then there is no orthogonal drawing. Rahman *et al.* [26] presented a liner-time algorithm to find a bend-minimum orthogonal drawing of a triconnected cubic plane graph. Rahman and Nishizeki [24] recently give a linear-time algorithm to find a bend-minimum orthogonal drawing of plane graphs with $\Delta \leq 3$. However, constructing a linear-time algorithm to obtain a bend-minimum orthogonal drawing of a plane graph with $\Delta \leq 4$ is still remained as an open problem.

An orthogonal drawing is called a *rectangular drawing* if it has no bend and each face is drawn as a rectangle, as illustrated in Fig. 1(d). A rectangular drawing has practical applications in VLSI floorplanning [18,19,25,28] and architectural floorplanning [20]. Thomassen [32] obtained a necessary and sufficient condition for a biconnected plane graph with $\Delta \leq 3$ to have a rectangular drawing when four vertices of degree two on the outer face are designated as convex corners of a rectangular drawing of the outer face. Linear-time algorithms are known to obtain a rectangular drawing of such a plane graph [1,17,25]. Recently Rahman *et al.* [28] give a necessary and sufficient condition for a plane graph of $\Delta \leq 3$ to have a rectangular drawing when no vertex is designated as a corner, and obtain a linear-time algorithm to find a rectangular drawing of a plane graph if it exists. However, constructing a linear-time algorithm for rectangular drawings of plane graphs of $\Delta \leq 4$ is still remained as an open problem.

A generalization of a rectangular drawing called a *box-rectangular drawing*, where each vertex is drawn as a rectangular box, has been emerged to meet some floorplanning requirements [27,15]. (See Fig. 1(e).) If a plane graph G has multiple edges or a vertex of degree 5 or more, then G has no rectangular drawing but may have a box-rectangular drawing. Rahman *et al.* [27] give a necessary and sufficient condition for a plane graph to have a box-rectangular drawing and obtain a linear-time algorithm to find a box-rectangular drawing if it exists. X. He [15] gives an alternate algorithm for finding a box-rectangular drawing of a plane graph if it exists.

References

1. J. Bhasker and S. Sahni, "A linear algorithm to find a rectangular dual of a planar triangulated graph," Algorithmica, vol.3, pp. 247–278, 1988.
2. T. C. Biedl, "Optimal orthogonal drawings of triconnected plane graphs," Proc. of SWAT'96, LNCS 1097, pp. 333–344, 1996.
3. N. Chiba, K. Onoguchi and T. Nishizeki, "Drawing planar graphs nicely," Acta Inform., vol.22, pp. 187–201, 1985.
4. N. Chiba, T. Yamanouchi and T. Nishizeki, "Linear algorithms for convex drawings of planar graphs," Progress in Graph Theory, J.A. Bondy and U.S.R. Murty (eds.), Academic Press, pp. 153–173, 1984.
5. M. Chrobak and G. Kant, "Convex grid drawings of 3-connected planar graphs," International Journal of Computational Geometry and Applications, vol.7 , pp. 211–223, 1997.
6. M. Chrobak and S. Nakano, "Minimum-width grid drawings of plane graphs," Computational Geometry: Theory and Applications, vol.10, pp. 29–54, 1998.
7. M. Chrobak and T. Payne, "A linear-time algorithm for drawing planar graphs on a grid," Information Processing Letters, vol.54, pp. 241–246, 1995.
8. G. Di Battista, P. Eades, R. Tamassia and I. G.Tollis, "Automatic graph drawing: an annotated bibliography," Computational Geometry: Theory and Applications, vol.4, pp. 235–282, 1994.
9. G. Di Battista, P. Eades, R. Tamassia and I. G. Tollis, Graph Drawing, Prentice Hall, NJ, 1999.
10. I. Fáry, "On straight lines representation of plane graphs," Acta Sci. Math. Szeged, vol.11, pp. 229–233, 1948.
11. H. de Fraysseix, J. Pach and R. Pollack, "How to draw a planar graph on a grid," Combinatorica, vol.10, pp. 41–51, 1990.
12. A. Garg and R. Tamassia, "A new minimum cost flow algorithm with applications to graph drawing," Proc. of Graph Drawing '96, LNCS 1190, pp. 201–226, 1996.

13. X. He, "On finding the rectangular duals of planar triangulated graphs," SIAM J. Comput., vol.22, no.6, pp. 1218–1226, 1993.

14. X. He, "Grid embedding of 4-connected plane graphs," Discrete & Computational Geometry, vol.17, pp. 339–358, 1997.

15. X. He, "A simple linear time algorithm for proper box-rectangular drawings of plane graphs," Journal of Algorithms, vol.4, no.1, pp. 82–101, 2001.

16. G. Kant, "Drawing planar graphs using the canonical ordering," Algorithmica, vol.16, pp. 4–32, 1996.

17. G. Kant and X. He, "Regular edge labeling of 4-connected plane graphs and its applications in graph drawing problems," Theoretical Computer Science, vol.172 , pp. 175–193, 1997.

18. K. Kozminski and E. Kinnen, "An algorithm for finding a rectangular dual of a planar graph for use in area planning for VLSI integrated circuits," Proc. 21st DAC, pp. 655–656, 1984.

19. T. Lengauer, Combinatirial Algorithms for Integrated Circuit Layout, John Wiley & Sons, Chichester, 1990.

20. S. Munemoto, N. Katoh and G. Imamura, "Finding an optimal floor layout based on an orthogonal graph drawing algorithm," J. Archit. Plann. Environment Eng. AIJ, vol.524, pp. 279–286, 2000.

21. K. Miura, S. Nakano and T. Nishizeki, "Grid drawings of four-connected plane graphs," Discrete & Computational Geometry, vol.26, pp. 73–87, 2001.

22. K. Miura, S. Nakano and T. Nishizeki, "Convex grid drawings of four-connected plane graphs," Proc. 11th Annual International Symposium on Algorithms and Computation (ISAAC'00), LNCS 1969, pp. 254–265, 2000.

23. T. Nishizeki, K. Miura and M. S. Rahman, Algorithms for drawing plane graphs, Trans. of IEICE, to appear.

24. M. S. Rahman and T. Nishizeki, "Bend-minimum orthogonal drawings of plane 3-graphs," Proc. of WG'02, LNCS 2573, pp. 265–276, 2002.

25. M. S. Rahman, S. Nakano and T. Nishizeki, "Rectangular grid drawings of plane graphs," Comp. Geom. Theo. Appl., vol.10, no.3, pp. 203–220, 1998.

26. M. S. Rahman, S. Nakano and T. Nishizeki, "A linear algorithm for bend-optimal orthogonal drawings of triconnected cubic plane graphs," Journal of Graph Alg. Appl., vol.3, no.4, pp. 31–62, 1999.

27. M. S. Rahman, S. Nakano and T. Nishizeki, "Box-rectangular drawings of plane graphs," Journal of Algorithms, vol. 37, no.2, pp. 363–398, 2000.

28. M. S. Rahman, S. Nakano and T. Nishizeki, "Rectangular drawings of plane graphs without designated corners," Comp. Geom. Theo. Appl., vol.21 no.3, pp. 121–138, 2002.

29. W. Schnyder, "Embedding planar graphs in the grid," Proc. 1st Annual ACM-SIAM Symp. on Discrete Algorithms, San Francisco, pp. 138–147, 1990.

30. W. Schnyder and W. Trotter, "Convex drawings of planar graphs," Abstracts of the AMS, vol.13, no.5, 92T-05-135, 1992.

31. S. K. Stein, "Convex maps," Proc. Amer. Math. Soc., vol. 2, pp. 464–466, 1951.

32. C. Thomassen, "Plane representations of graphs," (Eds.) J. A. Bondy and U. S. R. Murty, Progress in Graph Theory, Academic Press Canada, pp. 43–69, 1984.

33. W.T. Tutte, "How to draw a graph," Proc. London Math. Soc., vol.13, pp. 743–768, 1963.

34. K. Wagner, "Bemerkungen zum Vierfarbenproblem," Jahresbericht der Deutschen Mathematiker-Vereinigung, vol.46, pp. 26–32, 1936.

Linear Time Algorithm for Approximating a Curve by a Single-Peaked Curve

Jinhee Chun[1], Kunihiko Sadakane[2], and Takeshi Tokuyama[1]

[1] Graduate School of Information Sciences, Tohoku University,
Sendai, Japan
{jinhee, tokuyama}@dais.is.tohoku.ac.jp
[2] Graduate School of System Information Science, Kyushu University,
Fukuoka, Japan
sada@csce.kyushu-u.ac.jp

Abstract. Given a function $y = f(x)$ in one variable, we consider the problem of computing the single-peaked curve $y = \phi(x)$ minimizing the L_2 distance between them. If the input function f is a histogram with $O(n)$ steps or a piecewise linear function with $O(n)$ linear pieces, we design algorithms for computing ϕ in linear time. We also give an algorithm to approximate f with a function consisting of the minimum number of single-peaked pieces under the condition that each single-peaked piece is within a fixed L_2 distance from the corresponding portion of f.

1   Introduction

Given a function $y = f(x)$ defined on an interval $I = [0,1]$, we consider the problem of approximating f by a pyramidic function $y = \phi(x)$.

Here, a function is *pyramidic* if for any real number t, $\{x \in [0,1] : \phi(x) \geq t\}$ is either an interval or empty; in order words, the function has a unique maximal peak (the peak may be a flat interval). If the L_2 distance

$$D(f, \phi) = \int_0^1 (f(x) - \phi(x))^2 dx$$

is minimized, we call ϕ the optimal pyramidic approximation of f, and write it ϕ_f if we need to indicate the input function f explicitly. See Figure 1 to get intuition.

The problem is motivated from a data mining [6,7] problem, and also related to statistics. For this problem, an $O(n \log n)$ time algorithm has been announced [9] by one of the authors for a special case where the input function is a histogram. We give an $O(n)$ time algorithm for computing the optimal pyramidic approximation if f is a piecewise linear function with n linear pieces. It is easy to see that our method also works for a piecewise algebraic function. The algorithm is designed by using three different forms of the objective function, and also convex hull algorithms. Not only the algorithm is more efficient and general than that of [9], it is simpler.

T. Ibaraki, N. Katoh, and H. Ono (Eds.): ISAAC 2003, LNCS 2906, pp. 6–15, 2003.

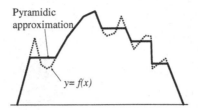

Fig. 1. Input polygonal function (dotted curve) and its optimal pyramidic approximation

A function $y = g(x)$ is called a piecewise unimodal approximation of $y = f(x)$ if g consists of k single-maximal-peak portions and the L_2 distance between each portion and the corresponding part of f is at most a given threshold ϵ. We can compute a piecewise unimodal approximation with the minimum number of maximal peaks in $O(n \log n)$ time by using the above-mentioned linear time algorithm.

2   Approximating a Histogram

Without loss of generality, we can assume f and ϕ_f are nonnegative functions, since we can vertically translate them without changing the distance between them. We first consider the case where the input f is a piecewise constant function (often called a *histogram*). That means $[0, 1]$ is divided into n subintervals $I_1, I_2, \ldots, I_n$, and f takes a constant value on each subinterval. We call these subintervals the step intervals. We write $I_k = (\ell_k, r_k]$ by using its left and right endpoints, and assume that $\ell_1 = 0$, $\ell_k = r_{k-1}$ $(k = 1, 2, \ldots, n)$, and $r_n = 1$. Precisely speaking, $I_1 = [0, r_1]$ (instead of $(0, r_1]$). Without loss of generality, we assume that the value of f on I_i is different from that of I_{i+1} for each $i = 1, 2, \ldots, n - 1$.

For an interval J, let $f(J) = \int_{x \in J} f(x)dx$, and let $|J|$ be the length of J. For a disjoint union F of intervals, $f(F)$ and $|F|$ means the sum of their values over the interval , respectively.

Figures 2 gives an example of pyramidic approximation of a histogram.

2.1   Properties of the Optimal Pyramidic Approximation

We show some properties of an optimal pyramidic approximation that are utilized to design efficient algorithms. The following lemma is obvious:

Lemma 1. *The optimal pyramidic approximation ϕ_f is a constant function on each I_j $(j = 1, 2, \ldots, n)$.*

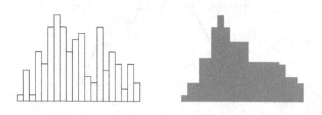

Fig. 2. Input histogram (left) and its optimal pyramidic approximation (right)

Let $\mathcal{I}$ be the set of subintervals of $[0, 1]$. We call $\Psi : t \in [0, \infty) \to \mathcal{I}$ a *pyramid map* (or *pyramid*) if $\Psi(t) \subseteq \Psi(t')$ if $t \geq t'$.

Consider a single-peaked function $y = \phi(x)$ defined on $[0, 1]$. Then, given a *height* t, $\Phi(t) = \{x \in [0, 1] : \phi(x) \geq t\}$ is a subinterval of $[0, 1]$, which we call the *horizontal section* of the region $\{(x, y) : x \in [0, 1], y \leq \phi(x)\}$ at $y = t$. Naturally, $\Phi(t)$ is a pyramid map. If ϕ is the optimal pyramidic approximation, each image of Φ is either empty or a union of intervals I_i $(i = 1, 2, \ldots, n)$.

The flat of ϕ at a height t is defined by $F(\phi, t) = \{x : \phi(x) = t\}$, which is the projection (to the x-axis) of the intersection of $y = \phi(x)$ with the horizontal line $y = t$. Obviously, a flat has at most two connected components, and each component is either a point or a union of step intervals.

An interval J is called a *balancing interval* for t if $\int_{x \in J}(f(x) - t)dx = 0$.

A flat is called balancing if each connected component is a balancing interval for its height.

Lemma 2. *If ϕ is the optimal pyramidic approximation of f, each flat $F = F(\phi, t)$ is balancing.*

Proof. It is sufficient to consider each connected component of F. If the component is a point, $f(x) = t$, and the statement is obvious. Thus, assume that the component is a closed interval, and the previous and next heights of ϕ be t_0 and t_1 (thus, $t_0 < t < t_1$). It follows from a elementary statistical fact that the value t minimizing $\int_{x \in J}(f(x) - t)^2 dx$ must be the mean value of $f(x)$ over J. It is easy to derive a contradiction if the mean value is not in the range of (t_0, t_1).

Corollary 1. *If ϕ is optimal, $\int_0^1 f(x)dx = \int_0^1 \phi(x)dx$.*

For the input function f, a single-peak function ϕ, and its corresponding pyramid map Φ, we define $H(f, \Phi) = \int_0^\infty (f(\Phi(t)) - t|\Phi(t)|)dt$ and $V(\phi) = \int_0^1 \phi^2(x)dx$. We remark that $f(\Phi(t)) - t|\Phi(t)| = \int_{x \in \Phi(t)}(f(x) - t)dx$; thus,

$H(f, \Phi) = \int_0^\infty \int_{x \in \Phi(t)}(f(x) - t)dxdt$.

Lemma 3. *1. ϕ gives the optimal pyramidic approximation if and only if it maximizes $H(f, \Phi)$.*

2. ϕ gives the optimal pyramidic approximation if and only if it maximizes $V(\phi)$ under the condition that each flat of ϕ is a balanced interval.

Proof. If we consider $H(f, \Phi)$ as a double integral with respect to t and x, and exchange the order of integrals, we have

$$H(f, \Phi) = \sum_F \{t_F f(F) - \frac{t_F^2}{2}|F|\} = \sum_F \int_{x \in F} t_F f(x) - \frac{t_F^2}{2} dx,$$

where the summation is taken over all flats F of ϕ. Thus,

$$2H(f, \Phi) - \int_0^1 f(x)^2 dx = \sum_F \int_{x \in F} 2t_F f(x) - t_F^2 - f(x)^2 dx$$

$$= -\int_0^1 (f(x) - \phi(x))^2 dx = -D(f, \phi).$$

Thus, maximizing $H(f, \Phi)$ means minimizing $D(f, \phi)$, since $\int_0^1 f(x)^2 dx$ is a fixed constant.

For each flat F of ϕ at a height t,

$$\int_{x \in F} (f(x) - \phi(x))^2 dx = \int_{x \in F} (f(x) - t)^2 dx$$

$$= -2t \int_{x \in F} (f(x) - t) dx - \int_{x \in F} t^2 dx + \int_{x \in F} f(x)^2 dx.$$

This equals $-\int_{x \in F} t^2 dx + \int_{x \in F} f(x)^2 dx$ if we assume that F is a balanced interval.

Thus, $D(f, \phi) = -V(\phi) + \int_0^1 f(x)^2 dx$, and ϕ minimizes $D(f, \phi)$ if and only if it maximizes $V(\phi)$ provided that each flat of ϕ is balanced.

Although it seems confusing to consider three (basically equivalent) objective functions, it is crucial to use $V(\phi)$ and $H(f, \Phi)$ in order to design an efficient algorithm for computing ϕ.

3   Algorithms for Histograms

The *top flat* of ϕ is the nonempty flat with the maximum height. The following lemma is easy to see:

Lemma 4. *If ϕ is the optimal pyramidic approximation, $f(x) = \phi(x)$ within the top flat.*

Since we assume that the values of f at adjacent intervals are different from each other, the above lemma implies that the top flat of the optimal pyramidic approximation consists of a single interval I_k for a suitable k. The interval I_k giving the top flat of ϕ is called the *peak interval*, and k is called the *peak index*.

We say the interval I_k is effective if there is no interval J properly containing I_k satisfying that $f(J) - f(x)|J| > 0$, where x is any point in I_k.

Lemma 5. *A peak index of an optimal pyramid must be effective.*

For a given effective index k, a single-peaked function ϕ whose peak I_k is called locally optimal if its corresponding pyramid map Φ maximizes $H(f, \Phi)$ under the condition that its top flat is I_k.

We first show how to compute the locally optimal pyramid with the given peak index k in linear time. Then, we proceed to a linear time algorithm for computing the (global) optimal pyramid.

3.1   Linear Time Algorithm for Computing a Local Optimal Pyramid

In this subsection, we fix an effective index k, and consider the local optimal pyramid Φ_k.

It is easy to see that each flat of a local optimal pyramid must be a balancing flat.

Let $I^k(t)$ be the interval J containing I_k maximizing $\int_{x \in J}(f(x) - t)dx$. If such interval is not unique, we chose the one with the minimum length.

Lemma 6. *If Φ_k is the local optimal pyramid, and $t \le t_{max}$, $\Phi_k(t) = I^k(t)$ if $t \le t_{max}$ and $\Phi_k(t) = \emptyset$ if $t > t_{max}$; here, $t_{max} = \max \phi(x)$.*

Proof. If $t > t'$, $I^k(t) \subseteq I^k(t')$, since otherwise we can see that $J = I^k(t) \cap I^k(t')$ also maximizes the objective function $\int_{x \in J}(f(x) - t)dx$, and contradict the minimality of length of $I^d(t)$. Thus, I^k defines a pyramid map, and it is clear that it maximizes $H(f, \Phi)$ under the condition that Φ has the peak index k.

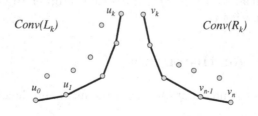

Fig. 3. $Conv(L_k)$ and $Conv(R_k)$

For $i = 1, 2, \ldots, n$, let u_i be the two-dimensional point defined by $u_i = (r_i, \int_0^{r_i} f(x)dx)$. Note that the x-coordinate value equals $\int_0^{r_i} 1 dx$, and recall that r_i is the right end of I_i. Similarly, we define $v_i = (1 - r_i, \int_{r_i}^1 f(x)dx)$.

We define two sets $L_k = \{u_0, u_1, u_2, \ldots, u_k\}$ and $R_k = \{v_k, v_{k+1}, \ldots, v_n\}$ of points in the two dimensional Euclidean plane, where u_0 is defined to be the origin, and v_n also becomes the origin. Note that points in L_k (resp. R_k) are sorted with respect to their x-coordinate values in an increasing (resp. decreasing) order. Let $Conv(L_k)$ and $Conv(R_k)$ be the lower convex hulls (lower chains of convex hulls) of L_k and R_k, respectively (Figure 3).

Lemma 7. *For a given height t, consider the tangent points $u_{p(t)}$ and $v_{q(t)}$ of lines with slope t to $Conv(L_k)$ and $Conv(R_k)$, respectively. Then, $I^k(t) = [r_{p(t)}, r_{q(t)}]$ if $p(t) \neq q(t)$ and $I^k(t) = \emptyset$ if $p(t) = q(t) = k$.*

Proof. Let $I^k(t) = [x_0, x_1]$(Figure 4). $[0,1] \setminus I^k(t)$ consists of two parts $[0, x_0)$ and $(x_1, 1]$. By definition, x_0 and x_1 are the values satisfying $x_0 \leq \ell_k$ and $x_1 \geq r_k$ and maximizing $\int_{x_0}^{x_1} (f(x) - t)dx$. Thus, x_0 is the value $x_0 \leq \ell_k$ minimizing $\int_0^{x_0} (f(x) - t)dx = \{\int_0^{x_0} f(x)dx\} - tx_0$. It is an elementary fact that this is attained at the tangent point of a line with slope t to $Conv(L_k)$, and thus $x_0 = r_{p(t)}$. We can similarly obtain the value of x_1.

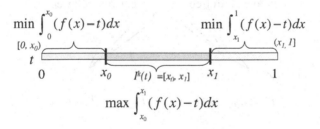

Fig. 4. $I^k(t) = [x_0, x_1]$

Thus, the pyramid map $\Phi_k(t) = I^k(t)$ can be obtained from $Conv(L_k)$ and $Conv(R_k)$ easily in linear time. Since the convex hull of a sorted point set can be computed in linear time, this gives a linear time algorithm.

3.2 Global Optimal Pyramid

Although L_k and R_k were defined for an effective index k, it can be similarly defined for every index k.

Suppose that the sorted list of the vertices of $Conv(L_k)$ is $u_{i(0)}, u_{i(1)}, \ldots, u_{i(m)}$ where $0 = i(0) < i(1) < \ldots < i(m) = k$, and let $t(i(s))$ be the slope between $u_{i(s)}$ and $u_{i(s+1)}$. We define $P(i(s)) = (r_{i(s+1)} - r_{i(s)})t(i(s))^2$. Let $W_1(L_k) = \sum_{s=0}^{m-1} P(i(s))$.

Similarly, the reversed sorted list of the vertices of $Conv(R_k)$ is $v_{j(1)}, v_{j(2)}, \dots,$
$v_{j(h)}$ where $n + 1 = j(1) > j(2) > \dots > j(h) = k$, and let $t'(j(s))$ be the slope between $v_{j(s)}$ and $v_{j(s+1)}$. We define $Q(j(s)) = (r_{j(s)} - r_{j(s+1)})t'(j(s))^2$. Let $W_2(R_k) = \sum_{s=1}^{h-1} Q(j(s))$.

Lemma 8. *If k is an effective index, $V(\Phi_k) = W_1(L_k) + W_2(R_k)$. If k is not an effective index, $W_1(L_k) + W_2(R_k) < V(\Phi)$, where Φ is the optimal pyramid.*

Proof. Obvious from the definition of $V(\Phi)$.

Thus, if we can compute $W_1(L_k)$ and $W_2(R_k)$ for all $k = 1, 2, \dots, n$ in linear time, we have done.

We define the lower convex hull trees $T^L = \cup_{1 \le k \le n} Conv(L_k)$ and $T^R = \cup_{1 \le k \le n} Conv(R_k)$, where the union is taken over all effective indices k (Figure 5). T^L forms a tree with the vertices $u_0, u_1, \dots, u_n$, and T^R forms a tree with the vertices $v_1, v_2, \dots, v_n$. Both tree have their root at the origin.

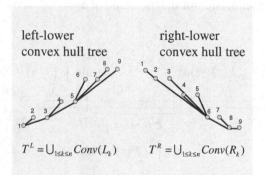

Fig. 5. Lower convex hull trees T^L and T^R

Lemma 9. *T^L and T^R can be computed in linear time.*

Proof. We run a plane-sweep convex hull algorithm adding points one-by-one in the sorted order updating the convex hull (Beneath-and-Beyond method [4], a version of Graham's scan [8]). We are only interested in the lower convex hull. When a new point is inserted, a part of the previous lower convex hull is deleted in the convex hull algorithm; however, in order to construct the lower convex hull tree, we keep it as the "old branch", so that the union of all branches form the lower convex hull tree. Similarly to the analysis of Graham's scan, this algorithm is linear time for a sorted set of point. See [5] for details.

For each vertex u_k in the tree, consider the unique path from the root to u_k. The path forms a convex chain $Conv(u_k)$. Let k' be the index of the parent of u_k in the tree. Then $W_1(L_k) = W_1(L_{k'}) + (r_k - r_{k'})t(r_k)^2$. Thus, $W_1(L_k)$ is computed in $O(1)$ time from $W_1(L_{k'})$.

Therefore, we can compute $W_1(L_k)$ for all $k = 1, 2, \ldots, n$ in $O(n)$ time. Similarly, we can compute $W_2(R_k)$ for all $k = 1, 2, \ldots, n$ in $O(n)$ time. Thus, we have the following:

Theorem 1. *The optimal pyramidic approximation of a histogram f with n steps can be computed in $O(n)$ time.*

4   Approximating a Piecewise Linear Function

If we do not mind computational complexity, our theory can be applied to every input function f on $[0, 1]$, since we can consider a sequence f_i $(i = 0, 1, \ldots)$ of step functions that uniformly converges to f, then the optimal pyramidal approximation ϕ_i of f_i uniformly converges to that of f.

However, if we consider the computational complexity, we should design an algorithm depending on the description of the function f. In this section, we consider the case where f is a piecewise linear function consisting of n linear pieces (f is not necessarily connected).

The interval $[0, 1]$ is subdivided into intervals $I_k = (\ell_k, r_k]$ $k = 1, 2, \ldots, n$, and f is a linear function in each interval I_k.

Instead of $Conv(L_k)$, we consider the function $F(x) = \int_0^x f(z)dz$ and let C_k^L be the lower convex hull of the curve defined by $y = F(x) : 0 \le x \le r_k$. $C_k'^L$ consists of parabolas and line segments.

We consider the union $T^L = \cup_{k=1}^n C_k^L$, which can be considered as a tree. Similarly, we define T^R.

We can construct T^L and T^R in linear time by modifying the plane-sweep algorithm for computing a convex hull, assuming that bitangent line between two parabolas can be computed in constant time.

Now, the rest is similar to the previous section. We note that a vertex in the tree need not correspond to an endpoint of the intervals I_k; precisely speaking, it can be an endpoint of bitangents of parabolas.

For each node $u = (x_u, y_u)$ in the tree T^L, we define $W^L(u)$ by the following recursion:
1. $W^L(u) = 0$ if u is the root $(0, 0)$
2. If $v = (x_v, y_v)$ is the parent of u, and the edge e between u and v is on the curve $y = g_e(x)$, $W^L(u) = W^L(v) + \int_{x_v}^{x_u} (\frac{d(g_e(x))}{dx})^2 dx$.

We can see that if f is piecewise constant, $W^L(u_k) = W_1(L_k)$. Similarly, we define $W^R(v)$ for each node v in the tree T^R.

If there are vertices u in T^L and v in T^R such that $x_u = x_v = x$, we define $W(x) = W^L(u) + W^R(v)$.

Lemma 10. *Consider x_0 which maximizes $W(x)$. Then, x_0 is the x-coordinate value of the peak of the optimal pyramidic approximation. Moreover, there exists* *such an x_0 that is the x-coordinate value of both a vertex T^L and a vertex in T^R.*

Theorem 2. *The optimal pyramidic approximation ϕ of a piecewise linear function f with n linear pieces can be computed in $O(n)$ time.*

Proof. We can compute $W^L(u)$ and $W^R(v)$ for all the vertices in linear time. Thus, we can find the peak of ϕ. Then, ϕ is obtained from the chains in T^L and T^R from the root to u and v, respectively.

5   Piecewise Unimodal Approximation of a Function

Although we have considered the problem where the output is single-peaked, we often need to approximate a function with a function with a small number of maximal peaks.

We consider the problem to approximate f with a function g that have the minimum number of pieces under the condition that each piece of g has at most one maximal peak and the L_2 distance between the piece and the corresponding portion of f is within a given threshold ϵ.

Let $y = f(x)$ be an input (piecewise linear) function. The following greedy algorithm computes a piecewise unimodal approximation of a given function f with a small number of pieces:

1. Compute the largest index k such that there exists a unimodal approximation g_0 of f within the interval $[0, r_k]$.
2. Compute the piecewise unimodal approximation g_1 of f within $[\ell_{k+1}, n]$ recursively.
3. Output the concatenation of g_0 and g_1.

The following lemma is easy to see:

Lemma 11. *The greedy algorithm outputs a piecewise unimodal approximation with the minimum number of pieces.*

Thus, we can apply an idea given by Agarwal et. al. [1] for computing the curve simplification. In contrast to the curve simplification where the method do not always give an optimal solution, we can compute the optimal solution for our problem.

Theorem 3. *A piecewise unimodal approximation with the minimum number of pieces can be computed in $O(n \log n)$ time.*

Proof. We apply a combination of the doubling strategy and the binary search to compute k in step 1. We check the condition whether f has a unimodal approximation (with an error less than ϵ) in the range $[0, r_{2^i}]$ or not for each $i = 0, 1, \ldots$. Suppose j is the first violating value of i. Then, k must satisfy that $2^{j-1} \le k < 2^j$. Now, we binary search in the range for k. Thus, it takes $O(2^j \log k) = O(k \log k)$ time for computing g_0. The rest of analysis is routine.

5.1   Concluding Remarks

It is also important to consider the case where the output has at most k peaks and the total L_2 distance is minimized. It is possible to solve it in polynomial time by running a dynamic programming algorithm by using our linear time algorithm given in the previous section as a subroutine; however, it is a little expensive. Practically, we can obtain a nice approximation by first running our greedy algorithm (for a suitable ϵ) to find a set P of positions of $K > k$ maximal peaks, then apply a dynamic programming to select k of them, and finally optimize each piece of the output between consecutive maximal peaks. However, we do not have theoretical guarantee of the approximation ratio of this method.

We often need to consider a different distance from the L_2 distance. The L_∞ distance looks easy to handle: If we want to decide whether we have a pyramidic approximation whose L_∞ distance from the input is at most (a given) ϵ, we can answer it in linear time easily. The optimization version can be solved in $O(n \log n)$ time if we apply parametric searching: however, we do not know a linear time algorithm for the optimization problem. The L_1-distance looks more difficult to deal with.

Two dimensional version [3] and higher dimensional version [2] of this problem has been considered in application to data mining, where the complexity of the problem highly depends on the definition of multi-variable pyramidic functions.

References

1. P. Agarwal, S. Hal-Peled, N. Mustafa, Y. Wang, Near Linear Time Approximation Algorithms for Curve Simplification in Two and Three Dimensions, Proc. 10th European Symp. on Algorithms, Springer LNCS 2461 (2002) pp. 29-41.
2. D. Chen, J. Chun, N. Katoh, T. Tokuyama, Efficient Algorithms for Constructing the Optimal Layered Data Segmentation, Working paper.
3. J. Chun, K. Sadakane, T. Tokuyama, Efficient algorithms for constructing a pyramid from a terrain, *Proceedings of JCDCG2002*, 2002.
4. H. Edelsbrunner, *Algorithms in Combinatorial Geometry*, ETACS Monograph on Theoretical Computer Science 10, Springer Verlag, 1987.
5. T. Fukuda, Y. Morimoto, S. Morishita, and T. Tokuyama, Mining Optimized Association Rules for Numeric Attributes, *Journal of Computer and System Sciences* **58** (1999) 1-12.
6. T. Fukuda, Y. Morimoto, S. Morishita, and T. Tokuyama, Data Mining with Optimized Two-Dimensional Association Rules, *ACM Trans. Database Systems* **26** (2001) 179-213.
7. Y. Morimoto, T. Fukuda, S. Morishita, and T. Tokuyama, Implementation and Evaluation of Decision Trees with Range and Region Splitting, *Constraints* (1997) 402-427.
8. F. P. Preparata and M. I. Shamos, *Computational Geometry – An Introduction*, Springer-Verlag, 1988 (2nd ed.).
9. T. Tokuyama, How to Reform a Terrain into a Pyramid, DIMACS Workshop on Geometric Graph Theory, 2002 (oral presentation).

A Dynamic Dictionary for Priced Information with Application[*]

Anil Maheshwari and Michiel Smid

School of Computer Science, Carleton University, Ottawa, Canada.
{anil,michiel}@scs.carleton.ca

Abstract. In this paper we design a dynamic dictionary for the priced information model initiated by [2,3]. Assume that a set S consisting of n elements is given such that each element has an associated price, a positive real number. The cost of performing an operation on elements of S is a function of their prices. The cost of an algorithm is the sum of the costs of all operations it performs. The objective is to design algorithms which incur low cost. In this model, we propose a dynamic dictionary, supporting insert, delete, and search for keys drawn from a linearly ordered set. As an application we show that the dictionary can be used in computing the trapezoidal map of a set of line segments.

1 Introduction

Priced Information Model: Assume that each input element has an associated price, a positive real number. When an algorithm performs an operation on element, then it is charged a cost which is a function of the price of the element. For example, the cost of a comparison operation between two elements could be the sum of their prices. The cost of an algorithm is the total sum of the costs of all operations it performs. In this paper we wish to design algorithms that incur low cost with respect to the "cheapest proof". A proof is a certificate that the output produced by the algorithm is correct. For example, if the problem is to search for a key in a sorted list, then the proof consists of either an element of the list that matches the query, or a pair of consecutive elements such that the key of the query is between their keys. The cost of the proof is proportional to either the price of the element that matches the query or the sum of the prices of the two neighboring elements to the query. The *competitive ratio* of an algorithm is defined to be the maximum ratio between the cost of the algorithm and the cost of the cheapest proof over all possible inputs. In this model, the solution to a problem involves (i) describing the cost of a cheapest proof, (ii) designing a competitive algorithm and (iii) analyzing its cost.

In this paper we propose a dynamic dictionary and use this to design a competitive algorithm for computing the trapezoidal map of a set of line segments; a fundamental problem in computational geometry. This study is inspired by the work of Charikar et al. [2,3] on *query strategies for priced information*. Their

---

[*] Work supported by NSERC.

motivation comes from the broad area of electronic commerce, where the priced information sources in several domains (e.g., software, legal information, propriety information, etc.) charge for their usage. The unit-cost comparison tree model has been traditionally used for evaluating algorithms. The work of [2,3,4,5] generalizes this model to accommodate variable costs. Geometric algorithms are usually designed and proven in the conventional "Real Random Access Machine" model of computation. Key features of this model include indirect addressing of any word in unlimited memory in unit time, words stored are infinite precision real numbers, and the basic operations (e.g., add, multiply, k-th root) are performed in constant time. To correctly implement a geometric algorithm, exact computation is extremely important. Unfortunately, the exact computation is very expensive and simple geometric tests, which take constant time in the Real RAM model, may require several operations. One way to model this is to associate prices to elements, and an operation involving an element needs to pay a cost which is a function of its price. Then an efficient algorithm aims to minimize the total cost of all the operations it performs.

Previous Work: We outline some of the fundamental problems such as searching, maximum finding, and sorting studied under the priced information model.

Theorem 1 ([2]). *For any cost function a query element can be searched in a sorted array of n-elements within a competitive ratio of $\log_2 n + O(\sqrt{\log n} \log \log n)$.*

Theorem 2 ([2]). *The maximum of n elements can be found within a competitive ratio of $2n - 3$ for any set of costs for the comparisons.*

What happens if the cost of the comparison operation is just the sum of the prices of the corresponding elements? In this case the problem of computing the maximum is much easier and can be solved by following a natural algorithm. Sort the elements w.r.t. their cost. Incrementally compute the maximum by examining the elements one by one, starting at the least cost element. The total cost of this algorithm is bounded by $2 \sum_{i=1}^{n} c_i$, where c_i is the price of the i-th element. Hence the competitive ratio of this algorithm is at most 2. It turns out that the general problem of sorting a set of items with arbitrary cost functions is highly non-trivial and has the flavor of the famous "Matching Nuts and Bolts" problem [6]. Given two lists of n numbers each such that one list is a permutation of the other, how should we sort the lists by comparisons only between numbers in different lists? In our setting comparisons within the list will be very expensive compared to comparisons across the list. If we modify the cost of the comparison operation to be the sum of the prices of the elements involved, then this problem can be solved quite easily. First sort the elements with respect to the price. Now incrementally sort the elements starting with the element with the least price. For example we can build a binary search tree to maintain the sorted order. It is easy to see that the cost of inserting an element is bounded by $2 \log_2 n$ times its cost, since all the elements in the tree have lower price when this element is inserted. Therefore this algorithm is $O(\log n)$ competitive.

New Results: In this paper we propose $O(\log n)$ competitive algorithms in the priced information model for the following problems; the cost of an operation is proportional to the sum of the prices of the elements involved in that operation.

1. A dynamic dictionary supporting insertion, deletion and searching of a key value in a linear ordered set consisting of n elements (Section 2).
2. The trapezoidal map of a set of n line segments (Section 3).

Result 1 can be viewed as a generalization of Theorem 1. Here we discuss dynamic dictionaries, whereas Theorem 1 is for static search queries. To the best of our knowledge Result 2 is the first instance where a problem from computational geometry has been studied under the priced information model.

2 Dynamic Dictionary

In this section we describe a dynamic search data structure in the priced information model. The elements are drawn from a total order. We allow a sequence of operations comprising of insertion of an element, deletion of an element and searching a query value. Each element has an associated price, and the cost of accessing an element is proportional to its price. Without loss of generality we will refer to the key value associated with an element x by x itself. Assume that the least possible price is 1. First we introduce an abstract data type and show how the various operations are performed and then outline how they are realized using 2-3 search trees.

2.1   Hierarchical Structure

Assume that currently the data structure consists of a set S of n elements. The elements are partitioned into cost groups, and elements within cost group i have prices in the range $(2^{i-1}, 2^i]$ for $i \geq 0$. Let $g(x)$ denote the cost group of the element $x \in S$. The elements are placed in a hierarchical structure $\mathcal{H}$ represented as a tree. The top level of $\mathcal{H}$ represents the whole set S. The hierarchy is described by the following recursive procedure, which is invoked by the call Hierarchy$(S,0)$. In a nutshell the main idea is to partition S recursively using the key values of groups. First partition S using the elements of the "cheapest" group (namely group 0 values) to obtain subsets $Z_0, \cdots, Z_k$. These subsets are recursively partitioned by the elements of "expensive" groups (i.e. groups consisting of elements with geometrically increasing prices). For an illustration see Figure 1. To simplify notation, a leaf node storing the value y_i will be referred to as the node y_i.

Procedure Hierarchy (X,i)

Input: A non-empty set X, such that $X \subseteq S$ and all elements of X are in the cost group i or bigger (i.e. each element of X has price $> 2^{i-1}$.)
Output: The hierarchical structure $\mathcal{H}$, for X, represented as a tree.

1. Compute the set $Y = \{x \in X : x \text{ in cost group } i\}$.
2. If $Y = \emptyset$ then Hierarchy $(X, i+1)$.
3. If $Y \neq \emptyset$ then

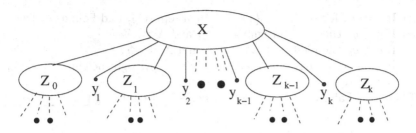

Fig. 1. Illustration of the hierarchy $\mathcal{H}$.

a) Let $Y = \{y_1, y_2, \cdots, y_k\}$, such that $y_1 < y_2 < \cdots < y_k$, for some $k \geq 1$.
b) Compute the sets $Z_j = \{z \in X \setminus Y : y_j < z < y_{j+1}\}, j = 1, 2, \cdots, k - 1$.
   Compute $Z_0 = \{z \in X \setminus Y : z < y_1\}$ and $Z_k = \{z \in X \setminus Y : z > y_k\}$.
c) For j, $j = 0, 1, \cdots, k$, if $Z_j \neq \emptyset$ then Hierarchy$(Z_j, i + 1)$.
d) Create a node representing X. Give this node children $r_0, y_1, r_1, \cdots, r_{k-1}, y_k, r_k$, where r_i $(0 \leq i \leq k)$ is the root of the tree representing Z_i.

The hierarchical structure $\mathcal{H}$ has the following properties. All elements of S appear as leaves in $\mathcal{H}$. A postorder traversal of the leaves of $\mathcal{H}$ results in the sorted order of the elements of S, and a node at level i in $\mathcal{H}$ (root is at level 0) represents only elements of groups $\geq i$.

2.2 Search

Next we describe the search procedure. The objective of the search for a query value q is to locate an element $x \in S$ such that $q = x$. In case there does not exists such an element in the set S, then report two elements $x, y \subset S$, such that $x < q < y$, and x and y are the left and right neighbors of q in the sorted order among the elements of $S \cup \{q\}$, respectively. The main idea is to sieve through the hierarchy, starting at the top level, and descending down by the aid of the y-values. The search terminates when it reaches a leaf node. The search procedure is described next.

Procedure Search(q, S)
Input: Set S stored in a hierarchical structure and a query value q.
Output: An element $x \in S$ such that $q = x$, if such x exists. Otherwise, the left and the right neighbors of q in S.

1. left-neighbor := nil and right-neighbor := nil.
2. $X := S$ and Found := False.
3. While $X \neq \emptyset$ and Found = False do
   Let $\{Z_0, y_1, Z_1, y_2, Z_2 \cdots, Z_{k-1}, y_k, Z_k\}$ be the children of the node representing X in the hierarchy $\mathcal{H}$, where $y_1 < y_2 < \cdots < y_k$, and all elements in the set Z_i, $i \in \{1, \cdots, k - 1\}$, have values in the range (y_i, y_{i+1}), elements in Z_0 have values smaller than y_1 and elements in Z_k have values larger than y_k (see Figure 1).

    a) If $q = y_j$, for some $j \in \{1 \cdots k\}$ then report y_j and Found := True.
    b) If $q < y_1$ then right-neighbor := y_1 and $X := Z_0$.
    c) If $q > y_k$ then left-neighbor := y_k and $X := Z_k$.
    d) If $y_j < q < y_{j+1}$ then left-neighbor := y_j, right-neighbor := y_{j+1} and $X := Z_j$.
4. If Found = False then report left-neighbor and right-neighbor.

Lemma 1. *Let x and y be the neighbors of q in $S \cup \{q\}$, and let the price of x be at least the price of y. Let $g(x)$ denote the group of x. Then* Search(q, S) *does not visit an element of any group having index bigger than $g(x)$.*

Proof Sketch: Consider the case where $q \notin S$. Let q have two neighbors $x, y \in S$. W.l.o.g. assume that $x < y$. Let x and y be in groups $g(x)$ and $g(y)$, resp. Observe that $g(y) \in \{0, \cdots, g(x)\}$. The search starts at S and then sieves through $\mathcal{H}$ using the y_i values of groups starting with group 0. In each step we consider the current set X which consists of elements of groups $\geq i$. We locate q among its children $\{Z_0, y_1, Z_1, y_2, Z_2 \cdots, Z_{k-1}, y_k, Z_k\}$, and depending upon the outcome we either terminate the search or proceed with one of the sets Z_j's. Note that $Z_j \subseteq X$ and elements of Z_j are of groups $\geq i + 1$. Consider the scenario when the search reaches the elements of group $g(y)$. Since $q < y$ and there is no element of S between q and y, the search procedure assigns y as the right neighbor of q (Step 3b or 3d). After that in each iteration of the while loop Step 3c will be executed till the set Z_j becomes empty. At that point the left neighbor of q will be x, since there are no elements of S between x and y, and $x < y$. Hence the search only visits elements up to the group $g(x)$. □

2.3 Insert

Next we discuss the procedure for inserting an element q belonging to the group $g(q)$ in the hierarchy $\mathcal{H}$. We first locate the left and the right neighbors, say x and y, respectively, of q in S using the Search(q, S) procedure. Without loss of generality we assume that $g(x) \geq g(y)$. Depending upon the relative order of $g(q)$, $g(x)$ and $g(y)$ we have different cases.
Case 1: $g(x) \geq g(y) \geq g(q)$. Starting at the leaf node containing x follow the path upwards in the hierarchy $\mathcal{H}$ and stop at the last node, say X, that represents only elements of groups $\geq g(q)$. Let Z_i be the child of X that contains x as one of its descendants. Let y_i and y_{i+1} be the left and the right neighbors of Z_i among the children of X. It is possible that none or only one of these neighbors exist; those cases can be handled using a similar approach. Observe that if $g(y) = g(q)$ then $y = y_{i+1}$, and if $g(y) > g(q)$ then y is a descendent of the node Z_i, since $y_i < x < q < y < y_{i+1}$. The insertion of node q is achieved by performing the following two operations: (a) Remove all elements in the set Z_i that have larger value than q. Form a new set Z_i' consisting of the removed elements. (b) Insert two new nodes between Z_i and y_{i+1} as children of X. The first one is the leaf node consisting of the element q, and the second one is Z_i' representing the hierarchy of elements in the set Z_i'.

Case 2: $g(q) \geq g(x) \geq g(y)$. Let node X be the parent node of the leaf node containing x in the hierarchy $\mathcal{H}$. Refer to node x as y_i and consider the node Z_i following the terminology used in Figure 1. Since the right neighbor of x is y before the insertion of q, and $g(x) \geq g(y)$, this implies that $Z_i = \emptyset$. Insertion of q is achieved by simply inserting q in the set Z_i.

Case 3: $g(x) \geq g(q) \geq g(y)$. Starting at the leaf node x traverse the path upwards in the hierarchy and stop at the last node, say X, which represents only elements of groups up to and including $g(q)$. If $g(x) = g(q) = g(y)$ then insert q as a child between x and y at the node X. If $g(q) > g(y)$ then insert q as the rightmost child at the node X.

Lemma 2. *Let q be the element to be inserted in the hierarchy $\mathcal{H}$. Let its neighbors in S be x and y, where $x < q < y$, and let $g(x) \geq g(y)$. Insertion of q, depending upon one of the above three cases, results in a new hierarchy $\mathcal{H}'$. The algorithm only visits elements up to the cost group $\max\{g(x), g(q)\}$.*

2.4   Delete

In this section we outline the procedure for deleting an element q from the hierarchy $\mathcal{H}$ storing the elements of the set S. First locate the neighbors x and y of q using the search procedure $\mathsf{Search}(S, q)$. This requires modifying the Search procedure as follows. After finding an element y_i that equals q among the children of the node X, the search continues for the left neighbor $x = \max\{Z_{i-1}\}$ and the right neighbor $y = \min\{Z_i\}$ of q. In the following we assume that $g(x) \geq g(y)$, the other case $g(y) \geq g(x)$ can be handled similarly.

Case 1: $g(x) \geq g(y) \geq g(q)$. Let node X be the parent of the leaf node containing $q = y_{i+1}$. Following the notation of Figure 1 let $\{Z_0, y_1, Z_1, \cdots, y_i, Z_i, q = y_{i+1}, Z_{i+1}, y_{i+2}, \cdots, Z_{k-1}, y_k, Z_k\}$ be the children of the node representing X, where $y_1 < y_2 < \cdots < y_k$ and all elements in the set Z_i have values in the range (y_i, y_{i+1}) for $i \in \{1, k-1\}$, and Z_0 has values smaller than y_1 and Z_k has values larger than y_k. Deletion of q can be achieved by removing the leaf node q and forming a new hierarchy by taking the union of the two hierarchies Z_i and Z_{i+1}.

Case 2: $g(q) \geq g(x) \geq g(y)$. Let node X be the parent node of the leaf node containing x in the hierarchy $\mathcal{H}$. Refer to node x as y_i and consider the node Z_i following the terminology used in Figure 1. Note that q is stored in the hierarchy at Z_i, and moreover this is the only element stored in this hierarchy, since $g(x) \geq g(y)$. Deletion of q is achieved by setting $Z_i := \emptyset$.

Case 3: $g(x) \geq g(q) \geq g(y)$. Remove the leaf node q.

Lemma 3. *Let q be the element to be deleted in the hierarchy $\mathcal{H}$. Let its neighbors in S be x and y, where $x < q < y$, and let $g(x) \geq g(y)$. Deletion of q, depending upon one of the above three cases, results in a new hierarchy $\mathcal{H}'$. The algorithm only visits elements up to the cost group $\max\{g(x), g(q)\}$.*

2.5   Implementation

We have described an abstract data type, called hierarchies, and the associated operations insert, delete and search. In this section we illustrate how we can realize this using *2-3 search trees*. A 2-3 tree is a tree in which each vertex, that is not a leaf, has 2 or 3 children, and every path from the root to a leaf is of the same length. A 2-3 tree can be used to store elements from a totally ordered set. This can be done by assigning the elements to the leaves of the tree in the left to the right order. Each internal node stores a set of intervals describing the range of key values in the left, middle and the right subtrees. The following theorem summarizes the relevant results on 2-3 trees.

Theorem 3. *([1]) Given a 2-3 tree on n elements, drawn from a totally ordered universe, each of the following operations can be performed in $O(\log n)$ time: (a) Insertion of an element. (b) Deletion of an element. (c) Searching for a key value. (d) Merging two 2-3 trees where all the key values in one tree are smaller than all the key values in the other tree. (e) Splitting a 2-3 tree into two 2-3 trees based on a key value, say q, where one tree will consist of all elements whose key values are $\leq q$ and the other tree will consist of all elements with key values $> q$.*

We represent the hierarchy $\mathcal{H}$ using 2-3 trees as follows. Recall that $\mathcal{H}$ was recursively defined, where a node X represents elements of groups $\geq i$ (see Figure 1 and the procedure Hierarchy(X, i)). Those children of node X which are leaves, namely $y_1, \cdots, y_k$, are represented in a 2-3 tree $T(X)$. In $T(X)$ the elements are stored at the leaves. Each child y_i of X is stored as a leaf node in $T(X)$, since a 2-3 tree stores elements only in its leaves. The leaf node corresponding to y_i, $1 \leq i \leq k$, in $T(X)$ stores a pointer to $T(Z_i)$, which is the recursively defined 2-3 tree for Z_i. The leaf node corresponding to y_1 stores an additional pointer to $T(Z_0)$. Next we illustrate how search, insert and delete can be performed.

Searching: For searching an element $q \in S$, we follow the procedure Search(q, S) on the tree $T(S)$ corresponding to the hierarchy $\mathcal{H}$ representing the set S. Refer to Figure 1 for the notation. The leaf nodes $\{y_1, \cdots, y_k\}$ of S are represented in a 2-3 tree $T(S)$. We locate q in $T(S)$ and as a result we either find a leaf node $y_j = q$ and the search terminates or find two leaf nodes y_j and y_{j+1} such that $y_j < q < y_{j+1}$. In that case we need to perform the search in the hierarchy Z_j, i.e. in the corresponding tree $T(Z_j)$, recursively.

Lemma 4. *An element can be searched in the hierarchical data structure storing the elements of the set S within a competitive ratio of $O(\log n)$, where $n = |S|$.*

Proof: The cheapest proof for membership of $q \in S$ is an element x_j that equals q, and the cheapest proof of non-membership is a pair of queries to two adjacent elements x_j and x_{j+1} such that $x_j < q < x_{j+1}$. Hence the cost of the cheapest proof is either the price of x_j or sum of the prices of x_j and x_{j+1}. Recall from the procedure Hierarchy that the leaf nodes associated to node X belong to the cost group i, i.e. the prices of these nodes are in the range $(2^{i-1}, 2^i]$. Let the search procedure examine elements in groups $0, 1, 2, \cdots, l$. The total number of elements in these groups is at most n, and the total number of comparisons made within a group with respect to the query q is at most $2 \log n + C$, for some constant C. Hence the cost of searching using the 2-3 tree data structure will be at most $(2 \log n + C) \sum_{i=0}^{l} 2^i \leq (2 \log n + C) 2^{l+1}$. As noted in Lemma 1, the search does not examine any elements of the groups larger than that of the neighbors of q in S. Therefore the cost of the cheapest proof is $> 2^{l-1}$. Hence the competitive ratio, i.e. the ratio of the cost of the algorithm to the cost of the cheapest proof is at most $\frac{(2\log n + C)2^{l+1}}{2^{l-1}} = 8\log n + 4C.\square$

Insert: Insertion of an element q in the hierarchy $\mathcal{H}$ requires searching for neighbors of q, possibly splitting part of the hierarchy from a leaf node up to an ancestor node (Case 1, Section 2.3), and inserting q as a leaf node. We have already discussed how searching can be realized.

The splitting can be realized as follows. Assume that we wish to split $\mathcal{H}$ with respect to the key value q as in Case 1 of the insert procedure in Section 2.3. Recall that each (non-leaf) node X of $\mathcal{H}$ is realized by a 2-3 tree, $T(X)$, and the leaves of $T(X)$ point to recursively defined 2-3 trees of the sub-hierarchies associated with X. Splitting $\mathcal{H}$ with respect to the key value q amounts to splitting each of the associated 2-3 trees on the path from the leaf node containing x up to the node in $\mathcal{H}$ representing groups $\geq g(q)$. Each of these 2-3 trees can be split with respect to the key value q resulting in two 2-3 trees. One of these trees represent key values smaller than q and the other one represents key values larger than q. The number of operations performed for each split is at most logarithmic in the size of the tree. The actual insertion of q in $\mathcal{H}$ can be done by inserting q in a 2-3 tree corresponding to the group $g(q)$, as dictated by one of the cases in Section 2.3.

The analysis of insertion is similar to that of searching. The cheapest proof involves the price of q and the sum of the prices of the neighbors of q in $S \cup \{q\}$. The total cost of performing the insertion is the sum of the costs of searching the neighbors of q and then performing the split and actual insertion. The searching is performed among the 2-3 trees representing groups $0, \cdots, g(x)$, where x is the neighbor of q with the highest price. The split is performed on the 2-3 trees representing groups $g(x)$ up to $g(q)$. Insertion of q is performed in a 2-3 tree representing the group $g(q)$. Hence each of the standard 2-3 tree operations (search, insert, split) are performed on 2-3 trees representing groups $0, \cdots, \max\{g(y), g(x), g(q)\}$, where x and y are neighbors of q in $S \cup \{q\}$. Similar to searching, the insertion of an element in the set S, $|S| = n$, can be done within a competitive ratio of $O(\log n)$.

Delete: Deletion of an element q from the hierarchy $\mathcal{H}$ requires searching for q and its neighbors in S, merging of two sub-hierarchies, and the deletion of the leaf node q. Merging of the two sub-hierarchies as required in Case 1 of Section 2.4 can be achieved as follows. Following the notation of Section 2.4, recall that x and y are neighbors of q in S, $x < y$, and $g(x) \geq g(y)$. The parent of the leaf node containing q is X in $\mathcal{H}$, and x (resp. y) is contained in the child node Z_i (resp. Z_{i+1}) of X. For each internal node X' (resp., Y') in $\mathcal{H}$ on the path from the leaf containing x (resp., y) up to Z_i (resp. Z_{i+1}), there is an associated 2-3 tree $T(X')$ (resp., $T(Y')$). Moreover the key values stored in $T(X')$ are smaller than in $T(Y')$ and each 2-3 tree represents key values of a particular cost group. Merging of the sub-hierarchies Z_i and Z_{i+1} is achieved by merging the corresponding 2-3 trees which belong to the same cost group. The total number of operations required to merge two 2-3 trees is given by Theorem 3. The actual deletion of q in $\mathcal{H}$ corresponds to deleting q from a 2-3 tree representing elements of the cost group $g(q)$, as given by one of the cases in Section 2.4.

Theorem 4. *A dynamic dictionary representing a set consisting of n priced elements drawn from a total order can be maintained. It supports insertion, deletion and searching of a key value and each of these operations can be achieved within a competitive ratio of $O(\log n)$ in the priced information model. The cost of an operation is the sum of the prices of the elements involved in that operation.*

3   Trapezoidal Maps

Let S be a set of n non-crossing line segments in the plane enclosed in a bounding box R. The *trapezoidal map* $\mathcal{T}(S)$ of S is obtained by drawing two vertical extensions from each endpoint of every segment $s \in S$. One of the extensions goes upwards and the other one downwards till it reaches either a segment of S or the boundary of R. The trapezoidal map is the subdivision induced by the segments in S, the bounding box R and the vertical extensions. Observe that each face of $\mathcal{T}(S)$ has one or two vertical sides and exactly two non-vertical sides, and hence each face is either a trapezoid or a triangle. The problem is to compute a trapezoidal map $\mathcal{T}(S)$ of a set S of n non-crossing line segments where each segment has an associated price. The cost of the cheapest proof for the trapezoidation is at least the total sum of the prices of all the boundary elements in all faces of $\mathcal{T}(S)$. The cost of a vertical extension l is the sum of the prices of the two segments in S to which l is incident.

Traditionally, in the uniform cost model, this problem is solved using the plane sweep paradigm as follows. Sort the end points of the segments with respect to increasing x-coordinate and insert them into an event queue. Sweep a vertical line from the left to the right and at each event point, the trapezoidal map of all the segments to the left has been computed. Maintain the y-sorted order of all segments intersecting the sweep line. At an event point either a segment is inserted in the sweep line data structure or it is deleted from it. When a segment is inserted/deleted the vertical extensions of its end-point are computed by finding out its neighbors in the y-sorted order of the segments maintained on the sweep line. Moreover after inserting/deleting the sweep line data structure is suitably updated.

In the cost model we make use of dynamic dictionaries to represent the y-sorted order of the segments intersecting the sweep line. The operations that are required on this data structure includes (a) inserting a new segment (i.e. insert a key value) (b) deleting an existing segment (i.e. delete a key value) (c) searching for neighbors of a query value. In addition to this we need an event list, which consists of end-points of segments in the x-sorted order.

Next we discuss the computation of the trapezoidal map $\mathcal{T}(S)$ of a set S consisting of n (possibly intersecting) segments. In addition to computing vertical extensions of the endpoints of segments, we need to compute vertical extensions

at each intersection point. Now the set of events includes endpoints of segments and intersection points. Observe that if two segments a and b intersect then they will be adjacent to each other on the sweep line at least once (e.g just before the sweep line reaches the intersection point). Event points are processed as follows:
Left endpoint: Suppose segment l needs to be inserted, and let a and b be the neighboring segments of l on the sweep line data structure, where a is above l and b is below l. First we locate a and b and then insert l in the sweep line data structure. Since a and l (and similarly b and l) have become adjacent, we check whether they intersect to the right of the sweep line. If so then their intersection point is inserted in the event queue. Draw upward (downward) vertical extension from the left endpoint of l to the segment a (resp. b).
Right endpoint: Suppose segment l needs to be deleted and let a and b be the neighboring segments as before. First locate l and its neighbors a and b. Draw vertical extensions from the right endpoint of l to a and b and delete l. Now a and b have become adjacent and it is possible that they intersect and their intersection point is to the right of the sweep line. If a and b have been adjacent at some point on the sweep line before l was even inserted then their intersection point is already present in the event queue. Therefore we search for the intersection point in the event queue, and if it is not present then we insert it.
Intersection point: Suppose the sweep line reaches the intersection point v of segments l and l' and let the segment a (resp. b) is just above (resp. below) v. Furthermore assume that l and a were adjacent, and similarly l' and b were adjacent, on the sweep line just before it reaches v. First locate v and the segments a and b on the sweep line data structure and draw the vertical extensions from v to a and b. Furthermore now the segments a and l', and similarly b and l, have become adjacent. Insert their intersection point into the event queue, if required.

Theorem 5. *The trapezoidal map of a set of n priced line segments can be computed within a competitive ratio of $O(\log n)$.*

References

1. AHO, HOPCROFT, AND ULLMAN. *The design and analysis of computer algorithms.* Addison-Wesley, 1974.
2. CHARIKAR, FAGIN, GURUSWAMI, KLEINBERG, RAGHAVAN, AND SAHAI. Query strategies for priced information. *Journal of Computer and System Sciences 64* (2002).
3. CHARIKAR, M., FAGIN, R., GURUSWAMI, V., KLEINBERG, J., RAGHAVAN, P., AND SAHAI, A. Query strategies for priced information (extended abstract). In *Proc. ACM Symp. on Theory of Computation* (New York, 2000), ACM, pp. 582–591.
4. GUPTA, AND KUMAR. Sorting and selection with structured costs. In *Proc. IEEE Symp. on Foundations of Comp. Sci.* (2001).
5. KANNAN, AND KHANNA. Selection with monotone comparison costs. In *Proc. ACM-SIAM Symp. on Discrete Algorithms* (2003).
6. KOMLOS, MA, AND SZEMEREDI. Matching nuts and bolts in O(n log n) time. *SIAM Journal on Discrete Mathematics 11* (1998).

Voronoi Diagram in the Flow Field

Tetsushi Nishida and Kokichi Sugihara

Department of Mathematical Informatics,
University of Tokyo, 7-3-1 Hongo, Bunkyo-ku, Tokyo 113-8656, Japan
{nishida,sugihara}@mist.i.u-tokyo.ac.jp

Abstract. A new concept called a boat-sail distance is introduced on the surface of water with flow, and it is used to define a generalized Voronoi diagram, in such a way that the water surface is partitioned into regions belonging to the nearest harbors with respect to this distance. The problem of computing this Voronoi diagram is reduced to a boundary value problem of a partial differential equation, and a numerical method for solving this problem is constructed. The method is a modification of a so-called fast marching method originally proposed for the eikonal equation. Computational experiments show the efficiency and the stableness of the proposal method.

1 Introduction

The concept of the Voronoi diagram is one of the most fundamental data structures in computational geometry, and its algorithms and applications have been studied extensively [4,7].

The Voronoi diagram has also been generalized in a variety of directions. A typical such direction is the generalization of the distance. The most fundamental Voronoi diagram is defined according to the Euclidian distance, while many generalized Voronoi diagrams are generated by replacing the Euclidean distance with other distances.

The first class of generalized distances are the distances that satisfy the distance axiom. This class includes L_1-distance, L_∞-distance, L_p-distance for $1 < p < \infty$ [6]. The second class contains weighted distances such as an additively weighted distance, a multiplicatively weighted distance, and the Laguerre distance [2]. There are still many other distances. They include a geodesic distance [1], a distance in a river [10], and a crystal-growth distance [5].

In this paper, we introduce still another generalization of the Voronoi diagram, which we encounter when a boat sails on the surface of water with flow. Suppose that we want to travel on the surface of water with a boat. If there is no flow of water, the boat can move in any direction at the same maximum speed. If the water flows, on the other hand, the speed of the boat is anisotropic; the boat can move faster in the same direction as the flow, while it move only slowly in the direction opposite to the flow direction. Modeling this situation, we introduce a boat-sail distance and define the Voronoi diagram associated with this distance.

T. Ibaraki, N. Katoh, and H. Ono (Eds.): ISAAC 2003, LNCS 2906, pp. 26–35, 2003.
© Springer-Verlag Berlin Heidelberg 2003

Next, we construct a numerical method for computing the boat-sail distance and the associated Voronoi diagram. For this purpose, we first reduce the problem to a boundary value problem of a partial differential equation. A similar idea was already used for the Euclidean distance, that is, the problem of computing the Euclidean distance was reduced to a boundary value problem of a partial differential equations called the eikonal equation [9]. Hence, our formulation can be considered a generalization of the eikonal equation.

2   Boat-Sail Distance and the Associated Voronoi Diagram

Let $\Omega \subset \mathbf{R}^2$ denote a two-dimensional domain with an (x, y) Cartesian coordinate system, and let $f(x, y) \in \mathbf{R}^2$ be a two-dimensional vector given at each point (x, y) in Ω. A physical interpretation is that Ω corresponds to the surface of water and $f(x, y)$ represents the velocity of the water flow. Hence, we call $f(x, y)$ the flow field. We assume that $f(x, y)$ is continuous in Ω.

Consider a boat that has the maximum speed F in any direction on the still water. Let Δt denote a short time interval. Suppose that the driver tries to move the boat at speed F in the direction v_F, where v_F is the unit vector, and hence the boat will move from the current point p to $p + \Delta t F v_F$ in time Δt if there is no water flow, as shown by the broken arrow in Fig 1. However, the flow of water also displaces the boat by $\Delta t f(x, y)$, and hence the actual movement Δu of the boat in time interval Δt is represented by $\Delta u = \Delta t F v_F + \Delta t f(x, y)$.

Consequently, the effective speed of the boat in the water flow is given by

$$\left| \frac{\Delta u}{\Delta t} \right| = |F v_F + f(x, y)| . \tag{1}$$

We assume that F is large enough to satisfy the condition $F > \max_{(x,y) \in \Omega} |f(x, y)|$.

Let p and q be two points in Ω, and let $c(s) \in \Omega$ denote a curve from p to q with the arc-length parameter s $(0 \leq s \leq \bar{s})$ such that $c(0) = p$ and $c(\bar{s}) = q$. Then, the time, say $\delta(c, p, q)$, necessary for the boat to move from p to q along the curve $c(s)$ with the maximum speed is obtained by

$$\delta(c, p, q) \equiv \int_0^{\bar{s}} \left| \frac{\Delta t}{\Delta u} \right| ds = \int_0^{\bar{s}} \frac{1}{|F v_F + f(x, y)|} ds . \tag{2}$$

Let C be the set of all paths from p to q. We define $d(p, q)$ by

$$d(p, q) \equiv \min_{c \in C} \delta(c, p, q) . \tag{3}$$

That is, $d(p, q)$ represents the shortest time necessary for the boat to move from p to q. We call $d(p, q)$ the *boat-sail distance* from p to q.

Next, we define a generalized Voronoi diagram with respect to the boat-sail distance. Let $P = \{p_1, p_2, \cdots, p_n\}$ be a set of n points, called boat harbors, in Ω. For $p_i \in P$, we define region $R(P; p_i)$ by

$$R(P; p_i) \equiv \bigcap_{j \neq i} \{p \in \Omega \mid d(p_i, p) < d(p_j, p)\}. \tag{4}$$

$R(P; p_i)$ represents the set of points which the boat at harbor p_i can reach faster than any other boats. The domain Ω is partitioned into $R(P; p_1)$, $R(P; p_2)$, $\cdots$, $R(P; p_n)$ and their boundaries. This partition is called the *Voronoi diagram for the boat-sail distance* or the *boat-sail Voronoi diagram* for short.

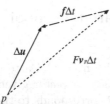

Fig. 1. Relation among the actual movement Δu, the water flow f and the boat velocity $F v_F$

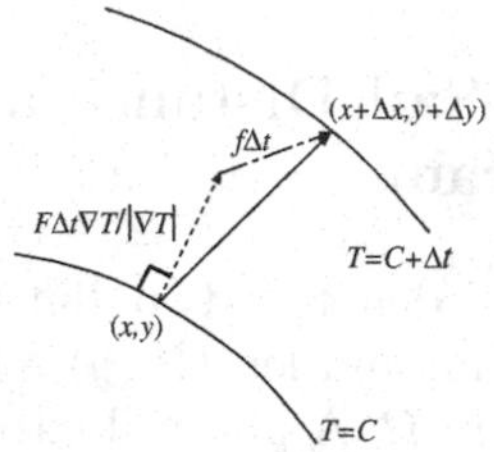

Fig. 2. Decomposition of the movement of a boat

3   Reduction to a Boundary Value Problem

Suppose that we are given the flow field $f(x, y)$ and the point $p_0 = (x_0, y_0)$ of the boat harbor in Ω. Let $T(x, y)$ be the shortest arrival time at which the boat departing p_0 at time 0 can reach the point $p = (x, y)$, that is, $T(x, y) \equiv d(p_0, p)$. In this section, we derive the partial differential equation that should be satisfied by the unknown function $T(x, y)$.

Let C be an arbitrary positive constant. The equation $T(x, y) = C$ represents a curve, any point on which can be reached in time C by the boat departing p_0 at time 0. As shown in Fig. 2, assume that the boat moving along the shortest path passes through the point (x, y) at time C and reaches the point $(x + \Delta x, y + \Delta y)$ at time $C + \Delta t$, where Δt is positive and small. Hence, in particular, we get

$$T(x + \Delta x, y + \Delta y) - T(x, y) = \Delta t. \tag{5}$$

If there is no flow, the shortest path should be perpendicular to the curve $T = C$, and hence, the progress of the boat during time interval Δt is represented by $F \frac{\nabla T}{|\nabla T|} \Delta t$. On the other hand, the displacement of the boat caused by the flow is $f \Delta t$. Hence, the total motion of the boat is represented by

$$F \frac{\nabla T}{|\nabla T|} \Delta t + f \Delta t. \tag{6}$$

Let us denote $T_x \equiv \frac{\partial T}{\partial x}$ and $T_y \equiv \frac{\partial T}{\partial y}$, respectively. Also let $g(x, y)$ and $h(x, y)$ denote the first and second components of $f(x, y)$. Then from the equation (6), we get

$$\Delta x = F \frac{T_x}{|\nabla T|} \Delta t + g \Delta t, \quad \Delta y = F \frac{T_y}{|\nabla T|} \Delta t + h \Delta t. \tag{7}$$

Hence, we get

$$T(x + \Delta x, y + \Delta y) = T(x, y) + T_x \Delta x + T_y \Delta y + \mathrm{O}((\Delta x)^2 + (\Delta y)^2)$$
$$= T(x, y) + T_x(F \frac{T_x}{|\nabla T|} + g) \Delta t + T_y(F \frac{T_y}{|\nabla T|} + h) \Delta t + \mathrm{O}(\Delta t^2).$$

Substituting this equation in equation (5), we get

$$F|\nabla T| = 1 - \nabla T \cdot f. \tag{8}$$

This is the partial differential equation that should be satisfied by the arrival time $T(x, y)$.

In what follows, we assume that $F = 1$ for simplicity. Hence, we consider the partial differential equation

$$|\nabla T| = 1 - \nabla T \cdot f, \tag{9}$$

together with the boundary condition

$$T(x_0, y_0) = 0. \tag{10}$$

4 Numerical Method Based on the Fast Marching Method

Standard methods for solving boundary value problems are the finite difference method and the finite element method. However, we cannot use these methods for our problem, because our partial differential equation is quadratic, but not linear. On the other hand, our equation has the property that the arrival time $T(x, y)$ is monotone increasing as we move along the shortest paths starting at p_0. A typical equation of this type is the eikonal equation $S|\nabla T| = 1$ [3], where T is the unknown function representing the arrival times, and S is a known speed of evolution that depends on the location (x, y), and the eikonal equation can be solved efficiently and stably by the fast marching method [8]. In this section, we modify the fast marching method and construct a numerical method for solving our boundary value problem.

4.1 Finite Difference Approximation

In Ω, we place the grid points $(x_i, y_i) = (i \Delta x, j \Delta y)$ for $i, j = 0, \pm 1, \pm 2, \cdots$, where Δx and Δy are small constants. For each grid point (x_i, y_i), we associate $T_{ij} = T(x_i, y_i)$. $T_{00} = T(x_0, y_0) = 0$ because of the boundary condition (10), while all the other T_{ij}'s are unknown variables.

Starting with the neighbors of (x_0, y_0), we want to compute T_{ij}'s point by point from smaller values to larger values. Hence, we use an upwind-like scheme.

Let us define

$$D_{ij}^{+x}T = \frac{T_{i+1,j} - T_{ij}}{\Delta x}, \quad D_{ij}^{-x}T = \frac{T_{ij} - T_{i-1,j}}{\Delta x},$$
$$D_{ij}^{+y}T = \frac{T_{i,j+1} - T_{ij}}{\Delta y}, \quad D_{ij}^{-y}T = \frac{T_{ij} - T_{i,j-1}}{\Delta y}.$$

Then, the upwind-like finite differences of first order are written by

$$D_{ij}^x T \equiv \max(D_{ij}^{-x}T, -D_{ij}^{+x}T, 0), \quad D_{ij}^y T \equiv \max(D_{ij}^{-y}T, -D_{ij}^{+y}T, 0). \tag{11}$$

If the values of the nearest and the second nearest girds from (x_i, y_i) have already been known, we can use the upwind-like finite differences of the second order [9].

Let us define g_{ij} and h_{ij} by $g(x_i, y_i)$ and $h(x_i, y_i)$, respectively. We replace ∇T by $(D_{ij}^x T, D_{ij}^y T)$ and f by (g_{ij}, h_{ij}) in our target equation (9), and thus we obtain the finite difference version of the equation:

$$(D_{ij}^x T)^2 + (D_{ij}^y T)^2 = (1 - (D_{ij}^x T)g_{ij} + (D_{ij}^y T)h_{ij})^2. \tag{12}$$

When we solve this equation, the value of T at the neighbor grid points, that are nearer to the harbor, have already been given. Hence, this equation is quadratic in the single unknown T_{ij}.

4.2   Algorithm

We solve our boundary value problem by the same strategy as the fast marching method by Sethian [8]. This method is similar to the Dijkstra method. We consider the grid structure the graph in which the vertices are grid points and the edges connect the four neighbors of each grid point. We start with the boat harbor at which $T_{ij} = 0$, and compute T_{ij}'s one by one from the nearest grid point. The only difference from the Dijkstra method is that the quadratic equation (12) is solved to obtain the value of T_{ij}.

In the next algorithm, the grid points are classified into three groups: "known" points, "frontier" points and "far" points. The "known" points are points at which the values T_{ij} are known. The "frontier" points are points that are not yet known but the neighbors of the "known" points. The "far" points are all the other points.

Suppose that there are n boat harbors, and they are numbered $1, 2, \cdots, n$. Let S_{ij} be the nearest harbor number at each grid point (x_i, y_i). The values S_{ij}'s specify the Voronoi regions of the boat-sail Voronoi diagram.

Algorithm 1 (Boat-sail Voronoi diagram)

Input: flow function $f(x, y)$ in Ω and the n harbors $q_1, q_2, \cdots, q_n$.
Output: Arrival time T_{ij} and the nearest harbor number S_{ij} at each grid point.
Procedure:

1. For $k = 1, 2, \cdots, n$, set $T_{ij} \leftarrow 0$ and $S_{ij} \leftarrow k$ for harbor q_k, and $T_{ij} \leftarrow \infty$ for all the other points.

2. Name the grid points $q_1, q_2, \cdots, q_n$ as "frontier", and all the other grid points as "far".
3. choose the "frontier" point $p = (x_i, y_i)$ with the smallest value of T_{ij}, and rename it as "known".
4. For all the neighbors of p that are not "known", do 4.1, 4.2 and 4.3.
    4.1 If p is "far", rename it as "frontier".
    4.2 Recompute the value of T_{ij} by solving the equation (12).
    4.3 If the recomputed value T_{ij} is smaller than the current value, update T_{ij} and also update S_{ij} as the harbor number of the neighbor grid points whose values are used in solving the equation (12).
5. If all the grid points are "known", stop. Otherwise go to Step 3.

Let N be the number of the grid points in Ω. Then, we can prove that Algorithm 1 runs in $O(N \log N)$ time; see Sethian [9] for the derivation of this time complexity.

4.3   Numerical Experiments

Using Algorithm 1, we constructed the Voronoi diagram in the flow field. Here we assumed that the water flows at the same speed uniformly left to right. Fig. 3 shows the Voronoi diagram for the flow of speed 0.4, generated by 10 generators randomly located in a square region.

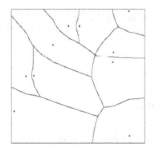

Fig. 3. Voronoi diagram by Algorithm 1 for a constant flow $f = (0.4, 0)$

In this case, the bisectors in this Voronoi diagram should essentially be hyperbola [10]. Almost all bisectors, however, are not hyperbola, that is, the bisectors have some distortions. The distortions arise along the vertical lines extended from the generators. In order to investigate the reason of this phenomenon, we plotted in Fig. 4 the isoplethic curve spreading from a single generator in uniform flow. In this situation, the isoplethic curves must essentially be circles. The computed isotropic curves, however, are destroied in the fan-shape area between the vertical line and the slanted line extending in the upper right direction.

The reason for this can be considered in the following way. As pointed out by Sethian [9], the fast marching method sometimes visits a grid point with larger arrival time before it visits a grid point with smaller arrival time. Let us consider the situation shown in Fig. 5, where the grid point 0 is the start point. The two broken half lines represent the set of points which have the fastest arrival time among the points on each line parallel to the x axis (the slopes of these lines are $\pm\tan|f|$). In this case, the actual arrival time at the grid point 2 is faster than the arrival time at the grid point 1. However, in the fast marching method, the grid point 1 is computed before the grid point 2 is computed. Consequently, the computation for the arrival time at the grid point 2 is carried out using the arrival time at the grid point 1, which is bigger than the true arrival time at the grid point 2. Hence, it is impossible to correctly compute the arrival time at the grid point 2.

Fig. 4. Isoplethic circle constructed by Algorithm 1

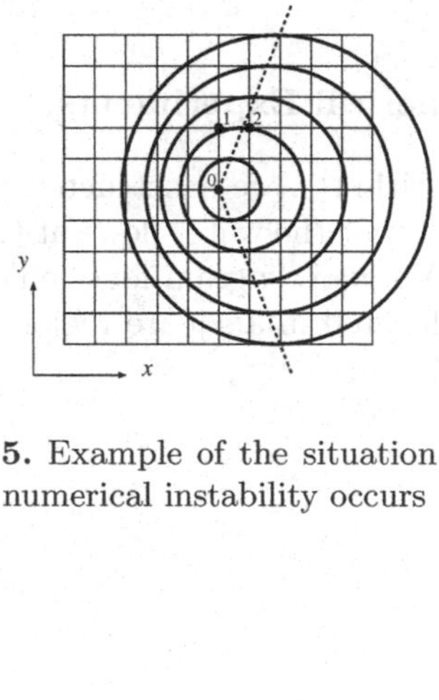

Fig. 5. Example of the situation such that numerical instability occurs

5   Improved Method

In the previous section, we explained why the scheme of the fast marching method can't work very well for our boundary value problem. In order to overcome the difficulty, here we will propose a new scheme which can compute the arrival times in a more stable manner.

For a while, let us assume that the flow be constant (g_c, h_c) over Ω. Supposed that the boat departs from the start point (x_s, y_s) at time 0. Then, location (x, y) of the boat at time t is represented by

$$(x - x_s - g_c t)^2 + (y - y_s - h_c t)^2 = F^2 t^2. \qquad (13)$$

As t can be considered the third axis, that is perpendicular to the x-y plane, the equation (13) represents the cone such that the cross-section generated by a cutting plain parallel to the x-y plain is a circle. Note that the axis of this cone is not perpendicular to the x-y plane unless $f = 0$.

Suppose that a flow vector f and a maximum speed F be given. Let t_1 and t_2 be the arrival times at (x'_1, y'_1) and (x'_2, y'_2), respectively, whose values have already been computed. The center (x_s, y_s) of the cone (13) is obtained by

$$x_s = \frac{1}{2}\left\{ x_1 + x_2 - \frac{(x_1 - x_2)F^2(t_1^2 - t_2^2)}{d^2} \right.$$

$$\left. \pm \frac{|y_1 - y_2|\sqrt{4F^2t_1^2t_2^2 - \{d^2 - F^2(t_1^2 + t_2^2)\}^2}}{d^2} \right\},$$

$$y_s = \frac{1}{2}\left\{ y_1 + y_2 - \frac{(y_1 - y_2)F^2(t_1^2 - t_2^2)}{d^2} \right.$$

$$\left. \mp \frac{\mathrm{sgn}(y_1 - y_2)(x_1 - x_2)\sqrt{4F^2t_1^2t_2^2 - \{d^2 - F^2(t_1^2 + t_2^2)\}^2}}{d^2} \right\}, \quad (14)$$

where $x_1 = x'_1 - g_c t$, $y_1 = y'_1 - h_c t$, $d^2 = (x_1 - x_2)^2 + (y_1 - y_2)^2$ and $\mathrm{sgn}(x)$ is the sign function; if $x > 0$, then $\mathrm{sgn}(x) = 1$ and if $x < 0$, then $\mathrm{sgn}(x) = -1$. After getting the center of the cone by the equation (14), we can compute the arrival time at any grid point by the equation (13).

From now on, we extend the above method to a general case, that is, we assume that the flow is not constant. Let $p = (x, y)$ be the position at which we want to compute the arrival time, and (g', h') be the flow at the grid point p. Let also t_1 and t_2 be the arrival times at the grid point (x_1, y_1) and (x_2, y_2). In addition, suppose that $|x - x_i| \leq 1$ and $|y - y_i| \leq 1$ for $i = 1$, 2, and that f can be regarded to be constant around p. Then, we can solve the equations (13) and (14), and we regard the obtained arrival time as the approximated solution.

Now, we are ready to construct a new method, which we name *cone approximation method*. The strategy is just to replace the first order differences in the fast marching method with this cone approximation. We, however, should deal with the way to choose grid points. In order to compute the arrival time by the cone approximation scheme, two grid points are definitely needed. However, if $D_{ij}^x T = 0$ or $D_{ij}^y T = 0$, then as only one of the four neighbour grid points has a value, one more grid point should be taken out from the "known" set.

There is one more factor we should consider in choosing the two grid points, say p_1 and p_2, because the estimation of a cone is unstable if p_1 and p_2 are too close. In order to conquer the difficulty, we will use p_1 and p_2 that are not too close to each other, that is, we widen the distance between p_1 and p_2. For that purpose, we fix a certain time t_0. Once the arrival time of any grid point comes between $(n - 1)t_0$ and nt_0 for some integer n, we select the grid points p_1 and p_2 in such a way that $|p_1 - p_2| = n$, and compute the equation (14) using these grid points.

Thus, we replace the step 4.2 in the algorithm with the following, where $\lceil u \rceil$ represents the smallest integer not smaller than u:

4.2' $n \leftarrow \lceil t/t_0 \rceil$, select p_1 and p_2 near p out of "known", in such a way that $|p_1 - p_2| = n$, and recompute T_{ij} by solving (13) and (14).

Fig. 6 shows the isoplethic curves computed by this method. In comparison with Fig. 4, we can see that Fig. 6 is much improved.

Fig. 6. Isoplethic circle constructed by the cone approximation

Finally, two examples of the Voronoi diagrams in the flow field are shown in Figs. 7 and 8. Fig. 7 shows the Voronoi diagram for a constant flow $f = (0.4, 0)$, generated by the same generators as in Fig. 3. Fig. 8 shows the Voronoi diagram for the flow field $f = (-0.3 \sin \theta, 0.3 \cos \theta)$, generated by the set of 10 generators randomly located in doughnut region: $0.25 < x^2 + y^2 < 1$.

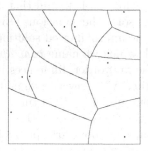

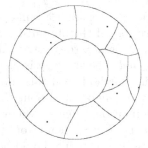

Fig. 7. Voronoi diagram by the cone approximation for a constant flow $f = (0.4, 0)$, generated by 10 generators

Fig. 8. Voronoi diagram for the flow field $f = (-0.3 \sin \theta, 0.3 \cos \theta)$, generated by 10 generators

6   Concluding Remarks

We first defined the boat-sail distance and the associated Voronoi diagram, next derived the partial differential equation satisfied by the first arrival time, thirdly constructed algorithms for computing the distances and the Voronoi diagrams, and finally showed computational experiments. The concept of the boat-sail distance is natural and intuitive, but the computation is not trivial. Actually the original definition of the boat-sail distance given by the equations (2) and (3) does not imply any explicit idea for computing this distance, because the shortest path is unknown. This seems the main reason why these concepts have not been studied from the computational point of view.

Our breakthrough toward efficient computation is that we succeeded in formulating the problem as the boundary value problem. The distance is defined according to the notion of the boat sailing, and hence a naive formulation will reach an initial value problem of a partial differential equation containing the time variable and its derivatives. In this paper, on the other hand, we concentrated on the first arrival time as the unknown function, and thus constructed an equation without time variable. Moreover, this partial differential equation is quadratic, which is not so simple as linear, but is still tractable. This formulation enables us to use the same idea as the fast marching method, which was originally proposed for the eikonal equation, and thus could construct efficient algorithms.

Acknowledgement. This work is supported by the 21st Century COE Program of the Information Science and Technology Strategic Core, and the Grant-in-aid for Scientific Research (S)15100001 of the Ministry of Education, Science, Sports and Culture of Japan.

References

1. B. Aronov: On the geodesic Voronoi diagram of point sites in a simple polygon. *Algorithmica*, vol. 4 (1989), pp. 109–140.
2. P. F. Ash and E. D. Bolker: Generalized Dirichlet tessellations. *Geometriae Dedicata*, vol. 20 (1986), pp. 209–243.
3. R. Courant and D. Hilbert: *Methods of Mathematical Physics Volume II*, Wiley, 1989.
4. S. Fortune: Voronoi diagrams and Delaunay triangulations. In D.-Z. Du and F. K. Hwang (eds.): *Computing in Euclidean Geometry*, World Scientific Publishing, Singapore, 1992, pp. 193–233.
5. K. Kobayashi and K. Sugihara: Crystal Voronoi diagram and its applications. *Future Generation Computer System*, vol. 18 (2002), pp. 681–692.
6. D.-T. Lee: Two-dimensional Voronoi diagrams in the L_p-metric. *Journal of the ACM*, vol. 27 (1980), pp. 604–618.
7. A. Okabe, B. Boots, K. Sugihara and S. N. Chiu: *Spatial Tessellations — Concepts and Applications of Voronoi Diagrams, Second Edition*. John Wiley and Sons, Chichester, 2000.
8. J. A. Sethian: Fast marching method. *SIAM Review*, vol. 41 (1999), pp. 199–235.
9. J. A. Sethian: *Level Set Methods and Fast Marching Methods, Second Edition*. Cambridge University Press, Cambridge, 1999.
10. K. Sugihara: Voronoi diagrams in a river. *International Journal of Computational Geometry and Applications*, vol. 2 (1992), pp. 29–48.

Polygonal Path Approximation: A Query Based Approach

Ovidiu Daescu and Ningfang Mi

Department of Computer Science, University of Texas at Dallas
Richardson, TX 75080, USA
{daescu,nxm024100}@utdallas.edu

Abstract. In this paper we present a new, query based approach for approximating polygonal chains in the plane. We give a few results related with this approach, some of more general interest, and propose a greedy heuristic to speed up the computation. We also give an $O(n \log n)$ time, factor 2 approximation algorithm with infinite beam criterion. Finally, we show that the query based approach can be used to obtain a subquadratic time exact algorithm with infinite beam criterion and Euclidean distance metric if some condition on the input path holds.

1 Introduction

A polygonal path or chain P in the plane, with n vertices, is defined as an ordered set of vertices $(p_1, p_2, \ldots, p_n)$, such that any two consecutive vertices p_i, p_{i+1} are connected by the line segment $\overline{p_i p_{i+1}}$, for $1 \leq i < n$. The polygonal path approximation problem asks to approximate a general polygonal path P by another polygonal path P' whose vertices are constrained to form an ordered subset of the vertices of P. Polygonal path approximation appears as a subproblem in many applications in geographic information systems (GIS), cartography, computer graphics, medical imaging and data compression. Efficient solutions to this problem may lead to better/faster solutions for more complex problems.

1.1 Problem Definition

Given a planar polygonal path $P = (p_1, p_2, \ldots, p_n)$, the polygonal path approximation problem is to find a path $P' = (p_{i_1} = p_1, p_{i_2}, \ldots, p_{i_m} = p_n)$ such that, for each $j \in \{1, 2, \ldots, m-1\}$: (i) $i_j < i_{j+1}$, where $i_j, i_{j+1} \in \{1, 2, \ldots, n\}$ and (ii) the subpath $(p_{i_j}, p_{i_j+1}, \ldots, p_{i_{j+1}})$ of P is contained in some *error tolerance* region of the line segment $\overline{p_{i_j} p_{i_{j+1}}}$. We will also consider the case when the vertices of the approximation are not restricted to a subset of the original path.

The *error tolerance* region of a line segment $\overline{p_i p_j}$ is defined by an error measure criterion. A few error criteria have been used in solving various polygonal path approximation problems, not necessarily of the form above [3, 8, 10, 14, 15, 18, 12, 19, 20, 21, 23, 2, 9, 5, 1]. If not otherwise specified, we consider the error criterion used in [14, 20, 23, 9], called the *infinite beam*

T. Ibaraki, N. Katoh, and H. Ono (Eds.): ISAAC 2003, LNCS 2906, pp. 36–46, 2003.

or *parallel-strip* criterion, with the Euclidean, L_2 measure of distance. With this criterion, the ϵ-tolerance region of a line segment $\overline{p_i p_j}$ is the set of points that are within distance ϵ from the line $L(\overline{p_i p_j})$ supporting $\overline{p_i p_j}$. If a subpath $P_{i_j, i_{j+1}} = (p_{i_j}, p_{i_j+1}, \ldots, p_{i_{j+1}})$ of P is contained in the ϵ-tolerance region of line segment $\overline{p_{i_j} p_{i_{j+1}}}$ of P', then $\overline{p_{i_j} p_{i_{j+1}}}$ is an ϵ-*approximating* segment for $P_{i_j, i_{j+1}}$. A path P' is an ϵ-*approximation* of P if each line segment $\overline{p_{i_j} p_{i_{j+1}}}$ of P', for $j = 1, 2, \ldots, m - 1$, is an ϵ-*approximating* segment. for the corresponding subpath of P. In addition, other commonly used error criteria are the tolerance zone [18, 20, 21] and uniform measure [2].

In this paper, we address the optimization version of the path approximation problem, called the **min-# problem**: Given a polygonal path P and a positive approximation error ϵ, find an ϵ-approximating path P' of P with the smallest number of vertices.

While the tolerance zone criterion would produce a compressed version that better captures the features of the original path, the motivation for studying the problem under infinite beam criterion is two fold. The first reason is that the best known solutions under tolerance zone compute approximating lines or semilines in order to obtain approximating segments. Thus, some of the results we develop may be useful for tolerance zone. The second reason is that infinite beam criterion gives a better degree of compression.

Lemma 1. *Let P' be an ϵ-approximating path of P with tolerance zone criterion. Then P' is an ϵ-approximating path of P with infinite beam criterion.*

1.2 Previous Work

Early results for the min-# problem, under various error criteria, were presented by Imai and Iri [18, 19, 20], Melkman and O'Rourke [21] and Toussaint [23]. Their graph based approach has been later exploited by most of the algorithms devoted to the problem [14, 8, 9, 2, 5]. However, with the exception of Agarwal and Varadarajan algorithms [2], all the other algorithms have quadratic or superquadratic time complexity. The algorithms in [2] combine the previous iterative graph based approach with divide and conquer and, using graph compression techniques and more complicated data structures, achieve $O(n^{4/3+\delta})$ time and space complexities, where $\delta > 0$ is an arbitrarily small constant. However, those algorithms work for L_1 distance metric and it has been left as an open problem in [2] to extend them to the more general, L_2 distance metric. Very recently, algorithms with running times that depend on the size of the output have been proposed in [11], by observing that only the edges of G that are needed by the shortest path computation in G need be computed. If the vertices of the approximating path are not required to be a subset of the vertices of the input, then faster algorithms are possible [16, 19, 15]. In [1], near-linear time algorithms are proposed for computing an approximating path with vertices among those of P.

Solutions to polygonal subdivision simplification problems are also based on polygonal path simplification. In [12], polygonal path simplification has been used to approximate a subdivision S with N vertices and M extra points in

$O(N(N + M) \log N)$ time. The simplification is only required to satisfy a set of constraints. If a minimum size simplification is sought, the problem becomes NP-hard [15] and, unless P=NP, one cannot obtain in polynomial time an approximation within a factor of $n^{1/5-\delta}$ of an optimal solution, for any $\delta > 0$ [13].

1.3   Our Results

Quadratic or near-quadratic time algorithms for planar min-# problem with L_2 distance metric have been developed almost two decades ago. However, no subquadratic time algorithms are known with L_2 metric and no nontrivial lower bound could be proved. In this paper we present a new, query based approach for solving the min-# problem that carries out the computation in a dual space. Our results imply an $O(n \log n)$ breadth first search procedure for some quadratic size graphs and an $O(n \log n)$ preprocessing, $O(\log n)$ query time solution for the following problem: Given a set of n equal radius disks $D_1, D_2, \dots, D_n$, construct a data structure that, for a query triplet (L, i, j), where L is a line and i and j are integers such that $1 \le i < j \le n$, answers whether L intersects all disks $D_i, D_{i+1}, \dots, D_j$. We further give an $O(n \log n)$ time, factor 2 approximation algorithm with infinite beam criterion. Finally, we show that the dual space approach can be used to obtain a subquadratic time exact algorithm with infinite beam criterion and L_2 distance metric if the following condition on the input path holds: $d(p_i, p_j) \notin [\epsilon, \epsilon\sqrt{2}]$, for $1 \le i < j \le n$ (in fact, it can be shown that it is enough to require that for each vertex $p_i \in P$, only a "small" (constant) number of vertices p_j are such that $d(p_i, p_j) \in [\epsilon, \epsilon\sqrt{2}]$). Although in a special case, this is the first subquadratic result for path approximation with L_2 distance metric. The algorithms we propose are simple, based on standard geometric operations, and thus suitable for efficient implementation. A basic version of our solution has been implemented and preliminary results are very promising when compared to previous algorithms.

2   Preliminaries

In this section, we briefly present the general structure of previous algorithms for solving the min-# problem. We exemplify the algorithms for the infinite beam criterion. To solve the min-# problem, those algorithms first build a path approximation, directed acyclic graph G. An optimal approximating path P' is then obtained by a shortest path computation in G. As observed in [9], in many cases one need not explicitly construct G: an optimal path can be computed while computing the ϵ-approximating segments. Let $D(p_i, \epsilon)$ denote the disk with center p_i and radius ϵ. The algorithms for computing the ϵ-approximating segments use an iterative, incremental approach to find the largest index j such that disks $D(p_{i+1}, \epsilon), D(p_{i+2}, \epsilon), \dots, D(p_j, \epsilon)$ admit a line transversal through p_i.

A more efficient approach [11] is to use a breadth first computation of the ϵ-approximating edges that simulates the breadth first shortest path computation in an ϵ-approximating graph G. The structure of the breadth first traversal

(BFT) approach is presented below, with *enqueue* and *dequeue* being the standard queue operations.

1: enqueue(1)
2: **for** $j = 2$ to n **do**
3:    $visit(j) = 0$.
4: **end for**
5: **repeat**
6:    $i =$ dequeue(), $j = i + 1$.
7:    **while** $D(p_{i+1}, \epsilon), D(p_{i+2}, \epsilon), \ldots, D(p_j, \epsilon)$ admit line transversal through p_i **do**
8:       If $!visit(j)$, check if $\overline{p_i p_j}$ is an ϵ-approximating segment; if yes, $visit(j) = 1$, set path length at p_j and enqueue(j).
9:       $j = j + 1$.
10:    **end while**
11: **until** p_n has been reached.

Lemma 2. *With the BFT approach, the shortest p_1-to-p_i path length at a vertex p_i of P is correctly computed when the vertex is enqueued and will not be updated by future computation.*

3   A Query Based Approach

From Lemma 2, it follows that it may be appropriate to combine the BFT algorithm described in the previous section with a query method for computing ϵ-approximating edges, rather than using the incremental method of computation. This may also be interesting for practical applications mentioned earlier, such as animation, where one may want to approximate various subpaths of P at different times. To this end, we divide the vertices of P in three categories: (1) *processed*: those visited by BFT that are no longer in the queue, (2) *active*: those visited by BFT that are in the queue and (3) *inactive*: those that have not yet been reached by the BFT. With a query method, one should be able to answer fast if $\overline{p_i p_j}$ is an ϵ-approximating segment without first having to compute information for vertices p_k, where $i < k < j$. Specifically, the following two operations should be supported.

- $Span(i)$: compute the largest index j such that the line segment $\overline{p_i p_j}$ could be an ϵ-approximating segment. Index j is the largest index such that the disks $D(p_{i+1}, \epsilon), D(p_{i+2}, \epsilon), \ldots, D(p_j, \epsilon)$ admit a line transversal through p_i.
- $Query(i, j)$: answer if the line segment $\overline{p_i p_j}$ is an ϵ-approximating segment.

Let V_1, V_2 and V_3 be the sets of processed, active and inactive vertices, and consider the BFT algorithm at some stage. The queue associated with the BFT contains a set of vertices such that the shortest path lengths of any two of them differ by at most one. We further augment the BFT algorithm with a greedy approach: vertices in V_2 are maintained in two priority queues having as keys the indices of vertices of P, such that a dequeue operation on each of the queues returns the largest index in the queue. The first priority queue corresponds to vertices V_2^1 that can be reached with $k - 1$ links and the second one to those vertices V_2^2 reachable with k links, for some integer k such that $2 \leq k \leq n - 2$.

Lemma 3. *The time to maintain the two priority queues is $O(f(m) \log(f(m)))$, where $f(m) = O(n)$ is the number of vertices of P that can be reached from p_1 with no more than $m - 1$ ϵ-approximating segments and m is the number of vertices of a min-# approximating path.*

Observe that it is possible to have $p_i \in (V_1 \cup V_2)$ and $p_j \in V_3$ such that $i > j$. However, only pairs of the form (i, j), with $p_i \in V_2^1$, $p_j \in V_3$ and $i < j$ should be considered for $Query(i, j)$ operations. Thus, we need to maintain the set of inactive vertices such that, when a vertex p_i is dequeued from the priority queue for V_2^1, the inactive vertices p_j, with $j > i$, are easily available.

Lemma 4. *Assuming $Span(i)$ is known, the inactive vertices for p_i can be found in $O(\log I + k)$ time, where I is the set of currently inactive vertices and k is the number of inactive vertices in I with indices between i and $Span(i)$. The set I of inactive vertices can be maintained in $O(n + f(m) \log n)$ time and $O(n)$ space.*

From Lemma 3 and Lemma 4 it follows that the time complexity of the greedy BFT algorithm depends on the time complexities for performing $Span(\cdot)$ and $Query(\cdot, \cdot)$ operations and the number of failed $Query(\cdot, \cdot)$ operations. We can extend Lemma 4 as follows. Let G be an unweighted directed graph with n vertices, such that for each $v_i \in G$ there are edges $(v_i, v_{i_1}), (v_i, v_{i_1+1}), \ldots, (v_i, v_{i_2}) \in G$. That is, G can be specified by its set of vertices and the index ranges (i_1, i_2) associated with each vertex $v_i \in G$. If a standard representation is used for storing G, $O(n^2)$ space is required, since G can have $O(n^2)$ edges. Computing single source shortest paths in G using standard breadth first search takes $O(n^2)$ time.

Lemma 5. *A single source shortest path tree in a graph G specified as above can be computed in $O(n \log n)$ time and $O(n)$ space.*

Let $d(p_i, p_j)$ denote the Euclidean distance between p_i and p_j. The following lemma bounds the time complexities of $Span(i)$ and $Query(i, j)$ operations.

Lemma 6. *For any pair (p_i, p_j), with $1 \leq i < j \leq n$, $Query(i, j)$ can be answered in $O(\log n)$ time. If $d(p_i, p_j) \notin [\epsilon, \epsilon\sqrt{2}]$, for $1 \leq i < j \leq n$, then $Span(i)$ can be answered in $O(\log n)$ time.*

To prove this lemma we first introduce some geometric structures. Let p_i and p_j, with $i < j$, be two vertices of P. For a vertex $p_k \in P$, with $i < k < j$, let σ_k denote the set of lines that are tangent to the disk $D(p_k, \epsilon)$. Using a standard point-line duality transform, σ_k is mapped to a hyperbola $H_k = (H_k^a, H_k^b)$ in the dual plane [17]. The upper branch H_k^a corresponds to tangents to the upper semicircle of $D(p_k, \epsilon)$ and the lower branch H_k^b corresponds to tangents to the lower semicircle. Each branch is an x-monotone and unbounded Jordan curve and $H_k^a \cap H_k^b = \Phi$. The dual of a line transversal of $D(p_k, \epsilon)$ corresponds to a point below the upper bound H_k^a and above the lower bound H_k^b. Observe that any pair (H_i^c, H_j^d) of hyperbolic branches intersects in at most one point, where $i \neq j$ and $c, d \in \{a, b\}$. This it true only for equal-radius disks; for different radii disks each pair can intersect in at most two points.

Let $\mathcal{L}_{ij}$ be the *lower envelope* of H_k^a and let $\mathcal{U}_{ij}$ be the *upper envelope* of H_k^b, for $k = i, i+1, \ldots, j$. Then, the line $L(\overline{p_i p_j})$ is a common transversal of the set of disks $\{D(p_{i+1}, \epsilon), D(p_{i+2}, \epsilon), \ldots, D(p_{j-1}, \epsilon)\}$ (the line segment $\overline{p_i p_j}$ is a valid approximation segment) iff its dual point lies between $\mathcal{L}_{ij}$ and $\mathcal{U}_{ij}$. Using the results in [22], it follows that the complexities of $\mathcal{L}_{ij}$, $\mathcal{U}_{ij}$ and the region $\mathcal{I}_{ij}$ sandwiched between them are $O(j - i)$ and that $\mathcal{I}_{ij}$ has at most one connected component. The last property is not true for different radii disks, in which case there could be $O(j - i)$ connected components. Since for a set of n equal-radius disks, the space of line transversals that are restricted to pass through a common point p can have $O(n)$ connected components [9,11], the line dual to p_i can have $O(j - i)$ disjoint segments in $\mathcal{I}_{ij}$. This is a key property that makes the min-# problem with infinite beam criterion somehow harder than with other error criteria (such as tolerance zone and uniform measure). It gives rise to the condition in Lemma 6: requiring that $d(p_i, p_j) \notin [\epsilon, \epsilon\sqrt{2}]$, for $1 \leq i < j \leq n$, assures that the line dual to p_i has at most one line segment in $\mathcal{I}_{ij}$ [11].

If we use a vertical error measure however, where the error region of a point is a vertical line segment instead of a disk, the space of line transversals that are restricted to pass through a common point can be easily seen to have at most one connected component.

Lemma 7. *The min-# problem with infinite beam criterion and vertical error measure can be solved in $O(n^{4/3+\delta})$ time and space, where $\delta > 0$ is an arbitrarily small constant.*

Proof. The result can be obtained by a simple modification of Agarwal and Varadarajan [2] min-# algorithm for x-monotone paths with uniform metric. For infinite beam criterion and vertical distance metric, the difference is that right (or left) oriented rays are replaced by lines (the path P is not monotone) and thus wedges are replaced by double wedges. The only places where this plays a role are in the computation of the lower and upper convex hulls (of the upper and lower endpoints of the vertical error segments) and in the computation of the double cone at p_i. The double cone at p_i can be found by computing the largest separating double cone of the two convex hulls, if such a separation is possible. This reduces to computing the tangents from p_i to the two convex hulls. Note that the convex hulls are used only to help compute the double cone at p_i, since only the double cone at p_i is important for the outcome of the algorithm. Then, to perform the incremental updating of the convex hulls and to compute the tangents in altogether $O(\log n)$ time, as in [2], it suffices to use the solution in [14], based on the on-line convex hull algorithm of Avis *et al.* [4].   □

We remark that a similar approach can be used with the L_1 metric. In that case, the space of line transversals to n L_1 disks, that are restricted to pass through a common point p, can have at most two connected components. This property is implicitly exploited by the subquadratic time algorithm in [2].

In what follows, we set up the data structures for computing $Span(i)$ and $Query(i, j)$. Let T be a complete binary tree such that the leaves of T are associated, in order, with the vertices of P. At each leaf l_i, we also store the hyperbolic branches H_i^a and H_i^b, the duals of the tangent lines to $D(p_i, \epsilon)$. For an internal node v in T, let i and j be the smallest and largest indices of the leaf descendants of v. We store at v the region $I(v) = \mathcal{I}_{ij}$ sandwiched between the lower envelope $\mathcal{L}_{ij}$ of $\{H_k^a \mid i \le k \le j\}$ and the upper envelope $\mathcal{U}_{ij}$ of $\{H_k^b \mid i \le k \le j\}$. We compute $I(v)$ for all vertices v of T using a divide-and-conquer method implemented by a bottom up traversal of T. The boundary of $I(v)$ is maintained as two monotone pieces, corresponding to the contributions of the lower and upper envelopes of the two sets of hyperbolic branches stored at the leaf descendants of v. Following similar arguments as in [5], $I(v)$ can be computed, for all vertices v in T, in a total of $O(n \log n)$ time. Note that in general the region $I(r)$ at the root r of T may be empty. We can use T to compute, in the same time bound, a family of trees $\mathcal{F} = \{T_1, T_2, \ldots, T_s\}$ such that T_1's leaves correspond to the longest possible prefix $D_1 = \{D(p_1, \epsilon), D(p_2, \epsilon), \ldots, D(p_{j_1}, \epsilon)\}$ that admits a line transversal, T_2's leaves correspond to the longest possible prefix starting at p_{j_1+1}, and so on. This implies the following result.

Lemma 8. *$\mathcal{F}$ can be used to compute an approximating path with vertices inside the error tolerance regions of the vertices of P and of size at most twice the size of an optimal approximation.*

Proof. For each $T_i \in \mathcal{F}$, pick a point in the intersection stored at the root of T_i and trim the dual line to a line segment with endpoints inside the first and last leaf of T_i, resulting in $|\mathcal{F}|$ line segments. Then join the resulting segments to form a path, which adds $|\mathcal{F}| - 1$ segments. Obviously, an optimal approximating path must have at least $|\mathcal{F}|$ vertices, from which the claim follows. Once $\mathcal{F}$ is available, the construction takes $O(|\mathcal{F}|)$ time. $\qquad\square$

Note that our solution is different from the greedy solutions in [15, 21, 1], which consider wedges instead of double wedges and/or may depend on some predefined stabbing order. Observe also that an $O(\log n)$ factor approximation can be obtained directly from T. Finally, it can be easily seen that the same results hold for other distance metrics, such as L_1 metric. We now give the proof for Lemma 6.

Proof (of Lemma 6). Let p_{ij} be the dual of the line $L(\overline{p_i p_j})$. To perform $Query(i, j)$ operation, we form a search path π_{ij} in $\mathcal{F}$, from the leaf l_i to the leaf l_j. Observe that l_i and l_j may be in the same tree or in different, adjacent trees of $\mathcal{F}$. We say that a node v of T is on the *right fringe* (*left fringe*) of π_{ij} if v is not on π_{ij} but it is a right (left) child of a node on π_{ij}. Noting that the query is a decomposable search problem, we can answer $Query(i, j)$ by determining if p_{ij} is inside $I(v)$ for each v that is a right (left) fringe node of π_{ij} (answering "true" if and only if it is inside them all). Using the approach in [5],

based on the fractional cascading technique of Chazelle and Guibas [6, 7], the
answer for $Query(i, j)$ can be obtained in $O(\log n)$ time. $Span(i)$ computation
proceeds in a similar way. We form a search path π_i in $\mathcal{F}$ as follows. We start
at l_i and go up the corresponding tree T_{l_i} storing l_i until we find a node with
nonempty intersection on the right fringe or we reach the root of T_{l_i}. If the root
has been reached, we go on a downward path in T_{l_i+1} (if it exists) until we find
a node with nonempty intersection on the left fringe. Let v be the root of that
subtree (right or left fringe) and let $l(p_i)$ be the dual line of p_i. We then compute the intersection of $l(p_i)$ with $I(v)$. The condition in the lemma assures that
$l(p_i) \cap I(v)$ has at most one connected component. If $v \in T_{l_i}$ and $l(p_i) \cap I(v) \neq \Phi$,
set $l(p_i) = l(p_i) \cap I(v)$. Then go up T_{l_i} until a node w on the right fringe of π_i
with $l(p_i) \cap I(w) = \Phi$ is found or the root of T_{l_i} has been reached (in this case
let w be the root of T_{l_i+1}), while updating $l(p_i)$ along the way. Then follow a
downward path (possibly in T_{l_i+1}) as follows. Let v be the current node and
let v_l and v_r be the left and right children of v. If $l(p_i) \cap I(v_l) \neq \Phi$ proceed
on right fringe of v with $l(p_i) = l(p_i) \cap I(v_l)$, else proceed on left fringe of v
with $l(p_i)$. The computation stops at some leaf l_j. Clearly, $Span(i) = j - 1$. The
computation for $Span(i)$ at a node in the tree is similar to that for $Query(i, j)$,
and thus $Span(i)$ can be answered in the same amount of time.   □

Corollary 1. *Given a set of n equal radius disks $D_1, D_2, \ldots, D_n$, in $O(n \log n)$
time one can construct a data structure of size $O(n \log n)$ such that, for a query
triplet (L, i, j), where L is a line and i and j are integers, $1 \leq i < j \leq n$, it can
be decided in $O(\log n)$ time whether L intersects all disks $D_i, D_{i+1}, \ldots, D_j$.*

The results in Lemma 3, Lemma 4 and Lemma 6 can be combined to obtain
an efficient algorithm for solving the min-# problem. Alternatively, we can use
Lemma 6 together with the divide and conquer procedure in [2] to obtain the
following result.

Lemma 9. *Under the condition in Lemma 6, the min-# problem with infinite
beam criterion and L_2 distance metric can be solved in $O(n^{4/3+\delta})$ time, where
$\delta > 0$ is an arbitrarily small constant.*

Although in a special case, this is the first subquadratic result for path approximation with L_2 distance metric. The result is useful especially when the
algorithm is used to approximate borders of fat planar regions and terrains,
and in medical imaging, where the condition stated in the lemma may be often
satisfied.

We conjecture that our results, under the condition of Lemma 6, can be
extended to tolerance zone criterion. A technical difficulty is in deciding whether
the line segment $\overline{p_i p_j}$ intersects all disks with index $i < k < j$, given that they
are intersected by $L(\overline{p_i p_j})$. It remains an open problem to extend these results
for general paths while maintaining subquadratic time.

4   Experimental Results

In this section, we report the results of our experiments and give comparisons for three algorithms for solving the min-# problem. The first two algorithms, i.e. the iterative, incremental approach and a breadth first traversal (BFT) approach are presented in Section 2. For the third algorithm, we use two priority queues having as keys the indices of vertices of P, such that a dequeue operation on each of the queues returns the largest index in the queue. In comparing the algorithms we let *sum_check* denote the sum of the check time of all vertices in P, where the check time of a vertex is the number of times it is visited during the computation.

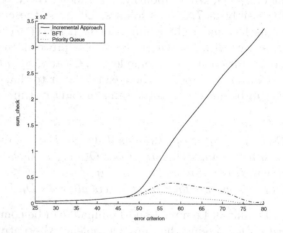

Fig. 1. Comparison of *sum_check* with different error tolerance

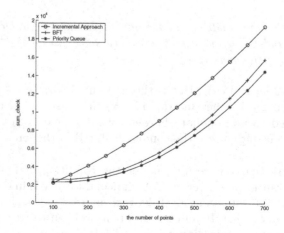

Fig. 2. Comparison of *sum_check* with diffrent number of points

We have generated two sets of test data with different error tolerance and varying number of vertices on the path, respectively. In each case of the first set, we randomly generate 1000 points in a $100 * 100$ area and test the inputs with different error tolerance ϵ. In each case of the second set, we randomly generate different number of points in a $10 * 10$ area and test the inputs with error tolerance 5. The results are illustrated in Fig. 1 and Fig. 2 and support our conclusion: (1) the incremental approach has the worst performance; (2) the BFT and the priority queue algorithms are much more efficient and (3) on average the priority queue is better than BFT. The difference in running times between the incremental and BFT approach increases as ϵ increases. This corresponds to the intuition that BFT should be much faster if coarser approximations are sought.

Acknowledgment. The authors thank Pankaj Agarwal for useful discussions.

References

1. P.K. Agarwal, S. Har-Peled, N. Mustafa, and Y. Wang. Near-linear time approximation algorithms for curve simplification. *Proc. of 10th Annual European Sympos. Algorithms*, pages 29–41, 2002.
2. P.K. Agarwal and K.R. Varadarajan. Efficient algorithms for approximating polygonal chains. *Discrete Computational Geometry*, 23:273–291, 2000.
3. H. Alt, J. Blomer, M. Godau, and H. Wagener. Approximation of convex polygons. *Proc. 10th Coll. on Autom., Lang., and Prog. (ICALP)*, pages 703–716, 1990.
4. D. Avis, H. ElGindy, and R. Seidel. Simple on-line algorithms for convex polygons. *Computational Geometry*, G.T. Toussaint, Ed., 1985.
5. G. Barequet, D.Z. Chen, O. Daescu, M.T. Goodrich, and J. Snoeyink. Efficiently approximating polygonal paths in three and higher dimensions. *Algorithmica*, 33(2):150–167, 2002.
6. B.Chazelle and L.J. Guibas. Fractional cascading: I. A data structuring technique. *Algorithmica*, 1:133–162, 1986.
7. B.Chazelle and L.J. Guibas. Fractional cascading: II. Applications. *Algorithmica*, 1:163–191, 1986.
8. W.S. Chan and F. Chin. Approximation of polygonal curves with minimum number of line segments or minimum error. *Intl. Journal of Computational Geometry and Applications*, 6(1):59–77, 1996.
9. D.Z. Chen and O. Daescu. Space-efficient algorithms for approximating polygonal curves in two dimensional space. *International Journal of Computational Geometry and Applications*, 13(2):95–112, 2003.
10. L.P. Cordella and G. Dettori. An $O(n)$ algorithm for polygonal approximation. *Pattern Recognition Letters*, 3:93–97, 1985.
11. O. Daescu. New results on path approximation. Manuscript, 2003.
12. M. de Berg, M. van Kreveld, and S. Schirra. Topologically correct subdivision simplification using the bandwidth criterion. *Cartog. and GIS*, 25:243–257, 1998.
13. R. Estkowski and J.S.B. Mitchell. Simplifying a polygonal subdivision while keeping it simple. *Proc. 17th ACM Symp. on Comput. Geom.*, pages 40–49, 2001.
14. D. Eu and G.T. Toussaint. On approximation polygonal curves in two and three dimensions. *CVGIP: Graphical Models and Image Processing*, 56(3):231–246, 1994.

15. L.J. Guibas, J.E. Hershberger, J.S.B. Mitchell, and J.S. Snoeyink. Approximating polygons and subdivisions with minimum link paths. *International Journal of Computational Geometry and Applications*, 3(4):383–415, 1993.
16. S.L. Hakimi and E.F. Schmeichel. Fitting polygonal functions to a set of points in the plane. *CVGIP: Graphical Models and Image Processing*, 53(2):132–136, 1991.
17. F. Hurtado, P. Ramos M. Noy, and C. Seara. Separating objects in the plane with wedges and strips. *Discrete Applied Mathematics*, 109:109–138, 2001.
18. H. Imai and M. Iri. Computational-geometric methods for polygonal approximations of a curve. *Computer Vision, Graphics and Image Processing*, 36:31–41, 1986.
19. H. Imai and M. Iri. An optimal algorithm for approximating a piecewise linear function. *Journal of Information Processing*, 9(3):159–162, 1986.
20. H. Imai and M. Iri. Polygonal approximations of a curve-formulations and algorithms. *Comput. Morphology*, pages 71–86, North–Holland, Amsterdam, 1988.
21. A. Melkman and J. O'Rourke. On polygonal chain approximation. *Computational Morphology*, pages 87–95, North–Holland, Amsterdam, 1988.
22. M. Sharir and P.K. Agarwal. *Davenport-Schinzel Sequences and Their Geometric Applications*, Cambridge University Press, 1995.
23. G.T. Toussaint. On the complexity of approximating polygonal curves in the plane. *Proc. IASTED International Symp. on Robotics and Automation*, 1985.

A Vertex Incremental Approach for Dynamically Maintaining Chordal Graphs

Anne Berry[1], Pinar Heggernes[2], and Yngve Villanger[2]

[1] ISIMA, Univ Clermont-Ferrand II, 63177 Aubiere, France. berry@isima.fr
[2] Informatics, Univ of Bergen, 5020 Bergen, Norway. {pinar, yngvev}@ii.uib.no

Abstract. For a chordal graph G, we study the problem of whether a new vertex u and a given set of edges between u and vertices of G can be added to G so that the resulting graph remains chordal. We show how to resolve this efficiently, and at the same time, if the answer is no, define a maximal subset of the proposed edges that can be added, or conversely a minimal set of extra edges that should be added in addition to the given set. Based on these results, we present a new algorithm which computes both a minimal triangulation and a maximal chordal subgraph of an arbitrary input graph in $O(nm)$ time. This time complexity matches the best known time bound for minimal triangulation, using a totally new vertex incremental approach. In opposition to previous algorithms, our process adds each new vertex without reconsidering any choice made at previous steps, and without requiring any knowledge of the vertices that might be added at further steps.

1 Introduction

Chordal graphs are a well studied class, with applications in many fields. One important aspect in applications is maintaining a chordal graph incrementally, and previous work has dealt with the problem of adding or removing an arbitrary *edge* while maintaining chordality [6], [16].

When the graph fails to be chordal, edges can be added or removed to obtain a chordal graph: either add edges until the graph becomes chordal, a process called *triangulation*, or remove edges until the graph becomes chordal, thus computing a *chordal subgraph*. Adding or removing a minimum number of edges has been shown to be NP-hard [17], [22]. However, adding or removing an inclusion minimal set of edges can be done in polynomial time. Given an arbitrary chordal subgraph (e.g., an independent set on the vertices of the graph) or supergraph (e.g, a complete graph on the same vertex set) of the input graph, edges can be added or removed one by one after testing that the resulting graph remains chordal, until no further candidate edge can be found. This ensures that minimality is achieved, by the results of [18]. The problem of maintaining a chordal graph by edge addition or deletion and the problem of computing a maximal chordal subgraph or a minimal chordal supergraph are thus strongly related.

The problem of adding an inclusion minimal set of *fill* edges, called *minimal triangulation*, has been well studied since 1976, and several $O(nm)$ time

T. Ibaraki, N. Katoh, and H. Ono (Eds.): ISAAC 2003, LNCS 2906, pp. 47–57, 2003.

algorithms exist for solving it [3], [4], [10], [18], though none of these algorithms uses an edge incremental approach as described above. However, the algorithm proposed in [7], which requires even less time when the fill is small, does use an edge deletion approach. The reverse problem of computing a maximal chordal subgraph has also been studied, and several $O(\Delta m)$ time algorithms exist, where Δ is the maximum degree in the graph [2], [11], [21].

In this paper, we present a new process for adding a *vertex* with a given set of incident edges to a chordal graph while maintaining chordality, which we are able to implement more efficiently than if we were to add the corresponding edges one by one. Our process is based on two new characterizations. The first is a characterization of a chordal graph by its edges, and the second is a characterization of the set of edges R incident to a vertex u which must be added to a chordal graph along with edge (u, v) to ensure that chordality is preserved. We show that we can compute this set R of edges in $O(n)$ time, by proposing a data structure which corresponds to a clique tree of the current chordal subgraph.

We use our results to compute both a minimal triangulation and a maximal chordal subgraph of a given arbitrary graph in $O(nm)$ time. This is done by an incremental process which repeatedly adds a new vertex u to the already constructed chordal graph H along with a maximal set of edges of the input graph between u and H, or a minimal set of extra edges between u and H in addition to original such edges.

Some of the existing algorithms which compute a maximal chordal subgraph or a minimal triangulation also use a vertex incremental process [2], [4], [5], [11], [18], [21], though none of them compute both chordal graphs at the same time. In addition, all these previous algorithms require knowing the whole graph in advance, as either vertices that are not yet processed are marked in some way to define the next vertex in the process, or edges are added between pairs of vertices that are not yet processed.

Our approach here is completely different from the previous ones, as it is more general: At each vertex addition step, we do not require the added vertex to be or to become simplicial, which enables us to process the vertices in any order. Moreover, we add only edges incident to the new vertex, so that we never need to reconsider or change the chordal graph which has been computed so far.

As a result, our process can add any vertex with any proposed neighborhood, and efficiently give a correction if the resulting graph fails to be chordal, either by computing a maximal subset of the edges to be added, or a minimal set of extra edges along with the proposed ones. In addition, the transitory chordal graph is maintained in a dynamic fashion, as making the desired or necessary additions to the graph does not require a recomputation from start, which would be the case for the other mentioned algorithms if the input graph was to be extended with new vertices after some steps or the end of the computation.

2   Graph Theoretic Background and Notation

We assume that all input graphs are simple and connected. For disconnected graphs, the results can be applied on each connected component. A graph is denoted $G = (V, E)$, with $n = |V|$, and $m = |E|$. A vertex sequence $v_1 - v_2 - \dots - v_k$ describes a *path* if (v_i, v_{i+1}) is an edge for $1 \leq i < k$. The *length* of a path is the number of edges in it. A *cycle* is a path that starts and ends with the same vertex. A *chord* of a cycle (path) is an edge connecting two non-consecutive vertices of the cycle (path). A *clique* is a set of vertices that are all pairwise adjacent. A *simplicial* vertex is one whose neighborhood induces a clique.

For the following definitions, we will omit subscript G when the graph is clear from the context. The *neighborhood* of a vertex v in G is $N_G(v) = \{u \neq v \mid (u, v) \in E\}$, and for a set of vertices A, $N_G(A) = \cup_{x \in A} N_G(x) - A$. $G(A)$ is the subgraph induced by a vertex set $A \subseteq V$, but we often denote it simply by A when there is no ambiguity. We would like to stress that when we say merely *subgraph* we do not necessarily mean an induced subgraph. Thus subgraph can be a proper subgraph on the same vertex set with fewer edges.

A subset S of V is called a *separator* if $G(V \setminus S)$ is disconnected. S is a *uv-separator* if vertices u and v are in different connected components of $G(V \setminus S)$, and a *minimal uv-separator* if no subset of S is a uv-separator. S is a *minimal separator* of G if there is some pair $\{u, v\}$ of vertices in G such that S is a minimal uv-separator. Equivalently, S is a minimal separator if there exist two connected components C_1 and C_2 of $G(V \setminus S)$ such that $N_G(C_1) = N_G(C_2) = S$.

A pair of non adjacent vertices $\{u, v\}$ is a *2-pair* in G if there is no chordless path of length 3 or more between u and v [14]. If G is not connected, then two vertices that belong to different connected components constitute a 2-pair by definition. If G is connected, it has been shown that $\{u, v\}$ is a 2-pair iff $N(u) \cap N(v)$ is a minimal uv-separator of G [1], [19].

A graph is *chordal* if it contains no chordless cycle of length ≥ 4. Consequently, all induced subgraphs of a chordal graph are also chordal. G is chordal iff every minimal separator of G is a clique [12]. Chordal graphs are the intersection graphs of subtrees of a tree [9], [13], [20], and the following result on this graph class gives a very useful tool which we will use as a data structure in our algorithm.

Theorem 1. ([9], [13], [20]) *A graph G is chordal iff there exists a tree T, whose vertex set is the set of maximal cliques of G, that satisfies the following property: for every vertex v in G, the set of maximal cliques containing v induces a connected subtree of T.*

Such a tree is called a *clique tree* [8], and each tree node of T is a vertex set of G corresponding to a maximal clique of G. We will not distinguish between cliques of G and their corresponding tree nodes. In addition, it is customary to let each edge (K_i, K_j) of T hold the vertices of $K_i \cap K_j$. Thus edges of T are also vertex sets. Although a chordal graph can have many different clique trees, these all share the following important properties that are related to an efficient implementation of our algorithm.

Theorem 2. ([9], [15]) *Let T be a clique tree of a chordal graph G. Every edge of T is a minimal separator of G, and for every minimal separator S in G, there is an edge $(K_i, K_j) = K_i \cap K_j = S$ in T.*

Theorem 3. ([8]) *T is a clique tree of G iff for every pair of distinct cliques K_i and K_j in G, the intersection $K_i \cap K_j$ is contained in every node of T (maximal clique of G) appearing on the path between K_i and K_j in T.*

Note that as a consequence, the intersection $K_i \cap K_j$ is also contained in every edge of T (minimal separator of G) appearing on the path between K_i and K_j in T. A chordal graph has at most n maximal cliques and $n-1$ minimal separators, and hence the number of nodes and edges in a clique tree is $O(n)$.

3   A New Characterization of Chordal Graphs

In this section we present a new characterization of chordal graphs that will be the basis of our algorithm.

Definition 1. *We will say that an edge (u, v) is mono saturating in $G = (V, E)$ if $\{u, v\}$ is a 2-pair in $G' = (V, E \setminus \{(u, v)\})$.*

Theorem 4. *A graph is chordal iff every edge is mono saturating.*

Proof. Let $G = (V, E)$ be chordal, and assume on the contrary that there is an edge $(u, v) \in E$ which is not mono saturating. Thus G' is connected, and $N(u) \cap N(v)$ is not a uv-separator in G'. Let us remove $N(u) \cap N(v)$ from G'. There is still a path connecting u and v in the remaining graph. Let p be a shortest such path. Now, p contains a vertex $x \in N(u)$ which is not adjacent to v, and a vertex $z \in N(v)$ which is not adjacent to u. Thus the following is a chordless cycle of length at least 4 in G: $u-p-v-u = u-x-\ldots-z-v-u$, which contradicts our assumption that G is chordal. For the other direction, let every edge in G be mono saturating, and assume on the contrary that G is not chordal. Thus there exists a chordless cycle C of length at least 4 in G. Let (u, v) be any edge of C. Since at least one other vertex of C must be removed to disconnect u and v in G', any minimal uv-separator of G' contains a vertex x of C, where $x \notin N(u)$ or $x \notin N(v)$. Therefore $N(u) \cap N(v)$ cannot be a uv-separator, which contradicts our assumption that every edge is mono saturating.

Corollary 1. *Given a chordal graph $G = (V, E)$, where $(u, v) \notin E$, the graph $(V, E \cup \{(u, v)\})$ is chordal iff $\{u, v\}$ is a 2-pair in G.*

As a consequence, while maintaining a chordal graph by adding edges, we could check every edge of the input graph to see if the endpoints constitute a 2-pair in the transitory chordal subgraph. However, this approach requires that we check every edge several times, as pairs of vertices can become 2-pairs only after the addition of some other edges. Our main result, to be presented as Theorem

5, gives a more powerful tool that allows examining each edge of the input graph only *once* during such a process, which yields our interesting time complexity.

Assume the following scenario: we are given a chordal graph G, and we want to add an edge (u, v) to G; since we want the resulting graph to remain chordal, we must allow addition of other necessary edges to achieve this, but we allow only addition of edges incident to u. (Vertex u is the most recently added vertex in the vertex incremental approach described in the next section.) Naturally, if we add every edge between u and the other vertices of G, the resulting graph is chordal. However, our main goal is to add as few edges as possible. Theorem 5 gives a necessary and sufficient condition for the addition of each such edge (u, v). Before we present it, we need the following definition for ease of notation.

Definition 2. *Given a chordal graph $G = (V, E)$ and any pair of vertices u and v in G such that $(u, v) \notin E$, $R(G, u, v) = \{(u, x) \mid x$ belongs to a minimal uv-separator of $G\}$. We will call $R(G, u, v)$ the set of required edges for (u, v) incident to u.*

Theorem 5. *Let $G = (V, E)$ be a chordal graph, let u and v be any two non-adjacent vertices of G, and assume that one wants to add edge (u, v) to G. $R(G, u, v)$ is an inclusion minimal set of edges that must be added to G along with edge (u, v) in order to obtain a chordal graph H.*

Proof. Assume that edge set $R(G, u, v) \cup \{(u, v)\}$ is added to G. We will show that H thus obtained is chordal. Observe first that (u, v) is mono saturating in H since every possible uv-separator of H is contained in $N_H(u)$, and thus does not appear on any chordless cycle of length more than 3, as we have seen in the proof of Theorem 4. Assume on the contrary that H is not chordal, and let C be a chordless cycle of length at least 4 in H. Then C must contain at least one newly added edge $(u, x) \in R(G, u, v)$. Let $C = u - y_1 - y_2 - \ldots - y_k - x - u$ with $k \geq 2$. Since edge (u, x) was added, x belongs to a minimal uv-separator S of G. Let C_1 and C_2 be two connected components of $G(V \setminus S)$ such that $N_G(C_1) = N_G(C_2) = S$. Assume without loss of generality that $u \in C_1$ and $v \in C_2$. Then every vertex of C belongs to $S \cup C_1$ since S is a clique in both G and H, and C is chordless. Thus in G, there is a chordless path p_1 containing $y_2 - \ldots - y_k - x$ between u and x, where all vertices of p_1 belong to $C_1 \cup S$. In addition there is also a chordless path p_2 between x and v (might be a single edge) passing only through vertices belonging to C_2. As a consequence, y_2 must belong to some minimal ux-separator of G, and thus also to some minimal uv-separator of G, since $p_1 - p_2$ is a chordless path between u and v in G. But then (u, y_2) belongs to $R(G, u, v)$ and has been added to H contradicting our assumption that $C = u - y_1 - y_2 - \ldots - y_k - x - u$ is a chordless cycle of H.

Now we will show that the set $R(G, u, v)$ is inclusion minimal. Assume on the contrary that (u, v) and a proper subset of $R(G, u, v)$ are added to G, and that the resulting graph H is chordal. Thus there is a vertex x belonging to a minimal uv-separator S of G such that (u, x) does not belong to H. Let C_1 be the connected component of $G(V \setminus S)$ that contains u and C_2 the one that contains v. In G there must be a chordless path p_1 between u and x with all intermediate vertices belonging to C_1, and p_2 between x and v with all intermediate vertices belonging to C_2. Let q_1 be a vertex of p_1 closest to x and adjacent to u, and let q_2 be an analogous vertex of p_2 (q_2 might be v), such that $u - p_1 - x - p_2 - v = u - p_{11} - q_1 - p_{12} - x - p_{21} - q_2 - p_{22} - v$. Then $u - q_1 - p_{12} - x - p_{21} - q_2 - u$ is a chordless cycle in H , giving us the desired contradiction.

Corollary 2. *Let $G = (V, E)$ be a chordal graph, and let u and v be any pair of non adjacent vertices in G. Then $H = (V, E \cup \{(u, v)\} \cup R(G, u, v))$ is a minimal triangulation of $(V, E \cup \{(u, v)\})$.*

4 A Vertex Incremental Algorithm for Simultaneous Maximal Subtriangulation and Minimal Triangulation

In this section we apply our results of Section 3 to the problem of computing a maximal chordal subgraph $H = (V, D)$ and a minimal triangulation $M = (V, F)$ of an arbitrary graph $G = (V, E)$, where $D \subseteq E \subseteq F$.

Our algorithm is based on the following vertex incremental principle. Start with an empty subset U of V, increase U with a new vertex u of G at each step, and do computations according to Theorem 5 to obtain a maximal chordal subgraph H of $G(U)$ or a minimal triangulation M of $G(U)$ on vertex set U at the end of each step. In the case of a maximal subtriangulation, we will allow adding only edges that belong to E between u and the vertices of H, whereas in the case of a minimal triangulation, the required edges between u and H will also be added. For this incremental approach, we first need the following two lemmas.

Lemma 1. *Given $G = (V, E)$, let $H = (U, D)$ be a maximal chordal subgraph of $G(U) = (U, E')$, where $U \subset V$ and $D \subseteq E' \subseteq E$. No edge belonging to $E' \setminus D$ can be contained in a maximal chordal subgraph of G that also contains H.*

Proof. Let (u, v) be any edge of $E' \setminus D$. Thus u and v both belong to the chordal subgraph H. Let $H' = (V, D')$ be a maximal chordal subgraph of G with $D \subset D'$, and assume on the contrary that (u, v) belongs to D'. Since induced subgraphs of chordal graphs are also chordal, $H'(U)$ is chordal and contains edge (u, v). But this contradicts the assumption that H is a maximal chordal subgraph of $G(U)$, since $H'(U)$ is a chordal subgraph of $G(U)$ that contains H as a proper subgraph.

Lemma 2. *Given $G = (V, E)$, let $M = (U, F)$ be a minimal triangulation of $G(U)$ with $U \subset V$. Then any minimal triangulation of $(V, E \cup F)$ obtained by introducing only edges with at least one endpoint in $V \setminus U$ is a minimal triangulation of G.*

Proof. Let $M' = (V, F')$ be a minimal triangulation of $(V, E \cup F)$ obtained by introducing only edges with at least one endpoint in $V \setminus U$. M' exists by Theorem 5, and M' is certainly a triangulation of G since it is chordal and contains all edges of G. Assume on the contrary that M' is not a minimal triangulation of G. Thus there is at least one edge in $F' \setminus E$ that can be removed. If this edge belongs to $F' \setminus (E \cup F)$, then this contradicts our assumption that M' is a minimal triangulation of $(V, E \cup F)$. Thus an edge (u, v) belonging to $F \setminus E$ can be removed from M' without destroying its chordality. However, since M is a minimal triangulation of $G(U)$, removing (u, v) creates a chordless cycle C of length at least 4 in M. Since no edge of $F' \setminus F$ have both its endpoints in U, $F' \setminus F$ does not contain a chord of C, and consequently the vertices belonging to C will induce a chordless cycle in M' if (u, v) is removed, giving the desired contradiction.

With the data structure proposed in the next section, computing and adding set $R(H, u, v)$ can be done in $O(n)$ time for each examined edge (u, v). Observe that every edge needs to be examined at most once, giving a total time complexity of $= O(nm)$. We are now ready to present our algorithm, and here we give the maximal chordal subgraph version.

Algorithm Incremental Maximal Subtriangulation (**IMS**)
Input: $G = (V, E)$.
Output: A maximal chordal subgraph $H = (V, D)$ of G.
Pick a vertex s of G; $U = \{s\}$; $D = \emptyset$;
for $i = 2$ to n **do**
   Pick a vertex $u \in N_G(U)$; $U = U \cup \{u\}$; $N = N_G(u) \cap U$;
   while N is not empty **do**
      Pick a vertex $v \in N$; $N = N \setminus \{v\}$;
      $X = \{x \mid x$ belongs to a minimal uv-separator of $H = (U, D)\}$;
      $R = \{(u, x) \mid x \in X\}$;
      if $R \subseteq E$ **then**
         $D = D \cup \{(u, v)\} \cup R$; $N = N \setminus X$;
   $H = (U, D)$;

Let us call **IMT** (Incremental Minimal Triangulation) the algorithm that results from removing line "**if** $R \subseteq E$ **then**" of Algorithm **IMS**. Thus in **IMT**, edge set $\{(u, v)\} \cup R$ is always added to the transitory graph for every examined edge (u, v). It can be proved by straight forward induction using Theorem 5 and Lemmas 1 and 2 that Algorithm **IMS** computes a maximal chordal subgraph and Algorithm **IMT** computes a minimal triangulation of the input graph. In Example 1, executions of both of these algorithms are shown on the same input graph. Figure 1 (a) shows **IMS** and (b) shows **IMT**.

Example 1. Consider Figure 1. The vertices of the input graph are processed in the order shown by the numbers on the vertices. At step 1, only vertex 1 is added to H. At step 2, vertex 2 and edge $(2, 1)$ are added, and similarly at steps 3 and 4, vertex 3 and edge $(3, 2)$, and vertex 4 and edge $(4, 1)$ are added, respectively. The first column of the figure shows graph H with thick lines on the

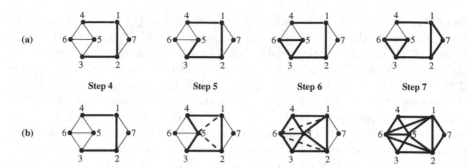

Fig. 1. The figure shows graph H in thick lines after steps 4, 5, 6, and 7 of (a) Algorithm **IMS** when computing a maximal chordal subgraph and (b) Algorithm **IMT** when computing a minimal triangulation.

input graph after these 4 steps. Graph H so far is the same for both a maximal chordal subgraph (a), and a minimal triangulation (b). We will explain the rest of the executions in more detail.

(a) At step 5, $N = \{3, 4\}$, and edge $(5, 3)$ is examined first. In this case, set X is empty, and edge $(5, 3)$ is thus added. For the addition of edge $(5, 4)$, $X = \{1, 2, 3\}$, and since required edges $(5, 1)$ and $(5, 2)$ are not present in G, edge $(5, 4)$ is not added. At step 6, $N = \{3, 4, 5\}$, and edge $(6, 3)$ is examined first and added since X is empty. For the addition of edge $(6, 4)$, $X = \{1, 2, 3\}$, and since required edges $(6, 1)$ and $(6, 2)$ are not present in G, edge $(6, 4)$ is not added. For the addition of edge $(6, 5)$, $X = \{3\}$, and $(6, 5)$ is added since edge $(6, 3)$ is present in G and in H.

(b) At step 5, edge $(5, 3)$ is added as in (a), and in addition, edge $(5, 4)$ is added along with the required edges $(5, 1)$ and $(5, 2)$. At step 6, edge $(6, 3)$ is added as in (a). For the addition of edge $(6, 4)$, $X = \{1, 2, 3, 5\}$ since the minimal $6, 4$-separators are $\{1, 5\}, \{2, 5\}$, and $\{3\}$. Thus edge $(6, 4)$ and required edges $(6, 1), (6, 2)$, and $(6, 5)$ are added to H.

Step 7 adds edges $(7, 1)$ and $(7, 2)$ in both (a) and (b) without requiring any additional edges in either case.

5   Data Structure and Time Complexity

The input graph G is represented by an adjacency list, and we use a clique tree T of H as an additional data structure to store and work on H. In order to achieve the total $O(nm)$ time bound, for each edge (u, v) of G to be examined we have to do the following two operations in $O(n)$ time: 1. Compute the union X of all minimal uv-separators in H, which gives the required edge set $R(H, u, v)$. 2. If $R(H, u, v) \cup \{(u, v)\}$ is to be added to H, update T to reflect this modification of H.

The main idea is to use a path P_{uv} of the clique tree T between a clique (tree node) C_u that contains u and a clique C_v that contains v, and compute

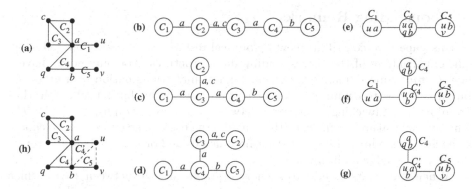

Fig. 2. A chordal graph H is given in (a), and (b) shows a clique tree of H, where $C_u = C_1$, $C_v = C_5$, and P_{uv} is the whole clique tree. After steps (c) and (d), path P_{uv} between C_1 and C_5 is in the desired form, and only this portion of the tree is shown after step (d). In step (e), u is placed in every clique on P_{uv}, and in step (f) C_4 is separated from the path since edge (u, q) is not intended. C_1 is removed in (g) since it becomes non maximal. The new corresponding graph H of which the modified tree is a clique tree is shown in (h).

the union of edges on this path that correspond to minimal uv-separators. For this operation, C_u and C_v are chosen so that no maximal clique between C_u and C_v on P_{uv} contains u or v, as illustrated in Figure 2 (a) and (b). In addition, T is modified so that path P_{uv} between C_u and C_v contains only distinct minimal uv-separators, as shown in Figure 2 (c) and (d). Now the union of the edges of P_{uv} give the desired vertex set X.

Unfortunately, the sum of the sizes of the edges on P_{uv} can be larger than $O(n)$. Thus if the tree nodes and tree edges of T are implemented in the traditional way as vertex lists containing vertices of each tree node and edge, then Operation 1 described above cannot be done in $O(n)$ time. For this reason, we present a new implementation of clique trees: Every edge (C_1, C_2) of T is implemented as two lists that we will call *difference lists*. One list contains vertices belonging to $C_1 \setminus C_2$. This list has two names; it is called both $add(C_2, C_1)$ and $remove(C_1, C_2)$. The other list contains vertices belonging to $C_2 \setminus C_1$. This list is called $add(C_1, C_2)$ and also $remove(C_2, C_1)$. Now, if every clique C of T contains pointers to its add and remove lists, then C actually does not need to store a list of vertices that it contains. To see how to compute X, let $P_{uv} = C_1 - C_2 - \ldots - C_k$; then $X = \cup_{i=2}^{k-1}(add(C_{i-1}, C_i) \setminus remove(C_i, C_{i+1}))$. Every vertex of G can appear in at most one add list and at most one remove list on this path due to Theorem 3, and thus computing X can be done in $O(n)$ time as described using a characteristic vector to store X. Further details of Operation 1, and details of Operation 2 are omitted in this extended abstract due to limited space. We refer the reader to Figure 2 (e) - (h).

6   Concluding Remarks

In this paper, we contribute new theoretical results on chordality as well as an efficient handling of the corresponding data structures. Not only do we have a new $O(nm)$ time dynamic algorithm for minimal triangulation of a graph G, but we are able to compute at the same time a maximal chordal subgraph, thus "minimally sandwiching" the graph between two chordal graphs: $H_1 \subseteq G \subseteq H_2$. This special feature of our algorithm enables the user, at no extra cost, to choose at each vertex addition step whether he wants to *add* or *delete* edges, or even to do so at each edge addition step.

When one wants to add to a chordal graph an edge between $\{u, v\}$ which is not a 2-pair, there is a succession of 2-pair edges incident to u that can be added first, making $\{u, v\}$ a 2-pair of the new graph thus obtained. Our main theorem precisely describes this set of edges as our set of required edges. It was not known earlier which edges needed to be added in order to ensure that $\{u, v\}$ becomes a 2-pair, and even less how to compute them efficiently.

References

1. S. Arikati and P. Rangan. An efficient algorithm for finding a two-pair, and its applications. *Disc. Appl. Math. Comb. Oper. Res.*, 31:71–74, 1991.
2. E. Balas. A fast algorithm for finding an edge-maximal subgraph with a TR-formative coloring. *Disc. Appl. Math.*, 15:123–134, 1986.
3. A. Berry. A wide-range efficient algorithm for minimal triangulation. In *Proceedings of the 10th Annual ACM-SIAM Symposium on Discrete Algorithms*, 1999.
4. A. Berry, J. Blair, and P. Heggernes. Maximum cardinality search for computing minimal triangulations. In L. Kucera, editor, *Graph Theoretical Concepts in Computer Science - WG 2002, LNCS 2573*, pages 1–12. Springer Verlag, 2002.
5. A. Berry, J-P. Bordat, P. Heggernes, G. Simonet, and Y. Villanger. A wide-range algorithm for minimal triangulation from an arbitrary ordering. Technical Report Reports in Informatics 243, University of Bergen, Norway, 2003.
6. A. Berry, A. Sigayret, and C. Sinoquet. Maximal sub-triangulation as improving phylogenetic data. Technical Report RR-02-02, LIMOS, Clermont-Ferrand, France, 2002.
7. J. R. S. Blair, P. Heggernes, and J. A. Telle. A practical algorithm for making filled graphs minimal. *Theoretical Computer Science*, 250:125–141, 2001.
8. J. R. S. Blair and B. W. Peyton. An introduction to chordal graphs and clique trees. In J. A. George, J. R. Gilbert, and J. W. H. Liu, editors, *Graph Theory and Sparse Matrix Computations*, pages 1–30. Springer Verlag, 1993. IMA Volumes in Mathematics and its Applications, Vol. 56.
9. P. Buneman. A characterization of rigid circuit graphs. *Discrete Math.*, 9:205–212, 1974.
10. E. Dahlhaus. Minimal elimination ordering inside a given chordal graph. In R. H. Möhring, editor, *Graph Theoretical Concepts in Computer Science - WG '97, LNCS 1335*, pages 132–143. Springer Verlag, 1997.
11. P. M. Dearing, D. R. Shier, and D. D. Warner. Maximal chordal subgraphs. *Disc. Appl. Math.*, 20:181–190, 1988.
12. G. A. Dirac. On rigid circuit graphs. *Abh. Math. Sem. Univ. Hamburg*, 25:71–76, 1961.

13. F. Gavril. The intersection graphs of subtrees in trees are exactly the chordal graphs. *J. Combin. Theory Ser. B*, 16:47–56, 1974.
14. R. Hayward, C. Hoàng, and F. Maffray. Optimizing weakly triangulated graphs. *Graphs and Combinatorics*, 5:339–349, 1989.
15. C-W. Ho and R. C. T. Lee. Counting clique trees and computing perfect elimination schemes in parallel. *Inform. Process. Lett.*, 31:61–68, 1989.
16. L. Ibarra. Fully dynamic algorithms for chordal graphs. In *Proceedings of the 10th Annual ACM-SIAM Symposium on Discrete Algorithms*, 1999.
17. A. Natanzon, R. Shamir, and R. Sharan. Complexity classification of some edge modification problems. *Disc. Appl. Math.*, 113:109–128, 2001.
18. D. J. Rose, R. E. Tarjan, and G. S. Lueker. Algorithmic aspects of vertex elimination on graphs. *SIAM J. Comput.*, 5:266–283, 1976.
19. J. Spinrad and R. Sritharan. Algorithms for weakly triangulated graphs. *Disc. Appl. Math.*, 59:181–191, 1995.
20. J. Walter. *Representations of rigid cycle graphs*. PhD thesis, Wayne State University, USA, 1972.
21. J. Xue. Edge-maximal triangulated subgraphs and heuristics for the maximum clique problem. *Networks*, 24:109–120, 1994.
22. M. Yannakakis. Computing the minimum fill-in is NP-complete. *SIAM J. Alg. Disc. Meth.*, 2:77–79, 1981.

Finding the Maximum Common Subgraph of a Partial k-Tree and a Graph with a Polynomially Bounded Number of Spanning Trees

Atsuko Yamaguchi and Hiroshi Mamitsuka

Bioinformatics Center, Institute for Chemical Research, Kyoto University
Gokasho, Uji, 611-0011, Japan
{atsuko,mami}@kuicr.kyoto-u.ac.jp

Abstract. The maximum common subgraph problem is NP-hard even if the two input graphs are partial k-trees. We present a polynomial time algorithm for finding the maximum common connected induced subgraph of two bounded degree graphs G_1 and G_2, where G_1 is a partial k-tree and G_2 is a graph whose possible spanning trees are polynomially bounded. The key idea of our algorithm is that for each spanning tree generated from G_2, a candidate for the maximum common connected induced subgraph is generated in polynomial time since a subgraph of a partial k-tree is also a partial k-tree. Among all of these candidates, we can find the maximum common connected induced subgraph for G_1 and G_2.

1 Introduction

The problem of finding the maximum common induced subgraph of two graphs is NP-hard [7], even for two graphs of bounded degree [10]. The subgraph isomorphism problem of two partial k-trees, i.e. graphs with tree-width k, is NP-complete [8,12], and thus the maximum common subgraph problem of two partial k-trees is also NP-hard.

In this paper, we present a polynomial time algorithm for the problem of finding the maximum common connected induced subgraph of a partial k-tree of bounded degree and a connected graph, the number of whose possible spanning trees is polynomially bounded. We note that the problem is NP-hard if the degree of input graphs is not bounded. This is easily shown by the following two facts. First, the problem is NP-hard for two almost trees if their degree is not bounded [1]. Second, the class of almost trees is a subclass of the graphs considered in this paper.

This problem is motivated by chemical structures (i.e. molecular graphs) found in molecular biology. Obviously the degree of a molecular graph is bounded, and the tree-width of a molecular graph in general is expected to be relatively small since a molecular graph is sparse. We actually checked the tree-width of approximately 10,000 chemical structures in a biological database (LIGAND database [9]) and found that the maximum tree-width of the structures

T. Ibaraki, N. Katoh, and H. Ono (Eds.): ISAAC 2003, LNCS 2906, pp. 58–67, 2003.

tested is four. Furthermore, in the literature of chemoinformatics as well as computational biology, induced subgraphs have been considered, instead of general (edge-induced) subgraphs (e.g. [5]). For all these reasons, we focus on induced subgraphs of a partial k-tree of bounded degree. Another finding regarding molecular graphs is that even in a molecular graph with a relatively large treewidth, say three, we often see that biconnected components are rather small and that the other parts naturally form a tree structure. This implies that the number of possible spanning trees in a molecular graph is relatively small. Therefore, we focus on a graph whose number of possible spanning trees is polynomially bounded.

The problem of finding the minimum tree-width of a graph is NP-hard [2]. However, polynomial time algorithms have already been proposed to solve the problem of determining whether a given graph is a partial k-tree or not when k is fixed [2,3,4,13]. One of these algorithms is based on tree-decomposition of the input graph.

In our algorithm as well, we start a tree-decomposition of one of our input graphs, the partial k-tree, G_1. We then generate all possible spanning trees from the other input graph, G_2. The key idea of our algorithm is that for each spanning tree generated from G_2, a candidate for the maximum common connected induced subgraph is generated in polynomial time since a subgraph of a partial k-tree is a partial k-tree. Among all of these candidates, we can find the maximum common connected induced subgraph for G_1 and G_2.

2   Preliminaries

All graphs in this paper are always finite and simple, i. e. they have no loops and no multiple edges. A graph is undirected unless indicated otherwise. For a graph G, we denote the set of vertices of G and the set of edges of G by $V(G)$ and $E(G)$, respectively. For a vertex v of a graph G, the *degree* of the vertex v is $|\{u \in V(G)|(u,v) \in E(G)\}|$. The degree of a graph G is the maximum degree of all vertices in $V(G)$. We denote by $sp(G)$ the number of possible spanning trees of G. For a polynomial function p, we call a class C of graphs a *polyclass*, if $sp(G) \leq p(|(G)|)$ holds for every graph $G \in C$. We note that the polyclass has already been considered. For example, in [6], Ding specified the conditions for a certain class of graphs to be defined as a polyclass.

A *subgraph* G' of a graph G is a graph such that $V(G') \subseteq V(G)$ and $E(G') \subseteq E(G)$. A *induced subgraph* G' of a graph G is a subgraph of G such that $E(G') = \{(u,v) \mid u,v \in V(G') \text{ and } (u,v) \in E(G)\}$. A *common induced subgraph* (hereafter abbreviated as CIS) of a graph G_1 and a graph G_2 is a triplet (G'_1, G'_2, ψ) of graphs such that G'_1 and G'_2 are induced subgraphs of G_1 and G_2, respectively, and ψ is an isomorphic mapping from G'_1 to G'_2. A *common connected induced subgraph* (hereafter abbreviated as CCIS) is a connected CIS, and a *maximum common connected induced subgraph* (hereafter abbreviated as MCCIS) of G_1 and G_2 is a CCIS (G'_1, G'_2, ψ) with the maximum $|V(G'_1)|$.

The *tree-decomposition* of a graph G is a pair (T, X), where T is a tree and $X : V(T) \to 2^{V(G)}$ that satisfies the following three conditions:

1. $\cup_{t \in V(T)} X(t) = V(G)$.
2. For every edge $(u,v) \in V(G)$, there exists a vertex $t \in V(T)$ such that $u,v \in X(t)$.
3. For any three vertices $r,s,t \in V(T)$, if s is on the path from r to t, $X(r) \cap X(t) \subseteq X(s)$.

The *width* of a tree-decomposition (T,X) is $\max_{t \in V(T)} |X(t) - 1|$. The *tree-width* of a graph G is the minimum width of all tree-decompositions of G. A k-*clique* of a graph G is a clique of G with k vertices. A k-*tree* is defined as follows:
1. The complete graph with $k+1$ vertices is a k-tree.
2. If G is a k-tree and $L \subseteq V(G)$ is a k-clique, a graph G' with $V(G') = V(G) \cup \{v\}$ and $E(G') = E(G) \cup \{(u,v) \mid u \in L\}$ is a k-tree.

A *partial k-tree* is a subgraph of a k-tree. It is known that the tree-width of a graph is k if and only if the graph is a partial k-tree [11]. Regarding partial k-trees, the following proposition was shown.

Proposition 1. (Gupta and Nishimura [8]) *The subgraph isomorphism problem of two partial k-trees is NP-complete if each of the two partial k-trees has all but k nodes of degree at most k.*

Thus, we can easily see that the maximum common subgraph problem of two partial k-trees with the same conditions of Proposition 1 is also NP-hard.

Here, regarding an almost tree, i.e. a connected graph G with $|E(G)| \leq |V(G)| + K$ for some constant K, the following proposition was shown.

Proposition 2. (Akutsu [1]) *The maximum common connected subgraph problem of two almost trees is NP-hard if the degree of the two almost trees is not bounded.*

Note that the class of almost trees with K is in a class of some polyclass C and in a class of a partial k-trees for some k. Thus, the problem of finding the maximum common connected subgraph of a partial k-tree and a graph in polyclass C is also NP-hard. In this paper, we consider the following problem and present a polynomial time algorithm for the problem. We emphasize that our algorithm is for a class, which is properly larger than that for which a polynomial time algorithm was proposed in [1].

Let d and k be fixed positive integers, and let C be a polyclass.

Definition 1. *(The maximum common connected induced subgraph problem of a degree-bounded partial k-tree and a degree-bounded graph in a polyclass C)*
Instance: *A partial k-tree G_1 of bounded degree d_1 and a graph G_2 in a polyclass C of bounded degree d_2.*
Problem: *Find an MCCIS of G_1 and G_2.* $\square$

3   Polynomial Time Algorithm

We present a polynomial time algorithm for finding an MCCIS of a partial k-tree of bounded degree and a graph of bounded degree in a polyclass.

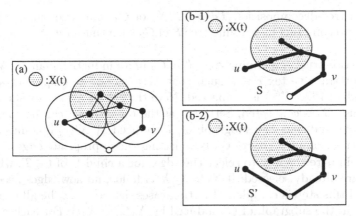

Fig. 1. (a) A graph G_2. (b-1) A spanning tree S such that (Td, S) is a suitable pair. (b-2) A spanning tree S' such that (Td, S') is not a suitable pair.

3.1 Basic Idea

We can easily see the following two claims.

Claim. A subgraph of a partial k-tree is a partial k-tree.

Claim. Let G_1 be a partial k-tree. Let (T, X) be a tree-decomposition of G_1. Let G_1' be a CIS of G_1. (T, X') is a tree-decomposition of G_1' of width at most k, where $X'(t) = X(t) \cap V(G_1')$.

For a tree-decomposition (T, X) of G_1 and a subgraph G_1' of G_1, we call (T, X') a *proper tree-decomposition* of G_1' and (T, X). To simplify notations, we permit the application of the tree-decomposition of a graph G_1' to a graph G_2' if G_1' and G_2' are isomorphic partial k-trees.

For a graph G_2, let G_2' be a induced subgraph of G_2 such that G_2' is a partial k-tree with a tree-decomposition $Td' = (T, X')$. For a vertex $t \in T$, let G_{2_t}' be a subgraph of G_2' induced by the vertices $V(G_2') - X'(t)$. Let S be a spanning tree of a graph G_2. For a vertex $t \in T$, let S_t be a subgraph of S constructed by the vertices $V(S) - X'(t)$. For G_{2_t}' with a tree-decomposition Td' and a spanning tree S, we call a pair (Td', S) *a suitable pair* if for every two vertices u, v in G_{2_t}', u and v are disconnected in S_t when u and v are disconnected in G_{2_t}'. Figure 1 shows an example of a suitable pair. Figure 1 (a) shows a graph G_2. A subgraph G_2' consists of black nodes and solid edges, and the large circles illustrates a tree-decomposition Td of G_2'. Figure 1 (b-1) shows a spanning tree S such that (Td, S) is a suitable pair. We can see that the two nodes u and v are disconnected in both graphs $G_2' - X(t)$ and $S' - X(t)$. Figure 1 (b-2) shows a spanning tree S' such that (Td, S) is not a suitable pair. This is because u and v are connected in the graph $S' - X(t)$ but they are disconnected in the graph $G_2' - X(t)$.

Lemma 1. *Let (G_1', G_2', ψ) be a CCIS of G_1 and G_2. For any tree-decomposition $Td = (T, X)$ of G_1, there exists a spanning tree S of G_2 such that (Td', S) is a suitable pair, where $Td' = (T, X')$ is a proper tree-decomposition of G_1' and (T, X).*

Proof. For a tree-decomposition $Td = (T, X)$ of G_1 and a common subgraph (G_1', G_2', ψ), we construct a spanning tree S of G_2 such that (Td', S) is a suitable pair.

First, we construct a spanning tree S' of G_2' in an inductive manner: We first choose an arbitrary vertex $r \in T$ such that $X'(r)$ is not an empty set and the subgraph induced by $X'(r)$ is connected. Note that there always exists such an r in T because G_2' is connected. Setting r as the root, tree T can be considered a directed tree, and since the subgraph of G_2' induced by $X'(r)$ is connected, we can construct a spanning tree of G_2' by selecting the appropriate edges.

We explain here the way to select the edges for a child t_c of $t \in T$, when the edges for t are already selected: If $X(t_c) \subseteq X(t)$ holds, no new edges need to be selected, and this step is complete. In other cases, let $c_1, \ldots, c_l$ be all connected components in the subgraph of G_2' induced by $X(t_c) - X(t)$. For each c_i, there is a vertex v_i in $X'(t)$ that is connected to vertices in c_i since G_2' is connected, and for each i, we make a spanning tree of the subgraph induced by $c_i \cup \{v_i\}$.

We can now obtain a subgraph S' of G_2' that is induced by edges selected as above. Obviously, S' is a spanning forest. Let t_p be the parent of t in T. Since the vertices in $X'(r)$ are connected in S' and each vertex in $X(t)$ is connected to some vertex in $X(t_p)$, we can say that S' is a spanning tree of G_2'.

Next, we construct a spanning tree S of G_2. For vertices in $V(G_2) - V(G_2')$, let $c_1', \ldots, c_l'$ be all connected components in the subgraph of G_2 induced by $V(G_2) - V(G_2')$. For each c_i', there is a vertex v_i' in G_2' that is connected to vertices in c_i' since G_2 is also connected, and for each i, we make a spanning tree of the subgraph induced by $c_i' \cup \{v_i'\}$. Through this process, we obtain a subgraph S of G_2 that is induced by S' and includes edges selected for vertices in $V(G_2) - V(G_2')$. Using a similar procedure for showing that S' is a spanning tree of G_2', we can show that S is a spanning tree of G_2.

Finally, we show that (Td', S) is a suitable pair. For $t \in T$ and two vertices v_1, v_2 in G_{2_t}', we assume that v_1 and v_2 are disconnected in G_{2_t}'. Let $t_1, \ldots, t_{k'}$ be children of t, and $t_{k'+1}$ be a parent of t. Since G_2' is connected, there exists a vertex v_1' in $\cup_{1 \le i \le k'+1} X(t_i)$ that is connected to v_1 in G_{2_t}'. Similarly, there exists a vertex v_2' in $\cup_{1 \le i \le k'} X(t_i)$ that is connected to v_2 in G_{2_t}'. Since in G_{2_t}', v_1 and v_1' are connected, v_2 and v_2' are connected, and v_1 and v_2 are disconnected, v_1' and v_2' are obviously disconnected in G_{2_t}'. Now we show that v_1' and v_2' are disconnected in S_t. First, we consider the case that both v_1' and v_2' are in $X(t_i)$ for some i $(1 \le i \le k'+1)$. In this case, v_1' and v_2' are disconnected in S_t because v_1' and v_2' are in different connected components. Second, we consider the case that v_1' is in $X(t_i)$ and v_2' is in $X(t_j)$ for $i \ne j$. There is no edge from a vertex in $X(t_i) - X(t)$ to a vertex in $X(t_j) - X(t)$ because of the definition of a tree-decomposition. Thus, v_1' and v_2' are disconnected in S_t because S_t is a spanning tree. Since S is a tree, v_1 and v_2 are also disconnected in S_t. Hence (Td', S) is a suitable pair. □

Let G_1 be a partial k-tree with a tree-decomposition $Td = (T, X)$. From Lemma 1, we can find an MCCIS of G_1 and G_2 using the following two steps:

1. For a spanning tree S in G_2, we find an MCCIS candidate (G'_{1S}, G'_{2S}, ψ) such that (Td', S) is a suitable pair, where Td' is a proper decomposition of G'_{1S} and Td.
2. We repeat step 1 for all possible spanning trees of G_2 and obtain the MCCIS from all the candidates.

In the next subsection, we focus on step 1 above. We describe a polynomial time algorithm to find an MCCIS candidate for a fixed tree-decomposition and a fixed spanning tree. When G_2 is restricted in a polyclass, the number of repetitions of step 2 is polynomially bounded, and thus we can show the following theorem.

Theorem 1. *The maximum common connected subgraph problem of a degree-bounded partial k-tree and a degree-bounded graph in a polyclass C is solvable in polynomial time.*

3.2 Our Proposed Algorithm

We introduce some notations before delving into the details of our algorithm. Hereafter, we assume that graph G_1 is always a partial k-tree with bounded degree d_1, and graph G_2 is always a graph with bounded degree d_2 in a polyclass. We further assume that a tree-decomposition $Td = (T, X)$ of G_1 and a spanning tree S of G_2 are fixed. We consider a tree T as a directed tree rooted by some vertex. For a vertex $t \in V(T)$, we denote a subtree of T rooted at t by $T(t)$. For $B \subseteq V(G_2)$, we further denote a set of connected components of $S - B$ by D_B. For a CIS (H_1, H_2, ψ) such that $V(H_1) \subseteq X(t)$ where $t \in V(T)$, we call a mapping from $D_{V(H_2)}$ to $\{t_1, \ldots, t_c\} \cup \{t_p\}$ (where $t_1, \ldots, t_c$ are children and t_p is a parent of the vertex t) an *allocation mapping* for (H_1, H_2, ψ). We further call a CIS of G_2 and a subgraph of G_1 induced by a vertex set $\cup_{t_p \in T(t)} X(t_p)$ a *partial CIS* $(G'_{1t}, G'_{2t}, \psi_t)$ for a vertex $t \in T$, if (Td', S) is a suitable pair where Td' is a proper tree-decomposition of G'_{1t} and (T, X). For an allocation mapping a for (H_1, H_2, ψ) with $V(H_1) \subseteq X(t)$, we call a partial CIS for t a *restricted CIS* $R_a = (G''_1, G''_2, \psi'')$ for a, if the following conditions hold:

1. $\psi''(u) = \psi(u)$ for every vertex $u \in V(H_1)$,
2. $\psi''^{-1}(v)$ is in $\{u \mid u \in X(s) - X(t), s \in V(T(a(c)))\}$ if v is in a component c, and
3. if there is no component that is assigned to a parent t_p, G''_1 is connected.

Note that if the procedure to find the maximum restricted CIS for an allocation mapping such that there is no component assigned to a parent of t is repeated, one of the maximum restricted CISs obtained will correspond to a maximum connected partial CIS for t.

We consider here an allocation mapping a of a triplet $f = (H_1, H_2, \psi)$ where $V(H_1) \subseteq X(t)$, and allocation mappings $a_1, \ldots, a_c$ such that a_i is an allocation mapping of a triplet $f_i = (H_1^i, H_2^i, \psi_i)$ where $V(H_1^i) \subseteq X(t_i)$. For given restricted CISs $R_{a_i} = (G_1^{i\,\prime\prime}, G_2^{i\,\prime\prime}, \psi_i'')$ of a_i ($i = 1, \ldots, c$), we call a triplet $R_a = (G''_1, G''_2, \psi'')$ a *composition* of f and $R_{a_i}(1 \le i \le c)$, if $V(G''_1) = \cup_{1 \le i \le c} V(G_1^{i\,\prime\prime}) \cup V(H_1)$ and $V(G''_2) = \cup_{1 \le i \le c} V(G_2^{i\,\prime\prime}) \cup V(H_2)$. We

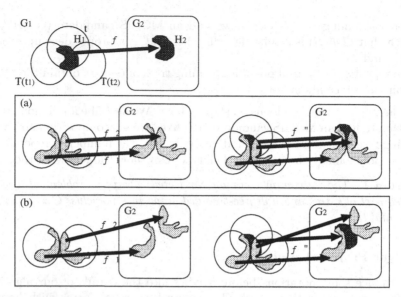

Fig. 2. (a) A possible composition and (b) a composition that is not a possible composition

further call a composition a *possible composition* if the composition satisfies the following two conditions:

1. $\psi''(u) = \psi_i(u)$ for all i such that $u \in V(G_1^i)$, and
2. ψ'' is an isomorphic mapping.

Obviously, a possible composition is a restricted CIS of the allocation mapping a. Figure 2 (a) shows an example of a possible composition, and Figure 2 (b) shows an example of a composition that is not a possible composition because ψ'' is not an isomorphic mapping.

We now show a polynomial time algorithm for finding a CCIS (G'_{1S}, G'_{2S}, ψ) of G_1 and G_2 such that for a given spanning tree S of G_2, (Td', S) is a suitable pair, where Td' is a proper tree-decomposition of G'_{1S} and $Td = (T, X)$. Figure 3 is the main algorithm and Figure 4 is the procedure (which we call *RestrictCIS*) that finds a maximum restricted CIS for an allocation mapping. We further show that this algorithm runs in polynomial time. If we prove that this algorithm runs in polynomial time, we will be able to find an MCCIS in polynomial time since the number of spanning trees of G_2 is polynomially bounded.

Let $n_1 = |V(G_1)|$ and $n_2 = |V(G_2)|$. Let $d = \max\{d_1, d_2\}$. Step 1 is done in $O(n_2^k)$ time and is polynomial because k is a constant. For Step 2, we can compute a BFS order in $O(n)$ time. In Step 3-1, we can obtain I_i in constant time since $|X(t_i)| \leq k$. In Step 3-2, we obtain K_{t_i} in $O(n_2^k)$ time since $|J| = O(n_2^k)$ and $|I_i|$ is a constant. Step 3-3 is done in $O(n_2^k) \times O((dk)!) = O(n_2^k)$ time. This comes from the fact that $|H_1|$ and $|H_2|$ are both at most k and the degree of $V(H_1)$ and $V(H_2)$ is at most d, so the number of connected components of S is bounded by dk and the number of children of t is also bounded by dk. In Step 3-4, for each allocation mapping, we compute a subgraph. Let $Q(n_1, n_2)$ be the

---

Input: A graph G_1 with a tree-decomposition $Td = (T, X)$, and a graph G_2 with a spanning tree S.

Output: An MCCIS (G'_{1S}, G'_{2S}, ψ) of G_1 and G_2 with the condition that (Td', S) is a suitable pair.

Step 1. Compute a collection P of all subsets of $V(G_2)$ such that the cardinality of a set in P is at most k. Given a graph Z that is a subgraph of G_2 induced by B, compute a set $J = \cup_{B \in P} J_B$, where J_B is a set of all subgraphs of Z.

Step 2. Choose a vertex r of T as a root and consider T as a rooted tree. Compute a BFS order $r = t_1, t_2, \ldots, t_m$ of vertices in T.

Step 3. For $i = m$ to 1,

  Step 3-1. Let Y be a graph that is a subgraph of G_1 induced by $X(t_i)$. Compute a set I_i of all subgraphs of Y.

  Step 3-2. Compute a set K_{t_i} of triplets (H_1, H_2, ψ') where $H_1 \in I_i$, $H_2 \in J_B$ and ψ' is an isomorphic mapping of H_1 and H_2.

  Step 3-3. For each triplet $f = (H_1, H_2, \psi')$ in K_{t_i}, compute a set F_f of all possible allocation mappings for f.

  Step 3-4. For each allocation mapping a of F_f, compute a maximum restricted CIS R_a for a using the procedure $RestrictCIS$.

  Step 3-5. Compute a maximum partial CCIS $(G'_{1t}, G'_{2t}, \psi_t)$ using the result of Step 3-3.

Step 4. For all vertices $t \in T$, scan a maximum partial CCIS for t, and output the one with the maximum number of vertices.

Fig. 3. The main algorithm

running time of the procedure $RestrictCIS$. Step 3-4 is done in $O(Q(n_1, n_2) \cdot n_2^k)$ since the number of allocation mappings is $O(n_2^k)$. Step 3-5 is done in $O(n_2^k)$ since the number of allocation mappings is $O(n_2^k)$.

We now show that the running time $Q(n_1, n_2)$ of the procedure $RestrictCIS$ is polynomial. Since $|X(t_i)| \leq k$ and the degree of each vertex in $V(H_1)$ is at most d, the c in the procedure $RestrictCIS$ is bounded by a constant dk. Furthermore, $|F_{f_j}| = O(n_2^k)$. Thus, the number of combinations of allocation mappings is $O(n_2^{dk^2})$. For a combination of allocation mappings, we can check whether the composition is a possible composition or not in constant time since it is enough to check vertices in $X(t_i)$ and $\cup_{1 \leq j \leq c} X(t_{ij})$ because (T, X) is a tree-decomposition of G_1. Overall, $Q(n_1, n_2) = O(n_2^{dk^2})$.

Step 3 repeats $O(n_1)$ times, and thus Step 3 runs in $O(n_1 \cdot n_2^{dk^2})$ time. Step 4 is done in $O(n_1)$. With all these results, the total running time of our algorithm is in $O(n_1 \cdot n_2^{dk^2})$.

Finally, we must show that a CCIS obtained by this algorithm is an MCCIS where (Td', S) is a suitable pair. Note here that the procedure $RestrictCIS$ checks that (Td', S) is always a suitable pair for a subgraph obtained by this algorithm. To show that a CCIS obtained by our algorithm is an MCCIS, we now prove the following lemma.

Lemma 2. *The procedure RestrictCIS outputs a maximum restricted CIS for a given allocation mapping.*

Input: An allocation mapping a of a triplet $f = (H_1, H_2, \psi)$ in K_{ti}, a set $\{t_{i1}, \ldots, t_{ic}\}$
of children of t_i in T, and for every possible triplet f_j for $t_{ij}(1 \leq j \leq c)$, $F_{f_j}(1 \leq j \leq c)$ with a maximum restricted CIS R'_a for every $a' \in F_{f_j}$.

Output: A maximum restricted CIS R_a for a.

    Step 1. Compute a set A of c allocation mappings such that for each element
        $(a_1, a_2, \ldots, a_c)$, a_j is in $F_{f_j}(1 \leq j \leq c)$.

    Step 2. For each element $(a_1, a_2, \ldots, a_c)$ in A, check whether the composition
        of $R_{a_j}(1 \leq j \leq c)$ and f is a possible composition or not. If true, add the
        composition to a set A'.

    Step 3. Output a restricted CIS with the maximum number of vertices using the
        compositions in A'.

Fig. 4. The procedure *RestrictCIS*

Proof. For the case that a node t is a leaf of T, it is trivial to show that this
lemma holds.

For the case that a node t has children $t_1, \ldots, t_j$, we first assume that we have
already obtained the maximum restricted CIS for each $a' \in F_{f_j}$. Let (G''_1, G''_2, ψ)
be a restricted CIS obtained by the procedure *RestrictCIS*. Let $a_1, \ldots, a_j$ be
the allocation mappings of the possible composition of (G''_1, G''_2, ψ) obtained.

Assume that there exists a restricted CIS $(G''_{1_{opt}}, G''_{2_{opt}}, \psi_{opt})$ for a with
$|V(G''_{1_{opt}})| > |V(G''_1)|$. Then, a child t_l $(1 \leq l \leq j)$ of t exists such that
$|V(G''_{1_{opt}}) \cap (\cup_{t' \in T(t_l)} X(t'))| > |V(G''_1) \cap (\cup_{t' \in T(t_l)} X(t'))|$. Let Td' (or Td_{opt}) be
a proper tree-decomposition of G''_1 (or $G''_{1_{opt}}$) and Td. Let $t_{l_1}, \ldots, t_{l_m}$ be the children of t_l in T. For a subgraph H_1 of G_1 induced by a vertex set $V(G''_{1_{opt}}) \cap X(t_l)$
and a subgraph H_2 of G_2 induced by a vertex set $\{\psi_{opt}(u) \mid u \in V(H_1)\}$,
we can obtain an allocation mapping a'_l of (H_1, H_2, ψ_{opt}) such that for every
connected component c of S_{t_l} and a vertex v in $c \cap V(G''_{2_{opt}})$, $\psi^{-1}_{opt}(v)$ is in
$V(T(a(c)))$. The allocation mapping a'_l exists: For any two children t_{l_g}, t'_{l_g} of
t_l, $\cup_{t' \in T(t_{l_g})} X(t') - X(t_l)$ and $\cup_{t' \in T(t'_{l_g})} X(t') - X(t_l)$ are disconnected, and
(Td_{opt}, S) is a suitable pair. Thus, for a connected component c of S_{t_l} there
exists a child t_{l_h} such that $\psi^{-1}_{opt}(v)$ is in $\cup_{t' \in T(t_{l_h})} X(t') - X(t_l)$ for every vertex
$v \in c$ where $\psi^{-1}_{opt}(v)$ is defined.

Furthermore, according to the definition of a restricted CIS, two restricted
CISs (G''_1, G''_2, ψ) and $(G''_{1_{opt}}, G''_{2_{opt}}, \psi_{opt})$ always have the same subgraph for
the nodes in $X(t)$, and (Td', S) and (Td_{opt}, S) are suitable pairs. Thus, by replacing a_l by a'_l, we can make a possible composition from j allocation mappings $a_1, \ldots, a_{l-1}, a'_l, a_{l+1}, \ldots, a_j$ and their maximum restricted CISs. Since
the number of vertices of the maximum restricted CIS for a'_l is at least
$|V(G''_{1_{opt}}) \cap (\cup_{t' \in T(t_l)} X(t'))|$, we can obtain a restricted CIS $(G''_{1_l}, G''_{2_l}, \psi_l)$ with
$|V(G''_{1_l})| > |V(G''_1)|$. This contradicts the restricted CIS chosen in the procedure
RestrictCIS since it tests for all combinations of allocation mappings and then
chooses a restricted CIS with the maximum number of vertices. $\qquad\square$

Now we have done the proof of Theorem 1.

4   Conclusion

In this paper, we presented a polynomial time algorithm for finding an MCCIS of G_1 and G_2, where G_1 is a partial k-tree of bounded degree and G_2 is a graph of bounded degree in a polyclass. We showed that an MCCIS of G_1 and G_2 exists in a set of all MCCIS candidates such that for a spanning tree S, (Td, S) is suitable pair by Lemma 1. Furthermore, we showed that for each spanning tree S, an MCCIS candidate can be found in polynomial time in Section 3.2. Thus, we confirmed that our algorithm runs in polynomial time and outputs an MCCIS. Our algorithm is designed to find a common structure from molecular graphs. Improvement of the time performance remains as future work as our algorithm is applied to massive amounts of molecular data.

Acknowledgment. This work was partially supported by Grant-in-Aid for Scientific Research on Priority Areas (C) "Genome Information Science" from the Ministry of Education, Culture, Sports, Science and Technology of Japan.

References

1. T. Akutsu: A polynomial time algorithm for finding a largest common subgraph of almost trees of bounded degree. *IEICE Trans. Fundamentals*, E76-A (1993), pp. 1488–1493.
2. S. Arnborg, D. G. Corneil, and A. Proskurowski: Complexity of finding embeddings in a k-tree. *SIAM J. on Algebraic and Discrete Methods*, 8 (1987), pp. 277–284.
3. S. Arnborg and A. Proskurowski: Linear time algorithms for NP-hard problems on graphs embedded in k-trees. *Discrete Appl. Math.*, 23 (1989), pp. 11–24.
4. H. L. Bodlaender: A linear-time algorithm for finding tree-decompositions of small treewidth. *SIAM J. Comput.*, 25 (1996), pp. 1305–1317.
5. D. M. Bayada, R. W. Simpson, and A. P. Johnson: An algorithm for the multiple common subgraph problem. *J. Chem. Inf. Comput. Sci.*, 32 (1992), pp. 680–685.
6. G. Ding: Graphs with not too many spanning trees. *Networks*, 25 (1995), pp. 193–197.
7. M. R. Garey and D. S. Johnson: Computers and Intractability: A Guide to the Theory of NP-Completeness, Freeman, 1987.
8. A. Gupta and N. Nishimura: The complexity of subgraph isomorphisms for classes of partial k-trees. *Theoret. Comput. Sci.*, 30 (2002), pp. 402–404.
9. S. Goto, Y. Okuno, M. Hattori, T. Nishioka, and M. Kanehisa: LIGAND: database of chemical compounds and reactions in biological pathways. *Nucleic Acids Res.*, 30 (2002), pp. 402–404.
10. V. Kann: On the approximability of the maximum common subgraph problem. *Proc. of 9th Ann. Symp. on Theoretical Aspects of Comput. Sci.*, Lecture Notes in Comput. Sci. 577, pp. 377–388, 1992.
11. J. van Leeuwen: *Handbook of Theoretical Computer Science, vol.A: Algorithm and Complexity*, Elsevier Science Pub. 1990.
12. J. Matoušek and R. Thomas: On the complexity of finding iso- and other morphisms for partial k-trees. *Discrete Math.*, 108 (1992), pp. 343–364.
13. D. Sanders: On linear recognition of tree-width at most four. *SIAM J. Discrete Math.*, 108 (1992), pp. 343–364.

Hotlink Enhancement Algorithms for Web Directories

(Extended Abstract)

Ori Gerstel[1], Shay Kutten[2], Rachel Matichin[3], and David Peleg[3]*

[1] Optical Networking Group, IBM T. J. Watson Research Center, Hawthorne, NY.
[2] Information Systems Group, Faculty of Industrial Engineering and Management,
Technion, Haifa, Israel. kutten@ie.technion.ac.il
[3] Department of Computer Science and Applied Mathematics, The Weizmann
Institute of Science, Rehovot, Israel. {rachelm,peleg}@wisdom.weizmann.ac.il.

Abstract. Consider a web site containing a collection of web pages with
data. Each page is associated with a weight representing the frequency
that page is accessed by users. In the tree hierarchy representation, accessing each page requires the user to travel along the path leading to
it from the root. By enhancing the index tree with additional edges
(hotlinks) one may reduce the access cost of the system. That is, the
hotlinks reduce the expected number of steps needed to reach a leaf
page from the tree root, assuming that the user knows which hotlinks to
take. The *hotlink enhancement* problem involves finding a set of hotlinks
minimizing this cost. The paper proposes a hotlinks structure allowing
a user with limited a-priori knowledge to determine which hotlink to
use at every given point. Then, a polynomial algorithm is presented for
solving the hotlink enhancement problem for such hotlinks on trees of
logarithmic depth. The solution is first presented for binary trees and
then extended to arbitrary degree trees. It is also shown how to generalize the solution to situations where more than one hotlink per node is
allowed. The case in which the distribution on the leaves is unknown is
discussed as well, and is given an algorithm guaranteeing (an optimal)
logarithmic upper bound on the expected number of steps down the tree.

1 Introduction

Finding desired information in a large and diverse database is a complex task.
When such a function is needed in a chaotic and large data collection such as
the World Wide Web, such a function becomes even harder yet crucial. There
are two basic ways to handle information finding in such a collection. One is
a "flat" approach which views the information as a non-hierarchical structure
and provides a query language to extract the relevant data from the database.
An example of this approach on the Web is the Google search engine [1]. The
other method is based on a hierarchical index to the database according to a

---

* Supported in part by a grant from the Israel Science Foundation.

T. Ibaraki, N. Katoh, and H. Ono (Eds.): ISAAC 2003, LNCS 2906, pp. 68–77, 2003.
© Springer-Verlag Berlin Heidelberg 2003

taxonomy of categories. Examples of such indices on the Web are Yahoo [6] and the Open Directory Service [7].

An advantage of the flat approach over the hierarchical one is that the number of human operations required to find a desired piece of information is much lower (if the right query is used). As opposed to that, in the hierarchical approach it is necessary to traverse a path in the taxonomy tree from the root to the desired node in the tree. Human engineering considerations further aggravate this problem since it is very hard to choose an item from a long list (a typical convenient number is 7–10). Thus, the degree of the taxonomy tree should be rather low and the average depth of it is therefore high. Another problem of the hierarchical approach is that the depth of an item in the taxonomy tree is not based on the access pattern. See, e.g., [8]. As a result, items which have very high access frequency may require long access paths each time they are needed, while items which are "unpopular" may still be very accessible in the taxonomy tree. We would like a solution that does not change the taxonomy tree itself, since this taxonomy is likely to be meaningful and useful for the user. The solution proposed in this paper leaves the tree unchanged, but adds an auxiliary structure that helps to user reach the destination faster.

A partial solution to this problem is currently used in the Web, and consists of a list of "hot" pointers which appears in the top level of the index tree and leads directly to the most popular items. We refer to a link from a hotlist to its destination as a *hotlink*. This approach is not scalable in the sense that only a small number of items can appear in such a list.

In the current paper we study a generalization of this "hotlist", allowing us to have such lists in multiple levels in the index tree — not just the top level. The resulting structure is termed a *hotlink-enhanced index structure* (or *enhanced structure* for short). It is proposed to base the decision concerning the hotlinks to be added on the statistics of visited items in the index. The goal is to minimize the expected number of links one has to follow from the root to an item. It is therefore possible to consider static systems where the hotlinks do not get updated often, and dynamic systems which follow the access pattern and dynamically change hotlinks on the fly. In this paper we consider the former, simpler system.

Let us formally define our problem. An index system is based on a fixed tree which classifies the data items in a hierarchical manner. For the sake of simplicity we assume that data resides only in leaves of the tree [1]. To this tree, hotlinks are added and updated dynamically, based on access statistics to the data items, yielding the hotlink-enhanced index structure.

When searching for an item, the user starts from the root of the enhanced structure and advances along tree edges and hotlinks towards the required destination. The original index tree contains a unique path leading from the root of the tree to the desired leaf. An implicit assumption underlying the common hierarchical approach is that at any node along the search in the tree, the user

---

[1] The case where data resides in internal nodes is easily modeled by adding leaves to the tree in the simpler model.

is able to select the correct link leading towards the desired leaf. This does not necessarily mean that the user knows the tree topology, but rather that the user has some general knowledge about the domain, and the links the user finds at any node reflect some natural partitioning of the domain. Thus, when the user sees several tree edges and hotlinks at a node, the user is capable of selecting the right link downwards in the tree.

Once hotlinks are added, the situation becomes more complex, as the resulting hotlink-enhanced index structure is no longer a tree but a directed acyclic graph (DAG), with multiple alternative paths for certain destinations. Again, an underlying assumption at the basis of the hotlink idea is that when faced with a hotlink in the current page, the user will be able to tell whether or not this hotlink may lead it to a closer point on the path to the desired destination. However, the considerations that led to adding the various hotlinks to the tree are not known to the user. Thus, when the user is at some node, the user can know only the hotlinks emanating from the current node (or, in the best case, also hotlinks emanating from previous nodes the user visited on the way from the root to the current node). In particular, the user cannot know whether any hotlinks emanate from descendents of the current node, or where do they lead.

The above discussion implies that any approach taken for designing a hotlink-enhanced index structure must take into account certain assumptions regarding the user's search policy. There could be a number of different models concerning the particular choices taken by the user. At the extreme lies a natural model that is probably too strong to be used in reality. This model captures situations where the user somehow knows the topology of the enhanced structure. Henceforth we refer to this model as the "clairvoyant" user model, which is based on the following assumption.

The clairvoyant user model: At each node in the enhanced structure, the user can infer from the link labels which of the tree edges or hotlinks available at the current page is on a shortest path (in the enhanced structure) to the desired destination. The user always chooses that link.

In contrast, the model proposed here is based on the assumption that the user does not have this knowledge. This forces the user to deploy a *greedy* strategy.

The greedy user model: At each node in the enhanced structure, the user can infer from the link labels which of the tree edges or hotlinks available at the current page leads to a page that is closest *in the original tree structure* to the desired destination. The user always chooses that link.

Note that by this assumption, whenever a user is looking at the page at node v in the hotlink-enhanced structure, the user is aware of all the tree edges and hotlinks in that page, but the user's knowledge about the rest of the tree corresponds only to the logical partitioning of the domain, namely, the original tree structure. In other words, the user is not aware of other hotlinks that may exist from other pages in the tree. This means that the user's estimate for the quality of a tree edge or hotlink leading from v to some node u is based solely on the height of u in the original tree (or equivalently the distance from u to the desired destination in the tree). An important implication is that following the greedy strategy does not necessarily lead to an optimal path in the hotlink-enhanced index structure.

This paper addresses the optimization problem faced by the index designer, namely, to find a set of hotlinks that minimizes the expected number of links (either tree edges or hotlinks) traversed by a greedy user from the root to a leaf. More formally, given a tree T, representing an index, a *hotlink* is an edge that does not belong to the tree. The hotlink *starts* at some node v and *ends* at (or *leads* to) some node u that is a descendant of v. (One may possibly consider a different model which allows to have hotlinks from a node v to a non-descendant node u residing in another subtree. In our model, however, such hotlinks will never be used, due to the greedy assumption.) We assume, without loss of generality, that u is not a child of v. Each leaf x of T has a weight $p(x)$, representing the proportion of the user visits to that leaf, compared with the total set of user's visits. Hence if normalized, $p(x)$ can be interpreted as the probability that a user wants to access leaf x. Another parameter of the problem is an integer K, specifying an upper bound on the number of hotlinks that may start at any given node. (There is no a-priori limit on the number of hotlinks that lead to a given node).

Let S be a set of hotlinks constructed on the tree (obeying the bound of K outgoing hotlinks per node) and let $D_S(v)$ denote the greedy path (including hotlinks) from the root to node v. The expected number of operations needed to get to an item is $f(T, p, S) = \sum_{v \in \mathcal{L}(T)} |D_S(v)| \cdot p(v)$. The problem of optimizing this parameter is referred to as the *hotlink enhancement* problem. Two different *static* problems arise, according to whether the probability distribution p is known to us in advance or not. Assuming a *known distribution*, our goal is to find a set of hotlinks S which minimizes $f(T, p, S)$ and achieves the optimal cost $\hat{f}(T, p) = \min_S \{f(T, p, S)\}$. Such a set is termed an *optimal* set of hotlinks. On the other hand, under the *unknown distribution* assumption, the worst-case expected access cost on a tree T with a set of hotlinks S is $\hat{f}(T, S) = \max_p \{f(T, p, S)\}$, and our goal is to find a set of hotlinks S minimizing $f(T, S)$ and achieving the optimal cost $\tilde{f}(T) = \min_S \{\tilde{f}(T, S)\}$.

For the latter problem, there exists an equivalent formulation, independent of the probability distributions, based on the observation that for every tree T and hotlink function S, $\tilde{f}(T, S) = \max_{v \in \mathcal{L}(T)} \{|D_S(v)|\}$, and therefore:

Lemma 1. *For every tree T, $\tilde{f}(T) = \min_S \{\max_{v \in \mathcal{L}(T)} \{|D_S(v)|\}\}$.*

Note that the above definitions can be repeated for the clairvoyant user model.

The clairvoyant user model, not used in the current paper, was discussed in previous papers. A proof of NP-hardness for adding hotlinks on DAGS was presented in [2] by a reduction from the problem of Exact Cover by 3-Sets (which is known to be NP-Complete) to that of hotlink enhancement for DAGs. An interesting analogy was presented for the clairvoyant user model between the problem of adding hotlinks and coding theory. One can think of the index tree as the coding of words (where in a binary tree, for example, a left move corresponds to '0' and a right move corresponds to '1'). Thus any leaf is a code-word in the code-alphabet. By adding a hotlink we actually add another letter to the alphabet. Consequently, Shannon's theorem suggests a lower bound for the problem. In particular, in binary trees, denoting by $H(p)$ the entropy of the access distribution on the leaves, and denoting by T^A the hotlink-enhanced index structure resulting from the original tree T with the hotlinks added by the algorithm A, $E[T^A, p] \geq H(p)/\log 3 = \frac{1}{\log 3} \sum_{i=1}^N p_i \log (1/p_i)$, and in trees of maximal degree Δ, $E[T^A, p] \geq H(p)/\log \Delta$. An approximation algorithm for adding hotlink to bounded degree trees for a clairvoyant user is presented in [3]. It turns out that this algorithm can also be used under our greedy user model. The approximation ratio of the algorithm depends on Δ, the maximum degree of the tree, and on the entropy of the access distribution (and is in general at least $\log(\Delta + 1)$). Recently, a polynomial time algorithm for approximating the hotlink assignment problem in the clairvoyant model was presented in [5]. This algorithm uses greedy choices at each iteration, and achieves an approximation ratio of 2. Another recent article [4] discusses the use of hotlink assignments in asymmetric communication protocols to achieve better performance bounds.

In this paper we present an algorithm for optimally solving the hotlink enhancement problem on trees in the greedy user model. The algorithm uses dynamic programming and the greedy assumption to limit the search operations. We also show how to generalize the solution to arbitrary degree trees and to hotlink enhancement schemes that allow up to K hotlinks per node. In contrast with the approximation algorithm of [3], which is polynomial for trees of bounded degree but arbitrary depth, our (exact) algorithm can be used for trees with unbounded degree, but its time complexity is polynomial only on trees of logarithmic depth.

Finally, we give an algorithm for handling settings when the distribution on the leafs is unknown. This algorithm provides a logarithmic bound on the expected number of steps to reach the desired leaf. Deriving a lower bound on the expected tour length of optimal solution, we then conclude that our algorithm ensures constant ratio approximation.

In the full paper we show that the NP-hardness proof of [2] for the hotlink enhancement problem on DAGs in the clairvoyant user model can be easily augmented to prove also the NP-hardness of the problem in the greedy model.

In what follows, Section 2 presents our algorithm for finding an optimal set of hotlinks and its analysis, and Section 3 discusses the particular case where the frequencies of visiting each page are unknown.

2   Known Distribution Model

Our algorithm makes use of the following properties of the problem (whose proofs are deferred to the full paper).

Lemma 2. *There exists an optimal solution to the hotlink enhancement problem in which no two hotlinks arrive at the same node.*

It is convenient to consider a hotlink from node u to node v as a pair of parentheses, where the start-node u of the hotlink marks the left parenthesis and the end-node v marks the right parenthesis. Using this representation, the hotlinks placed along any path from the root over the tree form a sequence of parentheses.

We say that a set of hotlinks S is *well-formed* if on any path from the root over the tree, the parentheses sequence of S on this path is well-formed, namely, hotlinks do not cross each other. Observe that for a well-formed set of hotlinks S, the greedy path from the root to any leaf v coincides with the shortest path in the hotlink-enhanced index structure. This means that the costs of a well-formed S in the greedy user model and in the clairvoyant user model are the same.

Lemma 3. *For every index tree T, there exists an optimal solution to the hotlink enhancement problem in the greedy user model which is well-formed.*

The usefulness of this lemma stems from the fact that it helps to narrow down the domain of potential solutions that needs to be searched (in the greedy user model) in order to find the optimal one.

We first restrict our discussion to n-node binary trees of depth $O(\log n)$ and to the case $K = 1$. We represent a solution S as a function $S : V \mapsto V$, with $S(v)$ being the endpoint of the hotlink starting at v.

For every node v in the tree T, let T_v denote the subtree of T consisting of v and all its descendants, and let $\mathcal{P}_v$ denote the path leading from the root to v in T. We generalize the definition of S to a function $S : V \mapsto 2^V$. For a node v, the set $S(v)$ is referred to as an *undetermined hotlink*, and interpreted as the collection of candidates to be the final endpoint of the hotlink from v. An (undetermined) hotlink function S is said to be *determined* or *fixed for* a node set $W \subseteq V$ if $S(w)$ is a singleton for every $w \in W$.

The cost associated with the solution S on the subtree T_v, assuming S is determined for $\mathcal{P}_v \cup T_v$, is $c(v, S) = \sum_{w \in \mathcal{L}(T_v)} |D_S(w)| \cdot p(w)$. The cost of S over the entire tree T with root r is thus $f(T, p, S) = c(r, S)$.

An (undetermined) hotlink function S is said to be *separated w.r.t. the node v* (or simply *v-separated*) if the nodes of $\mathcal{P}_v$ are partitioned into three disjoint sets, $\mathcal{P}_v = \mathcal{P}_v^F(S) \cup \mathcal{P}_v^I(S) \cup \mathcal{P}_v^O(S)$, called the *fixed-set*, *in-set* and *out-set*, such that (1) for every $w \in \mathcal{P}_v^F(S)$, $S(w)$ is a single descendant of w in $\mathcal{P}_v$, (2) for every $w \in \mathcal{P}_v^I(S)$, $S(w) \subseteq T_v$, and (3) for every $w \in \mathcal{P}_v^O(S)$, $S(w) \subseteq V \setminus (\mathcal{P}_v \cup T_v)$.

We remark that our algorithm will consider candidate solutions separated w.r.t. v in which for every node w in the in-set we have equality, i.e., $S(w) = T_v$, and similarly, for every node w in the out-set we have $S(w) = V \setminus (\mathcal{P}_v \cup T_v)$.

For two solutions S_1 and S_2 and a node set W, we say that S_1 *is compatible with S_2 on W* if $S_1(v) \subseteq S_2(v)$ for every node $v \in W$. S_1 is compatible with S_2 if it is compatible with S_2 on the entire node set of T.

Note that for an undetermined hotlink function S, the greedy path $D_S(w)$ is not necessarily defined for every leaf w of T. For the path to be uniquely defined as $D_S(w) = \langle root = v_0, v_1, \ldots, v_q = w \rangle$, it is required that the sequence of nodes $v_0, \ldots, v_q$ satisfies $S(v_i) = \{v_{i+1}\}$ for $i = 1, 2, \ldots, q-1$. In this case We say that S is *route-determined* for w. This means, in particular, that the cost of accessing w is determined.

Lemma 4. *(a) If a hotlink function S is determined for $\mathcal{P}_v \cup T_v$, then it is route-determined for every leaf w in T_v. (b) If a v-separated hotlink function S is determined for $\mathcal{P}_v^I \cup T_v$, then it is route-determined for every leaf w in T_v.*

Lemma 4 facilitates the use of dynamic programming on the problem, as it leads to the observation that the cost of any solution S over the subtree T_v is determined solely on the basis of its values on $\mathcal{P}_v \cup T_v$, and more importantly, the cost of any v-separated solution S over the subtree T_v is determined solely on the basis of its values on $\mathcal{P}_v^F \cup \mathcal{P}_v^I \cup T_v$. More formally, we have:

Lemma 5. *Consider two hotlink functions S_1 and S_2 that are both v-separated with the same fixed-set, $\mathcal{P}_v^F(S_1) = \mathcal{P}_v^F(S_2)$, and the same in-set, $\mathcal{P}_v^I(S_1) = \mathcal{P}_v^I(S_2)$. If S_1 and S_2 are determined in the same way on $\mathcal{P}_v^F \cup \mathcal{P}_v^I \cup T_v$, i.e., $S_1(w) = S_2(w)$ for every $w \in \mathcal{P}_v^F \cup \mathcal{P}_v^I \cup T_v$, then $c(v, S_1) = c(v, S_2)$.*

The recursive procedure Proc employed by the algorithm receives as its input a node v in the tree, and a v-separated partial hotlink function S of a specific form. Suppose v is of depth d from the root, and let $\mathcal{P}_v = (root = v_0, v_1, \ldots, v_d = v)$. Then S will be specified as a vector $\bar{s} = \langle s(0), \ldots, s(d-1) \rangle$, where

$$s(i) = \begin{cases} j, & S(v_i) = v_j \text{ for } i+2 \le j \le d, \\ I, & S(v_i) = T_v, \\ O, & S(v_i) = V \setminus (\mathcal{P}_v \cup T_v). \end{cases}$$

The goal of Procedure $\mathsf{Proc}(v, \bar{s})$ is to calculate the optimal completion of S on $\mathcal{P}_v^I(S) \cup T_v$, and its cost.

Procedure Proc operates as follows. If T_v is small enough (e.g., it contains fewer than K_0 nodes, for some constant K_0), then the best determination and its cost are found by exhaustive search, examining all possible completions.

Now suppose the tree T_v is larger than K_0 nodes. Denote the children of v by v_L and v_R. We aim to generate all possible v_L and v_R separated partial hotlinks that are compatible with S. The procedure goes over all possible ways of partitioning the set $\mathcal{P}_v^I$ (including v itself) into four disjoint sets named H_L, H_R, B_L and B_R. The set H_L will be interpreted as the set of nodes that have a hotlink directed to v_L (in any solution it is enough to have only one such hotlink). If $H_L = \emptyset$, then in the current completion there is no hotlink to be ended directly in node v_L. The set B_L will be interpreted as the collection of start points of hotlinks to be ended at the nodes of T_{v_L} except v_L itself (the left side sub tree). The sets B_R and H_R are defined analogously for the right hand side of the tree T_v. Thus we get all v_R separated and v_L separated hotlink functions possible from S.

For each such partition (H_L, H_R, B_L, B_R) constructed from S, the procedure does the following. It first generates the (partial) solution S_L derived from S by specifying that the hotlink from the node of H_L (if exists) ends at v_L, the hotlinks from the nodes of B_L (if exist) end inside T_{v_L}, and the hotlinks from the nodes of $H_R \cup B_R$ end outside $\mathcal{P}_{v_L} \cup T_{v_L}$. I.e., the vector representation of the generated S_L is

$$s_L(i) = \begin{cases} d+1, & i \in H_L, \\ O, & i \in \bar{B}_R \cup H_R, \\ s(i), & \text{otherwise.} \end{cases}$$

(Note that in particular, $s_L(i)$ remains I for nodes v_i of B_L, and maintains its previous value (which is either O or some $i + 2 \leq j \leq d$) for nodes outside $\mathcal{P}_v^I$.

The procedure similarly generates the partial solution S_R derived from S by following the specifications of the partition for the right subtree, T_{v_R}.

Then, the procedure is invoked recursively on $(v_L, \bar{s}_L)$ and $(v_R, \bar{s}_R)$, and returns cost values x_L and x_R respectively (accompanied with the determinations yielding them).

Of all the partitions examined, the procedure then selects the one yielding the lowest combined cost $x_L + x_R$ (along with the determination yielding it).

Note that the algorithm invokes the procedure by dynamic programming, rather than plain recursion. Namely, it maintains a table of determinations and costs $A(v, \bar{s})$, for every node v and partial solution $\bar{s}$ of the type described above. Whenever the procedure requires an answer for some pair $(v, \bar{s})$, the procedure first consults the table A. Hence each entry in the table must be computed only once, on the first occasion it is requested. (For example, B_L at v may be the same when in two different computations that differ in B_R.)

Lemma 6. *For every node v in T, and for every v-separated hotlink function S, procedure* Proc *returns a determination for $(v, \bar{s})$ of the minimal cost $c^*(v, S)$.*

To find the optimal cost, $\min_S \{f(T, p, S)\}$, we need to run $\mathsf{Proc}(r, \bar{0})$ where $\bar{0}$ is an empty vector and r is the root of the tree (there are no nodes in $\mathcal{P}_r$).

Let us first estimate the number of entries in table A. There are n possible values for v. For each v, we need to bound N_v, the number of legal vectors $\bar{s}$ that need to be considered. Note that the length of $\bar{s}$ is bounded by $Depth(T) = O(\log n)$. Observe also that for every $0 \leq i \leq d - 2$, where v is at depth d, there are at most $d - i$ possible values for $s(i)$ (namely, any $i + 2 \leq j \leq d$, plus the values I and O). Each $s(i)$ may assume up to $O(\log n)$ different values, and hence it seems as though there might be up to $(c \log n)^{c \log n}$ different $\bar{s}$ configurations overall, for constant c, which is superpolynomial. Fortunately, the number of legal solutions is restricted by the parenthesis requirement of Lemma 3. In particular, since the number of legal sequences of m parenthesis pairs is the m'th Katalan number, $K_m = \frac{1}{m+1}\binom{2m}{m}$, and there are $\binom{d+1+2m-1}{2m}$ ways to choose placements for those parentheses around d nodes taken $2m$ at a time with repetition allowed, the number of legal choices of m pairs of parentheses over d letters is bounded by $K_m \cdot \binom{d+2m}{2m}$. It can be readily verified that N_v, the number of entries corresponding to v, is bounded above by

$$N_v \leq \sum_{m=1}^{d} 2^{d-m} \frac{1}{m+1} \binom{2m}{m} \cdot \binom{d+2m}{2m} \leq 2^d \sum_{m=1}^{d} \binom{2m}{m} \cdot \binom{d+2m}{2m}$$

$$\leq 2^d \cdot d \cdot \binom{2d}{d} \cdot \binom{3d}{2d} \leq d \cdot 2^{6d} = O(\log n) \cdot 2^{O(\log n)} = O\left(n^{O(1)}\right).$$

Hence the number of invocations of the procedure is polynomial in n. Each invocation requires us to go over all the possible partitions of a set of size at most $O(\log n)$ into four subsets (two of which are at most singletons), hence its complexity is polynomial in n. Consequently, the entire algorithm is polynomial as well.

Theorem 1. *There exists a polynomial time algorithm for solving the hotlink enhancement problem with known probability distribution on n-leaf binary trees of depth $O(\log n)$.*

The solution as described above applies only to binary trees. In the full paper we outline the way to generalize it to trees of arbitrary degree. We also consider the case $K > 1$, i.e., where more than one outgoing hotlink is allowed at each node. Finally, in a dynamically changing environment, it may happen that after enhancing the tree once with new hotlinks we wish to repeat the process again and add additional hotlinks. In the full paper we show that our algorithm can be extended to handle this setting as well, by handling tree-dags, namely, DAGs created from a tree by adding only edges from a node to one of its descendants. (Note that the DAG generated by applying our algorithm to a tree is indeed a tree-DAG.)

Corollary 1. *There exists a polynomial time algorithm for solving the hotlink enhancement problem with known probability distribution on arbitrary degree n-leaf tree-DAGs of depth $O(\log n)$ where every node can have up to $K = O(1)$ outgoing hotlinks.*

3   Unknown Distribution

In this section we consider the case that the probabilities associated with each leaf are not known to us. In this case, constructing the best set of hotlinks for the instance at hand is out of the question. Nonetheless, it is possible to construct a generic set of hotlinks that will guarantee a global upper bound of $O(\log n)$ on the access cost. In fact, this can be achieved using a single hotlink per node.

We rely on the well-known fact that that given an n-node tree T, it is always possible to find a separating node v, whose removal breaks the tree into subtrees of size at most $n/2$. Using this fact, we define the hotlinks for our tree T rooted at r as follows. Let w_L and w_R be r's children in T. First, find a separator node v for T as in the lemma, and add a hotlink from r to v. Next, generate hotlinks for T_v, T_{w_L} and T_{w_R} by recursively applying the same procedure.

Letting $f(n)$ denote the maximum root-to-leaf distance in an n-node tree with hotlinks generated by the above procedure, we have to prove that $f(n) \leq c \log n$ for some constant c. This is established by noting that the construction guarantees that $f(n) \leq 1 + f(n/2)$. It follows that no matter what the probabilities are, the resulting cost using this construction is always $O(\log n)$, namely, for any n-node tree T, the algorithm described above constructs a hotlink function S such that $\tilde{f}(T, S) = O(\log n)$. Thus we have:

Theorem 2. *The hotlink enhancement problem with (known or unknown) probabilities has a polynomial time approximation algorithm with ratio $O(\log n)$.*

We now prove a lower bound on the expected access cost under an unknown probability distribution on the leaves. We assume that the tree T is Δ-ry, i.e., its degree is at most Δ, for some constant $\Delta \geq 1$, and that K hotlinks are allowed from each node.

Observe that if there is a hotlink leading to some node w in T, then the tree edge leading to w from its parent in T will never be used in a greedy route to any leaf of T_w. This observation implies that for any set of hotlinks S, the solution resulting from adding S to T is equivalent in cost to some $(\Delta + K)$-ry tree T' with *no hotlinks* at all. The tree T' can be obtained from the pair (T, S) by performing the following modification, for each hotlink leading from v to w: Eliminate the edge connecting w to its parent from the tree, and replace the hotlink by a tree edge connecting v to w. Hence the cost of any solution using up to K hotlinks on a Δ-ry tree is bounded from below by the cost of the best solution using no hotlinks on a $(\Delta + K)$-ry tree.

For an integer $\ell \geq 1$, the maximum number of distinct leaves reachable from the root in ℓ steps on a $(\Delta + K)$-ry tree is bounded by $(\Delta + K)^\ell$. This implies that a solution S in which each of the n nodes is reachable by a path of length ℓ or less, i.e., with $D_S(v) \leq \ell$, must satisfy $(\Delta + K)^\ell \geq n$, or, $\ell \geq \frac{\log n}{\log(\Delta + K)}$. Hence for constant Δ and K, $\ell = \Omega(\log n)$. Using Lemma 1 we get

Theorem 3. *(a) For any n-leaf Δ-ry tree T, if at most K hotlinks are allowed from each node, then $\tilde{f}(T) = \frac{\log n}{\log(\Delta + K)} - 1$. In particular, for constant Δ and K, $\tilde{f}(T) = \Omega(\log n)$. (b) For bounded degree trees, the hotlink enhancement problem with unknown probabilities and constant K has a polynomial time constant ratio approximation algorithm.*

References

1. http://www.google.com/.
2. Bose, P., Czywizowicz, J., Gasieniec, L., Kranakis, E., Krizanc, D., Pelc, A., and Martin, M. V., Strategies for hotlink assignments. *Proc. 11th Symp. on algorithms and computation (ISAAC 2000)*, pp. 23–34.
3. Kranakis, E., Krizanc, D., and Shende, S., Approximating hotlink assignments, *Proc. 12th Symp. on algorithms and computation (ISSAC 2001)*, pp. 756–767.
4. Bose, P., Krizanc, D., Langerman, S. and Morin, P., Asymmetric communication protocols via hotlink assignments, *Proc. 9th Colloq. on Structural Information and Communication Complexity*, June 2002, pp. 33–39.
5. Matichin, R., and Peleg, D., Approximation Algorithm for Hotlink Assignments in Web Directories, *8th Workshop on Algorithms and Data Structures*, Ottawa, Canada, Aug. 2003.
6. http://www.yahoo.com/.
7. www.dmoz.org
8. Attardi G., Di Marco S., Salvi D, Categorization by Context, *Journal of Universal Computer Science*, (1998), Springer Verlag. 4:9:719–736.

Finding a Length-Constrained Maximum-Density Path in a Tree

Rung-Ren Lin[1], Wen-Hsiung Kuo[2], and Kun-Mao Chao[1]

[1] Department of Computer Science and Information Engineering
{r91054, kmchao}@csie.ntu.edu.tw
[2] Department of Electrical Engineering National Taiwan University, Taipei, Taiwan.
b86058@ee.ntu.edu.tw

Abstract. Let $T = (V, E, w)$ be a rooted, undirected, and weighted tree with node set V and edge set E, where $w(e)$ is an edge weight function for $e \in E$. The *density* of a path, say $e_1, e_2, \ldots, e_k$, is defined as $\sum_{i=1}^{k} w(e_i)/k$. Given a tree with n edges, this paper presents two efficient algorithms for finding a maximum-density path of length at least L in $O(nL)$ time. One of them is further modified to solve some special cases such as full m-ary trees in $O(n)$ time.

Keywords: Algorithms, computational biology, network design, trees.

1 Introduction

Given a sequence of n real numbers and a lower bound L, Lin *et al.* [8] recently proposed an $O(n \log L)$-time algorithm for finding a segment of length at least L with the maximum average. Improvements to $O(n)$ were given independently by Goldwasser *et al.* [5] and Kim [7]. Lin *et al.* [9] implemented an algorithm that delivers k non-overlapping maximum-average segments of a given sequence of real numbers, for any fixed $k > 0$. The maximum-average segment problem arises naturally in several areas of sequence analysis. For example, given a DNA sequence, which segment of the sequence of length at least L has the highest GC ratio [4][6][11]? Given a multiple sequence alignment and scores the columns of the alignment, can we find a subalignment consisting of L or more consecutive columns of the alignment that has the highest cumulative average score [1][10]? On the other hand, Wu *et al.* [12] studied the problem of finding a path of length no great than a given upper bound, whose total weight is as large as possible.

In this paper, we study the problem of finding a maximum-density path in a weighted tree. Let $T = (V, E, w)$ be a rooted, undirected, and weighted tree with node set V and edge set E, where $w(e)$ is an edge weight function for $e \in E$. The *density* of a path, say $e_1, e_2, \ldots, e_k$, is defined as $\sum_{i=1}^{k} w(e_i)/k$. We propose two approaches for finding a maximum-density path in a tree. One approach is to compute for each node a maximum-density path starting at that node. The resulting algorithm can be easily adapted to a directed acyclic graph. The other approach is to locate for each internal node a maximum-density path that

T. Ibaraki, N. Katoh, and H. Ono (Eds.): ISAAC 2003, LNCS 2906, pp. 78–87, 2003.

takes such an internal node as a least common ancestor. Both approaches run in $O(nL)$ time. The later is further modified to solve some special cases such as full m-ary trees in $O(n)$ time.

Chao et al. [2] considered constrained alignments consisting of aligned pairs in nearly optimal alignments. These suboptimal alignments are represented as a directed acyclic graph [3]. The algorithms developed in this paper are useful in selecting, from among all high-scoring alignments, a subalignment that has the highest cumulative average score [1].

The rest of the paper is organized as follows. Section 2 describes the first approach which searches all possible paths starting from a specific node. An alternative approach, which searches all combinations of the *downward paths* of a least common ancestor (LCA) internal node, is given in Section 3. Section 4 discusses a special case that can be solved in linear time, and Section 5 concludes the paper with a few remarks.

2   Finding a Maximum-Density Path from Its End Node

To find a maximum-density segment of length at least L in a one-dimensional sequence, Huang [6] observed that there exists an optimal solution of length at most $2L - 1$. This property holds for the tree problem as well. Let $\mu(X)$ denote the density of path X in a tree.

Lemma 1. *There exists a length-constrained maximum-density path of length at most $2L - 1$.*

Proof. It can be proved by a counter argument. Let B denote the shortest path of length at least L such that the density is maximized. Suppose $|B| \geq 2L$. Bisect B into two subpaths, say C and D, such that the length of C and D are neither shorter than L. Without loss of generality, assume that $\mu(C) \geq \mu(D)$. We have $\mu(C) \geq \mu(CD) = \mu(B)$. A contradiction.   □

In order to find a maximum-density path starting from a given node, we classify the paths into two types. One is to stretch downward to its children only, called *downward paths*, and the other is to include at least its parent, called *upward paths*.

Let $D_K^1[i]$ and $D_K^2[i]$ denote the maximum density and the second-best density of those downward paths of length i starting from node K, respectively. The *downward table* of node K consists of $D_K^1[i]$ and $D_K^2[i]$ where $i = 1, 2, \ldots, 2L - 1$.

We can construct the downward tables by bottom-up dynamic programming. Suppose that internal node K has m children $K_1, K_2, \ldots, K_m$. Let e_j denote the edge (K, K_j), we have

$$\begin{cases} D_K^1[i] = \mathrm{max1}\{((i-1) * D_{K_j}^1[i-1] + w(e_j))/i, \ 1 \leq j \leq m\} \\ D_K^2[i] = \mathrm{max2}\{((i-1) * D_{K_j}^1[i-1] + w(e_j))/i, \ 1 \leq j \leq m\}. \end{cases}$$

Here the function max1 always selects the maximum density. If there exist at least two maximum-density downward paths, the function max2 selects the maximum density. Otherwise, max2 selects the second best density. Therefore, $D_K^1[i]$ and $D_K^2[i]$ denote the densities of the best two downward paths of length i from different child nodes. The nodes that determine its parent's downward table entries are called *contributors*. We also record those contributors in the downward table. Take the weighted tree in Figure 1 for example. Let us focus on node A. $D_A^1[1] = 7$, and its contributor is node D. $D_A^2[1] = 6$, and its contributor is node C. $D_A^1[2] = 8$, and its contributor is node C. If there is a tie, choose an arbitrary path. For the degenerated case where there is only one child, we leave D_K^2 undefined.

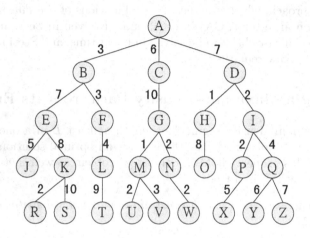

Fig. 1. A weighted tree with 26 nodes.

Lemma 2. *The downward tables of all nodes can be constructed in $O(nL)$ time.*

Proof. Assume internal node K has m children. For a fixed length i, it takes $O(m)$ time to determine $D_K^1[i]$ and $D_K^2[i]$. In total, it takes $O(mL)$ time to construct the downward table of node K with m children. By amortizing this cost to its m children, we spend $O(L)$ time for each child edge. Thus the time complexity of constructing the downward tables of all nodes are $O(nL)$, since there are n edges in the tree. □

The construction of *upward tables* is similar to that of downward tables. Let $U_K[i]$ denote the maximum density of those upward paths of length i starting from node K. Suppose that K' is the parent of node K, and e' denote the edge (K, K'). We have

$$U_K[i] = \max \begin{cases} ((i-1)*U_{K'}[i-1] + w(e'))/i \\ ((i-1)*D_{K'}^1[i-1] + w(e'))/i, \text{ if } K \text{ isn't the contributor of} \\ \qquad\qquad\qquad\qquad\qquad D_{K'}^1[i-1] \\ ((i-1)*D_{K'}^2[i-1] + w(e'))/i, \text{ if } D_{K'}^2[i-1] \text{ exists, and } K \text{ is} \\ \qquad\qquad\qquad\qquad \text{the contributor of } D_{K'}^1[i-1]. \end{cases}$$

The upward tables can be constructed in $O(nL)$ time and space by top-down dynamic programming. Once the downward table and the upward table of each node are constructed, a maximum-density path of the tree can be computed.

Lemma 3. *The density of a maximum-density path starting from node K is* $\max\{\max\{U_K[i], D_K^1[i]\}, L \le i \le 2L - 1\}$.

Proof. By Lemma 1, the length of a maximum-density path is in the range from L up to $2L - 1$. A path that starts from node K is either a downward path or an upward path. The downward table and the upward table of node K keep the densities of the maximum-density paths for each length. Thus, the density of a maximum-density path starting from node K is $\max\{\max\{U_K[i], D_K^1[i]\}$, $L \le i \le 2L - 1\}$.   □

Based on the downward tables and the upward tables, we can find the density of an optimal path starting from any specific node in $O(L)$ time. Therefore, in total it takes $O(nL)$ time to find the density of a length-constrained maximum-density in a tree. A simple backtracking procedure could be employed to deliver a maximum-density path.

3   Finding a Maximum-Density Path from Its LCA Node

This section presents an alternative approach for computing a maximum-density path. It locates for each internal node a maximum-density path that takes such an internal node as a least common ancestor. We first construct the downward tables as mentioned in Section 2. Table 1 is the downward table of node A in Figure 1. Each entry in Table 1 consists of two components, denoted as $a : b$, where a is the density and b is the contributor. Basically, for each internal node we want to compute a maximum-density path taking that internal as a least common ancestor. Such a path would be either a single downward path of length at least L, or a combination of two downward paths of length at least L in total. A naive algorithm takes $O(m^2 L^2)$ time to compute all combinations of a given node with m children. An improvement to $O(mL)$ is given in the following.

Table 1. The downward table of node A in Figure 1.

length	1	2	3	4
max1	7:D	8:C	6:C	7:B
max2	6:C	5:B	6:B	5:D

Define $Path(K, K_i)$ as the length-constrained maximum-density path which combines two non-overlapped downward paths starting from node K, and one of them is contributed by child-node K_i. That is, $Path(K, K_i)$ is a maximum-density path that contains edge (K, K_i), and node K is the highest node of such path.

We are now trying to compute $Path(K, K_i)$ in $O(L)$ time. For a one-dimensional sequence A of length $2*(2L-1)$, the left half elements are numbered from right to left as $L_1, L_2, ..., L_{2L-1}$, and the right half elements are numbered from left to right as $R_1, R_2, ..., R_{2L-1}$. For the downward table of node K, we put all entries that are contributed by K_i into the position L_j of sequence A, where j is the corresponding length of those entries in the downward table. $A[L_j]$ will be "null" if node K_i neither contributes $D_K^1[j]$ nor $D_K^2[j]$. We fill zero into $A[L_j]$ in this case. Then we put $D_K^1[j]$ into the position R_j of sequence A for each $1 \leq j \leq 2L-1$, unless if $D_K^1[j]$ is contributed by node K_i, we choose $D_K^2[j]$ instead. Now, elements that are numbered as L_j or R_j in sequence A stand for the density of length j. We can convert sequence A into *match sequence* B such that $(\sum_{i=1}^k B[L_i])/k = A[L_k]$ and $(\sum_{i=1}^k B[R_i])/k = A[R_k]$. The algorithm of converting a sequence to a match sequence is given in Figure 2. The converting algorithm runs in $O(L)$ time.

CONVERT(A)
Input: A real sequence $A = \langle a_1, a_2, \ldots, a_{4L-2} \rangle$.
Output: match sequence of A.
1 Init: $sumL \leftarrow a_{2L-1}$; $sumR \leftarrow a_{2L}$;
2 **for** $i \leftarrow 1$ **to** $2L - 2$ **do**
3   **if** (a_{2L-1-i} isn't null) **then**
4         $a_{2L-1-i} \leftarrow a_{2L-1-i} * (i+1)$ - $sumL$;
5         $sumL \leftarrow sumL + a_{2L-1-i}$;
6   **end if**
7     $a_{2L+i} \leftarrow a_{2L+i} * (i+1) - sumR$;
8     $sumR \leftarrow sumR + a_{2L+i}$;
9 **end for**

Fig. 2. Converting a given sequence into a match sequence.

For example, consider $Path(A, B)$ in Figure 1. The sequence that is filled in for $Path(A, B)$ is shown in the upper sequence of Figure 3, and its match sequence is shown in the lower one.

Based on the match sequence corresponding to $Path(K, K_i)$, the problem of finding $Path(K, K_i)$ is reduced to the problem of locating a maximum-average segment of length at least L in a one-dimensional sequence. However, our problem requires some additional constraints. The desirable segment is always starting from the left-half "non-null" element in a match sequence, and the right-most element of such segment is never less than the middle of the match sequence. The following lemma proves that the density of such segment equals to the density of $Path(K, K_i)$.

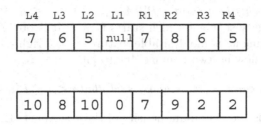

Fig. 3. An example of a match sequence.

Lemma 4. *Under the constraints mentioned above, the average of the maximum-average segment of length at least L found in the match sequence equals to the density of $Path(K, K_i)$.*

Proof. The maximum-density path of length at least L of a given LCA internal node is composed of either a single downward path of length at least L, or a combination of two downward paths of length at least L in total. Suppose that downward paths p and q are the best combination of such an LCA internal node. Let the length of p be denoted by $|p|$, and the length of q be denoted by $|q|$. If $|p| > |q|$ or $|p| < |q|$, we must combine $D_K^1[|p|]$ and $D_K^1[|q|]$. Otherwise we will get a worse combination. If $|p| = |q|$, the best combination is to add up $D_K^1[|p|]$ and $D_K^2[|q|]$.

Under the constraints mentioned above, the segments of the match sequence corresponding to $Path(K, K_i)$ are actually the combinations of two downward paths, in which one of these two downward paths is guaranteed to contain edge (K, K_i). Thus, the maximum-density segment of such match sequence represents $Path(K, K_i)$. □

Now we show how to solve the reduced one-dimensional sequence problem in linear time. Lin et al. [8] invented a data structure called a *right-skew segment*. A sequence $A = \langle a_1, a_2, \ldots, a_n \rangle$ is *right-skew* if and only if the average of any prefix $\langle a_1, a_2, \ldots, a_i \rangle$ is always less than or equal to the average of the remaining suffix subsequence $\langle a_{i+1}, a_{i+2}, \ldots, a_n \rangle$. Let $\mu(X)$ denote the average of segment X, and $\mu(a_i, a_j)$ denote the density of $A(i, j)$, where $A(i, j)$ stands for $\langle a_i, a_{i+1}, \ldots, a_j \rangle$. A partition $A = A_1 A_2 \cdots A_k$ is *decreasingly right-skew* if each segment A_i of the partition is right-skew and $\mu(A_i) > \mu(A_j)$ for any $i < j$. An example of the right-skew segments is shown in Figure 4.

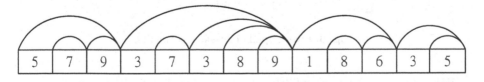

Fig. 4. An example of the right-skew segments.

We keep the *right-skew pointer* $P[i]$ for each $1 \leq i \leq n$. $P[i]$ is an index of the maximum-density segment which starts from i. It is obvious that $A(i, P[i])$ is a right-skew segment. Some desirable features of the right-skew segments are described in the following two lemmas due to [5].

Lemma 5. *There cannot exist i and j such that $i < j \leq P[i] < P[j]$.*

Proof. $A(i, P[i])$ is the maximum-density of those segments that starts from a_i. If $i < j \leq P[i] < P[j]$, it means two right-skew segments partially overlapped (see Figure 5). Since $P[i]$ stops at the end of the overlapped segment Y, it implies that $\mu(X) \leq \mu(Y)$. Likewise, $\mu(Y) \leq \mu(Z)$. Thus, we have $\mu(X) \leq \mu(Z)$. However, $P[i]$ stops at the end of Y instead of the end of Z. It contradicts the statement that $A(i, P[i])$ is the optimal segment of those starting from a_i. $\square$

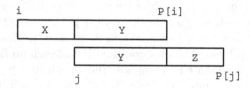

Fig. 5. A contradictive example of right-skew segments.

Lemma 6. *For a given $i < j \leq P[j] < P[i]$, we have $\mu(i, P[i]) < \mu(j, P[j])$.*

Proof. Partition $A(i, P[i])$ into three segments X, Y, and Z as shown in Figure 6, where Y is $A(j, P[j])$. Since $P[i]$ stops at the end of Z, it implies $\mu(Z) > \mu(XY)$. And $P[j]$ stops at the end of Y without stretching to the end of Z. It follows that $\mu(Y) > \mu(Z)$. So we have $\mu(Y) > \mu(Z) > \mu(X)$. Thus $\mu(i, P[i])$ is less than $\mu(j, P[j])$. $\square$

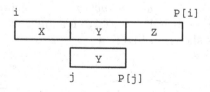

Fig. 6. Overlapped right-skew segments.

We have to record some additional information. Let S_k be a sorted list that contains all indices j for which $P[j] = k$. The arrays for Figure 4 are illustrated

Table 2. Recorded arrays for Figure 4.

	1	2	3	4	5	6	7	8	9	10	11	12	13
$A[i]$	5	7	9	3	7	3	8	9	1	8	6	3	5
$P[i]$	3	2	3	8	5	8	8	8	11	10	11	13	13
S_i			1,2,3		5			4,6,7,8		10	9,11		12,13

in Table 3. For instance, $S_8=\{4, 6, 7, 8\}$ implies that $P[4]$, $P[6]$, $P[7]$ and $P[8]$ are 8.

Let $G[i]$ represent the optimal index of a_i with a length-constraint, *i.e.*, $(i, G[i])$ is of length at least L. The algorithm for finding $Path(K, K_i)$ is shown in Figure 7.

FINDMAX(A)

Input: A match sequence $A = \langle a_1, a_2, \ldots, a_{4L-2} \rangle$ that is related with $Path(K, K_i)$.

Output: the density of $Path(K, K_i)$.

1 Init: $y \leftarrow 4L - 2$; $k \leftarrow 4L - 2$; $flag \leftarrow$ true;

2 **for** $i \leftarrow 2L - 1$ **downto** 1

3   **if** (a_i isn't null) **then**

4   **while** ($flag$ = true **and** $k \geq 2L$)

5             $k \leftarrow$ minimum but no less than $i + L$ in S_y;

6   **if** (k exists **and** $\mu(k, y) < \mu(i, k-1)$) **then** $y \leftarrow k - 1$;

7   **else** $flag \leftarrow$ false;

8   **end while**

9   **end if**

10    $G[i] \leftarrow y$;

11    $flag \leftarrow$ true;

12 **end for**

13 output the maximum $\mu(i, G[i])$, where $1 \leq i \leq 2L - 1$ **and** a_i isn't null

---

Fig. 7. Finding $Path(K, K_i)$ in linear time.

Lemma 7. *The algorithm shown in Figure 7 runs in linear time. It takes a match sequence, which is corresponding to $Path(K, K_i)$, as input, and outputs the density of $Path(K, K_i)$.*

Proof. As shown in Figure 7, variables k and y in **while** loop decrease only. Thus, the algorithm runs in linear time. In line 3, variable i is limited to start with a non-null element, and the right-most element is always not less than the middle of the input sequence. Therefore, the algorithm outputs the maximum density which is equal to the density of $Path(K, K_i)$. □

By lemma 7, the algorithm for finding the density of $Path(K, K_i)$ runs in $O(L)$ time. That is, each edge is handled in $O(L)$ time. Hence, the time complexity of finding the maximum-density paths of all internal nodes is $O(nL)$.

4   A Special Case

Now consider the case where the tree is a full m-ary tree. Imitate the steps mentioned in the Section 3. However, we only need to combine two downward paths when the internal node is of height at least $L/2$ as depicted in Figure 8.

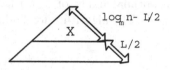

Fig. 8. A full m-ary tree with n nodes.

Lemma 8. *Finding a length-constrained maximum-density path in a full m-ary tree can be done in linear time.*

Proof. The time for constructing the downward tables for all nodes is $(\sum_{i=0}^{\log_m n} m^i * (\log_m n - i)) = O(n)$. Note that only those internal nodes of height at least $L/2$ (the area X in Figure 8) are qualified as a least common ancestor of a path of length at least L. For each qualified internal node, it takes $O(mL)$ time to find a length-constrained maximum-density path that takes such an internal node as a least common ancestor. Therefore, in total we have

$$(m^{(\log_m n - L/2)}) \times O(mL)) = \frac{nL}{m^{(L/2)-1}} = O(n).$$

$\square$

5   Concluding Remarks

Though our algorithm is for the tree with weighted edges, a straightforward modification will work properly for the tree with weighted nodes. Besides, the concept of constructing the downward tables can be used to solve the case where the graph is a directed acyclic graph. In the future, it is interesting to consider some other variants such as the problem of finding a size-constrained maximum-density subtree in a tree.

Acknowledgements. Rung-Ren Lin and Kun-Mao Chao were supported in part by an NSC grant 91-2213-E-002-129 from the National Science Council, Taiwan.

References

1. A. Arslan, Ö. Eğecioğlu, and P. Pevzner, A new approach to sequence comparison: normalized sequence alignment, *Bioinformatics*, 17:327–337, 2001.
2. K.-M. Chao, R.C. Hardison and W. Miller, Recent Developments in Linear-Space Alignment Methods: a Survey, *Journal of Computational Biology*, 1:271–291, 1994.
3. K.-M. Chao, On Computing all Suboptimal Alignments, *Information Sciences*, 105:189–207, 1998.
4. M. Gardiner-Garden and M. Frommer, CpG islands in vertebrate genomes, *J. Mol. Biol.*, 196:261–282, 1987.
5. M.H. Goldwasser, M.-Y. Kao, and H.-I. Lu., Fast algorithms for finding maximum-density segments of a sequence with applications to bioinformatics, *Proceedings of the 2nd Workshop on Algorithms in Bioinformatics (WABI)*, 157–171, 2002.
6. X. Huang., An algorithm for identifying regions of a DNA sequence that satisfy a content requirement, *CABIOS*, 10:219–225, 1994.
7. S.K. Kim., Linear-time algorithm for finding a maximum-density segment of a sequence. *Information Processing Letters*, 86:339–342, 2003.
8. Y.-L. Lin, T. Jiang, and K.-M. Chao, Efficient algorithms for locating the length-constrained heaviest segments. *Journal of Computer and System Sciences*, 65:570–586, 2002.
9. Y.-L. Lin, X. Huang, T. Jiang, and K.-M. Chao, MAVG: Locating Non-Overlapping Maximum Average Segments in a Given Sequence, *Bioinformatics*, 19:151–152, 2003.
10. N. Stojanovic, L. Florea, C. Riemer, D. Gumucio, J. Slightom, M. Goodman, W. Miller, and R.C. Hardison, Comparison of five methods for finding conserved sequences in multiple alignments of gene regulatory regions, *Nucleic Acids Res.*, 27:3899–3910, 1999.
11. D. Takai and P.A. Jones, Comprehensive analysis of CpG islands in human chromosomes 21 and 22, *PNAS*, 99:3740–3745, 2002.
12. B.Y. Wu, K.-M. Chao and C.Y. Tang, An efficient algorithm for the length-constrained heaviest path problem on a tree. *Information Processing Letters*, 69:63–67, 1999.

The Intractability of Computing the Hamming Distance

Bodo Manthey* and Rüdiger Reischuk

Universität zu Lübeck, Institut für Theoretische Informatik
Wallstraße 40, 23560 Lübeck, Germany
{manthey,reischuk}@tcs.uni-luebeck.de

Abstract. Given a string x and a language L, the Hamming distance of x to L is the minimum Hamming distance of x to any string in L. The edit distance of a string to a language is analogously defined.

First, we prove that there is a language in AC^0 such that both Hamming and edit distance to this language are hard to approximate; they cannot be approximated with a factor $O(n^{\frac{1}{3}-\epsilon})$, for any $\epsilon > 0$, unless $\mathrm{P} = \mathrm{NP}$ (n denotes the length of the input string).

Second, we show the parameterized intractability of computing the Hamming distance. We prove that for every $t \in \mathbb{N}$ there exists a language in AC^0 for which computing the Hamming distance is $\mathrm{W}[t]$-hard. Moreover, there is a language in P for which computing the Hamming distance is $\mathrm{W}[\mathrm{P}]$-hard.

Finally, we show that the problems of computing the Hamming distance and of computing the edit distance are in some sense equivalent by presenting reductions from the former to the latter and vice versa.

1   Introduction

Given a language L and a string x, one can ask whether there is a string in L in the "neighbourhood" of x and how to find such a string. On the other hand, one can ask for the minimum distance of any string in L to x. Hamming and edit distance are widely used for measuring the distance. One topic in which these problems arise is for example the field of error-correcting codes (see e.g. Spielman [15]). Another field is parsing theory. A main problem when designing a parser is recovery from syntax errors. This problem has been solved for context-free languages [1,8,11]. Furthermore, the problem of computing distances between strings has gained popularity in computational biology [5,9,13]. From the computational complexity point of view, it is interesting whether there are properties other than membership that can efficiently be computed for appropriate classes of languages [7].

Computing the Hamming distance of two strings is easy. Computing the edit distance of two strings can be done via dynamic programming. Pighizzini [14] presented a language in co-NTime(log) (a subclass of AC^0) for which computing

---

* Supported by DFG research grant Re 672/3.

T. Ibaraki, N. Katoh, and H. Ono (Eds.): ISAAC 2003, LNCS 2906, pp. 88–97, 2003.
© Springer-Verlag Berlin Heidelberg 2003

the edit distance is NP-hard. On the other hand, he showed that computing the edit distance to languages in 1NAuxPDA^P can be done in polynomial time and even in AC^1. 1NAuxPDA^P denotes the class of all languages that can be recognized by logarithmic space and polynomial time bounded nondeterministic Turing machines equipped a one-way input tape and an auxiliary pushdown store.

Intuitively, computing the edit distance seems to be harder than computing the Hamming distance. Thus, one might hope that Pighizzini's hardness result for computing the edit distance does not hold for computing the Hamming distance. However, we show that this is not the case and even improve the intractability bound. This will be done by showing that the problem is hard to approximate and intractable in the sense of parameterized complexity.

To be more precise, we present a language in AC^0 with the property that the Hamming distance of strings of length n to this language cannot be approximated in polynomial time with a factor $O(n^{\frac{1}{3}-\epsilon})$ unless P = NP. Furthermore, for a language L we consider the parameterized language where on input x we ask whether there is a string $y \in L$ within distance k. We prove that for every $t \in \mathbb{N}$ there is a language in AC^0 for which this is W[t]-hard. Moreover, we present a language in P for which this is W[P]-hard. Thus, it turns out that computing the Hamming distance is hard even for languages in small complexity classes. Finally, we reduce the problem of computing the Hamming distance to the problem of computing the edit distance and vice versa. Hence, both problems are in some sense equivalent with respect to their approximability.

2   Preliminaries

Let Σ be a finite alphabet. The length of a string x over Σ will be denoted by $|x|$. For two strings x and y of equal length, let $h(x, y)$ be the *Hamming distance* of x and y, i.e. the number of positions where x and y differ. The Hamming distance of a language L over Σ to a string $x \in \Sigma^*$ is the minimum Hamming distance of x to an element of L, i.e.

$$h(x, L) = \min\{h(x, y) \mid y \in L \text{ and } |y| = |x|\}\,.$$

If $\Sigma^{|x|} \cap L = \emptyset$, i.e. if there is no string of length $|x|$ in L, we define $h(x, L) = \infty$.

Let $\Delta \notin \Sigma$ denote the gap symbol and define $\Sigma' = \Sigma \cup \{\Delta\}$. An *alignment* of two strings x and y over Σ is a pair of strings $\tilde{x}$ and $\tilde{y}$ over Σ' such that $|\tilde{x}| = |\tilde{y}|$ and $\tilde{x}$ and $\tilde{y}$ are obtained from x and y, respectively, by inserting gap symbols. We assume that at neither position both $\tilde{x}$ and $\tilde{y}$ have a gap. We define the *edit distance* $d(x, y)$ of two strings x and y as

$$d(x, y) = \min\{h(\tilde{x}, \tilde{y}) \mid (\tilde{x}, \tilde{y}) \text{ is an alignment of } (x, y)\}\,.$$

The edit distance of two strings x and y is the minimum number of insertions, deletions, and substitutions of characters in x necessary to obtain y. In contrast to the Hamming distance, x and y do not have to be of the same length. In general, we can allow an arbitrary function that yields some penalty for each operation depending on the participating characters. See for example Gusfield [5] or Navarro [12] for a survey on computing edit distances between two or more sequences. To obtain the hardness results, it suffices to restrict ourselves to the simplest case where all insertions, deletions and substitutions have unit costs.

The edit distance of a string x to a language L is defined as

$$d(x, L) = \min\{d(x, y) \mid y \in L\}.$$

We consider the problem of computing the Hamming distance or the edit distance of a language and a string in two different ways, namely as an optimization problem and as a parameterized language.

Definition 1 (Optimization Problems). *Let $L \subseteq \{0,1\}^\star$ be a language. Then $\mathsf{OPT_H}(L)$ is the following optimization problem:*

1. *An instance of $\mathsf{OPT_H}(L)$ is a string $x \in \{0,1\}^\star$.*
2. *A solution to an instance x is a string $y \in L$ with $|y| = |x|$.*
3. *The measure is the Hamming distance between x and y, i.e. $h(x,y)$.*
4. *The goal is to find a string in L with minimum Hamming distance to x.*

$\mathsf{OPT_E}(L)$ *is similarly defined: We omit the length constraint, i.e. all $y \in L$ are feasible solutions, and we use the edit distance as measure.*

Definition 2 (Hamming/Edit Closure). *Let $L \subseteq \{0,1\}^\star$ be a language. Then $L_H = \{(x,k) \mid \exists y \in L : |x| = |y| \wedge h(x,y) \leq k\}$. L_E is similarly defined: We replace h by d and omit the constraint $|x| = |y|$. L_H and L_E are called the Hamming and edit closure of L, respectively.*

If $L \in \mathsf{NP}$, then both L_H and L_E are in NP as well. Throughout this work, we consider Hamming and edit closures as parameterized languages with k as parameter. Next, we define classes of Hamming and edit closures corresponding to classical complexity classes.

Definition 3 (Complexity Classes of Hamming/Edit Closures). *Let C be a class of languages. Then the class $\mathsf{C_H}$ of Hamming closures of languages in C is defined as $\mathsf{C_H} = \{L_H \mid L \in \mathsf{C}\}$. Analogously, the class $\mathsf{C_E}$ of edit closures of languages in C is defined as $\mathsf{C_E} = \{L_E \mid L \in \mathsf{C}\}$.*

The paper is organized as follows. In the next section we prove that the Hamming distance is hard to approximate. In Section 4 we focus our attention on Hamming closures. We show the intractability of Hamming closures in the sense of parameterized complexity. In Section 5 we present reductions from the problem of computing the Hamming distance to the one of computing the edit distance and vice versa. Finally, we raise some open problems in Section 6.

3   The Hamming Distance Is Hard to Approximate

In this section, we prove that there is a language $L \in \mathsf{AC}^0$ such that the Hamming distance to L cannot be approximated with a factor $O(n^{\frac{1}{3}-\epsilon})$, for any $\epsilon > 0$, for strings of length n unless $\mathsf{P} = \mathsf{NP}$.

We consider the optimization problem *Minimum Independent Dominating Set* (MIDS). An instance of MIDS is an undirected graph $G = (V, E)$. A solution is a subset $\tilde{V} \subseteq V$ of vertices that is both an independent set and a dominating set. $\tilde{V}$ is an independent set of G, if for every edge $\{u, v\} \in E$ at most one of the vertices u and v is in $\tilde{V}$. $\tilde{V}$ is a dominating set of G, if for every vertex $u \in V \setminus \tilde{V}$ there exists a node $v \in \tilde{V}$ with $\{u, v\} \in E$. The goal is to minimize the size of $\tilde{V}$. The problem MIDS is also known as *Minimum Maximal Independent Set*, since an independent dominating set is an independent set that cannot be extended. Halldórsson [6] showed that MIDS cannot be approximated with a factor $O(|V|^{1-\epsilon})$, for any $\epsilon > 0$, unless $P = NP$.

Consider the following language over the alphabet $\{0, 1, \#\}$:

$$L^{\mathsf{MIDS}} = \{ G_1 \# \ldots \# G_{m+1} \# \tilde{V} \mid G_\ell \in \{0, 1\}^{\binom{m}{2}}, \ \tilde{V} \in \{0, 1\}^m \text{ for some } m \in \mathbb{N},$$
$$G_1 = \ldots = G_{m+1}, \text{each } G_\ell \text{ is an encoding of the same } m\text{-vertex}$$
$$\text{graph } G, \text{ and } \tilde{V} \text{ encodes an independent dominating set of } G\}$$

An encoding G_ℓ ($1 \le \ell \le m+1$) consists of $\binom{m}{2}$ bits $(e_{i,j}^\ell)_{1 \le i < j \le m}$. (For simplicity, $e_{i,j}^\ell = e_{j,i}^\ell$ for $i > j$.) We have $e_{i,j}^\ell = 1$ iff $\{v_i, v_j\} \in E$. The set $\tilde{V}$ is encoded with m bits z_i ($1 \le i \le m$) with $z_i = 1$ iff $v_i \in \tilde{V}$.

Let us first show that $L^{\mathsf{MIDS}} \in AC^0$. We build the following circuit:

$$
\begin{aligned}
\text{DOM} \ &= \ \bigwedge_{i=1}^m \left(z_i \vee \bigvee_{j=1}^m (z_j \wedge e_{i,j}^1) \right), \\
\text{IND} \ &= \ \bigwedge_{i=1}^m \bigwedge_{j=1}^m \left((z_i \wedge z_j) \to \neg e_{i,j}^1 \right), \\
\text{EQU} \ &= \ \bigwedge_{i=1}^m \bigwedge_{j=i+1}^m \left(\bigwedge_{\ell=1}^{m+1} e_{i,j}^\ell \vee \bigwedge_{\ell-1}^{m+1} \neg e_{i,j}^\ell \right), \text{ and} \\
\text{OUTPUT} \ &= \text{DOM} \wedge \text{IND} \wedge \text{EQU}.
\end{aligned}
$$

We have DOM $= 1$ iff $\tilde{V}$ is a dominating set and IND $= 1$ iff $\tilde{V}$ is an independent set of G. Furthermore, EQU $= 1$ iff the matrices $(e_{i,j}^\ell)_{1 \le i < j \le m}$ encode the same graph G for any $1 \le \ell \le m+1$. Hence, OUTPUT $= 1$ iff the input is in L^{MIDS}. The circuit implementing the above formulas has constant depth and the circuit family is logarithmic space uniform. Thus, $L^{\mathsf{MIDS}} \in AC^0$. Let $n = \frac{m^3 + 3m + 2}{2}$ be the length of an input string encoding a graph with m vertices.

Theorem 1. *For any $\epsilon > 0$, $\mathsf{OPT_H}(L^{\mathsf{MIDS}})$ cannot be approximated in polynomial time with a factor $O(n^{\frac{1}{3}-\epsilon})$ for strings of length n unless $P = NP$.*

Proof. Let a graph $G = (V, E)$ with $|V| = m$ be given as an instance for MIDS. We create an input string x as an instance for $\mathsf{OPT_H}(L^{\mathsf{MIDS}})$ by encoding the graph G by $(e_{i,j}^\ell)_{1 \le i < j \le m}$ for $1 \le \ell \le m+1$ and setting $z_i = 0$ for all $1 \le i \le m$.

Since every graph has an independent dominating set, we have $h(x, L^{\mathsf{MIDS}}) \le m$. Thus, there exists a string $y \in L^{\mathsf{MIDS}}$ with $|x| = |y|$ and $h(x, y) \le m$. Since the encoding of the graph G consists of $m+1$ identical copies, all differences between x and such a y are within the encoding of $\tilde{V}$. Thus, y yields an independent dominating set of size $h(x, y)$ for G.

A factor $O(m^{1-\epsilon})$ approximation algorithm for $\mathsf{OPT_H}(L^{\mathsf{MIDS}})$ would yield an $O(m^{1-\epsilon})$ approximation for MIDS. From $m \in \Theta(n^{\frac{1}{3}})$, the theorem follows. $\square$

Theorem 2. *For any $\epsilon > 0$, $\mathsf{OPT_E}(L^{\mathsf{MIDS}})$ cannot be approximated in polynomial time with a factor $O(n^{\frac{1}{3}-\epsilon})$ for strings of length n unless $\mathsf{P} = \mathsf{NP}$.*

Proof. Consider the input string x created in the proof of Theorem 1. Any string $y \in L^{\mathsf{MIDS}}$ with $|y| \neq |x|$ fulfils $d(x, y) > m$. Thus, any string in L^{MIDS} with minimum edit distance to x has length n. A change within the graph encoding again causes at least a difference of $m + 1$. Hence, if $y \in L^{\mathsf{MIDS}}$ has minimum edit distance to x, then x and y differ only within the encoding of $\tilde{V}$. Let z_y be the encoding of $\tilde{V}$ in y. The edit distance of x and y is at least the number of 1's in z_y — the theorem is proved. $\square$

Thus, even in the small class $\mathsf{AC^0}$ there exists a language such that both Hamming and edit distance to this language are hard to approximate.

4   Parameterized Intractability of Hamming Closures

4.1   Parameterized Intractability of $\mathsf{P_H}$

The aim of this section is to analyze the complexity of Hamming closures of languages in P. On the one hand, we prove that the Hamming closures of languages in P are in $\mathsf{W[P]}$. On the other hand, there is a language in P the Hamming closure of which is $\mathsf{W[P]}$-hard.

Downey and Fellows [2] defined $\mathsf{W[P]}$ to be the class of parameterized languages that can be reduced to $\mathsf{EW\text{-}Circ\text{-}SAT}$. (Here, EW stands for *Exactly Weighted*. Downey and Fellows called the problem *Weighted Circuit Satisfiability*.)

$$\mathsf{EW\text{-}Circ\text{-}SAT} = \{(C, k) \mid C \text{ is a Boolean circuit and has a satisfying}$$
$$\text{assignment with weight } exactly \ k\}.$$

The weight of an assignment is the number of variables to which the value 1 has been assigned. We also consider the following variant of weighted circuit satisfiability:

$$\mathsf{W\text{-}Circ\text{-}SAT} = \{(C, k) \mid C \text{ is a Boolean circuit and has a satisfying}$$
$$\text{assignment with weight } at \ most \ k\}.$$

Lemma 1. $\mathsf{W\text{-}Circ\text{-}SAT}$ *is* $\mathsf{W[P]}$*-complete.*

Proof. First, we reduce $\mathsf{W\text{-}Circ\text{-}SAT}$ to $\mathsf{EW\text{-}Circ\text{-}SAT}$ to prove $\mathsf{W\text{-}Circ\text{-}SAT} \in \mathsf{W[P]}$. Let (C, k) be an instance for $\mathsf{W\text{-}Circ\text{-}SAT}$. Assume that C has n input bits. We add k new input bits $z_1, \ldots, z_k$ and construct the circuit C' as $C \wedge \bigvee_{i=1}^{k}(z_i \vee \overline{z_i})$. If C has a satisfying assignment with weight $k' \leq k$, then C' will be satisfied by the same assignment together with $z_1 = \ldots = z_{k'} = 0$ and $z_{k'+1} = \ldots = z_k = 1$. The assignment obtained has weight k and hence $(C', k) \in \mathsf{EW\text{-}Circ\text{-}SAT}$. On the other hand, any satisfying assignment for C' with weight k yields a satisfying assignment for C with weight at most k.

Second, we reduce EW-Circ-SAT to W-Circ-SAT to prove the W[P]-hardness of W-Circ-SAT. Let (C, k) be an instance for EW-Circ-SAT. We construct another circuit $C_{n,k}$ that on input x outputs 1 if the number of ones in x is exactly k. The circuit $C_{n,k}$ has size polynomial in n. Then $(C, k) \in$ EW-Circ-SAT iff $(C \wedge C_{n,k}, k) \in$ W-Circ-SAT — we have reduced EW-Circ-SAT to W-Circ-SAT.   □

Theorem 3. $P_H \subseteq W[P]$.

Proof. Consider an arbitrary language $L \in P$. We reduce L_H to W-Circ-SAT to show that $L_H \in W[P]$. Assume that $L \subseteq \Sigma^*$ for some finite alphabet $\Sigma = \{\alpha_1, \alpha_2, \ldots, \alpha_\sigma\}$. Let $g : \Sigma^* \to \{0,1\}^*$ be a homomorphism with $g(\alpha_i) = 0^{i-1}10^{\sigma-i}$. We consider the language $g(L) = \{g(x) \mid x \in L\}$. Clearly, $g(L) \in P$. Furthermore, we have $(x, k) \in L_H$ iff $(g(x), 2k) \in g(L)_H$. Since $g(L) \in P$, there is a logarithmic space uniform circuit family of polynomial size for deciding $g(L)$ (see e.g. Greenlaw et al. [4]). Let C_n be the circuit in this family for strings of length n. Assume that we have an input string $y = y_1 \ldots y_n$. We modify C_n slightly as follows to obtain a circuit $C_{n,y}$. If $y_i = 0$, then we leave the ith input bit unchanged. If $y_i = 1$, then we replace the ith input bit by itself followed by a NOT gate. Now C_n accepts y iff $C_{n,y}$ accepts 0^n. Furthermore, C_n accepts a string $\hat{y}$ iff $C_{n,y}$ accepts z with $z_i = y_i \oplus \hat{y}_i$, i.e. $C_{n,y}(z) = 1$ iff $C_n(\hat{y}) = 1$.

To summarize the above deliberations, we have $(x, k) \in L_H$ iff $(g(x), 2k) \in g(L)_H$ iff $(C_{|x| \cdot \sigma, g(x)}, 2k) \in$ W-Circ-SAT. Thus, the theorem is proved.   □

Now we prove that there is a language in P the Hamming closure of which is W[P]-hard. Therefore, we consider the circuit value problem:

$$\mathsf{CVP} = \{(C, x) \mid C \text{ is a Boolean circuit that outputs 1 on input } x\}.$$

Ladner [10] proved that CVP is P-complete. We consider the following variant of CVP, which is P-complete as well:

$$\mathsf{CVP'} = \{(\underbrace{C\#C\#\ldots\#C}_{(n+1) \text{ times}}, x) \mid (C, x) \in \mathsf{CVP} \text{ and } C \text{ has } n \text{ input bits}\}.$$

Theorem 4. $\mathsf{CVP'_H}$ *is* W[P]-*hard.*

Proof. Let (C, k) be an instance for W-Circ-SAT, such that C has n input bits. W.l.o.g. we assume $k \leq n$. Then $X = ((C\#C\#\ldots\#C, 0^n), k)$ is an instance of $\mathsf{CVP'_H}$ with $(C, k) \in$ W-Circ-SAT iff $X \in \mathsf{CVP'_H}$. Hence, we have reduced W-Circ-SAT to $\mathsf{CVP'_H}$.   □

4.2 Parameterized Intractability of $\mathsf{AC^0_H}$

A Boolean formula is called t-normalized, if it has the form "AND-of-ORs-of-ANDs-of- ... -of-Literals" with t alternations [2]. For example, CNF formulas are 2-normalized. Consider the parameterized language

$$\mathsf{W}\text{-}t\text{-SAT} = \{(F, k) \mid F \text{ is a } t\text{-normalized Boolean formula and has a}$$
$$\text{satisfying assignment with at most } k \text{ ones}\}.$$

W-t-SAT is W[t]-complete for all $t \geq 2$ while W-1-SAT is fixed parameter tractable [2]. Let us now encode a t-normalized formula F over n variables into a binary string. Therefore, we view F as a rooted tree T with vertices arranged in levels $V_1 \cup V_2 \cup \ldots \cup V_t$. The vertices in level V_ℓ ($1 \leq \ell \leq t-1$) are labelled with AND, if ℓ is odd, and with OR, if ℓ is even. Every vertex $v \in V_t$ is labelled with lit(v) which is either a variable or a negated variable. For every vertex $v \in V_\ell$ we have a set Adj(v) $\subseteq V_{\ell+1}$ that contains all those vertices in $V_{\ell+1}$ that serve as input bits for v. Thus, we can write F as (assume that t is even, if t is odd, then we have one more AND gate)

$$ F = \bigwedge\nolimits_{v_1 \in V_1} \bigvee\nolimits_{v_2 \in \mathrm{Adj}(v_1)} \bigwedge\nolimits_{v_3 \in \mathrm{Adj}(v_2)} \cdots \bigvee\nolimits_{v_t \in \mathrm{Adj}(v_{t-1})} \mathrm{lit}(v_t) . $$

We have $|V_1| \leq |V_2| \leq \ldots \leq |V_t|$, since T is a tree, and we can assume that $|V_t| \geq n$. Otherwise, there would be unused variables. We call $m = |V_t|$ the size of F. We can encode every subgraph induced by the vertices of $V_{\ell+1} \cup V_\ell$ by an $m \times m$-matrix $(e_{i,j}^\ell)_{1 \leq i,j \leq m}$. Hence, we can write F as

$$ F = \bigwedge\nolimits_{i_1=1}^{m} \bigvee\nolimits_{i_2=1}^{m} \bigwedge\nolimits_{i_3=1}^{m} \cdots \bigvee\nolimits_{i_t=1}^{m} \left((\bigwedge\nolimits_{\ell=1}^{t-1} e_{i_{\ell+1},i_\ell}^\ell) \rightarrow \mathrm{lit}(v_t) \right) . $$

Similar to the reduction presented in Section 4.1, we can create $m+1$ copies of each of these matrices. Thus, each t-normalized formula of size m can be evaluated by a circuit of depth $t+O(1)$ and polynomial size with $t \cdot m^2 \cdot (m+1)+m$ input variables. (W.l.o.g. we assume that we have m input variables. Otherwise we add $m-n$ variables that are never used.) The circuit family obtained (which is logarithmic space uniform) characterizes the language

t-VAL $= \{(M, x) \mid M$ is an encoding of a t-normalized formula F as

described above and outputs 1 on input $x \in \{0,1\}^m\}$.

Theorem 5. *For every $t \geq 2$, t-VAL$_\mathsf{H}$ is W[t]-hard.*

Proof. Let (F, k) be an instance for W-t-SAT and m be the size of F. We construct a circuit as described above with $t \cdot m^2 \cdot (m+1)+m$ input bits. The input X for the circuit is as follows. The first $t \cdot m^2 \cdot (m+1)$ bits encode the formula F. The last m bits are set to 0. Assume that $(F, k) \in$ W-t-SAT. We derive Y from X by setting a bit representing an input bit to 1, if the corresponding bit in the satisfying assignment for F is set to 1. Thus, $h(X, Y) \leq k$ and the circuit constructed accepts Y. On the other hand, assume that there is a Y with $h(X, Y) \leq k \leq m$ that is accepted by the circuit. Then X and Y encode the same formula and Y yields a satisfying assignment for F with weight at most k. Hence, we have reduced W-t-SAT to t-VAL$_\mathsf{H}$. ☐

Thus, for every $t \in \mathbb{N}$ there is a language $L \in \mathsf{AC}^0$ such that L_H is W[t]-hard.

5   Edit Distance versus Hamming Distance

5.1   Reduction from Computing the Hamming Distance to Computing the Edit Distance

Let L be a language to which we want to compute the Hamming distance. For every $x \in \{0,1\}^n$, let $x' = 0^n 1^n x_1 1^n 0^n 0^n 1^n x_2 1^n 0^n \ldots 0^n 1^n x_n 1^n 0^n$. We construct a language L' as

$$L' = \{x' \mid x = x_1 x_2 \ldots x_n \in L\}.$$

Thus, every string x of length n has a counterpart x' of length $(4 \cdot n + 1) \cdot n$. Consider the substring $0^n 1^n x_i 1^n 0^n$ of x'. We call the substrings $0^n 1^n$ and $1^n 0^n$ the left and right block, respectively, of x_i.

Lemma 2. *For every string x with $h(x, L) < \infty$, we have $h(x, L) = h(x', L') = d(x', L')$.*

Proof. Obviously, we have $h(x, L) = h(x', L')$ and $h(x', L') \geq d(x', L')$. Thus, it remains to show that $h(x', L') \leq d(x', L')$.

Let $|x| = n$. We can assume $L \cap \{0,1\}^n \neq \emptyset$, since $h(x, L) = \infty$ otherwise. Let $y' \in L'$ be a string with minimum edit distance to x'. Then $y' = 0^{n'} 1^{n'} y_1 1^{n'} 0^{n'} \ldots 0^{n'} 1^{n'} y_{n'} 1^{n'} 0^{n'}$ for some $n' \in \mathbb{N}$. If $n' \neq n$, then the difference of $|x'|$ and $|y'|$ is more than n and therefore $d(x', y') > n$. Thus, we can assume that $n' = n$. Consider now an optimal alignment $(\tilde{x}', \tilde{y}')$ of (x', y'). We have $h(\tilde{x}', \tilde{y}') \leq n$. Thus, we can assume that in the alignment considered, x_i is at most n positions away from y_i, because otherwise too many 0's or 1's will match a gap. Assume that x_i and y_i do not match, but x_i is at most n position away from y_i. Then either parts of the left block of x_i match parts of the right block of y_i or parts of the right block of x_i match parts of the left block of y_i. Thus, either there are a lot of 0's matching 1's in the other string or there are a lot of gaps both in $\tilde{x}'$ and $\tilde{y}'$. Due to the structure of x' and y', we can modify $\tilde{x}'$ and $\tilde{y}'$ to obtain an alignment with less or equal score. This way, we iteratively obtain a new alignment $(\tilde{x}'', \tilde{y}'')$ that contains no gaps. Since $\tilde{x}', \tilde{y}'$ is an optimal alignment we have $h(x', L') = h(\tilde{x}'', \tilde{y}'') = h(\tilde{x}', \tilde{y}') = d(x', y') = d(x', L')$.   □

Theorem 6. *Let L be a language such that $\mathsf{OPT_H}(L)$ cannot be approximated with a factor $f(n)$ for strings of length n. Then $\mathsf{OPT_E}(L')$ cannot be approximated with a factor $f(n)$ for strings of length $4 \cdot n^2 + n$.*

Proof. Due to Lemma 2, any algorithm that computes an $f(n)$-approximation for $\mathsf{OPT_E}(L')$ for strings of length $4 \cdot n^2 + n$ can be used for approximating $\mathsf{OPT_H}(L)$ for strings of length n.   □

An immediate consequence of the reduction presented in this section is the following corollary.

Corollary 1. *There is a language $L \in \mathsf{P}$ such that L_E is $\mathsf{W[P]}$-hard.*   □

5.2   Reduction from Computing the Edit Distance to Computing the Hamming Distance

Let $L \subseteq \{0,1\}^*$ be a language for which we want to compute the edit distance. We construct another language L' as follows:

$$L' = \{y \mid \exists x \in L : y \text{ is obtained from } x \text{ by inserting gaps}\}.$$

For a string x of length n we define $x' = \Delta^n x_1 \Delta^n \ldots \Delta^n x_n \Delta^n$.

Lemma 3. *For every $x \in \{0,1\}^*$ we have $d(x, L) = h(x', L')$.*

Proof. We start with $d(x, L) \geq h(x', L')$. Let $y \in L$ be a string with $d(x, y) = d(x, L)$. Let $(\tilde{x}, \tilde{y})$ be an optimal alignment of x and y. We can assume that to the left of x_1, between x_i and x_{i+1} (for $1 \leq i \leq n-1$), and to the right of x_n there are always at most n gap symbols in $\tilde{x}$. Thus, in $\tilde{x}$ we can insert gaps to obtain x' as defined above and in the same places in $\tilde{y}$ to obtain some $\hat{y}$. Clearly, $d(x, L) = h(x', \hat{y}) \geq h(x', L')$. It remains to show that $d(x, L) \leq h(x', L')$. Assume that we have a $y' \in L'$ with $h(x', y') = h(x', L')$. Then (x', y') is an alignment of (x, y), where y is obtained from y' by deleting all gap symbols. Thus, we have $d(x, L) \leq d(x, y) \leq h(x', y') = h(x', L')$. $\square$

Theorem 7. *Let L be a language such that $\mathsf{OPT_E}(L)$ cannot be approximated with a factor $f(n)$ for strings of length n. Then $\mathsf{OPT_H}(L')$ cannot be approximated with a factor $f(n)$ for strings of length $n^2 + 2 \cdot n$.*

Proof. Due to Lemma 3, any algorithm that computes an $f(n)$-approximation for $\mathsf{OPT_H}(L')$ for strings of length $n^2 + 2 \cdot n$ can be used for approximating $\mathsf{OPT_E}(L)$ for strings of length n. $\square$

We can extend the above results to languages over alphabets of size two using a homomorphism g mapping 0, 1, and Δ to 001, 010, and 100, respectively. Then we have $2 \cdot h(x', L') = h(g(x'), g(L'))$. Thus, if the Hamming distance to $g(L')$ cannot be approximated with a factor $f(n)$ for strings of length $3n$, then the Hamming distance to L' cannot be approximated with a factor $f(n)$ for strings of length n. Unfortunately, it might happen that $g(L') \notin \mathsf{AC}^0$ for some $L \in \mathsf{AC}^0$. Consider for example $L = \{x \mid x \in \{0,1\}^* \text{ and } |x| \text{ is even}\}$. Then L' and also $g(L')$ are essentially parity, which is known to be not in AC^0 [3]. Thus, there are languages $L \in \mathsf{AC}^0$ such that $g(L') \notin \mathsf{AC}^0$.

From the reduction presented we immediately obtain the following corollary.

Corollary 2. $\mathsf{P_E} \subseteq \mathsf{W[P]}$.

Proof. If $L \in \mathsf{P}$, then $L' \in \mathsf{P}$ and, by Theorem 3, $L'_H \in \mathsf{W[P]}$. Since we have reduced L_E to L'_H, we have $L_E \in \mathsf{W[P]}$. $\square$

6   Open Problems

An obvious open question is to find algorithms for approximating the Hamming or edit distance. On the other hand, we conjecture that significantly stronger lower bounds hold for the approximability of these problems.

The reduction from the problem of computing the Hamming distance to the one of computing the edit distance preserves the size of the alphabet. Furthermore, if the language to which we want to compute the Hamming distance is in AC^0, then so is the one constructed. In the reduction from the latter to the former, we used a third symbol (which could be avoided by an appropriate encoding), and the language constructed is not necessarily in AC^0, even if the original language is. Another question is whether there is a reduction avoiding this.

References

1. Alfred V. Aho and Thomas G. Petersen. A minimum distance error-correcting parser for context-free languages. *SIAM Journal on Computing*, 1(4):305–312, 1972.
2. Rodney G. Downey and Michael R. Fellows. *Parameterized Complexity*. Springer, 1999.
3. Merrick Furst, James B. Saxe, and Michael Sipser. Parity, circuits, and the polynomial-time hierarchy. *Mathematical Systems Theory*, 17(1):13–27, 1984.
4. Raymond Greenlaw, H. James Hoover, and Walter L. Ruzzo. *Limits to Parallel Computation: P-Completeness Theory*. Oxford University Press, 1995.
5. Daniel M. Gusfield. *Algorithms on Strings, Trees, and Sequences: Computer Science and Computational Biology*. Cambridge University Press, 1997.
6. Magnús M. Halldórsson. Approximating the minimum maximal independence number. *Information Processing Letters*, 46(4):169–172, 1993.
7. Lane A. Hemachandra. Algorithms from complexity theory: Polynomial-time operations for complex sets. In *Proc. of the SIGAL Int. Symp. on Algorithms*, volume 450 of *Lecture Notes in Computer Science*, pages 221–231. Springer, 1990.
8. Edgar T. Irons. An error-correcting parse algorithm. *Communications of the ACM*, 6(11):669–673, 1963.
9. Richard M. Karp. Mapping the genome: Some combinatorial problems arising in molecular biology. In *Proc. of the 25th Ann. ACM Symp. on Theory of Computing (STOC)*, pages 278–285, 1993.
10. Richard E. Ladner. The circuit value problem is log space complete for P. *SIGACT News*, 7(1):18–20, 1975.
11. Gordon Lyon. Syntax-directed least-errors analysis for context-free languages: A practical approach. *Communications of the ACM*, 17(1):3–14, 1974.
12. Gonzalo Navarro. A guided tour to approximate string matching. *ACM Computing Surveys*, 33(1):31–88, 2001.
13. Pavel A. Pevzner. *Computational Molecular Biology: An Algorithmic Approach*. MIT Press, 2000.
14. Giovanni Pighizzini. How hard is computing the edit distance? *Information and Computation*, 165(1):1–13, 2001.
15. Daniel A. Spielman. The complexity of error-correcting codes. In *Proc. of the 11th Int. Symp. on Fundamentals of Computation Theory (FCT)*, volume 1279 of *Lecture Notes in Computer Science*, pages 67–84. Springer, 1997.

Infinitely-Often Autoreducible Sets[*]

Richard Beigel[1], Lance Fortnow[2], and Frank Stephan[3][**]

[1] Department of Computer and Information Sciences, Temple University, Wachman Hall (038-24), 1805 North Broad Street, Philadelphia PA 19122-6094, USA, beigel@cis.temple.edu

[2] NEC Laboratories America, 4 Independence Way, Princeton, NJ 08540, USA, fortnow@nec-labs.com

[3] Mathematisches Institut, Im Neuenheimer Feld 294, Universität Heidelberg, 69120 Heidelberg, Germany, EU, fstephan@math.uni-heidelberg.de.

Abstract. A set A is autoreducible if one can compute, for all x, the value $A(x)$ by querying A only at places $y \neq x$. Furthermore, A is infinitely-often autoreducible if, for infinitely many x, the value $A(x)$ can be computed by querying A only at places $y \neq x$. For all other x, the computation outputs a special symbol to signal that the reduction is undefined. It is shown that for polynomial time Turing and truth-table autoreducibility there are sets A, B, C in EXP such that A is not infinitely-often Turing autoreducible, B is Turing autoreducible but not infinitely-often truth-table autoreducible, C is truth-table autoreducible with $g(n) + 1$ queries but not infinitely-often Turing autoreducible with $g(n)$ queries. Here n is the length of the input, g is nondecreasing and there exists a polynomial p such that $p(n)$ bounds both, the computation time and the value, of g at input of length n. Furthermore, connections between notions of infinitely-often autoreducibility and notions of approximability are investigated. The Hausdorff-dimension of the class of sets which are not infinitely-often autoreducible is shown to be 1.

1 Introduction

There is no known fast algorithm for the problem SAT. But the problem is still a bit accessible because one can reduce every formula ϕ to two subformulas $\phi[u \to 0]$ and $\phi[u \to 1]$ where the variable u is replaced by its possible values. Then ϕ is satisfiable if at least one of the subformulas is. Therefore the set SAT is called *autoreducible* since one can compute the membership of one element (here the formula ϕ) by analyzing whether some other formulas are in SAT. Of course, autoreducibility does not guarantee (efficient) solvability at all. But this property is still interesting as it tells a bit about the structure of the given problem.

Now consider any set where every element is chosen independently at random.

---

[*] For the complete version of this paper, see reference [7].

[**] Frank Stephan was supported by the Deutsche Forschungsgemeinschaft (DFG), Heisenberg grant Ste 967/1–1.

Intuitively the membership of x should not depend on the membership of the other elements. Indeed, random sets are not autoreducible. Ebert [11,12] gives the surprising result that one can nevertheless compute correctly the membership of an infinite number of elements of a random set from the membership of the other ones. The present work extends the study of this notion, called *infinitely-often autoreducible*.

Trakhtenbrot [19] introduced in the recursion theoretic context the notion of autoreducibility and found that many natural examples have this property. The notion of autoreducibility can easily be carried over to resource bounded reducibilities r like polynomial time Turing reducibility.

Definition 1.1. A set is r-autoreducible iff there is an r-reduction that computes for every x the value $A(x)$ from the oracle A without querying A at x.

For example, a many-one EXP-complete set A satisfies that A is many-one reducible to $\overline{A}$ via some function f; that is, $A(x) = \overline{A}(f(x)) = 1 - A(f(x))$. This guarantees that $f(x) \neq x$ for all x. So one has that A is autoreducible by a polynomial time Turing reduction which asks exactly one query: what is A at $f(x)$ and knowing this, let $A(x) = 1 - A(f(x))$.

In the present work, polynomial time truth-table and Turing reducibility are considered where the number of questions might also be bounded. Truth-table reducibility is different from Turing reducibility in the sense that the place of the n-th query does not depend on the oracle answers to the queries asked before and one can compute an explicit polynomially sized list of places queried. So the oracle is queried at many places in parallel and afterwards these answered are used by the program of the truth-table reduction without any further interaction with the oracle.

In complexity theory there are many natural examples of autoreducible sets besides the example SAT given above. Buhrman, Fortnow, Melkebeek and Torenvliet [10] showed that the Turing complete sets for EXP are Turing autoreducible while some of the Turing complete sets for the class EEXPSPACE are not. EEXPSPACE contains exactly those sets which are, for some polynomial p, computable in space $2^{2^{p(n)}}$. It is unknown whether all sets Turing complete for EEXP are autoreducible; settling this open question would separate some complexity classes which are not yet known to be different.

Random sets are not autoreducible, but Ebert [11,12] showed the surprising result that they are infinitely-often autoreducible which is defined as follows.

Definition 1.2. A set A is infinitely-often r-autoreducible iff there is an r-reduction M which at input x queries A only at places $y \neq x$. For infinitely many x, M computes $A(x)$ correctly, for all other x, M is undefined and signals this by outputting a special symbol.

The result that random sets are infinitely-often autoreducible received a lot of attention. Not only because one would not expect that it is possible to make predictions about the membership of x in a random set by looking which other y are in, but also because the proof of the result is an application of the solution of the hat problem. The hat problem was the topic of several newspaper articles, for example in the German weekly newspaper Die Zeit [9].

It is already well-known that there are sets which are not infinitely often autoreducible [5], but these examples are outside EXP, the class of all exponential time computable sets. EXP is the first deterministic time class known to contain nondeterministic polynomial time NP and polynomial space PSPACE. Therefore, it is natural to study the structure of the sets inside EXP and the main result of the present work is to show that there is a set A in EXP which is not infinitely-often Turing autoreducible. Furthermore, the major autoreducibility notions are separated by showing that there are sets in EXP which are autoreducible for the first reduction but not infinitely-often autoreducible by the second reduction; this is done in particular for Turing versus truth-table and for truth-table with $g(n) + 1$ queries versus Turing with $g(n)$ queries. This second result implies the separation of truth-table versus bounded truth-table. In the next section, the relations between notions of approximability and infinitely-often autoreducibility are investigated. Finally it is shown that there are quite many sets in EXP which are not autoreducible: the class of these sets has Hausdorff-dimension 1 in exponential time.

Notation 1.3.   The notation follows standard textbooks like the one of Odifreddi [17] with some exceptions: The function $x \to \log(x)$ denotes the logarithm of basis 2 with the exception that $\log(q) = 0$ for $q < 1$ in order to avoid to deal with too many exceptions in logarithmic expressions. The term $\log^*(x)$ denotes the number of iterations of log necessary to reach a number strictly below 1. So, $\log^*(0) = 0$, $\log^*(1) = 1$ and $\log^*(2^x) = \log^*(x) + 1$. A set D is called *supersparse*, iff, for all x, $D \cap \{x, x + 1, \ldots, 2^x\}$ contains at most $\log^*(x)$ many elements. $A \Delta D$ denotes the symmetric difference of A and D; the set $A \Delta D$ is called a *supersparse variant of A* if D is a supersparse set.

Note.   Due to page-constraints, this paper is only a short version of the corresponding technical report [7]. The interested reader might download it from

http://www.math.uni-heidelberg.de/logic/postscripts/tr62.ps

or request the full version from the authors.

2   Some Set in EXP Is Not Infinitely-Often Autoreducible

Note that a computation is exponential in the length (= logarithm) of x iff it is quasipolynomial in x itself. Thererfore one considers in the case of functionals quasipolynomial time bounds. More precisely, a partial functional f which assigns to inputs of the form $A(0)A(1)\ldots A(x)$ values $a_{x+1}a_{x+2}\ldots a_y$ is called a quasipolynomial time extension functional iff there is a constant c permitting to compute the extensions in time $x^{\log^c(x)}$. Following Lutz [15], one can introduce the following notion of resource-bounded genericity; see the survey of Ambos-Spies and Mayordomo [2] for further details.

Definition 2.1.   A set A is general generic iff, for every quasipolynomial time computable functional f,

- either $f(A(0)A(1)\ldots A(x))$ is undefined for almost all x
- or there are x, y such that $x < y$, $f(A(0)A(1)\ldots A(x)) = a_{x+1}a_{x+2}\cdots a_y$ and $A(z) = a_z$ for $z = x+1, x+2, \ldots, y$.

So, either "A almost always avoids f" or "A meets f".

General generic sets have to be distinguished from the weaker variant of generic sets as introduced by Ambos-Spies, Fleischhack and Huwig [1] which either meet or avoid every quasipolynomial time extension functionals which predicts only one bit whenever defined. Balcázar and Mayordomo [5] observed that these sets are not infinitely-often autoreducible.

Fact 2.2 [5]. *There are sets which are not infinitely-often autoreducible. In particular general generic sets have this property.*

On the other hand, Ambos-Spies, Neis and Terwijn [4] showed that the notions of generic sets and resource bounded randomness are compatible. As random sets are infinitely-often autoreducible (even infinitely-often truth-table autoreducible) [11,12], there are some generic sets which are infinitely-often autoreducible and Fact 2.2 really needs the stronger version of general generic sets.

General generic sets cannot be in EXP due to the quasipolynomial time bound. The following result shows that sets which are not infinitely-often autoreducible can be found in EXP. Note that many-one EXP-complete sets are (everywhere) autoreducible since they are many-one equivalent to their complement. Buhrman, Fortnow, van Melkebeek and Torenvliet [10] show that every Turing EXP-complete set is autoreducible.

Theorem 2.3. *There is a set in EXP which is not infinitely-often autoreducible with respect to Turing reducibility.*

Proof. Let $M_0, M_1, \ldots$ be an enumeration of all polynomial time autoreductions such that each M_e needs at most time $x + e$ at input x and queries the set A only at places $y \leq 2^x$ with $y \neq x$. Note that x is superpolynomial in $\log(x)$ and therefore, all polynomial time autoreductions are covered. The set A is constructed by a priority construction and satisfies at the end for every e one of the following two possibilities.

- There is a number x such that $M_e^A(x)$ outputs $b \in \{0, 1\}$ with $b \neq A(x)$.
- For almost every x, $M_e^A(x)$ is undefined.

The e-th requirement is then the first of these two conditions. The construction will be such that it either satisfies the e-th requirement explicitly or enforces the second condition implicitly.

The construction uses approximations A_x of A where $A_x(y) = A(y)$ for all x, y with $y < x$. So one has to simulate the construction only $x+1$ stages to know the value of A at x. Together with a proof that every stage needs time exponential in the length of x it follows that $A \in$ EXP. Recall from Notation 1.3 that $\log^*(x)$ denotes the number of iterations of the logarithm to be taken until the resulting value is smaller than 1: $\log^*(0) = 0$, $\log^*(1) = 1$ and $\log^*(2^x) = \log^*(x) + 1$.

Construction of A. Let A_x and $r_{e,x}$ be the values of A and r_e before stage x, in particular, $A_0 = \emptyset$ and $r_{e,0} = 0$ for all x.

In stage x one searches the least e such that there is a finite set D satisfying the following requirements where D is the set of the positions for which it is intended that A_{x+1} and A_x will differ.

Bound on e: $e \leq \log^*(x)$.

Respecting Restraints: $r_{e',x} < x$ for all $e' \leq e$.

Requirement e not yet done: There is no number $x' < x$ such that $M^{A_x}(x')$ queries A_x only at places below x and computes a wrong prediction for $A(x')$.

Requirement e needs attention: $M_e^{A_x \Delta D}(x)$ computes a prediction different from $(A_x \Delta D)(x)$; where $A_x \Delta D$ denotes the symmetric difference of A_x and D.

Size-constraint on D met: $D \subseteq \{x, x+1, x+2, \ldots, 2^x\}$ and D has at most $2^{-e-2} \cdot \log^*(x) - 2e$ elements.

If the above procedure finds an e (which is the minimal one possible) and D is the corresponding set mentioned above then

$$A_{x+1} = A_x \Delta D;$$
$$r_{e,x+1} = 2^x + 2;$$
$$r_{e',x+1} = r_{e',x} \text{ for all } e' \neq e;$$

else nothing changes, that is, $A_{x+1} = A_x$ and $r_{e',x+1} = r_{e',x}$ for all e'.

Verification. One first notes that in stage x the search considers only $\log^*(x)$ many values of e and for each of these, the search runs over computations which make at most $x + e$ queries where at most $2^{-e-2} \cdot \log^*(x) - 2e$ of the answers can differ from the current values of A_x as these queries hit elements in D. So, for each e, there are $O(x^{\log^*(x)})$ many possible computation paths. As $\log^*(x) \leq \log(x+2)$, the running time of step x of the algorithm is quasipolynomial in x, that is, exponential in $\log(x)$. As $A(x) = A_{x+1}(x)$, it follows that one can compute $A(x)$ by running the algorithm for the stages $0, 1, \ldots, x$ and so the overall running time is quasipolynomial in x, that is, $A \in \text{EXP}$.

Note that for sufficiently large x the bound $2^{-e-2} \cdot \log^*(x) - 2e$ becomes positive as e is a constant and $\log^*(x)$ is unbounded. Therefore, cardinality requirements do not hinder to satisfy the Requirement e for sufficiently large x.

By usual priority arguments, one can show that every e is found only finitely often by the search algorithm and that $r_{e,x}$ converges from below to a final value $r_{e,\infty}$.

Now it is shown that A is not infinitely-often autoreducible. Consider any autoreduction M_e which does not make any false prediction for A but might be undefined for some inputs. Let x be so large that $2^{-e-2} \cdot \log^*(x) - 2e > 2$ and $x > r_{e',\infty}$ for all $e' \leq e$. So the search does not return any $e' \leq e$ as otherwise the corresponding restraint would be increased again. It follows that $M_e^B(x)$ does not predict any value for input x on any set B of the form $A_x \Delta D$ with $|D| \leq 2^{-e-2} \cdot \log^*(x) - 2e - 1$ and $D \subseteq \{x, x+1, \ldots, 2^x\}$ – note that the search in the algorithm actually covers sets D with up to $2^{-e-2} \cdot \log^*(x) - 2e$ elements, but this one additional element might be needed to make the prediction to be different from $(A_x \Delta D)(x)$. On the other hand, it might happen that up to $\log^*(x)$ many requirements $e' > e$ act between stages x and 2^x. Due to the update rule of the restraints, each of them acts only once between these stages. Furthermore, each e' changes A at up to $2^{-e'-2} \cdot \log^*(2^x) - 2e' \leq 2^{-e'-2} \cdot \log^*(x) - 2e - 1$ many positions between x and 2^x. The symmetric difference of A and A_x contains below x no element and between x and 2^x at most $2^{-e-2} \cdot \log^*(x) - 2e - 1$ elements. So, $M_e^A(x)$ does also not predict any value for $A(x)$ and M_e^A is undefined for almost all inputs. ∎

3   On Truth-Table Autoreducibility

The topic of this section is the interrelation of autoreducibility notions with respect to truth-table reducibility, Turing-reducibility and the variants of these reducibilities where the number of queries is bounded. It is shown that only the trivial implications hold and that all differences between the notions can be witnessed by sets in EXP. Theorem 3.2 in particular shows that there is a set in EXP which is tt($n + 1$)-autoreducible but not infinitely-often Turing(n)-autoreducible, where n is the logarithm (= length) of the input. This implies that this set is tt-autoreducible but not btt-autoreducible.

The proof of the following theorem uses Kolmogorov complexity arguments to construct a starting set A_0 which is Turing but not tt-complete for EXP. Watanabe [20] first constructed such a set; his ideas are also based on Kolmogorov complexity arguments.

Theorem 3.1.   *There is a set A in EXP which is Turing autoreducible but not infinitely-often tt-autoreducible.*

Proof.   The construction is a modification of the one from Theorem 2.3 with the following two differences:

- The set A_0 is not empty but a set which is Turing complete (but not tt-complete) for EXP;
- Furthermore, $M_0, M_1, \ldots$ is a list of all polynomial time truth-table autoreductions which satisfy the same side conditions as in Theorem 2.3; that is, for any oracle X, $M_e^X(x)$ is computed in time $e + x$ and X is queried only at places $y \leq 2^x$ which are different from x.

The choice of A_0 is sensitive to the success of the construction because it must be guaranteed that one can compute all elements queried by M_e. This is done by placing the more difficult elements at positions which can be accessed by an adapted search but not by a nonadaptive truth-table reduction.

First one takes a sequence $b_0 b_1 \ldots$ of bits which is random for computations using computation time 2^{n^3} but can be computed in time 2^{n^6} and let B be the set of all numbers of the form $2^n + \sum_{m<n} 2^m \cdot b_m$. B is in EXP. Furthermore let C be a set which is many-one EXP-complete and contains 0. The set A_0 is then given by

$$A_0 = \{\langle b, c, d \rangle : b \in B, c \in C, c \leq b, d \in \mathbb{N}\}.$$

Now one uses that the e-th truth-table autoreduction M_e queries at most x many places and so any query of it has at most Kolmogorov complexity $\log(e) + \log(x) + k$ for a constant k where the Kolmogorov complexity is measured with respect to time bound x^3. It follows that every $\langle b, c, d \rangle$ queried satisfies that b has also this bound (plus perhaps a constant) and that, whenever $\langle b, c, d \rangle$ is in A_0, then $b = 2^n + \sum_{m < n} 2^m \cdot b_m$ for some $n \leq 3(\log(x) + \log(e) + k')$ and $c \leq b$ where k' is a suitable constant independent of e, x. So the algorithm to compute all the values of A_0 at places queried by M_e at x with $e \leq \log^*(x)$ is exponential in x and this gives that the set A is also in EXP.

The construction gives that A is not infinitely-often tt-autoreducible in the same way as the construction in Theorem 2.3 that the set constructed there is not infinitely-often Turing autoreducible. It remains to show that in this theorem the set A is Turing autoreducible.

Note that for fixed b, c and the two third majority of the numbers $y = \langle b, c, d \rangle$ with $0 \leq d \leq 3 \log^*(b + c) + 6$ satisfies that $A(y) = A_0(y)$. Thus one can every query whether $\langle b, c, 0 \rangle \in A_0$ reduce to polynomially many queries to A (omitting the query to x if it is among these queries) and so it is sufficient to give in the construction below the queries to A_0.

- For input x, compute the c such that $A(x) = C(c)$. This can be done without querying an oracle as C is many-one EXP-complete.
- For every $b \in B$, there is an n such that $b = 2^n + \sum_{m < n} 2^m \cdot b_m$. Then one of the following numbers is the next element of B: $b + 2^n, b + 2^{n+1}$ — the first one in case $b_n = 0$, the second one in case $b_n = 1$. So one can find for each member of B the next member of B by two queries to B and starting with 1, which is the minimum of B, one can find a $b \geq c$ such that $b \in B$ with $2 \log(c) + 2$ queries to B. Since $b \in B$ iff $\langle b, 0, 0 \rangle \in A_0$, this computation can also be done with the same number of queries to A_0.
- Having this $b \geq c$ such that $b \in B$, one can determine $A(x)$ with one query to A_0 as $x \in A$ iff $\langle b, c, 0 \rangle \in A_0$.

The so constructed algorithm is a Turing autoreduction as the size $\log(c)$ of c is polynomially bounded in the size $\log(x)$ of x. Furthermore, as $3 \log^*(b + c) + 6 \leq 3 \log(b + c) + 12$, the number of queries to A is only by a factor polynomial in x greater than the number of queries to A_0 and so the whole algorithm queries A only polynomially often. One can easily verify, that the running time of the algorithm is also polynomial. ∎

Theorem 3.2. *For every polynomial-time computable and nondecreasing function $g \in Poly(n)$ there is a set A in EXP such that A is $tt(g(n)+1)$-autoreducible but not infinitely-often Turing$(g(n))$-autoreducible.*

An autoreduction is a bounded truth-table reduction iff there is a constant k such that the reduction makes for every input at most k queries. If a set A is $tt(n+1)$-autoreducible but not infinitely-often Turing(n)-autoreducible, then A is clearly tt-autoreducible but not infinitely-often btt-autoreducible. This gives the following corollary.

Corollary 3.3. *There is a set in EXP which is truth-table autoreducible but not infinitely-often bounded truth-table autoreducible.*

4 Notions of Approximability

A set is called (a, b)-recursive iff there is a function f such that for all distinct $x_1, x_2, \ldots, x_b$ the function f computes a tuple $(y_1, y_2, \ldots, y_b)$ of bits such that at least a of the equations $A(x_k) = y_k$ are true. If there are a, b such that $1 \leq a \leq b$ and if there is a polynomial time computable function f such that A is (a, b)-recursive via f then A is called approximable [8] and if in addition $2a > b$ then A is called easily approximable.

In the Recursion Theoretic setting, every set which is $(1, b)$-recursive for some b is also autoreducible [14]. This does not carry over to complexity theory: Returning to the world of polynomial time computations, supersparse sets are $(1, 2)$-recursive but not Turing autoreducible. Supersparse sets are related to k-cheatable sets [6]. Nevertheless, approximable sets are still infinitely-often autoreducible.

Proposition 4.1. *Every approximable set is infinitely-often btt-autoreducible.*

Ogihara [18] also considered sets which are $(1, b(n))$-recursive where b is a function in $Poly(n)$ and the parameter n is $\log(\max\{1, x_1, x_2, \ldots, x_b\})$ where $x_1, x_2, \ldots, x_b$ is the input to the function to compute the approximation. This generalized notion does no longer enforce that A is infinitely-often autoreducible.

Example 4.2. *The set from Theorem 2.3 satisfies Ogihara's generalized approximability condition but is not infinitely-often Turing autoreducible.*

An easily approximable set A has the property that every set B Turing reducible to A is also tt-reducible to A. This property is called *T-easy*. The next theorem shows that every T-easy set is either infinitely-often autoreducible or satisfies Ogihara's generalized approximability notion with $a = 1$ and $b = \log^2(n)$.

Theorem 4.3. *Every set A satisfies at least one of the following properties.*

(a) *Not T-easy: There is a set B which is polynomial time Turing reducible but not polynomial time truth-table reducible to A;*
(b) *Infinitely-often tt-autoreducible: For infinitely many z, $A(z)$ can be computed by queries to places different from z;*
(c) *Generalized approximable: A is $(1, 1 + \log^2(n))$-recursive via some function computable in polynomial time.*

5 Hausdorff Dimension

Hausdorff [13] introduced a generalized notion of dimension for metric spaces; it also enables to measure the size of fractal objects. Lutz [16] adapted the notion for complexity theory in order to measure the size of subclasses of the natural numbers. The following definition – one among several equivalent ones – defines the Hausdorff-dimension in terms of the growth rate of the capital accumulated by a gambler who bets inductively on the bits of the characteristic functions of any set in the given class. Such growth rate functionals are called martingales.

Definition 5.1.   A quasipolynomial time computable functional f is called a *martingale*, iff it maps binary strings to positive numbers, the empty string to 1 and satisfies

$$2f(a_0a_1 \ldots a_x) = f(a_0a_1 \ldots a_x0) + f(a_0a_1 \ldots a_x1)$$

for all binary strings $a_0a_1 \ldots a_x$. The *Hausdorff-dimension* (with respect to EXP) of a class S is the infimum of all s such that there is a quasipolynomial time computable martingale f succeeding on every set in $A \in S$ with growth rate 2^{1-s}, that is, f satisfies

$$(\forall A \in S) \, (\exists^\infty x) \, [f(A(0)A(1) \ldots A(x)) \geq 2^{(1-s)x}].$$

Remark 5.2.   The class of all sets as well as the class EXP have Hausdorff-dimension 1.

Ambos-Spies, Merkle, Reimann and Stephan [3, Corollary 16] considered Hausdorff-dimension adapted to the class $E = \{A : (\exists c) \, (\exists M) \, (\forall x) \, [M \text{ computes } A(x)$ in time $c + x^c]\}$. They showed that the class of many-one autoreducible sets in E has Hausdorff-dimension 1. This fact directly carries over to EXP.

Fact 5.3.   *The class $\{A \text{ in EXP}: (\forall x) \, [A(x) = A(x^2)]\}$ consists only of many-one autoreducible sets and has Hausdorff-dimension 1. In particular, the classes of the many-one autoreducible, truth-table autoreducible and Turing autoreducible sets in EXP have Hausdorff-dimension 1.*

An interesting obvious question is to determine the Hausdorff-dimension of the class of those sets in EXP which are not infinitely-often r-autoreducible. The next theorem shows, that the Hausdorff-dimension is already 1 for the case of the polynomial time Turing reducibility; it then follows also for the other polynomial time reducibilities r. As Ebert [11,12] showed that every set which is x^3-random is already infinitely-often autoreducible, the class S is one of the natural witnesses that there are classes which have Hausdorff-dimension 1 and measure 0 with respect to quasipolynomial time martingales.

Theorem 5.4.   *The class of all sets in EXP which are not infinitely-often autoreducible has Hausdorff-dimension 1.*

Acknowledgments.   The authors would like to thank Klaus Ambos-Spies, Jack H. Lutz and Wolfgang Merkle for helpful discussions; furthermore, Jack H. Lutz proposed to investigate the Hausdorff-dimension of the class of sets in EXP which are not infinitely-often autoreducible.

References

1. Klaus Ambos-Spies, Hans Fleischhhack and Hagen Huwig. Diagonalizations over polynomial time computable sets. *Theoretical Computer Science* 51:177-204, 1997.
2. Klaus Ambos-Spies and Elvira Mayordomo. Resource-bounded measure and randomness. In A. Sorbi, editor, *Complexity, Logic, and Recursion Theory*, volume 187 of *Lecture Notes in Pure and Applied Mathematics*, pages 1–47, 1997.
3. Klaus Ambos-Spies, Wolfgang Merkle, Jan Reimann and Frank Stephan. Hausdorff dimension in exponential time. *Proceedings Sixteenth Annual IEEE Conference on Computational Complexity*, IEEE Computer Society, 210–217, 2001.
4. Klaus Ambos-Spies, Hans-Christian Neis and Sebastiaan A. Terwijn. Genericity and measure for exponential time. *Theoretical Computer Science*, 168:3–19, 1996.
5. José L. Balcázar and Elvira Mayordomo. A note on genericity and bi-immunity. *Proceedings of the Tenths Annual Structure in Complexity Theory Conference*, IEEE Computer Society Press, pages 193–196, 1995.
6. Richard Beigel. Bi-immunity results for cheatable sets. *Theoretical Computer Science*, 73:249–263, 1990.
7. Richard Beigel, Lance Fortnow and Frank Stephan. *Infinite-often autoreducible sets. Forschungsberichte Mathematische Logik und Theoretische Informatik*, 62 / 2003. Institut für Informatik, Universität Heidelberg, 2003. http://www.math.uni-heidelberg.de/logic/postscripts/tr62.ps
8. Richard Beigel, Martin Kummer and Frank Stephan. Approximable sets. *Information and Computation*, 120:304–314, 1995.
9. W. Blum. Denksport für Hutträger. *Die Zeit*, Hamburg, 03.05.2001. http://www.cecs.csulb.edu/~ebert/hatProblem/dieZeit.htm
10. Harry Buhrman, Lance Fortnow, Dieter van Melkebeek and Leen Torenvliet. Using autoreducibility to separate complexity classes. *Siam Journal on Computing*, 29(5):1497–1520, 2000.
11. Todd Ebert. *Applications of Recursive Operators to Randomness and Complexity*. PhD Thesis, University of California at Santa Barbara, 1998.
12. Todd Ebert, Wolfgang Merkle and Heribert Vollmer. *On the autoreducibility of random sequences*. Manuscript, 2002.
13. Felix Hausdorff. Dimension und äusseres Maß. *Mathematische Annalen*, 79:157–189, 1919.
14. Martin Kummer and Frank Stephan. Recursion theoretic properties of frequency computation and bounded queries. *Information and Computation*, 120:59–77, 1995.
15. Jack H. Lutz. Category and measure in complexity classes. *SIAM Journal on Computing*, 19:1100–1131, 1990.
16. Jack H. Lutz. Dimension in complexity classes. *Proceedings Fifteenth Annual IEEE Conference on Computational Complexity*, IEEE Computer Society, 158–169, 2000.
17. Piergiorgio Odifreddi. *Classical recursion theory*. North-Holland, Amsterdam, 1989.
18. Mitsunori Ogihara. Polynomial-time membership comparable sets. In *Proceedings of the 9th Conference on Structure in Complexity Theory*, IEEE Computer Society Press, 2–11, 1994.
19. Boris A. Trakhtenbrot. On autoreducibility. *Soviet Mathematics Doklady* 11:814–817, 1970.
20. Osamu Watanabe. A comparison of polynomial time completeness notions. *Theoretical Computer Science* 54:249–265, 1987.

Limiting Negations in Bounded-Depth Circuits: An Extension of Markov's Theorem

Shao Chin Sung[1] and Keisuke Tanaka[2*]

[1] School of Information Science
Japan Advanced Institute of Science and Technology
1-1 Asahidai Tatsunokuchi, Ishikawa 923-1292, Japan
son@jaist.ac.jp
[2] Department of Mathematical and Computing Sciences
Tokyo Institute of Technology
2-12-1 Ookayama Meguro-ku, Tokyo 152-8552, Japan
keisuke@is.titech.ac.jp

Abstract. From a theorem of Markov, the minimum number of negation gates in a circuit sufficient to compute any collection of Boolean
functions on n variable is $\ell = \lceil \log(n+1) \rceil$. Santha and Wilson [SIAM
Journal of Computing 22(2):294–302 (1993)] showed that in some classes
of bounded-depth circuits ℓ negation gates are no longer sufficient for
some explicitly defined Boolean function. In this paper, we consider a
general class of bounded-depth circuits in which each gate computes an
arbitrary monotone Boolean function or its negation. Our purpose is to
extend the theorem of Markov for such a general class of circuits. We
first show that a lower bound shown by Santha and Wilson becomes an
extension of Markov's lower bound by a small refinement. Then, we
present tight upper bounds on the number of negations for computing
an arbitrary collection of Boolean functions.

1 Introduction

Despite the importance of lower bounds on the circuit complexity of explicit
problems, the best bounds known are only linear. However, good lower bounds
are known for the complexity of monotone circuits, where negations are forbidden. In order to extend the results on monotone circuits to the general circuit
model, a natural intermediate step is the study of circuits with the limited number of negations, and this motivates the study on the complexity of negation-
limited circuits. For example, the negation-limited circuit complexity of inverters
[2,4], merging [1] and the relationship between the number of negations and circuit size [6] are studied.

When we consider the monotone circuit complexity, we have to consider only
a class of monotone functions. Once negations are permitted in the circuit, we can
also consider a class of non-monotone functions. Before studying the complexity

---

* Supported in part by Grant-in-Aid for Scientific Research, Ministry of Education,
Culture, Sports, Science, and Technology, Japan, 14780190.

T. Ibaraki, N. Katoh, and H. Ono (Eds.): ISAAC 2003, LNCS 2906, pp. 108–116, 2003.

of such a class, a natural question arises: how many negations are necessary to compute particular functions?

Markov [3] answered this question without any complexity theoretical consideration. From a theorem of Markov, the minimum number of negation gates in a circuit sufficient to compute an arbitrary Boolean function on n variables is $\lceil \log(n+1) \rceil$. The result of Fischer [4] shows that every function which can be computed by a polynomial-size logarithmic-depth circuit containing an arbitrary number of negations can be computed by a polynomial-size logarithmic-depth circuit containing only $\lceil \log(n+1) \rceil$ negations.

Santha and Wilson [5] considered polynomial-size constant-depth circuits and showed that $\lceil \log(n+1) \rceil$ negations are no longer sufficient. For threshold circuits and AC^0 circuits, they proved that several Boolean functions computable in constant depth cannot be computed in constant depth with $o(n^\epsilon)$ negations, for all $\epsilon > 0$. These results were derived from a lower bound on the number of negations in a general class of circuits in which each gate computes an arbitrary monotone Boolean function or its negation.

In this paper, we consider such a general class of circuits. Our purpose is to extend the theorem of Markov for such a general class of circuits. We study the necessary and sufficient number of negations for computing an arbitrary collection of Boolean functions. We first show that, by a small refinement, the lower bound shown by Santha and Wilson becomes an extension of Markov's lower bound, i.e., it matches Markov's lower bounds when depth of circuits are sufficiently large. Then, we show for an arbitrary collection F of Boolean functions a tight upper bound of the number of negations for computing F.

The rest of this paper is organized as follows. After giving some preliminaries, lower bounds and upper bounds for the number of negations for computing an arbitrary collection of Boolean functions are shown respectively in Section 3 and Section 4.

2 Preliminaries

A chain $\alpha = (\alpha^0, \ldots, \alpha^k)$ for some $1 \le k \le n$ is a vector of $\alpha^i = (\alpha_1^i, \alpha_2^i, \ldots, \alpha_n^i) \in \{0,1\}^n$ such that $\alpha^i \le \alpha^{i+1}$ (i.e., $\alpha_j^i \le \alpha_j^{i+1}$ for each $1 \le j \le n$). For a Boolean function f, an index $i \in \{1, 2, \ldots, k\}$ is a *decrease* of f over chain α if $1 = f(\alpha^{i-1}) > f(\alpha^i) = 0$. For a collection $F = \{f_1, \ldots, f_m\}$ of Boolean functions, an index $i \in \{1, 2, \ldots, k\}$ is a *decrease* of F over chain α if i is a decrease of f_j over chain α for some $1 \le j \le m$. By $d(F, \alpha)$ we denote the set of decreases of F over chain α. By $d(F)$ we denote the maximum value of $\#d(F, \alpha)$ among all chains α, where $\#S$ denotes the cardinality of a set S. A collection of Boolean functions F is called *monotone* if $d(F) = 0$.

From the definition of decreases, the following lemmas can be obtained immediately.

Lemma 1. *Let* $F = \{f_1, \ldots, f_m\}$ *be an arbitrary collection of Boolean functions, and let* g *be an arbitrary monotone function of* m *variables. Then, for every chain* α,

$$d(\{g(f_1,\ldots,f_m)\},\alpha) \subseteq d(F,\alpha).$$

Lemma 2. *Let f be an arbitrary Boolean function. Then, for every chain α,*

$$\#d(\{\neg f\},\alpha) \le \#d(\{f\},\alpha) + 1.$$

A *circuit* is a directed acyclic network in which inputs and gates are connected by directed wire. In-degree of an input must be 0, and in-degree of each gate is an arbitrary positive integer (i.e., unbounded). The *size* of a circuit is the number of gates in it, and the *depth* of a circuit is the length of a longest directed path in it. We say an input or a gate is in *level i*, for some non-negative integer i, if the length of a longest directed path to the input or the gate is i. It follows that all inputs are in level 0.

In this paper, we consider bounded-depth circuits in which each gate computes an arbitrary monotone Boolean function or its negation, i.e., each gate is unbounded fan-in. A gate is called a *monotone gates* if it computes a monotone Boolean function, and a gate is called a *negation gates* if it computes the negation of a monotone Boolean function.

3   Lower Bound on the Number of Negations

In this section, we show a lower bound on the number of negation gates in a depth-D circuit computing an arbitrary collection of Boolean functions. Let F be an arbitrary collection of Boolean functions. The result on the lower bound shown by Santha and Wilson [5] can be rewritten in terms of $d(F)$ as follows.

Proposition 1. *Every depth-D circuit computing F contains at least $D(d(F)+1)^{1/D} - D$ negation gates.*

Proof. Let C be a depth-D circuit computing F, and let G^ℓ, for $0 \le \ell \le D$, be the collection of Boolean functions each of which is computed by some gate in level ℓ', for some $\ell' \le \ell$, of C. Obviously, we have $F \subseteq G^D$, because each $f \in F$ is computed by some gate in C. It follows that $d(F,\alpha) \le d(G^D,\alpha)$ for every chain α, and thus, $d(F) \le d(G^D)$.

Suppose C contains ν negation gates, and let ν_ℓ, for $1 \le \ell \le D$, be the number of negation gates at level ℓ in C, i.e., $\nu = \sum_{\ell=1}^{D} \nu_\ell$. Level 0 consists of inputs $x_1,\ldots,x_n$, where $d(\{x_i\}) = 0$ for all $1 \le i \le n$, and thus $d(G^0) = 0$. From Lemma 1, for $1 \le \ell \le D$, $d(\{f\},\alpha) \subseteq d(G^{\ell-1},\alpha)$ if f is a function computed by a monotone gate in level ℓ, and from Lemma 2, $\#d(\{f\},\alpha) \le \#d(G^{\ell-1},\alpha)+1$ if f is a function computed by a negation gate in level ℓ. Since there are ν_ℓ negation gates in level ℓ, we have $d(G^\ell) \le (\nu_\ell + 1)(d(G^{\ell-1}) + 1) - 1$. Therefore, we have $d(G^D) \le \prod_{\ell=1}^{D}(\nu_\ell + 1) - 1$, and it implies

$$d(F) \le \prod_{\ell=1}^{D}(\nu_\ell + 1) - 1. \tag{1}$$

The product $\prod_{\ell=1}^{D}(\nu_\ell + 1)$ is maximized when $\nu_\ell = \nu/D$ for each $1 \leq \ell \leq D$, it follows that the number ν of negation gates in C is at least $D(d(F)+1)^{1/D} - D$.

$\square$

However, notice that the lower bound $D(d(F) + 1)^{1/D} - D$ tends to 0 when D grows, i.e., it does match the theorem of Markov. A small refinement of Proposition 1 can be made.

Since each ν_ℓ is integer, when $\nu = \sum_{\ell=1}^{D} \nu_\ell$ is fixed, $\prod_{\ell=1}^{D}(\nu_\ell+1)$ is maximized if $|\nu_k - \nu_\ell| \leq 1$ for every $1 \leq k, \ell \leq D$. Therefore, from $\nu = \sum_{\ell=1}^{D} \nu_\ell$ and (1), ν is minimized when, for each $1 \leq \ell \leq D$,

$$\nu_\ell \in \{\lfloor (d(F) + 1)^{1/D} \rfloor, \lfloor (d(F) + 1)^{1/D} \rfloor + 1\}.$$

Let $\sigma_D : N \to N$ be a function defined as follows.

$$\sigma_D(w) = D\lfloor (w+1)^{1/D} \rfloor - D + k,$$

where k is the smallest integer such that

$$\lceil (w+1)^{1/D} \rceil^k \lfloor (w+1)^{1/D} \rfloor^{D-k} \geq w + 1.$$

Then we have the following theorem.

Theorem 1. *Every depth-D circuit computing F contains at least $\sigma_D(d(F))$ negation gates.*

Notice that $\sigma_D(d(F)) = \lceil \log(d(F) + 1) \rceil$ for $D \geq \lceil \log(d(F) + 1) \rceil$. That is, Markov's lower bound $\lceil \log(d(F) + 1) \rceil$ of the number of negation gates can be derived from this theorem.

3.1   Special Cases

For some collections of Boolean functions, larger lower bounds of the number of negation gates can be obtained. Let $INV = \{INV_1, INV_2, \ldots, INV_n\}$ be a collection of Boolean function such that $INV_i(x) = \neg x_i$ for $1 \leq i \leq n$. Notice that $d(INV) = n$, and from Theorem 1, every depth-D circuit computing INV contains at least $\sigma_D(n)$ negation gates. However, it requires more negation gates.

Lemma 3. *Let D be a positive integer. Suppose there exists a depth-$(D + 1)$ circuit C computing INV such that C contains ν negation gates. Then, there exists a depth-$(D+1)$ circuit C' computing INV such that C' contains at most ν negation gates and has no negation gate in level $D + 1$.*

Proof. Let C be a depth-$(D + 1)$ circuit computing INV such that C contains ν negation gates. Suppose there exists a gate in level $D + 1$ which does not compute INV_i for any $1 \leq i \leq n$. Then by removing such a gate the resulting circuit also computes INV. Thus, we assume without loss of generality that all gates in level $D + 1$ are output gates, i.e., each gates in level $D + 1$ computes INV_i for some $1 \leq i \leq n$.

If all gates in level $D+1$ are monotone, then $C' = C$ is a circuit satisfying the lemma. Suppose there exists a negation gate in level $D+1$. Notice that each negation gate in level $D+1$ computes INV_i for some $1 \leq i \leq n$, and such a gate can be replaced by a negation gate with one input x_i and output $\neg x_i$. Then the resulting circuit C' contains the same number of negation gates as C and has no negation gate in level $D+1$.   □

Let C be a depth-$(D+1)$ circuit computing INV in which all gates in depth $D+1$ are monotone gates, and let G be the collection of Boolean functions each of which is computed by some gate in level ℓ of C, for some $\ell \leq D$. From Lemma 1, we have $d(G) = d(INV) = n$, and from Theorem 1, C contains at least $\sigma_D(n)$ negation gates. Therefore, the following theorem is obtained.

Theorem 2. *There exists a collection F of Boolean functions such that every depth-$(D+1)$ circuit computing F contains at least $\sigma_D(d(F))$ negation gates.*

4   Upper Bound on the Number of Negations

In this section, we show upper bounds on the number of negation gates in bounded-depth circuits. First we show that, for each non-negative integer ν, there exists a collection F of Boolean functions which can be computed by a depth-D circuit which contains $\sigma_D(d(F)) = \nu$ negation gates. Then we show that every collection of Boolean functions F can be computed by a depth-$(D+1)$ circuit which contains $\sigma_D(d(F))$ negation gates.

Let m be a positive integer, and let $\nu_1, \nu_2, \ldots, \nu_D \in \{\lfloor (m+1)^{1/D} \rfloor, \lfloor (m+1)^{1/D} \rfloor + 1\}$ satisfying $\sum_{\ell=1}^{D} \nu_\ell = \sigma_D(m)$, and for simplicity, let $\nu_{D+1} = 0$. Let $P_\ell = \prod_{k=\ell}^{D+1} (\nu_k + 1)$ for each $1 \leq \ell \leq D+1$. For $1 \leq \ell \leq D$ and $1 \leq j \leq \nu_\ell$, let g_j^ℓ be a Boolean function defined as follows.

$$g_j^\ell(x) = 1 \quad \text{iff} \quad \left(\sum_{i=1}^{m} h_i(x) \right) \bmod P_\ell < jP_{\ell+1},$$

where each h_i, for $1 \leq i \leq m$, is a monotone Boolean function. Let $G = \{g_j^\ell \mid 1 \leq \ell \leq D, 1 \leq j \leq \nu_\ell\}$.

Notice from the definition of σ_D that we have $P_1 \geq m+1$, and thus

$$g_j^1(x) = 1 \quad \text{iff} \quad \sum_{i=1}^{m} h_i(x) < jP_2. \tag{2}$$

Then, for each $1 \leq j \leq \nu_1$, $jP_2 \leq \sum_{i=1}^{m} h_i(x) < (j+1)P_2$ implies $g_1^1(x) = \cdots = g_j^1(x) = 0$ and $g_{j+1}^1(x) = \cdots = g_{\nu_1}^1(x) = 1$, and obviously, $(\sum_{i=1}^{m} h_i(x)) \bmod P_2 = \sum_{i=1}^{m} h_i(x) - jP_2$. Hence,

$$\left(\sum_{i=1}^{m} h_i(x) \right) \bmod P_2 = \sum_{i=1}^{m} h_i(x) - P_2 \sum_{j=1}^{\nu_1} \neg g_j^1(x)$$

$$= \sum_{i=1}^{m} h_i(x) + P_2 \sum_{j=1}^{\nu_1} g_j^1(x) - \nu_1 P_2.$$

By the similar argument, we have

$$\left(\sum_{i=1}^{m} h_i(x)\right) \bmod P_3 = \left(\sum_{i=1}^{m} h_i(x)\right) \bmod P_2 - P_3 \sum_{j=1}^{\nu_2} \neg g_j^2(x)$$

$$= \sum_{i=1}^{m} h_i(x) + P_2 \sum_{j=1}^{\nu_1} g_j^1(x) - \nu_1 P_2 + P_3 \sum_{j=1}^{\nu_2} g_j^2(x) - \nu_2 P_3,$$

and generally, we have, for $2 \leq \ell \leq D+1$,

$$\left(\sum_{i=1}^{m} h_i(x)\right) \bmod P_\ell = \sum_{i=1}^{m} h_i(x) + \sum_{k=1}^{\ell-1} P_{k+1} \sum_{j=1}^{\nu_k} g_j^k(x) - \sum_{k=1}^{\ell-1} \nu_k P_{k+1}. \qquad (3)$$

Hence, for $2 \leq \ell \leq D$ and $1 \leq j \leq \nu_\ell$,

$$g_j^\ell(x) = 1 \quad \text{iff} \quad \sum_{i=1}^{m} h_i(x) + \sum_{k=1}^{\ell-1} P_{k+1} \sum_{j=1}^{\nu_k} g_j^k(x) - \sum_{k=1}^{\ell-1} \nu_k P_{k+1} < j P_{\ell+1}. \qquad (4)$$

Moreover, from $P_{D+1} = 1$ and (3), we have

$$\sum_{i=1}^{m} h_i(x) = \sum_{k=1}^{D} \nu_k P_{k+1} - \sum_{k=1}^{D} P_{k+1} \sum_{j=1}^{\nu_k} g_j^k(x). \qquad (5)$$

Lemma 4. *The collection $G = \{g_j^\ell \mid 1 \leq \ell \leq D, 1 \leq j < \nu_\ell\}$ of Boolean functions defined above can be computed by a depth-D circuit which contains $\sigma_D(m)$ negation gates.*

Proof. A depth-D circuit satisfying the lemma can be constructed as follows. For each $1 \leq \ell \leq D$, the circuit contains exactly ν_ℓ gates in level ℓ, and each of such gates is a negation gate. That is, all gates of the circuits are negation gates.

We show that, for each $1 \leq \ell \leq D$ and $1 \leq j \leq \nu_\ell$, g_j^ℓ can be computed by a negation gate in level ℓ. From (2), each g_j^1 is the negation of a monotone Boolean function of $h_1(x), h_2(x), \ldots, h_m(x)$. Since each h_i is a monotone Boolean function of x, each g_j^1 is the negation of a monotone Boolean function of x. Thus, each g_j^1 can be computed by a negation gate in level 1. From (4), for $2 \leq \ell \leq D$ each g_j^ℓ is the negation of a monotone Boolean function of all $h_i(x)$ for $1 \leq i \leq m$ and all $g_j^k(x)$'s for $1 \leq k \leq \ell-1$, where each $g_j^k(x)$ is computed by some gate in level $k < \ell$. Thus, for $2 \leq \ell \leq D$, each g_j^ℓ can be computed by a negation gate in level ℓ. The proof is completed. $\qquad \square$

Suppose $m = n$ and each $h_i(x) = x_i$ for $1 \leq i \leq n$. Then (5) can be rewritten as follows.

$$\sum_{i=1}^{n} x_i = \sum_{k=1}^{D} \nu_k P_{k+1} - \sum_{k=1}^{D} P_{k+1} \sum_{j=1}^{\nu_k} g_j^k(x).$$

Let $\alpha = (\alpha^0, \cdots, \alpha^n)$ be a chain such that $\alpha_i^k = 1$ iff $i \leq k$ for each $0 \leq k \leq n$. Then, we have

$$\sum_{s=1}^{\ell-1} P_{s+1} \sum_{t=1}^{\nu_s} g_t^s(\alpha^{i-1}) > \sum_{s=1}^{\ell-1} P_{s+1} \sum_{t=1}^{\nu_s} g_t^s(\alpha^i)$$

for each $1 \leq i \leq n$, and thus $d(G, \alpha) = \{1, 2, \ldots, n\}$ (i.e., each i is a decrease of G over α). Therefore, $d(G) = n$. Notice that the depth-D circuit constructed in Lemma 4 computes G and contains exactly $\sigma_D(d(G))$ negation gates. Therefore, we obtain the following theorem.

Theorem 3. *For each non-negative integer ν, there exists a collection F of Boolean functions which can be computed by a depth-D circuit containing $\sigma_D(d(F)) = \nu$ negation gates.*

Now we are ready to show that every collection of Boolean functions F can be computed by a depth-$(D+1)$ circuit which contains $\sigma_D(d(F))$ negation gates.

Theorem 4. *Every collection F of Boolean functions can be computed by a depth-$(D+1)$ circuit which contains exactly $\sigma_D(d(F))$ negation gates.*

Proof. Let $F = \{f_1, \ldots, f_m\}$ be an arbitrary collection of Boolean functions. Let, for each non-negative integer i,

$$S_i = \{a \in \{0,1\}^n \mid \#d(F, \alpha) \leq d(F) - i \text{ for all chains } \alpha \text{ with } \alpha^0 = a\}.$$

Then, we have

$$\{0,1\}^n = S_0 \supseteq S_1 \supseteq \cdots \supseteq S_{d(F)} \supseteq S_{d(F)+1} = \emptyset, \qquad (6)$$

and $S_i = \emptyset$ for all $i \geq d(F) + 1$. Let t_i, for $0 \leq i \leq d(F)$, be the Boolean function defined by $t_i(x) = 1$ iff $x \in S_i$. Notice from (6) that we have, for each $x \in \{0,1\}^n$,

$$1 = t_0(x) \geq t_1(x) \geq \cdots \geq t_{d(F)}(x) \geq t_{d(F)+1}(x) = 0. \qquad (7)$$

Moreover $a \in S_i$ implies $\{b \in \{0,1\}^n \mid b \geq a\} \subseteq S_i$, since each b such that $b \geq a$ is in some chain α with $\alpha^0 = a$, and hence, each t_i is a monotone function.

For $0 \leq i \leq d(F)$ and $1 \leq j \leq m$, let

$$f_j^i(x) = \begin{cases} 0 & \text{if } x \notin S_i, \\ f_j(x) & \text{if } x \in S_i - S_{i+1}, \\ 1 & \text{otherwise (i.e., if } x \in S_{i+1}). \end{cases}$$

Now we show that each f_j^i is monotone, i.e., $d(f_j^i) = 0$, for $0 \leq i \leq d(f)$ and $1 \leq j \leq m$. Suppose $d(f_j^i) > 0$ for some i and j. Then there exists a chain α such that $d(f_j^i, \alpha) \neq \emptyset$. Let $k \in d(f_j^i, \alpha)$, i.e., $1 = f_j^i(\alpha^{k-1}) > f_j^i(\alpha^k) = 0$. It follows that $\alpha^{k-1} \in S_i$ and $\alpha^k \notin S_{i+1}$. Moreover, from $\alpha^{k-1} \leq \alpha^k$ and $\alpha^k \notin S_{i+1}$, we have $\alpha^{k-1} \notin S_{i+1}$ and $\alpha^{k-1} \in S_i - S_{i+1}$. Thus, there exists a chain β with

$\beta^0 = \alpha^k$ such that $\#d(F, \beta) = d(F) - i$, and it implies that $\#d(F, \gamma) = d(F) - i + 1$ for a chain γ with $\gamma^0 = \alpha^{k-1}$ and $\gamma^i = \beta^{i-1}$ for $i \geq 1$. However, it contradicts to $\alpha^{k-1} \in S_i - S_{i+1}$.

Now we are ready to show how F is computed. Let $\nu_1, \nu_2, \ldots, \nu_D \in \{\lfloor (d(F) + 1)^{1/D} \rfloor, \lfloor (d(F) + 1)^{1/D} \rfloor + 1\}$ satisfying $\sum_{\ell=1}^{D} \nu_\ell = \sigma_D(d(F))$. Recall that each t_i for $1 \leq i \leq d(F)$ is a monotone Boolean function. From Lemma 4 with $m = d(F)$ and $h_i = t_i$ for each $1 \leq i \leq d(F)$, the collection of Boolean function $G = \{g_j^\ell \mid 1 \leq \ell \leq D, 1 \leq j \leq \nu_\ell\}$, defined by,

$$g_j^\ell(x) = 1 \quad \text{iff} \quad \left(\sum_{i=1}^{m} t_i(x) \right) \bmod P_\ell < jP_{\ell+1},$$

can be computed by a depth-D circuit which contains $\sigma_D(d(F))$ negation gates. In order to complete the proof, it suffices to show that each f_j is a monotone Boolean function of x and all $g_j^k(x)$'s for $1 \leq k \leq D$ and $1 \leq j \leq \nu_k$, so that, each f_j can be computed by a monotone gate in level $D + 1$.

Notice that $f_j(x) = f_j^i(x)$ if $x \in S_i - S_{i+1}$, and $t_i(x) \wedge \neg t_{i+1}(x) = 1$ iff $x \in S_i - S_{i+1}$. Thus,

$$f_j = \bigvee_{i=0}^{d(F)} t_i \wedge \neg t_{i+1} \wedge f_j^i.$$

From $S_0 = \{0,1\}^n$ and $S_{d(F)+1} = \emptyset$, notice that t_0 and $t_{d(F)+1}$ are constant functions. From (7), we have $\neg t_{i+1}(x) = 1$ iff $\sum_{i'=1}^{d(F)} t_{i'}(x) \leq i$. Then, from (5) with $m = d(F)$ and $h_i = t_i$,

$$\neg t_{i+1}(x) = 1 \quad \text{iff} \quad \sum_{k=1}^{D} P_{k+1} \sum_{j=1}^{\nu_k} g_j^k(x) \geq \sum_{k=1}^{D} \nu_k P_{k+1} - i$$

Thus, $\neg t_{i+1}$ for each $1 \leq i \leq d(F)$ is a monotone function of all $g_j^k(x)$ for $1 \leq k \leq D$ and $1 \leq j \leq \nu_k$. Since each t_i for $1 \leq i \leq d(F)$ and each f_j^i for $0 \leq i \leq d(F)$ and $1 \leq j \leq m$ are monotone Boolean functions of x. Therefore, each f_j, for $1 \leq j \leq m$, is a monotone function of x and each $g_j^k(x)$ for $1 \leq k \leq D$ and $1 \leq j \leq \nu_k$. The proof is completed. $\square$

References

1. K. Amano, A. Maruoka , and J. Tarui. On the negation-limited circuit complexity of merging. *Discrete Applied Mathematics* 126(1): 3-8, 2003,
2. R. Beals, T. Nishino, and K. Tanaka. On the Complexity of Negation-Limited Boolean Networks. *SIAM Journal on Computing*, 27(5): 1334–1347, 1998.
3. A. A. Markov. On the inversion complexity of a system of functions. *Journal of the ACM*, 5(4):331–334, October 1958.
4. M. J. Fischer. The complexity of negation-limited networks – a brief survey. In *Lecture Notes in Computer Science 33*, pages 71–82. Springer-Verlag, 1974, Revised 1977 and 1996.

5. M. Santha and C. Wilson. Limiting negations in constant depth circuits. *SIAM Journal on Computing*, 22(2):294–302, April 1993.
6. S. C. Sung and K. Tanaka. An exponential gap with the removal of one negation gate. *Information Processing Letters*, 82(3):155–157, 2002.

Computational Complexity Measures of Multipartite Quantum Entanglement

(Extented Abstract)

Tomoyuki Yamakami

School of Information Technology and Engineering
University of Ottawa, Ottawa, Canada K1N 6N5

Abstract. We shed new light on entanglement measures in multipartite quantum systems by taking a computational-complexity approach toward quantifying quantum entanglement with two familiar notions—approximability and distinguishability. Built upon the formal treatment of partial separability, we measure the complexity of an entangled quantum state by determining (i) how hard to approximate it from a fixed classical state and (ii) how hard to distinguish it from all partially separable states. We further consider the Kolmogorovian-style descriptive complexity of approximation and distinction of partial entanglement.

1 Computational Aspects of Quantum Entanglement

Entanglement is one of the most puzzling notions in the theory of quantum information and computation. A typical example of an entangled quantum state is the Bell state (or the EPR pair) $(|00\rangle + |11\rangle)/\sqrt{2}$, which played a major role in, e.g., superdense coding [4] and quantum teleportation schemes [1]. Entanglement can be viewed as a physical resource and therefore can be quantified. Today, bipartite pure state entanglement is well-understood with information-theoretical notions of entanglement measures (see the survey [8]).

These measures, nevertheless, do not address computational aspects of the complexity of entangled quantum states. For example, although the Bell state is maximally entangled, it is computationally constructed from the simple classical state $|00\rangle$ by an application of the Hadamard and the Controlled-NOT operators. Thus, if the third party gives us a quantum state which is either the Bell state or any separable state, then one can easily tell with reasonable confidence whether the given state is truly the Bell state by reversing the computation since the minimal trace distance between the Bell state and separable states is at least $1/2$. This simple fact makes the aforementioned information-theoretical measures unsatisfactory from a computational point of view. We thus need different types of measures to quantify multipartite quantum entanglement.

We first need to lay down a mathematical framework for multipartite quantum entanglement and develop a useful terminology to describe a nested structure of entangled quantum states. In this paper, we mainly focus on pure quantum states in the Hilbert space $\mathbb{C}^{2^n}$ of dimension 2^n. Such a state is called, analogous to a classical string, a *quantum string* (or qustring, for short) *of length n.*

T. Ibaraki, N. Katoh, and H. Ono (Eds.): ISAAC 2003, LNCS 2906, pp. 117–128, 2003.

Any qustring of length n is expressed in terms of the standard basis $\{|s\rangle\}_{s\in\{0,1\}^n}$. Given a qustring $|\phi\rangle$, let $\ell(|\phi\rangle)$ denote its length. By Φ_n we denote the collection of all qustrings of length n and set Φ_∞ to be $\bigcup_{n\in\mathbb{N}^+} \Phi_n$, where $\mathbb{N}^+ = \mathbb{N} - \{0\}$. Ensembles (or series) of qustrings of (possibly) different lengths are of particular interest. We use families of *quantum circuits* [6,19] as a mathematical model of quantum-mechanical computation. A quantum circuit has input qubits and (possibly) ancilla qubits, where all ancilla qubits are always set to $|0\rangle$ at the beginning of computation. We fix a finite universal set of quantum gates, including the identity and the NOT gate. As a special terminology, we say that a property $\mathcal{P}(n)$ holds for *almost all* (or *any sufficiently large*) n in $\mathbb{N}$ if the set $\{x \in \mathbb{N} \mid \mathcal{P}(x)$ does not hold $\}$ is finite. All logarithms are conventionally taken to base two.

2   Separability Index and Separability Distance

We begin with a technical tool to identify the entanglement structure of an arbitrary quantum state residing in a multipartite quantum system. In a bipartite quantum system, any separable state can be expressed as a tensor product $|\phi\rangle\otimes|\psi\rangle$ of two qubits $|\phi\rangle$ and $|\psi\rangle$ and thus, any other state has its two qubits entangled with a physical correlation or "bonding." In a multipartite quantum system, however, all "separable" states may not have such a simple tensor-product form. Rather, various correlations of entangled qubits may be *nested*—or intertwined over different groups of entangled qubits. For example, consider the qustring $|\psi_{2n}\rangle = 2^{-n/2}\sum_{x\in\{0,1\}^n}|xx\rangle$ of length $2n$. For each $i \in \{1, 2, \ldots, n\}$, the ith qubit and the $n + i$th qubit in $|\psi_{2n}\rangle$ are entangled. The reordering of each qubit, nevertheless, unwinds its nested correlations and sorts all the qubits in the blockwise tensor product form $|\psi'_{2n}\rangle = (\frac{1}{\sqrt{2}}(|00\rangle + |11\rangle))^{\otimes n}$. Although $|\psi_{2n}\rangle$ and $|\psi'_{2n}\rangle$ are different inputs for a quantum circuit, such a reordering is done at the cost of additional $O(n)$ quantum gates. Thus, the number of those blocks represents the "degree" of the separability of the given qustring. Our first step is to introduce the appropriate terminology that can describe this "nested" bonding structure of a qustring.

We introduce the structural notion, *separability index*, which indicates the maximal number of entangled "blocks" that build up a target qustring of a multipartite quantum system. See [14] also for multipartite separability.

Definition 1.   *1. For any two qustrings $|\phi\rangle$ and $|\psi\rangle$ of length n, we say that $|\phi\rangle$ is isotopic to $|\psi\rangle$ via a permutation[1] σ on $\{1, 2, \ldots, n\}$ if $\sigma(|\phi\rangle) = |\psi\rangle$.*

2. A qustring $|\phi\rangle$ of length n is called k-separable if $|\phi\rangle$ is isotopic to $|\phi_1\rangle \otimes |\phi_2\rangle \otimes \cdots \otimes |\phi_k\rangle$ via a certain permutation σ on $\{1, 2, \ldots, n\}$ for a certain k-tuple $(|\phi_1\rangle, |\phi_2\rangle, \ldots, |\phi_k\rangle)$ of qustrings of length ≥ 1. This permutation σ is said

---

[1] Let σ be any permutation on $\{1, 2, \ldots, n\}$ and let $|\phi\rangle$ be any qustring of length n. The notation $\sigma(|\phi\rangle)$ denotes the qustring that results from permuting its qubits by σ; that is, $\sigma(|\phi\rangle) = \sum_x \alpha_x |x_{\sigma(1)}x_{\sigma(2)}\cdots x_{\sigma(n)}\rangle$ if $|\phi\rangle = \sum_x \alpha_x |x_1 x_2 \cdots x_n\rangle$, where $x = x_1 x_2 \cdots x_n$ runs over all binary strings of length n.

to achieve the k-separability of $|\phi\rangle$ *and the isotopic state* $|\phi_1\rangle \otimes |\phi_2\rangle \otimes \cdots \otimes |\phi_k\rangle$ *is said to have a* k-*unnested form. The series* $\boldsymbol{m} = (\ell(|\phi_1\rangle), \ell(|\phi_2\rangle), \ldots, \ell(|\phi_k\rangle))$ *is called a* k-*sectioning of* $|\phi\rangle$ *by* σ.

3. The separability index *of* $|\phi\rangle$, *denoted* $sind(|\phi\rangle)$, *is the maximal integer* k *with* $1 \leq k \leq n$ *such that* $|\phi\rangle$ *is* k-*separable.*

For any indices $n, k \in \mathbb{N}^+$ with $k \leq n$, let $QS_{n,k}$ denote the set of all qustrings of length n that have separability index k.

For clarity, we re-define the terms "entanglement" and "separability" using the separability indices. These terms are different from the conventional ones.

Definition 2. *For any qustring* $|\phi\rangle$ *of length* n, $|\phi\rangle$ *is* fully entangled *if its separability index equals* 1 *and* $|\phi\rangle$ *is* fully separable *if it has separability index* n. *For technicality, we call* $|\phi\rangle$ partially entangled *if it is of separability index* $\leq n - 1$. *Similarly, a* partially separable *qustring is a qustring with separability index* ≥ 2.

We assume the existence of a *quantum source of information*; namely, a certain physical process that produces a stream of quantum systems (i.e., qustrings) of (possibly) different lengths. Such a quantum source generates an ensemble (or a series) of qustrings. Of such ensembles, we are particularly interested in the ensembles of partially entangled qustrings. For convenience, we call them *entanglement ensembles*.

Definition 3. *Let* ℓ *be any strictly increasing function from* $\mathbb{N}$ *to* $\mathbb{N}$. *A series* $\Xi = \{|\xi_n\rangle\}_{n \in \mathbb{N}}$ *is called an* entanglement ensemble with size factor ℓ *if, for every index* $n \in \mathbb{N}$, $|\xi_n\rangle$ *is a partially entangled qustring of length* $\ell(n)$.

How close is a fully entangled state to its nearest partially separable state? Consider the fully entangled qustring $|\phi_n\rangle = (|0^n\rangle + |1^n\rangle)/\sqrt{2}$ for any $n \in \mathbb{N}$. For comparison, let $|\psi\rangle$ be any partially separable qustring of length n. By a simple calculation, the L_2-norm distance $\||\phi_n\rangle - |\psi\rangle\|$ is shown to be at least $\sqrt{2 - \sqrt{2}}$. The Bures metric $B(|\phi_n\rangle, |\psi\rangle) = 2(1 - F(|\phi_n\rangle, |\psi\rangle))$, where F is the fidelity,[2] is at least $2 - \sqrt{2}$ since we have $F(|\phi_n\rangle, |\psi\rangle) \leq 1/\sqrt{2}$ using the equality $F(|\phi_n\rangle, |\psi\rangle) = |\langle\phi_n|\psi\rangle|$. The trace distance[3] $\||\phi_n\rangle\langle\phi_n| - |\psi\rangle\langle\psi|\|_{\mathrm{tr}}$ is bounded below by $1/2$ using the inequality $1 - F(|\phi_n\rangle, |\psi\rangle)^2 \leq \||\phi_n\rangle\langle\phi_n| - |\psi\rangle\langle\psi|\|_{\mathrm{tr}}$ and the above bound for the fidelity.

This example motivates us to introduce the following notion of "closeness" similar to [13] using the trace norm. Note that the choice of a distance measure is not essential for our study.

Definition 4. *Let* $k, n \in \mathbb{N}^+$, $\delta \in [0, 1]$, *and let* $|\xi\rangle$ *be any qustring of length* n.

1. The k-separability distance *of* $|\xi\rangle$, *denoted* $sdis_k(|\xi\rangle)$, *is the infimum of* $\||\xi\rangle\langle\xi| - |\phi\rangle\langle\phi|\|_{\mathrm{tr}}$ *over all* k-*separable qustrings* $|\phi\rangle$ *of length* n.

---

[2] There are two different definitions in the literature. Following [11], we define the fidelity of two density operators ρ and τ as $F(\rho, \tau) = Tr(\sqrt{\sqrt{\rho}\tau\sqrt{\rho}})$.

[3] The trace norm of a linear operator X is defined as $\|X\|_{\mathrm{tr}} = \frac{1}{2}Tr(\sqrt{X^\dagger X})$ [11].

2. A qustring $|\xi\rangle$ is said to be (k,δ)-close to separable states if $sdis_k(|\xi\rangle) \le \delta$. Otherwise, $|\xi\rangle$ is (k,δ)-far from separable states.

3. Let k be any function from $\mathbb{N}$ to $\mathbb{N}^+$ and let δ be any function from $\mathbb{N}$ to $[0,1]$. An ensemble $\Xi = \{|\xi_n\rangle\}_{n\in\mathbb{N}}$ of qustrings is (k,δ)-close (infinitely-often (k,δ)-close, resp.) to separable states if $|\xi_n\rangle$ is $(k(n),\delta(n))$-close to separable states for almost all $n \in \mathbb{N}$ (for infinitely many $n \in \mathbb{N}$, resp.). We say that Ξ is (k,δ)-far (infinitely-often (k,δ)-far, resp.) from separable states if $|\xi_n\rangle$ is $(k(n),\delta(n))$-far from separable states for almost all $n \in \mathbb{N}$ (for infinitely many $n \in \mathbb{N}$, resp.).

Notice that $sdis_k(|\xi\rangle) = 0$ if $|\xi\rangle$ is k-separable. Moreover, the k-separability distance is invariant to permutation; namely, $sdis_k(\sigma(|\xi\rangle)) = sdis_k(|\xi\rangle)$ for any permutation σ. The previous example shows that the entanglement ensemble $\{(|0^n\rangle + |1^n\rangle)/\sqrt{2}\}_{n\in\mathbb{N}}$ are $(2, 1/2 - \epsilon)$-far from separable states for any constant $\epsilon > 0$. Our measure also has a connection to the geometric measure (see [16] for a review).

The notion of von Neumann entropy[4] has been proven to be useful for the characterization of entanglement of bipartite pure quantum states. The von Neumann entropy measures the *mixedness* of a mixed quantum state. Let $|\psi\rangle$ be any qustring of length n. For each $i \in \{1, \ldots, n\}$, let $\mathcal{H}_{\ge i}$ denote the Hilbert space corresponding to the last $n - i + 1$st qubits of $|\psi\rangle$. Consider the set $\mathcal{S} = \{S(Tr_{\mathcal{H}_{\ge i}}(|\psi\rangle\langle\psi|)) \mid i = 2, 3, \ldots, n\}$, where $Tr_{\mathcal{H}_{\ge i}}$ is the trace-out operator[5]. We define the *average entropy* of $|\psi\rangle$ as $E(|\psi\rangle\langle\psi|) = \frac{1}{n-1}\sum_{i=2}^{n} S(Tr_{\mathcal{H}_{\ge i}}(|\phi\rangle\langle\phi|))$. The following lemma then holds.

Lemma 1. *Let $n \in \mathbb{N}^+$, $|\xi\rangle \in \Phi_n$, and $k \in \{2, 3, \ldots, n\}$. If $sdis_k(|\xi\rangle) \le 1/e$, then $\min_{|\phi\rangle}\{|E(|\xi\rangle\langle\xi|) - E(|\phi\rangle\langle\phi|)|\} \le sdis_k(|\xi\rangle))(n - \log sdis_k(|\xi\rangle))$, where the minimization is taken over all k-separable qustrings in Φ_n.*

For Lemma 1, note that $|E(|\xi\rangle\langle\xi|) - E(|\phi\rangle\langle\phi|)| \le \frac{1}{n-1}\sum_{i=2}^{n}|S(Tr_{\mathcal{H}_{\ge i}}(|\xi\rangle\langle\xi|)) - S(Tr_{\mathcal{H}_{\ge i}}(|\phi\rangle\langle\phi|))|$. By the Fanne inequality (see, e.g., [11]), the difference $|S(Tr_{\mathcal{H}_{\ge i}}(|\xi\rangle\langle\xi|)) - S(Tr_{\mathcal{H}_{\ge i}}(|\phi\rangle\langle\phi|))|$ is at most $\|Tr_{\mathcal{H}_{\ge i}}(|\xi\rangle\langle\xi|) - Tr_{\mathcal{H}_{\ge i}}(|\phi\rangle\langle\phi|)\|_{tr} \cdot \log 2^{i-1} + \eta(\|Tr_{\mathcal{H}_{\ge i}}(|\xi\rangle\langle\xi|) - Tr_{\mathcal{H}_{\ge i}}(|\phi\rangle\langle\phi|)\|_{tr})$, which is bounded by $sdis_k(|\xi\rangle)[n - \log sdis_k(|\xi\rangle)]$, where $\eta(\gamma) = -\gamma\log\gamma$ for $\gamma > 0$.

3   Entanglement Distinguishability

We measure the complexity of each entangled state $|\phi\rangle$ by determining how hard it is to distinguish $|\phi\rangle$ from all k-separable states. Earlier, Vedral et al. [14] recognized the importance of distinguishability for quantifying entanglement.

---

[4] The von Neumann entropy $S(\rho)$ of a density operator ρ is $-Tr(\rho\log\rho)$, where the logarithm is taken to base 2. See, e.g., [11].

[5] For any bipartite quantum system $\mathcal{H} \otimes \mathcal{K}$, the *trace-out operator* (or *partial trace*) $Tr_{\mathcal{K}}$ is the mapping defined by $Tr_{\mathcal{K}}(\rho) = \sum_{j=1}^{n}(I \otimes \langle e_j|)\rho(I \otimes |e_j\rangle)$ for any density operator ρ of $\mathcal{H} \otimes \mathcal{K}$, where $\{|e_1\rangle, \ldots, |e_n\rangle\}$ is any fixed orthonormal basis of $\mathcal{K}$.

Fuchs and van de Graaf [7] took a cryptographic approach to quantum state distinguishing problems and briefly discussed computational indistinguishability of quantum states.

Cryptography has utilized the notion of "distinguishers" as, e.g., an adversary to a pseudorandom generator. Such a distinguisher is designed to distinguish between two different distributions of strings of fixed length with reasonable confidence. Since a quantum state can be viewed as an extension of a classical distribution, we can naturally adapt this cryptographic concept into a quantum context. For a quantum circuit C and a density operator ρ, the notation $C(\rho)$, ignoring ancilla qubits, stands for the random variable describing the measured output bit of C on input ρ. However, for a qustring $|\phi\rangle$, $C|\phi\rangle$ denotes the quantum state that results from $|\phi\rangle$ by an application of C.

Definition 5. *Let $\epsilon \in [0,1]$ and let ρ and τ be any two density operators of the same dimension. We say that a quantum circuit C ϵ-distinguishes between ρ and τ if $|\mathrm{Prob}_C[C(\rho) = 1] - \mathrm{Prob}_C[C(\tau) = 1]| \geq \epsilon$. This circuit C is called an ϵ-distinguisher of ρ and τ.*

Now, we introduce a special type of distinguisher, which distinguishes a given ensemble of partially entangled qustrings from k-separable states using only polynomially-many quantum gates. Let $|\phi\rangle$ be any k-separable qustring of length n that is isotopic to the state $|\phi_1\rangle \otimes |\phi_2\rangle \otimes \cdots \otimes |\phi_k\rangle$ via a permutation σ. Let $\boldsymbol{m} = (\ell(|\phi_1\rangle), \ldots, \ell(|\phi_k\rangle))$ be its k-sectioning. For notational convenience, we write $1^{\boldsymbol{m}}$ for $1^{\ell(|\phi_1\rangle)}01^{\ell(|\phi_2\rangle)}0 \cdots 1^{\ell(|\phi_k\rangle)}0$ whose length is exactly $n + k$. Let 1^σ be $1^{\sigma(1)}01^{\sigma(2)}0 \cdots 1^{\sigma(n)}0$ of length $n^2/2 + 3n/2$. Moreover, we write $1^{\sigma,\boldsymbol{m}}$ for $1^\sigma 01^{\boldsymbol{m}}0$. Note that the length of $1^{\sigma,\boldsymbol{m}}$ is $n^2/2 + 5n/2 + k + 2$.

Definition 6. *Let k be any function from $\mathbb{N}$ to $\mathbb{N} - \{0,1\}$ and ϵ be any function from $\mathbb{N}$ to $[0,1]$. Let ℓ and s be any functions from $\mathbb{N}$ to $\mathbb{N}$. Assume that ℓ is strictly increasing. Let $\Xi = \{|\xi_n\rangle\}_{n\in\mathbb{N}}$ be an ensemble of qustrings with size factor ℓ.*

1. A family $\{D_n\}_{n\in\mathbb{N}}$ of quantum circuits with $\ell(n)^2/2 + 7\ell(n)/2 + k(n) + 2$ input qubits and (possibly) ancilla qubits is called a non-uniform entanglement (k, ϵ)-distinguisher *(non-uniform infinitely-often entanglement (k, ϵ)-distinguisher, resp.) of Ξ if, for almost all n's (for infinitely many $n \in \mathbb{N}$, resp.), D_n $\epsilon(n)$-distinguishes between $|1^{\sigma,\boldsymbol{m}}\rangle|\xi_n\rangle$ and $|1^{\sigma,\boldsymbol{m}}\rangle|\phi\rangle$ for any k-separable qustring $|\phi\rangle$ of length $\ell(n)$ and any permutation σ that achieves the k-separability of $|\phi\rangle$ with $k(n)$-sectioning $\boldsymbol{m}$. In particular, if we want to emphasize a pair $(\sigma, \boldsymbol{m})$, we call D_n a* non-uniform (infinitely-often) entanglement ϵ-distinguisher *with respect to $(\sigma, \boldsymbol{m})$.*

2. The ensemble Ξ is called non-uniformly (k, ϵ, s)-distinguishable from separable states *if there is a non-uniform entanglement (k, ϵ)-distinguisher of Ξ that has size[6] at most $s(n)$. In contrast, Ξ is* non-uniformly (k, ϵ, s)-indistinguishable from separable states *if there is no s-size non-uniform infinitely-often entanglement (k, ϵ)-distinguisher of Ξ. In case where s is a polynomial, we simply say*

---

[6] The *size* of a quantum circuit is the total number of quantum gates in it.

that Ξ is non-uniformly (k, ϵ)-distinguishable from separable states *and* non-uniformly (k, ϵ)-indistinguishable from separable states, *respectively. Similarly, we can define the infinitely-often version of distinguishability and indistinguishability. For readability, we often drop the word "non-uniform" if it is clear from the context.*

We can also define a "uniform" entanglement distinguisher using a **P**-uniform family of quantum circuits (or equivalently, a multi-tape quantum Turing machine [2,17]).

Obviously, any ensemble of k-separable qustrings is (k, ϵ)-indistinguishable from separable states for any $\epsilon \geq 0$. The following lemma is an immediate consequence of Definition 6.

Lemma 2. *Let $\Xi = \{|\xi_n\rangle\}_{n \in \mathbb{N}}$ be any ensemble of qustrings with size factor ℓ.*

1. Let k, k' be any functions from $\mathbb{N}$ to $\mathbb{N} - \{0, 1\}$, let ϵ, ϵ' be any functions from $\mathbb{N}$ to $[0, 1]$, and let s, s' be any functions from $\mathbb{N}$ to $\mathbb{N}$. Assume that k', ϵ and s' majorize[7] k, ϵ', and s, respectively. If Ξ is (infinitely-often) (k, ϵ, s)-distinguishable from separable states, then Ξ is also (infinitely-often) (k', ϵ', s')-distinguishable from separable states.

2. Let $\boldsymbol{\sigma} = \{\sigma_n\}_{n \in \mathbb{N}}$ be any family of permutations σ_n on $\{1, 2, \ldots, \ell(n)\}$ for each n. Define $\boldsymbol{\sigma}(\Xi) = \{\sigma_n(|\xi_n\rangle)\}_{n \in \mathbb{N}}$. If Ξ is (infinitely-often) (k, ϵ, s)-distinguishable from separable states, then $\boldsymbol{\sigma}(\Xi)$ is (infinitely-often) $(k, \epsilon, s(n) + O(n))$-distinguishable from separable states.

Of course, there are entangled states that no quantum circuit can distinguish from separable states. For instance, if two qustrings are close to each other, then no polynomial-size quantum circuit can tell their difference. In what follows, we show that any entangled state close to separable states is indistinguishable.

Proposition 1. *Let k be any function from $\mathbb{N}$ to $\mathbb{N}^+$ and let ℓ be any function from $\mathbb{N}$ to $\mathbb{N}$. Any entanglement ensemble $\Xi = \{|\xi_i\rangle\}_{i \in \mathbb{N}}$ is $(k(n), sdis_{k(n)}(|\xi_n\rangle) + \delta)$-indistinguishable from separable states for any constant $\delta > 0$.*

Proposition 1 is proven by the inequality $|\mathrm{Prob}_C[C(|1^{\sigma, m}\rangle|\xi_n\rangle) = 1] - \mathrm{Prob}_C[C(|1^{\sigma, m}\rangle|\phi\rangle) = 1]| \leq \||\xi_n\rangle\langle\xi_n| - |\phi\rangle\langle\phi|\|_{\mathrm{tr}}$ for any k-separable state $|\phi\rangle$, which follows from the fact that $\|\rho - \sigma\|_{\mathrm{tr}} = \max_P\{Tr(P(\rho - \sigma))\}$, where the maximization is taken over all positive semidefinite contractive[8] matrices P.

We note that, for every qustring $|\xi\rangle \in \Phi_n$, there exists a positive operator-valued measure W such that $\max_{|\phi\rangle}\{|\langle\xi|W|\xi\rangle - \langle\phi|W|\phi\rangle|\} \geq sdis_k(|\xi\rangle)^2$, where the maximization is taken over all k-separable qustrings in Φ_n. Such a W is given, for example, as $W = I - |\xi\rangle\langle\xi|$. Lemma 4 will present its special case.

How do we construct our distinguisher? A basic way is to combine all distinguishers built with respect to different pairs of permutations and sectionings.

---

[7] For any two functions f, g from $\mathbb{N}$ to $\mathbb{R}$, we say that f *majorizes* g if $g(n) \leq f(n)$ for every $n \in \mathbb{N}$.

[8] A square matrix A is *contractive* if $\|A\| \leq 1$, where $\|A\| = \sum_{|\phi\rangle \neq 0}\{\||A|\phi\rangle\|/\||\phi\rangle\|\}$.

Suppose that we have s-size entanglement distinguishers with respect to permutations σ and $k(n)$-sectionings m targeting the same entanglement ensemble Ξ with size factor $\ell(n)$. Although the number of such pairs (σ, m) may be nearly $\ell(n)! \cdot \binom{\ell(n)-1}{k(n)}$, the following lemma shows that it is possible to build a $O(s)$-size distinguisher that works for all permutation-sectioning pairs.

Lemma 3. *Let Ξ be any entanglement ensemble with size factor ℓ. Let s be any strictly increasing function from $\mathbb{N}$ to $\mathbb{N}$. If, for every $n \in \mathbb{N}$, every permutation σ on $\{1, \dots, \ell(n)\}$, and every $k(n)$-sectioning m, there exists an $s(n)$-size ϵ-distinguisher of Ξ with respect to (σ, m), then there exists an $O(s(n)^c)$-size (k, ϵ)-distinguisher of Ξ, where c is an absolute positive constant.*

4 Entanglement Approximability

What types of entangled states are easily distinguishable from separable states? We first claim that any entangled state that is computationally "constructed" from the classical state $|0^m\rangle$ is distinguishable. The precise definition of constructibility is given as follows.

Definition 7. *Let s be any function from $\mathbb{N}$ to $\mathbb{N}$. An ensemble $\Xi = \{|\xi_n\rangle\}_{n \in \mathbb{N}}$ of qustrings with size factor $\ell(n)$ is* non-uniformly s-size constructible *if there exists a non-uniform family $\{C_n\}_{n \in \mathbb{N}}$ of quantum circuits of size at most $s(n)$ having $\ell(n)$ input qubits and no ancilla qubit such that, for every n, $C_n|0^{\ell(n)}\rangle = |\xi_n\rangle$, where $C_n|0^{\ell(n)}\rangle$ denotes the qustring obtained after the computation of C_n on input $|0^{\ell(n)}\rangle$. This family $\{C_n\}_{n \in \mathbb{N}}$ is called a* non-uniform s-size constructor *of Ξ.*

Consider a partially entangled qustring $|\xi\rangle$ of length n with $\delta = sdis_k(|\xi\rangle) > 0$. If $|\xi\rangle$ is computationally constructed from $|0^n\rangle$, then we can easily determine whether a quantum state given from the third party is exactly $|\xi\rangle$ by reversing the construction process to test whether it returns to $|0^n\rangle$. This induces a distinguisher D. This is seen as follows. For any k-separable state $|\phi\rangle$, we have $|\text{Prob}_D[D(|\xi\rangle) = 1] - \text{Prob}_D[D(|\phi\rangle) = 1]| \geq \delta^2$ since $\text{Prob}_D[D(|\phi\rangle) = 1] = F(|\xi\rangle, |\phi\rangle)^2$, which is bounded above by $1 - \delta^2$. Therefore, we obtain:

Lemma 4. *Let ℓ and s be any functions from $\mathbb{N}$ to $\mathbb{N}$ and k be any function from $\mathbb{N}$ to $\mathbb{N}^+$. Assume that ℓ is strictly increasing. For any ensemble $\Xi = \{|\xi_n\rangle\}_{n \in \mathbb{N}}$ of qustrings of size factor ℓ, if Ξ is s-size constructible, then it is $(k(n), sdis_{k(n)}(|\xi_n\rangle)^2, O(s(n)))$-distinguishable from separable states.*

Many fully entangled quantum states used in the literature are polynomial-size constructible. For instance, the entanglement ensemble $\{(|0^n\rangle + |1^n\rangle)/\sqrt{2}\}_{n \in \mathbb{N}}$ is $O(n)$-size constructible and its 2-separability distance is at least $1/2$. Thus, it is $(2, 1/4, O(n))$-distinguishable from separable states.

We further relax the computability requirement for partially entangled states. Below, we introduce quantum states that can be "approximated" rather than "constructed."

Definition 8. *Let s be any function from $\mathbb{N}$ to $\mathbb{N}$ and ϵ be any function from $\mathbb{N}$ to $[0,1]$. An ensemble $\Xi = \{|\xi_n\rangle\}_{n\in\mathbb{N}}$ of qustrings with size factor $\ell(n)$ is said to be* non-uniformly (ϵ, s)-approximable *(non-uniformly infinitely-often (ϵ, s)-approximable, resp.) if there exists a non-uniform family $\{C_n\}_{n\in\mathbb{N}}$ of quantum circuits of size at most $s(n)$ having $\ell(n)$ input qubits and $p(n)$ ancilla qubits $(p(n) \geq 0)$ such that, for almost all $n \in \mathbb{N}$ (for infinitely many $n \in \mathbb{N}$, resp.),*

$$\left\| Tr_{\mathcal{H}_n}(C_n|0^{p(n)+\ell(n)}\rangle\langle 0^{p(n)+\ell(n)}|C_n^\dagger) - |\xi_n\rangle\langle\xi_n| \right\|_{tr} \leq \epsilon(n),$$

where $\mathcal{H}_n$ refers to the Hilbert space corresponding to the $p(n)$ ancilla qubits of C_n. The family $\{C_n\}_{n\in\mathbb{N}}$ is called a non-uniform ϵ-approximator *(non-uniform infinitely-often ϵ-approximator, resp.) of Ξ. In particular, if Ξ is non-uniformly (infinitely-often) (ϵ, s)-approximable for a certain polynomial s, then we simply say that Ξ is* non-uniformly (infinitely-often) ϵ-approximable.

The "uniform" version of approximability can be defined using a **P**-uniform family of quantum circuits or a multi-tape quantum Turing machine. As seen before, we drop the phrase "non-uniform" in the above definition for simplicity unless otherwise stated. Clearly, any (ϵ, s)-constructible quantum state is (ϵ, s)-approximable.

The following lemma shows that any ensemble of qustrings has an exponential-size approximator; however, there exists an ensemble that is not approximated by any polynomial-size approximators.

Lemma 5. *1. Let ϵ be any function from $\mathbb{N}$ to $(0,1]$. Any ensemble of qustrings with size factor n has a non-uniform (ϵ, s)-approximator, where $s(n) = n^2 2^n \log^2 \frac{n^2 2^{2n}}{\epsilon(n)}$.*

2. For each constant $\epsilon > 0$, there exists an entanglement ensemble that is not $(\epsilon, n^{O(1)})$-approximable.

Lemma 5(1) follows from the Solovay-Kitaev theorem (see [11]). Lemma 5(2) uses the result in [9] that there exists a quantum state that is not approximated by any polynomial-size quantum circuits together with the fact that there is always an entangled state close to each separable state.

A role of approximators is to build distinguishers. We can show that approximability implies distinguishability if the target entanglement ensemble is far from separable states.

Proposition 2. *Let k be any function from $\mathbb{N}$ to $\mathbb{N} - \{0,1\}$ and ϵ, δ be any functions from $\mathbb{N}$ to $[0,1]$ such that $\delta(n) > \epsilon(n) + \sqrt{\epsilon(n)}$ for all n. For any (infinitely-often) (ϵ, s)-approximable entanglement ensemble, if it is (k, δ)-far from separable states, then it is (infinitely-often) $(k, \epsilon', O(s(n)))$-distinguishable from separable states, where $\epsilon'(n) = \frac{(\delta(n)-\epsilon(n))^2 - \epsilon(n)}{2}$.*

The proof of Proposition 2 is based on the fact that any (ϵ, s)-approximable entanglement ensemble $\Xi = \{|\xi_n\rangle\}_{n\in\mathbb{N}}$ can be distinguished from separable states by use of the Controlled-SWAP operator (see [5,10]). Let D_n be the circuit that runs an $(\epsilon(n), s(n))$-approximator C_n and then carries out the C-SWAP procedure (first apply the Hadamard H to the controlled bit $|0\rangle$, then

Controlled-SWAT, and finally H) and outputs the complement of the controlled bit. Let $|\psi\rangle$ be any qustring of length $\ell(n)$. It follows that $\mathrm{Prob}_{D_n}[D_n(|\psi\rangle) = 1] = 1/2 + Tr(\rho|\psi\rangle\langle\psi|)/2$, where $\rho = Tr_{\mathcal{H}_n}(C_n|0^m\rangle\langle 0^m|C_n^\dagger)$ for some appropriate m. On one hand, we have $\mathrm{Prob}_{D_n}[D_n(|\xi_n\rangle) = 1] \geq 1 - \epsilon(n)/2$. On the other hand, if $|\psi\rangle$ is $k(n)$-separable and $(k(n), \delta(n))$-far from separable states, then $\mathrm{Prob}_{D_n}[D_n(|\xi_n\rangle) = 1] < 1 - (\delta(n) - \epsilon(n))^2/2$. Therefore, $|\mathrm{Prob}_{D_n}[D_n(|\xi_n\rangle) = 1] - \mathrm{Prob}_{D_n}[D_n(|\psi\rangle) = 1]|$ is greater than $\epsilon'(n)$. Note that Proposition 2 also holds for the uniform case.

Recall from Proposition 1 that any entanglement ensemble close to separable states is indistinguishable from separable states. Conversely, we claim a general result that any entangled state that is far from separable states has exponential-size distinguishers by combining Proposition 2 with Lemma 5(1) as well as the fact that $n^2 2^n \log^2 \frac{n^2 2^{2n}}{\epsilon} \in O(2^{2n})$.

Corollary 1. *Let k be any function from $\mathbb{N}$ to $\mathbb{N} - \{0, 1\}$ and ϵ, δ be any functions from $\mathbb{N}$ to $[0, 1]$ with $\delta(n) > \epsilon(n) + \sqrt{\epsilon(n)}$ for any n. Every entanglement ensemble that is (k, δ)-far from separable states is $(k, \epsilon', O(2^{2n}))$-distinguishable from separable states, where $\epsilon'(n) = \frac{(\delta(n)-\epsilon(n))^2-\epsilon(n)}{2}$.*

Under the uniformity condition, we can show that distinguishability does not always imply approximability. To see this, consider the entanglement ensemble $\Xi = \{(|0^n\rangle + (-1)^{f(1^n)}|1^n\rangle)/\sqrt{2}\}_{n\in\mathbb{N}}$, where f is any recursive function from $\{1\}^*$ to $\mathbb{N}$, which is not computable by any P-uniform family of exponential-size Boolean circuits. This Ξ can be uniformly $(n, 1/\sqrt{2}, n^{O(1)})$-distinguishable but not uniformly $(1/\sqrt{2}, n^{O(1)})$-approximable; otherwise, we can build from an approximator of Ξ a family of exponential-size Boolean circuits that compute f. Therefore, we obtain:

Proposition 3. *There exists an entanglement ensemble of size factor n that is uniformly $(n, 1/\sqrt{2}, n^{O(1)})$-distinguishable from separable states and not uniformly $(1/\sqrt{2}, n^{O(1)})$-approximable.*

5   Descriptive Complexity of Entanglement

The recent work of Vitányi [15] and Berthiaume et al. [3] brought in the notion of quantum Kolmogorov complexity to measure the descriptive (or algorithmic) complexity of quantum states. In particular, Vitányi measured the minimal size of a classical program that approximates a target quantum state. We modify Vitányi's notion to accommodate the approximability of partially entangled qustrings using quantum circuits of bounded size.

Let us fix an appropriate universal deterministic Turing machine M_U and let $C(x|y)$ denote the Kolmogorov complexity of x conditional to y with respect to M_U; that is, the minimal nonnegative integer $|p|$ such that p is a classical program that produces x from y (i.e., $M_U(p, y) = x$ in finite time). Abbreviate

$C(x|\lambda)$ as $C(x)$. By identifying a quantum circuit D with its encoding[9] $\langle D\rangle$, we succinctly write $C(D)$ for $C(\langle D\rangle)$.

Definition 9. *Let s be any function from $\mathbb{N}$ to $\mathbb{N}$ and let $|\xi\rangle$ be any qustring of length n. The s-size bounded approximating complexity of $|\xi\rangle$, denoted $QCA^s(|\xi\rangle)$, is the infimum of $C(D) - \log F(|\xi\rangle, \rho)^2$ such that D is a quantum circuit of size at most $s(n)$ with ℓ inputs ($\ell \geq n$) and $\rho = Tr_{\mathcal{H}}(|\phi\rangle\langle\phi|)$, where $|\phi\rangle = D|0^\ell\rangle$ and $\mathcal{H}$ is the Hilbert space associated with the last $\ell - n$ qubits of D. Its conditional version $QCA^s(|\xi\rangle \| |\zeta\rangle)$ is defined by $C(D|\ell(|\zeta\rangle)) - \log F(|\xi\rangle\langle\xi|, \sigma)^2$, where $|\psi\rangle = D|\zeta\rangle|0^\ell\rangle$ and $\sigma = Tr_{\mathcal{H}}(|\psi\rangle\langle\psi|)$.*

More generally, we can define $QCA^s(\sigma)$ for any density operator σ. Similar to [15], $QCA^s(|\xi\rangle)$ is bounded above by $2n + c$ for any $|\xi\rangle \in \Phi_n$ (by considering a quantum circuit C that outputs $|x\rangle$ satisfying $F(|\xi\rangle, |x\rangle)^2 \geq 2^{-n}$) if $s(n) \geq n$.

We prove in the following lemma that any uniformly approximable entanglement ensemble has small approximating complexity. This lemma comes from the inequality $\|\rho - |\xi\rangle\langle\xi|\|_{\mathrm{tr}} \leq \sqrt{1 - F(\rho, |\xi\rangle)^2}$.

Lemma 6. *Let s be any function from $\mathbb{N}$ to $\mathbb{N}$ and let ϵ be any function from $\mathbb{N}$ to $[0, 1)$. Let $\Xi = \{|\xi_n\rangle\}_{n\in\mathbb{N}}$ be any entanglement ensemble. If Ξ is uniformly (ϵ, s)-approximable, then there exists an absolute constant $c \geq 0$ such that $QCA^s(|\xi_n\rangle \| |1^n\rangle) \leq c - \log(1 - \epsilon(n))$ for all $n \in \mathbb{N}$. In particular, if $\epsilon(n)$ is upper-bounded by a certain constant, then $QCA^s(|\xi_n\rangle \| |1^n\rangle) \leq d$ for some absolute constant $d \geq 0$.*

In connection to distinguishability, Sipser [12] defined the notion of distinguishing complexity, which measures the minimal size of a program that distinguishes a target classical string from all other strings. Translating this distinguishing complexity into a quantum context, we introduce the *k-separability distinguishing complexity* of a partially entangled state.

Definition 10. *Let s be any function from $\mathbb{N}$ to $\mathbb{N}$ and let $k \in \mathbb{N} - \{0, 1\}$. For any qustring $|\xi\rangle$ of length n, the s-size bounded k-separability distinguishing complexity of $|\xi\rangle$, denoted $sQCD_k^s(|\xi\rangle)$, is defined to be the infimum of $C(D|k) - \log \epsilon$ for any quantum circuit D of size at most $s(n)$ with $n^2/2 + 7n/2 + k + 2$ inputs and (possibly) ancilla qubits such that D ϵ-distinguishes between $|1^{\sigma, m}\rangle|\xi\rangle$ and $|1^{\sigma, m}\rangle|\phi\rangle$ for any k-separable qustring $|\phi\rangle$ of length n and any permutation σ that achieves the k-separability of $|\phi\rangle$ with k-sectioning $\mathbf{m}$. For convenience, we define $sQCD_{\sigma, \mathbf{m}}^s(|\xi\rangle)$ similarly by requiring conditions (i) and (ii) to hold only for the fixed pair $(\sigma, \mathbf{m})$. The conditional version $sQCD_k^s(|\xi\rangle \| |\zeta\rangle)$ is defined by $C(D|k, \ell(|\zeta\rangle)) - \log \epsilon$, where D takes $|1^{\sigma, m}\rangle|\psi\rangle|\zeta\rangle$ as input.*

It is important to note that if $|\xi\rangle$ is k-separable then $sQCD_k^s(|\xi\rangle)$ is *not defined* since ϵ becomes zero. The next lemma follows immediately from Definition 10.

---

[9] The notation $\langle D\rangle$ for a quantum circuit D denotes a fixed effective encoding of D such that the size of this coding is not smaller than the number of gates in D.

Lemma 7. *Let $k \geq 2$ and let $|\xi\rangle$ be any qustring.*

1. $\mathrm{sQCD}^s_{\sigma,m}(|\xi\rangle) \leq \mathrm{sQCD}^s_k(|\xi\rangle)$ *for any permutation σ and k-sectioning m.*
2. $\mathrm{sQCD}^s_{k+1}(|\xi\rangle) \leq \mathrm{sQCD}^s_k(|\xi\rangle)$ *if $k \leq \ell(|\xi\rangle) - 1$.*
3. *Let k,s be any functions from $\mathbb{N}$ to $\mathbb{N}$ with $k(n) \geq 2$ for all n. Let ϵ be any function from $\mathbb{N}$ to $(0,1]$. If an ensemble $\Xi = \{|\xi_n\rangle\}_{n \in \mathbb{N}}$ is uniformly (k,ϵ,s)-distinguishable from separable states, then there exists a constant $c \geq 0$ such that $\mathrm{sQCD}^s_{k(n)}(|\xi_n\rangle || 1^n)) \leq c - \log \epsilon(n)$ for all $n \in \mathbb{N}$. In particular, if $\epsilon(n)$ is bounded above by a certain constant, then $\mathrm{sQCD}^s_{k(n)}(|\xi_n\rangle || 1^n)) \leq d$ for some absolute constant $d \geq 0$.*

Note that if $\mathrm{sQCD}^s_k(|\xi\rangle) = C(D|k) - \log \epsilon$ as in Definition 10 then D is a (k,ϵ,s)-distinguisher of $|\xi\rangle$. By (the proof of) Proposition 1, ϵ cannot be less than or equal to $sdis_k(|\xi\rangle)$. This gives a lower bound of separability distinguishing complexity.

Proposition 4. *For any qustring $|\xi\rangle$ and any integer k with $2 \leq k \leq \ell(|\xi\rangle)$), if $sdis_k(|\xi\rangle) > 0$, then $\mathrm{sQCD}^s_k(|\xi\rangle) > -\log sdis_k(|\xi\rangle)$.*

At length, we exhibit two upper bounds of separability distinguishing complexity, which follow from Lemma 4 and Proposition 2. Note that Proposition 5 requires a calculation slightly different from Proposition 2.

Proposition 5. *Let $\Xi = \{|\xi_n\rangle\}_{n \in \mathbb{N}}$ be any entanglement ensemble with size factor ℓ. Let k,s be any functions from $\mathbb{N}$ to $\mathbb{N}$ with $2 \leq k(n) \leq \ell(n)$ for all n.*

1. If Ξ is s-size constructible, then there exist a constant $c \geq 0$ and a function $s'(n) \subset O(s(n))$ such that $\mathrm{sQCD}^{s'}_k(|\xi_n\rangle) \leq \mathrm{QCA}^s(|\xi_n\rangle) - 2\log sdis_{k(n)}(|\xi_n\rangle) + c$ for all $n \in \mathbb{N}$.

2. If Ξ is (ϵ,s)-approximable and $sdis_{k(n)}(|\xi_n\rangle) > 2\sqrt{\epsilon(n)}$ for all n, then there exist a constant $c \geq 0$ and a function $s'(n) \in O(s(n))$ such that, for all n's,

$$\mathrm{sQCD}^{s'}_k(|\xi_n\rangle) \leq \mathrm{QCA}^s(|\xi_n\rangle) - \log sdis_{k(n)}(|\xi_n\rangle) - \log\left(\frac{sdis_{k(n)}(|\xi_n\rangle) - 2\sqrt{\epsilon(n)}}{1 - \epsilon(n)^2}\right) + c.$$

References

1. C. H. Bennett, G. Brassard, C. Crépeau, R. Jozsa, A. Peres, and W. Wootters. Teleporting an unknown quantum state via dual classical and EPR channels. *Phys. Rev. Lett.*, **70** (1993), 1895–1899.

2. E. Bernstein and U. Vazirani. Quantum complexity theory. *SIAM J. Comput.*, **26**, 1411–1473, 1997.

3. A. Berthiaume, W. van Dam, and S. Laplante. Quantum Kolmogorov complexity. To appear in *J. Comput. System Sci.* See also ArXive e-print quant-ph/0005018, 2000.

4. C. H. Bennett and S. J. Wiesner. Communication via one and two-particle operations on Einstein-Podolsky-Rosen states. *Phys. Rev. Lett.*, **69** (1992), 2881–2884.

5. H. Buhrman, R. Cleve, J. Watrous, R. de Wolf. Quantum fingerprinting. *Phys. Rev. Lett.*, **87**:167902 (2001).

6. D. Deutsch. Quantum computational networks. *Proc. Roy. Soc. London.* A **425** (1989), 73–90.

7. C. A. Fuchs and J. van de Graaf. Cryptographic distinguishability measures for quantum-mechanical states. *IEEE Transactions on Information Theory*, **45** (1999), 1216–1227.
8. M. Horodecki. Entanglement measures. *Quant. Info. Comp.* **1** (2001), 3–26.
9. E. Knill. Approximating quantum circuits. ArXive e-print quant-ph/9508006, 1995.
10. H. Kobayashi, K. Matsumoto, and T. Yamakami. Quantum Merlin-Arthur proof systems: are multiple Merlins more helpful to Arthur? In this proceedings.
11. M. A. Nielsen and I. L. Chuang. *Quantum Computation and Information*. Cambridge University Press, 2000.
12. M. Sipser. A complexity theoretic approach to randomness. In *Proceedings of the 15th ACM Symposium on the Theory of Computing*, pp.330–335, 1983.
13. V. Vedral, M. B. Plenio, M. A. Rippin, and P. L. Knight. Quantifying entanglement. *Phys. Rev. Lett.* **78** (1997), 2275–2279.
14. V. Vedral, M. B. Plenio, K. Jacob, and P. L. Knight. Statistical inference, distinguishability of quantum states, and quantum entanglement. *Phys. Rev. A* **56** (1997), 4452–4455.
15. P. M. B. Vitányi. Quantum Kolmogorov complexity based on classical descriptions. *IEEE Transactions on Information Theory*, **47** (2001), 2464–2479.
16. T. C. Wei and P. M. Goldbart. Geometric measure of entanglement and applications to bipartite quantum states. ArXive e-print quant-ph/0307219, 2003.
17. T. Yamakami. A foundation of programming a multi-tape quantum Turing machine. In *Proceedings of the 24th International Symposium on Mathematical Foundations of Computer Science*, Lecture Notes in Computer Science, Vol.1672, pp.430–441, Springer-Verlag, 1999.
18. T. Yamakami. Quantum NP and a quantum hierarchy. In *Proceedings of the 2nd IFIP Conference on Theoretical Computer Science* (Foundations of Information Technology in the Era of Network and Mobile Computing), pp.323–336, Kluwer Academic Publishes, 2002.
19. A. C. Yao. Quantum circuit complexity. In *Proceedings of the 34th Annual Symposium on Foundations of Computer Science*, pp.352–361, 1993.

A New Simple Algorithm for the Maximum-Weight Independent Set Problem on Circle Graphs

Gabriel Valiente[*]

Department of Software, Technical University of Catalonia, E-08034 Barcelona

Abstract. The problem of finding an independent set of maximum weight for the chord model of a circle graph is solved in $O(\ell)$ time and $O(n)$ space, where n is the number of vertices and ℓ is the total chord length of the circle graph. The best previous algorithm required $O(dn)$ time and space, where d is the maximum number of intervals crossing any position on the line in the interval model of the graph. The algorithm is practical, requires only simple data structures to be implemented within the stated time and space bounds, and has small hidden constants.

1 Introduction

A circle graph is an undirected graph that is isomorphic to the intersection graph of a finite set of chords of a circle. The problem of finding a maximum-weight independent set of a circle graph is polynomially equivalent to finding a maximum-weight planar subgraph in a general graph with a fixed vertex ordering along the circumference of the circle (that is, a maximum-weight planar matching), and arises in various application areas, including polygon partition problems in computational geometry [2,13] and wiring and channel routing problems in VLSI design [5,10,19]. In the latter application area, a particular case of much interest is the maximum independent set problem on permutation graphs, which is polynomially equivalent to the noncrossing matching problem on bipartite graphs and was solved in $O(n \log n)$ time [11,12,20] and in $O(n \log \log n)$ time [14,15,21], on permutation graphs with n vertices.

Circle graphs can be recognized in polynomial time [4,6,16,18]. The current best algorithm takes $O(n^2)$ time [18] and produces an interval model of the input graph. In algorithms on circle graphs, it is usually assumed that either an interval model or a chord model of the input circle graph is given, and these geometric models can be easily transformed into each other [9, Sect. 11.3].

The problem of finding a maximum independent set of a circle graph was solved in $O(n^3)$ time in [7,13] and in $O(n^2)$ time [2,3,8,17,19], where n is the number of vertices of the graph. The best previous algorithm for this problem takes $O(dn)$ time and space, where d is the *density* of the graph, that is, the

---

[*] Partially supported by Spanish CICYT project MAVERISH (TIC2001-2476-C03-01)

T. Ibaraki, N. Katoh, and H. Ono (Eds.): ISAAC 2003, LNCS 2906, pp. 129–137, 2003.
© Springer-Verlag Berlin Heidelberg 2003

maximum number of intervals crossing any position on the line in the interval model of the graph [1].

In this paper, the problem of finding an independent set of maximum weight in a circle graph, given a chord model of the graph, is solved in $O(\ell) = O(dn)$ time and $O(n)$ space, where n is the number of vertices, ℓ is the total chord length, and d is the density of the circle graph.

2   Preliminaries

A circle graph is an undirected graph that is isomorphic to the intersection graph of a finite set of chords of a circle [9, Sect. 11.2]. Such a set of chords is called a *chord model* of the graph, when regarded as the edge set of an undirected graph whose vertex set is totally ordered along the circumference of the circle. A circle graph is shown in Fig. 1, along with a chord model of it.

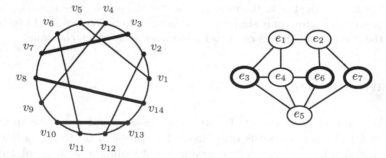

Fig. 1. A chord model (left) $G = (V, E)$ of a circle graph (right), where $V = [v_1, \ldots, v_{14}]$, $E = \{e_1, \ldots, e_7\}$, $e_1 = \{v_1, v_5\}$, $e_2 = \{v_2, v_{12}\}$, $e_3 = \{v_3, v_7\}$, $e_4 = \{v_4, v_9\}$, $e_5 = \{v_6, v_{11}\}$, $e_6 = \{v_8, v_{14}\}$, $e_7 = \{v_{10}, v_{13}\}$.

In general, algorithms on circle graphs work either with the chord model or with the *interval model* of a circle graph, in which the total order on the vertex set along the circumference of a circle is replaced by a total order along the line.

An interval model of a circle graph can be obtained from the chord model of the circle graph by a simple transformation, consisting in cutting the circumference of the circle at some point p which is not an endpoint of a chord [9, Sect. 11.3] and unfolding it at point p. The chord model can be reconstructed by wrapping around the circle the collection of intervals on the line.

Remark 1. Notice that, given a chord model of a circle graph, for each choice of point p in the previous transformation a different interval model is obtained, and both the density and the total chord length of the circle graph depend on the particular chord or interval model chosen, that is, on the choice of point p for the transformation between the chord model and the interval model of the circle graph.

An independent set of an undirected graph is an induced subgraph of the graph which has no edges. A maximal independent set of a graph is an independent set that is not properly included in any other independent set of the graph, and a maximum independent set of a graph is a (maximal) independent set of the graph with the largest number of vertices. A maximum independent set of a circle graph is highlighted in Fig. 1, for both the chord model and the circle graph itself.

For a weighted chord model $G = (V, E)$ of a circle graph, where there is a non-negative weight $w(e)$ associated with each chord $e \in E$, a maximum-weight independent set of G is a (maximal) independent set $I \subseteq E$ of G with the largest total chord weight.

Without loss of generality, it will be assumed that chords in a chord model of a circle graph are vertex-disjoint. As a matter of fact, as observed in [7], given a chord model $G = (V, E)$ of a circle graph, a vertex $v_i \in V$ which is adjacent with $t \geqslant 2$ chords, say $(v_i, v_j), (v_i, v_k), \ldots, (v_i, v_\ell)$, can be replaced by t consecutive (along the circumference of the circle) vertices $v_i^1, v_i^2, \ldots, v_i^t$, with chords $(v_i, v_j), (v_i, v_k), \ldots, (v_i, v_\ell)$ being replaced by chords $(v_i^1, v_j), (v_i^2, v_k), \ldots, (v_i^t, v_\ell)$. The transformation, illustrated in Fig. 2, preserves and reflects independent sets, because chords adjacent with the same vertex in the original circle graph are pairwise crossing in the result of the transformation. A connected circle graph with m chords and n vertices is thus transformed into a circle graph with m vertex-disjoint chords and at most $2m$ vertices. The same assumption was made in previous algorithms for the maximum-weight independent set problem on circle graphs [1,2,3,7,13,17,19].

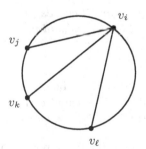 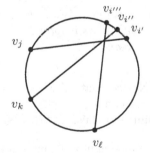

Fig. 2. Transformation of a circle graph with n chords and $2n$ vertices (left) into a circle graph with n vertex-disjoint chords and at most mn vertices (right), that preserves and reflects independent sets.

Notice that, because of the previous transformation of a chord model of a circle graph into another chord model with vertex-disjoint chords, and since a circle graph is isomorphic to the intersection graph of a finite set of chords of a circle, it follows that finding an independent set of maximum weight of a circle graph is polynomially equivalent to finding a maximum-weight planar subgraph (that is, a maximum-weight planar matching) of a general graph that is endorsed with a fixed vertex ordering along the circumference of the circle. In the rest of the paper, a chord model will be referred to as circle graph.

3   Finding a Maximum-Weight Independent Set

The problem of finding a maximum-weight independent set of a circle graph, although solvable in polynomial time, is not trivial, since there are families of circle graphs whose number of independent sets grow exponentially with the number of vertices [7]. However, the problem can be decomposed along the chords of the graph.

Definition 1. *Let $G = (V, E)$ be a circle graph. A maximum-weight independent set of G is denoted by $MIS(G)$. For all chords $(v_i, v_j) = e \in E$, a maximum-weight independent set of the subgraph of G induced by $\{v_k \in V \mid i < k < j\}$ is denoted by $MIS(e)$.*

A maximum-weight independent set of a circle graph with n chords can be found by dynamic programming in $O(n^2)$ time and space [19]. However, this involves the solution of subproblems that do not contribute to the solution of any larger problem. Unnecessary computation can be avoided by solving subproblems in nondecreasing order of chord length, because a chord can only contain shorter chords.

It will be assumed, without loss of generality, that all chords are ordered from lower to higher vertex number, that is, $i < j$ for all chords $(v_i, v_j) \in E$ in a circle graph $G = (V, E)$.

Definition 2. *Let $G = (V, E)$ be a circle graph. For all chords $(v_i, v_j) \in E$, the length of $e = (v_i, v_j)$ is $length(e) = j - i$. Chord (v_i, v_j) is said to contain chord (v_k, v_ℓ) if $i < k$ and $\ell < j$.*

Remark 2. Notice that $MIS(e) = \{e\}$ if $length(e) \leq 2$, because the shortest chord that can contain another chord has length 3. Notice also that chords are vertex-disjoint and thus, $|MIS(e)| \leq \lfloor (length(e) + 1)/2 \rfloor < length(e)$.

A maximum-weight independent set of the subgraph of a circle graph induced by those vertices that are comprised between the endpoints of a chord, can actually be found in time linear in the length of the chord.

Lemma 1. *Let $G = (V, E)$ be a circle graph, let $e \in E$, and assume $MIS(e')$ is known for all chords $e' \in E$ with $length(e') < length(e)$. Then, $MIS(e)$ can be found in $O(length(e))$ time and space.*

Proof. Let $G = (V, E)$ be a circle graph, let $e = (v_i, v_j) \in E$, and assume $MIS(e')$ is known for all chords $e' \in E$ with $length(e') < length(e)$. For all vertices $v_k \in V$ with $i < k < j$, let $T(k)$ be a maximum-weight independent set of the subgraph of G induced by $\{v_\ell \in V \mid k \leq \ell < j\}$.

Now, T is described by the following recurrence. $T(j) = \emptyset$. For all vertices v_k with $i < k < j$, $T(k) = T(k+1)$ if $outdeg(v_k) = 0$. Otherwise, let $e' = (v_k, v_\ell) \in E$ be the unique chord of G incident with vertex v_k. Then, $T(k) = T(k+1)$ if $l \geqslant j$ or, if $l < j$, $T(k)$ is the independent set of largest weight between $MIS(e') \cup T(\ell + 1)$ and $T(k+1)$.

Since $T(k)$ can be evaluated backwards for all k with $i < k < j$, it follows that $MIS(e) = \{e\} \cup T(i+1)$ can be found in $O(length(e))$ time. Further, since for all k with $i < k < j$, the set $T(k)$ need not be stored explicitly and can be represented by reference to either $MIS(e')$ and the set $T(\ell + 1)$, if there is a chord $e' = (v_k, v_\ell)$ contained in chord e, or the set $T(k+1)$ only, it follows from $|MIS(e)| < length(e)$ that $MIS(e)$ can be found using $O(length(e))$ space.   □

Lemma 2. *Let $G = (V, E)$ be a circle graph with n chords, and assume $MIS(e)$ is known for all chords $e \in E$. Then, $MIS(G)$ can be found in $O(n)$ time and space.*

Proof. For all vertices $v_i \in V$ with $1 \leqslant i \leqslant 2n$, let $T(i)$ be a maximum-weight independent set of the subgraph of G induced by $\{v_j \in V \mid i \leqslant j \leqslant 2n\}$. Now, T is described by the following recurrence. $T(2n) = \emptyset$. For all vertices v_i with $1 \leqslant i < 2n$, $T(i) = T(i+1)$ if $outdeg(v_i) = 0$. Otherwise, let $e = (v_i, v_j) \in E$ be the unique chord of G incident with vertex v_i. Then, $T(i)$ is the independent set of largest weight between $MIS(e) \cup T(j+1)$ and $T(i+1)$.

Since $T(i)$ can be evaluated backwards for all i with $1 \leqslant i \leqslant 2n$, it follows that $MIS(G) = T(1)$ can be found in $O(n)$ time. Further, since for all i with $1 \leqslant i \leqslant 2n$, the set $T(i)$ need not be stored explicitly and can be represented by reference to either $MIS(e)$ and the set $T(j+1)$ or the set $T(i+1)$ only, it follows that $MIS(G)$ can be found using $O(n)$ space.   □

Lemma 3. *Let $G = (V, E)$ be a circle graph with n chords, and let ℓ be the total chord length of G. Then, $MIS(G)$ can be found in $O(\ell)$ time and $O(n)$ space.*

Proof. The chords of G can be oriented from lower to higher-numbered vertices in $O(n)$ time using $O(1)$ space, and can be bucket sorted in nondecreasing order of chord length in $O(n)$ time using $O(n)$ space. For each chord $e \in E$ in nondecreasing order of chord length, $MIS(e)$ can be found in $O(length(e))$ time and space, by Lemma 1 and then, by Lemma 2, $MIS(G)$ can be found in $O(\ell)$ time using $O(\ell + n)$ space. Since the space used for computing $MIS(e)$ can be reused for each chord $e \in E$ and, furthermore, the n sets $MIS(e)$ themselves need not be stored explicitly and can be represented by reference to the sets they directly contain only, it follows that $MIS(G)$ can be found in $O(\ell)$ time and $O(n)$ space.
   □

Example 1. For the circle graph of Fig. 1, where $e_2 = (v_2, v_{12})$ and unit weight is assumed for all chords, $MIS(e_2)$ is computed as follows.

- $T(12) = \emptyset$

- $T(11) = T(12) = \emptyset$, because $outdeg(v_{11}) = 0$
- $T(10) = T(11) = \emptyset$, because $e_7 = (v_{10}, v_{13})$ is not contained in e_2
- $T(9) = T(10) = \emptyset$, because $outdeg(v_9) = 0$
- $T(8) = T(9) = \emptyset$, because $e_6 = (v_8, v_{14})$ is not contained in e_2
- $T(7) = T(8) = \emptyset$, because $outdeg(v_7) = 0$
- $T(6) = MIS(e_5) \cup T(12) = \{e_5\}$, because $e_5 = (v_6, v_{11})$ and $T(7) = \emptyset$
- $T(5) = T(6) = \{e_5\}$, because $outdeg(v_5) = 0$
- $T(4) = T(5) = \{e_5\}$, because $e_4 = (v_4, v_9)$ and $MIS(e_4) \cup T(10) = \{e_4\}$
- $T(3) = T(4) = \{e_5\}$, because $e_3 = (v_3, v_7)$ and $MIS(e_3) \cup T(8) = \{e_3\}$
- $T(2) = T(3) = \{e_5\}$, because $e_2 = (v_2, v_{12})$ is not contained in e_2
- $MIS(e_2) = \{e_2\} \cup T(2) = \{e_2, e_5\}$

Further, when computing $MIS(e_2)$, the shared representation of each set $T(k)$ with $2 < k < 12$ by reference to a maximum independent set (for some shorter chord) and/or to a previous set, is illustrated by the following diagram.

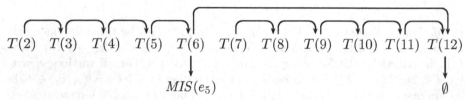

In a similar vein, the shared representation of each set $MIS(e)$ with $e \in E$, denoted herein by $I(e)$ for diagram layout reasons, by reference to zero or more previous maximum independent sets (for shorter chords) and to chord e itself, is illustrated by the following diagram, together with the shared representation of $MIS(G) = T(1)$.

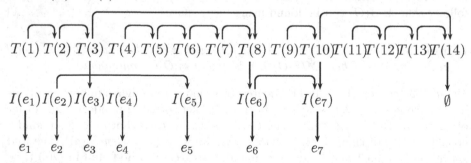

Now, a tight upper bound on the total length of the chords of a circle graph is given by the density times the number of vertices of the graph.

Theorem 1. *Let G be a circle graph with m chords and $n = 2m$ vertices, ℓ the total chord length of G, and let d be the density of G. Then, $\ell \leqslant dn$.*

Proof. For any fixed density d, the circle graph on $n = 2m = 2kd$ vertices with the largest total chord length ℓ, illustrated in Fig. 3 for $d = 4$ and $n = 24$, has $k = m/d = n/(2d)$ identical blocks, each of them with d chords of length d each. The total chord length is thus $\ell = kdd = nd$. $\square$

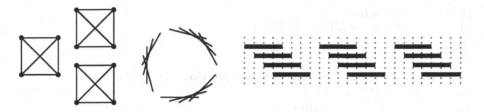

Fig. 3. The circle graph on $n = 24$ vertices with the largest total chord length $\ell = 84$, for a fixed density $d = 4$, has $n/(2d) = 3$ identical trapezoidal blocks of d identical chords each. No other circle graph of density $d = 4$ and $n = 24$ vertices can have a larger total chord length, because the chords, which must be vertex-disjoint, already fill up the space along d line segments.

Corollary 1. *Let $G = (V, E)$ be a circle graph with n chords. Then, $MIS(G)$ can be found in $O(dn)$ time and $O(n)$ space.*

Proof. Follows directly from Lemma 2 and Theorem 1.   □

3.1   Implementation Details

The procedure described in the proof of Lemmata 1–3 for computing a maximum-weight independent set in $O(\ell) = O(dn)$ time and $O(n)$ space, where ℓ is the total chord length, d is the density, and n is the number of chords of the circle graph, is put together in detailed pseudocode next. The presentation of the algorithm takes an adjacency-list representation of the circle graph as input.

Algorithm 1 *The following procedure finds a maximum-weight independent set MIS of the circle graph $G = (V, E)$, given in adjacency-list representation.*

```
 1: procedure maximum-weight independent set (V, E, MIS)
 2:    orient all edges e ∈ E from lower to higher-numbered vertices
 3:    bucket sort E in nondecreasing order of edge length
 4:    for all edges e = (vᵢ, vⱼ) ∈ E in order do
 5:        MIS[e] := {e}
 6:        if j − i ⩾ 3 then
 7:            T[j] := ∅
 8:            k := j − 1
 9:            while i < k do
10:                T[k] := T[k + 1]
11:                if outdeg(vₖ) ≠ 0 then
12:                    e′ := (vₖ, vₗ)
13:                    if ℓ < j and w(T[k]) < w(MIS[e′]) + w(T[ℓ + 1]) then
14:                        T[k] := MIS[e′] ∪ T[ℓ + 1]
15:                    end if
16:                end if
17:                k := k − 1
```

```
18:          end while
19:              MIS[e] := MIS[e] ∪ T[i + 1]
20:       end if
21:    end for
22:    for all vertices v_i ∈ V in reverse order do
23:       T[i] := ∅
24:       if outdeg(v_i) = 0 then
25:          if i < n then
26:              T[i] := T[i + 1]
27:          end if
28:       else
29:          e := (v_i, v_j)
30:          if w(MIS[e]) + w(T[j + 1]) > w(T[i]) then
31:              T[i] := MIS[e] ∪ T[j + 1]
32:          else
33:              T[i] := T[i + 1]
34:          end if
35:       end if
36:    end for
37:    MIS := T[1]
38: end procedure
```

The following choice of simple data structures allows to meet the time and space bounds stated in Corollary 1. Given a circle graph $G = (V, E)$ with n chords and $2n$ vertices, for each chord $e \in E$, $MIS(e)$ is represented by a MIS structure, consisting of a list of pointers to MIS structures, a pointer to a chord, and a weight. For each vertex $v_i \in V$, $T(i)$ is represented by a T structure, consisting of a pointer to a T structure, a pointer to a MIS structure, and a weight. Then, $MIS(G) = T(1)$ can be collected in $O(n)$ time by traversing the pointer structure.

4   Conclusions

The problem of finding a maximum-weight independent set of a circle graph is decomposed along the chords of the graph, and unnecessary computation is avoided by solving subproblems in nondecreasing order of chord length.

The algorithm presented in this paper runs in $O(\ell) = O(dn)$ time and $O(n)$ space, where ℓ is the total chord length, d is the density, and n is the number of chords of the circle graph. The best previous algorithm required $O(dn)$ time and space.

The algorithm is practical, requires only simple data structures to be implemented within the stated time and space bounds, and has small hidden constants.

References

1. A. Apostolico, M. J. Atallah, and S. E. Hambrusch. New clique and independent set algorithms for circle graphs. *Discrete Applied Mathematics*, 36(1):1–24, 1992.
2. T. Asano, T. Asano, and H. Imai. Partitioning a polygonal region into trapezoids. *Journal of the ACM*, 33(2):290–312, 1986.
3. T. Asano, H. Imai, and A. Mukaiyama. Finding a maximum weight independent set of a circle graph. *IEICE Transactions*, E74(4):681–683, 1991.
4. A. Bouchet. Reducing prime graphs and recognizing circle graphs. *Combinatorica*, 7(3):243–254, 1987.
5. J. Cong and C. L. Liu. Over-the-cell channel routing. *IEEE Transactions on Computer-Aided Design*, 9(4):408–418, 1990.
6. C. P. Gabor, K. J. Supowit, and W.-L. Hsu. Recognizing circle graphs in polynomial time. *Journal of the ACM*, 36(3):435–473, 1989.
7. F. Gavril. Algorithms for a maximum clique and a maximum independent set of a circle graph. *Networks*, 3(3):261–273, 1973.
8. O. Goldschmidt and A. Takvorian. An efficient algorithm for finding a maximum weight independent set of a circle graph. *IEICE Transactions*, E77-A(10):1672–1674, 1994.
9. M. C. Golumbic. *Algorithmic Graph Theory and Perfect Graphs*. Academic Press, New York, 1980.
10. H. Kim. An application algorithm for the via minimization problem in channel routing. In *Proc. 1990 Symp. on Applied Computing*, pages 150–154. IEEE, 1990.
11. H. Kim. Finding a maximum independent set in a permutation graph. *Information Processing Letters*, 36(1):19–23, 1990.
12. D. T. Lee and M. Sarrafzadeh. Maximum independent set of a permutation graph in k tracks. *International Journal of Computational Geometry and Applications*, 3(3):291–304, 1993.
13. R. Liu and S. C. Ntafos. On decomposing polygons into uniformly monotone parts. *Information Processing Letters*, 27(2):85–88, 1988.
14. E. Mäkinen. On the longest subsequence problem for permutations. *International Journal of Computer Mathematics*, 77(1):45–53, 2001.
15. F. Malucelli, T. Ottmann, and D. Pretolani. Efficient labelling algorithms for the maximum noncrossing matching problem. *Discrete Applied Mathematics*, 47(2):175–179, 1993.
16. W. Naji. Reconnaissance des graphes de cordes. *Discrete Mathematics*, 54(3):329–337, 1985.
17. R. C. Read, D. Rotem, and J. Urrutia. Orientations of circle graphs. *Journal of Graph Theory*, 6(3):325–341, 1982.
18. J. Spinrad. Recognition of circle graphs. *Journal of Algorithms*, 16(2):264–282, 1994.
19. K. J. Supowit. Finding a maximum planar subset of a set of nets in a channel. *IEEE Transactions on Computer-Aided Design*, 6(1):93–94, 1987.
20. P. Widmayer and C. K. Wong. An optimal algorithm for the maximum alignment of terminals. *Information Processing Letters*, 20(2):75–82, 1985.
21. M.-S. Yu, L. Y. Tseng, and S.-J. Chang. Sequential and parallel algorithms for the maximum-weight independent set problem on permutation graphs. *Information Processing Letters*, 46(1):7–11, 1993.

Polynomial Time 2-Approximation Algorithms for the Minmax Subtree Cover Problem

Hiroshi Nagamochi[1] and Kohei Okada[2]

[1] Toyohashi University of Technology,
Tempaku-cho, Toyohashi 441-8580, Japan.
naga@ics.tut.ac.jp
[2] Matsushita Electric Industrial Co., Ltd.,
Kadoma 1006, Osaka 571-8501, Japan.

Abstract. Let T be a tree such that edges are weighted by nonnegative reals, and p be a positive integer. The minmax subtree cover problem asks to find a set of p subtrees such that the union of the subtrees covers all vertices in T, where the objective is to minimize the maximum weight of the subtrees. Given a root r in T, the minmax rooted-subtree cover problem asks to find a set of p subtrees such that each subtree contains the root r and the union of the subtrees covers all vertices in T, where the objective is to minimize the maximum weight of the subtrees. In this paper, we propose an $O(p^2 n)$ time $(2 - \frac{2}{p+1})$-approximation algorithm to the first problem, and an $O(n \log \log_{1+\frac{\varepsilon}{2}} 3)$ time $(2 + \varepsilon)$-approximation algorithm to the second problem, where $\varepsilon > 0$ is a prescribed constant.

1 Introduction

Given a graph, the p–traveling salesmen problem (p–TSP) asks to find a set of p tours that cover all vertices in the graph, minimizing a given objective function. This type of problems arises in many applications such as the multi-vehicle scheduling problem [5]. Graphs are restricted as paths or trees in some applications such as the task sequencing problem [4], the delivery scheduling by ships on a shoreline [10] and the scheduling of automated guided vehicles. Thus the 1–TSP or p–TSP on these graphs and related problems have been studied extensively (e.g., [1,6,7,10]).

Among those problems, the following two problems are fundamental ones. Let $T = (V, E)$ be a tree such that each edge is weighted by nonnegative real. For a given integer $p \geq 2$ and a subset S of vertices in T such that each vertex $v \in S$ has a nonnegative weight. The *minmax subtree cover problem* (MSC for short) asks to find a set of p subtrees such that the union of the subtrees covers all vertices in S, where the objective is to minimize the maximum weight of the subtrees, where the weight of a subtree T' is the sum of the weights of edges in T' and the weights of vertices in S that are covered by T' (we regard that each vertex in S is covered by exactly one of the subtrees). Similarly, given a root r in T, the *minmax rooted-subtree cover problem* (MRSC for short) asks to find a set of p subtrees such that each subtree contains r and the union of the subtrees

T. Ibaraki, N. Katoh, and H. Ono (Eds.): ISAAC 2003, LNCS 2906, pp. 138–147, 2003.

covers all vertices in S, where the objective is to minimize the maximum weight of the subtrees. These two problems are NP-hard even for $p = 2$. For the MSC such that $S = V$ and $h(v) = 0$, $u \in V$, Averbakh and Berman [3] presented a $(2 - \frac{2}{p+1})$–approximation algorithm that runs in $O(p^{p-1}n^{p-1})$ time, where $n = |V|$. Afterwards, Nagamochi and Okada [8] considered the MSC with a general subset S of V, and gave a $(2 - \frac{2}{p+1})$–approximation algorithm that runs in $O((p-1)!n)$ time, which is linear for a fixed p, but remains to be exponential in p. It is known by Averbakh and Berman [2] that MRSC with $p = 2$ admits a linear time $\frac{4}{3}$-approximation algorithm. However, no polynomial approximation algorithms have been obtained for the MSC with $p \geq 2$ and the MRSC with $p \geq 3$.

In this paper, we propose an $O(p^2 n)$ time $(2 - \frac{2}{p+1})$–approximation algorithm to the MSC with $S = V$ and $p \geq 2$, and an $O(n \log \log_{1 + \frac{\varepsilon}{2}} 3)$ time $(2 + \varepsilon)$-approximation algorithm to the MRSC with $p \geq 2$. Both are the first polynomial time approximation algorithms to these minimax subtree cover problems.

The paper is organized as follows. In Section 1, we introduce some terminology to give the problem formulations of MSC and MRSC. In Section 2, we review some results on MSC, based on which a $(2 - \frac{2}{p+1})$-approximation algorithm is given. In Section 3, we first derive some upper and lower bounds on the optimal value to the MRSC, and then design a $(2 + \varepsilon)$-approximation algorithm to the MRSC.

2   Preliminaries

For a set A and an element $a \notin A$, we may denote set $A \cup \{a\}$ by $A + a$. Let T be a tree, where the vertex set and the edge set of a tree T are denoted by $V(T)$ and $E(T)$, respectively. Let $n = |V(T)|$. A vertex with degree 1 is called a *leaf* in a tree T, where the root with degree 1 in a rooted tree is not called a leaf. The set of leaves in a tree T is denoted by $L(T)$. A connected subgraph T' of T is called a *subtree* of T, and we denote this by $T' \subseteq T$. For a subset $X \subseteq V(T)$ of vertices, let $T\langle X \rangle$ denote the minimal subtree of T that contains X (where the leaves of $T\langle X \rangle$ will be vertices in X). In this paper, we say that $T\langle X \rangle$ is *induced* from T by X.

Let (T, w) denote a tree T such that each edge e is weighted by a nonnegative real $w(e)$. For two vertices u and v, the sum of weights in the path between u and v in T is denoted by $w(u, v)$. The tree may be denoted by (T, w, r) if a root $r \in V(T)$ is specified. The sum of edge weights in a subtree T' is denoted by $w(T')$.

Let S be a specified subset of $V(T)$ such that each vertex $v \in S$ has a nonnegative weight $h(v)$, where we may denote $h(u) = 0$ for a vertex $u \in V(T) - S$.

A collection $\mathcal{S}$ of subsets $S_1, S_2, \ldots, S_k$ of S is called a *partition* of S if their union is S, where some S_i may be empty. A collection $\mathcal{S}$ of S is called a *p-partition* of S if $|\mathcal{S}| = p$. We denote $\sum_{v \in S_i} h(v)$ by $h(S_i)$. Then the MSC is described as follows.

Minmax Subtrees Cover Problem:
   Input: An instance $I = (T, w, S, h, p)$ which consists of an edge-weighted tree (T, w), a weighted subset (S, h) and an integer $p \in [2, n]$.
   Feasible solution: A p-partition $S = \{S_1, S_2, \ldots, S_p\}$ of S.
   Goal: Minimize the cost $cost_I(S)$ of a partition S in I, where $cost_I(S) := \max_{S_i \in S}\{w(T\langle S_i \rangle) + h(S_i)\}$.

Similarly the MRSC can be described as follows.

Minmax Rooted-Subtrees Cover Problem:
   Input: An instance $I = (T, w, r, S, h, p)$ which consists of a rooted edge-weighted tree (T, w, r), a weighted subset (S, h) and an integer $p \in [2, n]$.
   Feasible solution: A p-partition $S = \{S_1, S_2, \ldots, S_p\}$ of S.
   Goal: Minimize the cost $cost_I(S)$ of a partition S in I, where $cost_I(S) := \max_{S_i \in S}\{w(T\langle S_i + r \rangle) + h(S_i)\}$.

3   Algorithm for MSC

In this section, we give an approximation algorithm to the MSC with $S = V(T)$. For an instance $I = (T, w, S, h, p)$ to the MSC, we denote the optimal value by $opt(I)$, and we say that a partition S of S *induces* edge-disjoint (resp., vertex-disjoint) subtrees if for any two $S_i, S_j \in S$, subtrees $T\langle S_i \rangle$ and $T\langle S_j \rangle$ are edge-disjoint (resp., vertex-disjoint). The following result has been shown by Nagamochi and Okada [8] based on the earlier work by Averbakh and Berman [3].

Lemma 1. [8] *For an edge-weighted tree (T, w), a weighted subset (S, h) and an integer $p \in [2, n]$, there exists a p-partition S of S with*

$$cost(S) \leq \max\left\{ \left(2 - \frac{2}{p+1}\right) \cdot \frac{w(T)}{p}, \ \max_{u \in S} h(u) \right\}$$

that induces edge-disjoint subtrees. Such an S can be obtained in $O(n)$ time.   □

   Interestingly if subtrees $T\langle S_i \rangle$, $S_i \in S$ are required to be vertex-disjoint in the MSC, then there is a polynomial time algorithm.

Theorem 1. [9] *Let (T, w, h) be a tree in which each edge e is weighted by a nonnegative real $w(e)$ and each vertex v is weighted by a nonnegative real $h(v)$. For a given integer $p \geq 2$, a set F of $(p-1)$ edges such that the maximum weight of subtrees in $(V(T), E(T) - F)$ is minimized can be found in $O(n + \rho p(p + \log \Delta))$ time, where ρ and Δ denote the radius and the maximum degree of tree T.*   □

   Unfortunately the worst ratio of $opt(I)$ to $cost_I(S)$ of a p-partition S of S that induces vertex-disjoint subtrees can be as large as $\frac{n}{p} - 1$. Consider an instance $I = (T, w, S, h, p)$ with a star T with $k \cdot p$ leaves and $w(e) = 0$, $e \in E(T)$ and $S = V(T)$ such that $h(s) = 0$ for the center s and $h(v) = 1$, $v \in V(T) - \{s\}$. Obviously

$opt(I) = k$ holds, but $cost_I(\mathcal{S}) \geq kp - (p-1)$ holds for any p-partition $\mathcal{S}$ that induces vertex-disjoint subtrees. Thus we cannot expect a good approximation just by applying the result in Theorem 1 to a given instance I.

In what follows, we consider the case where $S = V(T)$ in the MSC. In this case, we show that a given instance I can be modified so as to construct a 2-approximate solution by making use of Theorem 1. We convert a given instance $I = (T, w, S = V(T), h, p)$ into another instance $\tilde{I} = (\tilde{T}, w, V(\tilde{T}), h, p)$ of the MSC by the following procedure.

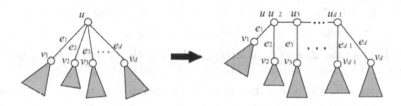

Fig. 1. Splitting a vertex u into vertices of degree 3.

LOWER_DEGREE

Step 1. For each non-leaf $v \in V(T) - L(T)$, we rename v by v', set $h(v') := 0$, and add a new vertex, called v, introducing a new edge $e_v = (v', v)$ with $w(e_v) = 0$, where we let the new v, which is a leaf, have the same weight $h(v)$ as before.

Step 2. For each vertex u with degree $d \geq 4$, execute the following procedure.

Let $e_1, e_2, \ldots, e_d$ be the edges incident to u. Split u into $d - 2$ vertices $u = u_2, u_3, \ldots, u_{d-1}$ introducing new vertices $u_3, u_4, \ldots, u_{d-1}$. Replace the end vertex u of each e_i, $i = 2, 3, \ldots, d - 1$ (resp., of e_1 and e_d) with u_i (resp., with u_2 and u_{d-1}). Join the split vertices $u_2, u_3, \ldots, u_{d-1}$ by $d - 3$ new edges $(u_2, u_3), \ldots, (u_{d-1}, u_d)$ (see Fig. 1). Let the weights of all introduced vertices edges to be zero while the edges $e_1, e_2, \ldots, e_d$ have the same weights as before. □

Let $\tilde{I} = (\tilde{T}, w, V(\tilde{T}), h, p)$ be the resulting instance, in which every vertex has degree at most three. Then it is not difficult to verify that the next two lemmas hold.

Lemma 2. *Let* $I = (T, w, V(T), h, p)$ *be an instance of the MSC, and* $\tilde{I} = (\tilde{T}, w, V(\tilde{T}), h, p)$ *be the instance of the MSC obtained from* I *by* LOWER_DEGREE. *Then* $opt(\tilde{I}) \leq opt(I)$. □

Lemma 3. *Let* $\tilde{I} = (\tilde{T}, w, V(\tilde{T}), h, p)$ *be an instance of the MSC on a tree* $\tilde{T}$ *in which every vertex is of degree* ≤ 3 *and every internal vertex* u *satisfies* $h(u) = 0$. *For a* p-partition $\tilde{S}$ *of* $V(\tilde{T})$ *that induces edge-disjoint subtrees in* $\tilde{I}$. *Then there is a* p-partition $\mathcal{S}^*$ *of* $V(\tilde{T})$ *with* $cost_{\tilde{I}}(\mathcal{S}^*) \leq cost_{\tilde{I}}(\tilde{S})$ *that induces vertex-disjoint subtrees in* $\tilde{I}$. □

Based on the above properties, we obtain the following algorithm to the MSC with $S = V(T)$.

Algorithm APPROX_1

Step 1. Convert a given instance $I = (T, w, V(T), h, p)$ of the MSC into an instance $\tilde{I} = (\tilde{T}, w, V(\tilde{T}), h, p)$ by procedure LOWER_DEGREE.

Step 2. By Theorem 1, find an optimal p-partition $\mathcal{S}^*$ of $V(\tilde{T})$ that induces vertex-disjoint subtrees in $\tilde{I}$.

Step 3. Output a p-partition $\mathcal{S} = \{S_i = S_i^* \cap V(T) \mid i = 1, \ldots, p\}$ of $V(T)$. □

Theorem 2. *For a given instance* $I = (T, w, V(T), h, p)$ *of the MSC, a p-partition $\mathcal{S}$ of $V(T)$ with $cost_I(\mathcal{S}) \leq (2 - \frac{2}{p+1})opt(I)$ that induces edge-disjoint subtrees can be obtained by APPROX_1 in $O(p^2 n)$ time.*

Proof. By Lemma 2, $opt(\tilde{I}) \leq opt(I)$ holds for the instance $\tilde{I}$ in Step 1. By Lemma 3, there exists a p-partition $\tilde{\mathcal{S}}$ of $V(\tilde{T})$ with $cost_{\tilde{I}}(\tilde{\mathcal{S}}) \leq (2 - \frac{2}{p+1})opt(\tilde{I})$ that induces edge-disjoint subtrees in $\tilde{I}$. By Lemma 3, $cost_{\tilde{I}}(\mathcal{S}^*) \leq cost_{\tilde{I}}(\tilde{\mathcal{S}})$ holds. Then by the construction of $\tilde{I}$, the p-partition $\mathcal{S}$ in Step 3 satisfies $cost_I(\mathcal{S}) \leq cost_{\tilde{I}}(\mathcal{S}^*)$. Also, $\mathcal{S}$ induces edge-disjoint subtrees since no edges in T are shared by the subtrees induced by $\mathcal{S}^*$. Hence $cost_I(\mathcal{S}) \leq (2 - \frac{2}{p+1})opt(I)$ holds. It is a simple matter to see that by Theorem 1, APPROX_1 can be implemented to run in $O(p^2 n)$ time. □

4   Algorithm for MRSC

In this section, we design an approximation algorithm to the MRSC. We first observe that the following condition can be assumed to an instance $I = (T, w, S, h, r, p)$ of the MRSC.

$$S = L(T) \text{ and } h(u) = 0 \text{ for all } u \in S. \tag{1}$$

To see this, we convert an instance $I = (T, w, S, h, r, p)$ into the following instance $I' = (T', w, S' = L(T'), h', r, p)$. We first create a new leaf v_u for each vertex $u \in S$ so that v_u is adjacent to u via a new edge e_u with weight $w(e_u) = h(u)$, and redefine the entire tree T' by $T\langle\{v_u \mid u \in S\}\rangle$, which discards the parts of T that are not necessarily covered. This can be done in $O(n)$ time. It is easy to see that an optimal solution $\mathcal{S}$ to I' is also optimal to I. Therefore, it suffices to consider the case where (1) holds in an instance I. In what follows, an instance I to the MRSC is denoted by $I = (T, w, r, p)$, and the optimal value to an instance $I = (T, w, r, p)$ is denoted by $opt(I)$ or $opt(T, w, r, p)$.

In a rooted tree T, let $Ch(v)$ denote the set of children of a vertex v. For a vertex u, let $d(u)$ denote the distance of u from r, i.e., $d(u) = w(r, u)$. For a subset $X \subseteq V(T)$, let $lca(X) \in V(T)$ denote the least common ancestor of all vertices in X, and $D(X)$ denote the set of all descendants of the vertices in X (including those in X). A *subtree rooted at* a vertex v is defined by a subtree $T\langle D(C') + v\rangle$ for some subset $C' \subseteq Ch(v)$.

For an instance $I = (T, w, r, p)$ of the MRSC, we easily see the following lower bound on $opt(I)$.

Lemma 4. $LB := \max\{\frac{w(T)}{p}, \max_{u \in L(T)} d(u)\} \leq opt(I)$. $\qquad\qquad\qquad\square$

By this and Lemma 1, we obtain a simple 3-approximation algorithm. The upper bound on the solution will be used to analyze the run time of a better 2-approximation algorithm.

Theorem 3. *For an instance* $I = (T, w, r, p)$ *of the MRSC, a p-partition* $\mathcal{S}$ *of* $L(T)$ *with* $cost_I(\mathcal{S}) \leq (3 - \frac{2}{p+1})LB$ *can be constructed in* $O(n)$ *time.*

Proof. From I, we construct an instance $I' = (T, w, S = L(T), h = 0, p)$ of the MSC. By Lemma 1, a p-partition $\mathcal{S}$ of $S = L(T)$ with $cost_{I'}(\mathcal{S}) \leq (2 - \frac{2}{p+1}) \cdot \frac{w(T)}{p}$ can be found in $O(n)$ time. For each $S_i \in \mathcal{S}$, let $r_i \in S_i$ be the vertex closest to r. Then $cost_I(\mathcal{S}) = \max_{1 \leq i \leq p}\{w(T\langle S_i \rangle + d(r_i))\} \leq cost_{I'}(\mathcal{S}) + \max_{u \in L(T)} d(u)$ $\leq (2 - \frac{2}{p+1}) \cdot \frac{w(T)}{p} + \max_{u \in L(T)} d(u) \leq (3 - \frac{2}{p+1})LB$. $\qquad\square$

To obtain a better performance guarantee, we consider a reverse problem of the MRSC. For an edge-weighted rooted tree (T, w, r) and a real $x > 0$, we try to estimate the least integer p such that $opt(T, w, r, p) \leq x$, which we denote by $p(T, w, r, x)$. Then we derive a lower bound on $p(T, w, r, x)$ based on a partition of a subset of the set $L(T)$ of leaves, which we call a *subpartition* of $L(T)$. A subpartition $\mathcal{L}' = \{L'_1, L'_2, \dots, L'_k\}$ of the set $L(T)$ of leaves is called *independent* if for any two L'_i and L'_j, the path between any leaf $u \in L'_i$ and r contains no edge in $T\langle L'_j + lca(L'_j)\rangle$ (i.e., $T\langle L'_i + r\rangle$ and $T\langle L'_j + lca(L'_j)\rangle$ are edge-disjoint).

Lemma 5. *Let* $\mathcal{L}' = \{L'_1, L'_2, \dots, L'_k\}$ *be an independent subpartition of the set* $L(T)$ *of leaves in an edge-weighted rooted tree* (T, w, r). *For each* L'_j, *let* $r'_j = lca(L'_j)$ *and* $d'_j = d(r'_j)$. *For any real* $x > \max_{1 \leq j \leq k} d'_j$, *it holds*

$$\sum_{1 \leq j \leq k} \frac{w(T\langle L'_j + r'_j\rangle)}{x - d'_j} \leq p(T, w, r, x).$$

Proof. Let $p = p(T, w, r, x)$, and consider a p-partition $L^*_1, L^*_2, \dots, L^*_p$ of $L(T)$ such that $\max_{1 \leq i \leq p} w(T\langle L^*_i + r\rangle) \leq x$. Let $w_i = w(T\langle L^*_i + r\rangle) (\leq x)$. It suffices to show that $x \sum_{1 \leq j \leq k} \frac{w(T\langle L'_j + r'_j\rangle)}{x - d'_j} \leq \sum_{1 \leq i \leq p} w_i (\leq px)$, which implies the lemma.

Let $E_{i,j} = E(T\langle L^*_i + r\rangle) \cap E(T\langle L'_j + r'_j\rangle)$, and $w_{i,j}$ be the sum of weights in $E_{i,j}$, where $w_{i,j} = 0$ if $E_{i,j} = \emptyset$. Since all edges in each $T\langle L'_j + r'_j\rangle$ are covered by the subtrees $T\langle L^*_i + r\rangle$, $i = 1, 2, \dots, p$, it holds

$$\sum_{1 \leq i \leq p} w_{i,j} \geq w(T\langle L'_j + r'_j\rangle), \quad 1 \leq j \leq k. \qquad (2)$$

For each L^*_i, let $J_i = \{j \mid E_{i,j} \neq \emptyset\}$ and $d^*_i = \max\{d'_j \mid j \in J_i\}$. By the independentness of $\mathcal{L}'$, we see that

$$w_i \geq d^*_i + \sum_{j \in J_i} w_{i,j}, \quad 1 \leq i \leq p.$$

From this and $w_i \leq x$, it holds

$$w_i \geq \frac{x(w_i - d_i^*)}{x - d_i^*} \geq \frac{x}{x - d_i^*} \sum_{j \in J_i} w_{i,j} \geq x \sum_{j \in J_i} \frac{w_{i,j}}{x - d_j'}.$$

Hence by (2) we have

$$\sum_{1 \leq i \leq p} w_i \geq x \sum_{1 \leq i \leq p} \sum_{j \in J_i} \frac{w_{i,j}}{x - d_j'} = x \sum_{1 \leq j \leq k} \frac{\sum_{1 \leq i \leq p} w_{i,j}}{x - d_j'} \geq x \sum_{1 \leq j \leq k} \frac{w(T\langle L_j' + r_j'\rangle)}{x - d_j'},$$

as required.   □

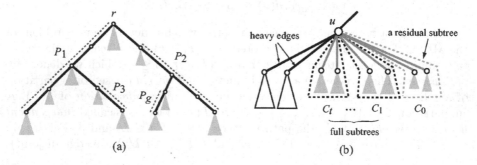

Fig. 2. Heavy edges in in a rooted tree T. (a) Thick lines show heavy edges. (b) A partition of the set of light children of a vertex u.

We consider the following two operations that modify an edge-weighted tree T rooted at r into another edge-weighted tree T' rooted at r. Let T_1 be a subtree of T rooted at a vertex r_1 (i.e., $T_1 = T\langle D(C')+r_1\rangle$ for some subset $C' \subseteq Ch(r_1)$). For an ancestor u of r_1 in T, we say that T_1 is *lifted up* to u if we detach T_1 at r_1 and then attach the T_1 at u, where the weight of each edge in the tree remains unchanged. Let v be a leaf in T, and $e = (u, v)$ be the edge incident to it. For a real $w \in (0, w(e))$, we say that e is *split* by the amount w if we reduce the weight of e to $w'(e) = w(e) - w$ and add a new leaf v' incident to u via a new edge $e' = (u, v')$ of weight $w'(e') = w$ while other edges have the same weights as before. Then we easily see the following property.

Lemma 6. *For an edge-weighted rooted tree (T, w, r), let (T', w, r) be an edge-weighted rooted tree obtained from T by applying a lifting or splitting operation. Then $opt(T', w', r, p) \leq opt(T, w, r, p)$ holds for any integer $p \geq 1$, and $p(T', w', r, x) \leq p(T, w, r, x)$ holds for any real $x > 0$.*   □

For a given real $x > 0$ and an edge-weighted rooted tree (T, w, r), a vertex v is called *heavy* if $w(T\langle D(\{v\})\rangle) + d(v) \geq x$ holds, or *light* otherwise. An edge $e = (u, v)$ with $v \in Ch(u)$ is called *heavy* if v is heavy. Then the set of heavy edges induces from T a subtree containing r, which we call the *heavy tree* and denote by T^* (see Fig. 2(a)).

The following algorithm converts a given tree (T, w, r) into another tree (T', w', r) by applying lifting and splitting operations, during which a partition $\mathcal{L}$ of the set $L(T)$ of leaves in T and an independent subpartition $\mathcal{L}'$ of the set $L(T')$ of leaves in T' are constructed.

Algorithm APPROX_2

Step 1. Let $\mathcal{L} := \mathcal{L}' := \emptyset$. For each heavy vertex u, we partition the set of light children of u into $C_0, C_1, C_2, \ldots, C_t$ such that

$$x - d(u) \le w(T\langle D(C_i) + u\rangle) \le 2(x - d(u)), \quad i = 1, 2, \ldots, t$$

and

$$w(T\langle D(C_0) + u\rangle) < x - d(u),$$

where we can find such a partition $C_0, C_1, \ldots, C_t$ since each light children $v \in Ch(u)$ satisfies $w(T\langle D(\{v\}) + u\rangle) < x - d(u)$. Call the subtree $T\langle D(C_i) + u\rangle$ *full*, and the subtree $T\langle D(C_0) + u\rangle$ with $C_0 \ne \emptyset$ *residual* (see Fig. 2(b)).

Step 2. Consider the heavy tree T^*. Let $g = |L(T^*)|$. We remove $g - 1$ edges from T^* so that the resulting forest consists of g paths $P_1, P_2, \ldots, P_g$ such that each P_i connects a leaf of T^* and an ancestor of the leaf (see Fig. 2(a)).

For each path P_i, we execute the following Steps 2a-2c.

Step 2a. We consider the residual subtrees $ST_1, ST_2, \ldots, ST_q$ incident to P_i, where the root of ST_i is denoted by r_i and r_i is an ancestor of r_{i+1}. We partition the set of these subtrees into $\mathcal{T}_1 = \{ST_1 = ST_{i_1}, ST_2, \ldots, ST_{i_2-1}\}$, $\mathcal{T}_2 = \{ST_{i_2}, \ldots, ST_{i_3-1}\}$, $\ldots$, $\mathcal{T}_j = \{ST_{i_j}, \ldots, ST_{i_{j+1}-1}\}$, $\ldots$, $\mathcal{T}_k = \{ST_{i_k}, \ldots, ST_q\}$ such that

$$x - d(r_{i_j}) \le w(\mathcal{T}_j) \le x - d(r_{i_j}) + x - d(r_{i_{j+1}-1}), \quad 1 \le j \le k - 1,$$

and

$$w(\mathcal{T}_k) \le x - d(r_{i_k}) + x - d(r_q),$$

where $w(\mathcal{T}_j)$ denotes $\sum_{ST_i \in \mathcal{T}_j} w(ST_i)$. See Fig. 3(a). (We can find such a partition $\mathcal{T}_1, \ldots, \mathcal{T}_k$ since $w(ST_j) < x - d(r_{i_j})$ holds for all j.) For $j = 1, 2, \ldots, k$, let L_j be the set of all leaves in the subtrees in $\mathcal{T}_j$.

Step 2b. For each $\mathcal{T}_j$, $j = 1, 2, \ldots, k-1$, we lift up subtrees in $\mathcal{T}_j$ at the vertex r_{i_j} and let $\mathcal{L} := \mathcal{L} \cup \{L_j\}$ and $\mathcal{L}' := \mathcal{L}' \cup \{L_j\}$. If $x - d(r_{i_k}) \le w(\mathcal{T}_k)$, then we also lift up subtrees in $\mathcal{T}_k$ to the vertex r_{i_k}, letting $\mathcal{L} := \mathcal{L} \cup \{L_k\}$ and $\mathcal{L}' := \mathcal{L}' \cup \{L_k\}$. Otherwise (if $w(\mathcal{T}_k) < x - d(r_{i_k})$) execute the next step for treating $\mathcal{T}_k$.

Step 2c. Let z be the end vertex of P_i that is a leaf of T^*, where possibly $z = r_q$ (see Fig. 3(b)). Since the edge between z and its parent is heavy, there is a full subtree T_0 rooted at z such that $x - d(z) \le w(T_0) < 2(x - d(z))$. Let L_0 be the set of leaves in the subtree in T_0.

Case-1: $w(T_0) + w(\mathcal{T}_k) < x - d(r_{i_k})$. Let $\mathcal{L} := \mathcal{L} \cup \{L_k \cup L_0\}$ and $\mathcal{L}' := \mathcal{L}' \cup \{L_0\}$.

Case-2: $x - d(r_{i_k}) \le w(T_0) + w(\mathcal{T}_k) < 2x - d(z) - d(r_{i_k})$. We lift up subtrees in $\mathcal{T}_k \cup \{T_0\}$ to the vertex r_{i_k}. Let $\mathcal{L} := \mathcal{L} \cup \{L_0 \cup L_k\}$ and $\mathcal{L}' := \mathcal{L}' \cup \{L_0 \cup L_k\}$.

Case-3: $w(T_0) + w(\mathcal{T}_k) \ge 2x - d(z) - d(r_{i_k})$. Let $\mathcal{L} := \mathcal{L} \cup \{L_0, L_k\}$. By applying lifting and splitting operations, we convert T_0 into two subtrees T_0' and T_0'' rooted at z such that $w(T_0') = x - d(z)$ and $w(T_0'') = w(T_0) - x + d(z)$. Then we lift up all subtrees in $\mathcal{T}_k \cup \{T_0''\}$ to r_{i_k}. For the set L_0' of leaves in T_0' and the set L_k' of leaves in the subtrees in $\mathcal{T}_k \cup \{T_0''\}$, let $\mathcal{L}' := \mathcal{L}' \cup \{L_0', L_k'\}$.

Step 3. For each of remaining full subtrees ST that are not processed in Step 2c, let L be the set of leaves in ST, and $\mathcal{L} := \mathcal{L} \cup \{L\}$ and $\mathcal{L}' := \mathcal{L}' \cup \{L\}$.   □

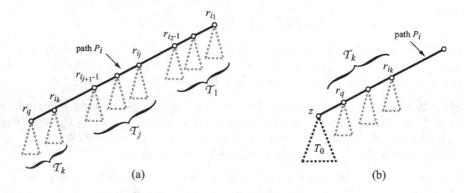

Fig. 3. Illustration for residual subtrees on a path P_i.

It is not difficult see that the above algorithm APPROX_2 can be implemented to run in linear time.

Lemma 7. *For a given tree (T, w, r) with a set $L(T)$ of leaves and a real $x > \max\{d(u) \mid u \in L(T)\}$, let (T', w', r), $\mathcal{L}$ and $\mathcal{L}'$ be respectively a tree, a partition of $L(T)$ and a subpartition of $L(T')$ obtained from (T, w, r) and x by APPROX_2. Then*
(i) *For each $L \in \mathcal{L}$, $w(T\langle L + r\rangle) \le 2x$.*
(ii) *For each $L' \in \mathcal{L}'$, $w'(T'\langle L' + lca(L')\rangle) \ge x - d'(lca(L'))$, where $d'(u)$ denotes the distance of a vertex u from r in (T', w', r).*
(iii) *$|\mathcal{L}| \le p(T, w, r, x)$.*

Proof. (i),(ii) Immediate from the algorithm. (iii) Obviously $|\mathcal{L}| = |\mathcal{L}'|$ and $\mathcal{L}'$ is an independent subpartition of $L(T')$. By the property (ii) and Lemma 5, we have $|\mathcal{L}'| \le \sum_{L' \in \mathcal{L}'} \frac{w'(T'\langle L' + lca(L')\rangle)}{x - d'(lca(L'))} \le p(T', w', r, x)$. Since (T', w', r) is obtained from (T, w, r) by lifting and/or splitting operations, it holds $p(T', w', r, x) \le p(T, w, r, x)$ by Lemma 6. This proves $|\mathcal{L}| \le p(T, w, r, x)$.   □

We are now ready to prove that the MRSC is nearly 2-approximable.

Theorem 4. *For a given instance $I = (T, w, r, p)$ of the MRSC and a specified $\varepsilon > 0$, a p-partition $\mathcal{L}$ of $L(T)$ such that $cost_I(\mathcal{L}) \leq (2 + \varepsilon)opt(I)$ can be found in $O(n \log \log_{1+\frac{\varepsilon}{2}} 3)$ time.*

Proof. Let $LB = \max\{\max_{u \in L(T)} d(u), \frac{w(T)}{p}\}$. Then $LB \leq opt(I) \leq 3LB$ holds by Lemma 4 and Theorem 3. For a specified $\varepsilon > 0$, we find two reals $x_1, x_2 \in [LB, 3LB]$ with $x_1 < x_2 \leq (1 + \frac{\varepsilon}{2})x_1$ such that the partitions $\mathcal{L}_1$ and $\mathcal{L}_2$ of $L(T)$ computed by APPROX_2 for x_1 and x_2, respectively satisfy $|\mathcal{L}_2| \leq p < |\mathcal{L}_1|$. Such x_1 and x_2 can be found by conducting to a binary search over the range $[LB, UB]$, during which APPROX_2 is invoked $O(\log t)$ times for the integer $t = \lceil \log_{1+\frac{\varepsilon}{2}} 3 \rceil$. By Lemma 7(iii), $p < |\mathcal{L}_1| \leq p(T, w, r, x_1)$ holds, indicating that $opt(I) > x_1$. On the other hand, by $|\mathcal{L}_2| \leq p$ and Lemma 7(i), we obtain a p-partition $\mathcal{L}$ of $L(T)$ such that $cost_I(\mathcal{L}) \leq 2x_2 < 2(1 + \frac{\varepsilon}{2})x_1 < (2 + \varepsilon)opt(I)$. $\square$

References

1. I. Averbakh and O. Berman, Sales-delivery man problems on treelike networks, Networks, 25 (1995), 45–58.
2. I. Averbakh and O. Berman, A heuristic with worst-case analysis for minmax routing of two traveling salesmen on a tree, Discrete Applied Mathematics, 68 (1996), 17–32.
3. I. Averbakh and O. Berman, $(p-1)/(p+1)$–approximate algorithm for p–traveling salesmen problems on a tree with minmax objective, Discrete Applied Mathematics, 75 (1997), 201–216.
4. J. Bruno and P. Downey, Complexity of task sequencing with deadlines, set-up times and changeover costs, SIAM J. Computing, 7 (1978), 393–581.
5. J. Desrosiers, Y. Dumas, M. M. Solomon and F. Soumis, Time constrained routing and scheduling, In M. O. Ball, T. L. Magnanti. C. L. Monma and G. L. Nemhauser (eds.): Handbooks in Operations Research and Management Science Volume 8: Network Routing, North-Holland, 1995, 35–139.
6. Y. Karuno and H. Nagamochi, 2-approximation algorithms for the multi-vehicle scheduling on a path with release and handling times, Discrete Applied Mathematics, 129, (2003), 433–447.
7. Y. Karuno and H. Nagamochi, A polynomial time approximation scheme for the multi-vehicle scheduling on a path with release and handling times, in: Proc. ISAAC'01, Lecture Notes in Computer Science, Vol. 2223 (Springer, Berlin, 2001) 36–47.
8. H. Nagamochi and K. Okada, A faster 2-approximation algorithm for the minmax p–traveling salesmen problem on a tree Discrete Applied Mathematics (to appear).
9. Y. Perl and U. Vishkin, Efficient implementation of a shifting algorithm, technique for the partitioning, Discrete Applied Mathematics, 12 (1985), 71–80.
10. H. Psaraftis, M. Solomon, T. Magnanti and T. Kim, Routing and scheduling on a shoreline with release times, Management Science, 36 (1990), 212–223.

Labeled Search Trees and Amortized Analysis: Improved Upper Bounds for NP-Hard Problems*

Jianer Chen[1], Iyad A. Kanj[2], and Ge Xia[1]

[1] Department of Computer Science, Texas A&M University
College Station, TX 77843-3112. {chen, gexia}@cs.tamu.edu
[2] School of CTI, DePaul University
243 S. Wabash Avenue, Chicago, IL 60604-2301 ikanj@cs.depaul.edu

Abstract. A sequence of exact algorithms to solve the VERTEX COVER and MAXIMUM INDEPENDENT SET problems have been proposed recently in the literature. All these algorithms appeal to a very conservative analysis that considers the size of the search tree, under a worst-case scenario, to derive an upper bound on the running time of the algorithm. In this paper we propose a different approach to analyze the size of the search tree. We use amortized analysis to show how simple algorithms, if analyzed properly, may perform much better than the upper bounds on their running time derived by considering only a worst-case scenario. This approach allows us to present a simple algorithm of running time $O(1.194^k + n)$ for the parameterized VERTEX COVER problem on degree-3 graphs, and a simple algorithm of running time $O(1.1254^n)$ for the MAXIMUM INDEPENDENT SET problem on degree-3 graphs. Both algorithms improve the previous best algorithms for the problems.

1 Introduction

Recently, there has been considerable interest in developing improved exact algorithms for solving well-known NP-hard problems [7,14]. This line of efforts was motivated by both practical and theoretical research in computational sciences. Practically, there are certain applications that require solving NP-hard problems precisely [10], while theoretically, this line of research may lead to a deeper understanding of the structure of NP-hard problems [4,9,11,13].

Two of the most extensively studied problems in this line of research are the MAXIMUM INDEPENDENT SET and the VERTEX COVER problems. For MAXIMUM INDEPENDENT SET (given a graph G, find a maximum independent set in G), since the initiation by Tarjan and Trojanowski [20] with an $O(1.259^n)$ time algorithm, there have been continuously improved algorithms for the problem [2,12,18]. For general graphs, the best algorithm for MAXIMUM INDEPENDENT SET is due to Robson [18], whose algorithm runs in time $O(1.211^n)$. Beigel [2]

* The first and third authors were partially supported by NSF under grants CCR-0000206 and CCR-0311590. The second author was partially supported by DePaul University Competitive Research Grant.

T. Ibaraki, N. Katoh, and H. Ono (Eds.): ISAAC 2003, LNCS 2906, pp. 148–157, 2003.

developed an algorithm of running time $O(1.083^e)$ for the problem, where e is the number of edges in the graph. Applying this algorithm to degree-3 graphs, we get the currently best algorithm of running time $O(1.1259^n)$ for the MAXIMUM INDEPENDENT SET problem on degree-3 graphs.

The VERTEX COVER problem (given a graph G and a parameter k, decide if G has a vertex cover of k vertices) has drawn much attention recently in the study of parameterized complexity of NP-hard problems [9]. This is also due to its applications in fields like computational biochemistry [15]. Since the development of the first parameterized algorithm by Buss (see [3]), which has running time $O(kn+2^k k^{2k+2})$, there has been an impressive list of improved algorithms for the problem [1,5,6,8,16,19]. Currently, the best parameterized algorithm for VERTEX COVER has running time $O(kn + 1.285^k)$ for general graphs [5], and the best parameterized algorithm for VERTEX COVER on degree-3 graphs has running time $O(kn + 1.237^k)$ [6].

The most popular technique for solving NP-hard problems precisely is the *branch-and-search* process, which can be depicted by a search tree model described as follows. Each node of the search tree corresponds to an instance of the problem. At a node α in the tree the search process considers a local structure in the problem instance corresponding to α, and enumerates some feasible partial solutions to the instance based on the specific local structure. Each such enumeration induces a new reduced problem instance that corresponds to a child of the node α in the search tree. The search process is then applied recursively to the children of α. The complexity of a branch-and-search process, which is roughly the size of the search tree, depends mainly on two things: how effectively the feasible partial solutions are enumerated, and how efficiently the instance size is reduced. In particular, all exact algorithms proposed in the literature for the MAXIMUM INDEPENDENT SET problem and the VERTEX COVER problem are based on this strategy, and most improvements were obtained by more effective enumerations of feasible partial solutions and/or more efficient reductions in the size of the problem instance [1,5,18,20].

A desirable local structure may not exist at a stage of the branch-and-search process. In this case, the branch-and-search process has to pick a less favorable local structure and make less effective branch and/or a less efficient instance-size reduction. Most proposed branch-and-search algorithms were analyzed based on the worst-case performance. That is, the computational complexity of the algorithm was derived based on the worst local structure occurring in the search process. Obviously, this worst-case analysis for a branch-and-search process is very conservative — the worst cases may appear very rarely in the entire process, while most other cases permit much better branching and reductions.

In the current paper, we suggest new methods to analyze the branch-and-search process. First of all, we label the nodes of a search tree to record the reduction in the parameter size for each branching process. We then perform an amortized analysis on each path in the search tree. This allows us to capture the following notion: an operation by itself may be very costly in terms of the size of the search tree that it corresponds to, however, this operation might be very beneficial in terms of introducing many efficient branches and reductions in the entire process. Therefore, the expensive operation can be well-"balanced" by the induced efficient operations.

This analysis has also enabled us to consider new algorithm strategies in a branch-and-search process. In particular, now we do not have to always strictly avoid expensive operations. To illustrate our analysis and algorithmic techniques, we propose a very simple branch-and-search algorithm (of few lines) for VERTEX COVER on degree-3 graphs, abbreviated VC-3. The algorithm also induces a new algorithm for MAXIMUM INDEPENDENT SET on degree-3 graphs, abbreviated IS-3. Using the new analysis and algorithmic strategies, we are able to show that the new algorithms improve the best existing algorithms in the literature. More specifically, our algorithm for VC-3 runs in time $O(n + 1.194^k)$, improving the previous best algorithm of running time $O(kn + 1.237^k k)$ [6], and our algorithm for IS-3 runs in time $O(1.1254^n)$, improving the previous best algorithm of running time $O(1.1259^n)$ [2]. Some of the proofs in this paper will be omitted due to the lack of space.

2   A Simple Algorithm for VC-3 and the Reduction Rules

Let $G = (V, E)$ be an undirected graph. For a subset V' of vertices in G, denote by $G(V')$ the subgraph of G induced by V'. For a subgraph H of G, denote by $G - H$ the subgraph of G obtained by removing all vertices in H. For a vertex u in G, denote by $N(u)$ the set of neighbors of u and by $d(u)$ the degree of u. A set C of vertices in G is a *vertex cover* for G if every edge in G has at least one endpoint in C. Denote by $\tau(G)$ the size of a minimum vertex cover of the graph G. An instance of the VERTEX COVER problem consists of a pair (G, k) asking whether $\tau(G) \leq k$. The VC-3 problem is the VERTEX COVER problem on graphs whose vertex degree is bounded by 3. Note that if every vertex in G has degree bounded by 3, and hence, can cover at most 3 edges, it is true that for any induced connected subgraph H of G with n_H vertices such that H is not a tree, we have $\tau(H) \geq n_H/3$. Let (G, k) be an instance of the VC-3 problem. The following proposition allows us to assume, without loss of generality, that the graph G contains at most $2k$ vertices.

Proposition 1 ([6]). *There is an algorithm of running time $O(k\sqrt{k})$ that, given an instance (G, k) of the VC-3 problem, constructs another instance (G_1, k_1), where the graph G_1 contains at most $2k_1$ vertices with $k_1 \leq k$, and such that the graph G has a vertex cover of at most k vertices if and only if the graph G_1 has a vertex cover of at most k_1 vertices.*

Let v be a degree-2 vertex in the graph with two neighbors u and w such that u and w are not adjacent. We construct a new graph G' as follows: remove the vertices v, u, and w and introduce a new vertex v_0 that is adjacent to all neighbors of the vertices u and w in G (of course except the vertex v). We say that the graph G' is obtained from the graph G by *folding* the vertex v.

Lemma 1 ([5]). *Let G' be a graph obtained by folding a degree-2 vertex v in a graph G, where the two neighbors of v are not adjacent to each other. Then $\tau(G) = \tau(G') + 1$. Moreover, a minimum vertex cover for G can be constructed from a minimum vertex cover for G' in constant time.*

We introduce some terminologies. A vertex folding on a degree-2 vertex v is *safe* if folding v does not create vertices of degree larger than 3. A cycle of length l in a graph is an *alternating cycle* if it contains exactly $\lfloor l/2 \rfloor$ degree-2 vertices of which no two are adjacent. Finally, a subgraph T in G is an *alternating tree* if: (1) T is induced by a subset of vertices in G; (2) T is a tree; (3) all leaves of T are of degree 3 in G; and (4) no two adjacent vertices in T are of the same degree in G. An alternating tree T is *maximal* if no alternating tree contains T as a proper subgraph.

Our algorithm takes as input a graph G and a parameter k and works by growing a partial minimum vertex cover C for G based on a branch-and-search process. If any search path finds a vertex cover of at most k vertices, the algorithm reports a success. Otherwise, the algorithm reports a failure. By *branching on a vertex set S* in which no two vertices are adjacent, we mean branching by either including all vertices in S in C, or including all vertices not in S but adjacent to vertices in S in C, then recursively working on the remaining graph.

The algorithm is given in Figure 1. The algorithm uses two subroutines **Fold**(v) and **Reducing**. The subroutine **Fold**(v) simply applies the safe folding operation to a degree-2 vertex v. We also implicitly assume that after each step, the algorithm calls a subroutine **Clean**, which eliminates all isolated vertices and degree-1 vertices (a degree-1 vertex is eliminated by including its neighbor in the partial cover C), and updates the graph G, the partial cover C, and the parameter k accordingly. In particular, we assume without loss of generality that at beginning of each step, the graph contains no vertices of degree less than 2.

Theorem 1. *The algorithm* **VC3-solver** *solves the VC-3 problem correctly.*

Proof. We explain how step 3 of **Reducing** works. The correctness of the other steps can be easily verified. Suppose that there is a cut in G, which is either a cut-vertex or a two-edge cut, whose removal results in at least one component H satisfying $2 \leq |V(H)| \leq 50$. Step 3 of **Reducing** removes H as follows.

If the cut is a cut-vertex u, let H_+ be the subgraph induced by H and u. We examine in constant time all minimum vertex covers of H_+. If any minimum vertex cover C_+ of H_+ contains u, we simply include C_+ in the partial cover C. If no minimum vertex cover of H_+ contains u, then if u has exactly one neighbor u' not in H, we include an arbitrary minimum vertex cover of H_+ and u' into the partial cover C; otherwise, u has two neighbors not in H. In this case we remove H and include an arbitrary minimum vertex cover of H_+ into the partial cover (note that u remains in the resulting graph).

If the cut consists of two edges (u, u') and (v, v'), we can assume without loss of generality that u and v are both in H, and that $u \neq v$ (otherwise the case is reduced to the case of a cut-vertex). Suppose first that $u' \neq v'$. We distinguish the following cases.

VC3-solver

Input: an instance (G, k) of VC-3

Output: a vertex cover C of G of size bounded by k in case it exists

1.   **while** there is a deg-2 vertex v where folding v is safe **do Fold**(v);

2.1 **if Reducing** is applicable **then** apply **Reducing** and **go to** step 1;

2.2 **else if** there is a deg-2 vertex v **then** branch on the two neighbors of v;

2.3 **else** branch on a deg-3 vertex v.

Reducing

0.   **if** there is a component H of size bounded by 50
     then compute a minimum vertex cover of H by brute force;

1.   **else if** there are two adjacent triangles (u, v, w) and (u, v, z)
     then include v in the cover;

2.   **else if** there is an alternating cycle K in G
     then include all deg-3 vertices on K in the cover;

3.   **else if** removing a cut-vertex or a two-edge cut results in a component
     $\qquad H$ with $2 \le |V(H)| \le 50$
     then remove H without any branching as explained in Theorem 1;

4.   **else if** there is a maximal alternating tree T of at least 4 vertices in G
     then branch on the vertices in T that are of deg-3 in G.

Fig. 1. The algorithm VC3-solver

(1) If there is a minimum vertex cover C_H for H that contains both u and v, then we include C_H in the partial cover C.

(2) If there is a minimum vertex cover C_H for H that includes u (resp. v) and every minimum vertex cover of H excludes v (resp. u), then we include C_H and v' (resp. u').

(3) If there are two minimum vertex covers C_u, C_v of H such that $u \in C_u$, and $v \in C_v$, then remove H, add an edge (u', v') in case it does not already exist, and reduce the parameter k by $\tau(H)$. When the algorithm returns a minimum vertex cover C' of the new graph, a minimum vertex cover of the original graph can be computed as follows. If the minimum vertex cover C' of the new graph contains u', then $C' \cup C_v$ is a minimum vertex cover for the original graph; otherwise, $C' \cup C_u$ is.

(4) If every minimum vertex cover for H excludes both u and v, then we consider two possibilities: (4.1) if the minimum size of a vertex cover for H containing both u and v is $\tau(H) + 2$, then we include a minimum vertex cover for H and u' and v'; (4.2) if the minimum size of a vertex cover for H containing both u and v is $\tau(H) + 1$, then we remove H, add a new vertex w', connect w' to u' and v', and reduce the parameter by $\tau(H)$. If the minimum vertex cover C' for the new graph excludes both u' and v', then C' plus a vertex cover of H including both u and v of minimum size, is a minimum vertex cover of the original graph; otherwise, C' includes both u' and v', and C' plus a minimum vertex cover of H is a minimum vertex cover of the whole graph.

Suppose now that $u' = v'$. If case (1) above applies, then we do the same as in case (1). Otherwise, we include an arbitrary minimum vertex cover of H and $u' = v'$ in the partial cover. It is easy to see that the above cases can be detected and implemented in constant time.   □

3   Analysis of the Algorithm

We analyze the time complexity of the algorithm **VC3-solver** in this section. Denote by $L(k)$ the number of leaves in the search tree of our algorithm looking for a vertex cover of size bounded by k. Let α be a node in the search tree with a corresponding parameter k' (i.e., the resulting parameter at α is k'). If we branch at α by reducing the parameter k' by k'_1, k'_2, ..., k'_s, in each branch respectively, then such a branch will be called a $(k'_1, k'_2, \ldots, k'_s)$-branch.

Previously, the size of the branching tree (number of leaves) was analyzed by considering the worst-case recurrence relation over all recurrence relations corresponding to the branching cases of the algorithm, and computing the size of the search tree corresponding to this recurrence relation. One can easily see that such analysis is very conservative since we do not always branch with the worst-case recurrence, and hence, the size of the search tree will be much smaller than the size of the search tree obtained in such a conservative analysis.

We present next a novel way of analyzing the size of the search tree. This can be achieved by looking at the set of operations performed by the algorithm as an interleaved set of operations. This allows us to counter-balance the effect of inefficient operations with efficient ones, thus providing a better upper bound on the size of the search tree. Our goal is to show that the size of the search tree corresponding to the running time of the algorithm on input (G, k) is not larger than the size of a search tree corresponding to (G, k) with all its branches satisfying the recurrence relation $L(k) \leq L(k-3) + L(k-5)$. This will allow us to conclude that the size of the search tree is $O(r^k)$, where $r \leq 1.194$ is the unique positive root of the polynomial $x^5 - x^2 - 1$.

The graph G is called *clean* if no vertex of degree 0 or 1 exists in G. The graph G is called *nice* if it is clean and no safe folding is applicable to any vertex in G. We will divide the operations performed by the algorithm into four categories.

1. **Folding** operations: the operations performed in step 1 of the algorithm **VC3-solver**.
2. $(1, 3)$ **branching** operations: the operations performed in step 2.3 of **VC3-solver** when we branch on a degree-3 vertex. These operations occur only when the graph becomes 3-regular.
3. $(2, 5)$ **branching** operations: the operations performed in step 2.2 of **VC3-solver** when we pick a degree-2 vertex and branch on its neighbors. Note that at this point of the algorithm the graph is nice, and hence, no safe folding is applicable. This means that the two vertices that we branch on have five neighbors, and the branch in this case is a $(2, 5)$-branch.
4. The operations performed in **Reducing** and those performed by **Clean**.

Let i be an operation[1] in any of the above categories. We define the following attributes for operation i: e_i the number of edges removed in operation i, v_i the number of vertices removed in operation i, and k_i the reduction in the parameter after operation i. We define the *surplus* s_i of operation i as follows. If i is a non-branching operation that reduces the parameter by k_i, then $s_i = k_i$. If i is the a-side (resp. b-side) of a branching operation (a, b), where $a \leq b$, then $s_i = a - 3$ (resp. $s_i = b - 5$). We define the amortized cost m_i of operation i by $m_i = 5e_i - 6v_i + 6s_i - 3k_i$. Note that if an operation i is followed by **Clean**, we will combine the amortized cost of **Clean** with m_i. Also note that for any non-branching operation $s_i = k_i$, therefore the amortized cost of such an operation is $m_i = 5e_i - 6v_i + 3k_i$.

Lemma 2. *Let C_0 be a connected component in G, and let m_0 be the amortized cost incurred by invoking **Clean** on C_0. If C_0 is not a tree then $m_0 \geq 0$, and if C_0 is a tree then $m_0 \geq -6$.*

Theorem 2. *Let i be an operation performed by **Reducing** followed by an invocation to **Clean**. Then i is not worse than a $(3, 5)$-branch and the amortized cost m_i of i is non-negative.*

Proposition 2. *Let G be a nice graph, and let $\mathcal{S}$ be a collection of disjoint induced trees in G that are joined to $G - \mathcal{S}$ by l edges. Then $|V(\mathcal{S})| \leq 4l - 5$.*

Proposition 3. *Let O be an operation that removes e_0 edges, v_0 vertices, reduces the parameter by k_0, and has surplus s_0. Let $m_0 = 5e_0 - 6v_0 + 6s_0 - 3k_0$ be the amortized cost of operation O.*
  (i) If O is a category 1 operation then $m_0 \geq 1$.
  (ii) If O is the 1-side branch in a category 2 operation then $m_0 = -6$.
  (iii) If O is the 3-side branch in a category 2 operation then $m_0 \geq -6$.
  (iv) If O is the 2-side branch in a category 3 operation then $m_0 = 0$.
  (v) If O is the 5-side branch in a category 3 operation then $m_0 \geq 1$.
  (vi) If O is a category 4 operation, then $m_0 \geq 0$.

Proof. A folding operation removes two vertices and at least two edges. Hence, $e_0 \geq 2$ and $v_0 = 2$. We also have $s_0 = k_0 = 1$ (since there is no branching). Thus, $m_0 \geq 1$. Now in the 1-side of the $(1, 3)$-branch exactly one vertex and three edges are removed. Since $s_0 = -2$ and $k_0 = 1$, we have $m_0 = -6$. Also, the remaining graph is clean, and **Clean** is not applicable. Similarly, for the 2-side of the $(2, 5)$-branch, 6 edges and 3 vertices are removed, and no degree-1 vertices are created since all the neighbors of the two vertices that we removed must be of degree-3 (otherwise we would have an alternating tree of size at least 5, which is not possible since **Reducing** is not applicable at this point). Since $s_0 = -1$

---

[1] When looking at the search tree, a branching operation will denote the two sides of the branch, whereas when looking at a certain path in the search tree, one side of a branching operation will be considered an operation by itself.

and $k_0 = 2$, we have $m_0 = 0$. In all the above cases, the subroutine **Clean** is not applicable since all the remaining vertices have degrees larger than one. This proves parts $(i), (ii), (iv)$.

The proofs of part (iii) and part (v) are similar. We prove part (iii). Note first that in the 3-side of the $(1, 3)$ branching we have $s_0 = -2$ and $k_0 = 3$. Also, we know that before this operation the graph G is 3-regular. Let u be the degree-3 vertex that we branch on, and let v, w, z be its neighbors. Let H be the graph induced by $\{u, v, w, z\}$. Since **Reducing** does not apply at this point, there cannot be more than one edge among v, w, z (otherwise, we would have two adjacent triangles). Suppose that there exists one edge among v, w, z. This means that there are exactly four edges connecting H to $G - H$. Note that in this case no component in $G - H$ can be a tree, otherwise, using Proposition 2, the graph induced by the vertices of the tree component plus the vertices of H has size bounded by 50, and is connected to the remaining graph by at most two edges (since the tree component has to be connected to $\{v, w, z\}$ by at least two edges), which is not possible at this stage of the algorithm since steps 0 and 3 of **Reducing** do not apply. Thus, we can assume that no component in $G - H$ is a tree, and hence by Lemma 2, the amortized cost of **Clean** in case it is invoked is non-negative. The number of edges and the number of vertices removed in this case is 8 and 4, respectively, giving $m_0 \geq 5e_0 - 6v_0 - 21 = -5$.

Now suppose that no edge exists among v, w, z, and hence, there are exactly six edges connecting H to $G - H$. By a similar argument to the above, we cannot have two different components in $G - H$ that are trees. Thus, in the worst case, the amortized cost of **Clean** is at least -6 by Lemma 2. The branch itself removes 9 edges and 4 vertices from the graph. Since the total amortized cost is the sum of the amortized cost of the branch and that of **Clean**, it follows that $m_0 \geq 5e_0 - 6v_0 - 27 = -6$.

To prove part (vi), note that a category 4 operation is either an operation that is performed in **Reducing** or one that is performed in **Clean**. If O is an operation that is performed in **Reducing**, then by Theorem 2, the amortized cost of O including the call to **Clean** is non-negative. Now if O is an operation in **Clean** that does not follow an operation in **Reducing**, by the above discussion, O must be the operation following a 3-side of a $(1, 3)$-branch, or a 5-side of a $(2, 5)$-branch (these cover all the cases in which **Clean** is called). By parts (iii) and (v) above, the negative part of the amortized cost of **Clean** was combined with the amortized cost of the operation, and the remaining part is positive. □

Based on Proposition 3, we give in Figure 2 the attribute values for any operation i in the four categories. The surplus s_i and the reduction in the parameter k_i of a category 4 operation i depend on the operation and are not specifically needed for our analysis. In all cases, either the amortized cost or a lower bound on it, is given in the table.

Definition 1. Let α be a node in the search tree $\mathcal{T}$ of the algorithm corresponding to (G, k). We define the *label* of α to be the reduction in the parameter along the branch in the tree from the parent of α to α. If α is the root of $\mathcal{T}$, then the label of α is k, where k is the original parameter.

Operations		reduction in k	surplus	amortized cost
Folding		1	1	1
(1, 3) branching	1-side	1	−2	−6
	3-side	3	−2	−6
(2, 5) branching	2-side	2	−1	0
	5-side	5	0	1
A category 4 operation i		k_i	s_i	$m_i \geq 0$

Fig. 2. The attribute values of the operations

Definition 2. Let $P = (\alpha_i, \ldots, \alpha_j)$ be a path in the search tree $\mathcal{T}$ corresponding to the execution of the algorithm. Let x_1 and x_3 be the numbers of nodes on P of labels 1 and 3 corresponding to the 1-side and the 3-side of the $(1, 3)$ branches, respectively, and x_2 be the number of nodes of label 2 corresponding to the 2-side of the $(2, 5)$ branches. Let d be the sum of the labels of all the nodes on P that correspond to folding operations plus the sum of all the surplus s_i over every category 4 operation i on P. The path P is said to be *compressible* if $d \geq 2x_1 + 2x_3 + x_2$.

Proposition 4. *Let $\mathcal{T}$ be the search tree corresponding to the execution of the algorithm on input (G, k). Suppose that all the branching operations performed by the algorithm can be classified as $(1, 3)$, $(2, 5)$, and other branching operations (a, b), where (a, b) is at least as efficient as a $(3, 5)$-branch. If every root-leaf path in $\mathcal{T}$ is compressible, then the number of leaves $L(k)$ in $\mathcal{T}$ is bounded by $O(r^k)$ where r is the unique positive root of the polynomial $x^5 - x^2 - 1$.*

Proposition 5. *Let $S = (\alpha_i, \alpha_{i+1}, \ldots, \alpha_{i+l-1}, \alpha_{i+l})$, $l > 0$, be a subpath of a path P in $\mathcal{T}$. Suppose that none of the nodes α_j, $i < j < i + l$, corresponds to a 3-regular graph. If α_{i+l} corresponds to a 3-regular graph then the subpath $S = (\alpha_i, \ldots, \alpha_{i+l-1})$ is compressible.*

Using Proposition 5, the attribute values given in Figure 2, and a detailed analysis, we can show the following lemma.

Lemma 3. *Every root-to-leaf path in the search tree $\mathcal{T}$ corresponding to the algorithm **VC3-solver** is compressible.*

Theorem 3. *The algorithm **VC3-solver** runs in time $O(1.194^k + n)$.*

Proof. By Lemma 3 and Proposition 4, the size of $\mathcal{T}$ is $O(r^k)$, where $r \leq 1.194$ is the positive root of the polynomial $x^5 - x^2 - 1$. Along every root-leaf path in $\mathcal{T}$ the time spent by the algorithm is linear in the size of the graph. Using the techniques in [17], the running time of the algorithm **VC3-solver** is $O(1.194^k + n)$. □

Using Theorem 3, and similar techniques to those in [5], we have:

Theorem 4. *The IS-3 problem can be solved in time $O(1.1254^n)$.*

References

1. R. BALASUBRAMANIAN, M. R. FELLOWS, AND V. RAMAN, An improved fixed parameter algorithm for vertex cover, *Inform. Process. Lett.* **65**, (1998), pp. 163–168.

2. R. BEIGEL, Finding maximum independent sets in sparse and general graphs, in *Proc. 10th ACM-SIAM Symp. on Discrete Algorithms* (SODA'99), (1999), pp. 856–857.

3. J. F. BUSS AND J. GOLDSMITH, Nondeterminism within P, *SIAM J. Comput.* **22**, (1993), pp. 560–572.

4. L. CAI AND D. JUEDES, On the existence of subexponential-time parameterized algorithms, available at http://www.cs.uga.edu/~cai/.

5. J. CHEN, I. A. KANJ, AND W. JIA, Vertex cover: further observations and further improvements, *J. Algorithms* **41**, (2001), pp. 280–301.

6. J. CHEN, L. LIU, AND W. JIA, Improvement on vertex cover for low-degree graphs, *Networks* **35**, (2000), pp. 253–259.

7. *DIMACS Workshop on Faster Exact Algorithms for NP-hard problems*, Princeton, NJ, (2000).

8. R. DOWNEY AND M. FELLOWS, Parameterized computational feasibility, in *Feasible Mathematics II*, P. Clote and J. Remmel, eds., Boston, Birkhäuser (1995), pp. 219–244.

9. R. DOWNEY AND M. FELLOWS, *Parameterized Complexity*, New York, Springer, (1999).

10. P. HANSEN AND B. JAUMARD, Algorithms for the maximum satisfiability problem, *Computing* **44**, (1990) pp. 279–303.

11. R. IMPAGLIAZZO, R. PATURI, AND F. ZANE, Which problems have strongly exponential complexity?, *J. Comput. System Sci.* **63-4**, (2001), pp. 512–530.

12. T. JIAN, An $O(2^{0.304n})$ algorithm for solving the maximum independent set problem, *IEEE Trans. Comput.* **35**, (1986) pp. 847–851.

13. D. JOHNSON AND M. SZEGEDY, What are the least tractable instances of max. independent set?, *Proc. 10th ACM-SIAM Symp. on Discrete Algorithms*, (1999), pp. 927–928.

14. D. S. JOHNSON AND M. A. TRICKS, EDS., *Cliques, Coloring and Satisfiability, Second DIMACS Implementation Challenges*, DIMACS Series on Discrete Mathematics and Theoretical Computer Science **26**, AMS, Providence, RI, (1996).

15. I. A. KANJ, Vertex Cover: Exact and Approximate Algorithms and Applications, *Ph.D. Dissertation*, Dept. of Computer Science, Texas A&M University, College Station, Texas, (2001).

16. R. NIEDERMEIER AND P. ROSSMANITH, Upper bounds for vertex cover further improved, *Lecture Notes in Computer Science* **1563**, (1999), pp. 561–570.

17. R. NIEDERMEIER AND P. ROSSMANITH, A general method to speed up fixed-parameter-tractable algorithms, *Inform. Process. Lett.* **73**, (2000), pp. 125–129.

18. J. M. ROBSON, Algorithms for maximum independent set, *J. Algorithms* **6**, (1977), pp. 425–440.

19. U. STEGE AND M. FELLOWS, An improved fixed-parameter-tractable algorithm for vertex cover, *Technical Report* **318**, Department of Computer Science, ETH Zurich, April 1999.

20. R. E. TARJAN AND A. E. TROJANOWSKI, Finding a maximum independent set, *SIAM J. Comput.* **7**, (1986), pp. 537–546.

A New Translation from Semi-extended Regular Expressions into NFAs and Its Application to an Approximate Matching Problem[*]

Hiroaki Yamamoto

Department of Information Engineering, Shinshu University,
4-17-1 Wakasato, Nagano-shi, 380-8553 Japan.
yamamoto@cs.shinshu-u.ac.jp

Abstract. Semi-extended regular expressions (SEREs) are regular expressions (REs) with intersection. Two algorithms for translating REs into nondeterministic finite automata (NFAs) are widely known, that is, Thompson construction and Glushkov construction. A trivial way for translating SEREs into NFAs is to use Thompson construction because it can easily be applied to SEREs. It seems to be difficult to directly apply Glushkov construction to SEREs. In this paper, we present a new translation from SEREs into NFAs using Glushkov construction and the modular decomposition technique by Yamamoto. Then, given an SERE r with m_r intersection operators, we can generate an NFA with at most $N_r + 1$ states and N_r^2 transitions in $O((m_r + 1)N_r^2)$ time and space. Here N_r is a number obtained from the decomposition of r, and is less than the number of states of an NFA obtained by the trivial translation (that is, the translation using Thompson construction). In addition, we will show an application to an approximate SERE matching problem.

1 Introduction

1.1 Background

Semi-extended regular expressions (SEREs) are regular expressions (REs) with intersection. Two algorithms for translating REs into nondeterministic finite automata (NFAs) are widely known, that is, Thompson construction and Glushkov construction. For example, see [5] for Thompson construction and [2,3,7] for Glushkov construction. Let r be an RE over an alphabet Σ, and let m be the length of r and s be the number of symbols of Σ occurring in r. Then, Thompson construction generates an NFA with at most $2m$ states and $4m$ transitions, while Glushkov construction generates an NFA with exactly $s + 1$ states and at most s^2 transitions. These constructions are used in many applications, such as pattern matching algorithm, compiler, text editor and so on.

A trivial way for translating SEREs into NFAs is to use Thompson construction because it can easily be applied to SEREs. On the other hand, it seems to

---

[*] This research has been supported by the REFEC

T. Ibaraki, N. Katoh, and H. Ono (Eds.): ISAAC 2003, LNCS 2906, pp. 158–167, 2003.

be difficult to directly apply Glushkov construction to SEREs. However, since an NFA by Glushkov construction has a fewer states than an NFA by Thompson construction, there is a possibility to get a more compact NFA for an SERE. Hence studying an extension of Glushkov construction to SEREs seems to be interesting.

In this paper, we present a new translation from SEREs into NFAs using the modular decomposition technique by Yamamoto [10] and Glushkov construction. The number of states of an NFA obtained from our translation is less than that of an NFA obtained by the translation using Thompson construction. In addition, we will show an application to the approximate SERE matching problem, which is NP-hard.

1.2   Outline of a New Translation

Up to now, any extensions of Glushkov construction to SEREs have never been known. The modular decomposition technique introduced by Yamamoto [10] seems to be very suitable for such an extension because it partitions an SERE into modules each of which represents an RE. We design a translation algorithm as follows.

Let r be an SERE over an alphabet Σ. As in [10], we first partition the parse tree of r into modules by intersection operators, and then transform each module into an NFA called *an augmented NFA* (A-NFA) using Glushkov construction. Next we construct an NFA, called *a CMT transition graph*, from A-NFAs, which exactly accepts the language generated by r. This time, we introduce a new structure called *a computation modular tree* (CMT) for such A-NFAs, which plays as a state of an NFA. Finally, we obtain an NFA with at most $N_r + 1$ states and N_r^2 transitions in $O((m_r + 1)N_r^2)$ time and space, where m_r denotes the number of intersection operators occurring in r. Here, N_r is defined as follows. Let $\mathcal{R}$ be the set of modules obtained from the parse tree of r and for any module $R \in \mathcal{R}$, let $\sharp R$ be the total number of symbols of Σ and intersection operators occurring in R. We introduce a concept of maximum independent subsets of $\mathcal{R}$ to analyze the algorithm. Then we define N_r to be $\sum_{H \in \mathcal{H}} \prod_{R \in H}(\sharp R + 1)$, where $\mathcal{H}$ is the collection of all maximum independent subsets of $\mathcal{R}$. If m_r is constant, then N_r becomes polynomial in s, where s is the number of symbols of Σ occurring in r. In fact, we have $N_r \leq (s + m_r + 1)^{m_r + 1}$. We remark that it is difficult to directly apply our technique to extended regular expressions (EREs).

If we use the trivial translation based on Thompson's, then we obtain an NFA with at most $\sum_{H \in \mathcal{H}} \prod_{R \in H}(2|R|)$, where $|R|$ denotes the length of the subexpression of r corresponding to R. Clearly, this number can be larger than number N_r. Furthermore, if m_r is constant, then the above number becomes polynomial in $|r|$. Hence our translation generates an NFA with a fewer states. We do not know whether or not the number of transitions is smaller. This depends on a given SERE.

1.3   Application to an Approximate SERE Matching Problem

We will present an algorithm to solve an approximate SERE matching problem as an application of our translation. The approximate SERE matching problem is as follows: Given an SERE r of length m, a text string x of length n and any number $d \geq 0$, find all the prefixes y of x with $edit(y, r) \leq d$. Here $edit(y, r) = \min_{z \in L(r)} \{edit(y, z)\}$, where $L(r)$ denotes the set of strings (that is, language) generated by r and the edit distance $edit(y, z)$ between two strings y and z is defined to be the minimum number of insertions, deletions, and/or substitutions required to transform y into z. For example, $edit(\ aaabb, aabbb) = 1$ and $edit(aaabb, abbb) = 2$.

For REs, several efficient approximate RE matching algorithms are presented [6,8,9]. On the other hand, we do not know any researches discussing the approximate SERE matching problem. In this paper, we will show that this problem is NP-hard, and then give an approximate SERE matching algorithm using our translation from SEREs into NFAs and the technique used in [6,9].

2   Semi-extended Regular Expressions

Let Σ be an alphabet. The semi-extended regular expressions (SEREs) over Σ are regular expressions (REs) with intersection and are recursively defined by union ($\vee$), concatenation ($\cdot$), closure ($*$) and intersection ($\wedge$) in the same way as REs. By m_r, we denote the number of intersection operators occurring in an SERE r, and by $L(r)$ we denote the language generated by r. Furthermore, we define the parse tree P_r of an SERE r as follows:

1. If $r = \emptyset$ (ϵ, a, respectively), then P_r is a tree consisting of just one node labeled by $\emptyset$ (ϵ, a, respectively).
2. If $r = r_1 \vee r_2$ ($r = r_1 \wedge r_2$, $r = r_1 r_2$, $r = r_1^*$, respectively), then P_r is a tree such that its root is labeled by $\vee$ ($\wedge$, $\cdot$, $*$, respectively) and the left subtree and the right subtree of the root are P_{r_1} and P_{r_2} ($*$ has only P_{r_1}), respectively.

3   A New Translation from SEREs into NFAs

3.1   Decomposition of an SERE and a Modular Tree

As in [10], we partition the parse tree of an SERE into subtrees. Let r be an SERE over an alphabet Σ and let P_r be the parse tree of r. Then, we partition P_r by nodes labeled with intersection $\wedge$ into subtrees such that (1) the root of each subtree is either a child of a node labeled with $\wedge$ in P_r or the root of P_r, (2) each subtree does not contain any interior nodes labeled by $\wedge$, (3) each leaf is labeled by $\emptyset$, ϵ, $a \in \Sigma$, or $\wedge$. If it is labeled by $\wedge$, then it is called *a universal leaf*. We call such a subtree *a module*.

Let R and R' be modules in the parse tree P_r. If a universal leaf u of R becomes the parent of the root of R' in P_r, then R is called *a parent of R'*, and conversely R' is called *a child of R* or *a child of R at u*. Thus there are two children at each universal leaf and these two modules are called *a universal pair*. If the root of a module R is the root of P_r, then R is called *the root module*. If a module R does not have any children, then R is called *a leaf module*. It is clear that such a parent-child relationship induces *a modular tree* $\mathcal{T}_r = (\mathcal{R}, \mathcal{E})$ such that (1) $\mathcal{R}$ is a set of modules, (2) $(R, R') \in \mathcal{E}$ if and only if R is the parent of R'. For any modules R and R' with $R \neq R'$, if there is a path R to R', then R is called an ancestor of R'.

Now we introduce a concept of maximum independent subsets of $\mathcal{R}$, which plays a crucial role in the analysis of our algorithm.

Definition 1. *An independent modular tree $\mathcal{T}'$ of r is a subtree of $\mathcal{T}_r$ such that (1) the root of $\mathcal{T}'$ is the same as $\mathcal{T}_r$, (2) for any module R in $\mathcal{T}'$, if there are $t \, (\geq 1)$ universal leaves $u_1, \ldots, u_t$ in R, then R has just two children R_1 and R_2 which are children at some universal leaf u_j.*

Definition 2. *We say that two modules R and R' are independent if R and R' satisfy the following conditions: (1) Each of R and R' is not an ancestor of the other, (2) there is an independent modular tree $\mathcal{T}_1$ such that both R and R' are modules in $\mathcal{T}_1$.*

Definition 3. *We say a subset H of $\mathcal{R}$ to be an independent subset of $\mathcal{R}$ if H consists of modules which are independent of each other. Especially, H is said to be a maximum independent subset if for any module $R \notin H$, $H \cup \{R\}$ is not independent.*

Definition 4. *Let r be any SERE over an alphabet Σ and let $\mathcal{R}$ be the set of modules obtained from the parse tree of r. Furthermore, let $\mathcal{H}$ be the collection of all maximum independent subsets of $\mathcal{R}$. Then we define N_r as follows:*

$$N_r = \sum_{H \in \mathcal{H}} \prod_{R \in H} (\sharp R + 1).$$

Here $\sharp R$ is the total number of symbols in Σ and intersection operators occurring in R. Clearly, $N_r < \prod_{R \in \mathcal{R}} (\sharp R + 1) \leq (s + m_r + 1)^{m_r + 1}$, and thus if m_r is a constant, then N_r becomes polynomial in s, where s is the number of symbols of Σ occurring in r.

Now, we introduce a new symbol σ_u, called *a modular symbol*, for each universal leaf u, and then, for each module R, we relabel every universal leaf u of R with modular symbol σ_u. By this relabeling, R can be viewed as a regular expression over $\Sigma \cup \{\sigma_u \mid u$ is a universal leaf of $R \}$.

Example 1. We here give a simple example for modular trees. Let $r = 1(((00)^*) \wedge ((000)^*))1$ be an SERE over $\{0, 1\}$. Then Fig. 1(a) shows an example of partition of the parse tree P_r for r. Fig. 1(b) shows the modular tree and it is the only independent modular tree. In Fig. 1, R_0 is the root module, R_1 and R_2 are leaf modules. The node u_1 of R_0 is a universal leaf. There are two maximum independent subsets $H_1 = \{R_0\}$ and $H_2 = \{R_1, R_2\}$ in the modular tree. Hence $N_r = 4 + 3 \times 4 = 16$ because $\sharp R_0 = 3$, $\sharp R_1 = 2$ and $\sharp R_2 = 3$.

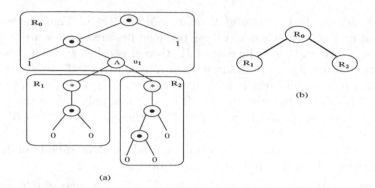

(a)

(b)

Fig. 1. The parse tree and its partition for $r = 1(((00)^*) \wedge ((000)^*))1$

3.2 Translating a Module into an NFA

Let $R_0, \ldots, R_{l-1}$ be modules obtained from an SERE r. As seen before, since each module R_j represents an RE, we can construct an NFA M_j for R_j. Although several translations from an RE to an NFA are known (see [1,2,3,5,7]), we translate R_j into M_j using Glushkov construction. We here omit the detail of the construction (for example, see [7]). The following proposition holds for Glushkov construction [2,3].

Proposition 1. *Let r be a regular expression of s symbols. Then we can construct an NFA M with just $s+1$ states and at most s^2 transitions in $O(s^2)$ time such that M accepts $L(r)$.*

We call this M_j an *augmented NFA* (A-NFA for short). In addition, if a module $R_{j'}$ is a child of R_j at u, then A-NFA $M_{j'}$ is said to be *associated with σ_u*. Obviously, for any universal leaf u, two A-NFAs are associated with the modular symbol σ_u. Then A-NFA M_j with an alphabet Σ and a set Γ of modular symbols has the following property.

Proposition 2. *1. The number of states is at most $\sharp R_j + 1$.*
   2. For any state q of M_j, all the transitions coming into q is by the same symbol $b \ (\in \Sigma \cup \Gamma)$.
   3. For any state q of M_j and any modular symbol $\sigma \in \Gamma$, the number of transitions from q by σ is at most one.

Note that the number of modular symbols in R_j is equal to the number of intersection operators.

Example 2. Fig. 2 gives A-NFAs for each module given in Fig. 1. As mentioned before, each A-NFA M_j is constructed from each module R_j by Glushkov construction. Here, M_1 and M_2 are associated with σ_{u_1}.

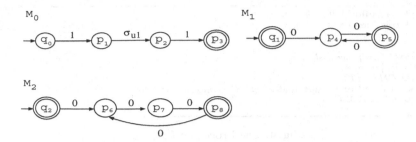

Fig. 2. A-NFAs by Glushkov construction for modules in Fig. 1

Function **BuildGraph**(r)
Input: SERE r;
Output: CMT transition graph $\mathcal{G}_r = (\mathcal{Q}, \mathcal{K}, \Sigma, T_0, T_f)$;

Step 1. Partition P_r into modules $R_0, \ldots, R_{l-1}$.
Step 2. Translate each module R_j $(0 \leq j \leq l-1)$ into an A-NFA M_j.
Step 3. $\mathcal{Q} := \{T_0, T_f\}$ and $\mathcal{K} := \emptyset$, where T_0 is the initial CMT.
Step 4. $BuildCMT(\mathcal{G}_r, T_0)$.
Step 5. Return $\mathcal{G}_r$.

Fig. 3. The function *BuildGraph*

3.3 Computation Modular Trees

Let r be an SERE over an alphabet Σ and let $x = a_1 \cdots a_n$ be a text string in Σ^*. Then suppose that the parse tree P_r is partitioned into l modules $R_0, \ldots, R_{l-1}$. Here R_0 is the root module. Let $M_0, \ldots, M_{l-1}$ be A-NFAs for each module. Then *a computation modular tree* (CMT for short) is defined as follows.

For each A-NFA M_j $(0 \leq j \leq l-1)$, we introduce *a state-node* U_j, which takes a state of M_j as its value. If a state-node does not have any state, then it is said to be empty. A computation modular tree $T = (\mathcal{U}, \mathcal{E})$ is the tree such that T has the same structure as the modular tree $\mathcal{T}_r$ except for taking state-nodes U_j as nodes instead of module R_j. Hence the root is the state-node U_0 for the root A-NFA M_0 and $\mathcal{E}$ corresponds to *edges* in $\mathcal{T}_r$. If (R_{j_1}, R_{j_2}) is a universal pair, then the pair (U_{j_1}, U_{j_2}) is also called *a universal pair*. For any state-node U, let $State(U)$ denote the state of U.

Let q_0 be the initial state of the root A-NFA M_0 and let T_0 be the CMT such that $State(U_0) = q_0$ and all the other state-nodes U_j are empty. Then T_0 is called *the initial CMT*. In addition, for any CMT T, T is called *an accepting CMT* if the state of U_0 in T is a final state of M_0.

3.4 A CMT Transition Graph

A CMT transition graph for an SERE r is a labeled directed graph $\mathcal{G} = (\mathcal{Q}, \mathcal{K}, \Sigma, T_0, T_f)$ such that

1. $\mathcal{Q} = \{T \mid T \text{ is a CMT obtained from } r\} \cup \{T_f\}$,

---

Procedure BuildCMT($\mathcal{G}, T$)
$\mathcal{G}$: CMT transition graph;
T: CMT;

1. $mark[T] := processed$,
2. $Next[T] := \emptyset$,
3. $NextCMT(\mathcal{G}, T)$,
4. for all $T' \in Next[T]$ such that $mark[T'] := unprocessed$ do
$\qquad BuildCMT(\mathcal{G}, T')$,

Fig. 4. The Procedure *BuildCMT*

Procedure NextCMT($\mathcal{G}, T$)
$\mathcal{G}$: CMT transition graph;
T: CMT;

1. if T is an accepting CMT, then $\mathcal{K} := \mathcal{K} \cup \{(T, T_f)\}$ and label (T, T_f) with ϵ,
2. for all state-nodes U_j in T do
$\qquad$ if $State(U_j)$ is a state of M_j such that it has transitions by modular symbols, then for all modular symbols σ, do
$\qquad$ a) copy T to T', and then $U_j := \emptyset$ in T',
$\qquad$ b) $U_{j_1} := q_{j_1}$ and $U_{j_2} := q_{j_2}$ in T', where M_{j_1} and M_{j_2} are associated with σ and q_{j_1} and q_{j_2} are the initial states of M_{j_1} and M_{j_2}, respectively,
$\qquad$ c) $Next[T] := Next[T] \cup \{T'\}$,
$\qquad$ d) $\mathcal{Q} := \mathcal{Q} \cup \{T'\}$, $\mathcal{K} := \mathcal{K} \cup \{(T, T')\}$, and label (T, T') with ϵ,
3. for all $a \in \Sigma$ do
$\qquad$ a) for all state-nodes U_j ($0 \leq j \leq l - 1$) in T' such that $State(U_j) \neq \emptyset$ do
$\qquad\qquad$ i. $P_j := \delta(State(U_j), a)$ on M_j,
$\qquad\qquad$ ii. if $P_j = \emptyset$ then go checking the next symbol,
$\qquad$ b) for all combinations $p_{j_1} \in P_{j_1}, \ldots, p_{j_e} \in P_{j_e}$ do
$\qquad\qquad$ i. let T' be a CMT such that all state-nodes are empty,
$\qquad\qquad$ ii. for all $j = j_1, \ldots, j_e$, $U_j := p_j$ in T',
$\qquad\qquad$ iii. $Next[T] := Next[T] \cup \{T'\}$, $\mathcal{Q} := \mathcal{Q} \cup \{T'\}$, $\mathcal{K} := \mathcal{K} \cup \{(T, T')\}$, and label (T, T') with a symbol a,
4. for all universal pairs (U_{j_1}, U_{j_2}) in T do /* check the intersection condition */
$\qquad$ a) if U_{j_1} and U_{j_2} both have final states, then
$\qquad\qquad$ i. copy T to T',
$\qquad\qquad$ ii. assign a state p to the parent U_j of U_{j_1} and U_{j_2} in T', where p is the state with $\delta(q, \sigma) = \{p\}$ on M_j and A-NFAs M_{j_1} and M_{j_2} are associated with σ,
$\qquad\qquad$ iii. $Next[T] := Next[T] \cup \{T'\}$, $\mathcal{Q} := \mathcal{Q} \cup \{T'\}$, $\mathcal{K} := \mathcal{K} \cup \{(T, T')\}$, and label (T, T') with ϵ,
5. for all newly generated CMTs T', $mark[T'] := unprocessed$.

Fig. 5. The Procedure *NextCMT*

2. $\mathcal{K} = \{(T, T') \mid T, T' \in Q\}$, where (T, T') is a directed edge from T to T' labeled by a symbol in $\Sigma \cup \{\epsilon\}$,
3. Σ is an alphabet,
4. $T_0 \in \mathcal{Q}$ is the initial CMT,
5. T_f is the special CMT, called the final CMT.

The final CMT T_f does not have any outgoing edges. We can view $\mathcal{G}$ as an NFA with ϵ-moves by regarding $\mathcal{Q}$ as the set of states, $\mathcal{K}$ as the transitions between states, the initial CMT as the initial state and T_f as the final state. Hence we can define the language $L(\mathcal{G})$ accepted by $\mathcal{G}$ in the standard way.

Now, to construct a CMT transition graph which accepts $L(r)$, we compute all CMTs reachable from the initial CMT T_0 according to transitions of A-NFAs. This time, we keep the following condition.

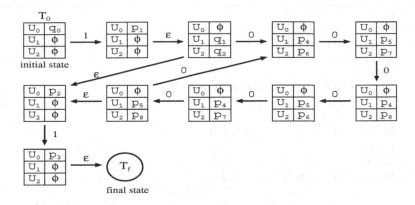

Fig. 6. CMT transition graph for $r = 1(((00)^*) \wedge ((000)^*))1$

- *Intersection condition*: Let M_{j_1} be an A-NFA such that M_{j_1} has a transition $p \in \delta(q, \sigma)$ for a state q and a modular symbol σ, and let M_{j_2} and M_{j_3} be two A-NFAs associated with σ. Then the transition from state q to state p is possible if and only if M_{j_2} and M_{j_3} reach the final states at same time.

Now let us describe the function *BuildGraph* that builds a CMT transition graph $\mathcal{G}_r$ which accepts $L(r)$ for a given SERE r. The detail is given in Fig. 3. The function *BuildGraph* first assigns only the initial CMT T_0 and the final CMT T_f to $\mathcal{G}_r$ and then invokes the procedure *BuildCMT* given in Fig. 4. The procedure *BuildCMT* computes CMTs reachable from T_0 using the technique of depth-first search. To compute all the transitions from a CMT T, *BuildCMT* invokes *NextCMT*. The procedure *NextCMT*$(\mathcal{G}, T)$ computes CMTs reachable from T by one step. To do this, *NextCMT* considers the following three cases: (a) transitions by modular symbols, (b) transitions by any symbol $a \in \Sigma$, (c) transitions by the intersection condition. *NextCMT* computes cases (a), (b) and (c) in 2, 3 and 4, respectively.

Example 3. Fig. 6 gives the CMT transition graph for A-NFAs given in Fig. 2. Each CMT has three state-nodes U_0, U_1 and U_2 which correspond to A-NFAs M_0, M_1 and M_2, respectively.

Let $\mathcal{G}_r = (\mathcal{Q}, \mathcal{K}, \Sigma, T_0, T_f)$ be the CMT transition graph generated by *BuildGraph*(r) for a given SERE r. The following Lemma 1 is obtained from the construction of $\mathcal{G}_r$ and Proposition 2.

Lemma 1. *Let T be any CMT of $\mathcal{G}_r$. Then, we have the following: (1) for any state-nodes U and U' in T, if two corresponding modules R and R' are independent, then at least one of U and U' is empty, (2) all incoming edges to T are labeled by the same symbol $b \in \Sigma \cup \{\epsilon\}$.*

In (2) of Lemma 1, if $b \in \Sigma$, then T is called an *S-node*, and if $b = \epsilon$, then T is called ϵ-node. Furthermore, from Lemma 1, we have the following lemma.

---

1. For $i = 0$
    a) for any $0 \le h \le L$, $E^h[T_0, 0] = 0$,
    b) for any CMT T such that $T \ne T_0$,
       $E^0[T, 0] = E^0[\overline{Pre}(T), 0] + \gamma$, where if T is an S-node, then $\gamma = 1$; otherwise 0,
    c) for any CMT T such that $T \ne T_0$ and $1 \le h \le L$,
       $E^h[T, 0] = \min\{E^h[\overline{Pre}(T), 0], E^{h-1}[Pre(T), 0]\} + \gamma$, where if T is an S-node, then $\gamma = 1$; otherwise 0,
    d) for any CMT T, $E[T, 0] = E^L[T, 0]$.
2. For $1 \le i \le n$,
    a) for any $0 \le h \le L$, $E^h[T_0, i] = i$,
    b) for any CMT T such that $T \ne T_0$,
       i. if T is an ϵ-node, then $E^0[T, i] = E^0[\overline{Pre}(T), i]$,
       ii. if T is an S-node, then $E^0[T, i] = \min\{E[T, i-1] + 1, E[\overline{Pre}(T), i-1] + \gamma, E^0[\overline{Pre}(T), i] + 1\}$, where $\gamma = 0$ if a_i matches the label; otherwise $\gamma = 1$,
    c) for any CMT T such that $T \ne T_0$ and $1 \le h \le L$,
       $E^h[T, i] = \min\{E^h[\overline{Pre}(T), i], E^{h-1}[Pre(T), i]\} + \gamma$, where if T is an S-node, then $\gamma = 1$; otherwise 0,
    d) for any CMT T, $E[T, i] = E^L[T, i]$.

Fig. 7. The recurrence for $E[T, i]$

Lemma 2. *The following holds for $\mathcal{G}_r$: (1) The number of CMTs in $\mathcal{Q}$ is at most $N_r + 1$, (2) the number of edges in $\mathcal{K}$ is at most N_r^2, and (3) $L(r) = L(\mathcal{G}_r)$.*

Let us investigate the running time of *BuildGraph*. By Lemma 2, the number of CMTs is $N_r + 1$. Since each CMT contains at most $2m_r + 1$ states, it takes $O(2m_r + 1)$ time for processing one CMT and one edge. Thus the total time to generate $\mathcal{G}_r$ is $O((m_r + 1)N_r^2)$. The space depends on the size of $\mathcal{G}_r$, it is also $O((m_r + 1)N_r^2)$. Therefore, we have the following theorem from Lemma 2.

Theorem 1. *Let r be any SERE with m_r intersection operators. Then we can translate r into an NFA, which consists of at most $N_r + 1$ states and N_r^2 transitions and accepts $L(r)$, in $O((m_r + 1)N_r^2)$ time and space.*

As an immediate corollary, we have the following corollary.

Corollary 1. *The emptiness problem of SEREs can be solved in $O((m_r + 1)N_r^2)$ time and space.*

4   Approximate SERE Matching Problem

4.1   Hardness

We can show the hardness of the approximate SERE matching problem by a reduction from 3SAT (see [4] for 3SAT).

Theorem 2. *The approximate SERE matching problem is NP-hard.*

4.2   Algorithm

Let r be an SERE over an alphabet Σ and $x = a_1 \cdots a_n$ be a text string of length n. Our algorithm first computes the CMT transition graph $\mathcal{G}_r = (\mathcal{Q}, \mathcal{K}, \Sigma, T_0, T_f)$, and then for all CMTs T, computes $E[T, i]$ that is the minimum value over all $edit(a_1 \cdots a_i, y)$ such that y is a string accepted at the CMT T. We first need to sort $\mathcal{Q}$ topologically according to $\mathcal{K}$. Then, let $\mathcal{G}_t = (\mathcal{Q}, \mathcal{K}_t)$ be the directed acyclic graph generated by this topological sort such that for any $(T_1, T_2) \in \mathcal{K} - \mathcal{K}_t$, if we add (T_1, T_2) to $\mathcal{G}_t$, then a loop occurs in $\mathcal{G}_t$. Let $\mathcal{K}_c = \mathcal{K} - \mathcal{K}_t$. Note that we can do such topological sort while generating $\mathcal{G}_r$.

Now let $Pre(T) = \{T' \mid (T', T) \in \mathcal{K}\}$ and $\overline{Pre}(T) = \{T' \mid (T', T) \in \mathcal{K}_t\}$. Furthermore, let $E[Pre(T), i] = \min_{T' \in Pre(T)} \{E[T', i]\}$ and $E[\overline{Pre}(T), i]$ is also defined similarly. Then $E[T, i]$ is defined by the recurrence of Fig. 7. In the recurrence, we are computing $E[T, i]$ for all CMTs in $\mathcal{Q}$ in topological order of CMTs L times, where $E^h[T, i]$ $(0 \le h \le L)$ denotes a temporary value of $E[T, i]$ after performing the $(h + 1)$-th computation. We here define the number L to be the minimum number of edges in $\mathcal{K}_c$ such that for any path P on $\mathcal{G}_r$, if L edges in $\mathcal{K}_c$ appear in P, then P contains a loop. Clearly, $L \le N_r$. As in [9], if we replace $E[T_0, i] = i$ with $E[T_0, i] = 0$ at 2-(a), then the value of $E[T, i]$ becomes the minimum edit distance over all the substrings ending at the position i of x. Then we have the following theorem.

Theorem 3. *Given an SERE r of length m, a text string x of length n and any number $d \ge 0$, we can solve the approximate SERE matching problem in $O((m_r + 1)N_r^3 n)$ time and $O((m_r + 1)N_r^2)$ space.*

References

1. A.V. Aho, Algorithms for finding patterns in strings, In J.V. Leeuwen, ed. Handbook of theoretical computer science, Elsevier Science Pub., 1990.
2. A. Bruggemann-Klein, Regular expressions into finite automata, Theoret. Comput. Sci., 120, 197–213, 1993.
3. C.H. Chang, and R. Paige, From regular expressions to DFA's using compressed NFA's, Theoret. Comput. Sci., 178, 1–36, 1997.
4. M.R. Garey, D.S. Johnson, Computers and Intractability: A Guide to the Theory of NP-Completeness, W.H.Freeman and Company, 1979.
5. J.E. Hopcroft and J.D. Ullman, Introduction to automata theory language and computation, Addison Wesley, Reading Mass, 1979.
6. E. Myers and W. Miller, Approximate Matching of Regular Expressions, Bull. of Mathematical Biology, 51, 1, 5–37, 1989.
7. G. Navarro and M. Raffinot, Compact DFA Representation for Fast Regular Expression Search, Proc. WAE2001, LNCS 2141, 1–12, 2001.
8. S. Wu and U. Manber, Fast Text Searching Allowing Errors, Communications of the ACM, 35, 10, 83–91, 1992.
9. S. Wu, U. Manber and E. Myers, A Sub-Quadratic Algorithm for Approximate Regular Expression Matching, J. of Algorithm, 19, 346–360, 1995.
10. H. Yamamoto, A New Recognition Algorithm for Extended Regular Expressions, ISAAC2001 Proc., LNCS 2223, 257–267, 2001.

The Quantum Query Complexity of 0-1 Knapsack and Associated Claw Problems

V. Arvind[1] and Rainer Schuler[2]

[1] The Institute of Mathematical Sciences, Chennai 600 113, India
arvind@imsc.res.in
[2] Theoretische Informatik, Universität Ulm, D-89069 Ulm, Germany
rsc@informatik.uni-ulm.de

Abstract. We give an $\tilde{O}(2^{n/3})$ quantum algorithm for the 0-1 Knapsack problem with n variables and an $\tilde{O}(2^{n/3}n^d)$ quantum algorithm for 0-1 Integer Linear Programs with n variables and d inequalities. To investigate lower bounds we formulate a *symmetric* claw problem corresponding to 0-1 Knapsack. For this problem we establish a lower bound of $\tilde{O}(2^{n/4})$ for its quantum query complexity and an $\tilde{O}(2^{n/3})$ upper bound. We also give a $2^{(1-\alpha)n/2}$ quantum algorithm for satisfiability of CNF formulas with no restrictions on clause size, but with the number of clauses bounded by cn for a constant c, where n is the number of variables. Here α is a constant depending on c.

1 Introduction

An active research area in quantum computing is to explore the possibility of developing quantum algorithms for different NP-hard problems that are faster than what we get by a direct application of Grover's search algorithm [7]. The goal is to discover quantum algorithms for algorithmic tasks that are significantly faster than classical algorithms (e.g. [7,4]). The limitation is that as yet there are only a few known techniques for designing quantum algorithms. The two central methods are essentially from Shor's factoring algorithm [11] and Grover's search algorithm [7].

In this paper, we consider quantum algorithms for certain NP-hard problems which have a special divide-and-conquer structure that can be exploited to design faster quantum algorithms. For example, we give an $\tilde{O}(2^{n/3})$ quantum algorithm for the 0-1 Knapsack problem with n variables. This is a consequence of a more general result for 0-1 Integer Linear Programs with n variables and d inequalities for which we give an $\tilde{O}(2^{n/3}n^d)$ quantum algorithm. For $d = o(n/\log n)$ this running time is bounded by $\tilde{O}(2^{n(1/3+\epsilon)})$ for every $\epsilon > 0$. It is to be noted that these problems admit $\tilde{O}(2^{n/2})$ time classical algorithms (for instances with n variables) by exploiting the same divide-and-conquer structure. Our algorithms are based on Grover's search algorithm and the method of amplitude amplification [7,5].

The next question we address is whether faster quantum algorithms for the above NP-hard problems are possible. To study this, we formulate a new claw-like problem (see [4] for claw problems) which we term as the *symmetric* claw

T. Ibaraki, N. Katoh, and H. Ono (Eds.): ISAAC 2003, LNCS 2906, pp. 168–177, 2003.

problem and study its quantum query complexity. The symmetric claw problem essentially captures the structure of 0-1 Knapsack and we study its complexity in the quantum query model [3,2]. For this problem we show a lower bound of $\tilde{O}(2^{n/4})$ in the quantum query model using the Ambainis' method [2]. The problem also has an $\tilde{O}(2^{n/3})$ upper bound given by essentially the same quantum algorithm that works for 0-1 Knapsack.

Finally, we consider the satisfiability problem for CNF formulas. Let CNF_c denote CNF formulas with the number of clauses bounded by cn for the given constant c, where n is the number of variables. There are no restrictions on the clause size of formulas in CNF_c. We give a $2^{(1-\alpha)n/2}$ quantum algorithm for satisfiability of inputs from CNF_c, where α is a constant depending on c. This gives us a faster quantum algorithm for satisfiability of formulas from CNF_c than the $2^{n/2}$ bound given by a direct application of Grover search. Classical algorithms significantly faster than exhaustive search are known for the k-CNF problem (see, e.g. [9]). To the best of our knowledge, the problem for unbounded clause size has not received attention.

We now give some preliminary definitions and explain the notation. The set $\{0,1\}^n$ denotes the set of binary strings of length n, and for a positive integer N we denote the set $\{1, 2, \ldots, N\}$ by $[N]$. Next, recall the definitions of 0-1 Knapsack and 0-1 Integer Linear Programs:

0-1 Knapsack. Given as input a list of positive integers $c_1, c_2, \ldots, c_n$ and a positive integer K, check if there is a subset $S \subseteq [n]$ such that $\sum_{i \in S} c_i = K$.

0-1 ILP. Given as input integers a_{ij} and b_i, $1 \leq j \leq n$ and $1 \leq i \leq d$, is the following set of linear inequalities feasible?

$$\sum_{j=1}^{n} a_{ij} x_j \leq b_i, \quad x_j \in \{0,1\}, \quad 1 \leq j \leq n \quad 1 \leq i \leq d.$$

We use standard definitions from quantum computing from [3,6]. In particular, we use the quantum query model (e.g. see [4,2]). In this model the input is a function $f : [N] \to [M]$ and the values of f is accessed by oracle queries. The complexity of computing some property of f is measured as the number of oracle queries. A quantum computation with T queries can be seen as a sequence of unitary transformations:

$$U_0 \to O \to U_1 \to \cdots O \to U_T,$$

where the unitary transform O implements the oracle access to f and the U_i are arbitrary unitary transformations which do not depend on the input f.

A central idea from quantum computing, which is a generalized form of Grover's search algorithm that we use throughout the paper is amplitude amplification [5]: Essentially, if we have a quantum algorithm $\mathcal{A}$ with success probability p then the success probability can be amplified to a constant by $O(\sqrt{1/p})$ calls to $\mathcal{A}$ and $\mathcal{A}^{-1}$. Amplitude amplification applies to search problems where a solution can be recognized efficiently.

A *range tree* (see [10] for details) is a data structure for storing a set S of N elements $\{x_1, x_2, \ldots, x_N\}$, each of which is a d-tuple of integers $x_i = (x_{i1}, x_{i2}, \ldots, x_{id})$. The data structure can be be built in time $N(log^{d-1}N)$ and needs space $N(log^{d-1}N)$. The specific property of interest that we require is that we can process *range queries* on a range tree in time $log^d N$ to retrieve one element, if it exists, of the set S that satisfies the query bounds. More precisely, given a d-tuple of real numbers $(a_1, a_2, \ldots, a_d)$, in time $O(log^d N)$ we can search for an element $x_i = (x_{i1}, x_{i2}, \ldots, x_{id})$ in the range tree such that $x_{ij} \le a_j$, $1 \le j \le d$.

2   0-1 Integer Linear Programs

Theorem 1. *There is an $\tilde{O}(2^{n/3}n^d)$ quantum algorithm with constant error probability that solves 0-1 integer linear programs with n variables and d inequalities.*

Proof. Let the input instance be

$$\sum_{j=1}^{n} a_{ij}x_j \le b_i, \quad 1 \le i \le d, x_j \in \{0,1\}, \quad 1 \le j \le n.$$

The goal is to find a feasible solution. We give a stepwise description of the quantum algorithm.

1. Partition the variables into two sets $A = \{x_1, \ldots, x_{n/3}\}$ and $B = \{x_{n/3+1}, \ldots, x_n\}$, where note that $|A| = n/3$ and $|B| = 2n/3$.
2. For each of the $2^{n/3}$ 0-1 assignments I to the variables in A define the d-tuple $y_I = (y_I(1), \ldots, y_I(d))$ of integers, where

$$y_I(i) = \sum_{j=1}^{n/3} a_{ij}I_j,$$

   where I_j is the value of variable x_j in assignment I.
3. Let $N = 2^{n/3}$. The set $X = \{y_I \mid I \text{ is a 0-1 assignment to } A\}$ is of size N. In time $\tilde{O}(N \log^{d-1} N)$ build a range tree (c.f. [10, Theorem 2.11]) to store the set X. The range tree has size $\tilde{O}(N \log^{d-1} N)$ and range queries can be processed in time $log^d N$. This completes the preprocessing phase.
4. Using the Hadamard transform prepare the uniform superposition over the set T of 0-1 assignments to the $2n/3$ variables in B:

$$|\psi\rangle = \frac{1}{2^{n/3}} \sum_{a \in T} |a\rangle.$$

5. Define a unitary transform U as the standard reversible implementation of the following classical subroutine f given $u \in T$ as input:
   (i) Compute $z_j = \sum_{j=n/3+1}^{n} a_{ij}u_j$, $1 \le i \le d$.

(ii) Let $\hat{z}_i = b_i - z_i$ for $1 \leq i \leq d$, giving a d-tuple of integers $(\hat{z}_1, \ldots, \hat{z}_d)$.

(iii) Search in the range tree for a y_I such that $y_I(1) \leq \hat{z}_1, \ldots, y_I(d) \leq \hat{z}_d$. Notice that this is a range query and it can be processed in time $\log^d N$ in the range tree date structure [10, Theorem 2.11].

(iv) If such a tuple y_I is in X then $f(u) = 1$. Otherwise, $f(u) = 0$.

6. With the initial state as the uniform superposition $|\psi\rangle$ and using the unitary transform U, apply Grover's search algorithm to search for $u \in T$ such that $f(u) = 1$.

It follows from the well-known analysis of Grover's algorithm and amplitude amplification [5,7] that the above algorithm has running time $\tilde{O}(2^{n/3} \log^d N) = \tilde{O}(2^{n/3} n^d)$, with constant success probability.

Corollary 1. *There is an $\tilde{O}(2^{n/3})$ time quantum algorithms with constant success probability for 0-1 Knapsack. Additionally, any NP-hard optimization problem that takes the form of a 0-1 Integer Linear Program with constant number of constraints has an $\tilde{O}(2^{n/3})$ time quantum algorithms with constant success probability.*

Proof. 0-1 Knapsack can be expressed as 0-1 integer linear programs with one inequality. Hence the algorithm of Theorem 1 yields the claimed quantum algorithm.

Consider any optimization problem that has a linear optimality function and the constraints can be expressed as a 0-1 integer linear program with d constraints. Using binary search we can reduce the optimization problem to feasibility of a 0-1 integer linear program with $d + 1$ constraints, which can be solved using the algorithm of Theorem 1 with running time $\tilde{O}(2^{n/3})$ for constant d. Thus, the corresponding optimization problem can also be solved in time $\tilde{O}(2^{n/3})$ with constant success probability.

Interestingly, if the 0-1 ILP is of the following form:

$$\text{minimize/maximize} \qquad \sum_i c_i x_i$$
$$\text{s.t.} \quad \sum_{j=1}^{n} a_{ij} x_j = b_i, \ \ 1 \leq i \leq d, x_j \in \{0,1\}, \ \ 1 \leq j \leq n,$$

then it is easy to see that essentially the same quantum algorithm presented in Theorem 1 solves this optimization problem in time $\tilde{O}(2^{n/3})$, independent of the number of equations d. The reason is that we do not have to maintain a range tree data structure as we do not have to process range queries. Just a sorted list would suffice as we only need to make exact queries in this case. The above kind of 0-1 ILP is referred to as the 0-1 Group Problem in Nemhauser and Wolsey's book [8]. An interesting instance of this problem is the following NP-hard problem: given a CNF formula F (no restrictions on clause size), search for a satisfying assignment that satisfies *exactly* one variable in each clause. This is clearly an instance of the above 0-1 ILP. Thus we have the following corollary.

Corollary 2. *There is an $\tilde{O}(2^{n/3})$ quantum algorithm that takes a CNF formula F with n variables as input (no restrictions on clause size or number of clauses) and searches, with constant success probability, for a satisfying assignment that satisfies exactly one variable in each clause.*

3   The Symmetric Claw Problem

In order to study how far we can exploit this idea of dividing the input, we examine in this section a black-box version of the 0-1 Knapsack problem which we term as the Symmetric Claw problem. For a pair of strings $x, y \in \{0,1\}^n$ let $x|_y$ denote the substring of x obtained by projecting it on the positions where y is 1. Likewise, let $x|_{\bar{y}}$ denote the substring of x obtained by projecting it on the positions where y is 0.

Definition 1. *The input to the symmetric claw problem is a function* $P : \{0,1\}^n \times \{0,1\}^n \rightarrow \{0,1\}^m \times \{0,1\}^m$ *where we write* $P(x,y) = (P_1(x,y), P_2(x,y))$ *for every* $x, y \in \{0,1\}^n$. *Additionally, the input function* P *is such that it fulfills the following promise symmetry conditions:*

1. *For* $x \in \{0,1\}^n$, *if* $P_1(x,y) = P_2(x,y)$ *for some* $y \in \{0,1\}^n$ *then* $P_1(x,y) = P_2(x,y)$ *for every* $y \in \{0,1\}^n$.
2. *For any* $x, x', y \in \{0,1\}^n$ *if* $x|_y = x'|_y$ *then* $P_1(x,y) = P_1(x',y)$. *Likewise, if* $x|_{\bar{y}} = x'|_{\bar{y}}$ *then* $P_2(x,y) = P_2(x',y)$.

Given such an input P *the symmetric claw problem is to find an* $x \in \{0,1\}^n$, *if it exists, such that* $P_1(x,y) = P_2(x,y)$ *for some* $y \in \{0,1\}^n$, *by querying* P *on* $(x,y) \in \{0,1\}^n \times \{0,1\}^n$.

Notice that the 0-1 Knapsack problem is an instance of the symmetric claw problem.

Remark 1. Consider a simpler version of the 0-1 Knapsack problem, where we seek a 0-1 assignment to variables $x_1, \ldots, x_n$ such that $\sum_{i=1}^{n} a_i x_i = 0$, given integers $a_1, \ldots, a_n$ as input.

For each $y \in \{0,1\}^n$ define a partition of the variable set $A = \{i \in [n] \mid y_i = 1\}$ and $B = \{i \in [n] \mid y_i = 0\}$. Define $P_1(x,y) = \sum_{i \in A} a_i x_i$ and $P_2(x,y) = -\sum_{i \in B} a_i x_i$.

It is easy to check that P_1 and P_2 fulfill conditions of Definition 1, making this version of 0-1 Knapsack an instance of the symmetric claw problem.

We first establish the upper bound result for symmetric claw problem. It is the same algorithm we described in the previous section.

Theorem 2. *There is an* $\tilde{O}(2^{n/3})$ *quantum algorithm with constant error probability for the symmetric claw problem in the quantum query model.*

Proof. The algorithm is along exactly the same lines as the algorithm in Theorem 1 for 0-1 ILP. In fact it is an easier version of that algorithm as we do not require range trees here. We fix $y \in \{0,1\}^n$ to be such that $y_i = 1$ for $1 \le i \le n/3$ and $y_i = 0$ for $n/3 + 1 \le i \le n$. Let $X_A = \{x \in \{0,1\}^n \mid x_i = 0$ for $n/3 + 1 \le i \le n\}$ and $X_B = \{x \in \{0,1\}^n \mid x_i = 0$ for $1 \le i \le n/3\}$. Compute and sort the list $\{P_1(x,y) \mid x \in X_A\}$ of size $2^{n/3}$ using a classical sorting algorithm in time $\tilde{O}(2^{n/3})$. This is the preprocessing phase. Prepare a superposition of $x \in X_B$ and search for $P_2(x,y)$ in the sorted list using a classical binary search implemented reversibly by a unitary transform. Now, using Grover's search we can find $x \in X_B$ such that $P_1(x', y) = P_2(x, y)$ for some $x' \in X_A$. At this point, using the properties of P_1 and P_2 we can put together a complete 0-1 assignment x'' from x and x' such that $P_1(x'', y) = P_2(x'', y)$. We can obtain x'' by concatenating the first $n/3$ bits from x' and the last $2n/3$ bits from x.

We now turn to the question of lower bounds. Using the technique of Ambainis [2] we establish a lower bound of $\Omega(2^{n/4})$ for the quantum query complexity of the symmetric claw problem. We first state the result in a form that we need for our setting.

Theorem 3. [2] *Let $\mathcal{F}$ be the set of input functions f, where $f : [M] \to [M]$, and let $\phi : \mathcal{F} \to \mathbb{Z} \times \mathbb{Z}$ be the function which we wish to compute. Let X, Y be two subsets of $\mathcal{F}$ such that $\phi(f) \neq \phi(g)$ for all $f \in X$ and $g \in Y$. Let $R \subseteq X \times Y$ such that:*

(i)   *For every $f \in X$ there are at least m different $g \in Y$ such that $(f, g) \in R$.*
(ii) *For every $g \in Y$ there are at least m' different $f \in X$ such that $(f, g) \in R$.*
(iii) *For every $f \in X$ and $x \in [N]$, there are at most l different $g \in Y$ such that $(f, g) \in R$ such that $f(x) \neq g(x)$.*
(iv) *For every $g \in Y$ and $x \in [N]$, there are at most l' different $f \in X$ such that $(f, g) \in R$ such that $f(x) \neq g(x)$.*

Any quantum algorithm that evaluates ϕ with constant success probability must make $\Omega(\sqrt{\frac{mm'}{ll'}})$ queries to the input function in the quantum query model.

Theorem 4. *Any quantum algorithm that solves the symmetric claw problem with constant success probability needs $\Omega(2^{n/4})$ queries in the quantum query model.*

Proof. We will prove the claimed lower bound by applying Theorem 3. The inputs consist of the class $\mathcal{F}$ of functions $P : \{0,1\}^n \times \{0,1\}^n \to \{0,1\}^n \times \{0,1\}^n$, where we write $P(x, y) = (P_1(x, y), P_2(x, y))$, and every P in $\mathcal{F}$ fulfills the conditions of the Definition 1. The goal of a quantum algorithm ϕ for the symmetric claw problem is to find $x \in \{0,1\}^n$ such that $P_1(x, y) = P_2(x, y)$ for some (and therefore, by the promise of Definition 1, every) y. Let NO denote the subset of "no" instances of $\mathcal{F}$ and YES the subset of "yes" instances. Define $X \subseteq$ NO as:

$X = \{P \in \mathcal{F} \mid P_1(x, y) \neq P_2(x, y) \ \forall x, y \in \{0,1\}^n, P_1(x, y) \neq P_1(x', y)$ if $x|_y \neq x'|_y$ and $P_2(x, y) \neq P_2(x', y)$ if $x|_{\overline{y}} \neq x'|_{\overline{y}}\}$.

We will define the subset Y of YES by first defining a relation $R \subseteq X \times$ YES and then setting $Y = \{P' \in \text{YES} \mid (P, P') \in R$ for some $P \in X\}$. We now define the relation R.

Given $P \in X$, for every $x \in \{0,1\}^n$ we define a distinct $P' \in$ YES and include (P, P') in R. Given $P \in X$ and $x \in \{0,1\}^n$, P' is obtained from P as follows:

- If $\sum_{i=1}^{n} y_i \geq n/2$ then define $P_1'(x,y) = P_1(x,y)$, and $P_2'(x,y) = P_1(x,y)$. Furthermore, for every $x' \in \{0,1\}^n$ such that $x'|_{\bar{y}} = x|_{\bar{y}}$ define $P_2'(x',y) = P_1(x,y)$. For such x', notice that by definition of X we have $P_1'(x',y) \neq P_1(x,y)$.
- If $\sum_{i=1}^{n} y_i < n/2$ then define $P_2'(x,y) = P_2(x,y)$, and $P_1'(x,y) = P_2(x,y)$. Furthermore, for every $x' \in \{0.1\}^n$ such that $x'|_y = x|_y$ define $P_1'(x',y) = P_2(x,y)$. For such x', notice that by definition of X we have $P_2'(x',y) \neq P_2(x,y)$.
- For all other pairs $(u,v) \in \{0,1\}^n \times \{0,1\}^n$ define $P_1'(u,v) = P_1(u,v)$ and $P_2'(u,v) = P_2(u,v)$.

Let P' be defined as above for a given $P \in X$ and $x \in \{0,1\}^n$. Notice that by construction P' is in YES and, furthermore, x is the unique element of $\{0,1\}^n$ such that $P_1'(x,y) = P_2'(x,y)$ for $y \in \{0,1\}^n$. Thus we define 2^n distinct elements $P' \in$ YES, one for every $x \in \{0,1\}^n$, such that $(P,P') \in R$. Therefore, in the terminology of Theorem 3, $m = 2^n$. For the remainder of the proof, we denote by P_x' the element $P' \in$ YES defined as above from an $x \in \{0,1\}^n$ and a given $P \in X$.

We next show that for any $P \in X$ and $(x,y) \in \{0,1\}^n \times \{0,1\}^n$ there are at most $2^{n/2}$ elements $P' \in Y$ such that $P(x,y) \neq P'(x,y)$ and $(P,P') \in R$. In terms of Theorem 3 this implies $l \leq 2^{n/2}$. We argue this in two cases:

(a) Suppose $\sum_{i=1}^{n} y_i \geq n/2$. Then notice from the definition of R that P_z' differs from P at (x,y) exactly when $x|_y = z|_y$. Thus, there are at most $2^{n/2}$ such elements P_z'.
(b) Suppose $\sum_{i=1}^{n} y_i < n/2$. Again, notice from definition of R that P_z' differs from P at (x,y) exactly when $x|_{\bar{y}} = z|_{\bar{y}}$. Thus, again, there can be at most $2^{n/2}$ such elements P_z'.

Finally, notice that $l' \leq m'$ always holds.

We can now apply the lower bound result Theorem 3. Since

$$\frac{mm'}{ll'} \geq \frac{m}{l} \geq \frac{2^n}{2^{n/2}},$$

The lower bound of $\Omega(\sqrt{\frac{mm'}{ll'}})$ given by Theorem 3 yields $\Omega(2^{n/4})$. This completes the proof.

4   Quantum Algorithm for CNF-SAT

In this section we use ideas from Section 2 to give a simple quantum search algorithm for CNF-SAT when the number of clauses is linearly bounded in the number of variables. Recall that $\text{CNF}_c = \{F \mid F$ is in conjunctive normal form with n variables and $F = C_1 \wedge C_2 \wedge \ldots \wedge C_m$ where $m \leq cn\}$.

Theorem 5. *For any constant $c > 0$ there is an $\tilde{O}(2^{(1-\alpha)n/2})$ quantum algorithm for satisfiability for inputs $F \in \text{CNF}_c$, where α is a constant such that $\alpha < 1/6$ and $H(\alpha) \leq \frac{1}{4c}$. Here, $H(\alpha)$ is the entropy function defined as $-\alpha \log_e \alpha - (1-\alpha) \log_e (1-\alpha)$.*

Proof. Let $\alpha < 1/6$ be a constant to be fixed later, as claimed in the statement. Let the input instance from CNF_c be $F = C_1 \wedge C_2 \wedge \ldots \wedge C_m$ from CNF_c with variables $x_1, x_2, \ldots, x_n$. Let $\frac{1}{\alpha} = k$, where we assume for simplicity of analysis that k is an integer. Partition the variable set $\{x_1, x_2, \ldots, x_n\}$ into k equal size sets $A_1, A_2, \ldots, A_k$, where $|A_i| = \alpha n$, $1 \le i \le k$. Suppose F is satisfiable and a^* is some fixed satisfying assignment for F. Denote by $\overline{A_i}$ the set of variables $\{x_1, \ldots, x_n\} \backslash A_i$ for each i. Denote by b_i^* the partial assignment given by a^* when restricted to variables in A_i. Similarly, let c_i^* denote the partial assignment given by a^* when restricted to variables in $\overline{A_i}$. We claim that there is an $i : 1 \le i \le k$ such that the partial assignment c_i^* satisfies at least $(1 - \alpha)m$ clauses of F. Suppose the claim is false. Then $\overline{A_i}$ satisfies at most $(1 - \alpha)m$ clauses of F for each i. Since a^* is a satisfying assignment, for each i there is a set S_i of *more than* αm clauses satisfied by the partial assignment b_i^* such that $S_i \cap S_j = \emptyset$ for $i \neq j$. This is impossible since there are only m clauses in F. The claim follows.

We now give a step-wise description of the algorithm. The algorithm is a loop with index $i : 1 \le i \le k$, where in the ith iteration it considers the partition of the variable set into A_i and $\overline{A_i}$. The algorithm succeeds when it considers a partition A_i and $\overline{A_i}$ such that c_i^* satisfies at least $(1 - \alpha)m$ clauses of the input F (such an index exists by the claim).

1. Partition the variable set into A_i and $\overline{A_i}$.
2. For $1 \le l \le \alpha m$ build a sorted table T_l consisting of the following set of pairs (u, b): $u \in \{0, 1\}^m$ is am m-bit string with exactly l 1's and b is a truth assignment to variables in A_i such that b satisfies each clause C_j for which $u_j = 1$, where $1 \le j \le m$. All other pairs (u, b) are discarded. Then, using a classical sorting algorithm and treating u in (u, b) as an m-bit integer key, sort the pairs in T_l in increasing order. This entire step can be done in time $\tilde{O}(\binom{m}{\alpha n} 2^{\alpha n})$.
3. Using the Hadamard transform prepare a uniform superposition of the truth assignments v to variables in $\overline{A_i}$. Let S be the set of all such truth assignments. Notice that $|S| = 2^{(1-\alpha)n}$. The superposition is

$$|\psi\rangle = \sqrt{\frac{1}{2^{(1-\alpha)n}}} \sum_{v \in S} |v\rangle.$$

4. Define a unitary transform U as the standard reversible implementation of the following classical subroutine f:
   (i) Compute the vector $u \in \{0, 1\}^m$ where $u_j = 1$ if and only if C_j is not satisfied by the partial assignment v.
   (ii) If u has more than αm 1's then $f(v)$ returns value 0 and stop.
   (iii) Otherwise, if u has l 1's in it, $1 \le l \le \alpha m$, then do a binary search for u in the table T_l. If (u, b) is found in T_l for some b then $f(v) = 1$ else $f(v) = 0$. Notice that if $f(v) = 1$ then v and b together give a satisfying assignment for F.

5. Now, starting with initial state as $|\psi\rangle$ and using the unitary transform U to implement f, apply Grover search to find $v \in S$ such that $f(v) = 1$.
6. Output the satisfying assignment (b, v).

To argue correctness it suffices to notice by our earlier claim that for some i, A_i and $\overline{A_i}$ is a partition such that in Step 3, $f(v) = 1$ for at least the partial assignment $v = c_i^*$ obtained from a^*. Thus, if F is satisfiable the algorithm will find a satisfying assignment with constant success probability in time $\tilde{O}(\binom{m}{\alpha m} 2^{\alpha n}) + \tilde{O}(2^{(1-\alpha)n/2})$, where the first term is the preprocessing time in Step 2, and the second term is the time for the Grover search. Since $m \leq cn$, an easy analysis yields $\binom{m}{\alpha m} \leq 2^{H(\alpha)cn}$ for large n. Thus, if we choose $\alpha < 1/6$ such that $(1 - \alpha)/2 \geq H(\alpha)c + \alpha$, then the overall time taken is $\tilde{O}(2^{(1-\alpha)n/2})$. It suffices to choose α such that $H(\alpha) < \frac{1}{4c}$.

5   Remarks

The question that arises is whether we can close the gap between the upper and lower bounds for the symmetric claw problem. Also, for the 0-1 ILP problem with n variables and d inequalities we do not have a better upper bound than $\tilde{O}(2^{n/3})n^d$. To study this issue in the quantum query model we define the simultaneous claw problem.

Definition 2. *Let $(f_i, g_i), 1 \leq i \leq d$ be functions where $f_i : [N] \to X$ and $g_i : [N] \to X$, where X is some set. The* simultaneous claw *problem is to find an $x \in [N]$ such that $f_i(x) = g_i(x)$ for each $i = 1, 2, \ldots, d$.*

We can also define a symmetric version of the simultaneous claw problem similar to Definition 1, but for simplicity we focus on this definition. It is known [4] that for $d = 1$ there is an $\tilde{O}(N^{3/4})$ upper bound and the recent new techniques of Aaronson [1] followed by Shi's sharpened results [12] imply an $\Omega(N^{2/3})$ lower bound for the problem. We note here that the simultaneous claw problem has a quantum upper bound of $\tilde{O}(N^{3/4} \log^d N)$. On the other hand, we are not able to strengthen the lower bound of $\Omega(N^{2/3})$ which already holds for a single claw pair (f, g). The following theorem is easy to prove.

Theorem 6. *There is a quantum algorithm that takes as input a collection $(f_i, g_i), 1 \leq i \leq d$ of functions where $f_i : [N] \to X$ and $g_i : [N] \to X$, where X is some set, which makes $\tilde{O}(N^{3/4} \log^d N)$ queries in the quantum query model and outputs a simultaneous claw $x \in [N]$, if it exists, such that $f_i(x) = g_i(x)$ for each $i = 1, 2, \ldots, d$.*

We recall the r-to-1 collision problem: given as input $f : [N] \to X$ with the promise that f is either 1-1 or r-to-1, the problem is to find $x \neq y \in [N]$ such that $f(x) = f(y)$. Recent results in [1,12] imply an $\Omega(N^{1/3})$ lower bound for the 2-to-1 collision problem. Analogous to the simultaneous claw problem we can define the simultaneous 2-to-1 collision problem which is given as input $f_i : [N] \to X, 1 \leq i \leq d$, with the promise that either all the f_i are 1-1 or all are 2-to-1, find a pair $x \neq y \in [N]$ if it exists such that $f_i(x) = f_i(y)$ for each i. We do not know anything better than the $\Omega(N^{1/3})$ lower bound of [12]. On the other hand, we have a straightforward algorithm that gives an upper bound for the problem.

Theorem 7. *There is a quantum algorithm that takes as input a collection $f_i, 1 \leq i \leq d$ of functions $f_i : [N] \rightarrow X$ where X is some set, makes $\tilde{O}(N^{3/4} \log^d N)$ queries in the quantum query model and outputs a simultaneous collision $x \neq y \in [N]$ such that $f_i(x) = f_i(y)$ for each $i = 1, 2, \ldots, d$, if it exists.*

References

1. S. AARONSON, Quantum Lower Bound for the Collision Problem. *Proceedings of the 34th Annual ACM Symp. on Theory of Computing*, 2002, pp. 635–642.
2. A. AMBAINIS, Quantum lower bounds by quantum arguments. *Journal of Computer and System Sciences*, 64(2002), pp. 750–767.
3. C.H. BENNETT, E. BERNSTEIN, G. BRASSARD, U. VAZIRANI, Strengths and weaknesses of quantum computing. *SIAM Journal on Computing*, 26(5), 1997, pp. 1510–1523.
4. HARRY BUHRMAN, RONALD DE WOLF, CHRISTOPH DURR, MARK HEILIGMAN, PETER HOYER, FREDERIC MAGNIEZ, MIKLOS SANTHA, Quantum Algorithms for Element Distinctness. *16th Annual Conference on Computational Complexity*, 2001, pp. 131–137.
5. G. BRASSARD, P. HOYER, M. MOSCA, A. TAPP, Quantum amplitude amplification and estimation. *In Quantum Computation and Quantum Information: A Millennium Volume, AMS Contemporary Mathematics Series*, 2002, to appear.
6. R. CLEVE, An introduction to quantum complexity theory. *quant-ph/9906111*, 1999.
7. L.K. GROVER, A fast quantum mechanical algorithm for database search. *Proceedings of 28th Symp of Theory of Computing*, 1996, pp. 212–219.
8. G.L. NEMHAUSER, L.A. WOLSEY, *Integer and Combinatorial Optimization*. Wiley-Interscience Series, New York, 1988.
9. RAMAMOHAN PATURI, PAVEL PUDLAK, FRANCIS ZANE, Satisfiability Coding Lemma, *Chicago Journal of Theoretical Computer Science*, 11, 31 December, 1999
10. F.P. PREPARATA, M.I. SHAMOS, *Computational Geometry: An Introduction*. Springer Verlag, New York Inc., 1985.
11. P.W. SHOR, Polynomial-time algorithms for prime factorization and discrete logarithms on a quantum computer. *SIAM Journal on Computing*, 26(5), 1997, pp. 1484–1509.
12. Y. SHI, Quantum lower bounds for the collision and the element distinctness problems. *Proceedings of the 43rd Symposium on the Foundations of Computer Science*, 513–519, 2002.

Non-interactive Quantum Perfect and Statistical Zero-Knowledge

Hirotada Kobayashi

Quantum Computation and Information Project,
Exploratory Research for Advanced Technology,
Japan Science and Technology Corporation,
5-28-3 Hongo, Bunkyo-ku, Tokyo 113-0033, Japan
hirotada@qci.jst.go.jp

Abstract. This paper introduces quantum analogues of non-interactive perfect and statistical zero-knowledge proof systems. Similar to the classical cases, it is shown that sharing randomness or entanglement is necessary for non-trivial protocols of non-interactive quantum perfect and statistical zero-knowledge. It is also shown that, with sharing EPR pairs a priori, the complexity class resulting from non-interactive quantum perfect zero-knowledge proof systems of perfect completeness has a natural complete promise problem. Using our complete promise problem, the Graph Non-Automorphism problem is shown to have a non-interactive quantum perfect zero-knowledge proof system.

1 Introduction

Zero-knowledge proof systems were introduced by Goldwasser, Micali, and Rackoff [10] and have been studied extensively from both complexity theoretical and cryptographic viewpoints. Because of their wide applicability in the domain of classical communication and cryptography, the quantum analogue of zero-knowledge proof systems is expected to play very important roles in the domain of quantum communication and cryptography.

Very recently Watrous [21] proposed a formal model of quantum statistical zero-knowledge proof systems. To our knowledge, his model is the only one for a formal model of quantum zero-knowledge proofs, although he considered only the case with an *honest verifier*. The reason why he put such a restriction seems to be that even his model may not give a cryptographically satisfying definition for quantum statistical zero-knowledge when the honest verifier assumption is absent. Indeed, generally speaking, difficulties arise when we try to define the notion of quantum zero-knowledge against dishonest verifiers by extending classical definitions of zero-knowledge in the most straightforward ways. See [11] for a discussion of such difficulties in security of quantum protocols. Nevertheless, the model of quantum statistical zero-knowledge proofs by Watrous is natural and reasonable at least in some restricted situations. One of such situations is the case with an honest verifier, which was discussed by Watrous himself. Another situation is the case of *non-interactive* protocols, which this paper treats.

T. Ibaraki, N. Katoh, and H. Ono (Eds.): ISAAC 2003, LNCS 2906, pp. 178–188, 2003.

Classical version of non-interactive zero-knowledge proof systems was introduced by Blum, Feldman, and Micali [2], and was later studied by a number of works [4,5,1,7,14,3,9,19]. Such non-interactive proof systems put an assumption that a verifier and a prover share some random string, and this shared randomness is necessary for non-trivial protocols (i.e., protocols for problems beyond BPP) of non-interactive quantum zero-knowledge proofs [7]. As for non-interactive statistical zero-knowledge proof systems, De Santis, Di Crescenzo, Persiano, and Yung [3] showed that the resulting complexity class NISZK has a complete promise problem, namely the Image Density (ID) problem. Goldreich, Sahai, and Vadhan [9] showed another two complete promise problems for NISZK, the Entropy Approximation (EA) problem and the Statistical Difference from Uniform (SDU) problem, from which they derived a number of properties of NISZK such as evidence of non-triviality of the class NISZK.

This paper focuses on quantum analogues of non-interactive perfect and statistical zero-knowledge proof systems. The notion of quantum zero-knowledge used in this paper is along the lines defined by Watrous [21]. Similar to the classical cases, it is shown that shared randomness or entanglement is necessary for non-trivial protocols (i.e., protocols for problems beyond BQP) of non-interactive quantum perfect and statistical zero-knowledge. It is proved that, with sharing EPR pairs a priori, the complexity class resulting from non-interactive quantum perfect zero-knowledge proof systems of perfect completeness has a natural complete promise problem, which we call the *Quantum State Closeness to Maximally Mixed (QSCMM)* problem, informally described as follows: given a description of a quantum circuit Q, is the output quantum state of Q close to the maximally mixed state or is it far from that? Note that our QSCMM problem may be viewed as a quantum variant of the SDU problem, which was shown NISZK-complete by Goldreich, Sahai, and Vadhan [9]. However, our proof for the completeness of the QSCMM problem is quite different from their proof for the classical case at least in the following two senses: (i) the completeness of the QSCMM problem is shown in a direct manner, while that of the classical SDU problem was shown by using other complete problems such as the ID problem and the EA problem, and (ii) our proof is rather quantum information theoretical. Using our complete problem, it is straightforward to show that the Graph Non-Automorphism (GNA) problem (or sometimes called the Rigid Graphs problem), which is not known in BQP, has a non-interactive quantum perfect zero-knowledge proof system of perfect completeness. Classically, the GNA problem can be reduced to the EA problem [19], and thus it is in NISZK. However, the protocol for the EA problem [9] makes use of hash functions, and is quite complicated. In contrast, both our reduction from a GNA instance to a QSCMM instance and our protocol for the QSCMM problem are remarkably simple.

One of the merits of considering non-interactive models is that the zero-knowledge property in such protocols does not depend on whether the verifier in the protocol is honest or not. Thus, our results may be the first non-trivial quantum zero-knowledge proofs secure even against dishonest quantum verifiers.

Familiarity with the basics of quantum computation and information theory is assumed throughout this paper. See [12,16,15], for instance.

2   Definitions

We start with a notion of polynomial-time preparable sets of quantum states introduced by Watrous [21]. Throughout this paper we assume that all input strings are over the alphabet $\Sigma = \{0, 1\}$, and $\mathbb{N}$ and $\mathbb{Z}^+$ denote the sets of natural numbers and nonnegative integers, respectively. We also use the notation $\mathbf{D}(\mathcal{H})$ for the set of mixed states in $\mathcal{H}$.

A collection $\{\rho_x\}$ of mixed states is *polynomial-time preparable* if there exists a polynomial-time uniformly generated family $\{Q_x\}$ of quantum circuits such that, for every x of length n, (i) Q_x is a quantum circuit over $q(n)$ qubits for some polynomially bounded function $q \colon \mathbb{Z}^+ \to \mathbb{N}$, and (ii) for the pure state $Q_x|0^{q(n)}\rangle$, the first $q_{\mathrm{out}}(n)$ qubits of it is in the mixed state ρ_x when tracing out the rest $q(n) - q_{\mathrm{out}}(n)$ qubits, where $q_{\mathrm{out}} \colon \mathbb{Z}^+ \to \mathbb{N}$ is a polynomially bounded function satisfying $q_{\mathrm{out}} \leq q$. In this context, the collection of the first $q_{\mathrm{out}}(n)$ qubits may be regarded as an output, and thus we also say that such a family $\{Q_x\}$ of quantum circuits is q-in q_{out}-out.

Now we give a definition of non-interactive quantum perfect and statistical zero-knowledge proof systems in terms of quantum circuits.

For each input x of length n, the entire system of our quantum circuit consists of $q(n) = q_{\mathcal{V}}(n) + q_{\mathcal{M}}(n) + q_{\mathcal{P}}(n)$ qubits, where $q_{\mathcal{V}}(n)$ is the number of qubits that are private to a verifier V, $q_{\mathcal{P}}(n)$ is the number of qubits that are private to a prover P, and $q_{\mathcal{M}}(n)$ is the number of message qubits sent from P to V. Furthermore, it is assumed that the verifier V and the prover P share EPR pairs a priori among their private qubits. Let $q_{\mathcal{S}}(n)$ be the number of the EPR pairs shared by V and P. It is also assumed that $q_{\mathcal{V}}$, $q_{\mathcal{M}}$, and $q_{\mathcal{S}}$ are polynomially bounded functions. Let $q_{\mathcal{V}_{\overline{\mathcal{S}}}} = q_{\mathcal{V}} - q_{\mathcal{S}}$ and $q_{\mathcal{P}_{\overline{\mathcal{S}}}} = q_{\mathcal{P}} - q_{\mathcal{S}}$.

A $(q_{\mathcal{V}}, q_{\mathcal{M}})$-*restricted quantum verifier* V is a polynomial-time computable mapping of the form $V \colon \Sigma^* \to \Sigma^*$. V receives a message of at most $q_{\mathcal{M}}(n)$ qubits from the prover, and uses at most $q_{\mathcal{V}}(n)$ qubits for his private space, including qubits of shared EPR pairs. For every x, $V(x)$ is interpreted as a description of a polynomial-time uniformly generated quantum circuit acting on $q_{\mathcal{V}}(n) + q_{\mathcal{M}}(n)$ qubits. One of the private qubits of V is designated as the output qubit.

A $(q_{\mathcal{M}}, q_{\mathcal{P}})$-*restricted quantum prover* P is a mapping of the form $P \colon \Sigma^* \to \Sigma^*$. P uses at most $q_{\mathcal{P}}(n)$ qubits for his private space, including qubits of shared EPR pairs, and sends a message of at most $q_{\mathcal{M}}(n)$ qubits to the verifier. For every x, $P(x)$ is interpreted as a description of a quantum circuit acting on $q_{\mathcal{M}}(n) + q_{\mathcal{P}}(n)$ qubits. No restrictions are placed on the complexity of the mapping P (i.e., $P(x)$ can be an arbitrary unitary transformation).

A $(q_{\mathcal{V}}, q_{\mathcal{M}}, q_{\mathcal{P}})$-*restricted non-interactive quantum proof system* consists of a $(q_{\mathcal{V}}, q_{\mathcal{M}})$-restricted quantum verifier V and a $(q_{\mathcal{M}}, q_{\mathcal{P}})$-restricted quantum prover P. Let $\mathcal{V} = l_2(\Sigma^{q_{\mathcal{V}}})$, $\mathcal{M} = l_2(\Sigma^{q_{\mathcal{M}}})$, and $\mathcal{P} = l_2(\Sigma^{q_{\mathcal{P}}})$ denote the Hilbert spaces corresponding to the private qubits of the verifier, the message qubits between the verifier and the prover, and the private qubits of the prover, respectively. A (q_V, q_M, q_P)-restricted non-interactive quantum proof system is q_S-shared-EPR-pairs if, for every x of length n, there are $q_S(n)$ copies of the EPR pair $(|00\rangle + |11\rangle)/\sqrt{2}$ that are initially shared by the verifier and the prover. Let $\mathcal{V}_S = l_2(\Sigma^{q_S})$ and $\mathcal{P}_S = l_2(\Sigma^{q_S})$ denote the Hilbert spaces corresponding to the verifier and the prover parts of these shared EPR pairs, respectively, and write $\mathcal{V} = \mathcal{V}_{\overline{S}} \otimes \mathcal{V}_S$ and $\mathcal{P} = \mathcal{P}_{\overline{S}} \otimes \mathcal{P}_S$. It is assumed that all the qubits in $\mathcal{V}_{\overline{S}}$, $\mathcal{M}$, and $\mathcal{P}_{\overline{S}}$ are initialized to the $|0\rangle$-state.

Given a verifier V, a prover P, and an input x of length n, define a circuit $(P(x), V(x))$ acting on $q(n)$ qubits to be the one applying $P(x)$ to $\mathcal{M} \otimes \mathcal{P}$ and $V(x)$ to $\mathcal{V} \otimes \mathcal{M}$ in sequence. The probability that (P, V) accepts x is defined to be the probability that an observation of the output qubit in the basis of $\{|0\rangle, |1\rangle\}$ yields $|1\rangle$, after the circuit $(P(x), V(x))$ is applied to the initial state.

In what follows, the circuits $P(x)$ and $V(x)$ may be simply denoted by P and V, respectively, if it is not confusing. Furthermore it is assumed that operators acting on subsystems of a given system are extended to the entire system by tensoring with the identity, when it is clear from context upon what part of a system a given operator acts.

The classes NIQPZK(a, b) and NIQSZK(a, b) of languages having non-interactive quantum perfect and statistical zero-knowledge proof systems with error probabilities a and b in completeness and soundness sides, respectively, are defined as follows.

Definition 1. *Given functions $a, b \colon \mathbb{Z}^+ \to [0, 1]$, a language L is in NIQPZK(a, b) (resp. NIQSZK(a, b)) if there exist polynomially bounded functions $q_V, q_M, q_S \colon \mathbb{Z}^+ \to \mathbb{N}$ and a (q_V, q_M)-restricted quantum verifier V such that, for every input x of length n,*

(i)   Completeness:
if $x \in L$, there exist a function $q_P \colon \mathbb{Z}^+ \to \mathbb{N}$ and a (q_M, q_P)-restricted quantum prover P, where P and V share $q_S(n)$ EPR-pairs a priori, such that (P, V) accepts x with probability at least $a(n)$,

(ii) Soundness:
if $x \notin L$, for any function $q_{P'} \colon \mathbb{Z}^+ \to \mathbb{N}$ and any $(q_M, q_{P'})$-restricted quantum prover P', where P' and V share $q_S(n)$ EPR-pairs a priori, (P', V) accepts x with probability at most $b(n)$,

(iii) Zero-Knowledge:
there exists a polynomial-time preparable set $\{\sigma_x\}$ of mixed states of $q_V(n) + q_M(n)$ qubits such that, if $x \in L$, $\sigma_x = \mathrm{tr}_\mathcal{P}(P|\psi_{\mathrm{init}}\rangle\langle\psi_{\mathrm{init}}|P^\dagger)$ (resp. $\|\sigma_x - \mathrm{tr}_\mathcal{P}(P|\psi_{\mathrm{init}}\rangle\langle\psi_{\mathrm{init}}|P^\dagger)\|_{\mathrm{tr}}$ is negligible in n) for the honest prover P, where $|\psi_{\mathrm{init}}\rangle$ is the initial state in which all the qubits except for the $q_S(n)$ shared EPR-pairs are in the $|0\rangle$-state.

A few notes are in order regarding our definitions of non-interactive quantum perfect and statistical zero-knowledge. First, note that the state $\mathrm{tr}_\mathcal{P}(P|\psi_{\mathrm{init}}\rangle\langle\psi_{\mathrm{init}}|P^\dagger)$ in Definition 1 corresponds to the "verifier's view". Second, Definition 1 requires the set $\{\sigma_x\}$ to be prepared in *worst-case* polynomial time *without fail*. This is in contrast to the common definitions of various classical zero-knowledge proofs in which the simulator is an *expected* polynomial-time machine or a worst-case polynomial-time machine *that may fail*. Third, similar to the QMA case [20,15], parallel repetition of non-interactive quantum perfect and statistical zero-knowledge proof systems can reduce completeness and soundness errors to be exponentially small while preserving the zero-knowledge property. Fourth, the classes NIQSZK and NIQPZK above, which are defined in terms of languages, can be naturally rephrased to those in terms of promise problems. Throughout this paper, we allow a little abuse of complexity classes and common complexity classes such as BPP and BQP are also considered to be those naturally rephrased in terms of promise problems. See [6] for detailed description on promise problems.

Finally, similar to the classical cases [7], shared randomness or entanglement is necessary for non-trivial protocols of non-interactive quantum perfect or statistical zero-knowledge. The proof is straightforward and thus omitted.

Theorem 2. *Without shared randomness or shared entanglement, any problem having non-interactive quantum perfect or statistical zero-knowledge proofs is necessarily in* BQP.

3   Complete Promise Problem for NIQPZK$(1, 1/2)$

This paper considers the promise problem called (α, β)-*Quantum State Closeness to Maximally Mixed* $((\alpha, \beta)$-*QSCMM)* problem, which is parameterized by constants α and β satisfying $0 \leq \alpha < \beta \leq 1$. Our promise problem is a variant of the (α, β)-*Quantum State Distinguishability* $((\alpha, \beta)$-*QSD)* problem and its complement, the (α, β)-*Quantum State Closeness* $((\alpha, \beta)$-*QSC)* problem, both of which were introduced and shown to be HVQSZK-complete (for any $0 \leq \alpha < \beta^2 \leq 1$) by Watrous [21]. As the (α, β)-QSD problem is a quantum analogue of the Statistical Difference (SD) problem [17], which is HVSZK-complete (and thus SZK-complete from the consecutive result HVSZK = SZK [8]), so the (α, β)-QSCMM problem is a quantum analogue of the Statistical Difference from Uniform Distribution (SDU) problem [9], which is NISZK-complete.

(α, β)-Quantum State Closeness to Maximally Mixed $((\alpha, \beta)$-QSCMM)

Input: A description of a quantum circuit Q acting over the Hilbert space $\mathcal{H}_{\text{in}} = \mathcal{H}_{\text{out}} \otimes \mathcal{H}_{\overline{\text{out}}}$, where $\mathcal{H}_{\text{in}}$ consists of q_{in} qubits and $\mathcal{H}_{\text{out}}$ consists of $q_{\text{out}} \leq q_{\text{in}}$ qubits.

Promise: For $\rho = \text{tr}_{\mathcal{H}_{\overline{\text{out}}}}(Q|0^{q_{\text{in}}}\rangle\langle 0^{q_{\text{in}}}|Q^{\dagger})$, we have either $\|\rho - I/2^{q_{\text{out}}}\|_{\text{tr}} \leq \alpha$ or $\|\rho - I/2^{q_{\text{out}}}\|_{\text{tr}} \geq \beta$.

Output: Accept if $\|\rho - I/2^{q_{\text{out}}}\|_{\text{tr}} \leq \alpha$, and reject if $\|\rho - I/2^{q_{\text{out}}}\|_{\text{tr}} \geq \beta$.

Now we show that the $(0, \beta)$-QSCMM problem is NIQPZK$(1, 1/2)$-complete for any $0 < \beta < 1$. Since parallel repetition works well for non-interactive quantum perfect zero-knowledge proofs, this implies the NIQPZK$(1, b)$-completeness for any bounded error probability b.

First we show that $(0, \beta)$-QSCMM is in NIQPZK$(1, 1/2)$. The proof uses the following well-known property in quantum information theory.

Theorem 3 ([18,13]). *For any pure states* $|\phi\rangle, |\psi\rangle \in \mathcal{H} \otimes \mathcal{K}$ *satisfying* $\text{tr}_\mathcal{K}|\phi\rangle\langle\phi| = \text{tr}_\mathcal{K}|\psi\rangle\langle\psi|$, *there exists a unitary transformation* U *over* $\mathcal{K}$ *such that* $(I_\mathcal{H} \otimes U)|\phi\rangle = |\psi\rangle$, *where* $I_\mathcal{H}$ *is the identity operator over* $\mathcal{H}$.

Lemma 4. $(0, \beta)$-QSCMM is in NIQPZK$(1, 1/2)$ for any $0 < \beta < 1$.

Proof. Let Q be a quantum circuit of the $(0, \beta)$-QSCMM, which is q-in q_{out}-out. Running $O(n)$ copies of Q in parallel for n exceeding the length of the input Q constructs a quantum circuit R of q'-in q'_{out}-out that outputs the associated mixed state ξ of q'_{out} qubits such that ξ either is $I/2^{q'_{\text{out}}}$ or satisfies $\|\xi - I/2^{q'_{\text{out}}}\|_{\text{tr}} > 1 - 2^{-n}$.

We construct a $(q'_{\text{out}}, q' - q'_{\text{out}})$-restricted quantum verifier V of a non-interactive quantum perfect zero-knowledge proof system of q'_{out}-shared-EPR-pairs (i.e., all the private qubits of V are particles of the shared EPR-pairs). Let the quantum registers $\mathbf{M}$ and $\mathbf{S}$ consist of the message qubits and the qubits in the verifier part of the shared EPR pairs, respectively. The verification procedure of V is as follows:

1. Receive a message in $\mathbf{M}$ from the prover.
2. Apply $R^\dagger$ on the pair of quantum registers $(\mathbf{M}, \mathbf{S})$.
3. Accept if $(\mathbf{M}, \mathbf{S})$ contains $0^{q'}$, and reject otherwise.

Hereafter, it is assumed that the output qubits of R and $R^\dagger$ correspond to the qubits in $\mathbf{S}$ in the applications of R and $R^\dagger$.

For the completeness, suppose that $\xi = I/2^{q'_{\text{out}}}$. Let $q_\mathcal{P} = q'_{\text{out}}$ be the number of private qubits of an honest prover (i.e., all the private qubits of the honest prover are particles of the shared EPR-pairs). Note that the pure state $|\phi\rangle = (R|0^{q'}\rangle) \otimes |0^{q_\mathcal{P}}\rangle$ of $q' + q_\mathcal{P}$ qubits is a purification of ξ. Since the initial state $|\psi_{\text{init}}\rangle \in \mathcal{V} \otimes \mathcal{M} \otimes \mathcal{P}$ of $q' + q_\mathcal{P}$ qubits is a purification of $I/2^{q'_{\text{out}}}$ and $\xi = I/2^{q'_{\text{out}}}$, from Theorem 3, there exists a unitary transformation P over $\mathcal{M} \otimes \mathcal{P}$ such that $(I_\mathcal{V} \otimes P)|\psi_{\text{init}}\rangle = |\phi\rangle$, where $I_\mathcal{V}$ is the identity operator over $\mathcal{V}$. Therefore,

$$(R^\dagger \otimes I_\mathcal{P})(I_\mathcal{V} \otimes P)|\psi_{\text{init}}\rangle = |0^{q' + q_\mathcal{P}}\rangle,$$

where $I_\mathcal{P}$ is the identity operator over $\mathcal{P}$. Thus V accepts the input with certainty.

For the soundness, suppose that $\|\xi - I/2^{q'_{\text{out}}}\|_{\text{tr}} > 1 - 2^{-n}$. Then, for arbitrarily large private space $\mathcal{P}'$ of a prover and any unitary transformation P' over $\mathcal{M} \otimes \mathcal{P}'$, letting $|\psi\rangle = (I_\mathcal{V} \otimes P')|\psi'_{\text{init}}\rangle$ for the initial state $|\psi'_{\text{init}}\rangle \in \mathcal{V} \otimes \mathcal{M} \otimes \mathcal{P}'$, we have

$$\|R|0^{q'}\rangle\langle 0^{q'}|R^\dagger - \text{tr}_{\mathcal{P}'}|\psi\rangle\langle\psi|\|_{\text{tr}} > 1 - 2^{-n},$$

since $\text{tr}_{\mathcal{M}}(R|0^{q'}\rangle\langle 0^{q'}|R^{\dagger}) = \xi$ and $\text{tr}_{\mathcal{M}}(\text{tr}_{\mathcal{P}'}|\psi\rangle\langle\psi|) = I/2^{q'_{\text{out}}}$. Therefore we have

$$\||0^{q'}\rangle\langle 0^{q'}| - R^{\dagger}(\text{tr}_{\mathcal{P}'}|\psi\rangle\langle\psi|)R\|_{\text{tr}} > 1 - 2^{-n}.$$

Thus, using the relation between the trace norm and fidelity, it follows that the probability that V accepts the input is negligible.

Finally, the fact that $R|0^{q'}\rangle\langle 0^{q'}|R^{\dagger} = \text{tr}_{\mathcal{P}}((I_{\mathcal{V}} \otimes P)|\psi_{\text{init}}\rangle\langle\psi_{\text{init}}|(I_{\mathcal{V}} \otimes P^{\dagger}))$ is polynomial-time preparable ensures the perfect zero-knowledge property. $\square$

Next we show the NIQPZK$(1, 1/2)$-hardness of $(0, \beta)$-QSCMM. For this, we state one fundamental property on trace norms without a proof.

Theorem 5. *For a constant α, $0 \le \alpha < 1$, let ρ be a mixed state of n qubits satisfying $\|\rho - I/2^n\|_{\text{tr}} \ge \alpha$. Then for any mixed state σ of n qubits and any constant β satisfying $0 \le \beta \le \alpha$, $\|(1 - \beta)\rho + \beta\sigma - I/2^n\|_{\text{tr}} \ge \alpha - \beta$.*

Lemma 6. *For any problem A in NIQPZK$(1, 1/2)$, there is a deterministic polynomial-time procedure that reduces A to the $(0, \beta)$-QSCMM problem for $0 < \beta < 1$.*

Proof. Let $A = \{A_{\text{yes}}, A_{\text{no}}\}$ be in NIQPZK$(1, 1/2)$. Then from the fact that parallel repetition works well for non-interactive quantum perfect zero-knowledge proof systems, there exist polynomially bounded functions $q_{\mathcal{V}}, q_{\mathcal{M}}, q_{\mathcal{S}} \colon \mathbb{Z}^+ \to \mathbb{N}$ and a $(q_{\mathcal{V}}, q_{\mathcal{M}})$-restricted quantum verifier V such that, for every input x of length n, (i) if $x \in A_{\text{yes}}$, there exist a function $q_{\mathcal{P}} \colon \mathbb{Z}^+ \to \mathbb{N}$ and a $(q_{\mathcal{M}}, q_{\mathcal{P}})$-restricted quantum prover P, who shares $q_{\mathcal{S}}(n)$ EPR-pairs with V a priori, such that (P, V) accepts x with certainty, and (ii) if $x \in A_{\text{no}}$, for any function $q_{\mathcal{P}'} \colon \mathbb{Z}^+ \to \mathbb{N}$ and any $(q_{\mathcal{M}}, q_{\mathcal{P}'})$-restricted quantum prover P', who shares $q_{\mathcal{S}}(n)$ EPR-pairs with V a priori, (P', V) accepts x with probability smaller than 2^{-n}. Without loss of generality, we assume that $q_{\mathcal{S}}(n) \ge n$.

Let $V(x)$ and $P(x)$ be the unitary transformations of the honest verifier V and the honest prover P, respectively, on a given input x. Let $\{\sigma_x\}$ be a polynomial-time preparable set such that, if the input x of length n is in A_{yes},

$$\sigma_x = \text{tr}_{\mathcal{P}}(P(x)|\psi_{\text{init}}\rangle\langle\psi_{\text{init}}|P(x)^{\dagger})$$

for the honest prover P. The existence of such a polynomial-time preparable set is ensured by the perfect zero-knowledge property. For convenience, we assume that, for every x of length n, the first $q_{\mathcal{M}}(n)$ qubits of σ_x correspond to the message qubits, the last $q_{\mathcal{V}_{\overline{S}}}(n) = q_{\mathcal{V}}(n) - q_{\mathcal{S}}(n)$ qubits of σ_x correspond to the private qubits of the verifier (not including the prior-entangled part), and the last qubit corresponds to the output qubit, of the original proof system, respectively.

Let $\mathbf{M}$, $\mathbf{S}$, and $\mathbf{V}$ be quantum registers, each of which consists of $q_{\mathcal{M}}(n)$, $q_{\mathcal{S}}(n)$, and $q_{\mathcal{V}_{\overline{S}}}(n)$ qubits, respectively. For every x, we construct a quantum circuit Q_x that corresponds to the following algorithm:

1. Prepare σ_x in the triplet $(\mathbf{M}, \mathbf{S}, \mathbf{V})$ of the quantum registers.

2. If one of qubits in the quantum register $\mathbf{V}$ contains 1, output $|0^{qs(n)}\rangle\langle 0^{qs(n)}|$.

3. Do one of the following two uniformly at random.

   3.1 Output the qubits in the quantum register $\mathbf{S}$.

   3.2 Apply $V(x)$ on the triplet $(\mathbf{M}, \mathbf{S}, \mathbf{V})$ of the quantum registers. Output $I/2^{qs(n)}$ if the last qubit in $\mathbf{V}$ contains 1, and output $|0^{qs(n)}\rangle\langle 0^{qs(n)}|$ otherwise.

Suppose that x is in A_{yes}. Then $\sigma_x = \text{tr}_{\mathcal{P}}(P(x)|\psi_{\text{init}}\rangle\langle\psi_{\text{init}}|P(x)^{\dagger})$ is satisfied. Note that $\text{tr}_{\mathcal{V_S}\otimes\mathcal{M}\otimes\mathcal{P}}(P(x)|\psi_{\text{init}}\rangle\langle\psi_{\text{init}}|P(x)^{\dagger}) = I/2^{qs(n)}$. Furthermore, for the state $P(x)|\psi_{\text{init}}\rangle\langle\psi_{\text{init}}|P(x)^{\dagger}$, the verification procedure of V accepts x with certainty. Hence the circuit Q_x constructed above outputs $I/2^{qs(n)}$ with certainty.

Now suppose that x is in A_{no}. We claim that the output ρ of Q_x satisfies $\|\rho - I/2^{qs(n)}\|_{\text{tr}} > c$ for some constant $0 < c < 1$.

First we assume that σ_x is of the form $\sigma'_x \otimes |0^{qv_{\overline{S}}(n)}\rangle\langle 0^{qv_{\overline{S}}(n)}|$.

From the soundness property of the original proof system, the verification procedure of V results in acceptance with probability smaller than 2^{-n}, for any mixed state $\xi \otimes |0^{qv_{\overline{S}}(n)}\rangle\langle 0^{qv_{\overline{S}}(n)}|$ in $\mathbf{D}(\mathcal{M}\otimes\mathcal{V})$ satisfying $\text{tr}_{\mathcal{M}\otimes\mathcal{V_S}}(\xi \otimes |0^{qv_{\overline{S}}(n)}\rangle\langle 0^{qv_{\overline{S}}(n)}|) = I/2^{qs(n)}$.

Therefore, if $\left\|\text{tr}_{\mathcal{M}\otimes\mathcal{V_{\overline{S}}}}(\sigma'_x \otimes |0^{qv_{\overline{S}}(n)}\rangle\langle 0^{qv_{\overline{S}}(n)}|) - I/2^{qs(n)}\right\|_{\text{tr}} < 2/3$, we have $\left\|\sigma'_x \otimes |0^{qv_{\overline{S}}(n)}\rangle\langle 0^{qv_{\overline{S}}(n)}| - \xi \otimes |0^{qv_{\overline{S}}(n)}\rangle\langle 0^{qv_{\overline{S}}(n)}|\right\|_{\text{tr}} < 2/3$ for some mixed state $\xi \otimes |0^{qv_{\overline{S}}(n)}\rangle\langle 0^{qv_{\overline{S}}(n)}|$ in $\mathbf{D}(\mathcal{M}\otimes\mathcal{V})$ satisfying $\text{tr}_{\mathcal{M}\otimes\mathcal{V_{\overline{S}}}}(\xi \otimes |0^{qv_{\overline{S}}(n)}\rangle\langle 0^{qv_{\overline{S}}(n)}|) = I/2^{qs(n)}$. It follows that the step 3.2 results in rejection and outputs $|0^{qs(n)}\rangle\langle 0^{qs(n)}|$ with probability greater than $1/3 - 2^{-n}$. Since $qs(n) \geq n$, this implies that Q_x outputs the mixed state ρ satisfying $\|\rho - I/2^{qs(n)}\|_{\text{tr}} > 1/6 - 3 \cdot 2^{-(n+1)}$.

On the other hand, if $\left\|\text{tr}_{\mathcal{M}\otimes\mathcal{V_{\overline{S}}}}(\sigma'_x \otimes |0^{qv_{\overline{S}}(n)}\rangle\langle 0^{qv_{\overline{S}}(n)}|) - I/2^{qs(n)}\right\|_{\text{tr}} \geq 2/3$, that is, if $\|\text{tr}_{\mathcal{M}}\sigma'_x - I/2^{qs(n)}\|_{\text{tr}} \geq 2/3$, from Theorem 5, Q_x outputs the mixed state ρ satisfying $\|\rho - I/2^{qs(n)}\|_{\text{tr}} \geq 1/6$, since the step 3.1 outputs $\text{tr}_{\mathcal{M}}\sigma'_x$.

Putting things together, the circuit Q_x outputs the mixed state ρ satisfying $\|\rho - I/2^{qs(n)}\|_{\text{tr}} > 1/7$ (for $n \geq 6$), if σ_x is of the form $\sigma'_x \otimes |0^{qv_{\overline{S}}(n)}\rangle\langle 0^{qv_{\overline{S}}(n)}|$.

To deal with general σ_x, notice that the step 2 outputs the state farthest away from $I/2^{qs(n)}$ with some probability p, or otherwise reduces σ_x to the state of the form $\sigma'_x \otimes |0^{qv_{\overline{S}}(n)}\rangle\langle 0^{qv_{\overline{S}}(n)}|$. For the latter case, the step 3 outputs the mixed state ρ' satisfying $\|\rho' - I/2^{qs(n)}\|_{\text{tr}} > 1/7$ (for $n \geq 6$) from the argument above. Thus, if x is in A_{no}, from Theorem 5, the circuit Q_x outputs the mixed state ρ satisfying $\|\rho - I/2^{qs(n)}\|_{\text{tr}} > \max\{1/7 - p, p - 2^{-n}\} > 1/15$ (for $n \geq 8$).

Now, constructing r copies of Q_x for appropriately chosen r to have a circuit $Q_x^{\otimes r}$ reduces A to the $(0, \beta)$-QSCMM problem for arbitrary $0 < \beta < 1$. $\qquad\square$

Thus we have the following theorem.

Theorem 7. $(0, \beta)$-*QSCMM is complete for* NIQPZK$(1, 1/2)$ *for* $0 < \beta < 1$.

4   Graph Non-automorphism is in NIQPZK$(1, 1/2)$

The *Graph Non-Automorphism (GNA)* problem is a variant of the *graph non-isomorphism (GNI)* problem, and is not known in BQP nor in NP.

Graph Non-Automorphism (GNA)

Input: A description of a graph G of n vertices.

Output: Accept if $\pi(G) \neq G$ for all non-trivial permutations π over n vertices and reject otherwise.

It is easy to show that any instance of GNA is reduced to an instance of $(0, \beta)$-QSCMM, and thus we have the following corollary.

Corollary 8. *GNA has a non-interactive quantum perfect zero-knowledge proof system of perfect completeness.*

Proof. We assume an appropriate ordering of permutations over n vertices so that each permutation can be represented with $q_{\mathcal{P}}(n) = \lceil \log n! \rceil$ qubits. Let π_i be the ith permutation according to this ordering for $0 \leq i \leq n! - 1$.

Let $\mathcal{P}$ be a Hilbert space consisting of $q_{\mathcal{P}}(n)$ qubits and $\mathcal{G}$ be a Hilbert space consisting of $q_{\mathcal{G}}(n) = O(n^2)$ qubits. Given a graph G of n vertices, consider the following quantum circuit Q_G behaving as follows.

1. Prepare the following quantum state in $\mathcal{P} \otimes \mathcal{G}$:

$$\frac{1}{\sqrt{2^{q_{\mathcal{P}}(n)}}} \sum_{i=0}^{n!-1} |i\rangle |0, \pi_i(G)\rangle + \frac{1}{\sqrt{2^{q_{\mathcal{P}}(n)}}} \sum_{i=n!}^{2^{q_{\mathcal{P}}(n)}-1} |i\rangle |1, i\rangle.$$

2. Output the qubits in $\mathcal{P}$.

If a given graph G has no non-trivial automorphism groups, every $\pi_i(G)$ is different from each other, and thus the output of Q_G is the mixed state $I/2^{q_{\mathcal{P}}(n)}$.

On the other hand, if a given graph G has a non-trivial automorphism group, the contents of qubits in $\mathcal{G}$ have at most $2^{q_{\mathcal{P}}(n)} - n!/2 < 3/4 \cdot 2^{q_{\mathcal{P}}(n)}$ variations, and the trace norm between $I/2^{q_{\mathcal{P}}(n)}$ and the output of Q_G is at least $1/4$.

Thus the constructed Q_G is an instance of $(0, 1/4)$-QSCMM.   □

5   Conjectures

We conjecture the following.

Conjecture 9. There is a (deterministic) polynomial-time procedure that, on an input $\langle Q, 1^n \rangle$ where Q is a description of a quantum circuit specifying a mixed state ρ of q_1 qubits, outputs a description of a quantum circuit R (having size polynomial in n and the size of Q) specifying a mixed state ξ of q_2 qubits such that (for α and β satisfying an appropriate condition)

$$\|\rho - I/2^{q_1}\|_{\mathrm{tr}} < \alpha \Rightarrow \|\xi - I/2^{q_2}\|_{\mathrm{tr}} < 2^{-n},$$
$$\|\rho - I/2^{q_1}\|_{\mathrm{tr}} > \beta \Rightarrow \|\xi - I/2^{q_2}\|_{\mathrm{tr}} > 1 - 2^{-n}.$$

Classically, Goldreich, Sahai, and Vadhan [9] implicitly proved a similar property to Conjecture 9. One of the troublesome points in applying a direct modification of their proof to our case is that the joint von Neumann entropy $S(A, B)$ for a composite system with two components A and B can be smaller than $S(A)$ and $S(B)$ (recall that classically the joint Shannon entropy $H(X, Y)$ is never smaller than $H(X)$ and $H(Y)$). Therefore, the classical technique of just discarding some part to reduce the entropy of output distribution no longer works well in the quantum case.

Under the assumption that Conjecture 9 holds, it is easy to modify the proofs of Lemma 4 and Lemma 6 to the statistical zero-knowledge case. Thus the following conjecture is provable if Conjecture 9 holds.

Conjecture 10. (α, β)-QSCMM is complete for NIQSZK for any α and β satisfying an appropriate condition.

References

1. M. Blum, A. De Santis, S. Micali, and G. Persiano. Non-interactive zero-knowledge. *SIAM Journal on Computing*, 20(6):1084–1118, 1991.
2. M. Blum, P. Feldman, and S. Mical. Non-interactive zero-knowledge and its applications (extended abstract). In *Proceedings of the Twentieth Annual ACM Symposium on Theory of Computing*, pages 103–112, 1988.
3. A. De Santis, G. Di Crescenzo, G. Persiano, and M. Yung. Image density is complete for non-interactive-SZK (extended abstract). In *Automata, Languages and Programming, 25th International Colloquium, ICALP '98*, volume 1443 of *Lecture Notes in Computer Science*, pages 784–795, 1998.
4. A. De Santis, S. Micali, and G. Persiano. Non-interactive zero-knowledge proof systems. In *Advances in Cryptology – CRYPTO '87, A Conference on the Theory and Applications of Cryptographic Techniques*, volume 293 of *Lecture Notes in Computer Science*, pages 52–72, 1987.
5. A. De Santis, S. Micali, and G. Persiano. Non-interactive zero-knowledge with preprocessing. In *Advances in Cryptology – CRYPTO '88, 8th Annual International Cryptology Conference*, volume 403 of *Lecture Notes in Computer Science*, pages 269–282, 1988.
6. S. Even, A. L. Selman, and Y. Yacobi. The complexity of promise problems with applications to public-key cryptography. *Information and Control*, 61(2):159–173, 1984.
7. O. Goldreich and Y. Oren. Definitions and properties of zero-knowledge proof systems. *Journal of Cryptology*, 7(1):1–32, 1994.
8. O. Goldreich, A. Sahai, and S. P. Vadhan. Honest-verifier statistical zero-knowledge equals general statistical zero-knowledge. In *Proceedings of the Thirtieth Annual ACM Symposium on Theory of Computing*, pages 399–408, 1998.

9. O. Goldreich, A. Sahai, and S. P. Vadhan. Can statistical zero knowledge be made non-interactive? or on the relationship of SZK and NISZK. In *Advances in Cryptology – CRYPTO '99, 19th Annual International Cryptology Conference*, volume 1666 of *Lecture Notes in Computer Science*, pages 467–484, 1999.

10. S. Goldwasser, S. Micali, and C. Rackoff. The knowledge complexity of interactive proof systems. *SIAM Journal on Computing*, 18(1):186–208, 1989.

11. J. van de Graaf. *Towards a formal definition of security for quantum protocols*. PhD thesis, Département d'Informatique et de Recherche Opérationnelle, Université de Montréal, December 1997.

12. J. D. Gruska. *Quantum Computing*. McGraw-Hill, 1999.

13. L. P. Hughston, R. O. Jozsa, and W. K. Wootters. A complete classification of quantum ensembles having a given density matrix. *Physics Letters A*, 183:14–18, 1993.

14. J. Kilian and E. Petrank. An efficient noninteractive zero-knowledge proof system for NP with general assumptions. *Journal of Cryptology*, 11(1):1–27, 1998.

15. A. Yu. Kitaev, A. H. Shen, and M. N. Vyalyi. *Classical and Quantum Computation*, volume 47 of *Graduate Studies in Mathematics*. American Mathematical Society, 2002.

16. M. A. Nielsen and I. L. Chuang. *Quantum Computation and Quantum Information*. Cambridge University Press, 2000.

17. A. Sahai and S. P. Vadhan. A complete problem for statistical zero knowledge. *Journal of the ACM*, 50(2):196–249, 2003.

18. A. Uhlmann. Parallel transport and "quantum holonomy" along density operators. *Reports on Mathematical Physics*, 24:229–240, 1986.

19. S. P. Vadhan. *A Study of Statistical Zero-Knowledge Proofs*. PhD thesis, Department of Mathematics, Massachusetts Institute of Technology, August 1999.

20. J. H. Watrous. Succinct quantum proofs for properties of finite groups. In *41st Annual Symposium on Foundations of Computer Science*, pages 537–546, 2000.

21. J. H. Watrous. Limits on the power of quantum statistical zero-knowledge. In *43rd Annual Symposium on Foundations of Computer Science*, pages 459–468, 2002.

Quantum Merlin-Arthur Proof Systems: Are Multiple Merlins More Helpful to Arthur?

Hirotada Kobayashi[1,2], Keiji Matsumoto[3,1], and Tomoyuki Yamakami[4]

[1] Quantum Computation and Information Project,
Exploratory Research for Advanced Technology,
Japan Science and Technology Corporation,
5-28-3 Hongo, Bunkyo-ku, Tokyo 113-0033, Japan
hirotada@qci.jst.go.jp
[2] Department of Information Science,
Graduate School of Science, The University of Tokyo,
7-3-1 Hongo, Bunkyo-ku, Tokyo 113-0033, Japan
[3] Foundations of Information Research Division, National Institute of Informatics,
2-1-2 Hitotsubashi, Chiyoda-ku, Tokyo 101-8430, Japan
keiji@nii.ac.jp
[4] School of Information Technology and Engineering, University of Ottawa,
800 King Edward Avenue, Ottawa, Ontario, Canada K1N 6N5
yamakami@site.uottawa.ca

Abstract. This paper introduces quantum "multiple-Merlin"-Arthur proof systems in which Arthur uses multiple quantum proofs unentangled with each other for his verification. Although classical multi-proof systems are obviously equivalent to classical single-proof systems, it is unclear whether quantum multi-proof systems collapse to quantum single-proof systems. This paper presents a necessary and sufficient condition under which the number of quantum proofs is reducible to two. It is also proved that using multiple quantum proofs does not increase the power of quantum Merlin-Arthur proof systems in the case of perfect soundness, and that there is a relativized world in which co-NP (actually co-UP) does not have quantum Merlin-Arthur proof systems even with multiple quantum proofs.

1 Introduction

Babai [3] introduced Merlin-Arthur proof systems in which powerful Merlin, a prover, presents a proof and Arthur, a verifier, probabilistically verifies its correctness with high success probability. The resulting complexity class MA has played important roles in computational complexity theory [3,5,4].

A quantum analogue of MA was first discussed by Knill [15] and studied intensively by Kitaev [12], Watrous [17], and several very recent works such as [11, 2]. In the most commonly-used version of quantum Merlin-Arthur proof systems, a proof presented by Merlin is a pure quantum state called a *quantum proof* and Arthur's verification process is a polynomial-time quantum computation. However, all the previous works only consider the model in which Arthur receives a single quantum proof, and no discussions are done so far on the model in which Arthur receives *multiple* quantum proofs unentangled with each other.

T. Ibaraki, N. Katoh, and H. Ono (Eds.): ISAAC 2003, LNCS 2906, pp. 189–198, 2003.

Classically, multiple proofs can be concatenated into a long single proof, and thus there is no advantage to use multiple proofs. However, it is unclear whether using multiple quantum proofs is computationally equivalent to using a single quantum proof, because knowing that a given proof is a tensor product of some pure states might be advantageous to Arthur. For example, in the case of two quantum proofs versus one, consider the following most straightforward Arthur's simulation of two quantum proofs by a single quantum proof: given a single quantum proof that is expected to be a tensor product of two pure states, Arthur first runs some pre-processing to rule out any quantum proof far from states of a tensor product of two pure states, and then performs the verification procedure for two-proof systems. It turns out that this straightforward method does not work well, since there is no positive operator-valued measurement (POVM) that determines whether a given unknown state is in a tensor product form or even maximally entangled, as is shown in Section 6. Other fact is that the unpublished proof by Kitaev and Watrous for the upper bound PP of the class QMA of languages having single-proof quantum Merlin-Arthur proof systems (and even the proof of QMA $\subseteq$ PSPACE [12,13]) no longer works well for the multi-proof cases with a straightforward modification. Also, the existing proofs for the property that parallel repetition of a single-proof protocol reduces the error probability to be arbitrarily small [14,17,13] cannot be applied to the multi-proof cases.

For these reasons, this paper introduces the multi-proof model of quantum Merlin-Arthur proof systems. Formally, we say that a language L has a (k, a, b)-*quantum Merlin-Arthur proof system* if there exists a polynomial-time quantum verifier V such that, for every input x of length n, (i) if $x \in L$, there exists a set of k quantum proofs that makes V accept x with probability at least $a(n)$, and (ii) if $x \notin L$, for any set of k quantum proofs, V accepts x with probability at most $b(n)$. The resulting complexity class is denoted by QMA(k, a, b). We often abbreviate QMA$(k, 2/3, 1/3)$ as QMA(k) throughout this paper.

This paper presents a necessary and sufficient condition under which the number of quantum proofs is reducible to two. Our condition is related to the possibility of amplifying success probabilities without increasing the number of quantum proofs. More formally, QMA$(k, a, b) = $ QMA$(2, 2/3, 1/3)$ for every constant $k \geq 2$ and any two-sided bounded error probability (a, b) if and only if QMA$(k, a, b) = $ QMA$(k, 2/3, 1/3)$ for every constant $k \geq 2$ and any two-sided bounded error probability (a, b).

Our proof for this also implies an interesting consequence for the case of perfect completeness. Namely, QMA$(k, 1, b) = $ QMA$(1, 1, 1/2)$ for every constant $k \geq 2$ and any bounded error probability b if and only if QMA$(2, 1, b) = $ QMA$(1, 1, 1/2)$ for any bounded error probability b.

It is also proved for the case of perfect soundness that, for every k and any error probability a, QMA$(k, a, 0) = $ QMA$(1, a, 0)$. With further analyses, the class NQP, which derives from another concept of "quantum nondeterminism" introduced by Adleman, DeMarrais, and Huang [1], is characterized by the union of QMA$(1, a, 0)$ for all error probability functions a. This bridges between two existing concepts of "quantum nondeterminism".

Finally, to see a limitation of QMA(k), this paper exhibits a relativized world in which QMA(k) does not contain co-NP (actually co-UP) for every k. As an immediate consequence, we have that, for every k, there exists a relativized world in which none of BQP, QMA(k), and co-QMA(k) coincides with each other.

Familiarity with the basics of quantum computation and information theory is assumed throughout this paper. The reader may refer to [10,16,13], for instance.

2   Quantum Merlin-Arthur Proof Systems

Here we formally define the multi-proof quantum Merlin-Arthur proof systems. One can define quantum Merlin-Arthur proof systems both in terms of quantum Turing machines and in terms of quantum circuits. From the computational equivalence of polynomial-time quantum Turing machines and polynomial-time uniform quantum circuits, these two models of quantum Merlin-Arthur proof systems are clearly equivalent in view of computational power. Here we formalize both of these two types of models. In the subsequent sections we will choose a suitable model from them depending on the situations. Throughout this paper all input strings are over the alphabet $\Sigma = \{0,1\}$, and $\mathbb{N}$ and $\mathbb{Z}^+$ denote the sets of natural numbers and nonnegative integers, respectively.

A *quantum proof of size s* is a pure quantum state of s qubits. Given polynomially bounded functions $q_V, q_M \colon \mathbb{Z}^+ \to \mathbb{N}$, a (q_V, q_M)-*restricted quantum verifier V for k-proof quantum Merlin-Arthur proof systems* is a polynomial-time computable mapping of the form $V \colon \Sigma^* \to \Sigma^*$. For every input x of length n, $V(x)$ is a description of a polynomial-time uniformly generated quantum circuit acting on $q_V(n) + k q_M(n)$ qubits. V receives k quantum proofs $|\phi_1\rangle, \ldots, |\phi_k\rangle$, each of size $q_M(n)$, and uses at most $q_V(n)$ qubits for his private computation. The probability that V accepts x is defined to be the probability that an observation of the output qubit (in the $\{|0\rangle, |1\rangle\}$ basis) yields $|1\rangle$, after the circuit $V(x)$ is applied to the state $|0^{q_V(n)}\rangle \otimes |\phi_1\rangle \otimes \cdots \otimes |\phi_k\rangle$. Or in terms of quantum Turing machines, a (q_V, q_M)-restricted quantum verifier V for k-proof quantum Merlin-Arthur proof systems is a multi-tape polynomial-time well-formed quantum Turing machine with two special tapes for an input and proofs other than the work tape. V receives k quantum proofs of size $q_M(n)$ in the proof tape and uses at most $q_V(n)$ cells in the work tape. The probability that V accepts the input is defined to be the probability that an observation of the output qubit (in the $\{|0\rangle, |1\rangle\}$ basis) yields $|1\rangle$, after V halts. More generally, the number of quantum proofs may not necessarily be a constant, and may be a function $k \colon \mathbb{Z}^+ \to \mathbb{N}$ of the input length n, but must be bounded polynomial in n.

Strictly speaking, the circuit-based (q_V, q_M)-restricted quantum verifier and the Turing-machine-based one may have different computational power for each fixed functions q_V and q_M. They are, however, "polynomially equivalent" and make no difference in the definition of the class QMA(k, a, b) below.

Definition 1. *Given a polynomially bounded function $k \colon \mathbb{Z}^+ \to \mathbb{N}$ and functions $a, b \colon \mathbb{Z}^+ \to [0,1]$, a language L is in* QMA(k, a, b) *if there exist polynomially bounded functions $q_V, q_M \colon \mathbb{Z}^+ \to \mathbb{N}$ and a (q_V, q_M)-restricted quantum verifier V for k-proof quantum Merlin-Arthur proof systems such that, for every x of length n,*

(i) if $x \in L$, there exists a set of quantum proofs $|\phi_1\rangle, \ldots, |\phi_{k(n)}\rangle$ of size $q_{\mathcal{M}}(n)$ that makes V accept x with probability at least $a(n)$,

(ii) if $x \notin L$, for any set of quantum proofs $|\phi_1\rangle, \ldots, |\phi_{k(n)}\rangle$ of size $q_{\mathcal{M}}(n)$, V accepts x with probability at most $b(n)$.

We say that a language L has a (k, a, b)-quantum Merlin-Arthur proof system if and only if L is in QMA(k, a, b). For simplicity, we abbreviate QMA$(k, 2/3, 1/3)$ as QMA(k) for each k.

3   Condition under Which QMA(k) = QMA(2)

Besides our central question whether quantum multi-proof Merlin-Arthur proof systems collapse to quantum single-proof systems, it is also unclear whether there are k_1 and k_2 with $k_1 \neq k_2$ such that QMA(k_1) = QMA(k_2). Towards settling these questions, here we give a condition under which QMA(k) = QMA(2) for every constant $k \geq 2$.

Formally, we consider the following condition on the possibility of amplifying success probabilities without increasing the number of quantum proofs:

(∗) For every constant $k \geq 2$ and any two-sided bounded error probability (a, b), QMA(k, a, b) coincides with QMA$(k, 2/3, 1/3)$.

Then we have the following theorem.

Theorem 2. QMA(k, a, b) = QMA$(2, 2/3, 1/3)$ for every constant $k \geq 2$ and any two-sided bounded error probability (a, b) if and only if the condition (∗) is satisfied.

The proof of Theorem 2 uses the following key lemma, which is proved later.

Lemma 3. For every $l \in \mathbb{N}$, every $r \in \{0, 1, 2\}$, and any two-sided bounded error probability (a, b) satisfying $a > 1 - (1 - b)^2/10 \geq b$, QMA$(3l + r, a, b) \subseteq$ QMA$(2l + r, a, 1 - (1 - b)^2/10)$.

Proof of Theorem 2. The "only if" part is obvious. We only show the "if" part.

Suppose that the condition (∗) holds. Then we have QMA$(3l + r, a, b)$ = QMA $(3l + r, 99/100, 1/100)$ for every $l \in \mathbb{N}$, $r \in \{0, 1, 2\}$, and any two-sided bounded error probability (a, b). Now from Lemma 3, we have QMA$(3l + r, 99/100, 1/100) \subseteq$ QMA$(2l + r, 99/100, 90199/100000)$, which implies that these two classes coincide with each other. Furthermore, (∗) ensures that QMA$(2l + r, 99/100, 90199/100000)$ = QMA$(2l + r, 99/100, 1/100)$. Thus, we have QMA$(3l + r, 99/100, 1/100)$ = QMA$(2l + r, 99/100, 1/100)$. We repeat this c times for some constant c of $O(\log_{3/2} k)$, and finally we obtain that QMA$(3l + r, a, b)$ = QMA$(2, 99/100, 1/100)$. Again from (∗), QMA$(2, 99/100, 1/100)$ = QMA$(2, a, b)$ for any two-sided bounded error probability (a, b). Therefore we have QMA(k, a, b) = QMA$(2, 2/3, 1/3)$ for every constant $k \geq 2$ and any two-sided bounded error probability (a, b).   □

Now we give a proof of Lemma 3. The proof uses a special operator called *controlled-swap* that exchanges the contents of two registers $\mathbf{S}_1$ and $\mathbf{S}_2$ if control register $\mathbf{B}$ contains 1, and does nothing otherwise. Consider the *C-SWAP algorithm* described below. A similar idea was used in [9] for the fingerprinting scheme. Given a pair of mixed states ρ and σ of n qubits of the form $\rho \otimes \sigma$, prepare quantum registers $\mathbf{B}$, $\mathbf{R}_1$, and $\mathbf{R}_2$. The register $\mathbf{B}$ consists of only one qubit that is initially set to the $|0\rangle$-state, while the registers $\mathbf{R}_1$ and $\mathbf{R}_2$ consist of n qubits and ρ and σ are initially set in $\mathbf{R}_1$ and $\mathbf{R}_2$, respectively.

C-SWAP Algorithm

1. Apply the Hadamard transformation H to $\mathbf{B}$.
2. Apply the controlled-swap operator on $\mathbf{R}_1$ and $\mathbf{R}_2$ using $\mathbf{B}$ as a control qubit. That is, swap the contents of $\mathbf{R}_1$ and $\mathbf{R}_2$ if $\mathbf{B}$ contains 1, and do nothing if $\mathbf{B}$ contains 0.
3. Apply H to $\mathbf{B}$. Accept if $\mathbf{B}$ contains 0, and otherwise reject.

We state the following without a proof, which is useful in proving Lemma 3.

Proposition 4. *The probability that the input pair of mixed states ρ and σ is accepted in the C-SWAP algorithm is exactly $1/2 + \operatorname{tr}(\rho\sigma)/2$.*

Proof of Lemma 3. The essence of the proof is the basis case where $k = 1$ and $r = 0$. We give the proof only for this particular case and leave the general case to the reader, since it is straightforward to modify our proof to the general case.

Let L be a language in QMA$(3, a, b)$. Given a $(3, a, b)$-quantum Merlin-Arthur proof system for L, we construct a $\left(2, a, 1 - (1 - b)^2/10\right)$-quantum Merlin-Arthur proof system for L in the following way.

Let V be the quantum verifier of the original $(3, a, b)$-quantum Merlin-Arthur proof system. For every input x of length n, suppose that each of quantum proofs V receives consists of $q_\mathcal{M}(n)$ qubits and the number of private qubit of V is $q_\mathcal{V}(n)$. Let $V(x)$ be the unitary transformation which the original quantum verifier V applies. Our new quantum verifier W of the $\left(2, a, 1 - (1 - b)^2/10\right)$-quantum Merlin-Arthur proof system prepares quantum registers $\mathbf{R}_1$, $\mathbf{R}_2$, $\mathbf{S}_1$, and $\mathbf{S}_2$ for quantum proofs and quantum registers $\mathbf{V}$ and $\mathbf{B}$ for private computation. Each of $\mathbf{R}_i$ and $\mathbf{S}_i$ consists of $q_\mathcal{M}(n)$ qubits, $\mathbf{V}$ consists of $q_\mathcal{V}(n)$ qubits, and $\mathbf{B}$ consists of a single qubit. W receives two quantum proofs $|D_1\rangle$ and $|D_2\rangle$ of $2q_\mathcal{M}(n)$ qubits, which are expected to be of the form $|D_1\rangle = |C_1\rangle \otimes |C_3\rangle$ and $|D_2\rangle = |C_2\rangle \otimes |C_3\rangle$, where each $|C_i\rangle$ is the ith quantum proof which the original quantum verifier V receives. Of course, each $|D_i\rangle$ may not be of the form above and the first and the second $q_\mathcal{M}(n)$ qubits of $|D_i\rangle$ may be entangled. Let $\mathcal{V}$, $\mathcal{B}$, each $\mathcal{R}_i$, and each $\mathcal{S}_i$ be the Hilbert spaces corresponding to the quantum registers $\mathbf{V}$, $\mathbf{B}$, $\mathbf{R}_i$, and $\mathbf{S}_i$, respectively. W runs the following protocol:

1. Receive $|D_1\rangle$ in registers $(\mathbf{R}_1, \mathbf{S}_1)$ and $|D_2\rangle$ in $(\mathbf{R}_2, \mathbf{S}_2)$.
2. Do one of the following two tests uniformly at random.
    2.1 SEPARABILITY TEST:
        Apply the C-SWAP algorithm over $\mathcal{B} \otimes \mathcal{S}_1 \otimes \mathcal{S}_2$, using $\mathbf{B}$, $\mathbf{S}_1$, and $\mathbf{S}_2$. Accept if $\mathbf{B}$ contains 0, and otherwise reject.
    2.2 CONSISTENCY TEST:
        Apply $V(x)$ over $\mathcal{V} \otimes \mathcal{R}_1 \otimes \mathcal{R}_2 \otimes \mathcal{S}_1$, using $\mathbf{V}$, $\mathbf{R}_1$, $\mathbf{R}_2$, and $\mathbf{S}_1$. Accept iff the result corresponds to the acceptance computation of the original quantum verifier.

The completeness of this protocol is immediate.

For the soundness property with the input $x \notin L$ of length n, consider any pair of quantum proofs $|D_1'\rangle$ and $|D_2'\rangle$, which are set in the pairs of the quantum registers $(\mathbf{R}_1, \mathbf{S}_1)$ and $(\mathbf{R}_2, \mathbf{S}_2)$, respectively. Let $\rho = \mathrm{tr}_{\mathcal{R}_1}|D_1'\rangle\langle D_1'|$ and $\sigma = \mathrm{tr}_{\mathcal{R}_2}|D_2'\rangle\langle D_2'|$. We abbreviate $b(n)$ as b, and let $\delta = (-1 + 2b + 4\sqrt{1 + b - b^2})/5$.

If $\mathrm{tr}(\rho\sigma) \leq \delta$, the probability α that the input x is accepted in the SEPARABILITY TEST is at most

$$\alpha \leq (1 + \delta)/2 = (2 + b + 2\sqrt{1 + b - b^2})/5 \leq (4 + 2b - b^2)/5 = 1 - (1 - b)^2/5.$$

Hence W accepts x with probability at most $(1 + \alpha)/2 \leq 1 - (1 - b)^2/10$.

On the other hand, if $\mathrm{tr}(\rho\sigma) > \delta$, the maximum eigenvalue λ of ρ satisfies $\lambda > \delta$. Thus there exist pure states $|C_1'\rangle \in \mathcal{R}_1$ and $|C_3'\rangle \in \mathcal{S}_1$ such that $F(|C_1'\rangle\langle C_1'| \otimes |C_3'\rangle\langle C_3'|, |D_1'\rangle\langle D_1'|) > \sqrt{\delta}$, since $\rho = \mathrm{tr}_{\mathcal{R}_1}|D_1'\rangle\langle D_1'|$. Similarly, the maximum eigenvalue of σ is more than δ and there exist pure states $|C_2'\rangle \in \mathcal{R}_2$ and $|C_4'\rangle \in \mathcal{S}_2$ such that $F(|C_2'\rangle\langle C_2'| \otimes |C_4'\rangle\langle C_4'|, |D_2'\rangle\langle D_2'|) > \sqrt{\delta}$. Thus, letting $|\phi\rangle = |C_1'\rangle \otimes |C_3'\rangle \otimes |C_2'\rangle \otimes |C_4'\rangle$ and $|\psi\rangle = |D_1'\rangle \otimes |D_2'\rangle$, we have $F(|\phi\rangle\langle\phi|, |\psi\rangle\langle\psi|) > \delta$. Therefore,

$$\||\phi\rangle\langle\phi| - |\psi\rangle\langle\psi|\|_{\mathrm{tr}} \leq \sqrt{1 - (F(|\phi\rangle\langle\phi|, |\psi\rangle\langle\psi|))^2} < \sqrt{1 - \delta^2}.$$

This implies that the input x is accepted in the CONSISTENCY TEST with probability at most $\beta < b + \sqrt{1 - \delta^2}$, since given any quantum proofs $|C_1'\rangle$, $|C_2'\rangle$, and $|C_3'\rangle$ the original quantum verifier V accepts the input x with probability at most b. Noticing that δ satisfies $(1 + \delta)/2 = b + \sqrt{1 - \delta^2}$, one can see that $\beta < 1 - (1 - b)^2/5$. Hence W accepts x with probability at most $(1 + \beta)/2 < 1 - (1 - b)^2/10$. $\square$

4   One-Sided Bounded Error Cases

First we focus on the cases with perfect completeness. Together with the fact that parallel repetition works well for single-proof quantum Merlin-Arthur proof systems, Lemma 3 implies the following. The proof is easy and thus omitted.

Theorem 5. QMA$(k, 1, b) = $ QMA$(1, 1, 1/2)$ *for every constant* $k \geq 2$ *and any bounded error probability* b *if and only if* QMA$(2, 1, b) = $ QMA$(1, 1, 1/2)$ *for any bounded error probability* b.

Now we turn to the cases with perfect soundness. For such cases, multiple quantum proofs do not increase the computational power.

Theorem 6. *For any polynomially bounded function* $k\colon \mathbb{Z}^+ \to \mathbb{N}$ *and any function* $a\colon \mathbb{Z}^+ \to (0, 1]$, QMA$(k, a, 0) = $ QMA$(1, a, 0)$.

Proof. For a language L in QMA$(k, a, 0)$, we show that L is also in QMA$(1, a, 0)$.

Let V be a quantum verifier of a $(k, a, 0)$-quantum Merlin-Arthur proof system for L. For every input x of length n, assume that V receives $k(n)$ quantum proofs of size $q(n)$. We define a new $(1, a, 0)$-quantum Merlin-Arthur proof system as follows: on input x of length n, the verifier W receives one quantum proof of size $k(n)q(n)$ and simulates V with this quantum proof.

The completeness property is clearly satisfied.

For the soundness property, assume that the input x of length n is not in L. Let $|D\rangle$ be any quantum proof of size $k(n)q(n)$. Let e_i be the lexicographically ith string in $\{0, 1\}^{k(n)q(n)}$. Note that, for each i, $1 \leq i \leq 2^{k(n)q(n)}$, V never accepts x when given $k(n)$ quantum proofs that form $|e_i\rangle$. Since any $|D\rangle$ is expressed as a linear combination of all $|e_i\rangle$, $1 \leq i \leq 2^{k(n)q(n)}$, W rejects x with certainty. $\square$

Let $\mathrm{EQMA}(k) = \mathrm{QMA}(k, 1, 0)$ and $\mathrm{RQMA}(k) = \mathrm{QMA}(k, 1/2, 0)$ for every k. Theorem 6 implies that $\mathrm{EQMA}(k) = \mathrm{EQMA}(1)$ and $\mathrm{RQMA}(k) = \mathrm{RQMA}(1)$. Furthermore, one can consider the complexity class $\mathrm{NQMA}(k)$ that combines two existing concepts of "quantum nondeterminism", $\mathrm{QMA}(k)$ and NQP.

Definition 7. *A language L is in $\mathrm{NQMA}(k)$ if there exists a function $a \colon \mathbb{Z}^+ \to (0, 1]$ such that L is in $\mathrm{QMA}(k, a, 0)$.*

$\mathrm{NQMA}(k) = \mathrm{NQMA}(1)$ is also immediate from Theorem 6. Actually, the following can be proved. This also gives a characterization of NQP by the union of $\mathrm{QMA}(1, a, 0)$ over all error probability functions a. The proof is omitted due to limitation of space.

Theorem 8. $\mathrm{EQMA}(1) \subseteq \mathrm{RQMA}(1) \subseteq \mathrm{NQMA}(1) = \mathrm{NQP}$.

5   Relativized Separation of QMA(k)

To see a limitation of $\mathrm{QMA}(k)$, here we show a relativized world in which $\mathrm{QMA}(k)$ does not contain co-UP.

Theorem 9. *For any polynomially bounded function $k \colon \mathbb{Z}^+ \to \mathbb{N}$, there exists an oracle A relative to which $\text{co-UP}^A \not\subseteq \mathrm{QMA}(k)^A$.*

The following is an immediate corollary of Theorem 9.

Corollary 10. *For any polynomially bounded function $k \colon \mathbb{Z}^+ \to \mathbb{N}$, there exists an oracle A relative to which none of BQP, $\mathrm{QMA}(k)$, and $\text{co-QMA}(k)$ coincides with each other.*

Proof. By Theorem 9, we have an oracle A such that $\text{co-NP}^A \not\subseteq \mathrm{QMA}(k)^A$. Since $\text{co-NP}^A \subseteq \text{co-QMA}(k)^A$, it follows that $\text{co-QMA}(k)^A \not\subseteq \mathrm{QMA}(k)^A$, and thus $\mathrm{QMA}(k)^A \neq \text{co-QMA}(k)^A$. That $\mathrm{BQP}^A \neq \mathrm{QMA}(k)^A$ follows from $\mathrm{QMA}(k)^A \neq \text{co-QMA}(k)^A$. $\square$

In what follows, we give the proof of Theorem 9. We use a so-called *block sensitivity* argument, whose quantum version was developed in [6]. Let $f \colon \Sigma^* \to [0, 1]$ be any relativizable function. If A is an oracle and $S \subseteq \Sigma^*$ be a subset of strings, then $A^{(S)}$ is the oracle satisfying that, for every y, $A(y) = A^{(S)}(y)$ if and only if $y \notin S$. For $\varepsilon > 0$ and an oracle A from an oracle collection $\mathcal{A}$, let the *lower* (resp. *upper*) ε-*block sensitivity* $\mathrm{bs}^A_{\varepsilon-}(f, A, |\phi\rangle)$

(resp. $bs_{\varepsilon+}^{\mathcal{A}}(f, A, |\phi\rangle)$) of f with an oracle A on an input $|\phi\rangle$ be the maximal integer l satisfying that there are l nonempty, disjoint sets $\{S_i\}_{i=1}^{l}$ such that, for every i, $1 \le i \le l$, (i) $A^{(S_i)} \in \mathcal{A}$, and (ii) $f^{A^{(S_i)}}(|\phi\rangle) \le f^A(|\phi\rangle) - \varepsilon$ (resp. $f^A(|\phi\rangle) \le f^{A^{(S_i)}}(|\phi\rangle) + \varepsilon$).

First, we give an upper bound for each of $bs_{\varepsilon-}^{\mathcal{A}}(f, A, |\phi\rangle)$ and $bs_{\varepsilon+}^{\mathcal{A}}(f, A, |\phi\rangle)$. The notation $\eta_M^A(|\phi\rangle)$ denotes the acceptance probability of M with an oracle A on an input $|\phi\rangle$. The proof is omitted due to limitation of space.

Proposition 11. *Let $\mathcal{A}$ be any set of oracles and let M be any well-formed oracle QTM whose running time $T(n)$ does not depend on the choice of oracles. Let $q: \mathbb{Z}^+ \to \mathbb{N}$ be a polynomially bounded function. For every x of length n, define $f^A(x) = \max\{\eta_M^A(|x\rangle \otimes |\phi\rangle)\}$ and $g^A(x) = \min\{\eta_M^A(|x\rangle \otimes |\phi\rangle)\}$, where the maximum and minimum are taken over all pure states $|\phi\rangle$ of $q(n)$ qubits. Then, for every oracle $A \in \mathcal{A}$, every input x of length n, and any constant $\varepsilon > 0$, both of $bs_{\varepsilon-}^{\mathcal{A}}(f, A, x)$ and $bs_{\varepsilon+}^{\mathcal{A}}(g, A, x)$ are at most $4T(n)^2/\varepsilon^2$.*

Now we give a proof of Theorem 9.

Proof of Theorem 9. Let $L^A = \{0^j \mid |A \cap \{0,1\}^j| = \emptyset\}$ for each $A \subseteq \{0,1\}^*$. Let $\mathcal{A} = \{A \mid \forall j [|A \cap \{0,1\}^j| \le 1]\}$. Obviously, $L^A \in \text{co-UP}^A$ for any set A in $\mathcal{A}$, and thus $L^A \in \Pi_1^P(A)$. We then show that $L^A \notin \text{QMA}(k)^A$ for a certain set A in $\mathcal{A}$.

Let $\{M_i\}_{i \in \mathbb{Z}^+}$ be an effective enumeration of all QTMs running in polynomial time. The construction of A is done by stages. For the base case, let $A_0 = \emptyset$. In the jth stage for $j > 0$, $A_j \subseteq \{0,1\}^j$ is to be defined. Our desired A is defined as $A = \bigcup_i A_i$.

Now consider the jth QTM M_j. Let $B = \bigcup_{i<j} A_i$. Note that $0^j \in L^B$. For simplicity, define $f^B(x) = \max\{\Pr_{M_j}[M_j(|x\rangle \otimes |\phi_1\rangle \otimes \cdots \otimes |\phi_{k(n)}\rangle) = 1]\}$ for every x of length n, where each $|\phi_i\rangle$, $1 \le i \le k(n)$, runs over all pure states of $q(n)$ qubits for some polynomially bounded function $q: \mathbb{Z}^+ \to \mathbb{N}$.

Suppose that $f^B(0^j) < 2/3$. Then we set A_j to be B and go to the next stage.

Now suppose that $f^B(0^j) \ge 2/3$. Let $B_i = B \cup \{s_i^j\}$, where s_i^j is the ith element in $\{0,1\}^j$. Clearly, $0^j \notin L^{B_i}$ for all i's. We show that there exists a number i such that $f^{B_i}(0^j) > 1/3$. If so, force A_j to be such B_i. Towards a contradiction, we assume that, for all i, $f^{B_i}(0^j) \le 1/3$. By our assumption, $f^B(0^j) - f^{B_i}(0^j) \ge 1/3$ for all i, $1 \le i \le 2^j$. It follows that $bs_{\frac{1}{3}-}^{\Sigma^*}(f, B, 0^j) \ge 2^j$, since $\{B_i\}_{i=1}^{2^j}$ is mutually disjoint. This contradicts Proposition 11. $\qquad\square$

6   Discussions

Here we show that there is no positive operator-valued measurement (POVM) that determines whether a given unknown state is in a tensor product form or even maximally entangled. Recall that the state $\rho = |\Psi\rangle\langle\Psi|$ is *maximally entangled* if $|\Psi\rangle$ can be written by $|\Psi\rangle = \sum_{i=1}^{d} \alpha_i |e_i\rangle \otimes |f_i\rangle$, $|\alpha_i|^2 = 1/d$, where $d = 2^n$ is the dimension of $\mathcal{H}$ and each $\{|e_1\rangle, \ldots, |e_d\rangle\}$ and $\{|f_1\rangle, \ldots, |f_d\rangle\}$ is an orthonormal basis of $\mathcal{H}$ [7]. Among all states, maximally entangled states are farthest away from states in tensor product form, and

$$\min_{|\Psi\rangle\in\mathcal{H}^{\otimes 2}} \max_{|\phi\rangle,|\psi\rangle\in\mathcal{H}} F(|\Psi\rangle\langle\Psi|, |\phi\rangle\langle\phi|\otimes|\psi\rangle\langle\psi|) = 1/\sqrt{d} = 2^{-n/2}$$

is achieved by maximally entangled states. Thus Arthur cannot rule out quantum proofs that are far from states of a tensor product of pure states.

Theorem 12. *Suppose one of the following two is true for a given proof* $|\Psi\rangle \in \mathcal{H}^{\otimes 2}$ *of $2n$ qubits:*

(a) $|\Psi\rangle\langle\Psi|$ *is in* $\mathsf{H}_0 = \{|\Psi_0\rangle\langle\Psi_0| \mid |\Psi_0\rangle \in \mathcal{H}^{\otimes 2}, \exists|\psi\rangle, |\phi\rangle \in \mathcal{H}, |\Psi_0\rangle = |\psi\rangle\otimes|\phi\rangle\}$,
(b) $|\Psi\rangle\langle\Psi|$ *is in* $\mathsf{H}_1 = \{|\Psi_1\rangle\langle\Psi_1| \mid |\Psi_1\rangle \in \mathcal{H}^{\otimes 2}$ *is maximally entangled*$\}$.

Then, in determining which of (a) and (b) is true, no POVM is better than the trivial strategy in which one guesses at random without any operation at all.

Proof. Let $M = \{M_0, M_1\}$ be a POVM on a given $|\Psi\rangle\langle\Psi|$. With M we conclude $|\Psi\rangle\langle\Psi| \in \mathsf{H}_i$ if M results in i, $i = 0, 1$. Let $\mathrm{P}^M_{i\to j}(|\Psi\rangle\langle\Psi|)$ denote the probability that $|\Psi\rangle\langle\Psi| \in \mathsf{H}_j$ is concluded by M while $|\Psi\rangle\langle\Psi| \in \mathsf{H}_i$ is true. We want to find the measurement that minimizes $\mathrm{P}^M_{0\to 1}(|\Psi\rangle\langle\Psi|)$ keeping the other side of error small enough. More precisely, we consider $\mathcal{E}$ defined and bounded as follows.

$$\mathcal{E} \overset{\text{def}}{=} \min_{M}\left\{\max_{\rho\in\mathsf{H}_0} \mathrm{P}^M_{0\to 1}(\rho) \;\middle|\; \max_{\rho\in\mathsf{H}_1}\mathrm{P}^M_{1\to 0}(\rho) \le \delta\right\}$$

$$\ge \min_{M}\left\{\int_{\rho\in\mathsf{H}_0} \mathrm{P}^M_{0\to 1}(\rho)\mu_0(\mathrm{d}\rho) \;\middle|\; \int_{\rho\in\mathsf{H}_1} \mathrm{P}^M_{1\to 0}(\rho)\mu_1(\mathrm{d}\rho) \le \delta\right\}$$

$$= \min_{M}\left\{\mathrm{P}^M_{0\to 1}\left(\int_{\rho\in\mathsf{H}_0}\rho\mu_0(\mathrm{d}\rho)\right) \;\middle|\; \mathrm{P}^M_{1\to 0}\left(\int_{\rho\in\mathsf{H}_1}\rho\mu_1(\mathrm{d}\rho)\right) \le \delta\right\},$$

where each μ_i is an arbitrary probability measure in H_i. It follows that $\mathcal{E}$ is larger than the error probability in distinguishing $\int_{\rho\in\mathsf{H}_0}\rho\mu_0(\mathrm{d}\rho)$ from $\int_{\rho\in\mathsf{H}_1}\rho\mu_1(\mathrm{d}\rho)$.

Take μ_0 such that $\mu_0(|e_i\rangle\langle e_i|\otimes|e_j\rangle\langle e_j|) = 1/d^2$ for each i and j, where $\{|e_1\rangle, \ldots, |e_d\rangle\}$ is an orthonormal basis of $\mathcal{H}$, and μ_1 such that $\mu_1(|g_{m,n}\rangle\langle g_{m,n}|) = 1/d^2$ for each m and n, where

$$|g_{m,n}\rangle = \frac{1}{d}\sum_{j=1}^{d}\left(e^{2\pi\sqrt{-1}jm/d}|e_j\rangle\otimes|e_{(j+n)\,\mathrm{mod}\,d}\rangle\right).$$

This $\{|g_{1,1}\rangle, \ldots, |g_{d,d}\rangle\}$ is an orthonormal basis of $\mathcal{H}^{\otimes 2}$ [8], and thus $\int_{\rho\in\mathsf{H}_0}\rho\mu_0(\mathrm{d}\rho) = \int_{\rho\in\mathsf{H}_1}\rho\mu_1(\mathrm{d}\rho) = I_{\mathcal{H}^{\otimes 2}}/d^2$. Hence we have the assertion. $\qquad\square$

7 Conclusions

This paper pointed out that it is unclear whether the multi-proof model of quantum Merlin-Arthur proof systems collapses to the single-proof model and proved several basic properties such as a necessary and sufficient condition under which the number of quantum proofs is reducible to two. However, the central question whether multiple quantum proofs are really more helpful to Arthur still remains open. The authors hope that this paper sheds light on new features of quantum Merlin-Arthur proof systems and quantum complexity theory.

Acknowledgements. The authors are grateful to John H. Watrous for providing us with an unpublished proof of QMA ⊆ PP, which was shown jointly by Alexei Yu. Kitaev and John H. Watrous. The first author thanks Richard E. Cleve and Lance J. Fortnow for their helpful comments.

References

1. L. M. Adleman, J. DeMarrais, and M.-D. A. Huang. Quantum computability. *SIAM Journal on Computing*, 26(5):1524–1540, 1997.
2. D. Aharonov and O. Regev. A lattice problem in quantum NP. In *44th Annual Symposium on Foundations of Computer Science*, 2003. To appear.
3. L. Babai. Trading group theory for randomness. In *Proceedings of the Seventeenth Annual ACM Symposium on Theory of Computing*, pages 421–429, 1985.
4. L. Babai. Bounded round interactive proofs in finite groups. *SIAM Journal on Discrete Mathematics*, 5(1):88–111, 1992.
5. L. Babai and S. Moran. Arthur-Merlin games: A randomized proof system, and a hierarchy of complexity classes. *Journal of Computer and System Sciences*, 36(2):254–276, 1988.
6. R. M. Beals, H. M. Buhrman, R. E. Cleve, M. Mosca, and R. de Wolf. Quantum lower bounds by polynomials. In *39th Annual Symposium on Foundations of Computer Science*, pages 352–361, 1998.
7. C. H. Bennett, H. J. Bernstein, S. Popescu, and B. Schumacher. Concentrating partial entanglement by local operations. *Physical Review A*, 53(4):2046–2052, 1996.
8. C. H. Bennett, G. Brassard, C. Crépeau, R. O. Jozsa, A. Peres, and W. K. Wootters. Teleporting an unknown quantum state via dual classical and Einstein-Podolsky-Rosen channels. *Physical Review Letters*, 70(13):1895–1899, 1993.
9. H. M. Buhrman, R. E. Cleve, J. H. Watrous, and R. de Wolf. Quantum fingerprinting. *Physical Review Letters*, 87(16):167902, 2001.
10. J. D. Gruska. *Quantum Computing*. McGraw-Hill, 1999.
11. J. Kempe and O. Regev. 3-local Hamiltonian is QMA-complete. *Quantum Information and Computation*, 3(3):258–264, 2003.
12. A. Yu. Kitaev. Quantum NP. Talk at the 2nd Workshop on Algorithms in Quantum Information Processing, DePaul University, Chicago, January 1999.
13. A. Yu. Kitaev, A. H. Shen, and M. N. Vyalyi. *Classical and Quantum Computation*, volume 47 of *Graduate Studies in Mathematics*. American Mathematical Society, 2002.
14. A. Yu. Kitaev and J. H. Watrous. Parallelization, amplification, and exponential time simulation of quantum interactive proof systems. In *Proceedings of the Thirty-Second Annual ACM Symposium on Theory of Computing*, pages 608–617, 2000.
15. E. H. Knill. Quantum randomness and nondeterminism. Technical Report LAUR-96-2186, Los Alamos National Laboratory, 1996.
16. M. A. Nielsen and I. L. Chuang. *Quantum Computation and Quantum Information*. Cambridge University Press, 2000.
17. J. H. Watrous. Succinct quantum proofs for properties of finite groups. In *41st Annual Symposium on Foundations of Computer Science*, pages 537–546, 2000.

A Faster Lattice Reduction Method Using Quantum Search

Christoph Ludwig

Technische Universität Darmstadt, Fachbereich Informatik
Alexanderstr. 10, 64283 Darmstadt, Germany
cludwig@cdc.informatik.tu-darmstadt.de

Abstract. We propose a new lattice reduction method. Our algorithm approximates shortest lattice vectors up to a factor $\leq (k/6)^{n/2k}$ and makes use of Grover's quantum search algorithm. The proposed method has the expected running time $O(n^3(k/6)^{k/8}A + n^4A)$. That is about the square root of the running time $O(n^3(k/6)^{k/4}A + n^4A)$ of Schnorr's recent random sampling reduction which in turn improved the running time to the fourth root of previously known algorithms. Our result demonstrates that the availability of quantum computers will affect not only the security of cryptosystems based on integer factorization or discrete logarithms, but also of lattice based cryptosystems. Rough estimates based on our asymptotic improvements and experiments reported in [1] suggest that the NTRU security parameter needed to be increased from 503 to 1277 if sufficiently large quantum computer were available nowadays.

Keywords: Lattice Reduction, Quantum Computers, NTRU, GGH

1 Introduction

Impact of Quantum Computers on Classical Cryptology. It is well known that quantum computers will be able to break cryptosystems that are based on the integer factorization problem or some discrete logarithm problem in polynomial time [2]. In particular, this affects RSA and elliptic curve cryptosystems, but also number field cryptosystems [3].

However, quantum computers are not believed to be able to solve NP-hard problems in polynomial time. The closest and shortest lattice vector problems (CVP and SVP) are known to be NP-hard [4,5,6]. Up to now, there was no evidence that the security of cryptosystems of GGH-type [7,8], that are based on SVP or CVP in arbitrary lattices, will be affected by the future availability of quantum computers. Neither is such a result known for NTRU. In fact, Regev's quantum reduction [9] of the $\Theta(n^{2.5})$-unique shortest vector problem applies to a class of lattices only which NTRU lattices do not belong to.

Classical Lattice Reduction Methods. Kannan's algorithm [10] computes a shortest lattice vector but it has an exponential running time. The renowned LLL algorithm [11] and its many variants compute in polynomial time a vector at most

T. Ibaraki, N. Katoh, and H. Ono (Eds.): ISAAC 2003, LNCS 2906, pp. 199–208, 2003.
© Springer-Verlag Berlin Heidelberg 2003

$(4/3 + \varepsilon)^{(n-1)/2}$ times as long as the shortest vectors in a given n-dimensional lattice. By applying Kannan's algorithm to blocks of length $2k$ in the lattice basis, Schnorr [12] improved the approximation factor of LLL to $(k/3)^{n/k}$ for sufficiently large k at the cost of an additional running time $O(n^3 k^{k+o(k)} A)$. (A covers the number of bit operations for the arithmetic on $O(n^2)$-bit integers.) The so called primal-dual method by Koy is claimed [13] to reduce the additional running time to $O(n^3 k^{k/2+o(k)} A)$ and still achieve an approximation factor $\leq (k/6)^{n/k}$. A variant of the $2k$-algorithm called BKZ (for Block Korkine-Zolotarev) [14] is widely used in practice, even though it is not proven to run in time polynomial in n.

Whenever the $2k$-method replaces the first base vector it takes only the first $2k$ base vectors into account. Schnorr [13] recently proposed an algorithm that is kind of complementary. It searches a replacement for the first base vector in the span of an LLL-reduced basis, but only the contribution of the last base vectors can be varied. If many such vectors are sampled, a sufficiently short vector will be found with high probability. The expected additional running time of this random sampling reduction (RSR) is $O(n^3 (k/6)^{k/4} A)$ and it guarantees an approximation factor $(k/6)^{n/2k}$. If the alloted running time is fixed, RSR reduces the approximation factor to about its 4th root compared with the primal-dual method.

Schnorr also proposed to replace the random sampling by a birthday sampling method that exploits the birthday paradox. The additional running time of his simple birthday reduction (SBR) is only $O(n^3 (4/3)^{k/3} (k/6)^{k/8} A)$, $k \geq 60$ according to [13], but it requires the storage of $(4/3)^{k/3} (k/6)^{k/8}$ additional lattice vectors. Even if $k = 60$ and $n = 100$, almost 10^{12} integers need to be stored. The massive space requirements raise doubts about the practicability of SBR.

Contribution of this Paper and Outline. We propose to replace the random sampling of vectors in Schnorr's algorithm by the technique of Grover's quantum search. We show that a quantum computer finds a sufficiently short vector with only $O((k/6)^{k/8})$ evaluations of a predicate that is as expensive to evaluate as one call to Schnorr's sampling algorithm. This leads to a quantum search reduction algorithm (QSR) that performs $O(n^3 (k^6)^{k/8} A)$ operations and achieves an approximation factor $\leq (k/6)^{n/2k}$. Hence, QSR improves in fixed time the approximation factor to about the square root compared with RSR and to about the 8th root compared with the primal-dual method.

Our result has an immediate effect on the security offered by all lattice based cryptosystems, including systems of GGH-type. But of particular interest is the impact of QSR on NTRU. If we transfer our improved running time bounds on the experimental results reported in [1] and require the security thresholds from the Lenstra-Verheul heuristic [15], we find that NTRU's security parameter need to be more than doubled. More precisely, the security parameter for NTRU's "highest security" parameter set had to be raised from 503 up to 1277 if quantum computers were available in 2005.

After some technical preliminaries and notations in section 2 we will outline Schnorr's random sampling reduction in section 3. Section 4 presents our proposed quantum reduction method. In section 5 we study the possible impact of the availability of sufficiently large quantum computers on NTRU. Section 6 points to possible further improvements of our algorithm and open research questions.

2 Preliminaries and Notation

All vector norms are Euclidean. A d-dimensional integral lattice $L = L(B)$ is the $\mathbb{Z}$-span of some linear independent lattice basis $B = \{b_1, \ldots, b_d\} \subset \mathbb{Z}^n$, i.e. $L = \{\sum_{i=1}^{d} a_i b_i : a_1, \ldots, a_d \in \mathbb{Z}\}$. By abuse of notation, we identify the basis B with the $n \times d$ matrix $B = [b_1, \ldots, b_d]$. For simplicity, we assume $d = n$.

We also assume $\max_j\{\|b_j\|\} = 2^{O(n)}$. Then the LLL algorithm operates on integers of bitlength $O(n^2)$. A denotes the the number of bit operations required for an arithmetic step on such integers.

Let $B = \hat{B}R$ be the Gram-Schmidt decomposition of B, i.e. the columns $\hat{b}_j$ of $\hat{B} \in \mathbb{Q}^{n \times n}$ are pairwise perpendicular and $R = (\mu_{i,j}) \in \mathbb{Q}^{n \times n}$ is unit upper triangular. In the following, whenever we pass B to an algorithm, we implicitly also pass $\hat{B}$ and R.

B is δ-LLL reduced $(1/4 \leq \delta < 1)$ if and only if

$$|\mu_{i,j}| \leq 1/2 \qquad \text{for all } 1 \leq i < j \leq n \quad \text{and}$$

$$\delta\|\hat{b}_j\|^2 \leq \|\mu_{j,j+1}\hat{b}_j + \hat{b}_{j+1}\|^2 \text{for all } 1 \leq j < n.$$

Then the first basis vector b_1 satisfies $\|b_1\| \leq \left(\delta - \frac{1}{4}\right)^{-\frac{n-1}{2}} \lambda_1$, where $\lambda_1 = \min\{\|u\| : 0 \neq u \in L(B)\}$ is the length of the shortest nonzero lattice vectors.

For many applications of lattice theory an approximate solution of a *Shortest Vector Problem* (SVP) is required for some approximation factor α: Given a basis B, find a nonzero lattice vector $v \in L$ such that $\|v\| \leq \alpha\lambda_1$. In high dimensional lattices, this is infeasible for very small approximation factors; in fact, the problem is NP-hard for randomized reductions if $\alpha < \sqrt{2}$ [6]. The LLL algorithm computes solutions to SVP with approximation factor $\alpha = 2^{(n-1)/2}$, though.

3 Schnorr's Random Sampling Reduction

In 2001, Schnorr proposed a novel algorithm for approximate solutions of the SVP. We present here only the essential parts of the algorithm; for a detailed description as well as proofs, cf. [13].

RSR is built around the sampling algorithm (SA). SA randomly chooses lattice vectors with Gram-Schmidt coefficients $\nu_1, \ldots, \nu_n$ that satisfy

$$\nu_j \in (-\tfrac{1}{2}, \tfrac{1}{2}] \text{for } 1 \leq j \leq n - k',$$

$$\nu_j \in (-1, 1] \text{ for } n - k' < j < n, \qquad (1)$$

$$\nu_n \in \{1, 2\}$$

for some integer k'. Denote $D_{n,k'} := (-\tfrac{1}{2}, \tfrac{1}{2}]^{n-k'} \times (-1, 1]^{k'-1} \times \{1, 2\}$.

Algorithm 1 (Sampling Algorithm (SA)). *Given a lattice basis B and an integer $1 \leq k' < n$, SA returns in $O(n^2)$ arithmetic steps a uniformly chosen $b = \widehat{B}\nu \in L(B)$ such that $\nu \in D_{n,k'}$.*

Based on empiric data, Schnorr makes two assumptions:

Assumption 1 (Randomness Assumption (RA)). *The coefficient vector $\nu = (\nu_1, \ldots, \nu_n)^t$ sampled by SA satisfies the following conditions:*

1. *The random variables $\nu_1, \ldots, \nu_{n-1}$ are uniformly distributed in the intervals $(-\frac{1}{2}, \frac{1}{2}]$ and $(-1, 1]$, respectively.*
2. *The random variables $\nu_1, \ldots, \nu_{n-1}$ are pairwise statistically independent.*

Note that (RA) is crucial only for coefficients ν_j with small index j.

Assumption 2 (Geometric Series Assumption (GSA)). *There is $0 < q < 1$ such that $\|\hat{b}_j\|^2 = q^{i-1}\|b_1\|^2$ for $1 \leq j \leq n$.*

In practice, of course, (GSA) holds approximately only, but the analysis remains valid as long the approximation is good enough. Schnorr [13] outlines how to "repair" bases that do not approximate (GSA) by reducing subbases.

Under these assumptions, SA will eventually yield a short lattice vector after expected $O((k/6)^{(k-1)/4})$ iterations:

Algorithm 2 (Sample Short Vector (SHORT)). *Let B be a δ-LLL reduced basis and let $k \geq 24$ be an integer subject to*

$$n \geq 3(k+1) + \frac{k-1}{4}\log_2\left(\frac{k}{6}\right). \tag{2}$$

Assume (RA) and (GSA) with $q < (6/k)^{1/k}$. On input k and B, SHORT computes in average $O(n^2(k/6)^{(k-1)/4})$ arithmetic steps a vector $b \in L(B)$ satisfying $\|b\|^2 \leq 0.99\|b_1\|^2$.

Once we found a short lattice vector b, an LLL update (LLLU) replaces b_1 by b and LLL reduces the resulting bases again. Since it is merely an update, this algorithm requires only $O(n^3)$ arithmetic steps.

Algorithm 3 (Random Sampling Reduction (RSR)). *Let B be a δ-LLL reduced basis and let $k \geq 24$ be an integer subject to (2). On input k and B, RSR computes under (RA) and (GSA) in average*

$$O\left(n^3\left(\frac{k}{6}\right)^{\frac{k-1}{4}}A + n^4 A\right)$$

bit operations a still δ-LLL reduced basis $B' = [b'_1, \ldots, b'_n]$ satisfying

$$\|b'_1\| \leq \left(\frac{k}{6}\right)^{\frac{n}{2k}}\lambda_1.$$

1: **while** $\|b_1\| > (k/6)^{(n-1)/2k}\|\hat{b}_n\|$ **do**   /* $O(n)$ iterations */

2:    $b \leftarrow \text{SHORT}(B, k)$
3:    $B \leftarrow \text{LLLU}(B, b)$
4: **end while**
5: **return** $B' \leftarrow B$

The loop condition implies $q < (6/k)^{1/k}$ whence the preconditions of SHORT are met. Since the input of RSR is already δ-LLL reduced, the approximation factor α after the i-th iteration satisfies $1 \leq \alpha \leq 0.99^i 2^{(n-1)/2}$. Therefore, RSR returns after $O(n)$ iterations.

All arithmetic steps operate on integers of length $O(n^2)$. Combining the complexity of SHORT and LLLU with the number of iterations in RSR, we get the average bit complexity $O(n^3(k/6)^{(k-1)/4}A + n^4A)$.

4   Quantum Search Reduction

Algorithm SHORT searches in the unsorted finite set of coefficient vectors $\nu \in D_{n,k'}$ with $\widehat{B}\nu \in L(B)$ for an element such that $\|\widehat{B}\nu\|^2 \leq 0.99\|b_1\|^2$. This is a setup where Grover's quantum search algorithm outperforms all classical search algorithms. For details on quantum computing in general and Grover's quantum search in particular we refer to [16] and [17,18], respectively.

Grover's quantum search QS makes use of a quantum operator called *black box oracle*. Let $S = \{0, \ldots, N-1\}$, $N = 2^n$. Given a (classical) algorithm that evaluates the predicate $f : S \rightarrow \{0,1\}$, we can easily construct a black box oracle O_f such that QS finds some $s \in S$ with $f(s) = 1$. More precisely, if there is a uniform circuit family evaluating f with $O(T_f(n))$ gates then O_f requires $O(T_f(n))$ quantum operations and ancilla qubits.

Algorithm 4 (Quantum Search (QS)). *Assume $M := |f^{-1}(\{1\})| > 0$. On input a black box algorithm O_f the quantum algorithm QS returns some $s \in S$ such that $f(s) = 1$.*

QS makes expected $\Theta((N/M)^{1/2})$ queries to O_f (even if M is unknown) and applies additional expected $\Theta((N/M)^{1/2})$ quantum operations on its $n+1$ qubit register.

Remark 1. QS can be easily modified to handle the case $M = 0$ at the cost of a small error probability [18]. However, in our particular application we know $M \geq 1$ whence we do not have to deal with sporadic errors

The idea underlying the quantum search reduction is to replace algorithm SHORT by a quantum search for a vector b satisfying $\|b\|^2 \leq 0.99\|b_1\|^2$. More precisely, we look for some sufficiently short b in

$$V_{B,k} = \left\{ v \in L(B) : v = \widehat{B}\nu, \; \nu \in D_{n,k'} \text{ with } k' = 1 + \left\lceil \tfrac{k-1}{4} \log_2 \left(\tfrac{k}{6} \right) \right\rceil \right\}.$$

Let $N = 2^{k'} = \min\left\{ 2^t : 2^t \geq 2\left(\tfrac{k}{6}\right)^{(k-1)/4} \right\}$. There is a (classical) $O(n^2A)$-time algorithm that enumerates $V_{B,k}$. In particular, $|V_{B,k}| = N$. The algorithm mimics Schnorr's algorithm SA; only the random bits are replaced by the input index.

Algorithm 5 (Enumerate $V_{B,k}$ (ENUM)). *Let B be a δ-LLL reduced basis with Gram-Schmidt decomposition $\widehat{B}R$, $R = [\mu_1, \ldots, \mu_n]$ and $k \geq 24$ be an integer subject to (2). On input B, k, and an index $0 \leq i < N$, ENUM computes in $O(n^2)$ arithmetic steps the vector v_i for some enumeration of $V_{B,k}$.*

1: $i_0 \leftarrow i \bmod 2$, $i \leftarrow \lfloor i/2 \rfloor$
2: $\nu = (\nu_1, \ldots, \nu_n)^t \leftarrow (i_0 + 1)\mu_n$, $b \leftarrow \nu_n b_n$
3: **for** $j = n - 1$ **downto** 1 **do**
4:     **if** $j \leq n - 1 - \lceil \frac{k-1}{4} \log_2 \left(\frac{k}{6} \right) \rceil$ **then**
5:         $c \leftarrow \lceil \nu_j \rfloor$
6:     **else**
7:         $i_0 \leftarrow i \bmod 2$, $i \leftarrow \lfloor i/2 \rfloor$
8:         $c \leftarrow \lceil \nu_j \rfloor - i_0$
9:     **end if**
10:    $b \leftarrow b - c b_j$, $\nu \leftarrow \nu - c \mu_j$
11: **end for**
12: **return** b

The vector returned by ENUM satisfies (1) because R is unit upper triangular. Since we restricted the coefficients in (1) to half-open intervals, the enumeration of $V_{B,k}$ is exhaustive.

The oracle black box of the quantum search is based upon the predicate $f_{B,k} : \{0, \ldots, N-1\} \to \{0,1\}$ with $f_{B,k}(i) = 1$ if and only if $\|\mathrm{ENUM}(B, k, i)\|^2 \leq 0.99\|b_1\|^2$. The evaluation of $f_{B,k}$ requires $O(n^2)$ arithmetic steps on integers of length $O(n^2)$, whence $O_{f_{B,k}}$ requires $O(n^2 A)$ quantum operations and $O(n^2 A)$ ancilla qubits.

We then have the following trivial algorithm to find sufficiently short vectors:

Algorithm 6 (Quantum Short Vector Search (QSHORT)). *Let B be a δ-LLL reduced basis and $k \geq 24$ be an integer subject to (2). On input B and k, QSHORT computes under (RA) and (GSA) with expected $O(n^2(k/6)^{k/8} A)$ operations on $O(n^2 A)$ qubits a lattice vector $b \in L(B)$ satisfying $\|b\|^2 \leq 0.99\|b_1\|^2$.*

1: $i \leftarrow \mathrm{QS}(O_{f_{B,k}})$
2: $b \leftarrow \mathrm{ENUM}(B, k, i)$
3: **return** b

Schnorr [13] shows $\Pr[\|b\|^2 \leq 0.99\|b_1\|^2] \geq \frac{1}{2} \left(\frac{k}{6} \right)^{(1-k)/4}$ under (RA) and (GSA) provided b is a vector sampled by SA. Since SA returns elements uniformly chosen from $V_{B,k}$, we have

$$M = N\Pr[\|b\|^2 \leq 0.99\|b_1\|^2] \geq 2 \left(\frac{k}{6} \right)^{\frac{k-1}{4}} \frac{1}{2} \left(\frac{k}{6} \right)^{\frac{1-k}{4}} = 1.$$

Therefore, QSHORT makes under (RA) and (GSA) expected

$$\Theta((N/M)^{1/2}) = O(N^{1/2}) = O\left(\left(\frac{k}{6}\right)^{(k-1)/8}\right)$$

queries to the black box $O_{f_{B,k}}$. The total number of expected elementary operations is $O(n^2(k/6)^{(k-1)/8}A)$. The space requirements of QSHORT are dominated by the black box $O_{f_{B,k}}$.

Replacing SHORT by QSHORT, RSR becomes a quantum algorithm QSR that achieves the same approximation factor with significantly less elementary operations.

Algorithm 7 (Quantum Search Reduction (QSR)). *Let $B = [b_1, \ldots, b_n]$ be a δ-LLL reduced basis and let $k \geq 24$ be an integer subject to (2). On input B and k, QSR computes under (RA) and (GSA) a still δ-LLL reduced basis $B' = [b'_1, \ldots, b'_n]$ satisfying*

$$\|b'_1\| \leq \left(\tfrac{k}{6}\right)^{\frac{n}{2k}} \lambda_1 .$$

QSR performs on average

$$O\left(n^3\left(\tfrac{k}{6}\right)^{(k-1)/8}A + n^4A\right)$$

operations.

```
1:  while ||b₁|| > (k/6)^((n-1)/2k)||b̂ₙ|| do          /* O(n) iterations */
2:      b ← QSHORT(B, k)
3:      B ← LLLU(B, b)
4:  end while
5:  return B
```

Like RSR, QSR executes the loop body $O(n)$ times and each iteration requires $O(n^2(k/6)^{(k-1)/8}A + n^3A)$ operations, yielding the stated operation bound.

5 Impact on NTRU

We discuss the impact of our proposed reduction algorithm QSR on NTRU if quantum computers were available. The NTRU cryptosystem attracted a lot of attention since it is very efficient. It is being standardized by the IEEE P1363 workgroup; another standard has already been published by the Consortium for Efficient Embedded Security [19].

The one-wayness of NTRU is based on the hardness of SVP in a certain class of lattices generated by convolution matrices. The resistance of NTRU against lattice reduction attacks has been studied in [1, §4.2 and Appendix] and [20]. The authors of these papers report experiments on a 200 MHz PC with the BKZ implementation found in Shoup's NTL library [21]. They tried to recover private keys in lattice dimension $2N$, $75 \leq N \leq 108$, for parameter sets relating to "moderate", "high", and "highest" security. We are not aware of any more recent data on lattice attacks against the one-wayness of NTRU.

It is noticeable that in the experiments, the block size had to be increased very quickly. For $N = 75$ a block size k between 4 and 6 sufficed to approximate the corresponding SVP well enough, but for $N = 108$ the required block size

Table 1. Estimated running time for recovering private NTRU keys (in MIPS-years)

N	$t_{\mathrm{BKZ}}(N)$	$t_{\mathrm{RSR}}(N)$	$t_{\mathrm{QSR}}(N)$
503	$1.2 * 10^{30}$	$3.3 * 10^{8}$	$5.8 * 10^{3}$
709	$6.5 * 10^{46}$	$\mathbf{2.8 * 10^{11}}$	$5.3 * 10^{5}$
809	$2.7 * 10^{53}$	$\mathbf{2.3 * 10^{13}}$	$4.8 * 10^{6}$
1277	$1.4 * 10^{89}$	$1.9 * 10^{22}$	$\mathbf{1.4 * 10^{11}}$
1511	$9.7 * 10^{106}$	$5.6 * 10^{26}$	$\mathbf{2.4 * 10^{13}}$

[15] considers $1.02 * 10^{11}$ and $2.07 * 10^{13}$ MIPS-years infeasible
in 2005 and 2015, respectively.

was already $k = 22$. From their experiments the authors extrapolated the running time t necessary to recover an NTRU key generated for highest security. Assuming a second on a 200 MHz PC is equivalent to 200 MIPS-seconds, they found

$$t_{\mathrm{BKZ}}(N) \geq e^{0.17564N - 19.04795} \text{ MIPS-years}.$$

The estimated cost of their attack for $N = 503$ is about 10^{30} MIPS-years. According to the Lenstra-Verheul heuristic [15], even $3 * 10^{21}$ MIPS-years are infeasible until 2050, i.e. NTRU's security margin with respect to this attack seemed plenty.

However, recall that QSR reduces the running time to about the 8th root compared with Koy's primal-dual method. The primal-dual method is already supposed to perform better than the BKZ reduction used in [1]. As a first approximation, we therefore estimate the running time of an attack with QSR as

$$t_{\mathrm{QSR}}(N) \geq e^{(0.17564N - 19.04795)/8} \text{ MIPS-years}.$$

Therefore, keys generated for NTRU-503 will be recovered after $\approx 10^{30/8} = 10^{3.75}$ MIPS-years and NTRU-503 cannot be considered secure anymore once QSR can be implemented.

But the speedup by QSR is only polynomial, whence the NTRU scheme itself won't be broken by QSR. It is sufficient to multiply NTRU's security parameter with a constant factor. Lenstra and Verheul claim that a running time of $1.02 * 10^{11}$ MIPS-years will be infeasible in 2005, $2.07 * 10^{13}$ will be infeasible in 2015. By our rough estimate, it would only be infeasible to recover an NTRU key in 2005 if $N \geq 1277$. Tab. (1) gives an overview of the estimated running times for recovering a private NTRU key generated with the parameters proposed for NTRU-503 if the attacker uses the BKZ implementation from NTL, Schnorr's random sampling reduction, and the proposed quantum search reduction, respectively. The shown values of N are minimal primes that can be considered secure against attacks with the RSR and QSR algorithm in 2005 and 2015, respectively.

6 Further Improvements and Research

Schnorr [13] reports that a variant of RSR that replaces any one of the first ten base vectors and updates the basis by BKZ rather than LLL is very effective. His extended sampling algorithm ESHORT returns a pair (b, i) such that $\|\pi_i(b)\|^2 = \sum_{j=i}^{n} \nu_j \|\hat{b}_j\|^2 \leq 0.99 \|\hat{b}_j\|^2$. We can implement an analog quantum search algorithm QESHORT by straightforward modifications to our predicate f. The time bounds for QESHORT do not change. Of course, we cannot bound the overall running time of the resulting reduction algorithm since we have no proven time bound for the BKZ algorithm.

As mentioned before, Schnorr also proposes a sampling reduction that exploits the birthday paradox. Unfortunately, he has to trade very much space for the additional speedup whence it is doubtful whether the simple birthday reduction (SBR) is practical. Anyway, the birthday paradox has also been used to accelerate Grover's search algorithm. Brassard, Høyer and Tapp [22] proposed an quantum algorithm that finds a collision in a hash function $h : X \rightarrow Y$ with at most $O(N^{1/3})$ evaluations of h, $N = |X|$. Thus, on the first glance, it seemed possible to construct a quantum variant of SBR that performs estimated $O(n^3(4/3)^{k/3}(k/6)^{k/12}A + n^4A)$ operations. Unfortunately, our attempt failed since [22] requires $N \geq 2|Y|$ which does not hold if we follow the construction of SBR. It therefore stays an open question whether QSR allows an additional speedup by a time-space trade-off.

7 Conclusion

We presented a quantum algorithm QSR that approximates shortest lattices vectors up to a factor $\leq (k/6)^{n/2k}$ where n is the lattice dimension and $k \geq 24$ is an almost arbitrary parameter. The expected running time of our algorithm is $O(n^3(k/6)^{k/8}A + n^4A)$ which is roughly the square root of the running time of the fastest known classical algorithm RSR. We reconsidered the security analysis of NTRU and found that an attack against NTRU-503 with our algorithm required only (roughly) estimated $5.8 * 10^3$ MIPS-years. An attack with QSR against NTRU would be infeasible only if NTRU's security parameter was raised up to 1277.

References

1. Hoffstein, J., Pipher, J., Silverman, J.H.: NTRU: A ring-based public key cryptosystem. In Buhler, J.P., ed.: Algorithmic Number Theory (ANTS III). Volume 1423 of LNCS., Springer-Verlag (1998)
2. Shor, P.W.: Polynomial-time algorithms for prime factorization and discrete logarithms on a quantum computer. SIAM J. Comput. 26 (1997) 1484–1509
3. Hallgren, S.: Polynomial-time quantum algorithm for Pell's equation and the principal ideal problem. In: Proceedings of the Thirty-Fourth Annual ACM Symposium on Theory of Computing, ACM Press (2002)

4. Emde Boas, P.v.: Another NP-complete partition problem and the complexity of computing short vectors in a lattice. Technical Report 81-04, University of Amsterdam, Department of Mathematics, Netherlands (1981)
5. Ajtai, M.: The shortest vector problem in L_2 is NP-hard for randomized reductions (extended abstract). In: Proceedings of the Thirtieth Annual ACM Symposium on Theory of Computing, ACM Press (1998) 10–19
6. Micciancio, D.: The shortest vector in a lattice is hard to approximate to within some constant. In: IEEE Symposium on Foundations of Computer Science. (1998) 92–98
7. Goldreich, O., Goldwasser, S., Halevi, S.: Public-key cryptosystems from lattice reduction problems. In Kaliski, Jr., B.S., ed.: Advances in Cryptology – Crypto'97. Volume 1294 of LNCS., Springer-Verlag (1997) 112–131
8. Micciancio, D.: Improving lattice based cryptosystems using the Hermite normal form. In Silverman, J.H., ed.: Cryptography and Lattices. Volume 2146 of LNCS., Springer-Verlag (2001) 126–145
9. Regev, O.: Quantum computations and lattice problems. In: The 43rd Annual IEEE Symposium on Foundations of Computer Science (FOCS'02), IEEE (2002) 520–529
10. Kannan, R.: Minkowski's convex body theorem and integer programming. Math. Oper. Research **12** (1987) 415–440
11. Lenstra, A.K., Lenstra, H.W., Lovász, L.: Factoring polynomials with rational coefficients. Math. Ann. **261** (1982) 515–534
12. Schnorr, C.P.: A hierachy of polynomial lattice basis reduction algorithms. Theoretical Computer Science **53** (1987) 201–224
13. Schnorr, C.P.: Lattice reduction by random sampling and birthday methods. In Alt, H., Habib, M., eds.: STACS 2003: 20th Annual Symposium on Theoretical Aspects of Computer Science. Volume 2607 of LNCS., Springer (2003) 146–156
14. Schnorr, C.P., Euchner, M.: Lattice basis reduction: Improved practical algorithms and solving subset sum problems. Math. Programming **66** (1994) 181–199
15. Lenstra, A.K., Verheul, E.R.: Selecting cryptographic key sizes. J. Cryptology **14** (2001) 255–293
16. Nielsen, M.A., Chuang, I.L.: Quantum Computation and Quantum Information. Cambridge University Press (2000)
17. Grover, L.K.: A fast quantum mechanical algorithm for database search. In: Proceedings of the Twenty-Eighth Annual ACM Symposium on Theory of Computing (STOC), ACM Press (1996) 212–219
18. Boyer, M., Brassard, G., Høyer, P., Tapp, A.: Tight bounds on quantum searching. arXiv e-print quant-ph/9605034 (1996)
19. Consortium for Efficient Embedded Security: EESS #1: Implementation aspects of NTRUEncrypt and NTRUSign. http://www.ceesstandards.org/documents/EESS1_11122002_v2.pdf (2002) Version 1.0.
20. Silverman, J.: Estimated breaking times for NTRU lattices. Technical Report 12, NTRU Cryptosystems, Inc. (1999)
21. Shoup, V.: NTL – a library for doing number theory. URL http://www.shoup.net/ntl/index.html (2001) Release 5.2.
22. Brassard, G., Høyer, P., Tapp, A.: Quantum cryptanalysis of hash and claw-free functions. In Lucchesi, C., Moura, A., eds.: LATIN'98: Theoretical Informatics. Volume 1380 of LNCS., Springer-Verlag (1998)

Three Sorting Algorithms Using Priority Queues

Amr Elmasry

Computer Science Department
Alexandria University
Alexandria, Egypt.
elmasry@cs.rutgers.edu

Abstract. We establish a lower bound of $B(n) = n\lceil\log n\rceil - 2^{\lceil\log n\rceil} + 1$[1] on the number of comparisons performed by any algorithm that uses priority queues to sort n elements. Three sorting algorithms using priority queues are introduced. The first algorithm performs the same comparisons as the classical Mergesort algorithm, but in a different order. The second algorithm performs at most $2n\log n + O(n)$ comparisons, with the advantage of being adaptive; meaning that it runs faster when the input sequence has some presortedness. In particular, we show that this algorithm sorts an already sorted sequence in linear time; a fact that is not obvious since there is no special checks to guarantee this behavior. The third algorithm is almost implicit; it can be implemented using the input array and less than n extra bits. The number of comparisons performed by this algorithm is at most $B(n) + 2.5n$. The three algorithms have the advantage of producing every element of the sorted output, after the first, in $O(\log n)$, and can be implemented to be practically efficient.

1 Introduction

A well known sorting paradigm is sorting using priority queues, with plenty of references in the literature [11]. A priority queue is a heap-ordered general tree. The values in the heap are stored one value per tree node. The value stored in the parent of a node is smaller than or equal to the value stored in the node itself. We thus find the minimum heap value stored in the tree root. There is no restriction on the number of children a node may have, and the children of a node are maintained in a list of siblings. These selection sort algorithms produce the sorted sequence by repeatedly deleting the root of the queue and outputting its value then reconstructing the priority queue to maintain the heap property, in an operation that we call *deletemin*. The classical example of tree selection is by using a tournament tree. A tournament tree can be constructed by starting with all the elements at the bottom level. Every adjacent pair of elements is compared and the smaller element is promoted to the next level. When a winner moves up from one level to another it is replaced by the one that should eventually move up into its former place (namely the smaller of the two keys below). Once the smallest element reaches the root and is deleted, we can proceed to sort by a

---

[1] All logarithms in this paper are to the base 2.

T. Ibaraki, N. Katoh, and H. Ono (Eds.): ISAAC 2003, LNCS 2906, pp. 209–220, 2003.
© Springer-Verlag Berlin Heidelberg 2003

top down method. The smallest descendent of the root is moved up, the smallest descendent of this latter element is moved up, and the process is repeated until reaching two empty nodes. This system of promotions is repeated with every *deletemin* operation. The number of comparisons performed by the tournament tree selection sort is at most $B(n) = n\lceil \log n \rceil - 2^{\lceil \log n \rceil} + 1$ [11].

We show that $B(n)$ is a lower bound on any selection sort algorithm that uses priority queues. It is well known that $\lceil \log n! \rceil < n \log n - 1.44n$ key comparisons is a lower bound for any comparison-based sequential sorting algorithm.

Our first algorithm performs the same comparisons performed by the Mergesort algorithm, but in a different order. See [7] for an analogous correspondence between other transformations on priority queues. In an abstract form, the Mergesort algorithm works as follows; the input sequence is split in two equal halves. Each half is recursively sorted, and these two sequences are then merged using the linear merge algorithm. Let $L(n)$ be the upper bound on the number of comparisons performed by the Mergesort algorithm. It is known that $B(n) \leq L(n)$ and $B(n) = L(n) = n \log n - n + 1$ when n is a power of 2 [11]. Our algorithm has an advantage over the Mergesort in that it requires $n - 1$ comparisons to produce the smallest element, and at most $\lceil \log n \rceil$ comparisons to produce each of the other elements. Hence, it is more suitable for order statistics.

Our second algorithm requires at most $2n \log n + O(n)$ comparisons. This algorithm is better than the first one when the input has fewer inversions. For an input sequence X of length n, the number of inversions $Inv(X)$ is defined

$$Inv(X) = |\{(i,j) \mid 1 \leq i < j \leq n \text{ and } x_i > x_j\}|.$$

In this sense, our second algorithm is an adaptive sorting algorithm. There are many defined measures of presortedness, and plenty of known adaptive sorting algorithms, see [4,5,12,13,15]. In particular, a common property of all adaptive sorting algorithms is that such algorithms run in linear time when the input sequence is sorted. We show that our second algorithm has this property. Experimental results illustrate that our second algorithm performs fewer comparisons as the number of inversions in the input decreases. Inspired by the experimental results, we conjecture that this algorithm is optimal with respect to the number of inversions. In other words, we conjecture that it runs in $O(n \log \frac{Inv(X)}{n} + n)$.

Another challenge is to implement the selection sort algorithms within the input array without using extra storage. In this line of thinking the following algorithms were introduced. The worst case number of key comparisons in Heapsort independently introduced by Floyd [6] and Williams [22] is bounded by $2n \log n + O(n)$. Bottom-up-Heapsort (Wegener [21]) is a variant of Heapsort with at most $1.5n \log n + O(n)$ comparisons in the worst case. MDR-Heapsort proposed by McDiarmid and Reed [14] and analyzed by Wegener [20] performs less than $n \log n + 1.1n$ comparisons in the worst case and extends the Bottom-up-Heapsort by using, with every element, one bit to encode on which branch the smaller element of its children can be found and another one to mark if this information is unknown. Weak-Heapsort introduced by Dutton [2] and analyzed by Edelkamp and Wegener [3] is more elegant and faster. Instead of two bits per element, Weak-Heapsort uses only one and requires at most $n \log n + 0.1n$ comparisons. Our third algorithm uses less than n extra bits in addition to the input array and requires at most $B(n) + 2.5n < n \log n + 1.6n$ comparisons.

All three algorithms rely on the notion of binomial queues. A binomial queue is a heap ordered tree that has the following structure. A binomial queue of rank r is constructed recursively by making the root of a binomial queue of rank $r-1$ the leftmost child of another binomial queue of rank $r-1$. A binomial queue of rank 0 consists of a single node. The rank of any node in a binomial queue equals the number of the children of this node. There are $\frac{n}{2^{i+1}}$ nodes of rank i in an n-node binomial queue, for all i from 0 to $\log n - 1$.

A basic operation for our algorithms is the pairing operation in which two queues are combined by making the root with the larger key value the leftmost child of the other root. Given a sequence of priority queues, a *halving* pass is implemented by combining these queues in pairs; every two adjacent queues are paired together starting from left to right (if the number of queues is odd, the rightmost queue is not paired). A *right-to-left incremental pairing* pass is implemented by combining the queues, in order from right to left, to form a single queue; each queue is paired with the single queue resulting from combining the queues to its right. A *multi-pass pairing* phase is implemented by repeatedly performing halving passes until a single queue is left. Given a sequence of n elements each stored in a single node, applying a multi-pass pairing phase, which requires $n - 1$ comparisons, the heap becomes a binomial queue. If n is not a power of 2 there will be some missing nodes from the above definition of a binomial queue. We call the queue at this moment the initial binomial queue. (Notice the similarity between building the initial binomial queue and building the Weak-Heap of Dutton [2].)

2   Algorithm 1

Given a sequence of n elements each stored in a single node, this selection sort algorithm starts by performing a multi-pass pairing phase, deleting the smallest element and printing its value. Then, a right-to-left incremental pairing pass is repeated $n - 1$ times, where each pass is followed by deleting the current smallest element from the queue and printing its value.

Lemma 1 *Using Algorithm 1, every element after the smallest requires at most* $\lceil \log n \rceil$ *comparisons to be produced.*

Proof. Omitted.   □

Lemma 2 *Algorithm 1 performs the same comparisons performed by the Merge-sort algorithm.*

Proof. Consider the multi-pass pairing phase. It is straight forward to observe that all the comparisons performed during this phase are also performed by the Mergesort algorithm. We define the following sorting algorithm, which we call algorithm *, as follows. When algorithm * is applied on a priority queue it outputs the element in the root, applies the same algorithm recursively on each of the resulting sub-queues from right to left, and finally merges the resulting sequences in an incremental fashion from right to left using the classical linear merge algorithm. In fact, algorithm * is another way to describe the Mergesort algorithm. What is left is to show that algorithm *, when applied on the initial binomial queue, performs the same set of comparisons performed by the right-to-left incremental pairing passes of Algorithm 1.

For any priority queue α, let $r(\alpha)$ represents the element at the root of α, $S(\alpha)$ represents the sorted sequence of the elements of α, and let α^* represents the set of comparisons performed by algorithm * when applied on α. Given two queues α and β, let $\alpha.\beta$ denote the queue resulting from pairing the two queues, and $r(\alpha) \# r(\beta)$ represents the comparison between $r(\alpha)$ and $r(\beta)$. We show that

$$(r(\alpha) \# r(\beta)) \cup (\alpha.\beta)^* = \alpha^* \cup \beta^* \cup merge(S(\alpha), S(\beta)) \tag{1}$$

Where $merge(a,b)$ stands for the set of comparisons performed by the classical linear merge algorithm when applied on the sorted sequences a and b. Assume without loss of generality that $r(\alpha) < r(\beta)$, in which case β will be linked to the root of α as its leftmost child. The way algorithm * works implies

$$(\alpha.\beta)^* = \alpha^* \cup \beta^* \cup merge(S(\alpha) - r(\alpha), S(\beta)).$$

The way the linear merge works implies

$$merge(S(\alpha), S(\beta)) = (r(\alpha) \# r(\beta)) \cup merge(S(\alpha) - r(\alpha), S(\beta)).$$

Equation (1) follows from the above facts.

Next, we show by backward induction on the comparisons performed by the right-to-left incremental pairing passes of Algorithm 1 that the same comparisons are performed if we apply algorithm *. The base case, which is in fact the last comparison, happens between two single nodes representing the largest two elements in the queues; in which case the two algorithms are trivially equivalent. Consider the priority queue at any moment of the algorithm, and let α and β be the rightmost two sub-queues. Applying Algorithm 1 on this queue results in the comparison $r(\alpha) \# r(\beta)$. Assuming the two algorithms perform the same comparisons from the point after this comparison and using (1), they are also equivalent before the comparison, and the induction hypothesis is true.   □

3   Algorithm 2

The pairing heap [8] is a self adjusting heap structure that uses pairing in its implementation. In the standard two-pass variant of the pairing heaps, the *deletemin* operation proceeds by applying a halving pass on the sequence of queues, followed by a right-to-left incremental pairing pass. It has been proven [8] that the amortized cost of the number of comparisons involved in the *deletemin* operation for the two-pass variant of the pairing heaps is at most $2 \log n + O(1)$.

Given a sequence of n elements each stored in a single node, Algorithm 2 starts by performing a multi-pass pairing phase to delete the smallest element and print its value. Then, a two-pass pairing phase, similar to the pairing heap *deletemin* operation is repeated $n-1$ times, where each two-pass phase is followed by deleting the current smallest element from the queue and printing its value.

Lemma 3 *Algorithm 2 runs in $O(n \log n)$ and requires at most $2n \log n + O(n)$ comparisons.*

Proof. We mention below the basic idea of the proof while the details are omitted. We use the fact that the amortized cost of a *deletemin* operation is $2 \log n + O(1)$ comparisons. An extra $O(n)$ credits are required to pay for the potential after the multi-pass pairing phase, while the actual cost of this phase is $O(n)$.   □

Lemma 4 *Given an input sequence of n elements that are sorted in ascending order from right to left, represented as n single nodes. Applying Algorithm 2 on this sequence requires less than $6n$ comparisons.*

Proof. Throughout the algorithm, when the value of a node is compared with its right sibling, the one to the left will have the larger value. Hence, the left node will be linked to the right node as its leftmost child.

The left spine of a node is defined to be the path from that node to the leftmost leaf of the sub-tree defined by this node. In other words, every node on the path is the leftmost child of its predecessor. The right spine is defined analogously. The halving passes are numbered, starting from t_0, the last halving pass of the first *deletemin* operation. We assume that the halving pass t takes place at time t. Consider any node x in the heap. Let $g_x(t)$ be the number of nodes on the left spine of x, after the halving pass t. Let $h_x(t)$ be the number of nodes on the left spine of the right sibling of x, after the same halving pass. If x does not have a right sibling, then $h_x(t)$ is equal to 0. Define $v_x(t)$ to be equal to $g_x(t) - h_x(t)$. We only consider the halving passes due to the fact that the values of $g(t)$ and $h(t)$ for all the nodes do not change during the right-to-left incremental pairing passes (except for the left sibling of the root of the rightmost queue, whose $h(t)$ decreases by one). We show by induction on time that for any node x, $v_x(t)$ is a positive non-decreasing function with time, and that this function increases if x is involved in a comparison during a halving pass. For the initial binomial queue, a property of binomial queues implies that the value of $v_x(t_0)$ is positive. This establishes the base case. Consider any node w and its right sibling z, such that w is linked to z as its leftmost child during the halving pass $t + 1$, for any $t \geq t_0$. The following relations follow:

$$h_w(t) = g_z(t) \tag{2}$$

$$g_w(t + 1) = g_w(t) \tag{3}$$

$$h_w(t + 1) \leq h_w(t) - 1 \tag{4}$$

$$g_z(t + 1) = g_w(t) + 1 \tag{5}$$

$$h_z(t + 1) \leq h_z(t) + 1 \tag{6}$$

Relation (6) is a result of the fact that the number of nodes of the left spine of the right sibling of z may increase by at most one in a halving pass. Using (3) and (4), then $v_w(t+1) > v_w(t)$, and the hypothesis is true for the node w at time $t+1$. Using the induction hypothesis for node w at time t, then $v_w(t) > 0$. This relation together with (2) and (5) implies $g_z(t+1) > g_z(t) + 1$. Using the latter relation and (6), then $v_z(t+1) > v_z(t)$, and the hypothesis is true for node z at time $t+1$. The hypothesis is then true for all the nodes.

Of the links of the halving passes, we distinguish between two types of links. If $v_z(t) = 1$, we call the link an A-link. If $v_z(t) \geq 2$, we call the link a B-link. The above analysis indicates that any node may gain at most one child by an A-link. Hence, the number of comparisons accompanying A-links is at most n.

We use the accounting method [19] for bounding the number of comparisons accompanying B-links. After the first *deletemin* operation, we maintain the invariant that the number of credits on a node x after any halving pass t is $\frac{h_x^2(t)}{2}$. In the initial binomial queue, $h_x(t_0)$ equals the rank of x (the number of children of x), r_x. Let C be the number of credits needed to keep the invariant hold for the initial binomial queue, then

$$C = \sum_x \frac{r_x^2}{2},$$

$$= \sum_{i=1}^{\log n - 1} \frac{i^2/2}{2^{i+1}} n$$

$$< 1.5n.$$

Next, we show that these credits are enough to pay for all the B-links, while maintaining the invariant. Let d be the difference between the sum of the number of credits on w and z before pass $t+1$ and those needed after pass $t+1$. Then

$$d = \frac{h_z^2(t)}{2} + \frac{h_w^2(t)}{2} - \frac{h_z^2(t+1)}{2} - \frac{h_w^2(t+1)}{2}.$$

Using (4) and (6), then

$$d \geq h_w(t) - h_z(t) - 1.$$

Using (2) together with the fact that for all the B-links $v_z(t) \geq 2$, then

$$d \geq 1.$$

This extra credit is used to pay for the comparison between w and z.

The above analysis implies that the total number of comparisons performed in the having passes is $2.5n$. This follows by adding the n comparisons bounding the A-links, and the $1.5n$ comparisons bounding the B-links. The number of comparisons performed in the right-to-left incremental pairing passes is bounded by the number of comparisons performed by the halving passes, for a total of at most $5n$ for both passes. The theorem follows by adding the $n - 1$ comparisons done in the multi-pass pairing phase.   □

4   Implementation Issues and Experimental Findings

The data structure we use to make these implementations efficient is the child, sibling representation, also known as the binary tree representation [11]. Each node has a left pointer pointing to its leftmost child and a right pointer pointing to its right sibling. The effect of the representation is to convert a heap-ordered tree into a half-ordered binary tree with empty right sub-tree, where by half-ordered we mean that the key of any node is at least as small as the key of any node in its left sub-tree.

It remains to investigate how our algorithms perform in practice. Since Algorithm 1 is another way to implement Mergesort, we need to relate it to the different ways known for implementing Mergesort. One of the well known methods to implement Mergesort is to use linked lists [11]. To save time in this implementation, the pointer manipulations are postponed as much as possible. Specifically, when the head of a list is found smaller than the head of the other, we keep traversing the first list until an element that is bigger than the head of the second list is encountered. The sub-list of the first list representing the elements smaller than the head of the second list are moved to the sorted output as a whole block. This saves several pointer manipulations, and improves the running time of the algorithm. On average, roughly speaking, more than half the work is saved about half the time. See [11] for more details. Several other tricks are used to improve the implementation of the linked list version of Mergesort [17]. Katajainen and Pasanen [9], and Reinhardt [16] show that Mergesort can be designed to achieve a bound of at most $n \log n - 1.3n + O(\log n)$ comparisons in the worst case. They [9,10] also gave a practical in-place Mergesort algorithm.

Consider the right-to-left incremental pairing passes. To save in the running time, we use a similar technique to the method that is mentioned above. After each iteration of the main loop, we keep the invariant that $value(l) > value(m)$, where l is the root of the rightmost queue, and m is the left sibling of l. The invariant is easily fulfilled before the loop, as follows. Let l be the root of the rightmost queue. We traverse the left siblings of l incrementally from right to left, as long as the values of the nodes are greater than the value of l. This list of siblings is linked to l, as $l's$ leftmost children, forming one sub-list in the same order. Within the main loop, a check is performed between the value of the left sibling of m and $value(m)$. If $value(m)$ is greater, l is linked to m as its leftmost child, and the iteration ends. Otherwise, we keep traversing the left sibling of the last traversed node, until a node whose value is smaller than $value(m)$ is encountered. The node l together with the whole list of left siblings of m (whose values are greater than $value(m)$) are linked as one sub-list forming the leftmost children of m, in the same order. This implementation saves several pointer manipulations, and improves the running time of the algorithm. On average, roughly speaking, more than half the work is saved about half the time. Another way of improving the running time of the algorithms is to use loop unfolding, a technique used in optimizing compilers. Here, we can save some commands and skip artificial variable renaming. By efficiently implementing Algorithm 1, we were able to beat the running time of the best implementations for Mergesort we know about. The results of these experiments are omitted from this version.

Other experiments were performed on Algorithm 2, supporting the hypothesis that it is an efficient adaptive sorting algorithm. In our experiments we compare the results of sorting an input sequence that has some presortedness, when applied to Algorithm 2, Splaysort and Binomialsort. Slaysort is an adaptive sorting algorithm that relies on repeated insertions in a splay tree [18]. As a consequence of the dynamic finger theorem for splay trees (see Cole [1]) Splaysort is an optimal adaptive sorting algorithm. Moffat et al. [15] performed experiments showing that Splaysort is efficient in practice. Binomialsort [4] is another optimal adaptive sorting algorithm that is practically efficient and easy to implement. Both algorithms run in $O(n \log \frac{Inv(X)}{n} + n)$.

The input sequence is randomly generated such that the expected and worst case number of inversions is controlled. We start with a sorted sequence and perform two phases of permutations. For a given value of a parameter k, we want to permute the sorted sequence to have at most kn inversions. In the first phase, the sorted sequence is broken into consecutive blocks of $\frac{n}{k}$ elements each. From each block we select one element at random, for a total of k elements. These k elements are then randomly permuted. The number of inversions produced by this process is at most $\frac{nk}{2}$. In the second phase, the sequence is broken into consecutive blocks of k elements each. The elements of each block are randomly permuted, for a total of at most another $\frac{nk}{2}$ inversions. A value of $k = 0$ means that the input sequence is sorted in ascending order. A small value of k, with respect to n, means that the input sequence is almost sorted. A value of k, which is as big as n, means that the input sequence is randomly sorted. The experiment is repeated 100 times for a different value of k and the average number of comparisons performed by each of the three algorithms is reported verses $\log k$. The experiments are performed on two values of n; for Table 1 $n = 1024$, and for Table 2 $n = 32768$.

The experiments are repeated with the input sequence reversed before being fed to the program. In other words, a value of $k = 0$ would now mean that the input sequence is inversely sorted. A small value of k means that the input sequence is almost inversely sorted. See Table 3.

The results of our experiments imply that Algorithm 2 always performs a fewer number of comparisons than Splaysort. It is also doing better than Binomialsort, except when the number of inversions is small. This suggests that the constant hidden in the linear term of the number of comparisons used by

Table 1. Comparisons per item to sort random sequences of n=1024. $Inv(X) < kn$

log k	0	1	2	3	4	5	6	7	8	9	10
Algorithm 2	3.2	3.2	3.5	3.9	4.7	5.6	6.5	8.0	8.7	10.8	11.1
Splaysort	2.0	3.1	3.9	5.0	5.7	6.8	8.4	10.4	11.8	13.7	15.5
Binomialsort	1.9	2.3	2.3	3.4	4.2	5.7	6.6	8.6	10.4	11.9	12.8

Table 2. Comparisons per item to sort random sequences of n=32768. $Inv(X) < kn$

$\log k$	0	1	2	3	4	5	6	7	8	9	10	11	12	13	14	15
Algorithm 2	3.3	3.3	3.5	3.9	4.5	5.1	6.0	6.9	7.8	8.8	9.9	11.1	12.5	14.0	15.1	17.3
Splaysort	2.0	3.2	4.4	4.9	5.8	6.5	7.6	8.8	10.2	11.7	13.3	15.1	16.9	18.9	20.8	25.2
Binomialsort	2.0	2.4	2.6	3.2	4.2	5.8	7.2	8.7	10.4	12.1	14.7	19.0	21.0	22.3	23.1	23.8

Table 3. Comparisons per item to sort random sequences of n=65536. $Inv(Rev(X)) \leq kn$, where $Rev(X)$ is the reversed sequence of X.

$\log k$	0	1	2	3	4	5	6	7	8	9	10	11	12	13	14	15
Algori. 2	1.5	1.6	2.4	3.4	4.3	5.2	6.1	7.0	7.9	8.9	10.1	11.0	12.5	13.6	14.8	17.5
Splay	2.0	3.1	3.87	5.1	5.8	6.6	7.6	8.8	10.1	11.5	13.2	14.9	16.7	18.7	21.3	23.2
Binomial	27.7	27.7	27.7	27.6	27.6	27.5	27.5	27.4	27.4	27.4	27.3	27.1	26.9	26.6	26.3	25.6

Binomialsort is smaller. When the input is almost inversely sorted, in contrast with Binomialsort, both Splaysort and Algorithm 2 are still adaptive.

5   Algorithm 3

The algorithm starts with building a binomial queue in the input array, by mapping every element of the binomial queue to a corresponding location in the array. The algorithm proceeds (similar to Heapsort) by repeatedly swapping the element that is the current minimum (first element of the array) with the last element of the unsorted part of the array. Each time, a *heapify* operation is performed on the binomial queue to maintain the heap property.

Heapifying Binomial Queues

Given an n-node binomial queue such that the value at its root is not the smallest value, we want to restore the heap property. The *heapify* operation proceeds by finding the node x with the smallest value among the children of the root and swapping its value with that of the root. This step is repeated with the node x as the current root, until either a leaf or a node that has a value smaller than or equal to all the values of its children is reached. For efficient implementation, an extra pointer is kept with every node x. This pointer points to the node with the smallest value among all the right siblings of x, including itself. We call this pointer, the pointer for the prefix minimum (pm). The pm pointer of the leftmost child of a node will, therefore, point to the node with the smallest value among all the children of the parent node. First, the path from the root to a leaf, where every node has the smallest value among its siblings, is determined by utilizing the pm pointers. No comparisons are required for this step. Next, the value at the root is compared with the values of the nodes of this path bottom up, until the correct position of the root is determined. The value at the root is then inserted at this position, and all the values at the nodes above this position are shifted up. The pm pointers of the nodes whose values moved up and those of all their left siblings are updated. To maintain the correct values in the pm pointers, the pm pointer of a given node x is updated to point to the smaller of the value of x and the value of the node pointed to by the pm pointer of the right sibling of x. At each level of the queue (except possibly for the level of the final destination of the old value of the root), either a comparison with the old value of the root takes place or the pm pointers are updated, but not both. See [4] for the details.

Lemma 5 *The time used by the heapify operation is $O(\log n)$. It requires at most $\lceil \log n \rceil + 1$ comparisons, and an $O(\log n)$ additional storage.*

Building a Binomial Queue in an Array

Given an n-element array, we build a binomial queue of rank i if the ith bit in the binary representation of n is 1. The smaller rank queues are mapped first in the array. The nodes of a binomial queue are mapped in a preorder fashion (the root is mapped to the first position of the array). The order in which the sub-queues are mapped is from right to left (right sub-queues first).

Being aware of the rank of a node of a binomial queue that is in location p in the array, the location of its right or left siblings as well as its leftmost child can be determined, as follows. If the rank of this node is r, the locations of its right sibling, left sibling and leftmost child will be $p - 2^{r-1}$, $p + 2^r$ and $p + 2^{r-1}$ respectively. During the onset of the algorithm, the sorted part is stored in the last locations of the array. Some nodes on the left spine of the largest queue will be losing their leftmost children. Hence the formula for the leftmost child for these nodes will be $p + 2^j$, where j is the largest integer less than or equal to $r - 1$ such that $p + 2^j$ is smaller than the boundary for the unsorted part of the array. The pm pointers are stored in the form of a number of bits per node that represents the difference in rank between the source node and the node it is pointing to. If the rank of the source node is r, its location in the array is p, and the value stored for the pm pointer is d, then the location of the node, that this pm pointer is pointing to, is $p - 2^r + 2^{r-d}$. The total number of bits representing these pointers is less than n. An initial binomial queue can be built in an array in a recursive manner. Given two binomial queues of rank $\log n - 1$ stored in the first and last $\frac{n}{2}$ locations of an array, the two queues are merged by comparing their roots and performing an $O(n)$ moves, if necessary, to maintain the above mapping criteria. The bits representing the pm pointer of the node that loses the comparison is calculated.

Lemma 6 *Algorithm 3 runs in $O(n \log n)$ and requires at most $n \log n + 1.6n$ comparisons. In addition to the input array, less than n extra bits are used.*

Proof. The phase of building the initial binomial queue in the array requires $n-1$ comparisons to build the queue, and $\frac{n}{2}$ comparisons to set the pm pointers (there are $\frac{n}{2}$ nodes that do not have right siblings). The number of moves done in this initial phase is $O(n \log n)$. A *heapify* operation is then applied $n-1$ times on the remaining unsorted elements. Using Lemma 5, the total number of comparisons needed in these operations is bounded by $\sum_{1 \leq k \leq n}(\lceil \log k \rceil + 1) = B(n) + n < n \log n + .1n$ (See [20] for the derivation of the bound on $B(n)$.). The bound on the number of comparisons follows by adding the above bound with the $1.5n$ comparisons of the initial phase. To represent the *pm* pointers, we need at most $\lceil \log i \rceil$ bits for each of at most $\frac{n}{2^i}$ of the nodes, for all i from 2 to $\log n$. Hence, the total number of bits is bounded by $\sum_{2 \leq i \leq \log n} \frac{\lceil \log i \rceil}{2^i} n < n$. □

6   A Lower Bound on Sorting Using Priority Queues

There are two main paradigms for sorting using priority queues. The first paradigm, which we used in the first two algorithms, maintains the elements to be sorted in a set of priority queues. It permits comparisons only between the elements of the roots of these priority queues. After such a comparison, the root that has the larger element is linked to the other root (becomes one of its children). Comparisons are performed until all the elements are combined into one queue. The root of this queue is removed and the smallest element is output, again leaving a set of priority queues. The process of combining the queues is repeated to produce the second smallest element, and so on. To establish a lower bound on such paradigm, we adopt the adversary that whenever the roots of two queues are compared, the queue with the smaller number of nodes becomes a child of the root of the other queue. The number of comparisons that a specific node wins is exactly the number of children of this node at the moment when this node is deleted as the smallest element. If the size of the combined queue at this time is i, the number of children of the root is at least $\lceil \log i \rceil$. Therefore, the total number of comparisons required by any sorting algorithm that uses this paradigm is at least $\sum_{1 \leq k \leq n} \lceil \log k \rceil = n \lceil \log n \rceil - 2^{\lceil \log n \rceil} + 1$.

The second paradigm, which we used in the third algorithm, uses a system of promotions. In such a paradigm, an initial priority queue structure is built using the first paradigm, the element in the root is deleted, and promotions start taking place. The promotions involve comparisons between elements in the sibling nodes, and the smallest among them is promoted to replace the vacant parent. We show next that this paradigm inherits the same rules as the first paradigm, and hence the same lower bound applies. More specifically, a feature of the first paradigm is that for two elements x and y to be compared, both x and y should have either never lost a comparison or otherwise the last time each of them has lost a comparison should have been to the same element. In a system of promotions, assume for the purpose of contradiction that x and y are to be compared together, and that the last time x lost the comparison to a and y lost the comparison to b. Now, for x and y to be compared, a and b should have been compared first. Assume without loss of generality that a wins with respect to b. It follows that x is to be compared with b. Since x is not to lose another comparison after it has lost to a, it follows that x wins with respect to

b (i.e. $x < b$). Since y lost the comparison to b (i.e. $b < y$), it follows that $x < y$. This precludes the possibility of x and y being compared. A contradiction!

Indeed, the two paradigms are equivalent and the stated lower bound applies for any algorithm that uses a mixture of these two paradigms.

References

1. R. Cole. *On the dynamic finger conjecture for splay trees. Part II: The proof.* SIAM J. Comput. 30 (2000), 44–85.
2. R. Dutton. *Weak-Heapsort.* BIT, 33 (1993), 372–381.
3. S. Edelkamp and I. Wegener. *On the performance of weak-heapsort.* STACS 2000.In LNCS 1770 (2000), 254–260.
4. A. Elmasry. *Priority queues, pairing and adaptive sorting.* 29th ICALP. In LNCS 2380 (2002), 183–194.
5. V. Estivill-Castro and D. Wood. *A survey of adaptive sorting algorithms.* ACM Comput. Surv. 24(4) (1992), 441–476.
6. R. Floyd. *ACM algorithm 245: Treesort 3.* Comm. of ACM, 7(12) (1964), 701.
7. M. Fredman. *A priority queue transform.* 3rd WAE, LNCS 1668 (1999), 243–257.
8. M. Fredman, R. Sedgewick, D. Sleator, and R. Tarjan. *The pairing heap: a new form of self-adjusting heap.* Algorithmica 1,1 (1986), 111–129.
9. J. Katajainen, T. Pasanen. *In-place sorting with fewer moves.* Information Processing Letters, 70(1) (1999), 31–37.
10. J. Katajainen, T. Pasanen and J. Teuhola. *Practical in-place Mergesort.* Nordic Journal of Computing, 3(1) (1996), 27–40.
11. D. Knuth. *The Art of Computer Programming. Vol III: Sorting and Searching.* Addison-wesley, second edition (1998).
12. C. Levcopoulos and O. Petersson. *Adaptive Heapsort.* J. of Alg. 14 (1993), 395–413.
13. H. Mannila. *Measures of presortedness and optimal sorting algorithms.* IEEE Trans. Comput. C-34 (1985), 318–325.
14. C. McDiarmid and B. Reed. *Building heaps fast.* J. of Alg. 10 (1989), 352-365.
15. A. Moffat, G. Eddy and O. Petersson. *Splaysort: fast, verstile, practical.* Softw. Pract. and Exper. Vol 126(7) (1996), 781–797.
16. K. Reinhardt. *Sorting in-place with a worst case complexity of $n \log n - 1.3n + O(\log n)$ comparisons and $\epsilon n \log n + O(1)$ transports.* LNCS (650) (1992), 489–499.
17. S. Roura. *Improving Mergesort for linked lists.* 7th ESA (1999), 267–276.
18. D. Sleator and R. Tarjan. *Self-adjusting binary search trees.* J. ACM 32(3) (1985), 652–686.
19. R. Tarjan. *Amortized computational complexity.* SIAM J. Alg. Disc. Meth. 6 (1985), 306-318.
20. I. Wegener. *The worst case complexity of McDiarmid and Reed's variant of Bottom-up Heapsort is less than $n \log n + 1.1n$.* Inform. and Comput., 97(1) (1992), 86–96.
21. I. Wegener. *Bottom-up-Heapsort, a new variant of Heapsort, beating on an average, Quicksort (if n is not very small).* Theor. Comp. science (118) (1993), 81–98.
22. J. Williams. *ACM algorithm 232: Heapsort.* Comm. of ACM 7(6) (1964), 347–348.

Lower Bounds on Correction Networks

Grzegorz Stachowiak

Institute of Computer Science, University of Wrocław, Przesmyckiego 20,
51-151 Wrocław, Poland, gst@ii.uni.wroc.pl

Abstract. Correction networks are comparator networks that sort inputs differing from sorted sequences of length N in a small number of positions. The main application of such networks is producing fault-tolerant sorting networks. We show the lower bound $1.44 \log_2 N$ on the depth of correction networks settling an open problem from [7]. This bound is tight since the upper bound $1.44 \log_2 N$ is known.

1 Introduction

Sorting is one of the most fundamental problems of computer science. A classical approach to sort a sequence of keys is to apply a comparator network. Apart from a long tradition, comparator networks are particularly interesting due to potential hardware implementations. They can be also implemented as sorting algorithms for parallel computers.

In our approach the elements (keys) to be sorted are stored in registers $r_1, r_2, \ldots, r_N$. A *comparator* $[i : j]$ is a simple device connecting registers r_i and $r_j (i < j)$. It compares the keys they contain and if the key in r_i is bigger, it swaps the keys. The general problem is the following. At the beginning of the computations the input sequence of keys is placed in the registers. Our task is to sort the sequence of keys applying a sequence of comparators. The sequence of comparators is the same for all possible inputs. We assume that comparators connecting disjoint pairs of registers can work in parallel. Thus we arrange the sequence of comparators into a series of comparator *layers* which are sets of comparators connecting disjoint pairs of registers. The total time needed by such a network to perform its computations is proportional to the number of layers of called the network's *depth*.

Much research concerning sorting networks was done in the past. Its main goals were to minimize the depth and the total number of comparators. The most famous results are asymptotically optimal AKS [1] sorting network of depth $O(\log N)$ and more 'practical' Batcher [2] network of depth $\sim \frac{1}{2} \log^2 N$ (logarithms in this paper are binary). Due to a very large constant hidden behind big O in AKS, Batcher network has much smaller depth for practical input sizes N. Another well known result is Yao's [8] construction of an almost optimal network to select t smallest (or largest) entries of a given input of size N (t-*selection* problem). His network has depth $\log N + (1 + o(1)) \log t \log \log N$ and $\sim N \log t$ comparators which matches lower bounds for that problem ($t \ll N$).

T. Ibaraki, N. Katoh, and H. Ono (Eds.): ISAAC 2003, LNCS 2906, pp. 221–229, 2003.

The analysis of comparator networks is most often based on the following useful lemma [4]

Lemma 1.1 (zero–one principle). *A comparator network is a sorting network if and only if it can sort any input consisting only of 0s and 1s.*

This lemma is the reason, why we consider inputs consisting only of 0s and 1s in the analysis of comparator networks. In this paper we deal with the problem of sorting sequences that differ by a small number of modifications t from a sorted sequence. These modifications can be either swaps between pairs of elements or changes on single positions. Such sequences we call *t-disturbed*. A comparator network that sorts such sequences we call a *t-correction* network. There are some potential applications in which we have to deal with sequences that differ not much from a sorted one. Assume we have a large sorted database with N entries. In some period of time we make t modifications of the database and want to have it sorted back by a comparator network. It can be better to design a specialized network of small depth to 'repair' the ordering and avoid using costly general sorting networks.

For the analysis of a t-correction network we can consider only t-disturbed sequences consisting of 0s and 1s. We note, that 0-1 sequence $x_1, \ldots, x_N$ is t disturbed if for some index b called the *border* at most t entries in $x_1, \ldots, x_b$ are 1s and at most t entries in $x_{b+1}, \ldots, x_N$ are 0s. These 1s (0s) we call *displaced*. We have a useful analog of zero-one principle for t-correction networks.

Lemma 1.2. *A comparator network is a t-correction network if it can sort any t-disturbed input consisting of 0s and 1s.*

The problem of construction t-correction networks arose when construction of fault-tolerant sorting networks was concerned. A comparator suffers a *passive fault* if it does nothing instead of sorting two elements. Assume that our aim is to construct a sorting network that is resistant to passive faults of any t (or less) of its comparators. One of approaches to this problem is to notice that if a 0-1 input is processed by an arbitrary sorting network suffering t passive faults, then the resulting output is t disturbed (see [6,9]). The idea is to add to this sorting network an additional t-correction unit in order to produce a fault tolerant sorting network. An additional requirement for this unit is that it has to be resistant to errors present in itself. Detailed conditions assuring fault tolerance of the whole network can be found in [7].

A nice construction of such a unit of depth $\sim 2 \log N$ for one fault can be found in Shimmler and Starke paper [6]. Later Piotrów [5] pipelined this network to obtain a unit for $t > 1$ of depth $O(\log N + t)$ having $O(Nt)$ comparators. The exact constants hidden behind these big O-s were not determined, but since Piotrów uses network [6] in his construction the constant in front of $\log N$ in $O(\log N + t)$ is at least 2. The best result as the constant in front of $\log N$ is concerned is included in [7] in which a network of depth $\alpha \log N(1 + \varepsilon) + ct/\varepsilon$ is described for any $\varepsilon > 0$. In this paper we denote $\Phi = \frac{1+\sqrt{5}}{2}$, $\alpha = 1/\log \Phi = 1.44 \ldots$.

Any unit making a sorting network resistant to t faults has to be a t-correction network, but we can have better t-correction networks. A nice result here is network of Kik, Kutyłowski, Piotrów [3] of depth $4 \log N + O(\log^2 t \log \log N)$. The best result concerning t-correction networks if we consider the leading constant is included in [7]. The network described there has depth $\alpha \log N (1 + \varepsilon) + c(\varepsilon) \log^2 t \log^2 N$.

As we mentioned our goal is to reduce the constant in front of $\log N$ in the depth of correction networks, which is most essential if t is small and N big. The best results concerning constructions of correction networks suggest α as a candidate for the tight bound for this constant. We prove in this paper that it is the case. Doing this we settle an open problem from [7].

2 One Displaced Element

In this section we consider the simplest possible case of correction network. Consider 0-1 inputs $x_1, \ldots, x_N$ that differ from sorted sequences by a single displaced 1. We call a comparator network sorting all such inputs a *simple correction network*. Note that sorting such an input means moving the single displaced 1 to the border register r_b in which at the beginning we have a 0. In this section we remind the construction from [7] of a simple correction network F_N of depth $\sim \alpha \log N$. Obviously a t-correction network for any t has to be a simple correction network. Any lower bound on a simple correction network is also a lower bound on any correction network. Conversely all the constructions of correction networks with leading constant α are based on the construction of F_N. This section serves mainly to introduce the denotations. Note, that in this section we describe F_N and the upper bound it gives in a more precise manner, than in [7].

To make easier understanding of the construction we first introduce the notion of *odd-even comparator network*. We view the registers with the smallest indexes to be on the top and those with the largest indexes to be on the bottom. A comparator $[i : j]$ has two end-registers: top r_i and bottom r_j. A comparator network is odd-even if it fulfills the following conditions:

- every comparator connects an even indexed register with an odd indexed register;
- in odd layers the bottom register of each comparator has an odd index;
- in even layers the bottom register of each comparator has an even index.

We assume, that our simple correction network F_N for inputs having a single displaced 1 is an odd-even network. Let the *distance* between registers r_i and r_j be the value $|j - i|$. Let the *length* of a comparator $[i : j]$ be the distance between r_i and r_j. To construct simple correction network F_N we make additional assumptions how it should look like:

- layer l consists of all possible comparators of length a_l (whose bottom register has parity of l);
- the sequence of comparator lengths a_l decreases as quickly as some geometric progression.

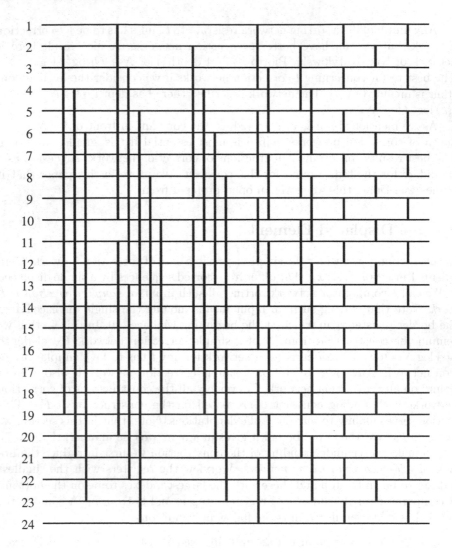

Fig. 1. Network F_{24}

Following these additional assumptions we can formulate a necessary and sufficient condition for such a network to sort any input with a single displaced 1. Let the distance of displaced 1 contained in register r_i from the border b be the value $b - i$ (b is the border index). Assume that in some layer l the displaced 1 is not moved by the comparator of length a_l because it is compared with a non displaced 1. In the next layer it is also not moved because it can be only in the bottom register of a comparator. Starting from the next layer it can start moving layer by layer with comparators of lengths $a_{l+2}, a_{l+3}, \ldots$. The network sorts the input if and only if this 1 always gets to the border (or covers the distance $a_l - 1$). This can be expressed by the inequality

$$a_l - 1 \leq a_{l+2} + a_{l+3} + \cdots + a_d$$

Now we should assign explicit values to the sequence a_l which is the sequence of comparator lengths.

First we recall the definition of Fibonacci numbers f_k:

$$f_0 = f_1 = 1,$$

$$f_k = f_{k-2} + f_{k-1}.$$

We define the numbers φ_k and ψ_k behaving similarly to f_k:

$$\varphi_0 = \varphi_1 = \psi_0 = \psi_1 = 1,$$

$$\psi_k = \varphi_{k-2} + \psi_{k-1} = 1 + \sum_{i=0}^{k-2} \varphi_i,$$

$$\varphi_k = \text{ the largest odd number smaller or equal } \psi_k.$$

Define $\mathrm{LG}(n)$ to be the smallest k such that $\psi_k \geq n$. The network F_N consists of $d = \mathrm{LG}(N)$ subsequent layers. The length of comparators in layer l is $a_l = \varphi_{d-l}$. We can check that our inequality

$$a_l - 1 \leq a_{l+2} + a_{l+3} + \cdots + a_d$$

now holds, because

$$\varphi_{d-l} - 1 \leq \psi_{d-l} - 1 - \varphi_{d-l-2} + \varphi_{d-l-3} + \cdots + \varphi_0.$$

At the beginning of the computations each displaced 1 is able to reduce its distance to the border to 0, because the largest distance to be covered is $N - 1$ and the latest layer on which a 1 has chance to be moved is 2. So we can check that

$$N - 1 \leq \psi_d - 1 \leq \varphi_{d-2} + \varphi_{d-3} + \cdots + \varphi_0.$$

This short justification proves, that F_N is indeed a simple correction network. We can note that the length φ_{d-1} of the comparators of the first layer was not used in the proof. In practical implementations we can exchange layer 1 of F_N by a layer consisting of comparators of length 1 which can reduce the layout of the network.

The depth d of F_N is $\sim \alpha \log N$ because of the following fact

Fact 2.1 $d = \mathrm{LG}(N) < \alpha \log N + \alpha \log(5)/2 + 1$

Proof. We have $N \leq \psi_d$ and $\psi_{d-1} < N$. It is easy to prove the following inequalities: $f_{k-1} \leq \psi_k \leq f_k$. Thus $f_{d-2} \leq \psi_{d-1} < N$. But f_k is the integer closest to $\Phi^{k+1}/\sqrt{5}$. So $\Phi^{d-1}/\sqrt{5} < N$ and $d < \alpha \log N + \alpha \log(5)/2 + 1$. $\square$

So we can formulate the following theorem

Theorem 2.2. *The network F_N is a simple correction network of depth d such that $d < \alpha \log N + \alpha \log(5)/2 + 1$.*

3   Lower Bounds

We prove two lower bounds. First we prove, that any odd-even simple correction network has at least as many layers as F_N. Then we prove that any correction network has the depth bigger than

$$\alpha \log N - \frac{\alpha}{2} \log 3$$

Theorem 3.1. *The network F_N has the smallest depth amongst all odd-even simple correction networks.*

The proof is based on the following lemma.

Lemma 3.2. *Assume that an odd-even comparator network is a simple correction network. Assume that b_{d-k} is the maximum length of a comparator that is used in layer $d - k$ to move a 1 for some 0-1 input with a single displaced 1. Then we have $b_{d-k} \leq \varphi_k$.*

Proof. Induction on k. Assume the lemma is true for $k', k' < k$ and prove it for k. Let the maximum length comparator in layer $d - k$ is $[i : j]$. There is some input in which the single displaced 1 is the x_m entry and this 1 is moved by comparator $[i : j]$. In such case $j \leq b$ where b is the border index. Let us take a new input in which the displaced 1 is x_m, but the border is $j - 1$. For such an input the displaced 1 is again in r_i, when $[i : j]$ from layer $d - k$ is used. But the 1 is not moved by this comparator. Then this 1 is forced to cover the distance $b_{d-k} - 1 = j - i - 1$ using the next layers. It is not moved by the layer $d - k + 1$. It can be moved by any of further layers $d - k'$ by the distance at most $b_{d-k'} \leq \varphi_{k'}$. So

$$b_{d-k} - 1 \leq b_{d-(k-2)} + b_{d-(k-3)} + \cdots + b_d \leq \varphi_{k-2} + \varphi_{k-3} + \cdots + \varphi_0 \leq \psi_k - 1.$$

Since b_{d-k} is an odd number it has to be not bigger, than φ_k. $\square$

Proof of the Theorem. Assume that we have an input having $N - 1$ 0s and a single 1 in r_1. The 1 is not moved by the first layer of an odd-even network because it cannot be on the top of a comparator at this layer. So it has to be moved to r_N by the next layers. Thus

$$N - 1 \leq b_2 + b_3 + \ldots b_d \leq \varphi_{d-2} + \varphi_{d-3} + \cdots + \varphi_0 \leq \psi_d - 1.$$

But $d = \mathrm{LG}(N)$ is the minimal depth, such that $N - 1 \leq \psi_d - 1$. $\square$

Now we formulate the main result of this paper. Note that the previous lower bound is exact and this bound is not. There is some constant gap between $\alpha \log N + \alpha \log(5)/2 + 1$ which the upper bound given by F_N and the lower bound we find. In fact there are examples of simple correction networks of slightly smaller depth than that of F_N.

Theorem 3.3. *Any simple correction network has depth bigger than*

$$\alpha \log N - \frac{\alpha}{2} \log 3$$

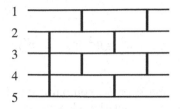 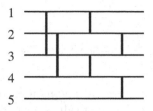

Fig. 2. The network F_5 has depth 4 and the optimal simple correction network for $N = 5$ has depth 3.

Proof of the Theorem. Assume we have an arbitrary (not necessarily odd-even) simple correction network on N registers. Its depth is d. Following the reduction made by Loryś (personal communication) we assign a value $v_{i,l}$ to each pair (i, l), where r_i is a register and l is a layer of the network. This value is the number of indexes j such that if the single displaced 1 is in r_j at the beginning of computations, then for some setting of border b it is in r_i just after the layer l. Let $v_{i,0} = 1$ is this value at the beginning of computations. Note, that $v_{i,d} = i$ for all i.

Fact 3.4 *If in l-th layer the comparator $[i : j]$ is present, then*

$$v_{i,l} \le v_{i,l-1} \quad and \quad v_{j,l} \le v_{i,l-1} + v_{j,l-1}$$

Proof. Only these 1s that were in r_i or r_j just before layer l can be in r_j just after layer l. □

In fact $v_{i,l} = v_{i,l-1}$, but we do not need this equality and its proof would require a few words of explanation.

Lemma 3.5. *If in l-th layer the comparator $[i : j]$ is present, then*

$$v_{i,l}^2 + v_{j,l}^2 \le \Phi^2(v_{i,l-1}^2 + v_{j,l-1}^2)$$

Proof. Consider a linear operator $A(v, w) \overset{\text{def}}{=} (w, v + w)$ on R^2. Euclidean norm of a vector (v, w) is defined as follows

$$\|(v, w)\| = \sqrt{v^2 + w^2}.$$

Note, that if $(v, w) = (v_{j,l-1}, v_{i,l-1})$, then

$$\sqrt{v_{i,l}^2 + v_{j,l}^2} \le \sqrt{v_{i,l-1}^2 + (v_{i,l-1} + v_{j,l-1})^2} = \|A(v_{j,l-1}, v_{i,l-1})\|$$

It is easy to check, that A has two eigenvalues: $\Phi, -1/\Phi$ for orthogonal eigenvectors: $(1, \Phi), (-\Phi, 1)$. Due to this fact

$$\|A(v, w)\| \le \Phi\|(v, w)\|$$

Thus

$$v_{i,l}^2 + v_{j,l}^2 \le \|A(v_{j,l-1}, v_{i,l-1})\|^2 \le \Phi^2 \|(v_{j,l-1}, v_{i,l-1})\|^2 = \Phi^2 (v_{i,l-1}^2 + v_{j,l-1}^2).$$

☐

Summing up inequalities from the last lemma over all comparators of the layer and adding values for not connected registers we get the following corollary

Corollary 3.6.

$$\sum_i v_{i,l}^2 \le \Phi^2 \sum_i v_{i,l-1}^2$$

To end up the proof of the theorem we note that $\sum_i v_{i,0}^2 = N$ and

$$\sum_i v_{i,d}^2 = \sum_i i^2 = \frac{1}{3}N^3 + \frac{1}{2}N^2 + \frac{1}{6}N > \frac{1}{3}N^3.$$

From the corollary we have

$$\sum_i v_{i,d}^2 \le \Phi^{2d} \sum_i v_{i,0}^2$$

or

$$\frac{1}{3}N^3 < \Phi^{2d} N$$

so

$$d > \alpha \log N - \frac{\alpha}{2} \log 3$$

☐

4   Conclusions

We proved, that a correction network for a single displaced 1 has depth bigger, than $\alpha \log N - \frac{\alpha}{2} \log 3$. An open question remains how many layers we have to add to deal with 2,3,4,... displaced 1s. In [7] we give a construction of 2-correction network of depth

$$\alpha \log N + c\sqrt{\log N}.$$

Does any 2-correction network have to have at least $\alpha \log N + c\sqrt{\log N}$ layers?

Acknowledgments. Author wishes to thank Mirek Kutyłowski, Krzysiek Loryś and Marek Piotrów for presenting the problems, helpful discussions and their encouragement to write this paper. Author wishes also to thank Maciek Warchoł for motivating him to keep on working on this problem.

References

1. M. Ajtai, J. Komlós, E. Szemerédi, Sorting in $c \log n$ parallel steps, *Combinatorica* 3 (1983), 1–19.
2. K.E. Batcher, Sorting networks and their applications, in *AFIPS Conf. Proc.* 32 (1968), 307–314.
3. M. Kik, M. Kutyłowski, M. Piotrów, Correction Networks, in *Proc. of 1999 ICPP*, 40–47.
4. D. E. Knuth, *The Art of Computer Programming*, Vol 3, 2nd edition, Addison Wesley, Reading, MA, 1975.
5. M. Piotrów, Depth Optimal Sorting Networks Resistant to k Passive Faults in *Proc. 7th SIAM Symposium on Discrete Algorithms* (1996), 242–251 (also accepted for *SIAM J. Comput.*).
6. M. Schimmler, C. Starke, A Correction Network for N-Sorters, *SIAM J. Comput.* 18 (1989), 1179–1197.
7. G. Stachowiak, Fibonacci Correction Networks, in *Algorithm Theory – SWAT 2000*, M. Halldórsson (Ed.), LNCS 1851, Springer 2000, 535–548.
8. A.C. Yao, Bounds on Selection Networks, *SIAM J. Comput.* 9 (1980), 566–582.
9. A.C. Yao, F.F. Yao, On Fault-Tolerant Networks for Sorting, *SIAM J. Comput.* 14 (1985), 120–128.

Approximate Regular Expression Searching with Arbitrary Integer Weights[*]

Gonzalo Navarro

Dept. of Computer Science, Univ. of Chile. gnavarro@dcc.uchile.cl

Abstract. We present a bit-parallel technique to search a text of length n for a regular expression of m symbols permitting k differences in worst case time $O(mn/\log_k s)$, where s is the amount of main memory that can be allocated. The algorithm permits arbitrary integer weights and matches the best previous complexities, but it is much simpler and faster in practice. In our way, we define a new recurrence for approximate searching where the current values depend only on previous values.

1   Introduction and Related Work

The need to search for regular expressions arises in many text-based applications, such as text retrieval, text editing and computational biology, to name a few. A *regular expression* (RE) is a generalized pattern composed of (i) basic strings, (ii) union, concatenation and Kleene closure of other REs [1]. We call m the length of our RE, not counting operator symbols. The alphabet is denoted by Σ, and n is the length of the text.

The traditional technique to search for a RE [1] first builds a nondeterministic finite automaton (NFA) and then converts it to a deterministic finite automaton (DFA), which is finally used to search the text in $O(n)$ time. This is worst-case optimal in terms of n. The main problem has been always the preprocessing time and space requirement to code the DFA, which can be as high as $O(2^{2m}|\Sigma|)$ if the classical Thompson's NFA construction algorithm [10] is used. Thompson's construction produces up to $2m$ states, but it has interesting properties, such as ensuring a linear number of edges and constant in/out-degree.

An alternative NFA construction is Glushkov's [3,2]. Although it does not provide the same regularities of Thompson's, this construction has other useful properties, such as producing the minimum number of states $(m+1)$ and that all the edges arriving at a node are labeled by the same character. The corresponding DFA needs only $O(2^m|\Sigma|)$ space, which is significantly less than the worst case using Thompson's NFA. Nevertheless, this is still exponential in m.

Two techniques have been classically used to cope with the space problem. The first is to use lazy DFAs, where the states are built only when they are reached. This ensures that no more than $O(n)$ extra space is necessary. The second choice [10] is to directly use the NFA instead of converting it to deterministic. This requires only $O(m)$ space, but the search time becomes $O(mn)$. Both approaches are slow in practice if the RE is large.

---

[*] Partially supported by Fondecyt grant 1-020831.

T. Ibaraki, N. Katoh, and H. Ono (Eds.): ISAAC 2003, LNCS 2906, pp. 230–239, 2003.

Newer techniques have provided better space-time tradeoffs by using hybrids between the NFA and the DFA. Based on the Four Russians technique, which precomputes large tables that permit processing several automaton states in one shot, it has been shown that $O(mn/\log s)$ search time is possible using $O(s)$ space [4]. The use of Thompson's automaton is essential for this approach which, however, is rather complicated. Simpler solutions obtaining the same complexities have been obtained later using bit-parallelism, a technique to pack several NFA states in a single machine word and update them as a single state. A first solution [12], based on Thompson's construction, uses a table of size $O(2^{2m})$ that can be split into t tables of size $O(2^{2m/t})$ each, at a search cost of $O(tn)$ table inspections. A second solution [8] uses Glushkov's automaton and uses t tables of size $O(2^{m/t})$ each, which is much more efficient in space usage. In both cases, $O(mn/\log s)$ search time is obtained using $O(s)$ space.

Several applications in computational biology, data mining, text retrieval, etc. need an even more sophisticated form of searching: An integer threshold k is given, so that we have to report the text substrings that can match the RE after performing several character insertions, deletions and substitutions, whose total *cost* or *weight* does not exceed k. Each operation may have a different weight depending on the characters involved. This problem is called "approximate regular expression searching", as opposed to "exact" searching.

Instead of being just active or inactive, every NFA node has now $k+2$ possible states, according to the weight of the differences needed to match the text (0 to k, or more than k). If one applies the classical DFA construction algorithm, the space requirement raises to $O((k+2)^{2m})$ using Thompson's NFA and $O((k+2)^m)$ using Glushkov's NFA. A dynamic programming based solution with $O(mn)$ time and $O(m)$ space exists [5]. Although this is an achievement because it retains the time complexity of the exact search version and handles real-valued weights, it is still slow. The Four Russians technique has been gracefully extended to this problem [13], obtaining $O(mn/\log_k s)$ time using $O(s)$ space. Again, this algorithm is rather complicated.

Since bit-parallel solutions have, for many related problems, yielded fast and simple solutions, one may wonder what have they achieved here. For the case of unitary costs (that is, all the weights are 1), bit-parallel solutions exist which resort to simulating $k+1$ copies of the NFA used for exact searching. They achieve $O(ktn)$ time using $O(2^{2m/t})$ space [12] or $O(2^{m/t})$ space [6]. This yields $O(kmn/\log s)$ time using $O(s)$ space, inferior to the achievement of the Four Russians technique. Despite this worse complexity, bit-parallel solutions are by far the fastest for moderate sized REs. Yet, they are restricted to unitary costs.

The aim of this paper is to overcome the technical problems that have prevented the existence of a simple $O(mn/\log_k s)$ time and $O(s)$ space bit-parallel solution to approximate RE searching with arbitrary integer weights. We build over Glushkov's NFA and represent the state of the search using $m\lceil 1+\log_2(k+2)\rceil$ bits. We then use t tables of size $O((k+2)^{m/t})$ and reach $O(tn)$ search time.

We use the following terminology for bit-parallel algorithms. A *bit mask* is a sequence of bits, where the lowest bit is written at the right. Typical bit operations are infix "|" (bitwise *or*), infix "&" (bitwise *and*), prefix "~" (bit complementation), and infix "$<<$" ("$>>$"), which moves the bits of the first argument (a bit mask) to higher (lower) positions in an amount given by the argument on the right. Additionally, one can treat the bit masks as numbers and obtain specific effects using the arithmetic operations "+", "−", etc. Exponentiation is used to denote bit repetition, e.g., $0^3 1 = 0001$, and $[x]_\ell$ represents an integer x using ℓ bits. Finally, $X \times x$, where X is a bit mask and x is a number, is the exact result of the multiplication, that is, a bit mask where x appears in the places where X has 1's.

An extended version of this paper, with all the details, can be found in [7].

2   A Bit-Parallel Exact Search Algorithm

We describe in this section the exact bit-parallel solution we build on [8]. The classical algorithm to produce a DFA from an NFA [1] consists in making each DFA state represent a set of NFA states that may be active at some point. Our way to represent the states of a DFA (i.e., the sets of states of an NFA) is a bit mask of $O(m)$ bits. The bit mask has in 1 the bits that belong to the set. We use set notation or bit mask notation indistinctly.

Glushkov's NFA construction algorithm can be found in [3,2]. We just remark some of its properties. Given a RE of m characters (not counting operator symbols), the algorithm defines $m + 1$ *positions* numbered 0 to m (one per position of a character of Σ in the RE, plus an initial position 0). Then, the NFA has exactly one state per position, the initial state corresponding to position 0. Two tables are built: $B(\sigma)$, the set of positions of the RE that contain character σ; and $Follow(x)$, the set of NFA states that can be reached from state x in one transition[1]. From these two tables, the transition function of the NFA is computed: $\delta : \{0 \ldots m\} \times \Sigma \to \wp(\{0 \ldots m\})$, such that $y \in \delta(x, \sigma)$ if and only if from state x we can move to state y by character σ. The algorithm gives also a set of final states, $Last$, which again will be represented as a bit mask.

Important properties of Glushkov's construction follow. (1) The NFA is ε-free. (2) All the arrows leading to a given NFA state are labeled by the same character: the one at the corresponding position. (3) The initial state does not receive any transition. (4) $\delta(x, \sigma) = Follow(x) \cap B(\sigma)$.

Property (4) permits a very compact representation of the DFA transitions. The construction algorithm is written so that tables B and $Follow$ represent the sets of states as bit masks. We use B as is and build a large table J, the deterministic version of $Follow$. That is, J is a table that, for every bit mask D representing a set of states, stores $J[D] = \bigcup_{i \in D} Follow(i)$. Then, by Property (4) it holds that, if the current set of active states is D and we read text character σ, then the new set of active states is $J[D] \cap B[\sigma]$. For search purposes, we set state 0 in $J[D]$ for every D and in $B[\sigma]$ for every σ, and report every text position j where $D \cap Last \neq \emptyset$. (In fact, state 0 needs not be represented, since it is always active when searching.)

---

[1] This is computed from the RE, since the NFA does not yet exist. Also, for simplicity, we assume that $Follow(0) = First$, the states reachable from the initial state.

Hence we need only $O(2^m + |\Sigma|)$ space instead of the $O(2^m|\Sigma|)$ space of the classical representation. Space-time tradeoffs are achieved by splitting table J. The splitting is done as follows. We build two tables J_1 and J_2, which give the set of states reached from states $0 \ldots \ell$ and $\ell + 1 \ldots m$, respectively, with $\ell = \lfloor (m+1)/2 \rfloor$. Then, if we accordingly split the current set of states D into left and right submasks, $D = D_1 : D_2$, we have $J[D] = J_1[D_1] \cup J_2[D_2]$. Tables J_1 and J_2 need only $O(2^{m/2})$ space each. This generalizes to using t tables, for an overall space requirement of $O(t2^{m/t})$ and a search cost of $O(tn)$ table accesses.

3   A New Recurrence for Approximate Searching

We start with an exact formulation for our problem. Let R be a RE generating language $L(R) \subseteq \Sigma^*$. Let m be the number of characters belonging to Σ in R. Let $T_{1 \ldots n} \in \Sigma^*$ be the text, a sequence of n symbols. The problem is, given R, T, and $k \in \mathbb{N}$, to report every text position j such that, for some $j' \leq j$ and $P \in L(R)$, $ed(T_{j' \ldots j}, P) \leq k$. The edit distance, $ed(A, B)$, is the minimum sum of weights of a sequence of character insertions, deletions and substitutions needed to convert A into B. The weights are represented by a function ω, where $\omega(a, b)$ is the cost to substitute character a by character b in the text, $\omega(a, \varepsilon)$ is the cost to delete text character a, and $\omega(\varepsilon, b)$ is the cost to insert character b in the text. Function ω satisfies $\omega(a, a) = 0$, nonnegativity, and triangle inequality.

The classical dynamic programming solution for approximate string matching [9], for the case where R is a simple string $P_{1 \ldots m}$, recomputes for every text position j a vector $C_{0 \ldots m}$, where $C_i = \min_{j' \leq j} ed(T_{j' \ldots j}, P_{1 \ldots i})$. Hence every text position j where $C_m \leq k$ is reported. C is initialized as $C_i = i$ and then updated to C' at text position j using dynamic programming:

$$C'_i \leftarrow \min(\omega(T_j, P_i) + C_{i-1}, \ \omega(T_j, \varepsilon) + C_i, \ \omega(\varepsilon, P_i) \mid C'_{i-1})$$

where $C'_0 = 0$. The first component refers to a character matching or substitution, the second to deleting a text character, and the third to inserting a character in the text. If we have a general RE R built using Glushkov's algorithm, with positions 1 to m, this generalizes as follows. We call L_i the set of strings recognized by the automaton if we assume that the only final state is i. Then $C_i = \min_{j' \leq j, P \in L_i} ed(T_{j' \ldots j}, P)$ is computed as follows:

$$C'_i \leftarrow \min(S_i(T_j) + \min_{i' \in Follow^{-1}(i)} C_{i'}, \ D(T_j) + C_i, \ I_i + \min_{i' \in Follow^{-1}(i)} C'_{i'}) \quad (1)$$

where $S_i(a) = \omega(a, R_i)$, $D(a) = \omega(a, \varepsilon)$, $I_i = \omega(\varepsilon, R_i)$, and R_i is the only character such that $B(R_i) = \{i\}$: Thanks to Property (2), we know that all the edges arriving at state i are labeled by the same character, R_i. C_0 is always 0 because it refers to the initial state, so $L_0 = \{\varepsilon\}$.

Note that the main difference in the generalization is that, in the case of a single pattern, every state i has a unique predecessor, state $i-1$. Here, the set of predecessor states, $Follow^{-1}(i)$, can be arbitrarily complex. In the third component of Recurrence (1) (insertions in the text) we have a potential dependence problem, because in order to compute C' for state i we need to have already computed C' for states that precede i, in an automaton that can perfectly contain cycles. There are good previous solutions to this circular dependence problem [5], but these are not easy to apply in a bit-parallel context.

We present a new solution now. We will use the form $i^{(r)}$ in minimization arguments, whose range is as follows: $i^{(0)} = i$ and $i^{(r+1)} \in Follow^{-1}(i^{(r)})$. Also, we will denote $S_{i^{(r)}} = S_{i^{(r)}}(T_j)$ and $D = D(T_j)$. Let us now unfold Recurrence (1):

$$C'_i \leftarrow \min (S_i + \min_{i^{(1)}} C_{i^{(1)}}, \ D + C_i,$$

$$I_i + \min_{i^{(1)}} \ \min(S_{i^{(1)}} + \min_{i^{(2)}} C_{i^{(2)}}, \ D + C_{i^{(1)}}, \ I_{i^{(1)}} + \min_{i^{(2)}} C'_{i^{(2)}}) \ )$$

where after a few manipulations we obtain

$$C'_i \leftarrow \min (D + C_i, \min_{i^{(1)}}(S_i + C_{i^{(1)}}), \min_{i^{(1)}}(I_i + S_{i^{(1)}} + \min_{i^{(2)}} C_{i^{(2)}}),$$

$$\min_{i^{(1)}}(I_i + D + C_{i^{(1)}}), \min_{i^{(1)}}(I_i + I_{i^{(1)}} + \min_{i^{(2)}} C'_{i^{(2)}}) \ )$$

The term $\min_{i^{(1)}}(I_i + D + C_{i^{(1)}})$ can be removed because, by definition of C_i, $C_i \leq \min_{i^{(1)}} I_i + C_{i^{(1)}}$ (third component of Recurrence (1) applied to the computation of C), and we have already $D + C_i$ in the minimization. We factor out all the minimizing operators and get

$$C'_i \leftarrow \min(D + C_i, \ \min_{i^{(1)},i^{(2)}} \ \min(S_i + C_{i^{(1)}}, I_i + S_{i^{(1)}} + C_{i^{(2)}}, \ I_i + I_{i^{(1)}} + C'_{i^{(2)}}))$$

By unfolding $C'_{i^{(2)}}$ and doing the same manipulations again we get

$$C'_i \leftarrow \min(D + C_i, \ \min_{i^{(1)},i^{(2)},i^{(3)}} \min (S_i + C_{i^{(1)}}, I_i + S_{i^{(1)}} + C_{i^{(2)}},$$

$$I_i + I_{i^{(1)}} + S_{i^{(2)}} + C_{i^{(3)}}, I_i + I_{i^{(1)}} + I_{i^{(2)}} + C'_{i^{(3)}}))$$

and we can continue until the latter term exceeds $k + C'_{i^{(r+1)}}$, which is not interesting anymore. The resulting recurrence does not depend anymore on C', and will become our working recurrence:

$$C'_i \leftarrow \min(D + C_i, \ \min_{r \geq 0} \ \min_{i^{(1)}...i^{(r)}} \sum_{0 \leq u < r} I_{i^{(u)}} + S_{i^{(r)}} + C_{i^{(r+1)}}) \qquad (2)$$

4   A Bit-Parallel Approximate Search Algorithm

We will represent the C_i vector in a bit mask. Each cell C_i will range in the interval $0 \ldots k + 1$, so we will need $\ell = \lceil \log_2(k + 2) \rceil$ bits to represent it. The reason is that, if a cell value is larger than $k + 1$, we can assume that its value is $k + 1$ and the outcome of the search will be the same [11]. For technical reasons that are made clear soon, we will need an extra bit per cell, which will always be zero. Since C_0 is always 0, it does not need to be represented. Hence we need $m(1 + \ell)$ bits overall. The bit mask will represent the sequence

---

CalcWeights (ω, B, k, m, ℓ)
1. $I \leftarrow 0^{(1+\ell)m}$
2.   **For** $c \in \Sigma$ **Do**
3. $D[c] \leftarrow (0[\min(\omega(c, \varepsilon), k+1)]_\ell)^m$
4. $S[c] \leftarrow 0^{(1+\ell)m}$
5.   **For** $i \in 1 \ldots m$ **Do**
6.   **If** $B[c]$ & $0^{m-i}10^{i-1} \neq 0^m$ **Then**
7. $I \leftarrow I \mid 0^{(1+\ell)(m-i)}0[\min(\omega(\varepsilon, c), k+1)]_\ell 0^{(1+\ell)(i-1)}$
8.   **For** $c' \in \Sigma$ **Do**
9. $S[c'] \leftarrow S[c'] \mid 0^{(1+\ell)(m-i)}0[\min(\omega(c', c), k+1)]_\ell 0^{(1+\ell)(i-1)}$

Fig. 1. Computation of tables I, D and S from ω and B.

of cells $C = 0[C_m]_\ell\, 0[C_{m-1}]_\ell \ldots 0[C_2]_\ell\, 0[C_1]_\ell$. We use as many computer words as needed to store C (a single cell will not be split among computer words).

From the parsing of the RE, we receive the tables B and $Follow$, where the sets are represented as bit masks of length $m + 1$ (see previous work for details [8]). We will preprocess B so as to produce bit-parallel versions of I_i, D and S_i. These will be called I, $D[\sigma]$ and $S[\sigma]$, respectively. The computation of these values from ω and B is shown in Figure 1.

We use a table J (an extended version of previous simpler table J), which maps bit masks of length $m(1 + \ell)$ into bit masks of length $m(1 + \ell)$, as follows:

$$J\,[\; 0[C_m]_\ell\, 0[C_{m-1}]_\ell \ldots 0[C_2]_\ell\, 0[C_1]_\ell\;] \;\; = \;\; 0[M_m]_\ell\, 0[M_{m-1}]_\ell \ldots 0[M_2]_\ell\, 0[M_1]_\ell$$

where

$$M_i \;\; = \;\; \min_{i' \in Follow^{-1}(i)} C_{i'}$$

That is, for each search state C, J indicates how the values in C propagate through NFA edges. If several states i' propagate to a single state i, we choose the minimum value. We account for the zeros propagated from the unrepresented initial state 0.

Let us now consider Recurrence (2). Assume that C is our current search state. The first part of the minimum $(D + C_i)$ is easily obtained in bit-parallel, as $E \leftarrow C + (0[D]_\ell)^m$. If D turns out to be larger than $k + 1$ we set $D = k + 1$. The result of the sum can give us values as large as $2(k + 1)$ in the counters. Our extra bit per cell can hold the overflow, but we have to replace the values of the overflown counters by $k + 1$ in order to continue our process. We detect the overflown counters by precomputing $W \leftarrow (10^\ell)^m$ and doing $Z \leftarrow E$ & W. Then, $Z \leftarrow Z - (Z \gg \ell)$ will be a sequence of all-0 or all-1 cells, where the all-1 ones correspond to the overflown counters. These are restored to $k + 1$ by doing $E \leftarrow (E$ & $\sim Z) \mid (0[k+1]_\ell)^m$ & $Z)$.

Let us call H the second, complex part of the main minimum of Recurrence (2). Once we obtain H, we have to obtain $C' \leftarrow Min(E, H)$, where Min takes the element-wise minimum over two sequences of values, in bit-parallel.

Bit-parallel minimum can be obtained with a technique similar to the one used above to restore overflown values. Say that we have to compute $Min(X, Y)$, where X and Y contain several counters (nonnegative integers) properly aligned. We need the extra highest bit per counter, which is always zero. We use mask W and perform the operation $Z \leftarrow ((X \mid W) - Y) \& W$. The result is that, in Z, each highest bit is set if and only if the counter of X is larger than that of Y. We now compute $Z \leftarrow Z - (Z >> \ell)$, so that the counters where X is larger than Y have all their bits set in Z, and the others have all the bits in zero. We now choose the minima as $Min(X, Y) \leftarrow (Y \& Z) \mid (X \& \sim Z)$.

We focus now on the most complex part: the computation of H. Let us consider $A = J[C] + S[T_j]$, and assume that we have again solved overflow problems in A^2. The i-th element of A is, by definintion of J, $A_i = S_i + \min_{i' \in Follow^{-1}(i)} C_{i'}$. Now, consider $J[A] + I$. Its i-th value is

$$I_i + \min_{i' \in Follow^{-1}(i)} A_{i'} = I_i + \min_{i' \in Follow^{-1}(i)} (S_{i'} + \min_{i'' \in Follow^{-1}(i')} C_{i''})$$
$$= \min_{i^{(1)}, i^{(2)}} (I_i + S_{i^{(1)}} + C_{i^{(2)}})$$

If we compute $J[J[A] + I] + I$, we have that its i-th value is $\min_{i^{(1)}, i^{(2)}, i^{(3)}} (I_i + I_{i^{(1)}} + S_{i^{(2)}} + C_{i^{(3)}})$, and so on. Let us define $f(A) = J[A] + I$ and $f^{(r)}(A)$ as the result of taking r times f over A. Then, we have that

$$f^{(r)}(A) = \min_{i^{(1)} \dots i^{(r)}} \left(\sum_{0 \leq u < r} I_{i^{(u)}} + S_{i^{(r)}} + C_{i^{(r+1)}} \right)$$

and hence the H we look for is

$$H[A] = Min \left(A, f(A), f^{(2)}(A), f^{(3)}(A), \dots \right)$$

To conclude, we have to report every text position where it holds $C_i \leq k$ for a final state i. The parsing yields an $(m + 1)$-bits long mask of final states, $Last$. We will precompute a mask $F = 0[F_m]_\ell \, 0[F_{m-1}]_\ell \dots 0[F_2]_\ell \, 0[F_1]_\ell$, so that $F_i = 1$ if i is final and $F_i = 0$ otherwise[3]. Hence, we have a match if and only if $C \& (F \times (2^\ell - 1)) \neq F \times (k + 1)$. Note that $F \times x$ is a bit mask of m counters X_i such that $X_i = x$ if $F_i = 1$ and $X_i = 0$ otherwise.

Figure 2 gives the search code. To initialize C we take H over an initial state where all the counters are $k + 1$. **Glushkov_Parse** is in charge of parsing the RE and delivering tables B, $Follow$ and bit mask $Last$. We then precompute all the tables using **Preprocess**.

The preprocessing is given in Figure 3. Although it looks complicated, it is conceptually simple. Function **Expand** takes a sequence of $m + 1$ bits, ignores the first, and introduces ℓ zero bits between each pair of bits, so as to align them to our representation. J is computed by ranging over all the $(k + 2)^m$

---

[2] The extra work for this can be avoided by precomputing all the allocated cells of H, as it will be clear soon.

[3] We assume that the initial state is not final, as otherwise the problem is trivial.

Search $(T_{1...n}, R, k, \omega)$
1. $(B, Follow, Last, m) \leftarrow$ **Glushkov_Parse**(R)
2. $(D, S, J, H, F, \ell) \leftarrow$ **Preprocess**$(B, Follow, Last, m, k, \omega)$
3. $C \leftarrow H[(0[k+1]_\ell)^m]$
4.   **For** $j \in 1 \dots n$ **Do**
5. $A \leftarrow J[C] + S[T_j]$
6. $C \leftarrow Min(C + D[T_j], H[A])$
7.   **If** C & $(F \times (2^\ell - 1)) \neq F \times (k+1)$ **Then** Report text position j

---

Fig. 2. Search algorithm. We disregard the restoring of overflows after additions.

possible search states, starting with a state where all the counters are $k+1$ and then computing all the possible values for state i, with the invariant that all the possible values of states $< i$ (with states larger than i having value $k+1$) are already computed. G is a bit mask that traverses all these possible values, and $curr$ is the current value of state i in G. $J[G]$ is computed as the minimum between what we already have with value $k+1$ for state i and the $curr$ value for the states in $Follow[i]$. **Next** computes the next value for G. The processing for H is very similar, except that we first compute $h[i, v]$ as the desired value of $H[A]$ when the i-th value of A is v and the rest is $k+1$. Then, we build all the combinations of A using h with the same technique as before. Note that we do not return I because it is embedded in the computation of H.

5   Analysis and Space-Time Tradeoffs

The search time of our algorithm is clearly $O(n)$. The preprocessing time includes $O(|\Sigma|^2 m)$ for **CalcWeights** and $O(k^2 m^2)$ to compute h (since for each of the km cells we iterate as long as we reduce some counter, which can happen only $m(k+1)$ times). However, the dominant preprocessing complexity is the $O((k+2)^m)$ space and time needed to fill J and H. If this turns out to be excessive, we can horizontally split tables J and H.

Let J be a table built over m counters. Let $C = C^1 : C^2$ be a splitting of mask C into two submasks, a left and a right submask. If we define J_1 and J_2 so that they propagate counters only from the first and second half of mask C, respectively, then $J[C^1 : C^2] = Min(J_1[C^1], J_2[C^2])$ because of the definition of J. (Note that J_1 and J_2 can propagate values to states of any half.) The same is valid for H: we can split the argument A into two halves A^1 and A^2, and preprocess the propagations of values from the first and second half in H_1 and H_2, so that $H[A^1 : A^2] = Min(H_1[A^1], H_2[A^2])$. In general, we can split J and H into t tables $J_1 \dots J_t$ and $H_1 \dots H_t$, such that J_i and H_i address the counters roughly from $(i-1)m/t$ to $im/k - 1$, that is, m/t counters. Each such table has $(k+2)^{m/t}$ entries, for a total space requirement of $O(t(k+2)^{m/t})$. Now, in order to perform each transition, we need to pay for t table accesses so as to compute $J[C^1 : C^2 : \dots C^t] = Min(J_1[C^1], J_2[C^2], \dots J_t[C^t])$ and

Expand(X, m, ℓ)
1. $EX \leftarrow 0^{(1+\ell)m}$
2.   **For** $i \in 1 \ldots m$ **Do**
3.   **If** X & $0^{m-i}10^i \neq 0^{m+1}$ **Then** $EX \leftarrow EX \mid 0^{(m-i)(1+\ell)}0^{\ell}10^{(i-1)(1+\ell)}$
4.   **Return** EX

Next(G, ℓ, m, lim)
1.   **For** $i \in 1 \ldots m$ **Do**
2. $val \leftarrow (G >> (1+\ell)(i-1))$ & $0^{(1+\ell)(m-1)}01^{\ell}$
3.   **If** $val < lim$ **Then**
4. $G \leftarrow G + 0^{(1+\ell)(m-i-1)}0^{\ell}10^{(1+\ell)(i-1)}$
5.   **Return** G
6. $G \leftarrow G$ & $1^{(1+\ell)(m-i-1)}0^{1+\ell}1^{(1+\ell)(i-1)}$

Preprocess (B, $Follow$, $Last$, m, k, ω)
1. $\ell \leftarrow \lceil \log_2(k+2) \rceil$
2. $(I, D, S) \leftarrow$ **CalcWeights** (ω, B, k, m, ℓ)
3. $F \leftarrow$ **Expand**($Last, m, \ell$)
       // Computation of J
4.   **For** $i \in 0 \ldots m$ **Do** $EFollow[i] \leftarrow$ **Expand**($Follow[i], m, \ell$)
5. $J[(0[k+1]_{\ell})^m] \leftarrow (0[k+1]_{\ell})^m - (EFollow[0] \times (k+1))$
6.   **For** $i \in 1 \ldots m$ **Do**
7. $G \leftarrow (0[k+1]_{\ell})^{m-i}0^{(1+\ell)i}$
8.   **For** $j \in 0 \ldots (k+2)^i - 1$ **Do**
9. $curr \leftarrow (G >> (1+\ell)(i-1))$ & $0^{(1+\ell)(m-1)}01^{\ell}$
10. $J[G] \leftarrow Min(J[G + 0^{(1+\ell)(m-i)}0[k+1-curr]_{\ell}0^{(1+\ell)(i-1)}],$
                   $(0[k+1]_{\ell})^m - (EFollow[i] \times (k+1-curr)))$
11. $G \leftarrow$ **Next**($G, \ell, m, k+1$)
       // Computation of H
12.   **For** $i \in 1 \ldots m$ **Do**
13.   **For** $v \in 0 \ldots k+1$ **Do**
14. $h[i, v] \leftarrow (0[k+1]_{\ell})^{m-i}0[v]_{\ell}(0[k+1]_{\ell})^{i-1}$
15.   **While** $h[i, v] \neq Min(h[i, v], J[h[i, v]] + I)$ **Do**
16. $h[i, v] \leftarrow Min(h[i, v], J[h[i, v]] + I)$
17. $H[(0[k+1]_{\ell})^m] \leftarrow (0[k+1]_{\ell})^m$
18.   **For** $i \in 1 \ldots m$ **Do**
19. $G \leftarrow (0[k+1]_{\ell})^{m-i}0^{(1+\ell)i}$
20.   **For** $j \in 0 \ldots (k+2)^i - 1$ **Do**
21. $curr \leftarrow (G >> (1+\ell)(i-1))$ & $0^{(1+\ell)(m-1)}01^{\ell}$
22. $H[G] \leftarrow Min(H[G + 0^{(1+\ell)(m-i)}0[k+1-curr]_{\ell}0^{(1+\ell)(i-1)}],$
                   $h[i, curr])$
23. $G \leftarrow$ **Next**($G, \ell, m, k+1$)
24.   **Return** (D, S, J, H, F, ℓ)

Fig. 3. Our preprocessing.

$H[A^1 : A^2 : \ldots A^t] = Min(H_1[A^1], H_2[A^2], \ldots H_t[A^t])$, which makes the search time $O(tn)$. If we have $O(s)$ space, then we solve for $s = t(k+2)^{m/t}$, to obtain a search time of $O(tn) = O(mn/\log_k s)$.

6   Conclusions

We have presented a bit-parallel algorithm to solve the problem of approximate searching for regular expressions with arbitrary integer weights. The algorithm is simple and has the same complexity of the best previous solution, namely $O(mn/\log_k s)$ time with $O(s)$ space. For lack of space we cannot present our experimental results in this paper, but they are available in [7]. There we show that, in practice, our algorithm clearly outperforms all previous solutions.

In our way, we have found a new recurrence for the problem, where the current values depend only on previous values. This is usually the main complication when combining the circular dependence of the classical recurrence (current values depending on current values) with the possible cycles of the automaton. We believe that our solution can be useful in other scenarios, for example the simpler problem of approximate string matching with integer weights.

References

1. A. Aho, R. Sethi, and J. Ullman. *Compilers: Principles, Techniques and Tools.* Addison-Wesley, 1985.
2. G. Berry and R. Sethi. From regular expression to deterministic automata. *Theor. Comp. Sci.*, 48(1):117–126, 1986.
3. V. Glushkov. The abstract theory of automata. *Russ. Math. Surv.*, 16:1–53, 1961.
4. E. Myers. A four-russian algorithm for regular expression pattern matching. *J. of the ACM*, 39(2):430–448, 1992.
5. E. Myers and W. Miller. Approximate matching of regular expressions. *Bull. Math. Biol.*, 51:7–37, 1989.
6. G. Navarro. Nr-grep: a fast and flexible pattern matching tool. *Software Practice and Experience*, 31:1265–1312, 2001.
7. G. Navarro. Approximate regular expression searching with arbitrary integer weights. Tech.Rep. TR/DCC-2002-6, Dept. of Computer Science, Univ. of Chile, July 2002. `ftp.dcc.uchile.cl/pub/users/gnavarro/aregexp.ps.gz`.
8. G. Navarro and M. Raffinot. Compact DFA representation for fast regular expression search. In *Proc. WAE'01*, LNCS 2141, pages 1–12, 2001.
9. P. Sellers. The theory and computation of evolutionary distances: Pattern recognition. *J. of Algorithms*, 1(4):359–373, 1980.
10. K. Thompson. Regular expression search algorithm. *CACM*, 11(6):419–422, 1968.
11. E. Ukkonen. Finding approximate patterns in strings. *J. of Algorithms*, 6:132–137, 1985.
12. S. Wu and U. Manber. Fast text searching allowing errors. *CACM*, 35(10):83–91, 1992.
13. S. Wu, U. Manber, and E. Myers. A subquadratic algorithm for approximate regular expression matching. *J. of Algorithms*, 19(3):346–360, 1995.

Constructing Compressed Suffix Arrays with Large Alphabets*

Wing-Kai Hon[1], Tak-Wah Lam[1], Kunihiko Sadakane[2], and Wing-Kin Sung[3]

[1] Department of Computer Science and Informations Systems,
The University of Hong Kong, Hong Kong,
{wkhon,twlam}@csis.hku.hk
[2] Department of Computer Science and Communication Engineering,
Kyushu University, Japan,
sada@csce.kyushu-u.ac.jp
[3] School of Computing, National University of Singapore, Singapore,
ksung@comp.nus.edu.sg

Abstract. Recent research in compressing suffix arrays has resulted in two breakthrough indexing data structures, namely, compressed suffix arrays (CSA) [7] and FM-index [5]. Either of them makes it feasible to store a full-text index in the main memory even for a piece of text data with a few billion characters (such as human DNA). However, constructing such indexing data structures with limited working memory (i.e., without constructing suffix arrays) is not a trivial task. This paper addresses this problem. Currently, only CSA admits a space-efficient construction algorithm [15]. For a text T of length n over an alphabet Σ, this algorithm requires $O(|\Sigma|n \log n)$ time and $(2H_0 + 1 + \epsilon)n$ bits of working space, where H_0 is the 0-th order empirical entropy of T and ϵ is any non-zero constant. This algorithm is good enough when the alphabet size $|\Sigma|$ is small. It is not practical for text data containing protein, Chinese or Japanese, where the alphabet may include up to a few thousand characters.

The main contribution of this paper is a new algorithm which can construct CSA in $O(n \log n)$ time using $(H_0 + 2 + \epsilon)n$ bits of working space. Note that the running time of our algorithm is independent of the alphabet size and the space requirement is smaller as it is likely that $H_0 > 1$. This paper also makes contribution to the space-efficient construction of FM-index. We show that FM-index can indeed be constructed from CSA directly in $O(n)$ time.

1 Introduction

The advance in information technology and bio-technology has generated an enormous amount of text data. In particular, a lot of such texts have no word

* This work was supported in part by the Hong Kong RGC Grant HKU-7024/01E; by the Grant-in-Aid of the Ministry of Education, Science, Sports and Culture of Japan; and by the NUS Academic Research Grant R-252-000-119-112.

T. Ibaraki, N. Katoh, and H. Ono (Eds.): ISAAC 2003, LNCS 2906, pp. 240–249, 2003.
© Springer-Verlag Berlin Heidelberg 2003

boundary. Typical examples include DNA, protein, Chinese, and Japanese. A simple piece of such texts can contain millions or even billions of characters. To assist users to locate their required information efficiently, it is vital to index the text using some data structures so as to exploit fast searching algorithms. For text with word boundary (e.g., English), inverted index [9] can be used; this data structure enables fast query and is space efficient. But inverted index cannot be used for text without word boundary. In this case, suffix tree [19] and suffix array [17] are the most useful data structures. They have applications in numerous areas including digital library [20], text data mining [24] and biological research [10].

Suffix tree is a powerful index because it allows us to search pattern using time linear to the pattern length, independent of the text size. For a sequence of n characters over an alphabet Σ, building a suffix tree takes $O(n)$ time. A pattern P can then be located in $O(|P| + occ)$ time, where occ is the number of occurrences. For suffix arrays, construction and searching takes time $O(n)$ [3,13] and $O(|P| \log n + occ)$, respectively. However, the suffix tree and the suffix array demands a lot of memory space. Both data structures require $O(n \log n)$ bits; the constant associated with suffix arrays is smaller, though. For human DNA (of length approximately 3 billion), the best known implementation of suffix tree and suffix array requires 40 Gigabytes and 13 Gigabytes, respectively [14]. For text data acquired from several years of a Chinese news source[1] (of length approximately 1.3 billion) [6], suffix tree and suffix array require 18 Gigabytes and 8 Gigabytes, respectively. Such memory requirement far exceeds the capacity of ordinary computers (PCs nowadays have up to 4 Gigabytes of main memory). To solve the memory space problem, it has been proposed to store the indexing data structure in the secondary storage [2,12]. But the searching time deteriorates a lot.

Recently, Grossi and Vitter [7] have proposed a space-efficient indexing data structure called compressed suffix array (CSA), which reduces the space requirement from $O(n \log n)$ bits to $O(n \log |\Sigma|)$ bits, and more importantly, the compressed suffix array still supports searching efficiently. Precisely, the searching time increases by a factor of at most $\log n$. In practice, a CSA for the human DNA occupies around 2 Gigabytes, and it is possible to store the CSA in the main memory of a PC.

To construct a compressed suffix array, a naive way is to build the suffix array first and then convert it to the compressed suffix array. This construction method takes $O(n \log n)$ time, but it requires much more than $O(n \log |\Sigma|)$-bit working space. In other words, it is feasible to store a CSA for human DNA in the main memory of a PC, but it is not feasible to build it on a PC. This definitely limits the application of CSA. To solve this working memory problem, Lam et al. [15] initiates the study of constructing the compressed suffix array directly. In particular, they gave an algorithm that uses only $O(n \log |\Sigma|)$ bits of memory and runs in $O(|\Sigma| n \log n)$ time. This algorithm can index the whole human DNA on a PC in 20 hours. The idea of [15] is to build the compressed

---

[1] The news source is the Central News Agency of Taiwan.

suffix array incrementally, character by character. With the help of a modified red-black tree, for every insertion of a character, the compressed suffix array can be updated in $O(|\Sigma| \log n)$ time. Since the text has n characters, the compressed suffix array can be obtained using $O(|\Sigma| n \log n)$ time.

For DNA (which has only four distinct characters) or texts of very small alphabet, the efficiency of the above algorithm is still acceptable. But for indexing other kinds of texts such as Chinese or Japanese, whose alphabet consists of at least a few thousand characters, the efficiency of the above algorithm deteriorates quickly. This paper gives a more practical algorithm for constructing compressed suffix arrays, reducing the time from $O(|\Sigma| n \log n)$ to $O(n \log n)$, while maintaining the $O(n \log |\Sigma|)$-bit space complexity.[2] In fact, our algorithm demands less working space; more precisely, it reduces the $(2H_0 + 1 + \epsilon)n$ space requirement in [15] to $(H_0 + 2 + \epsilon)n$, where ϵ is any non-zero constant, and H_0 is the 0-th order empirical entropy of the text. Note that H_0 is at most $\log |\Sigma|$ and is very likely to be bigger than 1. Thus, our algorithm allows us to index even longer text than the previous algorithm on ordinary PCs.

Instead of building a CSA character by character, the new algorithm partitions the text into $\log n$ segments where each segment is of length $n/\log n$. Suppose we have already built a CSA for the first i segments, we show that we can "merge" the $(i + 1)$-th segment with the CSA to form a bigger CSA in $O(n)$ time. Thus, the total time to build the whole compressed suffix array is $O(n \log n)$. Technically speaking, the new algorithm avoids using a balance tree of short sequences as an intermediate representation. The updating of such short sequences is inherently slow. Instead, we devise a more elegant representation based on Rice code [21,8].

In addition to CSA, Ferragina and Manzini [5] have proposed another scheme called FM-index to compress suffix arrays. The FM-index can match the storage requirement and searching efficiency of CSA, and it may be even better in some cases. Yet there is also no direct way to construct FM-index in the literature. Another contribution of this paper is the first algorithm for constructing FM-index using limited working space. We show that once CSA is constructed, we can build FM-index from CSA in $O(n)$ time without extra working storage.

The rest of this paper is organized as follows. Section 2 gives a review of suffix arrays and compressed suffix arrays. Section 3 presents the new construction algorithm of CSA, while Section 4 discusses the space-efficient construction of FM-index. We conclude the paper in Section 5.

2   Preliminaries

Let Σ be an alphabet, and $\$$ be a special character not in Σ. We assume that $\$$ is lexicographically smaller than any character in Σ, which is used to mark the end of a text. Consider a length-n text T defined on Σ, which is represented

---

[2] The quest for construction algorithm of text indices tailor-made for large alphabets is not a new idea. For instance, Farach [3] extends the linear-time suffix tree construction algorithm from constant-sized alphabet to general alphabets.

by an array $T[0..n] = T[0]T[1]...T[n]$, where $T[n] = \$$. For $i = 0, 1, 2, ..., n$, $T_i = T[i..n] = T[i]T[i+1]...T[n]$ denotes a suffix of T starting from the i-th position.

i	$T[i]$	T_i
0	a	acaaccg$
1	g	caaccg$
2	a	aaccg$
3	a	accg$
4	g	ccg$
5	g	cg$
6	c	g$
7	$	$

i	$SA[i]$	$T_{SA[i]}$
0	7	$
1	2	aaccg$
2	0	acaaccg$
3	3	accg$
4	1	caaccg$
5	4	ccg$
6	5	cg$
7	6	g$

i	$\Psi[i]$	$T[SA[i]]$
0	2	$
1	3	a
2	4	a
3	5	a
4	1	c
5	6	c
6	7	c
7	0	g

Fig. 1. Suffixes, suffix array, and compressed suffix array of $acaaccg\$$

A suffix array [17] is a sorted sequence of $n + 1$ suffixes of T, denoted by $SA[0..n]$. Formally, $SA[0..n]$ is a permutation of the set of integers $\{0, 1, ..., n\}$ such that, according to the lexicographic order, $T_{SA[0]} < T_{SA[1]} < \cdots < T_{SA[n]}$. See Figure 1 for an example. That is, $SA[i]$ denotes the starting position of the i-th smallest suffix of T. Note that $SA[0] = n$, so that for the remaining SA values, each can be represented in $\log n$ bits, and the suffix array can thus be stored using $(n + 1) \log n$ bits.[3] Given a text T together with the suffix array $SA[0..n]$, the occurrences of any pattern P in T can be found without scanning T again. Precisely, it takes $O(|P| \log n + occ)$ time, where occ is the number of occurrences.

For every $i = 0, 1, 2, ..., n$, define $SA^{-1}[i]$ to be the integer j such that $SA[j] = i$. Intuitively, $SA^{-1}[i]$ denotes the *lex-order* of T_i among the suffixes of T, which is the number of suffixes of T lexicographically smaller than or equal to the suffix T_i.

In general, to express the relation of a string X among the suffixes of T, we use $order(X, T)$ to denote the lex-order of X among all the suffixes of T. Thus, $SA^{-1}[i] = order(T_i, T)$.

Based on SA and SA^{-1}, the compressed suffix array [7,22] for a text T stores an array $\Psi[0..n]$ where $\Psi[i] = SA^{-1}[SA[i] + 1]$ for $i = 1, 2, ..., n$, while $\Psi[0]$ is defined as $SA^{-1}[0]$. See Figure 1 for an example.

Note that $\Psi[0..n]$ contains $n + 1$ integers. A trivial way to store the function requires $(n+1) \log n$ bits, which is the same space as storing the SA. Nevertheless, $\Psi[1..n]$ can always be partitioned into $|\Sigma|$ strictly increasing sequences, which allows it to be stored succinctly. This increasing property is illustrated in the rightmost table in Figure 1 and the correctness is proved based on the following lemmas.

---

[3] Throughout this paper, we assume that the base of the logarithm is 2.

Lemma 1. ([15]) *For every* $i < j$, *if* $T[SA[i]] = T[SA[j]]$, *then* $\Psi[i] < \Psi[j]$.

For any character $c \in \Sigma$, define l_c to be the maximum p such that $T_{SA[p-1]} < c$ and r_c to be the maximum p such that $T_{SA[p]} \leq c$.

Lemma 2. ([15]) *If* $l_c \leq r_c$, $\Psi[l_c \ldots r_c]$ *is strictly increasing.*

Corollary 1. $\Psi[1..n]$ *can be partitioned into at most* $|\Sigma|$ *strictly increasing sequences.*

Based on the increasing property, Grossi and Vitter [8] showed that Ψ can be encoded in $(H_0 + 2 + o(1))n$ bits using Rice code [21]. Moreover, each Ψ value can be retrieved in $O(1)$ time. Based on their encoding scheme, we observe a further property which is stated as follows.

Lemma 3. *Suppose that we can enumerate* $\Psi[i]$ *sequentially for* $i = 1, 2, \ldots, n$. *Then in* $O(n)$ *time, we can encode the* Ψ *function using* $(H_0 + 2 + o(1))n$ *bits.*

3 Our Algorithm

We want to construct $\Psi[1 \ldots n]$ for the text T. To do so, we first partiton the text into n/ℓ consecutive regions, say $T^1, T^2, \ldots, T^{n/\ell}$, each with $\ell = O(\frac{n}{\log n})$ characters.[4] The algorithm builds the Ψ function incrementally, starting with that of $T^{n/\ell}$, and then $T^{n/\ell-1}T^{n/\ell}, \ldots$ and finally obtains the required Ψ function of $T^1 T^2 \ldots T^{n/\ell} = T$. There are two main steps.

1. Base Step: Compute the Ψ function for $T^{n/\ell}$.
2. Merge Step: For $i = n/\ell - 1, n/\ell - 2, \ldots, 1$, compute the Ψ function of $T^i T'$ based on T^i and the Ψ function of T', where T' denotes the string $T^{i+1}T^{i+2} \ldots T^{n/\ell}$.

3.1 Time Complexity: Base Step

To compute the Ψ function of $T^{n/\ell}$, we first compute the SA for $T^{n/\ell}$ by suffix sorting. Since the length of $T^{n/\ell}$ is ℓ, suffix sorting takes $O(\ell \log \ell)$ time [16]. Afterwards, the SA^{-1} function can be computed in $O(\ell)$ time. Then together with the SA function, we obtain the Ψ function in $O(\ell)$ time. The overall time for the Base Step is therefore $O(\ell \log \ell)$.

3.2 Time Complexity: Merge Step

Consider $i \in \{1, 2, \ldots, n/\ell - 1\}$, and let $T^i = c_1 c_2 \cdots c_\ell$. Let $suf_1, suf_2, \ldots, suf_\ell$ to be the ℓ longest suffixes of $T^i T'$. Precisely, $suf_k = c_k c_{k+1} \cdots c_\ell T'$ for $k = 1, \ldots, \ell$.

The Iterative Step can be sub-divided into three parts:

---
[4] That is, we let $T^i = T[(i-1)\ell] \, T[(i-1)\ell + 1] \ldots T[i\ell - 1]$.

(a) Sort the suffixes $suf_1, suf_2, \ldots, suf_\ell$ to find the lex-orders of each suffix among themselves.
(b) For every suf_i, calculate $order(suf_i, T')$.
(c) Compute the Ψ function for $T^i T'$.

Part (a) can be done based on the following lemma.

Lemma 4. *The ℓ longest suffixes of $T^i T'$ can be sorted in $O(\ell \log \ell)$ time.*

Let $SA_{T'}$ denote the suffix array of T', $SA_{T'}^{-1}$ denote the inverse of the $SA_{T'}$, and $\Psi_{T'}$ denote the corresponding Ψ function of T'. For any character c, we use the notation of l_c and r_c to denote the maximum p such that $T'_{SA_{T'}[p-1]} < c$ and the maximum p such that $T'_{SA_{T'}[p]} \leq c$, respectively. The lemmas below show how to compute $order(c_k c_{k+1} \cdots c_\ell T', T')$ iteratively for $k = \ell, \ell - 1, \ldots, 1$, thus achieving Part (b).

Lemma 5. *Let X be any string and c be any character. Let B denote the set $\{b \mid b \in [l_c, r_c] \wedge \Psi_{T'}[b] \leq order(X, T')\}$. Then,*

$$order(cX, T') = \begin{cases} l_c - 1 & \text{if } B \text{ is empty} \\ \max\{b \mid b \in B\} & \text{otherwise} \end{cases}$$

Lemma 6. *Given the Ψ function of T'. Computing $order(c_k c_{k+1} \cdots c_l T', T')$ for all $1 \leq k \leq \ell$ can be done in $O(\ell \log n)$ time.*

We next discuss Part (c), which computes the Ψ function for $T^i T'$. Note that by definition, a Ψ function is basically an array of lex-orders of the suffixes of $T^i T'$ among themselves, enumerated in some specific order. To compute Ψ for $T^i T'$, we have to know $order(s, T^i T')$ for every suffix s of T'. We also need $order(suf_k, T^i T')$ for every $1 \leq k \leq l$.

In the following, we present a function f which maps the lex-orders for the existing suffixes of T' in T' to those in $T^i T'$, and a function g which maps the lex-orders for the newly added suffixes (i.e., the ℓ longest suffixes) to those in $T^i T'$. These two functions compute all the required lex-orders, and are then used to construct the required Ψ function of $T^i T'$.

Firstly, the following lemma shows the function f that relates $SA_{T'}^{-1}[m]$ and $SA_{T^i T'}^{-1}[m']$, where m and m' are positions in T' and $T^i T'$ that correspond to the same suffix of T' (i.e., $m' = m + |T^i|$).

Recall that suf_k denotes the string $c_k c_{k+1} \cdots c_\ell T'$.

Lemma 7. *Suppose $SA_{T'}^{-1}[m] = j$. Then $SA_{T^i T'}^{-1}[m']$ is equal to*

$$f(j) = j + \#(order(suf_k, T') \leq j),$$

where $\#(order(suf_k, T') \leq j)$ denotes the number of $order(suf_k, T')$ that is smaller than or equal to j, for $1 \leq k \leq \ell$.

Observation 1 *f is strictly increasing for $j \in [1, |T'|]$.*

Lemma 8. f *can be stored in* $o(n)$ *bits in* $O(n)$ *time, so that each* $f(j)$ *can be computed in constant time.*

The function g, which calculates the lex-orders of the remaining suffixes of $T^i T'$, is shown in the next lemma.

Lemma 9. *For all* $j \in [1, \ell]$, $\mathrm{SA}_{T^i T'}^{-1}[j]$ *is equal to*

$$g(j) = order(suf_j, T') + \#(suf_k \leq suf_j),$$

where $\#(suf_k \leq suf_j)$ *denotes the number of* suf_k *that is smaller than or equal to* suf_j, *for all* $1 \leq k \leq \ell$.

Observation 2 *For every* j, k, *if* $suf_j < suf_k$, *then* $g(j) < g(k)$. *In other words,* $g(k)$ *is strictly increasing in the ascending lex-order of* suf_k.

Lemma 10. *The values of the strictly increasing sequences* f *and* g *in Observations 1 and 2 are distinct and they span* $[1, |T^i T'|]$.

Based on Lemmas 7, 9 and 10, we are ready to describe how to accomplish Part (c). Let $\Phi = \Psi_{T'}$ and $\Phi' = \Psi_{T^i T'}$.

Lemma 11.
1. $\Phi'[f(j)] = f(\Phi[j])$ *for* $j = 1, 2, \ldots, |T'|$.
2. $\Phi'[g(\ell)] = f(\Phi[0])$.
3. $\Phi'[g(j)] = g(j+1)$ *for* $j = 1, 2, \ldots, \ell - 1$.

See Figures 2 and 3 for an example of the function Φ and Φ', and their relations with f and g.

i	$\mathrm{SA}_{T'}[i]$	$\Phi[i]$	$T'_{\mathrm{SA}_{T'}[i]}$
0	5	4	$
1	3	3	ac$
2	1	5	agac$
3	4	0	c$
4	0	2	cagac$
5	2	1	gac$

i	$\mathrm{SA}_{T^1 T'}[i]$	$\Phi'[i]$	$T_{\mathrm{SA}_{T^1 T'}[i]}$
0	8	8	$
1	6	4	ac$
2	2	6	acagac$
3	4	7	agac$
4	7	0	c$
5	1	2	cacagac$
6	3	3	cagac$
7	5	1	gac$
8	0	5	gcacagac$

Fig. 2. Functions Φ and Φ'. Φ and Φ' denote the Ψ functions for the text $T' = cagac$$ and the text $T^1 T' = gcacagac$$, respectively.

The algorithm to compute the required Φ' is as follows. By Lemma 10, merging the increasing sequences f and g gives the values from 1 to $|T^i T'|$. So we merge f and g, during which we compute the Φ' values sequentially by Lemma 11. A pseudo-code of the algorithm is shown in Figure 4.

Thus, we have the following lemma.

j	$f(j)$	$\Phi[j]$	$f(\Phi[j])$	j	$g(j)$	$g(j+1)$
0		4				
1	1	3	$\underline{4}$			
				3	2	$(\underline{6})$
2	3	5	$\underline{7}$			
3	4	0	$\underline{0}$			
				2	5	2
4	6	2	$\underline{3}$			
5	7	1	$\underline{1}$			
				1	8	$\underline{5}$

Fig. 3. Functions f and g. The $f(\Phi[j])$ and $g(j+1)$ values (underlined) form Φ' when we merge f and g. Note that $(\underline{6})$ denotes the special case of setting $\Phi'[g(j)]$ to $f(\Phi[0])$ when $j = \ell$.

```
j_f ← 1,   j_g ← 1.
for t = 0, 1, .., |T^i T'|
    if t = g(ℓ)
        Φ'[t] ← f(Φ[0]);
    else if t = f(j_f)
        Φ'[t] ← f(Φ[j_f]),   j_f++;
    else  Φ'[t] ← g(j_g + 1),   j_g++;
```

Fig. 4. Pseudo-code to construct Φ' sequentially.

Lemma 12. *Suppose that we have the lex-order of suf_j among the set $\{suf_k \mid 1 < k \le \ell\}$ and the $order(suf_j, T')$ for all $1 \le j \le \ell$, and the Ψ function of T'. Then the Ψ function for $T^i T'$ can be constructed in $(H_0 + 2 + o(1))n$ bits in $O(n)$ time.*

In conclusion, we have:

Lemma 13. *Given T^i and the Ψ function of T'. Computing the Ψ function of $T^i T'$ takes $O(\ell \log n + n)$ time.*

3.3   Overall Performance

Combining the results of Sections 3.1 and 3.2, we conclude the section with the following result:

Theorem 1. *Given a string T of length n, the Ψ function of T can be computed in $O(n \log n)$ time in $(H_0 + 2 + \epsilon)n$ bits space, for any $\epsilon > 0$.*

4   Space-Efficient Construction of FM-Index

Apart from CSA, there is another compressed index for suffix array called FM-index [5], which has demonstrated its compactness in size while showing competitive performance in searching a pattern recently [4]. The index is particularly suited for text with small-sized alphabet. The core part of the construction algorithm involves the Burrows-Wheeler transformation [1], which is a common procedure used in various data compression algorithms, such as bzip2 [23].

Precisely, the Burrows-Wheeler transformation transforms a text T of length n into another text W, where W is shown to be compressible in terms of the empirical entropy of T [18]. The transformed text W is defined such that $W[i] = T[SA[i] - 1]$ if $SA[i] > 0$, and $W[i] = \$$ if $SA[i] = 0$.

Given the Ψ of T, we observe that for any p, $SA[\Psi^k[p]] = SA[p] + k$ [22]. Now, by setting $p = \Psi[0] = SA^{-1}[0]$, and computing $\Psi^k[p]$ iteratively for $k = 1, 2, \ldots, n$, we obtain the values of $SA[\Psi^k[p]] = k$. Immediately, we can set $W[\Psi^k[p]] = T[k-1]$. Since each computation of Ψ takes $O(1)$ time, W can be constructed in $O(n)$ time.

Thus, we have the following theorem.

Theorem 2. *Given the text T and the Ψ function of T, the Burrows-Wheeler transformation on T can be output directly in $O(n \log |\Sigma|)$ bits space and in $O(n)$ time.*

Once the Burrows-Wheeler transformation is completed, the remaining steps for the construction of FM-index can be done in $O(n)$ time using negligible space in addition to the output index. Thus, we have the following result:

Theorem 3. *Given the text T and the Ψ function of T, the FM-index of T can be constructed in $O(n)$ time, using $O(n \log |\Sigma|)$ bits in addition to the output index.*

5   Concluding Remarks

We have presented an algorithm that constructs CSA in $(H_0 + 2 + \epsilon)n$ bits space, for some fixed $\epsilon > 0$. The running time is $O(n \log n)$, which is independent of the alphabet size. In contrast, the fastest known algorithm using comparable space requires $O(|\Sigma| n \log n)$ time.

We have also given the first algorithm for constructing FM-index using limited working space. We show that once CSA is constructed, we can build FM-index from CSA in $O(n)$ time without extra working storage.

In the literature, there is an algorithm that constructs CSA in $O(n \log \log |\Sigma|)$ time, but the working space is considerably increased to $O(n \log |\Sigma|)$ bits [11]. An interesting open problem is: Can we construct CSA in $o(n \log n)$ time, while using only $O((H_0 + 1)n)$ bits of working space?

References

1. M. Burrows and D. J. Wheeler. A Block-sorting Lossless Data Compression Algorithm. Technical Report 124, Digital Equipment Corporation, Paolo Alto, California, 1994.

2. D. R. Clark and J. I. Munro. Efficient Suffix Trees on Secondary Storage. In *Proc. ACM-SIAM SODA*, pages 383–391, 1996.
3. M. Farach. Optimal Suffix Tree Construction with Large Alphabets. In *Proc. IEEE FOCS*, pages 137–143, 1997.
4. P. Ferragina and G. Manzini. An experimental study of an opportunistic index. In *Proc. ACM-SIAM SODA*, pages 269–278, 2001.
5. P. Ferragine and G. Manzini. Opportunistic Data Structures with Applications. In *Proc. IEEE FOCS*, pages 390–398, 2000.
6. D. Graff and K. Chen. Chinese Gigaword, 2003. `http://` `//www.ldc.upenn.edu/Catalog/CatalogEntry.jsp?catalogId =LDC2003T09`.
7. R. Grossi and J. S. Vitter. Compressed Suffix Arrays and Suffix Trees with Applications to Text Indexing and String Matching. In *Proc. ACM STOC*, pages 397–406, 2000.
8. R. Grossi and J. S. Vitter. Compressed Suffix Arrays and Suffix Trees with Applications to Text Indexing and String Matching. Manuscript, 2001.
9. D. A. Grossman and O. Frieder. *Information Retrieval: Algorithms and Heuristics*. Kluwer Academic Publishers, Boston, 1998.
10. D. Gusfield. *Algorithms on Strings, Trees and Sequences: Computer Science and Computational Biology*. Cambridge University Press, New York, 1997.
11. W. K. Hon, K. Sadakane, and W. K. Sung. Breaking a Time-and-Sapce Barrier in Constructing Full-Text Indices. In *Proc. IEEE FOCS*, 2003. To appear.
12. E. Hunt, M. P. Atkinson, and R. W. Irving. A database index to large biological sequences. In *Proc. VLDB*, pages 410–421, 2000.
13. P. Ko and S. Aluru. Space Efficient Linear Time Construction of Suffix Arrays. In *Proc. CPM*, pages 200–210, 2003.
14. S. Kurtz. Reducing the Space Requirement of Suffix Trees. *Software Practice and Experiences*, 29:1149–1171, 1999.
15. T. W. Lam, K. Sadakane, W. K. Sung, and S. M. Yiu. A Space and Time Efficient Algorithm for Constructing Compressed Suffix Arrays. In *Proc. COCOON*, pages 401–410, 2002.
16. J. Larsson and K. Sadakane. Faster Suffix Sorting. Technical Report Technical Report LU-CS-TR:99-214, LUNDFD6/(NFCS-3140)/1-43/(1999), Lund University, 1999.
17. U. Manber and G. Myers. Suffix Arrays: A New Method for On-Line String Searches. *SIAM Journal on Computing*, 22(5):935–948, 1993.
18. G. Manzini. An Analysis of the Burrows-Wheeler Transform. *Journal of the ACM*, 48(3):407–430, 2001.
19. E. M. McCreight. A Space-economical Suffix Tree Construction Algorithm. *Journal of the ACM*, 23(2):262–272, 1976.
20. T. H. Ong and H. Chen. Updateable PAT-Tree Approach to Chinese Key Phrase Extraction using Mutual Information: A Linguistic Foundation for Knowledge Management. In *Proceedings of Asian Digital Library Conference*, 1999.
21. R. F. Rice. Some practical universal noiseless coding techniques. Technical Report JPL-79-22, Jet Propulsion Laboratory, Pasadena, California, 1979.
22. K. Sadakane. New Text Indexing Functionalities of the Compressed Suffix Arrays. *Journal of Algorithms*, in press.
23. J. Seward. The `bzip2` and `libbzip2` official home page, 1996. `http://sources.redhat.com/bzip2/`.
24. S. Shimozono, H. Arimura, and S. Arikawa. Efficient Discovery of Optimal Word Association Patterns in Large Text Databases. *New Generation Computing*, 18:49–60, 2000.

On the Geometric Dilation of Finite Point Sets

Annette Ebbers-Baumann, Ansgar Grüne, and Rolf Klein

Universität Bonn, Institut für Informatik I
D-53117 Bonn, Germany
{ebbers,gruene,klein}@cs.uni-bonn.de

Abstract. Let G be an embedded planar graph whose edges may be curves. For two arbitrary points of G, we can compare the length of the shortest path in G connecting them against their Euclidean distance. The maximum of all these ratios is called the *geometric dilation* of G. Given a finite point set, we would like to know the smallest possible dilation of any graph that contains the given points. In this paper we prove that a dilation of 1.678 is always sufficient, and that $\pi/2 = 1.570\ldots$ is sometimes necessary in order to accommodate a finite set of points.

Keywords: Computational geometry, detour, dilation, graph, network, spanner, stretch factor, transportation network.

1 Introduction

Transportation networks like waterways, railroad systems, or urban street systems can be modelled by a graph G in the plane whose edges are piecewise smooth curves that do not intersect, except at vertices of G.[1]

The quality of G as means of transport can be measured in the following way. For any two points, p and q, of G, let $\xi_G(p, q)$ denote a shortest path in G from p to q. Then the *dilation* of G is defined by

$$\delta(G) := \max_{p,q \in G} \frac{|\xi_G(p, q)|}{|pq|}. \tag{1}$$

The value of $\delta(G)$ measures the longest possible detour that results from using G instead of moving as the crow flies.

The above definition of $\delta(G)$ does not specify which points p, q of G to consider. There are two alternatives, corresponding to different applications.

Access to a railroad system is only possible at stations. In such a model we would use, as measure of quality, the *graph-theoretic dilation*, where only the *vertices* p, q of G are considered in definition (1). Here, only the lengths of the edges of G are of interest but not their geometric shapes.

---

[1] That is, we do not allow bridges at this stage, but it would, in principle, be possible to enlarge our model.

T. Ibaraki, N. Katoh, and H. Ono (Eds.): ISAAC 2003, LNCS 2906, pp. 250–259, 2003.
© Springer-Verlag Berlin Heidelberg 2003

Along urban streets, however, houses are densely distributed. Here it makes sense to include *all points* p, q of G in definition (1), vertices and interior edge points alike. This gives rise to the *geometric dilation* of graph G.

The graph-theoretic dilation has been extensively studied in the literature on spanners (see e. g. Eppstein's chapter in the Handbook of Computational Geometry [6] for a survey). One can efficiently construct spanners of bounded dilation and degree, whose weight is close to that of the minimum spanning tree, see Bose et al. [3]. Also, lower time bounds are known, see Chen et al. [4].

In contrast to this, the geometric dilation is a rather novel concept. So far, there are only three types of results. Icking et al. [9] and Aichholzer et al. [2] have provided upper bounds to the geometric dilation of planar curves in terms of their oscillation width, and Ebbers-Baumann et al. [5], Agarwal et al. [1], and Langerman et al. [11] have shown how to efficiently compute the geometric dilation of a given polygonal chain or cycle over n edges. Recently, Grüne [7] has given an algorithm for the related problem of computing the detour of a simple polygon.

Besides computing the dilation of given graphs, it is quite interesting to construct graphs of low dilation that contain a given finite point set.[2] In case of the graph-theoretic dilation the optimum solution must be a triangulation, since straight edges work best, and adding edges without creating new vertices never hurts. Yet, it seems not to be known how to efficiently compute the triangulation of minimum graph-theoretic dilation over a given vertex set. It is not even clear what maximum value the lowest possible dilation over all finite point sets can attain (see Problems 8 and 9 in [6]).

In this paper we are addressing the corresponding question for the geometric dilation. Given a finite point set P, we are interested in the smallest possible geometric dilation of any finite planar graph that contains all points of P, i. e., in the value of

$$\Delta(P) := \inf_{P \subset G, G \text{ finite}} \delta(G).$$

We call $\Delta(P)$ the *geometric dilation of the point set* P. Even for a set P of size 3, computing $\Delta(P)$ is a non-trivial task.

Our main interest in this paper is in the maximal value $\Delta(P)$ can attain, for an arbitrary finite point set, P. We are proving the following results.

1. There exist finite point sets whose geometric dilation is as large as $\pi/2 = 1.570\ldots$.
2. No finite point set can have a dilation larger than 1.678.

The first result is proven in Section 2, using Cauchy's surface area formula and a novel result on cycles in geometric graphs (Lemma 2). The second result will be shown in Section 3. We shall construct a periodic geometric graph G_∞ of dilation $1.6778\ldots$ that covers the plane, such that each finite point set is contained in a finite part G of a scaled copy of G_∞. While this construction is

---

[2] Observe that the complete graph over P does not solve this problem because the edge crossings would generate new vertices that must also be considered in definition (1).

certainly not efficient—the size of G depends on the rational coordinates of our input set—it serves well in establishing the upper bound.

2 A Lower Bound to the Geometric Dilation of Point Sets

In this section we show that some point sets can only be embedded in graphs of large geometric dilation. Our main result is the following.

Theorem 1. *Let P_n denote the vertex set of the regular n-gon on the unit circle. Then, we have $\Delta(P_n) = \pi/2 = 1,570\ldots$ for each $n \geq 10$.*

In order to prove Theorem 1, we will show that neither any graph with cycles nor a tree containing the given point set has a dilation smaller than $\pi/2$. As preparation we proof the following lemma.

Lemma 1. *Any closed curve C has dilation at least $\pi/2$.*

Proof. First, let C be a closed convex curve, and let δ denote its dilation. For each direction α, there is a unique pair of points (p_α, q_α), called a *partition pair*, that halves the perimeter $|C|$ of C; see Figure 1. We call

$$h(\alpha) = |p_\alpha q_\alpha|$$

the *partition distance* at angle α. Let $b(\alpha)$ be the breadth of C in orientation α. Clearly, $b(\alpha) \geq h(\alpha)$ holds. Moreover, we have $\frac{|C|/2}{h(\alpha)} \leq \delta$, by definition of the dilation.

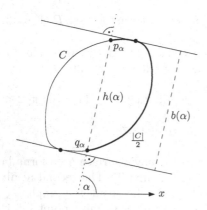

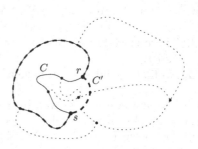

Fig. 1. The breadth of a convex curve is at least its partition distance.

Fig. 2. Cycle C' results from enlarging cycle C.

Thus, by Cauchy's surface area formula,

$$|C| = \int_0^\pi b(\alpha)\,d\alpha \geq \int_0^\pi h(\alpha)\,d\alpha \geq \int_0^\pi \frac{|C|/2}{\delta}\,d\alpha = \frac{\pi|C|}{2\delta},$$

hence $\delta \geq \pi/2$.

Next, let C be a closed non-convex curve. Again, for each orientation α there is a partition pair (p_α, q_α) of C. This can be shown by a continuity argument: Clearly, there is a partition pair (p_β, q_β) for *some* orientation β; as we let these points move along C in clockwise direction, at equal speed, each will eventually reach its partner's position. During this process, each possible orientation has been attained. Now let ch(C) denote the convex hull of C. Then, $|C| \geq |\text{ch}(C)|$ holds, and we have $b_{\text{ch}(C)}(\alpha) \geq h_C(\alpha)$. So, the proof for the convex case carries over. $\qquad\square$

Now, let G be an arbitrary geometric graph that contains a bounded face. In order to deal with this case we provide the following result.

Lemma 2. *Let G be a finite geometric graph in the plane that contains a bounded face. Then there exists a cycle, C in G such that for any two points, p and q of C there exists a shortest path $\xi_G(p,q)$ from p to q in G that is a subset of C.*

Proof. (Sketch.) We start with a cycle, C, that equals the boundary of a bounded face. As long as there are shorter connections between points on C than those provided by C, we use them to form a bigger cycle C' (see Figure 2), while maintaining the following.

Invariant. Let a, b be two points on cycle C. Then no shortest path in G connecting them uses any edge that passes through the interior of the bounded face encircled by C. $\qquad\square$

Together with Lemma 1 on the dilation of closed curves the subsequent theorem follows directly:

Theorem 2. *Each graph containing a bounded face has dilation at least $\pi/2$.*

It remains to show, that no graph without cycles, i. e. a tree, can provide a smaller dilation for embedding the vertex set P_n of a regular n-gon with $n \geq 10$.

Lemma 3. *Let tree T contain the point set P_n. Then $\delta(T) \geq \pi/2$ holds.*

Proof. Assume that tree T contains P_n, and that $\delta(T) < \pi/2$ holds. Then, if p, q are two neighboring points of P_n, the unique path $\xi(p,q)$ in T connecting them is of length at most $a\pi/2$, where

$$a = |pq| = 2\sin\left(\frac{\pi}{n}\right) \leq 2\sin\left(\frac{\pi}{10}\right) = \frac{\sqrt{5}-1}{2} = 0,618\ldots.$$

Let z be an arbitrary point on this path. Since z can be reached from p by a curve of length at most $a\pi/2$, its Euclidean distance from p cannot exceed this value. The same holds for q. Thus, z must be included in the lune formed by the two circles of radius

$$a\frac{\pi}{2} \le \frac{\sqrt{5}-1}{2}\frac{\pi}{2} = 0,9708\ldots < 1$$

centered at p and q; see Figure 3. Thus, no lune contains the unit circle's center. Now let us consider the arrangement of all lunes of neighboring points, as

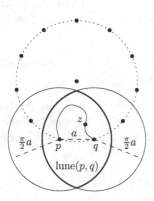

Fig. 3. The path between neighboring points is contained in their lune.

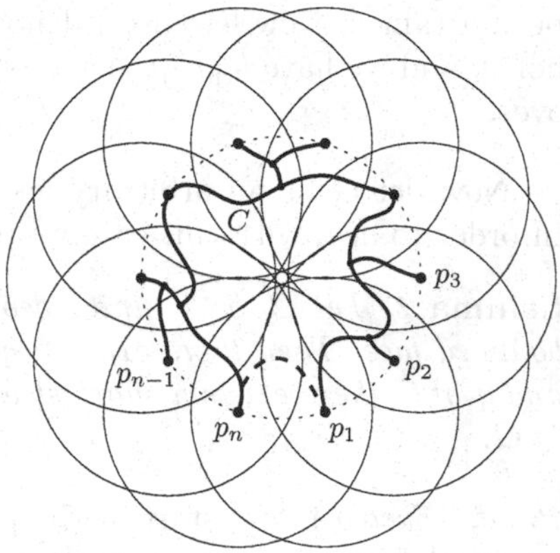

Fig. 4. The path C from p_1 to p_n is not contained in the lune of p_1 and p_n.

depicted in Figure 4, and assume that the points are labelled $p_1, p_2, \ldots, p_n$ in counterclockwise order. The concatenation

$$C = \xi(p_1, p_2)\xi(p_2, p_3)\ldots\xi(p_{n-1}, p_n)$$

is a path in T that is contained in, and visits, all lunes associated with these point pairs. Together with $\xi(p_n, p_1)$, which must be contained in the lune of p_n and p_1, C forms a closed path in T that encircles the center of the unit circle and is, thus, not contractible, contradicting the fact that T is a tree.   □

Now we can prove Theorem 1.

Proof. Clearly, for each n we have $\Delta(P_n) \le \pi/2$, because this is the dilation of the unit circle. Let $n \ge 10$. According to Theorem 2, any graph containing a cycle has a dilation $\delta(G) \ge \pi/2$. On the other hand according to Lemma 3 no tree containing P_n can provide a smaller dilation. So we have shown that no graph at all containing all points of P_n can have a dilation smaller than $\pi/2$.   □

The arguments displayed in the proof of Lemma 3 can also be used in proving the following result.

Corollary 1. *Let C be a closed curve, and let P_n be a set of n points evenly placed on C. Then the dilation of any tree containing P_n tends to infinity, as n grows.*

We want to point out that Theorem 1 does not hold for small values of n. Trivially, $\Delta(P_1) = \Delta(P_2) = 1$. For $n = 3$ we have the subsequent result.

Corollary 2. $\Delta(P_3) = \frac{2}{\sqrt{3}} = 1,157\ldots$.

To show this corollary the following technical lemma, stated here without proof, is useful.

Lemma 4. *Let v be a vertex of G where two edges meet at angle α, that is, the tangents to the piecewise smooth edges in the common vertex v form an angle α. Then, $\delta(G) \geq \frac{1}{\sin(\alpha/2)}$ holds.*

It follows the proof of Corollary 2.

Proof. We can achieve the bound $\Delta(P_3) = \frac{2}{\sqrt{3}}$ by the Steiner tree on P_3, i. e., by connecting the center of the unit circle by a straight segment to each point of P_3. These segments meet at an 120° angle. By Lemma 4, this causes a local dilation of $1/\sin(\alpha/2)$. In our case, no bigger value than $1/\sin(60°) = \frac{2}{\sqrt{3}}$ can occur.

In order to prove that no graph G containing P_3 can have a smaller dilation we need only consider the following cases. G cannot contain a cycle, because any cycle has a dilation of at least $\pi/2$ according to Lemma 1. Therefore G has to be either a simple chain or a tree with a vertex of degree at least 3. If G is a simple chain passing through the three points in the order p, q, r, then its dilation is at least $\frac{|pq|+|qr|}{|pr|} = 2$. Otherwise, G is a tree with a vertex of degree at least 3. But then we can be sure that its dilation is at least $\frac{2}{\sqrt{3}}$, by the angle argument of Lemma 4. □

3   An Upper Bound to the Geometric Dilation

In this section we will show that each finite point set can be embedded in a finite graph of geometric dilation at most 1.678. More precisely, we prove the following.

Theorem 3. *There is a periodic, plane covering graph G_∞ of dilation $1,67784\ldots$ such that each finite set of rational points is contained in a finite part of a scaled copy of G_∞.*

We proceed in three steps. First, we state a simple yet important technical result in Lemma 5. Then, the proof of Theorem 3 starts with the construction of a certain cycle, C. Graph G_∞ will then be obtained by taking the hexagonal grid of unit length, and replacing each vertex with a copy of C. The proof will be concluded by showing how to embed finite point sets in G_∞.

In determining the geometric dilation of graphs the following lemma is useful; it has first been used for chains in [5]. Observe that an analogous result for the graph-theoretic dilation does not hold.

Lemma 5. *The geometric dilation of a graph is always attained by two co-visible points.*

Proof. Assume that $\delta(G)$ is attained by points p, q that are not co-visible and have a minimal Euclidean distance, among all such pairs. Then the line segment pq contains a point r of G in its interior. Hence,

$$\delta(G) = \frac{\xi_G(p, q)}{|pq|} \le \frac{\xi_G(p, r) + \xi_G(r, q)}{|pr| + |rq|}$$

$$\le \max\left(\frac{\xi_G(p, r)}{|pr|}, \frac{\xi_G(r, q)}{|pq|}\right)$$

$$\le \delta(G).$$

Thus, the dilation of G is also attained by one of the pairs $(p, q), (q, r)$, a contradiction. $\qquad\square$

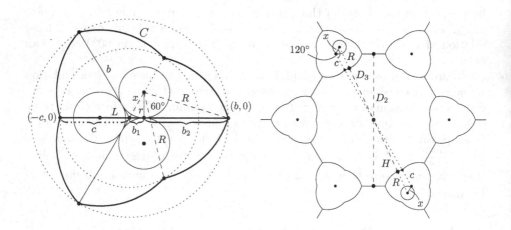

Fig. 5. The cycle C and the essentials of its construction.

Fig. 6. The periodic graph G_∞.

Now we give the proof of Theorem 3.

Proof. First, we construct a closed cycle, C, that will then be used in building a periodic graph, G_∞, of dilation $\delta(G) = 1,67784\ldots$. The cycle C is defined as follows. We draw the positive X−axis and two more half lines starting from the origin at angles of $120°$ and $−120°$, correspondingly. Next, we fix two numbers, $0 < c < b < 0.5$, that will be specified later, when optimizing the bound. Depending on b, c we draw three circles, each of which touches two of the three half lines at the distance $b_1 = \frac{b-c}{2}$ from the origin; see Figure 5. For their radius, r, and for the distance, x from their centers to the origin we obtain

$$\frac{x}{2} = x \, \cos 60° = b_1 = \frac{b - c}{2}$$

$$\frac{x\sqrt{3}}{2} = x\,\sin 60° = r,$$

which implies $x = b - c$ and $r = \frac{\sqrt{3}}{2}(b - c)$.

Now we consider the line segment, L, of length $b + c$ from $(-c, 0)$ to $(b, 0)$, and imagine that its midpoint is glued to the upper circle. As this circle rotates clockwise by $60°$, the right endpoint of L describes a circular arc of length $R\,\pi/3$, where

$$R = \sqrt{r^2 + b_2^2} = \sqrt{\frac{3}{4}(b - c)^2 + \frac{1}{4}(b + c)^2}$$

$$= \sqrt{b^2 - bc + c^2}.$$

After this rotation, line segment L is unglued from the upper circle, and glued to the left circle instead, that now rotates clockwise by $60°$, and so on. This results in a cycle C that consists of six circular arcs of length $R\,\pi/3$ each.

By construction, each pair of endpoints of the rotating line segment is a partition pair of C, because the endpoints of C are always moving with identical speed. Moreover, each such pair attains the maximum dilation of C. So, we have

$$D_1 := \delta(C) = \frac{\pi\,R}{b + c}.$$

Now we construct a periodic graph G_∞ that covers the plane. This graph is obtained by centering rotated copies of cycle C at the vertices of the regular hexagonal grid[3] of unit edge length, and cutting off those parts of the axes contained in those copies; see Figure 6.

Thanks to Lemma 5, we need only compute the dilation of the two faces occurring in G_∞, which are the cycle C and the boundary of the "dodecagonal" face. On the latter, two candidate partition pairs of points exist that might attain maximum dilation. In vertical direction, we have a pair whose dilation equals

$$D_2 = \frac{2\pi R + 3\,(1 - 2b)}{\sqrt{3}};$$

Observe that the numerator equals three times one third of the perimeter of cycle C, plus three times the length of a shortened unit edge, whereas the denominator measures the height of the hexagonal cell. The other candidate pair is obtained by intersecting, with the copies of C, the line H connecting the centers of two generating circles; see Figure 6. Since the diagonal of the hexagonal cell is of length 2, the distance between these intersection points equals

$$2\,(\sqrt{x^2 + 1 - 2x\cos 120°} - R),$$

by the law of cosines. This leads to

$$D_3 = \frac{2\pi R + 3\,(1 - 2b)}{2\,(\sqrt{x^2 + x + 1} - R)}.$$

---

[3] Without this refinement, the plain hexagonal grid would have a dilation of $\sqrt{3} = 1.7320\ldots$.

Analysis shows that the maximum of D_1, D_2, D_3 can be minimized to

$$D_1 \; = \; D_2 \; = \; D_3 \; = \; 1.6778\ldots$$

by putting

$$c = 0.1248\ldots \quad \text{and} \quad b = 0.1939\ldots$$

Now let us assume that we are given a finite set of rational points, $P = \{p_1, \ldots, p_n\}$, that must be embedded in a graph of low dilation. Assume that

$$p_i = (\frac{e_i}{f_i}, \frac{g_i}{h_i})$$

holds with natural numbers e_i, f_i, g_i, h_i. Let

$$K := (\frac{1}{2} - b) \, \frac{1}{\sqrt{3}} \, \frac{1}{\prod_j f_j} \, \frac{1}{\prod_j h_j} \, \min_j \frac{f_j}{e_j},$$

where b is the constant involved in constructing the cycle C. By a theorem of Dirichlet's, there are infinitely many integer pairs (r, s) satisfying

$$|\sqrt{3} - \frac{r}{s}| \; < \; \frac{1}{s^2} \; < \; \frac{K}{s}.$$

We choose one such pair and put

$$\gamma := \frac{1}{r} \, \frac{1}{\sqrt{3}} \, \frac{1}{\prod_j f_j} \, \frac{1}{\prod_j h_j},$$

and construct the graph G introduced above over a hexagonal grid of edge length γ. We are going to place the points p_i on (some of) the horizontal edges of the 12-gons, close to their mid points. This is possible because of two facts. First, each $Y-$coordinate g_i/h_i is an integer multiple of $\sqrt{3}\,\gamma$, the distance of two neighboring horizontal levels in G.

Second, each $X-$coordinate e_i/f_i is close enough to an integer multiple of the distance 3γ between two neighboring mid points of the same $Y-$level. Indeed,

$$\frac{\sqrt{3}s}{r} \, \frac{e_i}{f_i} \; = \; e_i \, s \prod_{j \neq i} f_j \prod_j h_j \; 3\gamma$$

is an integer multiple of 3γ, and we have

$$|\frac{\sqrt{3}s}{r} \, \frac{e_i}{f_i} - \frac{e_i}{f_i}| = \frac{e_i}{f_i} \, \frac{s}{r} \, |\sqrt{3} - \frac{r}{s}| < \frac{e_i}{f_i} \, \frac{s}{r} \, \frac{K}{s}$$

$$= \frac{e_i}{f_i} \, \min_j \frac{f_j}{e_j} \, (\frac{1}{2} - b) \, \gamma < (\frac{1}{2} - b) \, \gamma,$$

so that the point still lies on the horizontal edge. $\square$

This concludes the proof of Theorem 3 and, thus, of the main result of this section.

4   Concluding Remarks

In this paper we have, for the first time, studied the geometric dilation of geometric graphs. We have introduced the notion of the geometric dilation, $\Delta(P)$, of a finite set of points, P, as the minimal dilation of all finite graphs that contain P. We have shown that the vertices of the regular n−gon have dilation $\pi/2 = 1.570\ldots$, and that no finite point set has a dilation bigger than 1.678.

These results give rise to many further questions. How can we compute the geometric dilation of a given point set? How costly (in weight and computing time) is the construction of a geometric graph attaining (or: approximating) $\Delta(P)$? What is the precise value of

$$\Delta := \sup_{P \text{ finite}} \Delta(P)?$$

(We conjecture $\Delta > \pi/2$.) And finally, what happens if we extend this definition to non-finite sets, e. g. simple geometric shapes?

References

1. P. Agarwal, R. Klein, Ch. Knauer, and M. Sharir. Computing the detour of polygonal curves. Technical Report B 02-03, FU Berlin, January 2002.
2. O. Aichholzer, F. Aurenhammer, Ch. Icking, R. Klein, E. Langetepe, and G. Rote. Generalized self-approaching curves. *Discrete Appl. Math.*, 109:3–24, 2001.
3. P. Bose, J. Gudmundsson, and M. Smid. Constructing plane spanners of bounded degree and low weight. In *Proc. 10th European Symposium on Algorithms*, LNCS 2461, Springer-Verlag, pages 234–246, 2001.
4. D. Z. Chen, G. Das, and M. Smid. Lower bounds for computing geometric spanners and approximate shortest paths. *Discrete Appl. Math.*, 110:151–167, 2001.
5. A. Ebbers-Baumann, R. Klein, E. Langetepe, and A. Lingas. A fast algorithm for approximating the detour of a polygonal chain. In *Proc. 9th European Symposium on Algorithms*, LNCS 2161, Springer-Verlag, pages 321–332, 2001.
6. D. Eppstein. Spanning trees and spanners. In J.-R. Sack and J. Urrutia, editors, *Handbook of Computational Geometry*, pages 425–461. Elsevier, 1999.
7. A. Grüne. Umwege in Polygonen. Master's thesis, Institut für Informatik I, Universität Bonn, 2002.
8. J. Gudmundsson, Ch. Levcopoulos, G. Narasimhan, and M. Smid. Approximate distance oracles revisited. In *Proc. 13th Internat. Symp. ISAAC '02*, volume 2518 of *Lecture Notes Comput. Sci.*, pages 357–368, 2002.
9. Ch. Icking, R. Klein, and E. Langetepe. Self-approaching curves. *Math. Proc. Camb. Phil. Soc.*, 125:441–453, 1999.
10. R. Kato, K. Imai, and T. Asano. An improved algorithm for the minimum manhattan network problem. In *Proc. 13th Internat. Symp. ISAAC '02*, volume 2518 of *Lecture Notes Comput. Sci.*, pages 344–356, 2002.
11. S. Langerman, P. Morin, and M. Soss. Computing the maximum detour and spanning ratio of planar chains, trees and cycles. In *Proc. 19th Internat. Symp. Theoretical Aspects of Computer Sc., STACS '02*, volume 2285 of *Lecture Notes Comput. Sci.*, pages 250–261, 2002.
12. G. Narasimhan and M. Smid. Approximating the stretch factor of Euclidean graphs. *SIAM J. Comput.*, 30:978–989, 2000.

On Computing All Immobilizing Grasps of a Simple Polygon with Few Contacts

Jae-Sook Cheong, Herman J. Haverkort, and A. Frank van der Stappen

Institute of Information and Computing Sciences, Utrecht University,
P.O.Box 80.089, 3508 TB Utrecht, The Netherlands
{jaesook,herman,frankst}@cs.uu.nl

Abstract. We study the output-sensitive computation of all combinations of edges and vertices of a simple polygon P that allow a form-closure grasp with less than four point contacts. We present an $O(m^{4/3} \log^{1/3} m + K)$-time algorithm to compute all form-closure grasps using two frictionless point contacts, and an $O(n^2 \log^{O(1)} n + K)$-time algorithm to compute all such grasps with three point contacts. Here, n is the number of edges and m is the number of concave vertices of P. We also present an $O(n^2 \log^4 n + K)$-time algorithm that enumerates all edge triples with a second-order immobility grasp using Czyzowicz's conditions.

1 Introduction

Many applications such as robot hand grasping and manufacturing operations require an object to be *immobilized*, such that any motion of the object violates the rigidity of the object or the contacts.

An attractive theoretical model for immobility was formulated by Reuleaux in 1876 [13]. He defines a rigid body to be in *form closure* if a set of contacts along its boundary constrains all finite and *infinitesimal* motions of the body. This notion is stronger than immobility, as for instance an equilateral triangle with a point contact in the middle of each edge is immobilized, but is not in form closure (it permits an infinitesimal rotation around its center). Form closure depends only on the position of the contacts and their normals, and is invariant with respect to the curvature of body and contacts. This is not true for immobility in general (if we replace the equilateral triangle in the example by its inscribed circle, contacts and normals remain identical, but the body is no longer immobilized). Markenscoff et al. [9] and Mishra et al. [11] independently showed that, with the exception of a circle, any two-dimensional body can be put in form closure with four frictionless point contacts, and that almost any three-dimensional body can be put in form closure with seven such contacts. We will call a configuration of frictionless point contacts that put an object in form closure a *form-closure grasp*.

We consider the problem of computing all form-closure grasps of a polygonal part with at most four frictionless point contacts. The availability of *all* grasps of

T. Ibaraki, N. Katoh, and H. Ono (Eds.): ISAAC 2003, LNCS 2906, pp. 260–269, 2003.

a certain part allows a user—usually a machinist—to select the grasps that best meet specific additional requirements, such as accessibility, which may vary from one operation to another. As the computation of all grasps along a given combination of edges and concave vertices can be accomplished in constant time [12, 18], the algorithmic challenge is to efficiently report all combinations of edges and vertices that yield at least one grasp.

An algorithm to compute, for a simple n-vertex polygon, all the edge combinations that have a form-closure grasp with four contacts was presented by van der Stappen et al. [18]. The algorithm runs in $O(n^{2+\varepsilon} + K)$-time, where K is the number of edge quadruples reported. Brost and Goldberg [2] studied the same problem in modular settings, where the contact positions are restricted to a grid.

In general, four point contacts are required for planar objects, but sometimes form-closure grasps with fewer contacts are possible by using contacts in concave vertices of the object. Form-closure grasps with less than four contacts were first studied by Gopalakrishnan and Goldberg [8], who gave an $O(n^2)$-time algorithm to find all the concave vertex pairs that allow a two-contact form-closure grasp. In Section 2, we improve this to $O(m^{4/3} \log^{1/3} m + K)$, where m is the number of concave vertices of the polygon. All combinations of one concave vertex and two edges can be reported using a generalization of the algorithm by van der Stappen et al. We improve on that by presenting an $O(n^2 \log^{O(1)} m + K)$-time algorithm. Finally, we show how to report all combinations of two concave vertices and one edge in $O(n^2 \log^{O(1)} n + K)$-time.

In Section 3, we turn our attention away from form closure to general immobility. Analogous to the above, we call a configuration of frictionless point contacts that immobilizes a rigid body an *immobility grasp*. Czyzowicz et al. [5] provided a necessary and sufficient geometric condition for a simple polygon without parallel edges to be immobilized by three point contacts. A more general analysis applicable to arbitrary objects was given by Rimon and Burdick [14, 15,16], who define the term *second-order immobility*, as it not only takes position and normal, but also curvature of object, contacts, and possible motions into account.

An algorithm that reports, for a simple n-vertex polygon without parallel edges, all the edge triples that yield at least one immobility grasp was given by van der Stappen et al. [18]. Its running time is $O(n^2 \log^2 n + K')$, where K' is the number of triples considered according to some criterion. This criterion is necessary, but not sufficient, and so the algorithm may consider triples that do not yield immobility grasps. We resolve this shortcoming by giving a truly output-sensitive algorithm with a running time of $O(n^2 \log^4 n + K)$-time, where K is the number of edge triples yielding immobility grasps.

2 Form-Closure Grasps with Less than Four Contacts

A wrench in two-dimensional space is a three-component vector (f_x, f_y, τ), where (f_x, f_y) is a force and τ is the torque induced by the force. A point contact to

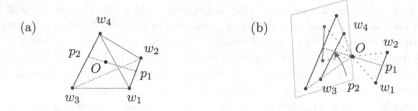

Fig. 1. (a) Illustrating Lemma 1. (b) The origin O lies in $\overline{p_1 p_2}$, where $p_1 \in \overline{w_1 w_2}$ and $p_2 \in \overline{w_3 w_4}$.

an object P at position p can be seen as able to apply the wrench $(n_x, n_y, n \times p)$ to P, where n is the inward normal of P at p.

Our results on form-closure grasps are based on the following characterization of form closure [7,11,12,17].

Theorem 1. *Given a set of $k \geq 4$ wrenches $w_1, w_2, \cdots w_k$ on an object P. Then the following three conditions are equivalent:*

(i) P is in form closure.
(ii) Any wrench w can be written as $w = \lambda_1 w_1 + \cdots + \lambda_k w_k$, with $\lambda_i \geq 0$.
(iii) The origin lies in the interior of the convex hull of $w_1, w_2, \cdots, w_k$.

The equivalence of (ii) and (iii) can be verified easily. The equivalence of (i) and (ii) relies on the fact that the contacts together can be seen to apply any wrench that is a non-negative combination of the individual contact wrenches. Intuitively, the object is in form closure if and only if any wrench applied to the object can be cancelled by such a non-negative combination of contact wrenches.

Placing a point contact at a concave vertex of P provides *two* contact wrenches w_1 and w_2, as the contact touches two edges at the same time. Therefore, by making use of contacts at concave vertices, form-closure grasps with less than four point contacts can be achieved.

In the following, we define the segment $\overline{pq}$ to be the *relatively open* segment connecting p and q, that is, the set $\overline{pq} := \{\lambda p + (1 - \lambda)q \mid 0 < \lambda < 1\}$. We need a simple geometric lemma.

Lemma 1. *Let w_1, w_2, w_3, w_4 be four points in $\mathbb{R}^3$. The origin O lies in the interior of the convex hull of $w_1, \ldots, w_4$ if and only if there are points $p_1 \in \overline{w_1 w_2}$ and $p_2 \in \overline{w_3 w_4}$ such that $O \in \overline{p_1 p_2}$.*

Proof. The "if" direction is trivial. Suppose therefore that the origin O lies strictly inside the tetrahedron formed by w_1, w_2, w_3 and w_4. Consider the plane Π containing w_1, w_2, and O. It intersects the segment $\overline{w_3 w_4}$ in a point p_2. The intersection of the tetrahedron with Π is the triangle $\triangle w_1 w_2 p_2$. The point O lies in the interior of this triangle, and so the line Op_2 intersects $\overline{w_1 w_2}$ in the required point p_1.   □

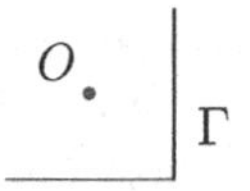

Fig. 2. The screen Γ, seen from above

We now build a *screen* Γ in wrench space. Γ is the union of two vertically infinite slabs, namely (see Fig. 2)

$$\Gamma := \{(x, -1, z) \mid -1 \leq x < 1, z \in \mathbb{R}\} \cup \{(1, y, z) \mid -1 \leq y < 1, z \in \mathbb{R}\}.$$

Any non-vertical line through the origin intersects Γ in exactly one point. A non-vertical plane intersects Γ in the union of two line segments. We will project wrenches $w \neq O$ onto Γ as follows: Consider the line ℓ through w and the origin O, and let $\pi(w) := \ell \cap \Gamma$. If w lies between O and $\pi(w)$, we color $\pi(w)$ *blue*. If O lies between w and $\pi(w)$, we color $\pi(w)$ *red*.

A segment $\overline{w_1 w_2}$ is projected onto Γ by projecting each point $w \in \overline{w_1 w_2}$. It is easy to see that the projection $\pi(\overline{w_1 w_2})$ consists of at most three segments on Γ, where each segment is either blue or red.

Lemma 2. *Given an object with four contact wrenches w_1, w_2, w_3, w_4. The object is in form-closure if and only if a red part of $\pi(\overline{w_1 w_2})$ intersects a blue part of $\pi(\overline{w_3 w_4})$, or vice versa.*

Proof. By Theorem 1 and Lemma 1, the object is in form closure if and only if there exist $p_1 \in \overline{w_1 w_2}$ and $p_2 \in \overline{w_3 w_4}$ such that $O \in \overline{p_1 p_2}$. This implies that $\pi(p_1) = \pi(p_2)$, and the colors of the projections differ. □

In the following we will make use of two data structures that we introduce now.

A *triangle search structure* is a data structure that stores a set Q of q points in $\mathbb{R}^2$ and supports queries of the following form: Given a query triangle Δ, report the points in $\Delta \cap Q$. We use the structure by Matoušek [10], which can be built in time $O(q^2)$ and has query time $O(\log^3 q + k)$, where k is the number of points reported.

A *segment intersection structure* is a data structure that stores a set S of r line segments in $\mathbb{R}^2$, and supports queries of the form: Given a query segment s, report all segments $s' \in S$ with $s \cap s' \neq \emptyset$. Such a structure can be built in time $O(r^2 \log^{O(1)} r)$, it has query time $O(\log^{O(1)} r + k)$, where k is the number of segments reported [1,10].

Pairs of concave vertices. We wish to report all pairs of concave vertices which allow a form-closure grasp by placing two frictionless point contacts at these vertices. For each concave vertex, we compute the two wrenches w and w' corresponding to it, and project the segment $\overline{ww'}$ onto Γ. Let $s(v) := \pi(\overline{ww'})$ be the projection. By Lemma 2, two concave vertices v and v' have a form-closure grasp if and only if $s(v)$ and $s(v')$ form a red-blue intersection in Γ.

The family $\{s(v)\}$ consists of at most $3m$ red and blue segments in Γ, where m is the number of concave vertices of P. It remains to compute all red-blue intersections in this set, a problem that can be solved in time $O(m^{4/3} \log^{1/3} m + K)$ [3]. Note that for this computation, we can simply flatten out Γ into a planar strip of width 4. In the worst case, K is $\Theta(n^2)$. There are classes of polygons for which K is zero.

Theorem 2. *Given a polygon with m concave vertices, all K form-closure grasps formed by two concave vertices can be computed in time $O(m^{4/3} \log^{1/3} m + K)$.*

Triples of one concave vertex and two edges. Form closure may also be achieved by placing three frictionless point contacts, one at a concave vertex v, and one each on two edges e and e'. We now give an algorithm to report all such triples (v, e, e'). Again, we have four wrenches $w_1, \ldots, w_4$, where $w_1 \in \hat{e}$, $w_2 \in \hat{e}'$, and w_3, w_4 are the two wrenches corresponding to the concave vertex v. Here, $\hat{e}$ is the set of wrenches corresponding to the possible placement of contacts on the edge e. All such wrenches have a common force vector, and so $\hat{e}$ is a vertical segment in wrench space.

Let $r(e, e') := \bigcup \{\pi(\overline{ww'}) \mid w \in \hat{e}, w' \in \hat{e}'\}$. The region $r(e, e')$ is the union of at most three trapezoids with two vertical sides, where each trapezoid is either all red or all blue. For a concave vertex v, let $s(v)$ be as above. By Lemma 2, a triple (v, e, e') allows a form-closure grasp if and only if a blue part of $s(v)$ intersects a red trapezoid of $r(e, e')$, or vice versa.

It remains to solve the following problem in the plane: Given a set of m line segments and a set of n^2 trapezoids, find all intersections between a line segment and a trapezoid. We observe that a segment s intersects a trapezoid r if and only if the midpoint of s lies in r, or if s intersects one of the sides of r. We test the two cases separately. We build, in time $O(m^2)$, a triangle search structure storing the midpoints of the segments. We can then report the k segment midpoints inside a trapezoid by two triangle queries in time $O(\log^3 m + k)$. We also build, in time $O(m^2 \log^{O(1)} m)$, a segment intersection structure. We can then find the k segments intersecting the boundary of a trapezoid by four segment intersection queries in time $O(\log^{O(1)} m + k)$.

It follows that, after $O(m^2 \log^{O(1)} m)$ preprocessing, we can report all k segments intersecting a given trapezoid in time $O(\log^{O(1)} m + k)$. Since there are $O(n^2)$ trapezoids, the total running time is $O(n^2 \log^{O(1)} m + K)$. In the worst case, K is $\Theta(n^3)$. There are classes of polygons for which K is $\Theta(n^2)$.

Theorem 3. *Given a polygon with m concave vertices and n vertices in total, all K form-closure grasps formed by one concave vertex and two edges can be computed in time $O(n^2 \log^{O(1)} m + K)$.*

Triples of two concave vertices and one edge. Placing two point contacts at a pair of concave vertices v, v' may not achieve form closure. Placing one more contact in the interior of an appropriate edge e, however, can achieve form closure with v and v'. Here, we present an algorithm to report all such triples (v, v', e).

Consider a pair of concave vertices v, v' that does not achieve form closure. Let w_1, w_2 and w_3, w_4 be the wrenches induced by v and v', respectively, and let $W := \{w_1, w_2, w_3, w_4\}$. By Theorem 1, the origin O does not lie in the interior of the convex hull of W. An additional edge contact achieves form closure if and only if O lies in the interior of the convex hull of $W \cup \{w\}$, where w is the wrench induced by the contact.

Let $W' := W \cup \{O\}$. The convex hull of W' is a convex polytope with four or five vertices, one of which is O. Consider a facet f incident to O, and let H be the open half-space bounded by the supporting plane of f not containing W'. If O lies in the interior of the convex hull of $W \cup \{w\}$, for some w, then $w \in H$. Conversely, if this is true for every facet incident to O, then O does lie in the interior of the convex hull of $W \cup \{w\}$.

It follows that an edge e can achieve form closure together with v and v' if and only if the wrench-space segment $\hat{e}$ intersects the intersection of three or four half-spaces. The bounding planes of these half-spaces pass through O, and so we can again project everything onto a two-dimensional screen. Here, we do not wish to identify wrenches that are symmetric around the origin, and so we use a screen Γ' enclosing the origin as follows:

$$\Gamma' := \{(x, y, z) \mid \max(|x|, |y|) = 1, z \in \mathbb{R}\}.$$

We project the n segments $\hat{e}$ onto Γ'. We build, in time $O(n^2)$, a triangle search structure on the endpoints of the projections. We also build, in time $O(n^2 \log^{O(1)} n)$, a segment intersection structure on the projected segments.

We then consider each pair (v, v') of concave vertices in turn. We compute the wrenches W induced by the two vertices, the convex hull of $W \cup \{O\}$, and the intersection R of the three or four half-spaces relevant. We then compute $R' := R \cap \Gamma'$, a polygonal area of constant complexity. We triangulate R', and find the k segment endpoints inside R' by a constant number of triangle queries in time $O(\log^3 n + k)$. Furthermore, we find all k segments intersecting the boundary of R' in time $O(\log^{O(1)} n + k)$ by a constant number of segment intersection queries.

Since there are $\Theta(m^2)$ pairs of concave vertices, the total running time is $O(n^2 \log^{O(1)} n + K)$.

Theorem 4. *Given a polygon with m concave vertices and n vertices in total, all K form-closure grasps formed by two concave vertices and one edge can be computed in time $O(n^2 \log^{O(1)} n + K)$.*

3   Immobility Grasps with Three Contacts

We introduce some notations and definitions used in this section. Let the edges of the simple polygon P be oriented counter-clockwise around P, that is, P lies locally to the left of each edge. We denote the normal to an edge at its start and

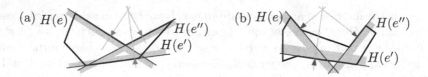

Fig. 3. The edges e, e', e'' in (a) are a triangle triple, while those in (b) are not.

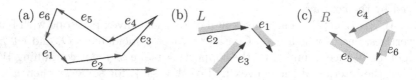

Fig. 4. (a) A polygon with directed edges. (b) The edges in L, and (c) in R.

end point by $s_0(e)$ and $s_1(e)$, respectively. Let $\hat{s}(e)$ be the infinite slab bounded by $s_0(e)$ and $s_1(e)$, that is, the union of all normals through points of e. Since placing a contact at a convex vertex may damage the part, convex vertices are not generally accepted as contact positions. If contacts are allowed to be at concave vertices, the corresponding slab boundaries should be included in the slabs $\hat{s}(e)$. In this section, however, we do not include any slab boundaries.

Let $l(e)$ be the supporting line of e, and let $H(e)$ be the open half-plane bounded by $l(e)$ lying locally to the left of e, that is, locally containing P (see Fig. 3). When the intersection of $H(e)$, $H(e')$ and $H(e'')$ forms a (finite) triangle, then e, e', e'' are said to be a *triangular triple*. (Compare Fig. 3 (a) with (b).) A necessary and sufficient condition for three edges to have a configuration of three point contacts to immobilize a simple polygon is provided by Czyzowicz et al. [5].

Lemma 3 (Czyzowicz et al. [5]). *There are three point contacts that immobilize a polygon on three edges e, e', e'' if and only if:*

(i) $\hat{s}(e) \cap \hat{s}(e') \cap \hat{s}(e'') \neq \emptyset$ (common intersection condition), and
(ii) $H(e) \cap H(e') \cap H(e'')$ is a triangle (triangular triple condition).

We take a similar approach as in [18]. Interval trees and orthogonal range search trees [6] will be used to find all the edge triples that have a common normal intersection, and among these, triangular triples will be filtered out using orthogonal range search trees and convex layer structures [4]. These data structures will be combined as a multi-level data structure.

The sketch of the global approach is as follows. For each edge e of P we build a data structure. This structure will be queried with each of the remaining $n - 1$ edges e', to report all edges e'' such that e, e', e'' satisfy the conditions of Lemma 3.

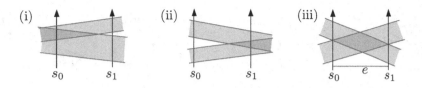

Fig. 5. Illustration of Lemma 4.

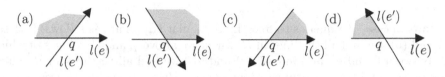

Fig. 6. (a) $(a' > 0) \wedge (l(e') \in L)$, (b) $(a' < 0) \wedge (l(e') \in L)$, (c) $(a' > 0) \wedge (l(e') \in R)$, and (d) $(a' < 0) \wedge (l(e') \in R)$. The intersection of $H(e)$ and $H(e')$ is shaded.

From now on, we focus on an edge e. We choose a coordinate system such that $l(e)$ is the x-axis oriented left to right. We divide the remaining edges into two groups L and R, depending on whether it forms an angle between $-\frac{\pi}{2}$ and $\frac{\pi}{2}$ with the positive x-axis or not (see Fig. 4 (b) and (c)). We also define the *top boundary* of a slab as the boundary lying above the other (see Fig. 5). The following is a necessary and sufficient condition for three edges to have a non-empty common normal intersection region (see Fig. 5).

Lemma 4 (van der Stappen et al. [18]). *Two normal slabs $\hat{s}(e')$ and $\hat{s}(e'')$ have a common normal intersection with $\hat{s}(e)$ if and only if:*

(i)   *the open intervals $s_0(e) \cap \hat{s}(e')$ and $s_0(e) \cap \hat{s}(e'')$ overlap, or*
(ii) *the open intervals $s_1(e) \cap \hat{s}(e')$ and $s_1(e) \cap \hat{s}(e'')$ overlap, or*
(iii) *the top boundaries of $\hat{s}(e')$ and $\hat{s}(e'')$ intersect in $\hat{s}(e)$.*

In cases (i) and (ii), we will use an interval tree to identify all the intervals that overlap a given interval $s_0(e) \cap \hat{s}(e')$ or $s_1(e) \cap \hat{s}(e')$. In case (iii), observe that the order of the top boundary positions at $s_0(e)$ and $s_1(e)$ are swapped. Let $x(e')$ and $y(e')$ be the y-coordinate of the intersection point at $s_0(e)$ and $s_1(e)$, respectively, and define $x(e''), y(e'')$ likewise. The top boundaries intersect each other in $\hat{s}(e)$, if $((x' < x'') \wedge (y' > y''))$, or if $((x' > x'') \wedge (y' < y''))$. All the edges satisfying condition (iii) with e' can be reported using a two-dimensional orthogonal range search tree. This allows us to report the edges that have a common normal intersection with e and e'.

Among these edges, the triangular triples will be filtered out using duality. Let a' be the slope of $l(e')$, and let q be $l(e) \cap l(e')$. Recall that the directed line $l(e)$ is the positive x-axis. The slope a' can be either positive or negative. In each case, there are two different directions of $l(e')$, that is, $l(e')$ is from L or R. We therefore distinguish four cases for $l(e)$ and $l(e')$ as in Fig. 6.

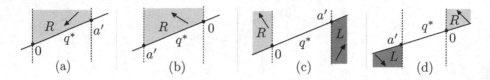

Fig. 7. The query regions in the dual space.

In each case, the queries to find the triangular triples are as follows. In cases (a) and (b), we find all the lines in R, which are above q, and the slopes of which are between 0 and a', and in case (c) and (d), we find all the lines in R, which are above q, and the slopes of which are smaller than 0 (case (c)) or greater than 0 (case (d)), and find all the lines in L, which are below q, and the slopes of which are greater than a' (case (c)) or smaller than a' (case (d)). Fig. 7 shows the query regions in the dual space of $l(e'')$'s, where the dual of $q(a_q, b_q)$ is a line $q^* : a_q x + b_q$. The dual points of L and R are first stored in one-dimensional orthogonal range search trees according to the slopes, and the points at each node are stored in a convex layer structure for half-plane queries. This concludes the description of the data structure.

Now we analyze the time complexity of this algorithm. Cases (i) and (ii) in Lemma 4 use one-dimensional interval trees with one-dimensional range search trees (for L and R) at the second level, and a convex layer structure at the third level. Case (iii) in Lemma 4 uses a three-dimensional range search tree with a convex layer structure at the fourth level.

The range search trees and convex layer structures use linear space. One-dimensional interval trees use $O(n \log n)$ space. All have $O(n \log n)$ construction time, and $O(\log n)$ query time. Three-dimensional range search trees use $O(n \log^2 n)$ storage, have $O(n \log^2 n)$ construction time, and $O(\log^3 n)$ query time. In total, cases (i) and (ii) use $O(n \log n)$ storage, have $O(n \log^2 n)$ construction time, and $O(\log^3 n + K)$ query time. Case (iii), on the other hand, uses $O(n \log^2 n)$ storage, has $O(n \log^3 n)$ construction time, and $O(\log^4 n + K)$ query time in total. These multi-level data structures are built for each edge, so the whole algorithm runs in $O(n^2 \log^4 n + K)$ time using space $O(n \log^2 n)$.

Theorem 5. *All K edge triples (e, e', e'') of a simple polygon with n edges such that there are three point contacts that immobilize the polygon on these edges can be reported in $O(n^2 \log^4 n + K)$-time.*

If we exploit concave vertices, two contacts can immobilize a simple polygon: one at a concave vertex v and the other in the interior of an edge e. We can report these in time $O(mn)$ by brute force, where m is the number of concave vertices. A faster algorithm is possible, by observing that a pair (v, e) admits a two-contact immobility grasp if and only if there is a three contact form-closure grasp with one contact in v and two on e. Such pairs can be reported using the techniques of Section 2, in time $O(n^{4/3} \log^{1/3} n + K)$.

Acknowledgments. We thank Günter Rote for pointing out an error in an earlier version of this work, and Otfried Cheong for helpful discussions.

References

1. P. K. Agarwal and J. Erickson. Geometric range searching and its relatives. In B. Chazelle, J. E. Goodman, and R. Pollack, editors, *Advances in Discrete and Computational Geometry*, volume 223 of *Contemporary Mathematics*, pages 1–56. American Mathematical Society, Providence, RI, 1999.

2. R. Brost and K. Goldberg. A complete algorithm for designing planar fixtures using modular components. In *IEEE Transactions on Robotics and Automation*, volume 12, pages 31–46, 1996.

3. B. Chazelle. Cutting hyperplanes for divide-and-conquer. *Discrete & Computational Geometry*, 9(1):145–158, 1993.

4. B. Chazelle, L. J. Guibas, and D. T. Lee. The power of geometric duality. In *IEEE Symposium on Foundations of Computer Science*, pages 217–225, 1983.

5. J. Czyzowicz, I. Stojmenovic, and J. Urrutia. Immobilizing a shape. *International Journal of Computational Geometry and Applications*, 9(2):181–206, 1999.

6. M. de Berg, M. van Kreveld, M. Overmars, and O. Schwarzkopf. *Computational Geometry: Algorithms and Applications*. Springer-Verlag, 1997.

7. A. J. Goldman and A. W. Tucker. Polyhedral convex cones. *Linear Inequalities and Related Systems*, pages 19–40, 1956.

8. G. Gopalakrishnan and K. Goldberg. Gripping parts at concave vertices. In *IEEE International Conference on Robotics and Automation (ICRA)*, pages 1590–1596, May 2002.

9. X. Markenscoff, L. Ni, and C. H. Papadimitriou. The geometry of grasping. *International Journal of Robotics Research*, 9(1):61–74, 1990.

10. J. Matoušek. Range searching with efficient hierarchical cuttings. *Discrete Comput. Geom.*, 10(2):157–182, 1993.

11. B. Mishra, J. T. Schwartz, and M. Sharir. On the existence and synthesis of multifinger positive grips. *Algorithmica*, 2:541–558, 1987.

12. V.-D. Nguyen. Constructing force-closure grasps. *International Journal of Robotics Research*, 7(3):3–16, 1988.

13. F. Reuleaux. *The Kinematics of Machinery*. Macmilly and Company, 1876. Republished by Dover in 1963.

14. E. Rimon and J. W. Burdick. New bounds on the number of frictionless fingers required to immobilize planar objects. *J. of Robotic Systems*, 12(6):433–451, 1995.

15. E. Rimon and J. W. Burdick. Mobility of bodies in contact—part I: A second-order mobility index for multiple-finger graps. *IEEE Transactions on Robotics and Automation*, 14:696–708, 1998.

16. E. Rimon and J. W. Burdick. Mobility of bodies in contact—part II: How forces are generated by curvature effects. *IEEE Transactions on Robotics and Automation*, 14:709–717, 1998.

17. K. Salisbury. *Kinematic and force analysis of articulated hands*. PhD thesis, Stanford University, 1982.

18. A. F. van der Stappen, C. Wentink, and M. H. Overmars. Computing immobilizing grasps of polygonal parts. *International Journal of Robotics Research*, 19(5):467–479, 2000.

Optimal Point Set Projections onto Regular Grids

José Miguel Díaz-Báñez[1], Ferran Hurtado[2], Mario Alberto López[3], and
J. Antoni Sellarès[4]

[1] Departamento de Matemática Aplicada II, Universidad de Sevilla, España
[2] Departament de Matemática Aplicada II, U.P.C, Barcelona, España
[3] Department of Computer Science, University of Denver, Denver, Colorado, USA
[4] Institut d'Informàtica i Aplicacions, Universitat de Girona, Girona, España

Abstract. The problem of determining nice (regular, simple, minimum crossing, monotonic) and non-degenerate (with distinct x-coordinate, non-collinear, non-cocircular, non-parallel) orthogonal and perspective images of a set of points or a set of disjoint line segments has been studied extensively in the literature for the theoretical case of infinite resolution images. In this paper we propose to extend the study of this type of problems to the case where the images have finite resolution. Applications dealing with such images are common in practice, in fields such as computer graphics and computer vision. We derive algorithms that solve the simplest problem of obtaining an optimal orthogonal image of a two-dimensional or three-dimensional point set. Due to the high cost of the proposed algorithms we also present algorithms that provide approximate solutions to the problems with better complexity.

1 Introduction

An object in two-dimensional and three-dimensional space is often represented by a set of points and line segments that act as its features. An optimal projection of an object is one that gives an image in which the features of the object, relevant for some task, are visible without ambiguity so that the image is as simple and readable as possible: no two points are projected to the same point, the projection of a segment is not reduced to a point, the number of crossings of the projection of a set of segments is minimum, no two projected points have the same x-coordinate, no three projected points are collinear, no four projected points are cocircular, no two projected segments are parallel, etc. The terms *nice* and *non degenerate projections* refers to these requirements and to many others. The problem of determining nice and non-degenerate orthogonal and perspective projections of sets of points and disjoint line segments has been studied extensively in the literature for the theoretical case of infinite resolution images [1,2,3,4].

In the finite resolution model a d-dimensional point projects onto a cell (pixel) of a regular grid (all cells are disjoint but identical k-dimensional hypercubes, for $k < d$). For clarity, when the dimensionality of the grid is important, we explicitly refer to the grid as a *graduated line* or *graduated plane*, for example.

T. Ibaraki, N. Katoh, and H. Ono (Eds.): ISAAC 2003, LNCS 2906, pp. 270–279, 2003.

In this paper we consider orthogonal projections only. Furthermore, without loss of generality, we assume unit size grid cells (hypercubes of side length equal to one). Other cell sizes can be reduced to unit cells by scaling the input set about the origin. We present both exact and approximation algorithms for the following problems:

1. Given a set of points in $\mathbb{R}^2$, determine a graduated line ℓ in $\mathbb{R}^2$ such that the maximum number of input points that project to the same cell of ℓ is minimum (or within a small factor of the minimum).

2. Given a set of points in $\mathbb{R}^3$, determine a graduated line ℓ or graduated plane π in $\mathbb{R}^3$ such that the maximum number of input points that project to the same cell of ℓ or π is minimal (or within a small factor of the minimal).

Definition 1. *Let d and k be positive integers such that $k < d$. An instance of the $P(d, k)$ problem is a set of points $\mathcal{P}$ in $\mathbb{R}^d$. A solution to this instance is a k-dimensional graduated hyper-plane π such that the maximum number m of points of $\mathcal{P}$ projected to the same cell of π is minimal. We refer to m as the cost of the solution.*

In [5,6] a similar, but different problem is studied. Given a set of points in the plane the problem is to find an optimal set of b equally spaced parallel lines such that the maximum number of points in a region bounded by two consecutive lines is minimized. In [7] a regular grid is considered. Notice that for these problems, unlike ours, the distance between adjacent parallel lines is not fixed beforehand.

2   Two-Dimensional Case

The graduated line $\ell = \ell(\theta, u, v)$ is the line obtained from the x-axis by composing a rotation by angle $\theta \in [0, \pi)$ around the origin o with a translation by vector (u, v). The point (u, v) is called the origin of the graduated line. Each number $z \in \mathbb{Z}$ defines a cell $c_z = [l_z, r_z]$ in ℓ that is obtained from cell $[z, z + 1)$ of the x-axis by the composite transformation described above. A region of the plane bounded by two lines orthogonal to ℓ through consecutive cell boundaries is called a *bucket* and the participating lines are the *bucket boundaries*. Equivalently, a bucket is the locus of points in the plane that project to the same cell.

Remark 1. Let ℓ be a graduated line with unit normal n and unit direction vector d. Let ℓ' be the graduated line obtained by translating ℓ by $zd + rn$, for any $z \in \mathbb{Z}$ and $r \in \mathbb{R}$. Then lines ℓ and ℓ' determine the same bucket sets.

Definition 2. *Two graduated lines whose bucket sets produce exactly the same partition of a point set $\mathcal{P}$ are said to be equivalent with respect to $\mathcal{P}$.*

A solution to an instance $\mathcal{P}$ of $P(2, 1)$ is a graduated line ℓ that minimizes the maximum number of points of $\mathcal{P}$ in a bucket determined by ℓ. Clearly, if ℓ is an optimal solution so is any graduated line equivalent to ℓ.

Lemma 1. *Let ℓ be a solution to an instance $\mathcal{P}$ of $P(2, 1)$. There exists a graduated line ℓ_0 equivalent to ℓ such that a point of $\mathcal{P}$ lies on the boundary of a bucket of ℓ_0.*

Proof. Let $\mathcal{P} = \{p_1, \ldots, p_n\}$ be a point set. For $1 \leq i \leq n$ let p_i^* denote the projection of p_i onto ℓ, and d_i, the distance from p_i^* to the left endpoint l_i of the cell containing p_i^*. Suppose that $d_j = \min_{1 \leq i \leq n}\{d_i\}$. Then the translation that moves point l_j to point p_j transforms line ℓ to the desired line ℓ_0.

Our algorithm to solve P(2,1) is based on two key ideas:

1. As a consequence of Lemma 1, we only need to consider graduated lines that have a bucket boundary passing through a point p_i of $\mathcal{P}$. Furthermore, from Remark 1, we can assume that p_i is the origin of the graduated line.
2. Let ℓ be a graduated line with origin p_i. Every rotation of ℓ by an angle θ about its origin produces a partition of $\mathcal{P}$ into buckets. Since $\ell = \ell(\theta, u, v)$ and $\ell = \ell(\pi + \theta, u, v)$ produce equivalent partitions, it suffices to consider angles in $[0, \pi)$. A radial sweep of ℓ about p_i produces a finite number of different partitions of $\mathcal{P}$. As ℓ rotates from $\theta = 0$ to π, the current partition changes only at angles where the left boundary line of a bucket passes through a point p_j of $\mathcal{P}$, $p_j \neq p_i$. At this instant, p_j changes from one bucket to the adjacent one. Consequently, in searching for the optimal solution for a fixed origin, it suffices to examine the finite collection $\mathcal{A}$ of these angles.

The algorithm, which we call **MGL2**, proceeds in two steps:

1. For each point p_i of $\mathcal{P}$ perform a radial sweep around p_i to find the graduated line ℓ_i with origin p_i that minimizes the maximum number of points of $\mathcal{P}$ that fall in the same bucket. Call this minimum number m_i.
2. Report the line ℓ that corresponds to $\min\{m_1, \ldots, m_n\}$.

We now elaborate on Step 1. Consider the iteration with the sweep centered at p_i. Without loss of generality assume that $p_i = o = (0,0)$ as, otherwise, a simple translation of $\mathcal{P}$ makes this true. Let $C(p, r)$ denote the circle of radius r centered at p, and $\ell(k, \theta)$, the line obtained by rotating the boundary line $x = k$ about o by angle θ. We wish to determine the value(s) of θ for which an input point p_j lies on $\ell(k, \theta)$. Each such value corresponds to an event of the sweep. Note that if $d(o, p_j) < k$ the rotated line cannot possibly contain p_j. Otherwise, the above equation has one or two solutions, depending on whether p_j lies on the boundary or outside, respectively, of the circle $C(o, k)$. In fact, the solutions correspond to the lines through p_j tangent to the circle. The points of tangency (hence the values of θ) can be found as the intersection of the circle $C(p_i, k)$ with circle $C(m, \frac{1}{2}\mathrm{dist}(p_i, p_j))$ where m is the midpoint of segment $p_i p_j$. Note that we may substitute θ by $\theta - \pi$ if $\theta \geq \pi$ as the sweep is performed in the range $[0, \pi)$.

This procedure, which yields at most two events, is repeated for integer values of k that satisfy $|k| \leq \mathrm{dist}(p_i, p_j)$. Once all events have been collected they are processed in ascending order by θ. Before the first event the "status" of the sweep is initialized by computing the number of points that belong to each bucket for a graduated line with $\theta = 0$ and the largest such count is identified. Each event modifies the status by updating these bucket counts and computing the largest count. The minimum m_i of these counts corresponds to the best graduated line ℓ_i centered at p_i.

The complexity of **MGL2** is dominated by the sorting of angles on $\mathcal{A}$. Each execution of this step requires $O(|\mathcal{A}|\log|\mathcal{A}|)$ time and $O(|\mathcal{A}|)$ space. If $t_i = \max_{1\leq j\leq n}\{\text{dist}(p_i, p_j)\}$, then $|\mathcal{A}| = O(t_i n)$ and the i-th iteration of the algorithm requires $O(t_i n\log t_i n)$ time. Thus, the total execution time is $O(tn^2\log tn)$, where $t = \max\{t_i\}$. The space required is $O(tn)$. We have proven the following:

Theorem 1. *An instance* $\mathcal{P}$ *of problem* P(2,1) *can be solved in* $O(tn^2\log tn)$ *time and* $O(tn)$ *space, where* t *is the diameter of* $\mathcal{P}$.

2.1 Approximate Solutions to P(2, 1)

When the origin (u, v) of the graduated line is fixed, and the only degree of freedom is the rotation angle θ, we obtain a restricted instance AP(2,1) of problem P(2,1). When the angle θ of the projection line is fixed, but we are allowed to shift the projection line over itself, we obtain a restricted instance SP(2,1) of problem P(2,1). It is natural to consider solutions to the restricted instances AP(2,1) and SP(2,1) as approximations to the solution of P(2,1).

The solution to problem AP(2,1) can be obtained by performing one iteration of Step 1 of **MGL2**, using $p = (u, v)$ (instead of p_i) as the designated origin.

Theorem 2. *An instance of problem* AP(2, 1) *can be solved in* $O(tn\log tn)$ *time and* $O(tn)$ *space, where* $t = \max_{1\leq j\leq n}\{dist(p, p_j)\}$.

It is not difficult to prove the following:

Theorem 3. *An instance of problem* SP(2, 1) *can be solved in* $O(n\log n)$ *time.*

Lemma 2. *Let* ℓ *be a projection with cost* C *and let* C' *be the cost of a projection* ℓ' *obtained by shifting* ℓ *by an arbitrary amount. Then,* $\frac{1}{2}\leq\frac{C'}{C}\leq 2$.

Proof. It suffices to concentrate on positive shifts smaller than the pixel size. This means that, after an arbitrary shift, the worst thing that can happen is that the contents of two buckets are combined into one, thus at most doubling the cost of the more expensive of the two. Since no bucket contains more than C points, we have $C' \leq 2C$. Conversely, the cost of a bucket could be reduced by shifting. For some $0 \leq i \leq j$, a bucket with j points will contribute, after shifting, i and $j - i$ points, respectively, to two neighboring buckets. This implies that for some $0 \leq i \leq C$, $C' \geq \max(i, C-i) \geq \lceil C/2\rceil$ which completes the proof.

Theorem 4. *Let* C *be the cost of an optimal solution to an instance* $\mathcal{P}$ *of* P(2,1) *and let* t *denote the diameter of* $\mathcal{P}$. *There is an algorithm that runs in* $O(tn\log tn)$ *time that finds an answer with cost no bigger than* $2\,C$

Proof. Let $\ell = \ell(\theta, u, v)$ be an optimal solution to P(2,1). Let $\ell_i = \ell(\alpha_i, x_i, y_i)$ be the best solution found during the i-th iteration of Step 1 of algorithm **MGL2**, i.e., while using (x_i, y_i) as the pivot point. Clearly, $\text{cost}(\ell_i) \leq \text{cost}(\ell(\theta, x_i, y_i))$ as ℓ_i is optimal for pivot (x_i, y_i). Furthermore, for some $s \geq 0$, there is a line $\ell' = \ell(\theta, x_i + s\cos\theta, y_i + s\sin\theta)$ which is equivalent to the optimal ℓ. Since the supporting lines of $\ell(\theta, x_i, y_i)$ and ℓ' are one and the same, Lemma 2 implies that $\text{cost}(\ell(\theta, x_i, y_i)) \leq 2\,\text{cost}(\ell')$. Thus, we have $\text{cost}(\ell_i) \leq \text{cost}(\ell(\theta, x_i, y_i) \leq 2\,\text{cost}(\ell') = 2\,\text{cost}(\ell)$.

Notice that most of the useful work of **MGL2** is already done during the first iteration! Later iterations can only yield small improvements, if any.

3   Three-Dimensional Case

3.1   Graduated Lines

The graduated line $\ell = \ell(\theta, \varphi, u, v, w)$ is the line obtained from the x-axis by composing a rotation by angle $\pi - \varphi$, $\varphi \in [-\pi/2, \pi/2]$ around the y-axis, a rotation by angle θ, $\theta \in [0, 2\pi]$ around the z-axis and a translation by vector (u, v, w). The point (u, v, w) is called the origin of the graduated line ℓ. Each number $z \in \mathbb{Z}$ defines a cell $c_z = [l_z, r_z)$ in ℓ that is obtained from cell $[z, z+1)$ of the x-axis by the composite transformation described above. A region of space consisting of all points that project to the same cell is called a *bucket*. A bucket is bounded by two planes orthogonal to ℓ through consecutive cell boundaries.

Remark 2. Let ℓ be a graduated line with unit direction vector d and let n be any unit vector normal to ℓ. Let ℓ' be the graduated line obtained by translating ℓ by $zd + rn$, for any $z \in \mathbb{Z}$ and $r \in \mathbb{R}$. Then lines ℓ and ℓ' determine the same bucket sets.

A solution to an instance $\mathcal{P}$ of P(3,1) is a graduated line that minimizes the maximum number of points of $\mathcal{P}$ that lie in the same bucket. As before, two graduated lines whose bucket sets produce the same partition of a point set $\mathcal{P}$ are said to be equivalent with respect to $\mathcal{P}$.

Lemma 3. *Let ℓ be a solution to an instance $\mathcal{P}$ of* P(3, 1). *There exists a graduated line ℓ_0 equivalent to ℓ with a point of $\mathcal{P}$ lying on a boundary plane of a bucket of ℓ_0.*

We are going to describe an algorithm, which we call **MGL3**, to solve P(3,1). The algorithm is based, as algorithm **MGL2**, on two key ideas:

1. As a consequence of Lemma 3, it suffices to consider graduated lines that have a bucket boundary passing through a point p_i of $\mathcal{P}$. Furthermore, from Remark 2 we can assume that p_i is the origin of the graduated line.
2. Each graduated line with origin $p_i = o$ determines a partition of $\mathcal{P}$ into buckets and the set of all such graduated lines produces a finite number of different partitions of $\mathcal{P}$. The set of all graduated lines is obtained from the x-axis by composing a rotation by angle $\pi - \varphi$ around the y-axis and a rotation by angle θ around the z-axis. During such motions, the current partition changes only at angles θ, φ where the left boundary plane of a bucket passes through a point p_j of $\mathcal{P}$, $p_j \neq p_i$. At this instant, p_j changes from one bucket to the adjacent one. Consequently, in searching for the optimal solution for a fixed origin, it suffices to consider the finite collection of curves $\mathcal{C}$ of the 2-dimensional space parametrized by the angles θ and φ for which such event occurs, since in any cell of the arrangement determined by $\mathcal{C}$ the partition of $\mathcal{P}$ remains constant.

The algorithm proceeds in two steps:

1. For each point p_i of $\mathcal{P}$ find the graduated line ℓ_i of origin p_i that minimizes the maximum number of points of $\mathcal{P}$ that fall in the same bucket. Call this minimum number m_i.
2. Report the line ℓ that corresponds to $\min\{m_1, \ldots, m_n\}$.

We now elaborate on Step 1. For $p_i = o$, consider the iteration with the motion of the x-axis that generates all the graduated lines with origin p_i. Let $S(p, r)$ denote the sphere of radius r centered at p. Denote by $\pi(k, \theta, \varphi)$ the plane obtained by rotating the plane $x = k$ by an angle $\pi - \varphi$ around the y-axis and then by an angle θ around the z-axis. We wish to determine the values of θ, φ for which an input point p_j lies on $\pi(k, \theta, \varphi)$. Each such pair of values θ, φ corresponds to an event of the motion. Note that if $d(p_i, p_j) < k$ the rotated plane cannot possibly contain p_j. For $|k| \leq dist(p_i, p_j)$, the solutions of the above equation correspond to the planes through p_j tangent to the sphere $S(p_i, k)$. The points of tangency determine a curve $X_{j,k}$ of the 2-dimensional space defined by the angles θ, φ that can be found as the intersection circle $C_{j,k}$ between the sphere $S(p_i, k)$ and the sphere $S(m, \frac{1}{2}dist(p_i, p_j))$ where m is the midpoint of segment $p_i p_j$.

This procedure is repeated for integer values of k that satisfy $|k| \leq dist(p_i, p_j)$. Since in the bijection between points of the 2-dimensional space determined by angles θ, φ of coordinates (θ, φ) and points of the unit sphere centered at p_i of polar coordinates (θ, φ), the curve $X_{j,k}$ is in correspondence with a circle on this unit sphere, the maximum number of intersection points between any couple of curves $X_{j,k}$ and $X_{j',k'}$ is bounded by 2. We break each $X_{j,k}$ curve, at its points of vertical tangency, into x-monotone curves. Finally, we construct the arrangement determined by the collection $\mathcal{C}$ of all such x-monotone curves.

We initialize the number of points that belong to each bucket for a graduated line with $\theta = \varphi = 0$ and the largest such count is identified. Then, starting in the cell that corresponds to $\theta = \varphi = 0$, we make a breadth first search in the dual graph of the arrangement of $\mathcal{C}$. For each new cell of the arrangement we update the bucket counts and we compute the largest count. The minimum m_i of these counts is reported as the best graduated line ℓ_i centered at p_i.

The complexity of **MGL3** is dominated by the construction of the arrangement of $\mathcal{C}$. The arrangement of a collection of n x-monotone curves, each pair of which intersect in at most 2 points, can be computed using an incremental approach in time $O(n\lambda_4(n))$ and space $O(n^2)$, where $\lambda_4(n)$ is roughly linear in n [8]. In our case, since there are $t_i = \max_{1 \leq j \leq n}\{dist(p_i, p_j)\}$ curves in $\mathcal{C}$, the construction of the arrangement of $\mathcal{C}$ requires $O(t_i n \lambda_4(t_i n))$ time and $O(t_i^2 n^2)$ space. Thus, the total execution time of the algorithm is $O(t n^2 \lambda_4(t n))$, where $t = \max\{t_i\}$. The space required is $O(t^2 n^2)$. We have proven the following result:

Theorem 5. *An instance $\mathcal{P}$ of problem $P(3, 1)$ can be solved in $O(t n^2 \lambda_4(t n))$ time and $O(t^2 n^2)$ space, where t is the diameter of $\mathcal{P}$.*

3.2 Approximate Solutions to P(3, 1)

A good approximate solution to an instance of P(3,1) can be obtained in a manner similar to that used to approximate P(2,1). Since the argument is essentially the same as that used in Section 2.1 we provide only the main result:

Theorem 6. *Let C be the cost of an optimal solution to* P(3, 1). *There is an algorithm that runs in $O(tn\lambda_4(tn))$ time that finds an answer with cost no bigger than $2C$.*

3.3 Graduated Planes

The graduated plane $\pi = \pi(\alpha, \theta, \varphi, u, v, w)$ is the plane obtained from the xy-coordinate plane by composing a rotation by angle $\alpha \in [0, \pi]$ around the z-axis, a rotation by angle $\pi - \varphi, \varphi \in [-\pi/2, \pi/2]$ around the y-axis, a rotation by angle $\theta \in [0, 2\pi]$ around the z-axis and a translation by vector (u, v, w). The point (u, v, w) is the *origin* of the graduated plane π. The graduated lines obtained by transforming the x and y-coordinate lines with the composite transformation described above are called the graduated axes of π. Each couple of numbers $z_1, z_2 \in \mathbb{Z}$ define a cell c_{z_1, z_2} in π obtained from the cell $[z_1, z_1 + 1) \times [z_2, z_2 + 1)$ of the xy-plane, by the the composite transformation described above. A region of space consisting of all points that project to the same cell is called a *bucket*. A bucket is bounded by four planes orthogonal to π that pass through the four boundaries of a cell.

Remark 3. Let π be a graduated plane with unit normal n and let d_x and d_y be unit direction vectors of the graduated axes of π. Let π' be the graduated plane obtained by translating π by $z_x d_x + z_y d_y + rn$, for any $z_x, z_y \in \mathbb{Z}$ and $r \in \mathbb{R}$. Then planes π and π' determine the same bucket sets.

A solution to an instance $\mathcal{P}$ of P(3,2) is a graduated plane that minimizes the maximum number of points of $\mathcal{P}$ that lie in the same bucket. As before, two graduated planes whose bucket sets produce the same partition of $\mathcal{P}$ are said to be equivalent with respect to $\mathcal{P}$.

Lemma 4. *Let π be a solution to an instance $\mathcal{P}$ of* P(3, 2). *There exist a graduated plane π_0 equivalent to π such that a point of $\mathcal{P}$ lies on a bottom boundary plane of a bucket of π_0.*

Proof. Let $\mathcal{P} = \{p_1, \ldots, p_n\}$ be a point set and $\mathcal{P}^* = \{p_1^*, \ldots, p_n^*\}$, where p_i^* is the projection of p_i onto π, $1 \le i \le n$. Denote by c_i the cell containing p_i^*, $1 \le i \le n$. For each p_k^* of $\mathcal{P}^*$ let db_k be the distance from p_k^* to the bottom side b_k of the cell c_k. Suppose that $db_i = \min_{1 \le k \le n}\{db_k\}$. The translation on the direction of the y-axis that moves the line b_i on the point p_i^* moves plane π to the desired plane π_0. Observe that, in general, there does not exist a graduated plane equivalent to π such that a point of $\mathcal{P}$ lies on one of its bottom-left boundary lines.

Next we sketch an algorithm **MGPG** to solve P(3,2). The problem can be discretized according two key ideas:

1. As a consequence of Lemma 4 it suffices to determine graduated planes that have a bottom bucket boundary passing through a point p_i of $\mathcal{P}$. Furthermore, from Remark 3, we can assume that p_i belongs to the bottom side of the transformed cell $[0, 1) \times [0, 1)$ of the xy-plane. To fulfill this condition, we can translate $\mathcal{P}$ so that p_i is the origin o and consider only graduated planes with origin $(-u, 0, 0)$, $u \in [0, 1)$.

2. The set of graduated planes passing through $p_i = 0$ and whose origin is $(-u, 0, 0)$, $u \in [0, 1)$ is obtained from the xy-coordinate plane by composing a a rotation by angle α around the z-axis, a rotation by angle $\pi - \varphi$ around the y-axis, a rotation by angle θ around the z-axis and a translation by vector $(-u, 0, 0)$. Each of these graduated planes determines a partition of $\mathcal{P}$ into buckets and the set of all such graduated planes produces a finite number of different partitions of $\mathcal{P}$. During the motion of the xy-coordinate plane, the current partition changes only at angles α, θ, φ and values u where the left boundary plane passes through a point p_j of $\mathcal{P}$ or the bottom boundary plane passes through a point p_k of $\mathcal{P}$, $p_j, p_k \neq p_i$. At these instants, p_j or p_k change from one bucket to the adjacent one. Consequently, in searching for the optimal solution for a point p_i, it suffices to consider the finite collection of hyper-surfaces $\mathcal{H}$ of the 4-dimensional space determined by the angles $\alpha \in [0, \pi]$, $\theta \in [0, 2\pi]$, $\varphi \in [-\pi/2, \pi/2]$ and the value $u \in [0, 1)$ for which such events occur, since in any cell of the arrangement determined by $\mathcal{H}$ the partition of $\mathcal{P}$ remains constant.

Algorithm **MGPG**, similarly to the previous ones, proceeds in two steps:

1. For each $p_i \in \mathcal{P}$ find the graduated plane π_i that minimizes the maximum number of points of $\mathcal{P}$ that fall in the same bucket. Call this minimum m_i.
2. Report the plane π that corresponds to $\min\{m_i \mid 1 \leq i \leq n\}$.

During Step 1, for each $1 \leq i \leq n$, it is necessary to consider an arrangement determined by a finite collection of hyper-surfaces $\mathcal{H}$ of a 4-dimensional space. The number t_i of hyper-surfaces in $\mathcal{H}$ is in $O(\max_{1 \leq m \leq n} \text{dist}(p_i, p_m))$. Since we only need to encode the adjacency relationship among 4-dimensional cells of the arrangement we compute the vertical decomposition of the arrangement and then we compute the adjacency relationship of cells in the decomposition [9]. Then we initialize the number of points that belong to each bucket for a graduated plane with $\theta = \varphi = u = 0$ and the largest such count is identified. Finally we traverse $\mathcal{H}$ by using the adjacency relationship of the cells in its vertical decomposition. For each new cell of the arrangement we update the bucket counts and we compute the largest count. The minimum m_i of these counts is reported as the best graduated plane π_i.

The complexity of **MGPG** is dominated by the construction of the arrangement of hypersurfaces. The number of cells of the vertical decomposition of an arrangement of n surfaces in $\mathbb{R}^d$ is $O(n^{2d-4}\lambda_q(n))$, where q is a constant depending on the maximum degree of the surfaces, and the vertical decomposition of the arrangement can be computed in randomized expected time $O(n^{2d-3+\epsilon})$, using the random-sampling technique [10]. In our case, the vertical decomposition of S can be constructed in $O((t_i n)^{5+\epsilon})$ time and $O((t_i n)^4 \lambda_q(t_i n))$ space. Thus, if $t = \max\{t_i\}$ we have the following result:

Theorem 7. *An instance $\mathcal{P}$ of problem $P(3,2)$ can be solved in $O(n(tn)^{5+\epsilon})$ expected time and $O((tn)^4 \lambda_q(tn))$ space.*

3.4   Approximate Solutions to $P(3,2)$

Using an approach similar to that of Section 2.1 we can use an arbitrary origin (u_1, v_1, w_1) to derive an approximation algorithm whose cost differs from the optimal by no more than a constant factor and whose complexity is lower than that of **MGPG**. We start by showing that shifting a graduated plane over itself changes the quality of the solution by at most a factor of four.

Lemma 5. *Let d_x and d_y be unit direction vectors for the axes of a graduated plane π with cost C. Let C' be the cost of a graduated plane π' obtained by shifting π by vector $r_x d_x + r_y d_y$, for any $r_x, r_y \in \mathbb{R}$. Then, $\frac{1}{4} \le \frac{C'}{C} \le 4$.*

Proof. First, we can assume that $0 \le r_x, r_y < 1$ as shifting π by $(r_x \bmod 1)d_x + (r_y \bmod 1)d_y$ results in a plane equivalent to π'. Thus, after shifting, the worst that can happen is that the contents of four buckets are combined into one, at most quadrupling the cost of the solution. Since no bucket of π has more than C points we have $C' \le 4C$. Conversely, the cost of a bucket can be reduced by shifting. Take a bucket of π with C points. After shifting, these points will be distributed among at most four buckets. At least one of these buckets must have no fewer than $\lceil C/4 \rceil$ points which implies that $C' \ge \lceil C/4 \rceil$.

Now let $\pi_0 = \pi(\alpha_0, \theta_0, \varphi_0, u_0, v_0, w_0)$ be an optimal solution for an instance of $P(3,2)$. Also let $\pi_1 = \pi(\alpha_1, \theta_1, \varphi_1, u_1, v_1, w_1)$ be the best solution over all possible values of α, θ, and φ for an arbitrary but fixed origin (u_1, v_1, w_1). Clearly, $\text{cost}(\pi_1) \le \text{cost}(\pi(\alpha_0, \theta_0, \varphi_0, u_1, v_1, w_1))$ as π_1 is optimal for (u_1, v_1, w_1). Furthermore, for some (u', v', w'), there is a graduated plane $\pi' = \pi(\alpha_0, \theta_0, \varphi_0, u', v', w')$ through (u_1, v_1, w_1) which is parallel and equivalent to the optimal π_0. Since $\pi(\alpha_0, \theta_0, \varphi_0, u_1, v_1, w_1)$ can be obtained from π' by a translation along the direction vectors of the axes of π', Lemma 5 implies that $\text{cost}(\pi(\alpha_0, \theta_0, \varphi_0, u_1, v_1, w_1)) \le 4\,\text{cost}(\pi')$. Thus, we have $\text{cost}(\pi_1) \le \text{cost}(\pi(\alpha_0, \theta_0, \varphi_0, u_1, v_1, w_1) \le 4\,\text{cost}(\pi') = 4\,\text{cost}(\pi_0)$. We still need to find the optimal projection for a fixed (u_1, v_1, w_1). For this purpose we create an arrangement of hyper-surfaces parametrized by α, θ and φ, in a manner similar to that outlined in the previous section. All points in the same cell of the arrangement correspond to graduated planes with the same origin that produce the same partition of $\mathcal{P}$. Using the results of [10] the optimal α, θ and φ can be found in $O((tn)^{3+\epsilon})$ expected time, where t is the diameter of $\mathcal{P}$. We have proven the following result.

Theorem 8. *Let C be the cost of an optimal solution to $P(3,2)$. There is an algorithm that runs in expected time $O((tn)^{3+\epsilon})$ that finds an answer with cost no bigger than $4\,C$.*

Acknowledgments. The authors would like to thank G. Toussaint and A. Mesa for organizing the workshop at which this research was initiated. The first author was supported in part by grants BFM2000-10, MCyT: BFM2000-1052 and II Plan Propio de Apoyo a Programas Internacionales de la Universidad de Sevilla. The second author was partially supported by Projects MCYT-FEDER BFM2002-0557, MCYT-FEDERBFM2003-0368 and Gen. Catalunya 2001SGR00224. The third author was supported in part by the National Science Foundation under grant DMS-0107628. The fourth author was supported in part by grants TIC2001-2392-C03-01 and Gen. Catalunya DURSI-2001SGR-00296.

References

1. P. Bose, M. F. Gómez, P. Ramos and G. Toussaint, "Drawing Nice Projections of Objects in Space", *Journal of Visual Communication and Image Representation*, Vol 10(2), pp. 155–172, 1999.
2. F. Gómez, F. Hurtado, J.A. Sellarès and G. Toussaint, "Nice Perspective Projections", *Journal of Visual Communication and Image Representation*, Vol 12, No 4, pp. 387–400, 2001.
3. F. Gómez, F. Hurtado, J.A. Sellarès and G. Toussaint, "On Degeneracies Removable by perspective Projection", *International Journal of Mathematical Algorithms*, Vol 2, pp. 227–248, 2001.
4. F. Gómez, S. Ramaswami and G. Toussaint, "On Computing General Position Views of Data in Three Dimensions", *Journal of Visual Communication and Image Representation*, Vol 13(4), pp. 401–424, 2002.
5. T. Asano and T. Tokuyama, "Algorithms for Projecting Points to Give the Most Uniform Distribution with Applications to Hashing", *Algorithmica*, Vol 9, pp. 572–590, 1993.
6. P.K. Agarwal, B.K. Bhattacharya and S. Sen, "Improved Algorithms for Uniform Partititons of Points", *Algorithmica*, Vol 32, No 4, pp. 521–539, 2002.
7. P. Bose, A. Maheshwari, P. Morin and J. Morrison, "The Grid Placement Problem", *Proc. 7th Int. Works., WADS 2001, LNCS 2125*, pp. 180–191, 2001.
8. M. Sharir and P.K. Agarwal, *"Davenport-Schinzel sequences and their geometric aplications"*, Cambridge University Press, 1995.
9. M. Sharir, "Recent Developments in Theory of Arrangements of Surfaces", *Lecture Notes in Computer Science*, Vol 1738, pp. 1–21, Springer-Verlag 2000.
10. B. Chazelle, H. Edelsbrunner, L.J. Guibas and M. Sharir, "A singly-exponential stratification scheme for real semi-algebraic varieties and its applications", *Proc. 16th Internat. Colloq. Automata Lang. Program., Lecture Notes Comput. Sci.* Vol. 372, Springer-Verlag, pp. 179–192, 1989.

An Approximation Algorithm for Dissecting a Rectangle into Rectangles with Specified Areas

Hiroshi Nagamochi[1] and Yuusuke Abe[2]

[1] Toyohashi University of Technology, Tempaku-cho, Toyohashi, 441-8580 Japan.
naga@ics.tut.ac.jp
[2] NEC Software Tohoku, Ltd.,
1-10-23 Ichiban-cho, Aoba-ku, Sendai, 980-0811 Japan.

Abstract. Given a rectangle R with area α and a set of n positive reals $A = \{a_1, a_2, \ldots, a_n\}$ with $\sum_{a_i \in A} a_i = \alpha$, we consider the problem of dissecting R into n rectangles r_i with area a_i $(i = 1, 2, \ldots, n)$ so that the set $\mathcal{R}$ of resulting rectangles minimizes an objective function such as the sum of perimeters of the rectangles in $\mathcal{R}$, the maximum perimeter of the rectangles in $\mathcal{R}$, and the maximum aspect ratio $\rho(r)$ of the rectangles $r \in \mathcal{R}$, where we call the problems with these objective functions PERI-SUM, PERI-MAX and ASPECT-RATIO, respectively. We propose an $O(n \log n)$ time algorithm that finds a dissection $\mathcal{R}$ of R that is a 1.25-approximation solution to the PERI-SUM, a $\frac{2}{\sqrt{3}}$-approximation solution to the PERI-MAX, and has an aspect ratio at most $\max\{\rho(R), 3, 1 + \max_{i=1,\ldots,n-1} \frac{a_{i+1}}{a_i}\}$, where $\rho(R)$ denotes the aspect ratio of R.

1 Introduction

Optimization problems of partitioning or arranging rectangles appear in many applications such as the data assignment problem in parallel computers [1],[8],[14], the module arrangement problem in VLSI design [7] [13], [15], database mining and the graph drawing problem. For example, in a parallel computer in which data stored in a matrix-shaped memory space is need to be allocated to each processor, it is often required to partition an entire matrix into small matrices. It is known that this problem can be formulated as a problem of dissecting a rectangle into small rectangles [1]. On the other hand, problems of dissecting a rectangle into rectangles have been studied as basic issues in mathematics [5], [6], [9], [10].

In this paper, we consider the following problem. We are given a rectangle R_0 with area α and a set of n positive reals $A_0 = \{a_1, a_2, \ldots, a_n\}$ with $\sum_{a_i \in A_0} a_i = \alpha$, and we wish to dissect R_0 into n rectangles r_i with area a_i $(i = 1, 2, \ldots, n)$ so that the resulting rectangles become as square as possible. In this paper, we introduce three types of functions that measure the "squareness" of a set $\mathcal{R}$ of rectangles $\{r_i \mid i = 1, 2, \ldots, n\}$. For a rectangle r, let $h(r)$ and $w(r)$ denote its height and width, respectively, and define its *perimeter* and *aspect ratio* by $p(r) := h(r) + w(r)$ and $\rho(r) := \frac{\max\{h(r), w(r)\}}{\min\{h(r), w(r)\}}$. For a set $\mathcal{R}$ of rectangles, we

T. Ibaraki, N. Katoh, and H. Ono (Eds.): ISAAC 2003, LNCS 2906, pp. 280–289, 2003.

define $ps(\mathcal{R}) := \sum_{r\in\mathcal{R}} p(r)$, $pm(\mathcal{R}) := \max_{r\in\mathcal{R}} p(r)$, and $\rho(\mathcal{R}) := \max_{r\in\mathcal{R}} \rho(r)$. We consider the next three rectangle dissection problems,

- **The total perimeter minimization problem (PERI-SUM):** Dissect R_0 into a set $\mathcal{R}$ of rectangles so as to minimize the sum $ps(\mathcal{R})$ of perimeters of the resulting rectangles.
- **The maximum perimeter minimization problem (PERI-MAX):** Dissect R_0 into a set $\mathcal{R}$ of rectangles so as to minimize the maximum perimeter $pm(\mathcal{R})$ of the resulting rectangles.
- **The maximum aspect ratio minimization problem (ASPECT-RATIO):** Dissect R_0 into a set $\mathcal{R}$ of rectangles so as to minimize the maximum aspect ratio $\rho(\mathcal{R})$ of the resulting rectangles.

Note that the PERI-SUM is equivalent to the problem of minimizing the total length $cl(\mathcal{R})$ of cutting lines to cut out the rectangles in $\mathcal{R}$ from R_0, where we call the problem CUT. In the special case where $a_1 = a_2 = \cdots = a_n$ holds in a set A_0 of reals, Kong et al. [11], [12] have proved that the PERI-MAX can be solved in polynomial time, and Bose et al. [4], [3] have proved that the CUT can be solved in $O(6^n)$ time and is approximable within factor of $1 + \frac{\rho+1}{2\sqrt{n\rho}-\rho-1}$ for $\rho = \rho(R_0)$. It is, however, known [1] that the problem of testing whether a given rectangle can be dissected into squares with specified areas is NP-hard. This implies that all the above three problems are NP-hard too. In the case that R_0 is a square, Beaumont et al. [2] proposed a 1.75-approximation algorithm for the PERI-SUM and a $\frac{2}{\sqrt{3}}$-approximation algorithm for the PERI-MAX.

In this paper, we present a simple $O(n\log n)$ time algorithm for the above three problems with an arbitrary rectangle R_0. We do not need to change our algorithm to the three problems. Our algorithm delivers a dissection $\mathcal{R}$ of R_0 that satisfies the following three properties at the same time: (i) $\mathcal{R}$ is a 1.25-approximation solution to the PERI-MAX, (ii) $\mathcal{R}$ is a $\frac{2}{\sqrt{3}}$-approximation solution to the PERI-SUM, and (iii) $\rho(\mathcal{R})$ is bounded from above by $\max\{\rho(R_0), 3, 1 + \max_{i=1,\ldots,n-1} \frac{a_{i+1}}{a_i}\}$.

The paper is organized as follows. In Section 2, we describe our dissection algorithm after introducing terminology. In Sections 3, 4 and 5, we analyze the performance of our algorithm in terms of the ASPECT-RATIO, PERI-MAX and PERI-SUM, respectively. In Section 6, we give some concluding remarks.

2 Algorithm

For a rectangle R, we denote the area of R by $a(R)$, and call a longest edge of the four edges of R a *long edge* of R. A *dissection* of a rectangle R is a collection of rectangles such that the union of the rectangles forms R without generating overlaps between any two rectangles. A dissection $\mathcal{R}$ of a rectangle R is called *slicing* if $|\mathcal{R}| = 1$ or if there is a dissection $\{R_1, R_2\}$ of R such that $\mathcal{R}$ consists of a slicing dissection $\mathcal{R}_1$ of a rectangle R_1 and a slicing dissection $\mathcal{R}_2$ of a rectangle R_2. For a set $A = \{a_1, a_2, \ldots, a_p\}$ of positive reals, an *A-dissection* of a rectangle R is a dissection $\mathcal{R} = \{r_1, r_2, \ldots, r_p\}$ of R such that $a(r_i) = a_i$ for each i.

Given a rectangle R_0, and a set $A_0 = \{a_1, a_2, \ldots, a_n\}$ of n positive reals, our algorithm computes a slicing A_0-dissection $\mathcal{R}$ of R_0 by the following recursive procedure. Assume that $a_1 \leq a_2 \leq \cdots \leq a_n$. Then we find an adequate 2-partition $A_1 = \{a_1, a_2, \ldots, a_k\}$ and $A_2 = \{a_{k+1}, a_{k+2}, \ldots, a_n\}$ of A_0, and then dissect R_0 into two rectangle R_1 and R_2 such that $a(R_i) = \sum_{a_j \in A_i} a_j$, $j = 1, 2$ by cutting the long edges of R. For each of the two subproblems (R_1, A_1) and (R_2, A_2), we apply the same procedure. In this way, we can construct a slicing A_0-dissection of R_0. The criteria for determining a 2-partition A_1 and A_2 of A_0 is on the basis of the next simple lemma.

Lemma 1. *Let A be a set of m nonnegative reals $b_1 \leq b_2 \leq \cdots \leq b_m$. Let $\alpha = \sum_{1 \leq i \leq m} b_i$, and k be the integer such that $\sum_{1 \leq i \leq k-1} b_i < \frac{\alpha}{3} \leq \sum_{1 \leq i \leq k} b_i$. Then one of the following (i) and (ii) holds.*

(i) $\frac{\alpha}{3} \leq b_m$.
(ii) $b_m < \frac{\alpha}{3}$, $k \leq m - 2$ and $\sum_{1 \leq i \leq k} b_i < \frac{5\alpha}{9}$ (and $\sum_{1 \leq i \leq k} b_i < \frac{\alpha}{2}$ holds if $b_{m-1} \leq \frac{\alpha}{6}$).

Proof. Assume that $b_m < \frac{\alpha}{3}$ (otherwise we have (i)). Let $x = \sum_{1 \leq i \leq k-1} b_i (< \frac{\alpha}{3})$. Then A contains at least three reals that follow b_{k-1}, since otherwise we would have $b_m \geq \frac{\alpha - x}{2} > \frac{\alpha}{3}$. Hence $k \leq m - 2$ and $b_k \leq \frac{\alpha - x}{3}$. From this, $\sum_{1 \leq i \leq k} b_i \leq x + \frac{\alpha - x}{3} = \frac{\alpha + 2x}{3} < \frac{5\alpha}{9}$ ($\sum_{1 \leq i \leq k} b_i < \frac{\alpha}{3} + \frac{\alpha}{6} = \frac{\alpha}{2}$ if $b_{m-1} \leq \frac{\alpha}{6}$), as required. $\square$

Based on the lemma, we dissect a given rectangle R_0 with a set A_0 of reals by procedure DISSECT(R_0, A_0), which is defined as follows.

DISSECT(R, A)
Input: A rectangle R, and a set $A = \{a_i, a_{i+1}, \ldots, a_{i+|A|-1}\}$ of positive reals such that $|A| \geq 2$, $a_i \leq a_{i+1} \leq \cdots \leq a_{i+|A|-1}$ and $\sum_{a \in A} a = a(R)$, where $h(R) \leq w(R)$ is assumed without loss of generality.
Output: An A-dissection $\{r_i, r_{i+1}, \ldots, r_{i+|A|-1}\}$ of R.

    if $\frac{1}{3} \sum_{a \in A} a \leq \max_{a \in A} a$
    then /* (i) in Lemma 1 holds for A */
      $A_1 := \{a_i, a_{i+1}, \ldots, a_{i+|A|-2}\}$; $A_2 := \{a_{i+|A|-1}\}$;
    else /* (ii) in Lemma 1 holds for A */
      Let k be the least integer such that the sum of the smallest reals in A
      is at least $\frac{1}{3} \sum_{a \in A} a$;
      $A_1 := \{a_i, a_{i+1}, \ldots, a_{i+k-1}\}$; $A_2 := \{a_{i+k}, \ldots, a_{i+|A|-1}\}$;
    endif;
    $h(R_1) := h(R_2) := h(R)$;
$$w(R_1) := w(R) \cdot \frac{\sum_{a_j \in A_1} a_j}{\sum_{a_j \in A} a_j}; \quad w(R_2) := w(R) \cdot \frac{\sum_{a_j \in A_2} a_j}{\sum_{a_j \in A} a_j};$$
    for $j = 1, 2$ do
      Let $\mathcal{R}_j := \{R_j\}$ if $|A_j| = 1$, $\mathcal{R}_j := $DISSECT$(R_j, A_j)$ otherwise;
    endfor;
    Return $\mathcal{R}_1 \cup \mathcal{R}_2$.

Lemma 2. *Given a rectangle R_0 and a set A_0 of n positive reals such that $\sum_{a_i \in A_0} a_i = a(R_0)$, DISSECT($R_0, A_0$) returns a slicing A_0-dissection of R_0 in $O(n \log n)$ time.* □

To analyze the performance of the algorithm, we introduce some terminology. Let $\mathcal{R} = \{r_1, r_2, \ldots, r_n\}$ be an A_0-dissection of R_0 output by DISSECT(R_0, A_0). Let $\mathcal{R}'$ denote the set of all rectangles R that are the input for some recursive call of DISSECT during the execution of the DISSECT(R_0, A_0). A rectangle $r \in \mathcal{R}$ is called *simple*, and a rectangle $R \in \mathcal{R}'$ is called *compound*. A compound rectangle R which consists of rectangles R' and R'' may be denoted by $R' \cup R''$. During DISSECT, a rectangle $R \in \mathcal{R}'$ is partitioned into two rectangles $R_1, R_2 \in \mathcal{R} \cup \mathcal{R}'$, where R_1 and R_2 in DISSECT are called the *left child* and the *right child* of R, and R is called the *parent* of R_1 and R_2. A subset $A \subseteq A_0$ of reals that are assigned to a rectangle $R \in \mathcal{R} \cup \mathcal{R}'$ by DISSECT (i.e., R is to be A-dissected by DISSECT) is denoted by $A(R)$. Hence $a(R) = \sum_{a_i \in A(R)} a_i$ holds. With the parent-child relations, we consider the inclusion tree $\mathcal{T}$ with a node set $\mathcal{R} \cup \mathcal{R}'$ such that R_0 is the root and nodes for $\mathcal{R}$ are the leaves. In the tree $\mathcal{T}$, we define *ancestors* and *descendants* among rectangles in $\mathcal{R} \cup \mathcal{R}'$.

Theorem 1. *Given a rectangle R_0 and a set $A_0 = \{a_1, a_2, \ldots, a_n\}$ of $n(\geq 2)$ positive reals such that $a_1 \leq a_2 \leq \cdots \leq a_n$ and $\sum_{a_i \in A_0} a_i = a(R_0)$, let $\mathcal{R} = \{r_1, r_2, \ldots, r_n\}$ be a slicing A_0-dissection of R_0 output by DISSECT(R_0, A_0), where $a(r_i) = a_i$, $a_i \in A_0$. Let $\mathcal{R}'$ be the set of all rectangles that are the input of some recursive call of DISSECT during DISSECT(R_0, A_0). Then the following (I)–(III) hold.*

(I) *For each $r \in \mathcal{R} \cup \mathcal{R}'$,*

$$\rho(r) \leq \max\left\{ \rho(R_0),\ 3,\ 1 + \max_{i=1,\ldots,n-1} \frac{a_{i+1}}{a_i} \right\}. \tag{1}$$

(II) *For the maximum perimeter $pm(\mathcal{R})$ of $\mathcal{R}$ and the optimal value OPT_{pm} to the RERI-MAX with instance (R_0, A_0),*

$$\frac{pm(\mathcal{R})}{OPT_{pm}} \leq \frac{2}{\sqrt{3}} \quad (\simeq 1.1547).$$

(III) *For the perimeter sum $ps(\mathcal{R})$ of $\mathcal{R}$ and the optimal value OPT_{ps} to the RERI-SUM with instance (R_0, A_0),*

$$\frac{ps(\mathcal{R})}{OPT_{ps}} \leq \frac{5}{4}.$$

□

We remark that Theorem 1(III) implies the next approximability result on the CUT, which provides a similar performance due to Bose et al. [3] in the case of $a_1 = a_2 = \cdots = a_n \in A_0$.

Corollary 1. *A slicing A_0-dissection $\mathcal{R}$ in Theorem 1 satisfies*

$$\frac{cl(\mathcal{R})}{OPT_{cl}} \leq \frac{5}{4} + \frac{\rho+1}{4\max\{1, 2\sum_{a_i \in A_0} \sqrt{a_i} - 1 - \rho\}},$$

where $\rho = \rho(R_0)$ and OPT_{cl} denote the minimum length of the cutting lines in an A_0-dissection of R. □

3   Analysis for ASPECT-RATIO

In this section, we prove Theorem 1(I) together with some basic properties on dissections constructed by DISSECT.

Lemma 3. *Let R_1 and R_2 be the left and right children of a compound rectangle $R \in \mathcal{R}'$, and let $a_\ell \leq a_{\ell+1} \leq \cdots \leq a_m$ be the reals in $A(R)$. Then*
(i) $\rho(R_2) \leq \max\{\rho(R), 3\}$.
(ii) $\rho(R_1) \leq \max\{\rho(R), 3, 1 + \frac{a_m}{a_{m-1}}\}$. *Moreover if $\rho(R) \leq \rho(R_1) > 3$, then R_2 is a simple rectangle with $a(R_2) = a_m > \frac{2}{3}a(R)$ and $\rho(R_1) \leq 1 + \frac{a_m}{a_{m-1}}$.*

Proof. Without loss of generality assume $w(R) \geq h(R)$. Then $h(R_1) = h(R_2) = h(R)$. Let $x = \sum_{a_i \in A(R_1)} a_i$ and $y = \sum_{a_i \in A(R_2)} a_i$, where $\frac{y}{x+y} \geq \frac{1}{3}$ by the choice of $A(R_1)$ and $A(R_2)$ in DISSECT. Then $w(R_1) = \frac{x \cdot w(R)}{x+y}$ and $w(R_2) = \frac{y \cdot w(R)}{x+y}$.

(i) If $w(R_2) \leq h(R_2)$, then $\rho(R_2) = \frac{h(R)}{w(R_2)} = \frac{h(R)(x+y)}{y \cdot w(R)} = \frac{x+y}{y \cdot \rho(R)} \leq 3$. Hence if $\rho(R_2) > 3$, then $w(R_2) > h(R_2)$ and thereby $\rho(R) > \rho(R_2)$, as required.

(ii) As in (i), if $w(R_1) \leq h(R_1)$ and $\frac{x}{x+y} \geq \frac{1}{3}$ hold, then we have $\rho(R_1) \leq 3$. Hence if $\rho(R_1) > 3$, then $w(R_1) > h(R_1)$ or $\frac{x}{x+y} < \frac{1}{3}$ holds. Assume that $\rho(R) \leq \rho(R_1)$ (otherwise we have $\rho(R) > \rho(R_1)$ as desired). Then $w(R_1) \leq h(R_1)$ and thereby $\frac{x}{x+y} < \frac{1}{3}$, implying that $A(R)$ must have been partitioned into $A(R_1)$ and $A(R_2)$ with $a_m \in A(R)$ such that $\frac{a_m}{x+y} = \frac{y}{x+y} > \frac{2}{3}$. Therefore, we see that $R_2 = \{a_m\}$ is simple, $\frac{2}{3}\sum_{\ell \leq i \leq m} a_i < a_m$ and $\rho(R_1) = \frac{h(R)}{w(R_1)} = \frac{h(R)(x+y)}{x \cdot w(R)} = \frac{x+y}{x \cdot \rho(R)} \leq 1 + \frac{y}{x} \leq 1 + \frac{a_m}{a_{m-1}}$. □

The lemma says that for the children R_1 and R_2 of a rectangle R, it holds $\max\{\rho(R_1), \rho(R_2)\} \leq \max\{\rho(R), 3, 1 + \frac{a_m}{a_{m-1}}\}$ for $a_m = \max_{a \in A(R)}$. From this we obtain (1) by induction, proving Theorem 1(I).

Before closing this section, we show some lemmas that are necessary to prove Theorem 1(III) (the proofs are omitted). A compound rectangle $R' \in \mathcal{R}'$ is called a *key rectangle* if $\rho(R) \leq 3 < \rho(R')$ holds for at least one R' of the children of R.

Lemma 4. *Let $R \in \mathcal{R}'$ be a key rectangle. Then a child R' of R with $\rho(R') > 3$ is the left child of R and the right child R'' of R is a simple rectangle with $\rho(R') \leq 3$ and $a(R'') > \frac{2}{3}a(R)$. Moreover R is the left child of its parent $\tilde{R}$ (if any).* □

Lemma 5. *For a key rectangle* $R \in \mathcal{R}'$, *let* $\tilde{R}$ *be the parent of* R *and* R_y *be the right child* R_y *of* $\tilde{R}$. *Then* R_y *consists of at most two simple rectangles* r, *each of which satisfies* $\rho(r) \leq 3$ *if* $\rho(\tilde{R}) \leq 3$ *or if* $\rho(R_y) \leq 3$. *Furthermore, if* R_y *consists of two simple rectangles* $R_{y_1}, R_{y_2} \in \mathcal{R}$, *then the slicing pattern of* $\tilde{R} = R_z \cup R_x \cup R_{y_1} \cup R_{y_2}$ *is one of the three cases shown in Fig. 1(a)-(c), where* R_z *and* R_x *denote the left and right children of* R, *respectively.* □

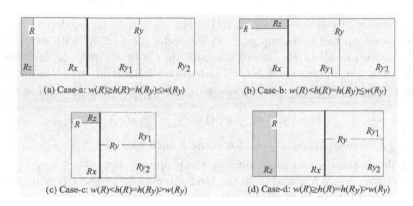

Fig. 1. Illustration for possible slicing patterns for a key rectangle $R = R_z \cup R_x$ and its sibling $R_y = R_{y_1} \cup R_{y_2}$.

4 Analysis for RERI-MAX

In this section, we prove Theorem 1(II). It suffices to show that $\frac{p(r_i)}{OPT_{pm}} \leq \frac{2}{\sqrt{3}}$ for each simple rectangle $r_i \in \mathcal{R}$. Note that $OPT_{pm} \geq p(r_n) \geq 2\sqrt{a_n}$ and that $p(r) = h(r) + w(r) = (\rho + 1)\sqrt{a(r)/\rho(r)}$ for any rectangle r. Then if $\rho(r_i) \leq 3$, i.e., $p(r_i) \leq \frac{4\sqrt{a_i}}{\sqrt{3}}$, then we have $p(r_i)/OPT_{pm} \leq 4\sqrt{a_i/3}/(2\sqrt{a_n}) \leq 2/\sqrt{3}$.

We consider the case where $\rho(r_i) > 3$. Assume $h(r_i) > w(r_i)$ without loss of generality. For the r_i, let $R \in \mathcal{R}' \cup \{r_i\}$ be the highest ancestor of r_i in $\mathcal{T}$ such that the long edges of r_i are contained in the long edges of R (possibly $R = r_i$). Hence $h(R) \geq h(r_i) > w(r_i) = w(R)$. If R has no parent (i.e., $R = R_0$), then it is obvious that $p(r_i)$ cannot be smaller in any A_0-dissection of R_0 (since $h(R_0) \geq h(r_i) > w(r_i) = w(R_0)$), indicating that $OPT_{pm} \geq p(r_i)$. Then assume that R has a parent $\tilde{R} = R \cup r'$. We first show that the sibling r' of R is a simple rectangle. By the choice of R and the property that $h(R) \geq h(r_i) > w(r_i) = w(R)$, we have $w(\tilde{R}) \geq h(\tilde{R}) = h(r') = h(R)$. Let $\rho = \rho(R)(> 3)$. Since $w(R) + w(r') = w(\tilde{R}) \geq h(\tilde{R}) = h(R) = \rho w(R)$, we have $\frac{a(r')}{a(R)} = \frac{w(r')}{w(R)} \geq \rho - 1$ and $\frac{a(R)}{a(\tilde{R})} = \frac{w(R)}{w(\tilde{R})} \leq \frac{1}{\rho} < \frac{1}{3}$, where the latter implies that $\tilde{R}$ has been dissected into R and r' by applying condition (i) of Lemma 1, indicating that r' is simple and $a(r') \leq a_n$. Therefore

$$\frac{p(r_i)}{OPT_{pm}} \leq \frac{p(R)}{2\sqrt{a_n}} \leq \frac{\frac{\rho+1}{\sqrt{\rho}}\sqrt{a(R)}}{2\sqrt{a(r')}} \leq \frac{\frac{\rho+1}{\sqrt{\rho}}\sqrt{a(R)}}{2\sqrt{(\rho-1)a(R)}} \leq \frac{\rho+1}{2(\rho-1)} \leq 1.$$

This proves Theorem 1(II).

5   Analysis for RERI-SUM

In this section, we prove Theorem 1(III). For each $a_i \in A_0$, we denote by LB_i a lower bound on the minimum $p(r_i)$ of the rectangle $r_i \in \mathcal{R}'$ with $a(r_i) = a_i$ in an A_0-dissection $\mathcal{R}'$ of R_0 (where the minimum is taken over all A_0-dissections of R_0). For the optimal value OPT_{ps} to the PERI-SUM with R_0 and A_0, it holds $OPT_{ps} \geq \sum_{1 \leq i \leq n} LB_i$. Hence to prove $\frac{ps(\mathcal{R})}{OPT_{ps}} \leq \frac{5}{4}$, it suffices to show $\frac{\sum_{1 \leq i \leq n} p(r_i)}{\sum_{1 \leq i \leq n} LB_i} \leq \frac{5}{4}$. For this, we partition $\sum_{1 \leq i \leq n} p(r_i)$ into $p_1, p_2, \ldots, p_k$ and $\sum_{1 \leq i \leq n} LB_i$ into $L_1, L_2, \ldots, L_k$ for some k such that $\frac{p_j}{L_j} \leq \frac{5}{4}$, $j = 1, 2, \ldots, k$, which shows the desired inequality by the property that $\frac{a+b}{x+y} \leq \max\{\frac{a}{x}, \frac{b}{y}\}$ for any positive reals a, b, x and y. In the next subsection, we show how to partition $\sum_{1 \leq i \leq n} p(r_i)$ into such numbers.

5.1   A Charging Scheme

We define *forced rectangles* $R \in \mathcal{R} \cup \mathcal{R}'$ as follows. The R_0 is a forced rectangle. If $a_n \geq a(R_0)/2$ holds (where the right child $R_2 = r_n$ of R_0 is a forced rectangle), then the left child R_1 of R_0 is defined to be a forced rectangle. Any rectangle $R \in \mathcal{R} \cup \mathcal{R}'$ whose long edges are both contained in the long edges of a forced rectangle is defined to be a forced rectangle. Observe that, for any forced simple rectangle $r_i \in \mathcal{R}$, $\min\{h(r_i), w(r_i)\}$ cannot be larger in any other A_0-dissection of R_0, implying that $LB_i \geq w(r_i) + h(r_i)$.

For a rectangle $R \in \mathcal{R} \cup \mathcal{R}'$, we define a carry function $C(R)$ by

$$C(R) = \begin{cases} 0 & \text{if } R \text{ is simple and forced,} \\ \max\{h(R) - 3w(R), w(R) - 3h(R), 0\} & \text{if } R \text{ is simple but not forced,} \\ \max\{h(R) - 2w(R), w(R) - 2h(R), 0\} & \text{if } R \text{ is compound.} \end{cases}$$

Let r_i be a non-forced simple rectangle. Then, it holds $\frac{p(r_i) - C(r_i)}{2\sqrt{a_i}} \leq \frac{5}{4}$. For each non-forced simple rectangle $r_i \in \mathcal{R}$ with $\rho(r_i) > 3$, we call $C(r_i) > 0$ the *extra cost* from r_i, and we charge the extra cost $C(r_i)$ to the lowest ancestor R of r_i in $\mathcal{T}$ that satisfies one of the following conditions:

(1) R is a key rectangle and has the parent $\tilde{R}$ with $\rho(\tilde{R}) \leq 3$.
(2) R is a key rectangle and has the parent $\tilde{R}$ which is a forced rectangle with $\rho(\tilde{R}) > 3$.
(3) R is a forced rectangle.

Such a rectangle R' for r_i is called the *charged rectangle* of r_i, where we say that charged rectangles in (1)-(3) are of types (1)-(3), respectively. The next lemma can be shown by an induction.

Lemma 6. *Let $R \in \mathcal{R}'$ be a compound rectangle, and $\mathcal{R}_R \subseteq \mathcal{R}$ be the set of simple rectangles which are descendants of R and whose charged rectangles are ancestors of R.*
(i) If $\rho(R) \leq 3$, then $\mathcal{R}_R = \emptyset$ or R is a key rectangle.
(ii) If $\rho(R) > 3$, then $\sum_{r_i \in \mathcal{R}_R} C(r_i) \leq C(R)$. □

5.2 Charged Rectangle of Type (1)

Consider a charged rectangle $R \in \mathcal{R}'$ of type (1), which has the parent $\tilde{R}$ with $\rho(\tilde{R}) \leq 3$. Let R_y be the sibling of R. Since R is a key rectangle, it consists of the left child R_z and the right child R_x. By Lemma 4, R_x is a simple rectangle $r_i \in \mathcal{R}$ with $\rho(r_i) \leq 3$, R and R_y are the left and right children of their parent $\tilde{R} = R_x \cup R_y \cup R_z$, and R_y consists of at most two simple rectangles. Let $\rho = \rho(\tilde{R})$. By Lemma 5 and $\rho \leq 3$, each simple rectangle r in R_y satisfies $\rho(r) \leq 3$. Hence by Lemma 6, extra costs charged to R are all from R_z and bounded by $C(R_z)$. We show that the total extra cost charged to R can be handled over the two or three simple rectangles in $R_x \cup R_y$. Assume without loss of generality $1 = h(\tilde{R}) \leq w(\tilde{R}) = \rho$.

Case-1: R_y is a simple rectangle $r_j \in \mathcal{R}$. We prove that $\frac{p(R_x)+p(R_y)+C(R_z)}{LB_i+LB_j} \leq \frac{5}{4}$. Let $x = a(R_x)$, $y = a(R_y)$ and $z = a(R_z)$. We use trivial lower bounds $LB_i \geq 2\sqrt{x}$ and $LB_j \geq 2\sqrt{y}$.

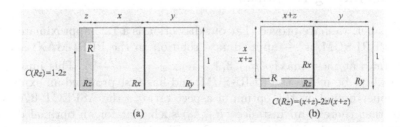

Fig. 2. Illustration for slicing patterns in Case-1; (a) shows the case of $w(R_x \cup R_z) \geq h(R_x \cup R_z)$ and (b) shows the case of with $w(R_x \cup R_z) < h(R_x \cup R_z)$.

Subcase-(1a) $w(R_x \cup R_z) \geq 1$ (see Fig. 2(a)). We have

$$\frac{p(R_x) + p(R_y) + C(R_z)}{LB_i + LB_j} \leq \frac{(1+x) + (1+y) + (1-2z)}{2\sqrt{x} + 2\sqrt{y}}. \tag{2}$$

We can prove that (2) is at most $\frac{5}{4}$ (the proof is omitted).

Subcase-(1b) $w(R_x \cup R_z) < 1$ (see Fig. 2(b)). We have

$$\frac{p(R_x) + p(R_y) + C(R_z)}{LB_i + LB_j} \leq \frac{(x + z + \frac{x}{x+z}) + (1 + y) + (x + z - \frac{2z}{x+z})}{2\sqrt{x} + 2\sqrt{y}}. \tag{3}$$

We can show that (3) is at most $\frac{5}{4}$ (the proof is omitted).

Case-2: R_y consists of two simple rectangles $r_j = R_{y_1}, r_k = R_{y_2} \in \mathcal{R}$. As examined in Lemma 5, there are three slicing patterns Cases-a,b and c shown in Fig. 1(a)-(c), respectively. Since we can treat Cases-a and b by applying above proof for Case-(1) to the rectangles R_z, R_x and R_{y_1}, we consider Case-c in the following. Note that $\rho \leq 2$ in Case-c since $h(R) \geq w(R)$ and $h(R_y) \geq w(R_y)$. We prove

$$\frac{p(R_x) + p(R_{y_1}) + p(R_{y_2}) + C(R_z)}{LB_i + LB_j + LB_k} \leq \frac{5}{4}.$$

Let $z = a(R_z)$, $x = a(R_x)$, $y_1 = a(R_{y_1})$, $y_2 = a(R_{y_2})$. Since $LB_i \geq 2\sqrt{x}$, $LB_j \geq 2\sqrt{y_1}$ and $LB_k \geq 2\sqrt{y_2}$, it suffices to show that

$$\frac{(\frac{x}{x+z} + x + z) + (1 + 2y_1 + 2y_2) + (x + z - \frac{2z}{x+z})}{2\sqrt{x} + 2\sqrt{y_1} + 2\sqrt{y_2}} \tag{4}$$

is at most $\frac{5}{4}$ (the proof is omitted).

The proof for the case where a charged rectangle is of type (2) or (3) is omitted due to the space limitation.

6   Concluding Remarks

In this paper, we have proved that our dissection is a 1.25-approximate solution to the PERI-SUM, a $\frac{2}{\sqrt{3}}$-approximate solution to the PERI-MAX, and has a aspect ratio at most $\max\{\rho(R_0), 3, 1 + \max_{i=1,\ldots,n-1} \frac{a_{i+1}}{a_i}\}$. This improves the previous best bound to the PERI-SUM, and has first provided an explicit form of an upper bound on the optimum aspect ratio to the ASPECT-RATIO. We remark that there is an instance (R_0, A_0) such that for an optimal dissection $\mathcal{R}^*$ and an optimal *slicing* dissection $\mathcal{R}$, $\rho(\mathcal{R})/\rho(\mathcal{R}^*)$ cannot be bounded by any constant. This implies that obtaining a solution with a constant relative error in the ASPECT-RATIO needs to design an algorithm that can find a *non-slicing* dissection.

References

1. O. Beaumont, V. Boudet, F. Rastello and Y. Robert, Matrix multiplication on heterogeneous platforms, IEEE Transaction Parallel and Distributed Systems, vol.12, no.10, 2001, pp. 1033–1051.

2. O. Beaumont, V. Boudet, F. Rastello and Y. Robert, Partitioning a square into rectangles: NP-completeness and approximation algorithms, Algorithmica, vol.34, 2002, pp. 217–239.

3. P. Bose, J. Czyzowicz, E. Kranakis, D. Krizanc and D. Lessard, Near optimal-partitioning of rectangles and prisms. Proc. the 11th Canadian Conference on Computational Geometry, UBC, Vancouver, British Columbia, Canada, August 15–18, 1999.

4. P. Bose, J. Czyzowicz and D. Lessard, Cutting rectangles in equal area pieces. Proc. the 10th Canadian Conference on Computational Geometry, McGill University, Montreal, Québec, Canada, August 10–12, 1998, pp. 94–95.

5. G. Frederickson, Dissections Plane and Fancy, Cambridge University Press, 1997.

6. R. L. Graham, Fault-free tilings of rectangles, In The Mathematical Gardner (Ed. D. A. Klarmer), Belmont, CA; Wadsworth, 1981, pp. 120–126.

7. T. F. Gonzalez, M. Razzari and M.-T. Shing and S.-Q. Zheng, On optimal guillotine partitions approximating optimal d-box partitions, Computational Geometry, vol.4, 1994, pp. 1–11.

8. S. Khanna, S. Muthukrishnan and M. Paterson, On approximating rectangle tiling and packing, Proc. of the ninth annual ACM-SIAM symposium on Discrete algorithms, 1998, pp. 384–393.

9. R. Kenyon, Tiling a rectangle with the fewest squares, Journal of Combinatorial Theory, A-76, 1996, pp. 272–291.

10. C. Kenyon and R. Kenyon, Tiling a polygon with rectangles, Proc. of the 33rd Annual Symposium on Foundations of Computer Science. Pittsburgh, PN, October, 1992, pp. 610–619.

11. T. Y. Kong, D. M. Mount and M. Wermann, The decomposition of a square into rectangles of minimal perimeter, Discrete Applied Mathematics, vol.16, 1987, pp. 239–243.

12. T. Y. Kong, D. M. Mount and A. W. Roscoe, The decomposition of a rectangle into rectangles of minimal perimeter, SIAM Journal of Computing, vol.17, no.6, 1988, pp. 1215–1231.

13. A. Lingas, R. Y. Pinter, R. L. Rivest and A. Shamir, Minimum edge length partitioning of rectilinear polygons, Proc. of 20th Annual Allerton Conference on Communication, Control, and Computing, 1982, pp. 53–63.

14. K. Lory and K. Paluch, Rectangle tiling, in: Proc. APPROX2000, Lecture Notes in Computer Science, Vol. 1913 (Springer, Berlin, 2000) pp. 206–213.

15. L. Stockmeyer: Optimal orientations of cells in slicing floorplan designs, Information and Control, vol. 57, 1983, pp. 91–101.

A Faster Algorithm for Two-Variable Integer Programming

Friedrich Eisenbrand and Sören Laue

Max-Planck-Institut für Informatik, Stuhlsatzenhausweg 85, 66123 Saarbrücken,
Germany {eisen,soeren}@mpi-sb.mpg.de

Abstract. We show that a 2-variable integer program, defined by m
constraints involving coefficients with at most φ bits can be solved with
$O(m + \varphi)$ arithmetic operations on rational numbers of size $O(\varphi)$.
This result closes the gap between the running time of two-variable integer programming with the sum of the running times of the Euclidean
algorithm on φ-bit integers and the problem of checking feasibility of an
integer point for m constraints.

1 Introduction

Integer programming is the problem of maximizing a linear function over the
integer vectors which satisfy a given set of inequalities. A wide range of combinatorial optimization problems can be modeled as integer programming problems. But integer programming is not only related to combinatorics. The *greatest
common divisor* of two numbers a and $b \in \mathbb{Z}$ is the smallest integer combination
$x\,a + y\,b$ such that $x\,a + y\,b \geqslant 1$. This is an integer program in two variables.
This fact links integer programming also to the algorithmic theory of numbers.

The Euclidean algorithm requires $O(\varphi)$ arithmetic operations, if φ is the
binary encoding length of the input. Checking an integer point for feasibility,
requires to test it for all the constraints. In this paper we prove that an integer
program $\max\{c^t x \mid Ax \leqslant b,\, x \in \mathbb{Z}^2\}$, where $c \in \mathbb{Z}^2$, $A \in \mathbb{Z}^{m \times 2}$ and $b \in \mathbb{Z}^m$
involve coefficients with at most φ bits, can be solved with $O(m + \varphi)$ arithmetic operations on rationals of binary encoding length $O(\varphi)$. In the arithmetic
complexity model, this is the best one can hope for if one believes that greatest-common-divisor computation requires $\Omega(\varphi)$ arithmetic operations.

Related Work

The two-variable integer programming problem has a long history. Polynomiality
was established by Hirschberg and Wong [8] and Kannan [10] for special cases
and by Scarf [17,18] for the general case. Then, Lenstra [15] proved that integer
programming in arbitrary fixed dimension can be solved in polynomial time.

Afterwards, various authors were looking for faster algorithms for the two-dimensional case. Here is a table which summarizes the development of the last
20 years. In this table, m denotes the number of constraints and φ denotes the
maximal binary encoding length of an involved coefficient.

T. Ibaraki, N. Katoh, and H. Ono (Eds.): ISAAC 2003, LNCS 2906, pp. 290–299, 2003.
© Springer-Verlag Berlin Heidelberg 2003

Method for integer programming	complexity
Feit [6]	$O(m \log m + m\varphi)$
Zamanskij and Cherkasskij [21]	$O(m \log m + m\,\varphi)$
Kanamaru, Nishizeki and Asano [9]	$O(m \log m + \varphi)$
Eisenbrand and Rote [5]	$O(m + (\log m)\,\varphi)$
Clarkson [2] combined with Eisenbrand [4] [1]	$O(m + (\log m)\,\varphi)$
This paper	$O(m + \varphi)$

Checking a point for feasibility	$\Theta(m)$
Greatest common divisor computation	$O(\varphi)$

For comparison, we have also given the complexity of greatest-common-divisor computation and of checking whether a given integer point is feasible. Thus the last two lines of the table is the goal that one should aim for. This paper achieves this goal.

Our algorithm is the fastest algorithm in the *arithmetic complexity model*. Here, the basic arithmetic operations $+,-,*,/$ are unit-cost operations. This is in contrast to the *bit-complexity model*, where bit-operations are counted. In this model, the algorithm in [5] is the fastest known so far. Its complexity is $O(m + \log m \, \log \varphi)M(\varphi)$, where $M(\varphi)$ is the bit-complexity of φ-bit integer multiplication. In the bit-model, our algorithm can also be analyzed to require $O(m + \log m \, \log \varphi)M(\varphi)$ if the occurring shortest vector queries are individually carried out with Schönhage's algorithm [19].

It is well known, see, e.g. [4,5,9] that, by means of an appropriate unimodular transformation, we can assume that the objective is to maximize the value of the first component. In fact, a reduction of a general integer programming problem to this special objective function requires one extended gcd-computation and a constant number of arithmetic operations. Thus we define the integer programming problem as follows.

Problem 1 (2IP). Given a system of inequalities $Ax \leqslant b$, where $A \in \mathbb{Z}^{m \times 2}$ and $b \in \mathbb{Z}^m$, determine an integer point $x^* \in \mathbb{Z}^2$ which satisfies $Ax \leqslant b$ and has maximal first component $x^*(1)$, or assert that $Ax \leqslant b$ is integer infeasible.

In the following, the letter m denotes the number of constraints of $Ax \leqslant b$ and φ is an upper bound on the binary encoding length of each constraint $a^t x \leqslant \beta$ of $Ax \leqslant b$. We can also assume that the polyhedron $\{x \in \mathbb{R}^2 \mid Ax \leqslant b\}$ is bounded, thus that the constraints define a *convex polygon* $P = \{x \in \mathbb{R}^2 \mid Ax \leqslant b\}$.

The main idea of our approach is to dissect the polygon into *four* specially structured polygons and to solve the integer programming problem for each of them separately. To do so, we need to check their lattice width. This can be approximated by shortest vector queries for inscribed triangles. Since the polygons have a special structure, the corresponding triangles have similar shapes. This allows us to batch the shortest vector queries for them so that they can be carried out in time $O(\log \varphi)$ for each query after $O(\varphi)$ preprocessing time. Then, our algorithm follows a prune-and-search technique.

---

[1] This is a randomized method for arbitrary fixed dimension

2   Preliminaries from Algorithmic Number Theory

In this section, we review some basics from algorithmic number theory, which are necessary to develop our algorithm.

2.1   The Euclidean Algorithm and Best Approximations

The Euclidean algorithm for computing the *greatest common divisor* $\gcd(a_0, a_1)$ of two integers $a_0, a_1 > 0$ computes the remainder sequence $a_0, a_1, \ldots, a_{k-1}, a_k \in \mathbb{N}_+$, where a_i, $i \geqslant 2$ is given by $a_{i-2} = a_{i-1}q_{i-1} + a_i$, $q_i \in \mathbb{N}$, $0 < a_i < a_{i-1}$, and a_k divides a_{k-1} exactly. Then $a_k = \gcd(a_0, a_1)$. The *extended Euclidean algorithm* keeps track of the unimodular matrices $M^{(j)} = \prod_{i=1}^{j} \left(\begin{smallmatrix} q_i & 1 \\ 1 & 0 \end{smallmatrix} \right)$, $0 \leqslant j \leqslant k - 1$. One has $\left(\begin{smallmatrix} a_0 \\ a_1 \end{smallmatrix} \right) = M^{(j)} \left(\begin{smallmatrix} a_j \\ a_{j+1} \end{smallmatrix} \right)$. The extended Euclidean algorithm requires $O(\varphi)$ arithmetic operations on $O(\varphi)$-bit integers, if the binary encoding length of a_0 and a_1 is $O(\varphi)$, see also [13,1].

The fractions $M_{1,1}^{(i)}/M_{2,1}^{(i)}$ are called the *convergents* of $\alpha = a_0/a_1$. A fraction x/y, $y \geqslant 1$ is called a *best approximation*,[2] if one has $|y\alpha - x| < |y'\alpha - x|$ for all other fractions x'/y', $0 < y' \leqslant y$. A best approximation to α is a convergent of α, see, e.g. [12].

2.2   Lattices

A 2-*dimensional (rational) lattice* Λ is a set of the form $\Lambda(A) = \{\, Ax \mid x \in \mathbb{Z}^2 \,\}$, where $A \in \mathbb{Q}^{2\times 2}$ is a nonsingular rational matrix. The matrix A is called a *basis* of Λ. One has $\Lambda(A) = \Lambda(B)$ for $B \in \mathbb{Q}^{2\times 2}$ if and only if $B = AU$ with some *unimodular matrix* U, i.e., $U \in \mathbb{Z}^{2\times 2}$ and $\det(U) = \pm 1$. Every lattice $\Lambda(A)$ has a unique basis of the form $\left(\begin{smallmatrix} a & b \\ 0 & c \end{smallmatrix} \right) \in \mathbb{Q}^{2\times 2}$, where $c > 0$ and $a > b \geqslant 0$, called the *Hermite normal form, HNF* of Λ, see, e.g. [20]. The Hermite normal form can be computed with an extended-gcd computation and a constant number of arithmetic operations.

A *shortest vector* of a lattice Λ is a nonzero vector $v \in \Lambda - \{0\}$ with minimal ℓ_∞-norm $\|v\|_\infty = \max\{|v(i)| \mid i = 1, 2\}$. There are many algorithms known to compute a shortest vector of a 2-dimensional lattice [7,14,19]. The following approach is very useful for our purposes.

Proposition 1 ([3] [3]). *Let $\Lambda \subseteq \mathbb{Q}^2$ be a rational lattice which is given by its Hermite normal form $\left(\begin{smallmatrix} a & b \\ 0 & c \end{smallmatrix} \right)$. A shortest vector of Λ with respect to the ℓ_∞-norm is either $\left(\begin{smallmatrix} a \\ 0 \end{smallmatrix} \right)$ or $\left(\begin{smallmatrix} b \\ c \end{smallmatrix} \right)$, or a vector of the form $\left(\begin{smallmatrix} -x\,a+y\,b \\ y\,c \end{smallmatrix} \right)$, where the fraction x/y is a best approximation of the number b/a.*

Later, we will have to deal with the following problem for which we provide an algorithm below.

---

[2] In [12] this is referred to as *best approximation of the second kind*

[3] In [3] this assertion is stated for integral lattices. It is easy to see that it also holds for rational lattices

Problem 2. Given a lattice basis $A \in \mathbb{Q}^{2\times2}$ and a sequence of K positive rational numbers $\alpha_1, \ldots, \alpha_K$, find a shortest vector w.r.t. the ℓ_∞-norm for each of the lattices Λ_i generated by the matrices $\begin{pmatrix} 1 & 0 \\ 0 & \alpha_i \end{pmatrix} \cdot A$, for $i = 1, \ldots, K$.

Lemma 1. *Let $A \in \mathbb{Q}^{2\times2}$ and $\alpha_1, \ldots, \alpha_K$ be parameters of Problem 2, where A and each of the α_i have binary encoding length $O(\varphi)$. Then Problem 2 can be solved with $O(\varphi + K \log \varphi)$ arithmetic operations on rational numbers of size $O(\varphi)$.*

Proof. First we compute the Hermite normal form $\begin{pmatrix} a & b \\ 0 & c \end{pmatrix}$ of A with the extended Euclidean algorithm. Then we compute all convergents x_j/y_j, $j = 1, \ldots, k$ of b/a with the extended Euclidean algorithm. From this, the convergents come out with the following property. The sequence $|-x_j a + y_j b|$ is monotonously decreasing and the sequence $y_j c$ is monotonously increasing and nonnegative.

By Proposition 1 and since a best approximation of b/a is a convergent of b/a, for each of the α_i, we have to determine the convergent x_j/y_j of b/a such that $\|\begin{pmatrix} -x_j a + y_j b \\ y_j \alpha_i c \end{pmatrix}\|_\infty$ is minimal. For this, we search the position j_i in the list of convergents, where $|-x_{j_i} a + y_{j_i} b| \geqslant y_{j_i} \alpha_i c$ and $|-x_{j_i+1} a + y_{j_i+1} b| < y_{j_i+1} \alpha_i c$. If $|-x_j a + y_j b| \geqslant y_j \alpha_i c$ holds for all convergents x_j/y_j, then j_i shall be the second-last position. Similarly, if $|-x_j a + y_j b| \leqslant y_j \alpha_i c$ for all convergents x_j/y_j, then j_i shall be the first position. The shortest vector of Λ_i is then the shortest vector among the vectors

$$\begin{pmatrix} -x_{j_i} a + y_{j_i} b \\ y_{j_i} \alpha_i c \end{pmatrix}, \begin{pmatrix} -x_{j_i+1} a + y_{j_i+1} b \\ y_{j_i+1} \alpha_i c \end{pmatrix}, \begin{pmatrix} a \\ 0 \end{pmatrix}, \begin{pmatrix} b \\ \alpha_i c \end{pmatrix}. \tag{1}$$

Since there are at most $O(\varphi)$ convergents of b/a, this position j_i, can be computed with binary search in $O(\log \varphi)$ many steps. Thus we have the desired running time of $O(\varphi + K \log \varphi)$.

2.3 The Flatness Theorem

A central concept of our algorithm, as in Lenstra's algorithm [15], is the lattice width of a convex body. Let $K \subseteq \mathbb{R}^d$ be a convex body. The width of K along a direction $c \in \mathbb{R}^d$ is defined as $w_c(K) = \max\{c^t x \mid x \in K\} - \min\{c^t x \mid x \in K\}$. The lattice width $w(K)$ of a K is defined as the minimum $w_c(K)$ over all nonzero vectors $c \in \mathbb{Z}^d - \{0\}$. Thus if a convex body has lattice width ℓ with a corresponding direction $c \in \mathbb{Z}^d$, then all its lattice points can be covered by at most $\lfloor \ell \rfloor + 1$ parallel hyperplanes of the form $c^t x = \delta$, where $\delta \in \mathbb{Z} \cap [\min\{c^t x \mid x \in K\}, \max\{c^t x \mid x \in K\}]$. If a convex body does not contain any lattice points, then it must be *thin* in some direction, or equivalently its lattice width must be small. This is known as Khinchin's Flatness Theorem [11].

Theorem 1 (Flatness theorem). *There exists a constant $f(d)$ depending only on the dimension d, such that each full-dimensional convex body $K \subseteq \mathbb{R}^d$ containing no integer point has width at most $f(d)$.*

How can the width of a convex body be computed? In this paper, we only need to do this for triangles. Let $T = \text{conv}(u, v, w) \subseteq \mathbb{R}^2$ be a triangle. The width is invariant under translation. Thus the width of T is the width of the triangle $T' = \text{conv}(0, v - u, w - u)$. The width of T' along a vector $c \in \mathbb{R}^2$ is then bounded from below by $\max\{|c^t(v - u)|, |c^t(w - u)|\}$ and bounded from above by $2 \max\{|c^t(v - u)|, |c^t(w - u)|\}$. Let $A_T \in \mathbb{R}^2$ be the matrix $A_T = \left(\begin{smallmatrix} (v-u)^t \\ (w-u)^t \end{smallmatrix} \right)$. The width along c thus satisfies the following relation

$$\|A_T\, c\|_\infty \leqslant w_c(T) \leqslant 2\,\|A_T\, c\|_\infty. \tag{2}$$

This means that the width of T is bounded from below by the length of the shortest (infinity norm) vector of $\Lambda(A_T)$ and bounded from above by twice the length of the shortest vector of $\Lambda(A_T)$. Furthermore, if $v = A_T\, c$ is a shortest vector, then the following relation holds

$$w_c(T) \leqslant w(T) \leqslant 2\,w_c(T). \tag{3}$$

In the sequel, we call a vector $c \in \mathbb{Z}^2$, such that $v = A_T\, c$ is a shortest vector of $\Lambda(A_T)$, a *thin direction* of T. A shortest vector of $\Lambda(A_T)$ w.r.t. the ℓ_∞-norm will be denoted as a *shortest vector of the triangle* T. Its length is denoted by $SV(T)$.

3   Partitioning the Polygon

In a first step, we partition the polygon into four parts. Two of the parts belong to a class of polygons for which one already knows an $O(m + \varphi)$ algorithm for their corresponding integer programs [5]. In the following sections, we will deal with the other two polygons.

First we compute the rightmost point and the leftmost point of P and we consider the line g through these two points, see Figure 1. This line dissects P into an upper part P_U and a lower part P_L. Next we compute vertices of P_U and P_L which have largest distance from the line g and draw a vertical line h_U and h_L through these points. The line h_U dissects P_U again in two parts, an upper-left polygon P_{Ul} and an upper-right polygon P_{Ur}. The line h_L partitions P_L into two parts, a lower-left polygon P_{Ll} and a lower-right polygon P_{Lr}. The optimum integer point in P is the maximum of the optima of these four polygons. This partition can be found with linear programming. Using the algorithm of Megiddo [16], this requires $O(m)$ operations. Notice that the binary encoding length of each constraint describing the four polygons remains $O(\varphi)$.

The polygons P_{Ul} and P_{Ll} are *lower polygons* in the terminology of Eisenbrand and Rote [5]. This is because they have a line-segment parallel to the objective line as an edge and there are two parallel lines trough the endpoints of this edge which enclose the polygon.[4] Thus Proposition 1 and Theorem 2

---

[4] In [5] the objective is to find a highest integer point, while we find a rightmost integer point

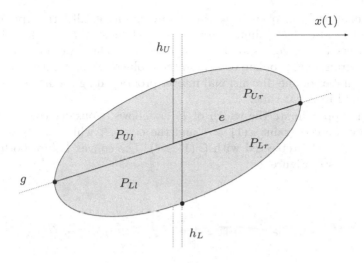

Fig. 1. The dissection of the polygon P. The arrow is the $x(1)$-direction in which we optimize.

of [5] implies that the integer program over P_{Ul} and P_{Ll} can be solved in with $O(m + \varphi)$ arithmetic operations on rationals with $O(\varphi)$ bits.

The polygons P_{Ur} and P_{Lr} are the ones we need to take care of. The polygon P_{Ur} has a special structure. It has an edge e, such that each point of P_{Ur} lies vertically above e and the two vertical lines through the endpoints of this edge enclose the polygon. Furthermore, the vertical line through the vertex on the left of e, defines a facet of P_{Ur}. All the other facets, from left to right, have decreasing slope and each slope is at most the slope of e. A polygon of this kind will be called a polygon of *upper-right* kind in the sequel. Notice that P_{Lr} becomes an upper-right polygon, when it is reflected around the $x(1)$ axis. Therefore we concentrate now on the solution of integer programming problems over polygons of upper-right kind.

4   A Prune-and-Search Algorithm

In the following, let P be a polygon of upper-right kind. We now present an $O(m + \varphi)$ algorithm for this case. Similar to the algorithm in [5] we use the prune-and-search technique of Megiddo [16] to solve the optimization problem over P.

The idea is to search for a parameter ℓ, such that the truncated polygon $P_\ell = P \cap (x(1) \geq \ell)$ has width $w(P_\ell)$ between $f(2) + 1$ and $4(f(2) + 1)$. If we have found such an ℓ, we know two important things. First, the flatness theorem guarantees that P_ℓ is feasible and thus that the optimum of the integer programming problem over P lies in P_ℓ. Furthermore, all lattice points of P_ℓ, and therefore also the optimum, must lie on at most $4(f(2)+1)+1$ parallel line segments in the corresponding flat direction. Thus, we have reduced the integer programming problem over P to the problem of finding an optimum of a constant number of one-dimensional integer programming problems, which then can be solved in linear time.

We will approximate the width of P_ℓ as follows. Consider the edge f of P_ℓ induced by the constraint $x(1) \geqslant \ell$ and the edge e', which emerges from the lower edge e of P intersected with $(x(1) \geqslant \ell)$. The convex hull of both edges is a triangle T_ℓ, see, Figure 2.

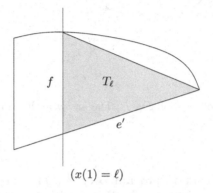

$$(x(1) = \ell)$$

Fig. 2. The polygon P_ℓ and the triangle T_ℓ.

Obviously, we have $T_\ell \subseteq P_\ell$. It is easy to see that if we scale T_ℓ by a factor of 2 and translating T_ℓ appropriately, then it includes P_ℓ. Hence, the width $w(P_\ell)$ satisfies $w(T_\ell) \leqslant w(P_\ell) \leqslant 2\,w(T_\ell)$. From Section 2.3 we can conclude $\mathrm{SV}(T_\ell) \leqslant w(P_\ell) \leqslant 4\,\mathrm{SV}(T_l)$. Thus, we are interested in a parameter ℓ, such that the shortest vector of T_ℓ has length $f(2)+1$.

We start with m constraints and maintain two numbers ℓ_{thick} and ℓ_{thin}. In the beginning, ℓ_{thick} is the $x(1)$-component of the left endpoint of the edge e and ℓ_{thin} is the $x(1)$-component of the right endpoint of the edge e. If $\mathrm{SV}(T_{\ell_{thick}}) \leqslant f(2)+1$, then P itself is flat and we are done. Otherwise we keep the following invariant.

> The shortest vector of $T_{\ell_{thick}}$ has length at least $f(2)+1$ and the shortest vector of $T_{\ell_{thin}}$ has length at most $f(2)+1$.

The idea is to prune constraints, while we search for the correct position ℓ, which cannot be facet defining for the intermediate part of the polygon $P \cap (x(1) \geqslant \ell_{thick}) \cap (x(1) \leqslant \ell_{thin})$, see Figure 3.

One iteration is as follows. We pair up all m constraints yielding $m/2$ intersection points. Then we compute the x-median ℓ_{med} of the intersection points.

Now we distinguish three cases. One is that ℓ_{med} lies to the right of ℓ_{thin}. In this case, we can delete from each pair of intersection points to the right of the median, the constraint with the smaller slope. We can do this, since this constraint cannot be facet-defining for the intermediate polygon. Similarly, if ℓ_{med} lies to the left of ℓ_{thick}, we can delete from each pair on the left of the median the constraint with the larger slope.

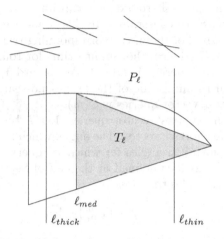

Fig. 3. The prune-and-search algorithm for a polygon of the upper-right kind

The more interesting case is the one, where ℓ_{med} lies in-between ℓ_{thick} and ℓ_{thin}. Then we compute the length of the edge f which is induced by $x(1) \geqslant \ell_{med}$. This edge is simply the line-segment spanned by the intersection of $x(1) = \ell_{med}$ with e and by the lowest intersection point of the line $x(1) = \ell_{med}$ with all m constraints.

Now we compute the shortest vector of $T_{\ell_{med}}$. If its length is smaller than $f(2) + 1$, then we set ℓ_{thin} to ℓ_{med} and delete from each intersection point that lies to the right of ℓ_{med} the constraint with the smaller slope. Otherwise we set ℓ_{thick} to ℓ_{med} and delete from each intersection point that lies to the left of ℓ_{med} the constraint with the larger slope.

We repeat this prune and search procedure until we have found a position ℓ, where the shortest vector of T_ℓ is $f(2) + 1$ or we identified a constant number of constraints, which can be facet defining for $P \cap (x(1) \geqslant \ell_{thick}) \cap (x(1) \leqslant \ell_{thin})$.

In the first case, we know that the optimum lies in P_ℓ and we have a flat direction of P_ℓ, namely the vector $c \in \mathbb{Z}^2 - \{0\}$ such that $v = A_{T_\ell} c$ is a shortest vector of T_ℓ. Thus the optimum is the largest of the optima of the integer programs over the constant number line segments $P_\ell \cap (c^t x = \delta)$, where $\delta \in \mathbb{Z} \cap [\min\{c^t x \mid x \in P_\ell\}, \max\{c^t x \mid x \in P_\ell\}]$. In the second case, we know that the optimum lies in $P_{\ell_{thick}}$. Furthermore, $P_{\ell_{thick}}$ can be partitioned into $P_{\ell_{thin}}$, and the polygon $P \cap (x(1) \geqslant \ell_{thick}) \cap (x(1) \leqslant \ell_{thin})$. The first polygon is flat.

The second polygon is defined by a constant number of constraints, for which integer programming can be solved with $O(\varphi)$ arithmetic operations.

Analysis

We will prove that the presented algorithm runs in $O(m + \varphi)$ using rational numbers of size $O(\varphi)$.

Suppose we are in the i-th round of the prune-and-search algorithm and suppose we are left with m_i constraints. In this round we compute $m_i/2$ intersection points, the median of them, the corresponding triangle T_ℓ and query for the shortest vector of T_ℓ. Hence, the running time for round i, without considering the shortest vector queries, is $O(m_i)$. We discard $1/4$ of the constraints. Therefore, the overall running time of the prune-and-search algorithm without considering the shortest vector queries is $O(m)$.

Let us consider the shortest vector queries. Let T be the first triangle, for which we compute the shortest vector. The angle, which is enclosed by the edges f and e' is the same for all triangles for which we query a shortest vector. Let A_T be the matrix of T as it is defined at the end of Section 2.3. The matrices A_{T_ℓ} of the following triangles thus satisfy

$$A_{T_\ell} = \beta_\ell \cdot \left(\begin{smallmatrix} 1 & 0 \\ 0 & \alpha_\ell \end{smallmatrix} \right) \cdot A_T, \tag{4}$$

with rational numbers α_ℓ and β_ℓ which can be computed from T and T_ℓ in constant time. The length of the shortest vector of T_ℓ is equal to β_ℓ times the length of the shortest vector of the lattice $\Lambda\left(\left(\begin{smallmatrix} 1 & 0 \\ 0 & \alpha_\ell \end{smallmatrix} \right) \cdot A_T \right)$. Hence, we can apply Lemma 1. As we perform $O(\log m)$ queries, the total number shortest vector queries can be computed with $O(\varphi + \log m \cdot \log \varphi)$ arithmetic operations on rational numbers of size $O(\varphi)$. Thus the total running time amounts to $O(m + \varphi + \log m \cdot \log \varphi) = O(m + \varphi)$ arithmetic operations on rational numbers of binary encoding length $O(\varphi)$, which proves our main result.

Theorem 2. *A two-variable integer programming problem* $\max\{c^t x \mid Ax \leqslant b, x \in \mathbb{Z}^2\}$, *where* $A \in \mathbb{Z}^{m \times 2}$ *and* $b \in \mathbb{Z}^m$ *and* $c \in \mathbb{Z}^2$ *involve only coefficients of binary encoding length* $O(\varphi)$, *can be solved with* $O(\varphi + m)$ *arithmetic operations on rational numbers of size* $O(\varphi)$.

Acknowledgement. We thank the anonymous referees for their valuable comments and suggestions.

References

1. A. V. Aho, J. E. Hopcroft, and J. D. Ullman. *The Design and Analysis of Computer Algorithms*. Addison-Wesley, Reading, 1974.
2. K. L. Clarkson. Las vegas algorithms for linear and integer programming when the dimension is small. *Journal of the Association for Computing Machinery*, 42:488–499, 1995.

3. F. Eisenbrand. Short vectors of planar lattices via continued fractions. *Information Processing Letters*, 79(3):121–126, 2001.
4. F. Eisenbrand. Fast integer programming in fixed dimension. Technical Report MPI-I-2003-NWG2-002, Max-Planck-Institut für Informatik, Saarbrücken, Germany, 2003. to appear in the Proceedings of ESA 2003.
5. F. Eisenbrand and G. Rote. Fast 2-variable integer programming. In K. Aardal and B. Gerards, editors, *Integer Programming and Combinatorial Optimization, IPCO 2001*, volume 2081 of *LNCS*, pages 78–89. Springer, 2001.
6. S. D. Feit. A fast algorithm for the two-variable integer programming problem. *Journal of the Association for Computing Machinery*, 31(1):99–113, 1984.
7. C. F. Gauß. *Disquisitiones arithmeticae*. Gerh. Fleischer Iun., 1801.
8. D. S. Hirschberg and C. K. Wong. A polynomial algorithm for the knapsack problem in two variables. *Journal of the Association for Computing Machinery*, 23(1):147–154, 1976.
9. N. Kanamaru, T. Nishizeki, and T. Asano. Efficient enumeration of grid points in a convex polygon and its application to integer programming. *International Journal of Computational Geometry & Applications*, 4(1):69–85, 1994.
10. R. Kannan. A polynomial algorithm for the two-variable integer programming problem. *Journal of the Association for Computing Machinery*, 27(1):118–122, 1980.
11. R. Kannan and L. Lovász. Covering minima and lattice-point-free convex bodies. *Annals of Mathematics*, 128:577–602, 1988.
12. A. Y. Khintchine. *Continued Fractions*. Noordhoff, Groningen, 1963.
13. D. Knuth. *The art of computer programming*, volume 2. Addison-Wesley, 1969.
14. J. C. Lagarias. Worst-case complexity bounds for algorithms in the theory of integral quadratic forms. *Journal of Algorithms*, 1:142–186, 1980.
15. H. W. Lenstra. Integer programming with a fixed number of variables. *Mathematics of Operations Research*, 8(4):538–548, 1983.
16. N. Megiddo. Linear programming in linear time when the dimension is fixed. *Journal of the Association for Computing Machinery*, 31:114–127, 1984.
17. H. E. Scarf. Production sets with indivisibilities. Part I: generalities. *Econometrica*, 49:1–32, 1981.
18. H. E. Scarf. Production sets with indivisibilities. Part II: The case of two activities. *Econometrica*, 49:395–423, 1981.
19. A. Schönhage. Fast reduction and composition of binary quadratic forms. In *International Symposium on Symbolic and Algebraic Computation, ISSAC 91*, pages 128–133. ACM Press, 1991.
20. A. Schrijver. *Theory of Linear and Integer Programming*. John Wiley, 1986.
21. L. Y. Zamanskij and V. D. Cherkasskij. A formula for determining the number of integral points on a straight line and its application. *Ehkon. Mat. Metody*, 20:1132–1138, 1984.

Efficient Algorithms for Generation of Combinatorial Covering Suites

Adrian Dumitrescu

Department of Computer Science,
University of Wisconsin–Milwaukee,
ad@cs.uwm.edu

Abstract. In this note we describe efficient algorithms for generating tests that cover a prescribed set of combinations of a software system's input parameters. Our methods for obtaining uniform t-wise coverage are based on repeatedly coloring the vertices of a graph such that the vertices in each t-subset have different colors in at least one of the colorings. The resulting algorithm is compared to other known algorithms for uniform coverage, a greedy algorithm and a randomized algorithm, in particular. The size of its output test suite is then related to a new lower bound that we obtain on the minimal size of a test suite.

Keywords: Combinatorial covering suite, Software testing, Automatic test generation.

1 Introduction

Development and production of high-quality software at a reasonable price is a critical issue for today's society, when the safety and quality of life is increasingly dependent on software systems. Software testing is an important but expensive part of the software development process, as it often consumes between 1/3 and 1/2 of this cost [7].

In this note, we address black-box testing, which ensures that a program meets its specification from a functional perspective. The number of possible black-box test cases is equal to the number of all possible valid settings of the input parameters of the system and thus in general is extremely large. Consequently testers have resorted to restricting the number of input combinations fed into the system under test, by only requiring that all pairwise (and more generally t-wise) combinations of input parameters are covered. For example, covering all pairwise combinations means that for any two parameters P_1 and P_2, and any valid values v_1 for P_1 and v_2 for P_2, there is a test in which P_1 is set to v_1 and P_2 is set to v_2.

The efficient construction of combinatorial covering suites has important applications in the process of testing software and hardware systems. A short example (cf. [17]) is as follows. Before shipping new machines to customers, running some final tests is desired. There are 16 switches on the back of each machine, that have to be set, each with two positions. Testing all possible $2^{16} = 65,536$

T. Ibaraki, N. Katoh, and H. Ono (Eds.): ISAAC 2003, LNCS 2906, pp. 300–308, 2003.

possible combinations is infeasible, but testing all 2^3 combinations for each sub-set of three switches is possible. Not more than 17 test vectors are necessary: 0000000000000000 and all the cyclic shifts of 0000101101110111 are sufficient for this task [17]. The same principle (and test sequence) can be applied for testing a software system with 16 inputs if every output of the software system depends on at most three input parameters (or one wants to test the interactions of all triples of parameters). A higher degree of testing of interactions between input parameters can be achieved using t-wise coverage (for some $t \geq 2$): the test se-quence will discover all errors if each output of the system depends on at most t input parameters.

A technical challenge that remains in applying this technique in software testing is the issue of efficiently constructing the covering test suite. This issue is important, because the number of test cases, as well as the time necessary to obtain them directly influences the amount of resources needed to test a software system.

1.1 Covering Suites

Throughout this note, let $[m]$ denote the set $\{1, 2, \ldots, m\}$, and $\log x$ stand for $\log_2 x$. We follow some of the terminology in [10]. Consider a software system with k parameters whose domains are the finite sets $D_1, \ldots, D_k$. We write $l_i = |D_i|$, $i = 1, \ldots, k$. The actual domains are in fact not important, but only their sizes; we will therefore assume that $D_j = \{0, 1, \ldots, l_j - 1\}$. A test suite with N test vectors is a matrix $A = (a_{ij} : 1 \leq i \leq N, 1 \leq j \leq k)$, where $a_{ij} \in D_j$ for all i and j. The rows of the matrix are called test vectors, or simply tests. A test suite A can be also viewed as a sequence $\mathcal{T}$ of N test vectors.

We say that a test suite A is a t-wise covering suite with parameters $l_1, \ldots, l_k$, $(t \leq k)$, if for any subset $\{j_1, \ldots, j_t\}$ of t columns of A, and for any t-tuple of values $T \in D_{j_1} \times \ldots \times D_{j_t}$, there exists at least one row r in A, such that $(a_{r,j_1}, \ldots, a_{r,j_t}) = T$. We speak in this case of *uniform coverage*. The *covering suite number* $h_t(l_1, \ldots, l_k)$ is then defined as the minimum integer N such that there exists a t-wise covering suite with N tests for k domains of sizes $l_1, \ldots, l_k$. Other names used in the literature for t-wise covering suites are covering arrays, (k, t)-universal sets, and t-surjective arrays. If all k domains are of the same size l — which we refer to as the *uniform range* case — we write $h_t(l^k)$ instead of $h(l, \ldots, l)$. Similarly, we write $h_t(l^2, m^3)$ instead of $h(l, l, m, m, m)$ for example. We call the matrix of a t-wise covering suite with k domains of size l a (k, t, l)-*universal test matrix*. If the domains are ordered by their size, say $l_1 \geq \ldots \geq l_k$, then clearly $h_t(l_1, \ldots, l_k) \geq l_1 \ldots l_t$ [10].

The uniform case $l = 2$ (all the domains are binary) and $t = 2$ (pairwise coverage), was solved by Rényi [15], Katona [11], Kleitman and Spencer [12]: for all $k \geq 2$, $h_2(2^k) = N$, where N is the smallest integer such that

$$\binom{N-1}{\lceil N/2 \rceil} \geq k.$$

A test suite of this size may be constructed as follows: the first test is the 0 vector in all coordinates. The columns of the remaining $N-1$ rows each contain exactly $\lceil N/2 \rceil$ ones, and each column is constructed by choosing a different $\lceil N/2 \rceil$-subset of the rows [10]. Asymptotically $h_2(2^k)$ satisfies

$$h_2(2^k) = \log k + \frac{1}{2} \log \log k + O(1). \tag{1}$$

For the uniform case $l = 2$ and $t = 3$ (3-wise coverage), the best known bounds are

$$3.21256\ldots \log k (1 + o(1)) \le h_3(2^k) \le 7.56444\ldots \log k (1 + o(1)),$$

where the lower bound is due to Kleitman and Spencer [12], while the upper bound is due to Sloane [17].

An extensive literature is devoted to constructing covering suites using orthogonal arrays, intersecting codes, or algebraic techniques — see [10,17] and the references therein. However these methods are complicated and in many cases do not work for an arbitrary given number of parameters, or of domain-size.

Seroussi and Bshouty [16] have shown that a generalized version of the problem of finding a minimal t-covering suite — where only a prescribed collection of t-sets of parameters needs to be covered — is NP-complete, using a reduction from graph 3-coloring. We refer to this case as non-uniform coverage. Thus finding polynomial time algorithms for generating optimal covering suites in the general case remains unlikely. However, to efficiently compute covering suites whose sizes are close to optimal remains a topic of continued interest.

In our note we present algorithms for efficient generation of combinatorial covering suites, and whose modular design allows for the resulting covering suites to be stored in a compact form. In Section 2 we address pairwise coverage, we continue with t-wise coverage in Section 3, and we conclude with a short discussion of non-uniform ranges and post-processing in Section 4.

The non-uniform coverage demand comes also from practical considerations, since outputs of the software system seldom depend on the same number of input parameters. A technique which in many cases reduces a given testing problem to one with a smaller number of parameters (and thus easier to solve) appears in [2].

2   Pairwise Coverage

The reported effectiveness of test sets with a low degree of coverage (such as pairwise or triple) is a major motivation for the combinatorial design approach [5]. In this section we outline a simple algorithm for generating covering suites in the uniform case (with k domains of size l) and $t = 2$ (pairwise coverage), and then implicitly get an upper bound on $h_2(l^k)$. We however note that better constructions are known for this case and that we feature our algorithm only for its simplicity and to illustrate the simplest case (for $t = 2$ colors) of our coloring approach detailed in Section 3. For example, Kobayashi et. al. proposed an algebraic method for pairwise coverage which yields a good upper bound on $h_2(l^k)$ and which works well even in the non-uniform range case.

We next outline the algorithm. The following fact is probably well known.

Lemma 1. *The edge set of the complete graph on the k vertices $\{0, \dots, k-1\}$ can be expressed as a union of the sets of edges of $m = \lceil \log k \rceil$ complete bipartite graphs (A_i, B_i), $i = 1, \dots, m$ on the same set of vertices. More precisely for each edge (j_1, j_2), $0 \le j_1 < j_2 \le k-1$, there exists i, such that $j_1 \in A_i$, $j_2 \in B_i$ and $(j_1, j_2) \in E(A_i, B_i)$. Moreover, each such bipartition can be generated in linear time.*

Proof. Put $m = \lceil \log k \rceil$; m represents the number of bits necessary to represent in binary all integers in the range $\{0, \dots, k-1\}$. For any such integer j, let j_i be the i-th bit in the binary representation of j. We assume that the vertex set of the complete graph is $\{0, \dots, k-1\}$. For $i = 1, \dots, m$, let $A_i = \{j \in \{0, \dots, k-1\} \mid j_i = 0\}$ and $B_i = \{j \in \{0, \dots, k-1\} \mid j_i = 1\}$ specify the bipartitions. It is easy to see that each edge (j_1, j_2), $0 \le j_1 < j_2 \le k-1$ is covered as required. All edges of these bipartite graphs are also present in the complete graph, which concludes the proof. □

Set $m = \lceil \log k \rceil$. The algorithm — which we refer to as $\mathcal{A}_1$ — generates the following tests. For each pair of parameters values (u, v), $u, v \in [l]$, $u \ne v$, output m vectors, each corresponding to a bipartition of the vertex set (of k parameters) in Lemma 1: if (A_i, B_i) is the i-th bipartition, the j-th component $(1 \le j \le k)$ of the i-th output vector w is set as follows. If $j \in A_i$, set $w[j] \leftarrow u$, and if $j \in B_i$, set $w[j] \leftarrow v$. For each pair of parameters values (u, u), $u \in [l]$, output a vector w all of whose components are equal to u.

The resulting sequence of vectors is a pairwise covering suite, as we show next. Take any pair of parameters (j_1, j_2), $j_1 < j_2$, and any pair of values $(u, v) \in [l]^2$. The case $u = v$ is taken care in the second part of the algorithm. In the case $u \ne v$, there exists a bipartition (A_i, B_i), such that $j_1 \in A_i$ and $j_2 \in B_i$, thus the parameter j_1 is set to u and the parameter j_2 is set to v in the vector corresponding to this bipartition, which is generated when the value pair (u, v) is considered in the first part of the algorithm.

For instance, the covering suite generated for $l = 3$, $k = 7$ is shown in Table 1, and corresponds to the bipartite graphs $A_1 = \{0, 1, 2, 3\}$, $B_1 = \{4, 5, 6\}$, $A_2 = \{0, 1, 4, 5\}$, $B_2 = \{2, 3, 6\}$, and $A_3 = \{0, 2, 4, 6\}$, $B_3 = \{1, 3, 5\}$.

The size of the output covering suite is

$$N_1 = l(l-1)\lceil \log k \rceil + l,$$

which also provides an upper bound on $h_2(l^k)$. Incidentally, the upper bound N_g (see below) on the number of tests derived in [3] using the greedy algorithm is at least twice ours, although their algorithm may output shorter covering suites.

$$N_g = l^2 \times \lceil \log \binom{k}{2} + \log l^2 \rceil.$$

Table 1. Pairwise coverage for seven parameters with three values each

P_0	P_1	P_2	P_3	P_4	P_5	P_6
0	0	0	0	1	1	1
0	0	1	1	0	0	1
0	1	0	1	0	1	0
0	0	0	0	2	2	2
0	0	2	2	0	0	2
0	2	0	2	0	2	0
1	1	1	1	0	0	0
1	1	0	0	1	1	0
1	0	1	0	1	0	1
1	1	1	1	2	2	2
1	1	2	2	1	1	2
1	2	1	2	1	2	1
2	2	2	2	0	0	0
2	2	0	0	2	2	0
2	0	2	0	2	0	2
2	2	2	2	1	1	1
2	2	1	1	2	2	1
2	1	2	1	2	1	2
0	0	0	0	0	0	0
1	1	1	1	1	1	1
2	2	2	2	2	2	2

We note that for $l = 2$, the size of the covering suite is roughly twice the size of the optimal in (1). We also note that Gargano, Körner and Vaccaro have shown that for very large values of k, the minimal number of test cases is $\sim \frac{l}{2} \log k$ [8], although their methods are non-constructive and the linear dependence on l for moderate k is unlikely [3,6].

3 t-Wise Coverage

In this section we show how the approach in Section 2 can be extended to obtain t-wise coverage in the uniform case (with k domains of size l). This approach can be used for any $t \geq 2$, so we can obtain an alternative method for pairwise coverage ($t = 2$).

The algorithm — which we refer to as $\mathcal{A}_2$ — has two phases. Fix a palette of t colors, say $[t] = \{1, \ldots, t\}$. In the first phase, repeatedly color uniformly and randomly the vertices of the complete graph on k vertices, until each unordered t-tuple is *multicolored* in at least one such coloring, i.e, each element of the t-tuple is colored by a different color in that coloring. Say n colorings have been used to achieve this property. In the second phase, for each ordered t-tuple of parameter values $(v_1, \ldots, v_t) \in [l]^t$, output n vectors, each corresponding to one of the above colorings. For a given coloring c, the j-th component ($1 \leq j \leq k$)

of the output vector w is set according to its color: if $c(j) = i$, set $w[j] \leftarrow v_i$, $i = 1, \ldots, t$.

The next lemma shows that the resulting sequence of vectors is a t-wise covering suite.

Lemma 2. *For each t-tuple of values $(v_1, \ldots, v_t) \in [l]^t$, and each t-tuple of parameters $i_1 < \ldots < i_t$, there exists a test vector w such that $w[i_j] = v_j$, $j = 1, \ldots, t$.*

Proof. Take a coloring c (which gives a test in the output suite) for which all parameters $i_1, \ldots, i_t$ have different colors, i.e., $\{c(i_1), \ldots, c(i_t)\} = [t]$. Let $\tau = (\tau_1, \ldots, \tau_t)$ be a permutation of $[t]$, such that $c(i_j) = \tau_j$, $j = 1, \ldots, t$. Let $\sigma = (\sigma_1, \ldots, \sigma_t) = \tau^{-1}$ be the inverse of τ. Consider the t-tuple of values $(v_{\sigma_1}, \ldots, v_{\sigma_t})$. In the output vector w corresponding to coloring c and the above t-tuple of values,

$$w[i_j] = v_{\sigma_{\tau_j}} = v_j,$$

since by definition of σ, $\sigma_{\tau_j} = j$. $\qquad\square$

Next we estimate n so that the resulting sequence is a t-wise covering suite. Fix a t-tuple U of parameters. The probability that U is not multicolored is

$$P_t = Prob[U \text{ is not multicolored}] = \frac{t^t - t!}{t^t}.$$

The probability that U is not multicolored in any of the n colorings is P_t^n, so the expected number of such t-tuples is $\binom{k}{t} P_t^n$. Requiring this to be < 1, and since $\binom{k}{t} < k^t$, for $t \geq 2$, it is enough to take

$$n = \left\lceil \frac{t \log k}{\log \frac{1}{P_t}} \right\rceil.$$

The size of the test sequence output by our algorithm is not more than $N_2 = \left\lceil \frac{t \log k}{\log \frac{1}{P_t}} \right\rceil l^t$. Thus

$$h_t(l^k) \leq \left\lceil \frac{t \log k}{\log \frac{1}{P_t}} \right\rceil l^t.$$

For fixed t (which holds for most practical applications), this becomes

$$N_2 = O((\log k) \cdot l^t). \qquad (2)$$

A different randomized algorithm for t-wise coverage — which we refer to as $\mathcal{A}'$ — is presented in [14,9]. That algorithm selects instead a collection of N' random vectors $\in [l]^k$: for each vector, each component is selected uniformly and randomly from $[l]$. Via the probability 'union bound', if

$$N' = \left\lceil \frac{t \log k + t \log l}{\log \frac{l^t}{l^t - 1}} \right\rceil,$$

t-wise coverage is obtained [14]. For fixed t, this becomes $N' = O((\log k + \log l) \cdot l^t)$. The size of the test sequence given by our algorithm $\mathcal{A}_2$ is (under the same assumption) a slight improvement for large l over the above bound, since the logarithmic dependence on l is removed. Besides that, the space and time requirements of $\mathcal{A}_2$ are much smaller that those of $\mathcal{A}'$: the former only needs to verify that all $\binom{k}{t}$ t-tuples of parameters have been covered (i.e., multicolored), while the latter needs to check that all $\binom{k}{t}l^t$ value t-tuples have been covered. Notice that $\binom{k}{t}l^t \gg \binom{k}{t}$!

In addition, if one wants to store enough information for obtaining covering suites for a large family of (k, t, l) instances, this becomes very easy to do using $\mathcal{A}_2$, and it uses very small space. Indeed, once a set of colorings is obtained for a given pair (k, t), it can be used as a seed to obtain covering suites for all (k, t, l) instances (i.e., for any value of l). Moreover, the space needed to store a set of colorings for a given (k, t) instance is much smaller than that needed for storing a complete covering suite for a (k, t, l) instance for a single l: the number of colorings is much smaller than the number of test vectors in a covering suite, and the number of bits per entry is usually smaller ($\lceil \log t \rceil$ versus $\lceil \log l \rceil$).

Next, we give a (straightforward) extension of the lower bound in [16] on the size of minimal t-wise covering suites for the binary case $l = 2$ to arbitrary l. We note that for fixed t and l and large k, the covering suite output by algorithm $\mathcal{A}_2$ is within a multiplicative constant factor of the optimal (cf. (2) above).

Theorem 1. *For all $k \geq t \geq 2$ and $l \geq 2$,*

$$h_t(l^k) \geq \max(l^t, l^{t-2} \cdot \lceil \log (k - t + 2) \rceil).$$

Proof. The first term in the maximum is justified by the trivial lower bound $h_t(l^k) \geq l^t$. To justify the second, let M be a (k, t, l)-universal test matrix of dimensions $m \times k$. For any $x \in [l]^{t-2}$, denote by M_x the matrix of rows of M whose last $t - 2$ coordinates agree with x. If m_x is the number of rows of M_x, then

$$m = \sum_{x \in [l]^{t-2}} m_x.$$

The minimum m_x, corresponding to some $\xi = \xi_1 \xi_2 \ldots \xi_{t-2} \in [l]^{t-2}$, satisfies

$$m_\xi \leq \frac{m}{l^{t-2}}. \tag{3}$$

Let $k' = k - t + 2$, and let M' be the $m_\xi \times k'$ matrix consisting of the first k' columns of M_ξ. We claim that M' is $(k', 2, l)$-universal. Indeed, assuming that for two column indices $j_1, j_2 \leq k'$, a value pair (v_1, v_2) is missing, then the t-tuple $v_1 v_2 \xi_1 \xi_2 \ldots \xi_{t-2}$ is missing from M at indices $j_1, j_2, k' + 1, \ldots, k$, contradicting the assumption that M is (k, t, l)-universal. Hence M' is $(k', 2, l)$-universal, thus also $(k', 2, 2)$-universal. By [1] (and also implied by [12], see also (1)), $m_\xi \geq \lceil \log k' \rceil = \lceil \log (k - t + 2) \rceil$. Combining with (3), we obtain

$$m \geq l^{t-2} m_\xi \geq l^{t-2} \cdot \lceil \log (k - t + 2) \rceil,$$

which completes the proof.   □

Corollary 1. *If $k - t = k^{\Omega(1)}$, then*

$$h_t(l^k) = \Omega(l^{t-2} \log k).$$

4 Other Aspects and Concluding Remarks

4.1 Non-uniform Ranges

Applications having large variations in the domain-size of the input parameters are a rule rather than an exception in software [4]. Two algorithms $\mathcal{A}_3$ and $\mathcal{A}_4$ are obtained by adapting algorithms $\mathcal{A}_2$ and $\mathcal{A}'$ respectively.

Algorithm $\mathcal{A}_3$ reduces the non-uniform case to the uniform one. It first sets $l = \max(l_1, \ldots, l_k)$, and then uses algorithm $\mathcal{A}_2$ (or $\mathcal{A}'$) to generate a t-wise covering suite for k domains of size l. Then for each test vector in this suite, and for each $i = 1, \ldots, k$, arbitrarily assigns its i-th entry to a value in its valid range if it lies outside its range. Clearly the result is a t-wise covering suite of the same size.

An algorithm similar to $\mathcal{A}'$ is algorithm $\mathcal{A}_4$: random vectors $\in D_1 \times \ldots \times D_k$ are chosen until coverage is obtained: i.e., for each vector, its i-th component is selected uniformly and randomly from D_i.

4.2 Post-processing: The Greedy Algorithm

Cohen et. al. have presented a greedy algorithm for test generation which for a fixed t, shows that the size of the test suite which provides t-wise coverage grows logarithmically in the number of parameters k [4,3]. As remarked in [3], the proof of the logarithmic growth for the greedy algorithm assumes that at each step, it is possible to find a test vector that covers the maximum number of uncovered t-tuples. Since there are an exponential number of test vectors (l^k), this may be computationally unfeasible. Therefore they outlined a heuristic random greedy variant of the algorithm to get around this problem, by using a random order in setting parameter values in their algorithm.

A different approach is to make use of the greedy algorithm in a post-processing optimization step. Once a covering suite $\mathcal{T}$ is obtained, it is fed as input to the greedy algorithm. Since the size of $\mathcal{T}$ is "small", the greedy algorithm can efficiently find a test vector that covers the maximum number of uncovered t-tuples, and thus in the end, it may produce as output only a subset $\mathcal{T}'$ of the covering sequence $\mathcal{T}$. This optimization step can be applied to any of the suites output by our algorithms $\mathcal{A}_1, \mathcal{A}_2, \mathcal{A}_3, \mathcal{A}_4$ presented earlier, or obtained by any other method.

4.3 Concluding Remarks

In this note we have outlined alternative algorithms for generating test suites which achieve uniform coverage of the software's input parameters. Our algorithms are efficient and extremely simple to implement. In addition, their design does not use sophisticated mathematical techniques, and the number of tests generated favorably compares with a general lower bound we have given. Moreover, their modular design allows for the resulting covering suites to be stored in a compact form. In combination with the use of the greedy algorithm as a post-processing optimization step, they provide a practical tool in the software testing process.

References

1. A. K. Chandra, L. T. Kou, G. Markowsky and S. Zaks, On sets of boolean n-vectors with all k-projections surjective, *Acta Informatica*, **20** (1983), 103–111.
2. C. Cheng, A. Dumitrescu and P. Schroeder, Generating small test suites for non-uniform instances, *Third International Conference on Quality Software* (QSIC 2003), Dallas, November 2003, accepted.
3. D. M. Cohen, S. R. Dalal, M. L. Fredman and G. C. Patton, The AETG system: an approach to testing based on combinatorial design, *IEEE Transactions on Software Engineering*, **23**(7) (1997), 437–444.
4. D. M. Cohen, S. R. Dalal, A. Kajla and G. C. Patton, The automatic efficient test generator (AETG) system, *Proceedings of the 5-th International Symposium on Software Reliability Engineering*, IEEE, 1994, 303–309.
5. D. M. Cohen, S. R. Dalal, J. Parelius and G. C. Patton, The combinatorial design approach to automatic test generation, *IEEE Software*, **13** (1996), 83–89.
6. D. M. Cohen and M. L. Fredman, New techniques for designing qualitatively independent systems, *Journal of Combinatorial Designs*, **6**(6) (1998), 411–416.
7. S. R. Dalal and C. M. Mallows, Factor-covering designs for testing software, *Technometrics*, **40**(3) (1998), 234–243.
8. L. Gargano, J. Körner and U. Vaccaro, Sperner capacities, *Graphs and Combinatorics*, **9** (1993), 31–46.
9. A. P. Godbole, D. E. Skipper and R. A. Sunley, t-Covering arrays: upper bounds and Poisson approximations, *Combinatorics, Probability and Computing*, **5** (1996), 105–117.
10. A. Hartman, Software and hardware testing using combinatorial covering suites, to appear in *Interdisciplinary Applications of Graph Theory, Combinatorics and Algorithms* (ed. M. Golumbic), manuscript, July 2002.
11. G. O. H. Katona, Two applications (for search theory and truth functions) of Sperner type theorems, *Periodica Mathematica Hungarica*, **3** (1973), 19–26.
12. D. J. Kleitman and J. Spencer, Families of k-independent sets, *Discrete Mathematics*, **6** (1973), 255–262.
13. N. Kobayashi, T. Tsuchiya and T. Kikuno, A new method for constructing pairwise covering designs for software testing, *Information Processing Letters* **81**(2) (2002), 85–91.
14. M. Naor, L. J. Schulman and A. Srinivasan, Splitters and near-optimal derandomization, *Proceedings of the 36-th Annual Symposium on Foundations of Computer Science* (FOCS), 1995, 182–191.
15. A. Rényi, *Foundations of Probability*, Wiley, New york, 1971.
16. G. Seroussi and N. H. Bshouty, Vector sets for exhaustive testing of digital circuits, *IEEE Transactions on Information Theory*, **34**(3) (1988), 513–522.
17. N. J. A. Sloane, Covering arrays and intersecting codes, *Journal of Combinatorial Designs*, **1** (1993), 51–63.

A Better Approximation for the Two-Machine Flowshop Scheduling Problem with Time Lags

Yoshiyuki Karuno[1] and Hiroshi Nagamochi[2]

[1] Kyoto Institute of Technology, Sakyo, Kyoto 606-8585, Japan
karuno@ipc.kit.ac.jp
[2] Toyohashi University of Technology, Toyohashi, Aichi 441-8580, Japan
naga@ics.tut.ac.jp

Abstract. In this paper we consider the two-machine flowshop scheduling problem with time lags. The problem has been known to be strongly NP-hard and 2-approximation algorithms have been obtained. We give a $(11/6)$-approximation algorithm that runs in $O(n \log n)$ time for an instance with n jobs.

1 Introduction

The two-machine flowshop scheduling problem with time lags is described as follows. There are n jobs to be processed on two machines, where all jobs have to pass through the machines following the same *processing route* (i.e., in the *flowshop* manner, and hence each job must be processed on the first machine and then on the second machine). Neither machine can process more than one job at a time, and no preemption is allowed. Each job has a non-negative *time lag*, which is the minimum time interval between the completion time of the job on the first machine and its starting time on the second machine. The objective is to find an optimal schedule of jobs that minimizes the makespan (i.e., the maximum completion time of all jobs).

The scheduling problems with time lags appear in many applications such as flexible manufacturing system (FMS) environment. Cutting machines often require intermediate operations such as washing, cooling, drying, and so on, before or after cutting operations. Thus, a straightforward interpretation is to consider the time lags as processing times on a *non-bottleneck machine* (i.e., a machine that can process any number of jobs at a time) (e.g., see Mitten [6]) situated between the two machines for such intermediate operations. The time lag can also be viewed as the actual transportation time of a job from the first machine to the second machine when the transportation device such as a conveyor system connecting the two machines is always available. Due to this, the time lags are sometimes referred to as the *transportation times* in the literature (e.g., see Strusevich [7]). Actually, there exist many FMS's with intermediate stations which perform the intermediate operations, and with conveyor systems (e.g., see an investigation book [1]).

In a general schedule to the two-machine flowshop problem with time lags, the processing orderings of jobs on the two machines are allowed to be different. Such

T. Ibaraki, N. Katoh, and H. Ono (Eds.): ISAAC 2003, LNCS 2906, pp. 309–318, 2003.

a schedule is called a *non-permutation* schedule. On the other hand, a schedule is called a *permutation* schedule if the two machines process the jobs in the same ordering. If only permutation schedules are allowed, the problem is referred to as permutation version. It has been known that the permutation version of the problem can be solved in $O(n \log n)$ time (e.g., see Lawler, Lenstra, Rinnooy Kan and Shmoys [5]), and that the makespan of an optimal permutation schedule (i.e., a permutation schedule with the minimum makespan among all permutation schedules) is at most twice of the optimal (see Dell'Amico [3]). For the original version of the problem where non-permutation schedules are allowed, it is easy to provide a problem instance for which the use of non-permutation schedules yields a shorter makespan than that by the use of only permutation schedules. However, Dell'Amico [3] has proved that the original version of the problem is strongly NP-hard. In the same paper [3], he has presented three 2-approximation $O(n \log n)$ time algorithms and introduced a tabu search approach. When all time lags are zero, the problem is identical to the traditional two-machine flowshop scheduling problem, which has been analyzed by Johnson [4]. He has proved the well known result such that an optimal schedule to the problem is given by a permutation schedule and such a schedule can be obtained in $O(n \log n)$ time [4].

If the processing routes of jobs are not given in advance, but have to be chosen, the two-machine system is referred to as *openshop* instead of flowshop. Strusevich [7] has presented a 1.5-approximation $O(n \log n)$ time algorithm for the two-machine openshop scheduling problem with time lags.

For the two-machine flowshop scheduling problem with time lags, reducing the best-known approximation bound of 2 was left as an attractive future work in [7]. In this paper, we prove that the bound can be improved by designing an algorithm that delivers a $(11/6)$-approximation solution in $O(n \log n)$ time.

The remainder of this paper is organized as follows. In Section 2, we describe the problem formulation and some basic properties, and review previously proposed heuristics. In Section 3, we present a collection of new heuristics. Each heuristic may deliver a schedule with a makespan exceeding $(11/6)$ times the optimal. In Section 4, however, we show that the best schedule among these heuristic solutions yields a makespan at most $(11/6)$ times the optimal.

2   Preliminaries and Basic Properties

We denote the two machines by A and B. Each job j of set $J = \{1, 2, \ldots, n\}$ has to be processed on the first machine A and then on the second machine B (i.e., in the flowshop manner). The processing times of a job j on A and B are given by a_j and b_j, respectively. We assume that each job $j \in J$ has its own time lag, denoted by l_j (i.e., the minimum time interval which must elapse between the completion of job j on machine A and its start on machine B). We denote by $I = (J, a, l, b)$ an instance of the problem. For an instance I, let $opt(I)$ be the minimum makespan for processing all jobs in I.

Let $\pi = [\lambda; \mu]$ be a schedule to a problem instance, where $\lambda = (\lambda_1, \lambda_2, \ldots, \lambda_n)$ and $\mu = (\mu_1, \mu_2, \ldots, \mu_n)$ are the processing orderings of the jobs on A and

B, respectively. Note that the permutation version of the problem allows only permutation schedules $\pi = [\lambda; \mu]$ such that $\lambda = \mu$ (i.e., $\lambda_j = \mu_j$ for all $j = 1, 2, \ldots, n$). In this paper, we prove the next result.

Theorem 1. *For the two-machine flowshop scheduling problem $I = (J, a, l, b)$ with time lags, there is a pair of a subset $J' \subseteq J$ of jobs and a permutation σ on J' such that, for any permutations λ and μ on $J - J'$, schedule $\pi = [(\lambda, \sigma); (\sigma, \mu)]$ is a $(11/6)$-approximation solution, and such a pair can be obtained in $O(n \log n)$ time, where n denotes the number of jobs.*

For a problem instance I and a schedule π to I, let $T(\pi; I)$ be the makespan of π. Furthermore, we define the following notions. Given an instance $I = (J, a, l, b)$, let J^a and J^b be the subsets of jobs such that

$$J^a = \{j \mid a_j > b_j\}; \quad J^b = \{j \mid a_j \leq b_j\}, \tag{1}$$

and for a subset $J' \subseteq J$, let

$$a(J') = \sum_{j \in J'} a_j; \quad b(J') = \sum_{j \in J'} b_j, \tag{2}$$

where we define $a(\emptyset) = b(\emptyset) = 0$.

By using (2), an immediate lower bound on the minimum makespan $opt(I)$ is described as follows.

$$opt(I) \geq \max\left\{a(J), b(J), \max_{j \in J}\{a_j + l_j + b_j\}\right\}. \tag{3}$$

In the remainder of this section, we explain three heuristics obtained in the work by Dell'Amico [3], each of which delivers a 2-approximation solution to the problem. These heuristics will be used as the subroutines in our algorithm proposed in the next section.

For a given instance $I = (J, a, l, b)$, let $I_1 = (J, a, l' = 0, b)$ be the instance such that for each job $j \in J$, the processing time on machine A is a_j, the time lag is $l'_j = 0$ and the processing time on machine B is b_j. This is an instance of the traditional two-machine flowshop scheduling problem, and hence an optimal solution π_1 to I_1 can be obtained in $O(n \log n)$ time by Johnson's algorithm [4]. The following procedure finds an optimal schedule to I_1.

Procedure JOHNSON
Input: An instance $I_1 = (J, a, l' = 0, b)$.
Output: An optimal schedule π_1 to I_1.
begin
1   Partition the set J into two subsets J^a and J^b by (1)
2   Let σ_b be a sequence consisting of all jobs in J^b
     in the non-decreasing order of their processing times a_j
3   Let σ_a be a sequence consisting of all jobs in J^a
     in the non-increasing order of their processing times b_j

4   Output a permutation schedule $\pi_1 = [(\sigma_b, \sigma_a); (\sigma_b, \sigma_a)]$ of all jobs in J,
     and halt
end. /* JOHNSON */

Since the instance I_1 is a relaxation of the original instance I, we obtain

$$T(\pi_1; I_1) \le opt(I).$$

When we use the schedule π_1 to the original instance I as a heuristic solution,
we can easily see that

$$T(\pi_1; I) \le T(\pi_1; I_1) + \max_{j \in J}\{l_j\} \le 2 \cdot opt(I). \tag{4}$$

Heuristic 1. The first 2-approximation algorithm is now described as follows.
First construct the instance $I_1 = (J, a, l' = 0, b)$ from a given instance I, and then
apply procedure JOHNSON to I_1. The schedule π_1 obtained by the procedure
is a 2-approximation solution to the original instance I.

   In addition, we remark that a 2-approximation solution π to I can be obtained
by applying procedure JOHNSON to the instance $I_1' = (a' = a + l, l' = 0, b' =
l + b)$ such that for each job $j \in J$, the processing time on A is $a_j' = a_j + l_j$, the
time lag is $l_j' = 0$ and the processing time on B is $b_j' = l_j + b_j$, and that such a
schedule π is an optimal permutation schedule among all permutation schedules
to I (e.g., see Lawler, Lenstra, Rinnooy Kan and Shmoys [5]).

   For a given instance $I = (J, a, l, b)$, let $I_2 = (J, a' = 0, l' = a + l, b)$ be the
instance such that for each job $j \in J$, the processing time on machine A is
$a_j' = 0$, the time lag is $l_j' = a_j + l_j$ and the processing time on machine B is
b_j. Since the new time lag l_j' can be viewed as the *release time* of job j, I_2 is
an instance of the single-machine scheduling problem with release times which
can be solved in $O(n \log n)$ time (e.g., see Brucker [2]). The following procedure
computes an optimal schedule to I_2.

Procedure RELEASE
Input: An instance $I_2 = (J, a' = 0, l' = a + l, b)$.
Output: An optimal solution π_2 to I_2.
begin
1   Let σ be a sequence consisting of all jobs in J
     in the non-decreasing order of their time lags l_j'
2   Output a permutation schedule $\pi_2 = [\sigma; \sigma]$, and halt
end. /* RELEASE */

Since the instance I_2 is also a relaxation of the original instance I, we have

$$T(\pi_2; I_2) \le opt(I).$$

On the other hand, the makespan of π_2 in the original instance I satisfies that

$$T(\pi_2; I) \le a(J) + T(\pi_2; I_2) \le 2 \cdot opt(I).$$

Heuristic 2. The second 2-approximation algorithm is described as follows. It constructs the instance $I_2 = (J, a' = 0, l' = a + l, b)$ from a given instance I, and then applies procedure RELEASE to I_2. The resulting schedule π_2 is a 2-approximation solution to I.

Heuristic 3. For the last 2-approximation algorithm we construct the instance $I_3 = (J, a, l' = l + b, b' = 0)$ such that for each job $j \in J$, the processing time on machine A is a_j, the time lag is $l'_j = l_j + b_j$ and the processing time on machine B is $b'_j = 0$. I_3 is an instance of the single-machine scheduling problem with delivery times, and hence an optimal schedule to the instance I_3 can be obtained in $O(n \log n)$ time by the following procedure (e.g., see also Brucker [2]).

Procedure DELIVERY
Input: An instance $I_3 = (J, a, l' = l + b, b' = 0)$.
Output: An optimal solution π_3 to I_3.
begin
1   Let σ be a sequence consisting of all jobs in J
      in the non-increasing order of their time lags l'_j
2   Output a permutation schedule $\pi_3 = [\sigma; \sigma]$, and halt
end. /* DELIVERY */

Similarly to the previous two relaxations, we have

$$T(\pi_3; I_3) \leq opt(I),$$

and for the resulting schedule π_3 to the original instance I as a heuristic solution, it holds that

$$T(\pi_3; I) \leq T(\pi_3; I_3) + b(J) \leq 2 \cdot opt(I).$$

Before closing this section, we remark that there is an instance I such that for any permutation schedule π, $T(\pi; I)$ is twice as large as the optimal $opt(I)$. Such an instance $I = (J, a, l, b)$ is given by $a_j = b_j = 1$ for all $j \in J$, $l_1 = n$ and $l_j = 0$ for all $j \in J - \{1\}$, where $opt(I) = n + 2$ and $T(\pi; I) = 2n + 1$ [3]. This implies that we cannot expect a performance guarantee better than 2 even if we select the best schedule among those constructed by the above three heuristics, any of which outputs only permutation schedules.

3   Algorithm

In this section we introduce two new heuristics, each of which may deliver a schedule with a makespan exceeding $(11/6)$ times the optimal. With these new heuristics and Heuristic 3, we construct three solutions. We will show in the next section that the best schedule among the three solutions yields a makespan at most $(11/6)$ times the optimal.

In what follows, we assume without loss of generality that

$$a(J) \geq b(J) > 0,$$

since any schedule has the same makespan if it is executed in the reverse orderings of the jobs on both machines for the instance obtained by switching the processing times a_j and b_j for each job j. Let r denote the constant r $(0 < r \leq 1)$ such that

$$b(J) = r \cdot a(J). \tag{5}$$

First, we use Heuristic 3 to a given instance $I = (J, a, l, b)$ to obtain a schedule $\pi_1 = [\sigma_1; \sigma_1]$ such that

$$T(\sigma_1; I_1) \leq opt(I).$$

By (5), we have

$$T(\pi_1; I) \leq T(\sigma_1; I_1) + b(J) \leq opt(I) + r \cdot a(J). \tag{6}$$

For some instances such as the one described at the end of the previous section, it is advantageous to process jobs with long time lags first on A, but last on B. Our first new heuristic constructs such a schedule by distinguishing jobs with long time lags from jobs with short time lags by introducing an adequate threshold h^* on time lags. We also need a new lower bound to analyze the performance of such non-permutation schedules. To make the analysis for deriving our new lower bound and for determining the threshold easier, we convert a given instance I into a *symmetric instance* $\tilde{I} = (J, \tilde{a}, l, \tilde{b})$ with $\tilde{a}_j = \tilde{b}_j$, $j \in J$, by defining

$$\tilde{a}_j := a_j \text{ and } \tilde{b}_j := a_j \text{ for each job } j \in J^a;$$

$$\tilde{a}_j := b_j \text{ and } \tilde{b}_j := b_j \text{ for each job } j \in J^b$$

for the partition J^a and J^b of J in (1). Let

$$\Delta a = \tilde{a}(J) - a(J) \ (= b(J^b) - a(J^b)); \quad \Delta b = \tilde{b}(J) - b(J) \ (= a(J^a) - b(J^a)).$$

Clearly, $opt(I) \leq opt(\tilde{I})$ holds since $\tilde{a}_j \geq a_j$ and $\tilde{b}_j \geq b_j$ for all $j \in J$. However, any schedule to I can be executed for $\tilde{I}$ by taking at most another $\Delta a + \Delta b$ time units in the makespan. Thus,

$$opt(\tilde{I}) \leq opt(I) + \Delta a + \Delta b. \tag{7}$$

Let α $(0 < \alpha \leq 1)$ denote the constant such that

$$a(J^b) + b(J^a) = \alpha \cdot a(J). \tag{8}$$

By definitions, we have

$$\begin{aligned}
\Delta a + \Delta b &= b(J^b) - a(J^b) + a(J^a) - b(J^a) \\
&= b(J^b) + b(J^a) + a(J^a) + a(J^b) - 2a(J^b) - 2b(J^a) \\
&= a(J) + b(J) - 2\alpha \cdot a(J) \\
&= (1 + r - 2\alpha)a(J),
\end{aligned} \tag{9}$$

and

$$\tilde{a}(J) = \frac{1}{2}(\tilde{a}(J) + \tilde{b}(J)) = \frac{1}{2}(a(J) + b(J) + \Delta a + \Delta b)$$
$$= \frac{1}{2}(1 + r + 1 + r - 2\alpha)a(J)$$
$$= (1 + r - \alpha)a(J). \tag{10}$$

In the symmetric instance $\tilde{I}$, for a real $h \in [0,1]$, we define sets of jobs $J^>(h)$ and $J^\geq(h)$ by

$$J^>(h) = \{j \in J \mid l_j > h \cdot \tilde{a}(J)\}; \quad J^\geq(h) = \{j \in J \mid l_j \geq h \cdot \tilde{a}(J)\}.$$

Then there exists a real $h^* \in [0.5, 1]$ such that

$$\tilde{a}(J^\geq(h^*)) = (2h^* - 1)\tilde{a}(J), \tag{11}$$

or

$$\tilde{a}(J^\geq(h^*)) > (2h^* - 1)\tilde{a}(J) \geq \tilde{a}(J^>(h^*)), \tag{12}$$

since $\tilde{a}(J^\geq(h))$ is a non-increasing function with respect to h.

We now derive a new lower bound on $opt(I)$.

Lemma 1. $opt(I) \geq [(2h^* - 1)(1 + r - \alpha) + \alpha]a(J)$.

Proof: Consider an optimal schedule π^* to $\tilde{I}$, where we assume without loss of generality that π^* starts at time 0 and there is no idle time on machine A.

Case-1: Some job $j \in J^\geq(h^*)$ finishes on A in π^* at time t which is equal to $h^*\tilde{a}(J)$ or later. Then $T(\pi^*; \tilde{I}) \geq t + l_j \geq h^*\tilde{a}(J) + h^*\tilde{a}(J) \geq 2h^*\tilde{a}(J)$. This implies that $opt(\tilde{I}) \geq 2h^*\tilde{a}(J)$.

Case-2: All jobs $j \in J^\geq(h^*)$ finish on A in π^* earlier than time $h^*\tilde{a}(J)$. Again, since $l_j \geq h^*\tilde{a}(J)$, none of jobs in $j \in J^\geq(h^*)$ cannot start its processing on B at time $h^*\tilde{a}(J)$ or earlier. Hence, since $\tilde{a}_j = \tilde{b}_j$ for all $j \in J$, machine B has at least $\tilde{b}(J^\geq(h^*)) = \tilde{a}(J^\geq(h^*))$ idle time before time $h^*\tilde{a}(J)$. This implies that $opt(\tilde{I}) \geq \tilde{a}(J) + \tilde{a}(J^\geq(h^*)) \geq \tilde{a}(J) + (2h^* - 1)\tilde{a}(J) = 2h^*\tilde{a}(J)$.

By (7), (9) and (10), we get

$$opt(I) \geq opt(\tilde{I}) - (\Delta a + \Delta b) \geq 2h^*\tilde{a}(J) - (\Delta a + \Delta b)$$
$$= 2h^*(1 + r - \alpha)a(J) - (1 + r - 2\alpha)a(J)$$
$$= \left[(2h^* - 1)(1 + r - \alpha) + \alpha\right]a(J),$$

proving the lemma. $\qquad \square$

By using the above h^* as the threshold between long time lags and short time lags, our first new heuristic is described as follows.

Heuristic 4. Define $J_{long} = J^\geq(h^*)$ in the case (11) and $J_{long} = J^>(h^*)$ in the case (12). Let $J_{short} = J - J_{long}$. We consider the instance $\hat{I} = (J, a, \hat{l} = 0, b)$

which is obtained from I by setting $\hat{l}_j := 0$ for each job $j \in J$. We can find an optimal permutation $\hat{\pi} = [\sigma, \sigma]$ to $\hat{I}$ in $O(n \log n)$ time by Johnson's algorithm (see procedure JOHNSON in Section 2). Thus

$$T(\hat{\pi}; \hat{I}) = opt(\hat{I}) \le opt(I).$$

Let σ_{short} be the subsequence of σ that consists of the jobs in J_{short}, and λ_{long} and μ_{long} be two arbitrary permutations on J_{long}.

Now we consider schedule $\pi_2 = [(\lambda_{long}, \sigma_{short}); (\sigma_{short}, \mu_{long})]$. We see that

$$T(\pi_2; \hat{I}) \le T(\hat{\pi}; \hat{I}) + \tilde{a}(J_{long})$$

since moving jobs $j \in J_{long}$ at the head of a schedule on A and jobs $j \in J_{long}$ at the tail of a schedule on B increases the makespan at most by $a(J_{long}) + b(J_{long}) - \sum_{j \in J_{long}} \min\{a_j, b_j\} = \sum_{j \in J_{long}} \max\{a_j, b_j\} = \tilde{a}(J_{long})$. We claim that

$$T(\pi_2; I) \le \max\{T(\pi_2; \hat{I}) + \max\{l_j \mid j \in J_{short}\},\ opt(I) + a(J_{long}) + b(J_{long})\}.$$

To see this, we introduce the time lags l_j only for the jobs $j \in J_{short}$. This increases the makespan at most by $\max\{l_j \mid j \in J_{short}\}$. If the time τ to process all jobs in J_{short} in this schedule is at least $opt(I)$, then all jobs in J_{long} can be started on B without requiring any idle time (since $opt(I) \ge \max\{l_j \mid j \in J_{long}\}$). On the other hand, if the τ is less than $opt(I)$, then $T(\pi_2; I) \le a(J_{long}) + opt(I) + b(J_{long})$. This proves the claim. We consider these two cases. For the former case, we have by $\max\{l_j \mid j \in J_{short}\} \le h^* \tilde{a}(J)$,

$$T(\pi_2; I) \le opt(I) + \tilde{a}(J_{long}) + h^* \tilde{a}(J) \le opt(I) + (2h^* - 1)\tilde{a}(J) + h^* \tilde{a}(J)$$
$$= opt(I) + (3h^* - 1)(1 + r - \alpha)a(J). \tag{13}$$

For the latter case, we have

$$T(\pi_2; I) \le opt(I) + a(J_{long}) + b(J_{long}) \le opt(I) + \tilde{a}(J_{long}) + \tilde{b}(J_{long})$$
$$\le opt(I) + 2 \cdot (2h^* - 1)\tilde{a}(J)$$
$$= opt(I) + (4h^* - 2)(1 + r - \alpha)a(J). \tag{14}$$

Note that $3h^* - 1 \ge 4h^* - 2$ holds since $h^* \le 1$.

Finally we introduce our second new heuristic which delivers a good schedule for small α (see (8)).

Heuristic 5. We partition the set J of jobs into two subsets J^a and J^b by (1). Then we construct the instance $I_a = (J^a, a, l, b' = 0)$ from I which contains only jobs in J^a and their processing times on B are set to be zero while other parameters remain unchanged.

Similarly consider the instance $I_b = (J^b, a' = 0, l, b)$ from I which contains only jobs in J^b and their processing times on A are set to be zero while other parameters remain unchanged.

Let σ_a and σ_b be optimal permutations to these instances I_a and I_b, which can be found in $O(n \log n)$ time (see procedures DELIVERY and RELEASE in Section 2). Based on σ_a and σ_b, we construct a schedule $\pi_3 = [(\sigma_b, \sigma_a); (\sigma_b, \sigma_a)]$ to I.

Since the instances I_a and I_b are the relaxations of I, we have

$$T(\sigma_a; I_a) = opt(I_a) \leq opt(I); \quad T(\sigma_b; I_b) = opt(I_b) \leq opt(I),$$

and we can see that the makespan of π_3 in I satisfies that

$$T(\pi_3; I) \leq a(J^b) + \max\{T(\sigma_a; I_a), T(\sigma_b; I_b)\} + b(J^a) \leq opt(I) + \alpha \cdot a(J). \quad (15)$$

4   Performance Analysis

From (6), (13) and (15) and Lemma 1, the best schedule π^{apx} among those obtained by Heuristics 3, 4 and 5 satisfies

$$T(\pi^{apx}; I) \leq opt(I) + \min\{r, \alpha, (3h^* - 1)(1 + r - \alpha)\} \cdot a(J)$$
$$\leq opt(I) + \frac{\min\{r, \alpha, (3h^* - 1)(1 + r - \alpha)\}}{\max\{1, (2h^* - 1)(1 + r - \alpha) + \alpha\}} \cdot opt(I).$$

We show in this section that for any $r \in (0, 1]$, $\alpha \in (0, 1]$ and $h^* \in [0.5, 1]$,

$$f(\alpha, h^*) = \frac{\min\{r, \alpha, (3h^* - 1)(1 + r - \alpha)\}}{\max\{1, (2h^* - 1)(1 + r - \alpha) + \alpha\}}$$

is at most $5/6$, which proves Theorem 1. Clearly $f(\alpha, h^*) \leq 5/6$ if $r \leq 5/6$ or $\alpha \leq 5/6$ holds. In what follows, we assume that $r \in (5/6, 1]$ and $\alpha \in (5/6, 1]$. Note that $1 + r - \alpha > 0$ holds since $r > 5/6$ and $\alpha \leq 1$.

(1) Assume $(2h^* - 1)(1 + r - \alpha) + \alpha \leq 1$, i.e.,

$$h^* \leq \frac{1 - \alpha}{2(1 + r - \alpha)} + \frac{1}{2}. \quad (16)$$

Since $(3h^* - 1)(1 + r - \alpha)$ is an increasing function with respect to h^*, we have

$$f(\alpha, h^*) \leq (3h^* - 1)(1 + r - \alpha)$$
$$\leq \left(3\left(\frac{1 - \alpha}{2(1 + r - \alpha)} + \frac{1}{2}\right) - 1\right)(1 + r - \alpha) \quad \text{(by (16))}$$
$$= \frac{3(1 - \alpha)}{2} + \frac{(1 + r - \alpha)}{2} \leq \frac{5 - 4\alpha}{2} \quad \text{(since } r \leq 1\text{)}$$
$$< \frac{5}{6} \quad \left(\text{since } \alpha > \frac{5}{6}\right).$$

(2) Assume $(2h^* - 1)(1 + r - \alpha) + \alpha > 1$, i.e.,

$$h^* > h' = \frac{1 - \alpha}{2(1 + r - \alpha)} + \frac{1}{2}. \tag{17}$$

We can see that $u(\alpha, h^*) = \alpha / \{(2h^* - 1)(1 + r - \alpha) + \alpha\}$ is a decreasing function with respect to h^*, and

$$v(\alpha, h^*) = \frac{(3h^* - 1)(1 + r - \alpha)}{(2h^* - 1)(1 + r - \alpha) + \alpha} = \frac{(3h^* - 1)(1 + r - \alpha)}{2(1 + r - \alpha)h^* - (1 + r - 2\alpha)}$$

$$= \frac{3}{2} + \frac{1 + r - 4\alpha}{4(1 + r - \alpha)h^* - 2(1 + r - 2\alpha)}$$

is an increasing function with respect to h^*, where $1 + r - 4\alpha < 0$ holds since $r \leq 1$ and $\alpha > 5/6$. Moreover, it holds that $u(\alpha, 0.5) = 1 > v(\alpha, 0.5) = (1 + r - \alpha)/2\alpha$ and $u(\alpha, 1.0) = \alpha/(1 + r) < v(\alpha, 1.0) = 2(1 + r - \alpha)/(1 + r)$ since $5/6 < r \leq 1$ and $5/6 < \alpha \leq 1$. These imply that $f(\alpha, h^*) = \min\{u(\alpha, h^*), v(\alpha, h^*)\}$ takes the maximum when $h^* = h''$ such that

$$h'' = \frac{1}{3} + \frac{\alpha}{3(1 + r - \alpha)}, \tag{18}$$

i.e., $u(\alpha, h'') = v(\alpha, h'')$. Clearly, $f(\alpha, h') \leq f(\alpha, h'')$ holds even if $h' > h''$. Then we have

$$f(\alpha, h^*) \leq \frac{\alpha}{(2h'' - 1)(1 + r - \alpha) + \alpha} = \frac{3\alpha}{6\alpha - (1 + r)} \quad \text{(by (18))}$$

$$< \frac{5}{6} \quad \left(\text{since } r \leq 1 \text{ and } \alpha > \frac{5}{6}\right).$$

Therefore, Theorem 1 has been proved.

References

1. Association of Mechanical Technology of Japan (ed.): A Collection of FMS's in Japan (in Japanese). Machinist Publisher, Tokyo (1982)
2. Brucker, P.: Scheduling Algorithms (Third Edition). Springer, Berlin (2001)
3. Dell'Amico, M.: Shop problems with two machines and time lags. Operations Research **44** (1996) 777–787
4. Johnson, S. M.: Optimal two- and three-stage production schedules with setup times included. Naval Research Logistics Quarterly **1** (1954) 61–68
5. Lawler, E. L., Lenstra, J. K., Rinnooy Kan, A. H. G. and Shmoys, D. B.: Sequencing and scheduling: Algorithms and complexity. In: Graves, S. C., Rinnooy Kan, A. H. G. and Zipkin, P. H. (eds.): Handbooks in Operations Research and Management Science. Vol. 4. Logistics of Production and Inventory. Elsevier, Amsterdam (1993) 445–522
6. Mitten, L. G.: Sequencing n jobs on two machines with arbitrary time lags. Management Science **5** (1959) 293–297
7. Strusevich, V. A.: A heuristic for the two-machine open-shop scheduling problem with transportation times. Discrete Applied Mathematics **93** (1999) 287–304

On Minimizing Average Weighted Completion Time: A PTAS for the Job Shop Problem with Release Dates[*]

Aleksei V. Fishkin[1], Klaus Jansen[1], and Monaldo Mastrolilli[2]

[1] Institut für Informatik und Praktische Mathematik,
Christian-Albrechts-Universität zu Kiel, Olshausenstrasse 40, 24118 Kiel, Germany,
{avf,kj}@informatik.uni-kiel.de
[2] IDSIA-Istituto Dalle Molle di Studi sull'Intelligenza Artificiale, Manno,
Switzerland, monaldo@idsia.ch

Abstract. We consider the non-preemptive job shop scheduling problem with release dates and the average weighted completion time objective. We propose here a polynomial-time approximation scheme (PTAS) for the case when the number of machines is constant and each job consists of at most a constant number of operations. This substantially improves on previous results [4], adds to a number of techniques [1,2,6,10,22], and gives some answers to the questions mentioned in [20,23].

Keywords: Approximation, PTAS, job shop, scheduling.

1 Introduction

In this paper we consider the non-preemptive job shop scheduling problem with release dates, a fixed number of machines, a fixed number of operations per job, and the average weighted completion time objective, denoted as $Jm \,|op \leq \mu, r_j|$ $\sum w_j C_j$ [15,19]. Formally, we are given a set of m machines $M = \{1, 2, \dots, m\}$ and a set of n jobs $J = \{1, 2, \dots, n\}$. Each job j $(j = 1, 2, \dots, n)$ consists of $\mu \geq 2$ operations $o_{1j}, \dots, o_{\mu j}$ that have to be processed in the given order, has a weight w_j, which defines its importance, and a release date r_j, before which it cannot be started. Each operation o_{ij} $(i = 1, 2, \dots, \mu)$ requires a machine $\tau_{ij} \in M$ and has a processing time p_{ij}. Each job can be processed only by one machine at a time and each machine can process only one job at a time. Here we assume that m and μ are fixed and the goal is to find a non-preemptive feasible schedule which minimizes *average weighted completion time* $\sum w_j C_j$, where C_j denotes the completion time of job j.

[*] Supported by EU-project CRESCCO, IST-2001-33135, by EU-project APPOL I & II, IST-1999-14084, IST-2001-32007, by SNSF project 21-55778.98, and grant HPRN-CT-1999-00106.

T. Ibaraki, N. Katoh, and H. Ono (Eds.): ISAAC 2003, LNCS 2906, pp. 319–328, 2003.
© Springer-Verlag Berlin Heidelberg 2003

Previous Results. The first polynomial-time approximation scheme (PTAS) for a strongly NP-hard scheduling problem minimizing the average weighted completion time was given for scheduling jobs with no release dates on identical parallel machines $P||\sum w_j C_j$ [22]. Then recently it has been proved in [1, 6] that there are PTASs for many different variants of classical scheduling problems with release dates and the average weighted completion time objective. These include scheduling on identical parallel machines $P|r_j|\sum w_j C_j$, on related machines $Q|r_j|\sum w_j C_j$, and on a fixed number of unrelated machines $Rm|r_j|\sum w_j C_j$ with and without preemptions.

The job shop scheduling problem is an important generalization of scheduling on parallel machines. However, it seems to be harder for approximating even in the case of unit weights and no release dates. Regarding the worst-case complexity, problem $J2|op \leq 2|\sum C_j$ with two machines and at most two operations per job is already strongly NP-hard [12]. This negative result was strengthened in [17], where it was proven that the general job shop scheduling problem $J||\sum C_j$ with arbitrary (not fixed) number of machines m and number of operations per job μ is MAX-SNP-hard. Contrasting this with the fact that for identical parallel machines only the general problem $P||\sum C_j$ is strongly NP-hard, while $Pm||\sum C_j$ is just weakly NP-hard, indicates that computing optimal or approximate schedules for the job shop version is likely to be much harder.

Indeed, for about 20 years only a simple $O(m)$-approximation algorithm for $J||\sum C_j$ [14] has been known. Then, in [4] it that shown that there is a $(5.78+\varepsilon)$-approximation algorithm for problem $Jm|op \leq \mu, r_j|\sum w_j C_j$. Later, a general $O((\log(m\mu)/\log\log(m\mu))^2)$- approximation algorithm for problem $J|r_j|\sum w_j C_j$ was presented in [20].

New Results. Here we obtain a PTAS for $Jm|op \leq \mu, r_j|\sum w_j C_j$. In order to be able to cope with the problem we employ the well-known input transformation technique [24] and refine some recent sophisticated approximation techniques for the average completion time objective function. These partially include the interval time-partitioning technique [4,16], the techniques of geometric rounding, time stretching, and weight-shifting [1,3], our techniques of LP relaxation and rounding [2,10], and our PTAS for the makespan version of the problem [9,18]. Our main goal is to perform several *transformations* that simplify the input without dramatically increasing the objective value such that the final result is amenable to a fast dynamic programming solution. At the beginning, we round all processing times and release dates to integer powers of $(1+\varepsilon)$. This breaks the time line into contiguous *geometrically increasing intervals* $I_x = ((1+\varepsilon)^x, (1+\varepsilon)^{x+1}]$, $x \in \mathbb{Z}$, where release dates only happen at the beginning of intervals. Furthermore, we round weights such that all w_j/p_j are distinct. Next, we define *main* and *negligible* operations of a job. Here, negligible operations are very small and can be rounded to zero, whereas main operations are very big and can rounded to some particular fractions of the total job length. This makes the problem structure much simpler. We show that any job completes within a constant number of intervals in a schedule, and partition all jobs into a constant number of subsets sharing similar characteristics, called *profile*. Our next idea is to classify the jobs as huge and tiny. In particular, a job is *huge* with respect to an interval if its length is at least ε^2/q^* times the size of the interval, and *tiny* otherwise. For one interval I_x, all huge jobs of the same profile and *size* (a power of $1 + \varepsilon$) can be prioritized by decreasing weights w_j, whereas all tiny jobs of the same profile can be prioritized by decreasing ratio w_j/p_j, called a modified Smith's rule [28]. In order to prove the latter statement we define the value of parameter q^*. We first use a subroutine for "assigning" tiny jobs to intervals, and then as a subroutine for "packing" jobs in single intervals. For the first step we use an LP formulation and a special rounding procedure from [18]. For the second step, we use an adopted PTAS for the makespan version of the problem [9]. Finally, the weight-shifting technique is applied. If too many jobs are released at interval I_x, some of them have to wait to be processed. Shifting refers to the process of moving the excess jobs to the next interval I_{x+1}. We enforce special *compact instances* in which there is only a constant number of jobs at any release date. Then, we apply dynamic programming which integrates all previous components. The obtained PTAS is a sequence of the former instance transformations coupled with the dynamic programming algorithm. By an appropriate combination of these ideas and a careful analysis of the algorithm, we prove the following result:

Theorem 1. *There is a PTAS for $Jm|op \le \mu, r_j| \sum w_j C_j$ that computes for any fixed m, μ and $\varepsilon > 0$ accuracy, $(1 + \varepsilon)$-approximate solutions in $O(n \log n)$ time.*

This substantially improves on previous results [4]. Furthermore, we show that a right combination of all ideas – the input transformation technique, the idea of intervals, the idea of huge-tiny jobs, the weight-shifting technique, an LP relaxation (formulation), rounding, a PTAS for the makespan version of the problem, and dynamic programming – is quite a powerful method for the design of PTASs for problems with the average weighted completion time objective function. Indeed, these generalizations significantly add to a number of techniques [1,2,6,10, 22]. One of the most interesting aspects here is that we do not really use a PTAS for the makespan version of the problem as a subroutine, that was previously considered as an interesting question in [20], but rather as a part of our proof technique. Furthermore, following the same line of ideas we can prove the existence of PTASs for many other scheduling models, e.g. open shop, flow shop, dag shop, and their preemptive or multiprocessor versions. Accordingly, we can prove that there are PTASs for the two-machine flow shop problem $F2|| \sum C_j$ and for the two-machine open shop problem $O2|| \sum C_j$, that was mentioned in [23] as a result which can be the first step to understanding the approximability of shop scheduling problems with the sum of completion time objective function.

The paper is organized as follows. In Section 2 we give some simple preliminary results, which can be also found in [1,6,10]. In Sections 3 and 4 we define negligible operations and perform the main structuring step of the algorithm. In Section 4.1 we define job profiles and give some related definitions. In Section 4.2 we formulate a modified Smith's rule. In Section 5 we complete the algorithm.

2   Preliminaries

To simplify notation we will use throughout the paper that $1/\varepsilon$ is integer (and in particular $\varepsilon < 1/2^{m\mu}$), and use OPT to denote the objective value of the optimal schedule. For an operation o_{ij}, we use S_{ij} and C_{ij} to denote the start and completion time of o_{ij}. For a job j we will use C_j and S_j to denote the completion and start time of j, and use $\ell_j = \sum_{i=1}^{\mu} p_{ij}$ to denote the length of j. For a job set X, we will use $D(X)$ to denote the total length of the jobs in X, that is $\sum_{j \in X} \ell_j$.

As a preliminary step of our algorithm, here we perform some basic *transformations* that simplify the input problem. Many of our transformations are thought modifications applied to the optimal schedule to argue that some schedule nearly as good has very simple structure. In this case, Then, we say that *with $1+\varepsilon$ loss*, we can *assume* some properties in any schedule. Others our transformations are actual simplifying modifications of the instance that run in polynomial time and do not increase the objective value too much. Then, we say that *with $1 + \varepsilon$ loss* and in $O(n)$ time, we can *enforce* some properties in an instance. For a more clear understanding, see lemmas in the next two paragraphs.

Geometric Rounding. The first simplification creates a well-structured set of lengths, release dates, and weights:

Lemma 1. *With $1 + 3\varepsilon$ loss and in $O(n)$ time, we can enforce all ℓ_j and r_j be integer powers of $1 + \varepsilon$ and all w_j/ℓ_j be distinct.*

Proof Sketch. Multiply all r_j and ℓ_j by $1+\varepsilon$, and then *decrease* each date and length to the next *lower* integer power of $1+\varepsilon$. Since $\ell_j(1+\varepsilon) = \sum_{i=1}^{\mu}(1+\varepsilon)p_{ij}$, we decrease all $(1 + \varepsilon)p_{ij}$ by the same factor as ℓ_j. The objective value of the final schedule is at most $(1 + \varepsilon)OPT$. Regarding weights, we multiply all w_j by $1 + \varepsilon$, and then *decrease* some of them by small values until all w_j/ℓ_j differ. This increases the objective function value by at most a factor of $1 + \varepsilon$.   □

This result guarantees that there are only a small number of distinct processing times and release dates to worry about, and lets us break the time line into *geometrically increasing intervals*, where release dates only happen at the beginning of intervals, that is useful for later techniques and dynamic programming.

For an arbitrary integer x, define $R_x = (1 + \varepsilon)^x$. We partition $(0, \infty)$ into disjoint intervals of the form $I_x := [R_x, R_{x+1})$. We will use $|I|_x$ to refer to the size value $(R_{x+1} - R_x) = \varepsilon R_x$, which is ε times its start time. Now all release dates are of the form $R_x = (1 + \varepsilon)^x$ for some integer x.

Schedule-Stretching. We can enforce that no operation starts too early or crosses too many intervals:

Lemma 2. *With $1 + \varepsilon$ loss, we can assume $S_{ij} \geq \varepsilon p_{ij}$ for all jobs j.*

Proof Sketch. Multiply all C_{ij} by $1 + \varepsilon$ and increase S_{ij} to match (without changing p_{ij}). The objective value of the final schedule is at most $(1 + \varepsilon)OPT$, and all starting times $(1 + \varepsilon)C_{ij} - p_{ij} \geq (1 + \varepsilon)p_{ij} - p_{ij}$ are at least εp_{ij}.   □

Lemma 3. *With $1 + \varepsilon$ loss, we can assume that each operation crosses at most $s^* = \lceil \log_{1+\varepsilon}(1 + \frac{1}{\varepsilon}) \rceil$ intervals.*

Proof Sketch. By the above lemma, all $C_{ij} = S_{ij} + p_{ij} \le S_{ij} + S_{ij}/\varepsilon = S_{ij}(1 + \frac{1}{\varepsilon})$. If $S_{ij} \in [R_x, R_{x+1})$, s^* intervals following I_x cover $[S_{ij}, (1 + \frac{1}{\varepsilon}) S_{ij}]$. $\qquad\square$

3   Main and Negligible Operations

Consider a job j. Let $\ell_j = \sum_{i=1}^{\mu} p_{ij}$ be its length. Let operations o_{ij} ($i = 1, \dots, \mu$) be indexed by $i_1, i_2, \dots, i_\mu$ such that $p_{i_1 j} \ge p_{i_2 j} \ge \dots \ge p_{i_\mu j}$. Then, if there exist some $k \in \{1, \dots, \mu\}$ such that

$$\varepsilon^{4\mu} \cdot p_{i_k j} > \sum_{s=k+1}^{\mu} p_{i_s j}, \tag{1}$$

then we select the smallest value of k and define operations $o_{i_{k+1} j}, \dots, o_{i_\mu j}$ be *negligible*, and operations $o_{i_1 j}, \dots, o_{i_k j}$ be *main*.

Lemma 4. *Each main operation o_{ij} has processing time $p_{ij} \ge \varepsilon^{5\mu^2} \cdot \ell_j$.*

Proof Sketch. Omitted. $\qquad\square$

4   Main Structuring Step

Here we perform several main transformations that structure the problem. By combining several techniques we eliminate all negligible operations and round all main operations:

Lemma 5. *With $1 + 3\varepsilon$ loss and in $O(n)$ time, for all jobs j we can enforce all operation processing times $p_{ij} = \pi_{ij} \cdot \ell_j$, where*

$$\pi_{ij} \in \left\{ z \cdot \varepsilon^{5\mu^2 + 2} \mid z = 0, 1 \dots, \frac{1}{\varepsilon^{5\mu^2 + 2}} \right\}.$$

Proof Sketch. Omitted. $\qquad\square$

Similarly, we can move release dates.

Lemma 6. *With $1 + \varepsilon$ loss and in $O(n)$ time, we can enforce r_j be at least $\varepsilon^{10\mu^2} \cdot \ell_j$ for all jobs j.*

Proof Sketch. Omitted. $\qquad\square$

Finally, we can prove that no job can cross too many intervals.

Lemma 7. *With $1 + \varepsilon$ loss, each job crosses at most a constant number of intervals e^*.*

Proof Sketch. Omitted. $\qquad\square$

4.1   Profiles, Huge and Tiny Jobs, Local Profiles and Patterns

Here we introduce some important definitions. We first define job profiles. Informally, two jobs have the same profile if they have the same sequence of required processors, and although they can differ in length, their operation processing times correspond to the same sequence of length multiples. Next, we define huge and tiny jobs. Here we introduce a special parameter q^* which value is defined later in Lemma 12, respectively. Finally, we define local profiles and patterns for tiny jobs. This allows us to formulate Smith's rule for tiny jobs in Section 4.2.

Profiles. Consider a job j. By Lemma 5, each operation o_{ij} $(i = 1, \ldots, \mu)$ has processing time $\pi_{ij} \cdot \ell_j$ and requites machine τ_{ij}. Then, μ-tuples $\pi_j = (\pi_{ij})_{i=1}^{\mu}$ and $\tau_j = (\tau_{ij})_{i=1}^{\mu}$ are called the *execution* and *machine* profile of job j, respectively.

We say that two jobs have the same profile $\varphi = (\pi, \tau)$, if they have the same execution profile π and machine profile τ. Notice that two jobs of profile φ can only differ in their length and release dates. Furthermore, as a consequence of Lemma 5 we can prove the following:

Lemma 8. *The number of distinct profiles is bounded by a constant ν^*.*

Huge and Tiny Jobs. We say that a job j is *huge* in an interval I_x if its length $\ell_j \geq \varepsilon^2 |I|_{x(j)}/q^*$, and *tiny* otherwise. The value of parameter $q^* \gg 1$ is defined later in Lemma 12, respectively. We will write H_x and T_x to denote sets of huge and tiny jobs released at R_x (H for huge and T for tiny). As in Lemma 2, we use time-stretching to "clean up" a schedule:

Lemma 9. *With $1 + \varepsilon$ loss, we can assume that no tiny operation crosses an interval in a schedule.*

Furthermore, by using Lemmas 1 and 6 we can prove the following:

Lemma 10. *There is at most a constant number $z^* = O(q^*)$ of distinct sizes (ℓ_j powers of $1 + \varepsilon$) in H_x.*

Local Profiles and Patterns. Take an optimal schedule. Consider a tiny job j. Let $x(j)$ be the index for which $R_{x(j)} = r_j$. Let $y(j)$ and $z(j)$ be whose indices for which $S_j \in I_{y(j)}$ and $C_j \in I_{z(j)}$. Then, job j runs in intervals $I_{y(j)}, \ldots, I_{z(j)}$. By Lemma 9, no operation of job j crosses an interval. Hence, the set O_j of all operations $o_{1j}, \ldots, o_{\mu j}$ "splits" into a constant number of subsets, $O_j^{y(j)}, \ldots, O_j^{z(j)}$, where each subset $O_j^x \subseteq O_j$ consists of operations which "fall" into interval I_x, for $x = y(j), \ldots, z(j)$.

Now assume that tiny job j has some profile $\varphi = (\pi, \tau)$, where two μ-tuples $\pi = (\pi_i)_{i=1}^{\mu}$ and $\tau = (\tau_i)_{i=1}^{\mu}$. Then, we have that $\pi_i = \pi_{ij}$ and $\tau_i = \tau_{ij}$ for all operations $o_{ij} \in O_j$. Informally, we can say that the operations of set O_j "form" profile $\varphi = (\pi, \tau)$. If we restrict ourselves to the operations of set O_j^x, we can define a $2|O_j^x|$-tuple $\bar{\varphi}^x = (\bar{\pi}^x, \bar{\tau}^x)$ such that $\bar{\pi}_i^x = \pi_{ij}$ and $\bar{\tau}_i^x = \tau_{ij}$ for all operations $o_{ij} \in O_j^x$. In this case, we can also say that the operations of set O_j^x "form" *local profile* $\bar{\varphi}^x$ in interval I_x, $x = y(j), \ldots, z(j)$. In other words,

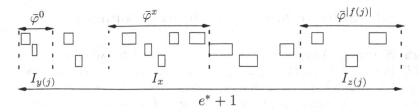

Fig. 1. Local profiles $\bar{\varphi}^0, \bar{\varphi}^1, \ldots, \bar{\varphi}^{|f(j)|}$ of job j

operations of tiny jobs "locally" form "profiles". Notice that operations of two tiny jobs with different profiles can "form" the same local profile in an interval.

We say that a tiny job j has *pattern* $f(j) = < \bar{\varphi}^0, \bar{\varphi}^1, \ldots, \bar{\varphi}^{|f(j)|} >$ in a schedule if starting in interval $I_{y(j)}$ it completes in interval $I_{y(j)+|f(j)|} = I_{z(j)}$, and in each interval $I_{y(j)+k}$ the operations of tiny job j "form" local profile $\bar{\varphi}^k$, for $k = 0, \ldots, |f(j)|$. For an illustration see Figure 1. Notice some local profiles $\bar{\varphi}^k$ can be empty, but the combination of all local profiles gives the profile of tiny job j. By Lemma 7 any tiny job crosses at most a constant number e^* of intervals. By Lemma 8 there is at most a constant number ν^* of profiles. Hence, we can prove the following:

Lemma 11. *There is at most a constant number $\bar{\nu}^*$ of distinct local profiles, and at most a constant number f^* of distinct patterns.*

4.2 Scheduling Tiny Jobs: Smith's Rule

We first need to introduce some notations. Consider an optimal schedule. Then, for a tiny job j we can define two indices $x(j) \leq y(j)$ and pattern $f(j)$ such that job j is released at $R_{x(j)}$, starts at $S_j \in I_{y(j)}$ having pattern $f(j)$ and completes at $C_j \in I_{y(j)+|f(j)|}$.

Smith's rule. Let k and j be two tiny jobs with $x(k) \leq x(j)$ (here $r_k \leq r_j$) and $\frac{w_j}{\ell_j} < \frac{w_k}{\ell_k}$ (see Lemma 1). We say that tiny jobs *obey* Smith's rule if $y(k)+|f(k)| \leq y(j) + |f(j)|$ ($C_k \leq C_j$) for all such pairs of jobs j and k. In other words, if the two jobs are available in an interval, then job k of greater value w_k/ℓ_k completes not later than job j with respect to intervals $I_{y(k)}, I_{y(j)}$ and patterns $f(k), f(j)$. Here we are interested in the following result:

Lemma 12. *The value of parameter $q^* = O(\varepsilon, m, \mu)$ can be defined such that with $1 + 7\varepsilon$ loss, for each profile φ we can assume that tiny jobs of profile φ obey Smith's rule in a schedule.*

Proof Sketch. Omitted. $\square$

5   Weight-Shifting and Dynamic Programming

Weight-Shifting. Assume that at some release date R_x we have a lot of huge jobs (H_x) and tiny jobs (T_x). Which jobs can wait until the next interval? Take one profile φ. The jobs of $H_x(\varphi)$ having the same size must complete by decreasing weights w_j. By Lemmas 10 and 12, there is at most a constant number of such sizes. By Lemma 12, the jobs of $T_x(\varphi)$ must complete by decreasing w_j/ℓ_j. By Lemma 7, all jobs that start in I_x must complete within the next e^* intervals. We only select the jobs that can be potentially scheduled in I_x:

Lemma 13. *With $1+O(\varepsilon)$ loss and in $O(n\log n)$ time, we can enforce $D(T_x) \leq t^* \cdot |I|_x$ and $|H_x| \leq H^*$ at each release date R_x, where t^* and H^* are some constant.*

At each release date R_x we partition the ordered set of tiny jobs $T_x(\varpi)$ into subsets of roughly equal size $\approx \varepsilon^2|I|_x/2q^*$ (but less than $\varepsilon^2|I|_x/q^*$). Then, we merge the jobs of each such subset into a new tiny job of profile φ.

Lemma 14. *With $1+O(\varepsilon)$ loss and in $O(n\log n)$ time, we can enforce $|T_x| \leq T^*$ and $|H_x| \leq H^*$ at each release date R_x, where T^* and H^* are some constant.*

Finally, by the ideas of Lemmas 9, 7 and the results of Lemma 14 we can prove the following:

Lemma 15. *With $1 + \varepsilon$ loss, each job completes within d^* intervals after its release, where d^* is some constant.*

Dynamic Programming. We partition the time line into a sequence of *blocks*, where each block i consists of d^* consecutive intervals. The basic idea is to use dynamic programming with blocks as units. The jobs of block i run either in block i or $i+1$. A *pseudo-schedule* S_i describes a possible placement of the jobs of blocks i. The dynamic programming entry $E(i, S_i)$ stores the minimum weighted completion time achievable by completing all jobs released before or in block i while leaving pseudo-schedule S_i for block $i+1$. Given all table entries for block $i-1$, the values for block i can be computed as follows.

$$E(i, S_i) = \min_{S_{i-1}}\{E(i-1, S_{i-1}) + W(i, S_{i-1}, S_i)\},$$

where $W(i, S_{i-1}, S_i)$ is the minimum weighted completion time achievable by scheduling the jobs in intervals of block i with respect to the *incoming* pseudo-schedule S_{i-1} and the *outgoing* pseudo-schedule S_i, respectively. Both the feasibility test and computation of $W(i, S_{i-1}, S_i)$ can be done in $O(1)$ time. Since there are at most $O(n)$ blocks the entire table $E(\cdot)$ can be computed in $O(n)$ time. The combination of all above steps and the dynamic programming algorithm gives a PTAS with $O(n\log n)$ running time. This completes the proof of Theorem 1.

References

1. F. Afrati, E. Bampis, C. Chekuri, D. Karger, C. Kenyon, S. Khanna, I. Millis, M. Queyranne, M. Skutella, C. Stein, and M. Sviridenko. Approximation schemes for minimizing average weighted completion time with release dates. In *Proceedings 40th IEEE Symposium on Foundations of Computer Science*, pages 32–43, 1999.
2. F. Afrati, E. Bampis, A. V. Fishkin, K. Jansen, and C. Kenyon. Scheduling to minimize the average completion time of dedicated tasks. In *Proceedings 20th Conference on Foundations of Software Technology and Theoretical Computer Science*, LNCS 1974, Springer Verlag, pages 454–464, 2000.
3. F. Afrati and I. Milis. Designing PTASs for MIN-SUM scheduling problems. In *Proceedings 13th International Symposium on Fundamentals of Computation Theory*, LNCS 2138, pages 432–444. Springer Verlag, 2001.
4. S. Chakrabarti, C. A. Phillips, A. S. Schulz, D. B. Shmoys, C. Stein, and J. Wein. Improved scheduling algorithms for minsum criteria. In *Proceedings 23rd International Colloquium on Automata, Languages and Programming*, LNCS 1099, pages 646–657. Springer Verlag, 1996.
5. C. Chekuri. *Approximation algorithms for scheduling problems*. PhD thesis, Department of Computer Science, Stanford University, 1998.
6. C. Chekuri and S. Khanna. A PTAS for minimizing weighted completion time on uniformly related machines. In *Proceedings 28th International Colloquium on Automata, Languages and Programming*, LNCS 2076, pages 848–861. Springer Verlag, 2001.
7. C. Chekuri, R. Motwani, B. Natarajan, and C. Stein. Approximation techniques for average completion time scheduling. In *Proceedings of 8th Annual ACM-SIAM Symposium on discrete Algorithms*, pages 609–618, 1997.
8. B. Chen, C. N. Potts, and G. J. Woeginger. *Handbook of combinatorial optimization (D.-Z. Du and P. M. Paradalos eds.)*, chapter A review of machine scheduling: complexity, algorithms and approximability, pages 21–169. Kluwer, 1998.
9. A. V. Fishkin, K. Jansen, and M. Mastrolilli. Grouping techniques for scheduling problems: Simpler and faster. In *Proceedings 9th Annual European Symposium*, LNCS 2161, pages 206–217, Arhus, 2001. Springer Verlag.
10. A. V. Fishkin, K. Jansen, and L. Porkolab. On minimizing average weighted completion time of multiprocessor tasks with release dates. In *Proceedings 28th International Colloquium on Automata, Languages and Programming*, LNCS 2076, pages 875–886, Crete, 2001. Springer Verlag.
11. M. R. Garey and D. S. Johnson. *Computers and intractability: A guide to the theory of NP-completeness*. Freeman, San Francisco, CA, 1979.
12. M. R. Garey, D. S. Johnson, and R. Sethi. The complexity of flowshop and jobshop scheduling. *Mathematics of Operation Research*, 1:117–129, 1976.
13. L. A. Goldberg, M. Paterson, A. Srinivasan, and E. Sweedyk. Better approximation guarantees for job-shop scheduling. In *Proceedings 8th Symposium on Discrete Algorithms*, pages 599–608, 1997.
14. T. Gonzales and S. Sahni. Flowshop and jobshop schedules: Complexity and approximation. *Operations Research*, 26:36–52, 1978.
15. R. L. Graham, E. L. Lawler, J. K. Lenstra, and A. H. G. Rinnooy Kan. Optimization and approximation in deterministic scheduling: A survey. *Annals of Discrete Mathematics*, 287–326, 1979.
16. L. A. Hall, A. S. Schulz, D. B. Shmoys, and J. Wein. Scheduling to minimize average time: Off-line and on-line algorithm. *Mathematics of Operation Research*, pages 513–544, 1997.

17. H. Hoogeveen, P. Schuurman, and G. Weoginger. Non-approximability results for scheduling problems with minsum criteria. In *Proceedings 6th Conference on Integer Programming and Combinatorial Optimization*, LNCS 1412, pages 353–366. Springer Verlag, 1998.

18. K. Jansen, R. Solis-Oba, and M. Sviridenko. Makespan minimization in job shops: A polynomial time approximation scheme. In *Proceedings 31st Annual ACM Symposium on Theory of Computing*, pages 394–399, Atlanta, 1999. To appear in SIAM Journal on Discrete Mathematics.

19. E. L. Lawler, J. K. Lenstra, A. H. G. Rinnooy Kan, and D. B. Shmoys. *Logistics of Production and Inventory*, volume 4 of *Handbooks in Operation Research and Management Science*, chapter Sequencing and scheduling: Algorithms and complexity, pages 445–522. North-Holland, Amsterdam, 1993.

20. M. Queyranne and M. Sviridenko. New and improved algorithms for minsum shop scheduling. In *Proceedings 11th Annual ACM-SIAM Symposium on Discrete Algorithms*, pages 871–878, 2000.

21. A. S. Schulz. *Polytopes and scheduling*. PhD thesis, Technical University of Berlin, Germany, 1996.

22. P. Schuurman and G. J. Woeginger, Polynomial time approximation algorithms for machine scheduling: Ten open problems. *Journal of Scheduling*, 2: 203–213, 1999.

23. P. Schuurman and G. J. Woeginger. Polynomial time approximation algorithms for machine scheduling: Ten open problems. *Journal of Scheduling*, 2:203–213, 2000.

24. P. Schuurman and G. J. Woeginger. Approximation schemes – a tutorial. To appear in the book Lectures on Scheduling, edited by R. H. Moehring, C. N. Potts, A. S. Schulz, G. J. Woeginger and L. A. Wolsey., 2002.

25. D. B. Shmoys. Using linear programming in the design and analysis of approximation algorithms: Two illustrative examples. In *Proceedings 1st International Workshop on Approximation Algorithms for Combinatorial Optimization Problems*, LNCS 1444, pages 15–32. Springer Verlag, 1998.

26. D. B. Shmoys, C. Stein, and J. Wein. Improved approximation algorithms for shop scheduling problems. *SIAM Journal of Computing*, 23:617–632, 1994.

27. M. Skutella. *Approximation and randomization in scheduling*. PhD thesis, Technical University of Berlin, Germany, 1998.

28. W. E. Smith. Various optimizers for single-stage production. *Naval Research Logistic Quarterly*, 3:59–66, 1956.

29. E. Torng and P. Uthaisombut. Lower bounds for SRPT-subsequence algorithms for non-preemptive scheduling. In *Proceedings 10th ACM-SIAM Symposium on Discrete Algorithms*, pages 973–974, 1999.

Online Scheduling of Parallel Jobs with Dependencies on 2-Dimensional Meshes*

Deshi Ye[1] and Guochuan Zhang[1,2]

[1] Department of Mathematics,
Zhejiang University, Hangzhou 310027, China
[2] Institut für Informatik und Praktische Mathematik,
Christian-Albrechts-Universität zu Kiel,
Olshausenstrasse 40, 24098 Kiel, Germany
gzh@informatik.uni-kiel.de.

Abstract. We study an on-line problem of scheduling parallel jobs on 2-dimensional meshes. Parallel jobs arrive dynamically according to the dependencies between them, which are unknown before the jobs appear. Each job may need more than one processor simultaneously and is required to be scheduled on a submesh of the processors which are located on a 2-dimensional mesh, i.e., a job must be scheduled on a rectangle of given dimensions. The objective is to minimize the maximum completion time (makespan). We deal with an UET job system, in which all job processing times are equal. We show a lower bound of 3.859 and present a 5.25-competitive algorithm. It significantly improves a previous lower bound of 3.25 and a previous upper bound of 46/7. We consider also the rotated 2-dimensional mesh, in which the parallel jobs can be rotated. A lower bound of 3.535 is proven and an on-line algorithm with competitive ratio of at most 4.25 is derived.

1 Introduction

In the classical scheduling theory, it is assumed that a job can be executed only by one processor. This assumption is too restrictive in the case of parallel computer system and modern production system where jobs can be processed on several machines in parallel. Therefore, the scheduling model of parallel jobs has been proposed, see, e.g., [4,12,8,7,3,6]. In many applications, a network topology is specified for the processors, which may impose serious restrictions on the job types that can be executed on particular processors, only those processors connected to each other can execute a job together. Parallel processors with a specific network topology can be viewed as a graph where each node represents a processor and each edge represents the communication link between the two nodes (processors). The network topologies can be *Hypercubes, Lines*, and *Meshes*. A parallel system is a *PRAM* (Parallel Random Accessing Machine), if its underlying network topology is a complete graph. In addition there are

* Supported by EU-Project CRESCCO (IST-2001-33135) and NSFC (10231060).

T. Ibaraki, N. Katoh, and H. Ono (Eds.): ISAAC 2003, LNCS 2906, pp. 329–338, 2003.
© Springer-Verlag Berlin Heidelberg 2003

precedence constraints on the jobs, i.e. some special order in which jobs have to be started (they can be expressed in term of chains, trees, series parallel orders, interval order and so on).

On-line scheduling of parallel jobs with or without precedence constraints is studied by Feldmann et al. [7,6] and Sgall [10]. In [6,10] it is shown that the worst-case performance of any deterministic or randomized on-line algorithm for scheduling parallel jobs with precedence constraints and unknown processing times is rather dismal, even if the precedence constraints among the jobs are known in advance. Bischof et al. [1,2] study the case that there is some a priori knowledge about the processing times of the individual jobs but the dependencies are unknown to the scheduler. They first consider the problem that the job processing times are equal. Such a job system is denoted by UET. For the *PRAM* topology, they present a 2.7-competitive algorithm and a lower bound of 2.691 for any deterministic on-line algorithms. For the hypercube network topology, they give a best possible on-line algorithm with competitive ratio of 2. For two-dimensional meshes, they derive a 46/7-competitive algorithm and a lower bound 3.25 for any deterministic on-line algorithm. Secondly, they consider the model with runtime ratio restriction (the quotient of the longest and shortest processing times) for *PRAM*s. When the shortest processing time is known, a family of job systems with runtime ratio $T_R \geq 2$ is given that bounds the the competitive ratio of any deterministic on-line algorithm by $(T_R + 1)/2$ from below. An on-line algorithm with competitive ratio of $T_R/2 + 4$ is provided for the job system with runtime ratio $\leq T_R$. If the assumption that the shortest processing time is known is dropped, a modified algorithm with competitive ratio of $T_R/2 + 5.5$ is given.

Note that for an UET job system there are already optimal or nearly optimal on-line algorithms if the network topology is a *hypercubes* or a *PRAM*. However, there is a big gap between the best known lower bound and the upper bound for the two-dimensional mesh topology. In this paper, we are concerned with on-line scheduling of an UET job system on two-dimensional meshes and improve the previous results by Bischof [1]. A two-dimensional mesh $N_1 * N_2$ is a parallel system consisting of $N_1 \times N_2$ processors $\{p_{ij} | 0 \leq i < N_1, 0 \leq j < N_2\}$ where processor p_{ij} is directly connected with processors $p_{i,j\pm1}$, $p_{i\pm1,j}$ (if they exist). Each job has a unit processing time and must be scheduled on a rectangle of given dimensions. Job J_i is characterized by (a_i, b_i), meaning J_i requires an $a_i * b_i$ submesh. We call this topology a *normal 2-d mesh*. On the other hand, it is also reasonable to assume that parallel jobs can be rotated, which means that job J_i can also be scheduled on a $b_i * a_i$ submesh, where the processors in each node of the mesh are identical. Such a topology is called a *rotated 2-d mesh*. There are precedence constraints among jobs. A job is available if and only if its predecessors have been completed. The precedences are unknown in advance and an on-line algorithm is only aware of available jobs and has no knowledge about their successors. The goal is to minimize the maximum job completion time (the makespan).

For normal 2-d meshes we give a lower bound of 3.859 for any deterministic on-line algorithms and present a 5.25-competitive algorithm which adopts Steinberg's algorithm [11] as a subroutine. Then we consider the rotated 2-d mesh topology. A 4.25-competitive algorithm is given. Slightly revising the instance borrowed from [5] shows that the competitive ratio of any on-line algorithm is at least 3.535.

The remainder of this paper is organized as follows. Section 2 gives preliminaries. In Section 3, we give lower bounds for any on-line algorithm on normal 2-d meshes and on rotated 2-d meshes. On-line algorithms are presented in Section 4. Conclusions are given in Section 5.

2   Preliminaries

To evaluate an on-line algorithm we adopt the standard measure - *competitive ratio*, which is defined as follows. For any instance L, let $T_A(L)$ and $T_{opt}(L)$ be the makespans given by an on-line algorithm A and by an optimal off-line algorithm, respectively. The optimal off-line algorithm has full information on the jobs, including the dependencies between them. The on-line algorithm A is called ρ-*competitive* if $T_A(L) \leq \rho T_{opt}(L)$ holds for any job list L. The *competitive ratio* R_A of algorithm A is defined as

$$R_A = \sup_L \{T_A(L)/T_{opt}(L)\}$$

For simplicity we may use T_A and T_{opt} instead of $T_A(L)$ and $T_{opt}(L)$ if no confusion is caused.

Regarding the two-dimensional mesh as a rectangular bin and the jobs (with unit processing times) as rectangles (items), the problem of scheduling a set of available jobs at each unit time interval can be regarded as a 2-dimensional bin packing problem. A job (a_i, b_i) has a width a_i and a height b_i. The makespan of a schedule is just the number of bins used for packing all jobs. Note that the on-line issue is only with respect to the precedences: a job is available if and only if its predecessors have been completed. We distinguish the jobs by levels. The jobs in level 1 are available at the beginning. A job belongs to level i if its predecessor(s) falls in level $i - 1$, for $i \geq 2$.

In this paper, we adopt Steinberg's algorithm [11] as a subroutine of our algorithm. In 2-dimensional bin packing, we are given a list of rectangles $R = (R_1, \cdots, R_l)$, where rectangle R_i has a width a_i and a height b_i. Let $a_L = \max\{a_i | 1 \leq i \leq l\}$, $b_L = \max\{b_i | 1 \leq i \leq l\}$, $s_i = a_i b_i$ and $S_L = \sum_{i=1}^{l} s_i$. Then we get the following lemma.

Lemma 2.1. [11] *If the following inequalities hold*

$$a_L \leq u, \quad b_L \leq v \quad and \quad 2S_L \leq uv - (2a_L - u)_+(2b_L - v)_+$$

then it is possible to pack the rectangles of R into a rectangle with a width u and a height v by Steinberg's algorithm, where $x_+ = \max(x, 0)$.

Remark. Note that if the height (the width) of any rectangle is at most $v/2$ (at most $u/2$), the rectangles with total area at most $(uv)/2$ can be packed into a rectangle (bin) with a width u and a height v.

3   Lower Bounds

In [2,1], Salzer numbers [9] are used to construct an instance for a lower bound of 2.691 for the $PRAM$ network topology. We extend the idea to the normal 2-d mesh topology. The Salzer number t_i is defined as follows. $t_1 = 2$, $t_{i+1} = t_i(t_i - 1) + 1$ for $i \geq 1$. Define $h_\infty = \sum_{i=1}^{\infty} \frac{1}{t_i - 1} > 1.69103$.

Theorem 3.1. *No on-line algorithms can have competitive ratios lower than* $h_\infty^2 + 1 > 3.859$.

Proof. Let $k > 0$ be an arbitrarily large integer. From the definition of Salzer numbers, we have $\sum_{i=1}^{k} 1/t_i + 1/(t_{k+1} - 1) = 1$, $\prod_{i=1}^{k} t_i = t_{k+1} - 1$. We choose N such that $N > (k+1)(t_{k+2} - 1)$. Consider a mesh $N * N$. Let $A_i = \lfloor \frac{N}{t_i} \rfloor + 1$, where t_i's are Salzer numbers, for $i = 1, \ldots, k$. Set $A_{k+1} = N - \sum_{i=1}^{k} A_i - 1$. Then $N/(t_{k+1} - 1) > A_{k+1} \geq N/(t_{k+1} - 1) - (k+1) > 0$.

The job system consists of l levels, where $l \geq k^3$. The $(i + (k+1)(j-1))$-st level consists of $l - (i-1) - (j-1)(k+1)$ jobs with size (A_i, A_j), $i = 1, \cdots, k+1$ and $j = 1, \cdots, k+1$. The last $l - (k+1)^2$ levels form a chain of $l - (k+1)^2$ jobs with size $(1, 1)$. At each level, one of the jobs is the predecessor of all jobs of the next level. Note that jobs at the same level have the same size.

Dependencies are assigned dynamically by the adversary. In the optimal solution, we first process the available job which is the predecessor of the next level. Then we divide in height of the mesh into $k + 2$ shelves. The j-th shelf has a height of A_j, $1 \leq j \leq k+1$, and the $(k+2)$-nd (the last) shelf has a height of one. We assign (A_i, A_j) into shelf of height A_j and a job of the chain is assigned into a shelf with height 1. It results in a schedule with length of l. The schedule is illustrated as follows.

Time intervals	Jobs scheduled
$(0, 1]$	$\{(A_1, A_1)\}$
$(1, 2]$	$\{(A_1, A_1), (A_2, A_1)\}$
$(2, 3]$	$\{(A_1, A_1), (A_2, A_1), (A_3, A_1)\}$
$\cdots$	$\cdots$
$((k+1)^2 - 1, (k+1)^2]$	$\{(A_1, A_1), (A_2, A_1), \ldots, (A_{k+1}, A_{k+1})\}$
$((k+1)^2, (k+1)^2 + 1]$	$\{(A_1, A_1), (A_2, A_1), \ldots, (A_{k+1}, A_{k+1}), (1, 1)\}$
$\cdots$	$\cdots$
$(l-1, l]$	$\{(A_1, A_1), (A_2, A_1), \ldots, (A_{k+1}, A_{k+1}), (1, 1)\}$

Contrary to the optimal schedule, the job which is the predecessor of all jobs in the next level must be scheduled last among the jobs in the same level by any on-line scheduler, since all the jobs in a level have the same size and the on-line scheduler can not distinguish them. Note that $N/(t_{k+1} - 1) > A_{k+1} \geq$

$N/(t_{k+1} - 1) - (k + 1)$. It implies that at most $(t_i - 1)(t_{k+1} - 1)$ jobs of size (A_i, A_{k+1}) can be scheduled together on the mesh. It is also easy to check that at most $(t_i - 1)(t_j - 1)$ jobs of size (A_i, A_j), $(1 \leq i, j \leq k + 1)$ can be scheduled together on the mesh by any on-line scheduler. Thus the length generated by the on-line scheduler is at least

$$\sum_{j=1}^{k+1}\sum_{i=1}^{k+1} \lceil \frac{l - (i - 1) - (j - 1)(k + 1)}{(t_i - 1)(t_j - 1)} \rceil + l - (k + 1)^2$$

$$\geq \sum_{j=1}^{k+1}\sum_{i=1}^{k+1} \frac{l - (k + 1)^2}{(t_i - 1)(t_j - 1)} + l - (k + 1)^2$$

$$= ((\sum_{i=1}^{k+1} \frac{1}{t_i - 1})^2 + 1)(l - (k + 1)^2)$$

Recall that the optimal schedule has a length of l and $l \geq k^3$. For $k \to \infty$, the competitive ratio of any on-line algorithm can be arbitrarily close to $h_\infty^2 + 1$. □

Epstein [5] showed that the competitive ratio of any bounded space online algorithm for two dimensional bin packing is at least 2.535 if the items can be rotated. In the instance eight types of items are introduced. Let $\delta > 0$ be a sufficiently small constant. Consider square bins of side length 1. Items of type 1 are squares of side length $1/2 + \delta$; items of type 2 are squares of side length $1/3 + \delta$; items of type 3 are rectangles of width $2/3 - \delta$ and height $1/3 + 2\delta$; items of type 4 are rectangles of width $2/3 - 2\delta$ and height $1/3 + 3\delta$; items of type 5 are rectangles of width $11/21 - 4\delta$ and height $10/63 + 2\delta$; items of type 6 are rectangles of width $32/63 - 4\delta$ and height $31/189 + 2\delta$; items of type 7 are squares of side length $1/7 + \delta$; items of type 8 are tiny squares, where eight items, exactly one of which from each type, can fit in a bin since the items are rotatable. We can use the same instance from [5] by adding precedence constraints among the jobs (items): A (critical) job of type i is the predecessor of all jobs of type $i + 1$ for $i = 1, \ldots, 7$, and the jobs of type 8 form a chain. There are $l - i + 1$ jobs of Type i, for $i = 1, \ldots, 8$, where $l > 0$ is an arbitrarily large integer. We can assume that the last scheduled job of Type i $(i = 1, \ldots, 7)$ by any on-line algorithm is the critical job. It is not difficult to prove the following lower bound by using the similar arguments from [5].

Theorem 3.2. *No on-line algorithms can have competitive ratios lower than* 3.535 *for scheduling on a rotated 2-d mesh.* □

4   Online Algorithms

For convenience, in this section we normalize an $N_1 * N_2$ mesh as a unit square (bin). A job J_i, denoted also by (a_i, b_i), has a width $a_i \leq 1$ and a height $b_i \leq 1$. The *work* of a job is defined as the number of requested processors divided by $N_1 \times N_2$. In other words, the work of job J_i, is the area $a_i b_i$ of job J_i.

The *efficiency* of a schedule at any time t is defined to be the number of busy processors at time t divided by $N_1 \times N_2$. Therefore, the efficiency of a schedule at any time can be viewed as the total work of the jobs in a bin. It is also called the efficiency of the bin. For any time unit, assigning jobs to the processors on a mesh can be regarded as packing rectangles into a square bin without any overlap. The resulting makespan by a schedule is exactly the number of bins used for packing the jobs.

We divide the jobs into *big*, *long*, *wide* and *small* jobs. A job is called big if both its width and its height are larger than $1/2$. A job is called small if both its width and its height are at most $1/2$. A job is long if its height is larger than $1/2$ but its width is at most $1/2$. A job is wide if its width is larger than $1/2$ but its height is at most $1/2$.

In the following we first present an (off-line) algorithm, which schedules available jobs into bins. Then applying this algorithm to the jobs level by level, we get an on-line algorithm.

Algorithm *RP.*

1. Group the jobs. In this step we just group the jobs into different bins. The jobs assigned to a bin are packed in the next step.
   - Put big jobs each in a bin.
   - Put long jobs with First-Fit to the partially filled bins (by big jobs) if the total width of the jobs is at most 1. If a long job can not fit in any of the partially-filled bins, open a new bin for it.
   - Open new bins for wide jobs and pack them with First-Fit. A job can be put to a bin if the total height of the jobs is at most one.
   - Consider all partially filled bins with total work of jobs packed less than $1/2$. Put small jobs into them with First-Fit as long as the total work of jobs is at most $1/2$. If a small job can not fit in any of the partially filled bins (i.e., the total work will exceed $1/2$ if the small job is put into the bins), open a new bin for it.
2. Pack the jobs.
   - If a bin contains no small jobs, these jobs can be easily packed into a bin since either the total height of them or the total width of them is no more than 1.
   - If a bin contains no big job but some small jobs, the total work of the jobs in this bin is at most $1/2$ and either all jobs are not wide or all jobs are not long. By Steinberg's algorithm, these jobs can be packed into a bin.
   - If a bin contains a big job as well as some small jobs, this bin can be packed as follows. Let x be the total width of the big job and the long jobs (if any). Clearly, $x < 1$. Otherwise, the total work of them is over $1/2$, and no small jobs can be accepted in the step for grouping jobs. Among the small jobs, let T_1 be the ones with width larger than $1 - x$ and let T_2 be the ones with width at most $1 - x$. Place the big job to the leftmost bottom of the bin. Put long jobs one by one upon the big job to the left. Put jobs of T_1 one by one on the right of the big job. Put

jobs of T_2 to the free space above the long jobs by Steinberg's algorithm. This free space is exactly a rectangle with width $1 - x$ and height 1. The following figure (Figure 1) gives an illustration of the packing.

Lemma 4.1. *The above packing is feasible.*

Proof. We only need to consider the last case that a bin contains a big job as well as some small jobs. Let a_{max} and b_{max} be the width and the height of the big job, respectively. Let $s(T_1)$ be the total work of jobs in T_1. Assume that the total height of jobs in T_1 is larger than $1 - b_{max}$. Then $s(T_1) > (1 - b_{max})(1 - x)$. On the other hand, the total work of the big job and the long jobs is at least $a_{max}b_{max} + (x - a_{max})/2$. Let $s(B)$ be the total work of the jobs in the bin.

$$s(B) > a_{max}b_{max} + (x - a_{max})/2 + (1 - b_{max})(1 - x)$$
$$= 1/2 + a_{max}(b_{max} - 1/2) + (1 - x)(1/2 - b_{max})$$
$$= 1/2 + (a_{max} + x - 1)(b_{max} - 1/2)$$
$$> 1/2$$

It gives a contradiction. Therefore, the total height of jobs in T_1 is at most $1 - b_{max}$. These jobs can be packed to the right of the big job .

We turn to T_2. Let $s(T_2)$ be the the total work of jobs in T_2. $s(T_2) < 1/2 - x/2 = (1 - x)/2$. In other words, the total work of jobs in T_2 is less than the half of the area of a rectangle with width $1 - x$ and height 1. The height of any job in T_2 is at most $1/2$ (they are small jobs) and their width is no more than $1 - x$. Using Steinberg's algorithm the jobs can be packed into the free space of the bin (a rectangle with width $1 - x$ and height 1). $\qquad\square$

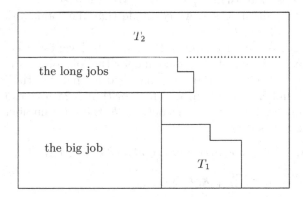

Fig. 1. An illustration of the packing with a big job

In a packing given by algorithm RP, a bin is called a W-bin if it contains wide jobs, an L-bin if it contains a big job or long jobs, an S-bin if it contains only small jobs.

Lemma 4.2. *At a level if $m \geq 3$ bins are used, then the total work of the jobs is at least $m/3 - b/12 - 1/2$, where b is the number of big jobs of the level.*

Proof. We divide the m bins into two groups. G_1 consists of L-bins and S-bins, while G_2 consists of W-bins. Let $p = |G_1|$ and $q = |G_2|$. $m = p + q$. We first assume that $p \neq 1$ and $q \neq 1$. Consider G_1.

Case 1. There are no big jobs, i.e., $b = 0$. Except the last bin there are at most one bin with efficiency less than $1/3$. To observe this, if a bin B_i has efficiency less than $1/3$, then all jobs assigned to the succeeding bins have size larger than $1/6$ (otherwise they should have been assigned to B_i). And any two jobs can be put into a bin. Therefore except B_i and perhaps the last bin all the other bins have efficiency larger than $1/3$. On the other hand, the sum of efficiency of B_i and the last bin is more than $1/2$. It follows that the total work of the jobs in G_1 is more than $(p - 2)/3 + 1/2 = p/3 - 1/6$.

Case 2. $b \geq 1$. Note that each bin containing a big job has efficiency larger than $1/4$. If all the bins containing a big job have efficiency at least $1/3$, we obtain the same bound for the total work of the jobs as in Case 1. Assume that at least one of such bins has efficiency less than $1/3$. Then all the other bins except the last one, which contain no big jobs, have efficiency larger than $1/3$. Moreover, the sum of efficiency of a bin with a big job and the last bin is larger than $1/2$. It implies that the total work of the jobs is at least $(b-1)/4 + (p-b-1)/3 + 1/2 = p/3 - b/12 - 1/12$.

Now we consider G_2. Since G_2 contains no big jobs, it is easy to obtain, analogously as Case 1, that the total work of the jobs in G_2 is more than $q/3 - 1/6$.

Thus the total work of the jobs in the level is more than $(p+q)/3 - b/12 - 1/3 = m/3 - b/12 - 1/3$.

If $p = 1$, the total work of the jobs is more than $q/3 - 1/6 = m/3 - 1/2$. If $q = 1$, the total work of the jobs is more than $m/3 - 1/2$ if $b = 0$, and the total work of the jobs is more than $m/3 - b/12 - 5/12$ if $b \geq 1$.

By considering all the cases, we conclude that the total work of the jobs is at least $m/3 - b/12 - 1/2$. □

Algorithm $N2d$. Apply algorithm RP to the jobs level by level. As the jobs of level i have been assigned, start a schedule for the jobs of level $i + 1$.

Let l be the maximum number of bins used for packing the jobs in a level. Let k_i be the number of levels in which algorithm $N2d$ uses exactly i bins for packing the jobs, for $i = 1, 2, \ldots l$. Denote by b_i the total number of big jobs in the levels using i bins.

Theorem 4.3. *The competitive ratio of algorithm $N2d$ is at most 5.25.*

Proof. Clearly, $T_{N2d} = \sum_{i=1}^{l} i k_i$ and

$$T_{opt} \geq \sum_{i=1}^{l} k_i. \tag{1}$$

By Lemma 4.2, the total work of all jobs is at least $\sum_{i=3}^{l}(k_i(i/3 - 1/2) - b_i/12)$. Then

$$T_{opt} \geq \sum_{i=3}^{l}(i k_i/3 - b_i/12 - k_i/2). \tag{2}$$

On the other hand, any two big jobs can not be processed at the same time. It implies that

$$T_{opt} \geq \sum_{i=3}^{l} b_i. \tag{3}$$

Summing up the inequalities (1) multiplying by 2, (2) multiplying by 3, (3) multiplying by 1/4, we have

$$(2 + 3 + 1/4)T_{opt} \geq \sum_{i=1}^{l} 2k_i + \sum_{i=3}^{l}(ik_i - b_i/4 - 3k_i/2) + \sum_{i=3}^{l} b_i/4$$
$$\geq \sum_{i=1}^{l} ik_i = T_{N2d}.$$

It follows that $T_{N2d} \leq 5.25 T_{opt}$. $\square$

Corollary 4.4. *If there are only small jobs and long jobs (or wide jobs), the competitive ratio of algorithm N2d is at most 4.*

Proof. At a level if $i \geq 2$ bins are used, the total work of the jobs at this level is larger than $(i - 2)/3 + 1/2 = i/3 - 1/6$. Adopt the same terminology as in the proof of Theorem 4.3. We have $T_{opt} \geq \sum_{i=2}^{l}(ik_i/3 - k_i/6)$. Then

$$3T_{opt} \geq \sum_{i=2}^{l}(ik_i - k_i/2). \tag{4}$$

Summing inequalities (1) and (4) we get

$$4T_{opt} \geq \sum_{i=1}^{l} k_i + \sum_{i=2}^{l}(ik_i - k_i/2) \geq \sum_{i=1}^{l} ik_i = T_{N2d}.$$

$\square$

Corollary 4.5. *If there are no wide jobs (or no long jobs), the competitive ratio of algorithm N2d is at most 4.25.*

Proof. At a level if two bins are used, the total work of the jobs at this level is larger than 1/2. Similarly as the proof of Theorem 4.3, we have

$$T_{opt} \geq k_2/2 + \sum_{i=3}^{l}(ik_i/3 - b_i/12 - k_i/2). \tag{5}$$

Summing up the inequalities (1), (5) multiplying by 3, (3) multiplying by 1/4, we have $T_{N2d} \leq 4.25 T_{opt}$. $\square$

Finally we consider the problem of scheduling parallel jobs on a rotated 2-d mesh. For job $J_i = (a_i, b_i)$, we can schedule it on a submesh $a_i * b_i$ or a submesh $b_i * a_i$, where the processors at each node are identical.

Algorithm R2d: Rotate the jobs such that $a_i \geq b_i$. Then apply algorithm N2d.

Theorem 4.6. *The competitive ratio of algorithm R2d is at most 4.25.*

Proof. It follows directly from Corollary 4.5. $\square$

5   Conclusions

In this paper, we investigate on-line scheduling of parallel jobs on two dimensional meshes. The dependencies among jobs are unknown to the on-line scheduler. A job appears only when all its predecessors have been completed. Parallel jobs may require several processor and the job processing times are identical. We give a lower bound of 3.859 and an upper bound of 5.25 on the normal 2-d mesh, which improves the previous lower bound of 3.25 and upper bound of 46/7. On the rotated 2-d mesh where the parallel jobs may rotate, a lower bound of 3.535 and a 4.25-competitive on-line algorithm are given. It is interesting to improve both the present lower bound and upper bound. We guess that the tight bound is much closer to the lower bound of 3.859 for the normal 2-d mesh.

Acknowledgment. We would like to thank Leah Epstein for pointing out the reference [5] and the helpful comments to improve the lower bound for the rotated case.

References

1. S. Bischof, Efficient algorithm for on-line scheduling and load distribution in parallel systems, Ph.D. Thesis, Institut für Informatik, Technische Universität München, 1999.
2. S. Bischof, E. W. Mayr, On-line scheduling of parallel jobs with runtime restrictions, *Theoretical Computer Science* **268** (2001), 67–90.
3. M. Drozdowski, Scheduling multiprocessor tasks – an overview, *European Journal on Operations Research* **94** (1996), 215–230.
4. J. Du and J. Leung, Complexity of scheduling parallel task systems, *SIAM Journal on Discrete Mathematics* **2** (1989), 473–487.
5. L. Epstein, Two dimensional packing: the power of rotation, accepted to the 28th International Symposium on Mathematical Foundations of Computer Science (MFCS2003), Bratislava, Slovak.
6. A. Feldmann, M.-Y. Kao, J. Sgall, and S.-H. Teng, Optimal on-line scheduling of parallel jobs with dependencies, *J. Combin. Optim.* **1** (1998), 393–411.
7. A. Feldmann, J. Sgall, and S.-H. Teng, Dynamic scheduling on parallel machines, *Theoretical Computer Science* (Special Issue on Dynamic and On-line Algorithms) **130** (1994), 49–72.
8. W. Ludwig and P. Tiwari, Scheduling malleable and nonmalleable parallel tasks, Proc. 5th ACM-SIAM Symposium on Discrete Algorithms, 1994, pp. 167–176.
9. H.E. Salzer, The approximation of numbers as sums of reciprocals, *Amer. Math. Monthly* **54** (1947), 135–142.
10. J. Sgall, On-line scheduling on parallel machines, Ph.D. Thesis, School of Computer Science, Carnegie Mellon University, Pittsburgh, PA, 1994.
11. A. Steinberg, A strip-packing algorithm with absolute performance bound two, *SIAM Journal on Computing* **26** (1997), 401–409.
12. J. Turek, J. Wolf, and P. Yu, Approximation algorithms for scheduling parallelizable tasks, Proc. 4th ACM Symposium on Parallel Algorithms and Architectures, 1992, pp. 323–332.

Efficient Algorithms for Descendent Subtrees Comparison of Phylogenetic Trees with Applications to Co-evolutionary Classifications in Bacterial Genome

Yaw-Ling Lin[1]* and Tsan-Sheng Hsu[2]

[1] Department of Computer Science and Information Management, Providence
University, 200 Chung Chi Road, Shalu, Taichung, Taiwan 433. yllin@pu.edu.tw
[2] Institute of Information Science Academia Sinica, Nankang 115 Taipei, Taiwan 115.
tshsu@iis.sinica.edu.tw

Abstract. A phylogenetic tree is a rooted tree with unbounded degree
such that each leaf node is uniquely labelled from 1 to n. The descendent subtree of of a phylogenetic tree T is the subtree composed by all
edges and nodes of T descending from a vertex. Given a set of phylogenetic trees, we present linear time algorithms for finding all leaf-agree
descendent subtrees as well as all isomorphic descendent subtrees.

The *normalized cluster distance*, $d(A, B)$, of two sets is defined by
$d(A, B) = \Delta(A, B)/(|A| + |B|)$, where $\Delta(A, B)$ denotes the symmetric
set difference of two sets. We show that computing all pairs normalized
cluster distances between descendent subtrees of two phylogenetic trees
can be done in $O(n^2)$ time. Since the total size of the outputs will be
$\Theta(n^2)$, the algorithm is thus computationally optimal.

A nearest subtree of a subset of leaves is such a descendent subtree that
has the smallest normalized cluster distance to these leaves. Here we
show that finding nearest subtrees for a collection of pairwise disjoint
subsets of leaves can be done in $O(n)$ time.

Several applications of these algorithms in areas of bioinformatics is
considered. Among them, we discuss the 2CS (Two component systems)
functional analysis and classifications on bacterial genome.

Keywords: Algorithm, phylogenetic trees, subtrees comparison, co-
evolutionary classification.

1 Introduction

Trees are widely used to represent evolutionary, historical, or hierarchical relationships in various fields of classification. Biologists use the information contained in the DNA sequences of a collection of organisms, or taxa, to infer the

---

* This work is supported in part by the National Science Council, Taiwan, R.O.C,
grant NSC-91-2213-E-126-004.

T. Ibaraki, N. Katoh, and H. Ono (Eds.): ISAAC 2003, LNCS 2906, pp. 339–351, 2003.

evolutionary relationships among those taxa. *Phylogenetic trees* typically represent the evolutionary history of a collection of extant species or the line of descent of some genes, and may also be used to classify individuals (or populations) of the same species. Numerous phylogenetic inference methods, e.g. maximum parsimony, maximum likelihood, distance matrix fitting, subtrees consistency, and quartet based methods have been proposed over the years [15,1,14,26,17,27,4]; furthermore, it is rather common to compare the same set of species w.r.t. different biological sequences or different genes, hence obtaining various trees. The resulting trees may agree in some parts and differ in others. In general, one is interested in finding the largest set of items on which the trees agree. This fact motivates the compelling need to compare different trees in order to achieve consensus or extract partial agreements. For measuring the similarity / difference between trees, several distance measures have been proposed [9], e.g. the symmetric difference metric [23], the nearest-neighbor interchange metric [29], the subtree transfer distance [2], the Robinson and Foulds (RF) metric [24], and the quartet metric [11,6].

There have been many suggestions for how to infer the consensus tree from a profile of trees in the literature [7,12,3,10]. Among them, many extensively investigated results concerning the *maximum agreement subtree problem* (MAST). Also known as the *maximum homeomorphic agreement subtree* [5], the problem is: given a set of rooted trees whose leaves are drawn from the same set of items of size n, find the largest subset of these items so that the portions of the trees restricted to the subset are isomorphic. Amir and Keselman [3] show that the problem is NP-hard even for 3 unbounded degree trees. The problem is also hard to approximate. Hein *et al.* [19] show that the MAST for three trees with unbounded degree cannot be approximated within ratio $2^{\log^\delta n}$ in polynomial time for any $\delta < 1$, unless NP $\subset$ DTIME$[2^{\text{polylog } n}]$. On the positive side, polynomial time algorithms are obtainable for three or more bounded degree trees [3, 12], even though the time complexity is exponential in the bound for the degree. Efficient algorithms for the MAST problem for instances of two trees have been widely investigated in literature. Farach and Thorup [13] give an $O(n^{1.5} \log n)$ time algorithm for two arbitrary degree trees. Cole *et al.* [8] show that the MAST of two binary trees can be found in $O(n \log n)$ time, while the MAST of two degree d trees can be found in $O(\min\{n\sqrt{d} \log^2 n, nd \log n \log d\})$ time.

With the rapid expansion in genomic data, the age of large-scale biomolecular sequence analysis has arrived. An important line of research in post-genome analysis is to analyze the evolution and co-evolution genes clustering of genomic sequences. Facing the known algorithmic difficulties of MAST problem discussed above, here we turn our attention to the problem of comparing the *descendent subtrees* among a set of different phylogenetic trees according to their Robinson-Foulds distance metric.

The Robinson-Foulds distance metric [24] is a commonly used similarity measure, which is closely related to the notion of symmetric set difference [16]. Formally, let $A, B \subset S$ be two clusters of genes set S. The *symmetric set difference*, $\Delta(A, B)$, is defined by $\Delta(A, B) = |A \cup B \setminus A \cap B| = |A \setminus B| + |B \setminus A|$. Further, the *normalized cluster distance*, a RF-like metric, $d(A, B)$, is defined as $d(A, B) = \frac{\Delta(A,B)}{|A|+|B|}$ The normalized cluster distance between two sets is considered to be a rough measurement of the *degree of difference* between them. Note that $0 \leq d(A, B) \leq 1$; $d(A, B) = 0$ if $A = B$, and $d(A, B) = 1$ if $A \cap B = \emptyset$. In other words, the smaller value of $d(A, B)$ implies a greater *similarity* of A, B.

Consider a rooted (unbounded degree) phylogenetic tree T with n leaves such that each leaf is labelled with a distinct number from 1 to n. Here we assume that each internal node of T has at least two children; thus the total size of T is bounded by $O(n)$. Let v be a (internal or leaf) vertex of T. The *descendent subtree* of T descending from v, denoted by $T[v]$, is the subtree of T composed by all edges and nodes of T descending from v. Furthermore, we use $L_T(v)$ to denote the set of all descendent leaves of v in T. That is, $L_T(v) = \{x \mid x \text{ a leaf of } T[v]\}$. Furthermore, for clarity of presentation, we sometimes omit the subscript T and use $L(v)$ as a shorthand of $L_T(v)$ when the context is clear. Note that $L(v) = \{v\}$ if v itself is a leaf.

Let T_i, T_j be two rooted trees whose leaves are drawn from the same set $\{1, \ldots, n\}$. Two descendent subtrees of T_i, T_j, namely $T_i[v_i]$ and $T_j[v_j]$, are called *leaf-agree* if $L_{T_i}(v_i) = L_{T_j}(v_j)$. Two *leaf-agree isomorphic* (or just *isomorphic*) subtrees, denoted by $T_i[v_i] \cong T_j[v_j]$, are defined recursively as the following: Either $v_i \in T_i$ and $v_j \in T_j$ are two leaf nodes with the same label; otherwise, the children of v_i (say $\{v_{i1}, \ldots, v_{im}\}$) and the children of v_j (say $\{v_{j1}, \ldots, v_{jm}\}$) can be but into one-to-one corresponding such that $T_i[v_{i1}] \cong T_i[v_{i1}], \ldots$, and $T_i[v_{im}] \cong T_i[v_{im}]$.

In this paper, we consider the following problems:

Definition 1 (all-pair-descendent-subtree). *Given two rooted trees, $\{T_1, T_2\}$ whose leaves are drawn from the same set S, compute the all pairs normalized cluster distances between each pair of descendent leaves. That is, output the set $\{d(L_{T_1}(u), L_{T_2}(v)) \mid u \in T_1, v \in T_2\}$.*

Definition 2 (near-subtree). *Given a rooted trees T with leaf nodes S and a subset $V \subset S$, compute the nearest descendent subtree of T with respect to V. That is, find a vertex $v^* \in T$ such that $d(V, L_T(v^*)) = \min\{d(V, L_T(v)) \mid v \in T\}$.*

Definition 3 (leaf-agree-subtree). *Given a set of rooted trees, $\{T_1, T_2, \ldots, T_k\}$ whose leaves are drawn from the same set S, find the all leaf-agree subtrees of these trees. That is, output the set $\{(v_1, v_2, \ldots, v_k) \mid v_1 \in T_1, v_2 \in T_2, \ldots, v_k \in T_k, L_{T_1}(v_1) = L_{T_2}(v_2) = \cdots = L_{T_k}(v_k)\}$.*

Definition 4 (isomorphic-subtree). *Given a set of rooted trees, $\{T_1, T_2, \ldots, T_k\}$ whose leaves are drawn from the same set S, find all isomorphic subtrees of these trees. That is, output the set $\{(v_1, v_2, \ldots, v_k) \mid v_1 \in T_1, v_2 \in T_2, \ldots, v_k \in T_k, T_1[v_1] \cong T_2[v_2] \cong \cdots \cong T_k[v_k]\}$.*

The rest of the paper is organized as the following. In Section 2, we show that computing all pairs normalized cluster distances between all paired subtrees of two trees can be done in $O(n^2)$ time. Since the total size of the outputs will be

$\Theta(n^2)$, the algorithm is thus computationally optimal. In Section 3, we show that finding nearest subtrees for a collection of pairwise disjointed subsets of leaves can be done in $O(n)$ time. In Section 4, we show that finding all leaf-agree-subtrees as well as the isomorphic subtrees of $\{T_1, T_2, \ldots, T_k\}$ can be solved in $O(kn)$ time, which are optimal linear time algorithms proportional to the size of the input trees. Section 5 discusses the biological applications in more depth.

2 All Pairs Subtrees Comparison

Here we discuss the problem of all pairs subtree comparison. A naive algorithm would need to compute all the normalized distances of all pairs of subtrees of given paired trees using $O(n^2)$ comparisons with each comparison takes $O(n)$ time; thus a totally $O(n^3)$ operations are needed.

The goal here is to compute all paired distances within $O(n^2)$ time. Note that the total size of the outputs will be $\Theta(n^2)$. An $O(n^2)$ time algorithm is thus computationally optimal. The idea here is trying to find a recurrence formula such that the normalized cluster distance of a parent node can be computed from its children in time proportional to the number of its children. Let u be a node of a phylogenetic tree T_1, and v be a node of another phylogenetic tree T_2 such that v is the parent of $\{v_1, \ldots, v_m\}$. Now the target is to compute $\Delta(u, v)$ from $\{\Delta(u, v_1), \ldots, \Delta(u, v_m)\}$ in $O(m)$ time. Here, for easier description, we use $\Delta(u, v)$ as a short-hand notation of $\Delta(L(u), L(v))$.

Lemma 1 (constant time $\Delta(A, B)$ calculation). *Let A, B_1, B_2 be 3 sets with $B_1 \cap B_2 = \emptyset$. It follows that $\Delta(A, B_1 \cup B_2) = \Delta(A, B_1) + \Delta(A, B_2) - |A|$.*

Proof. It is easily verified that $\Delta(X, Y) = |X| + |Y| - 2|X \cap Y|$ for any two sets X, Y. Now we have

$$
\begin{aligned}
\Delta(A, B_1 \cup B_2) &= |A| + |B_1 \cup B_2| - 2|A \cap (B_1 \cup B_2)| \\
&= |A| + |B_1| + |B_2| - 2|A \cap (B_1 \cup B_2)| \\
&= |A| + |B_1| + |B_2| - 2|A \cap B_1| - 2|A \cap B_2)| \\
&= |A| + |B_1| - 2|A \cap B_1| + |A| + |B_2| - 2|A \cap B_2)| - |A| \\
&= \Delta(A, B_1) + \Delta(A, B_2) - |A|
\end{aligned}
$$

since $B_1 \cap B_2 = \emptyset$. $\qquad\square$

The following result shall be easily deduced from Lemma 1 by induction.

Corollary 1. *Let $A, B_1, \ldots, B_k$ be $k + 1$ sets such that $(\forall i \neq j)(B_i \cap B_j = \emptyset)$. It follows that $\Delta(A, B_1 \cup \cdots \cup B_k) = (1 - k)|A| + \sum_{i=1}^{k} \Delta(A, B_i)$.*

Note that Lemma 1 implies that $\Delta(u, v)$ can be calculated from $\Delta(u, v_1)$ and $\Delta(u, v_2)$ in constant time when $|L(u)|$ is precomputed. Given a pair of phylogenetic trees T_1 and T_2, we can store at each node $u \in T_1, v \in T_2$ with its associated descendants size $|L(u)|$ and $|L(v)|$. Further, for each node $u \in T_1$ we can store an array consisting of $\Delta(u, \cdot)$'s so that whenever we need to decide the value $d(u, v)$, it can be computed as $d(u, v) = \Delta(u, v)/(|L(u)| + |L(v)|)$.

Theorem 1. *Computing all paired subtree distances can be done in $O(n^2)$ time.*

ALL-PAIR(T_1, T_2)
Input: Two phylogenetic trees T_1 and T_2 with leaves $\{1, 2, \ldots, n\}$.
Output: All pairs $\Delta(u, v)$'s for all $u \in T_1, v \in T_2$.

1 Compute $|L(u)|$'s, $|L(v)|$'s, level(u)'s, level(v)'s for all $u \in T_1, v \in T_2$.
2 **for each** $u \in T_1$ in increasing order of level(u) **do** $\quad \triangleright$ bottom up.
3 $\quad$ **for each** $v \in T_2$ in increasing order of level(v) **do**
4 $\quad\quad$ **if** both u, v are leaf nodes **then** $\quad \triangleright$ initial condition.
5 $\quad\quad\quad$ $\Delta(u, v) \leftarrow 0$ if $u = v$; otherwise, $\Delta(u, v) \leftarrow 2$
6 $\quad\quad$ **else if** u is a leaf **then** let v be the parent of $\{v_1, \ldots, v_j\}$;
7 $\quad\quad\quad$ $\Delta(u, v) \leftarrow 1 - j + \sum_{i=1}^{j} \Delta(u, v_i)$ $\quad \triangleright$ Note that $(1 - j) = (1 - j)|L(u)|$.
8 $\quad\quad$ **else** let u be the parent of $\{u_1, \ldots, u_k\}$;
9 $\quad\quad\quad$ $\Delta(u, v) \leftarrow (1 - k)|L(v)| + \sum_{i=1}^{k} \Delta(u_i, v)$

Fig. 1. Computing all pairs $\Delta(T_1, T_2)$'s in $O(n^2)$ time.

Proof. We propose an $O(n^2)$ time algorithm, ALL-PAIR(T_1, T_2), shown in Figure 1. The algorithm essentially builds up all $\Delta(\cdot, \cdot)$'s in a bottom up manner. The correctness of the algorithm is easily followed by Corollary 1 and the correctness of the computation ordering.

To ensure the correct computation ordering, we introduce the following notations. Recall that the *v-descendant subtree*, denoted by $T[v]$, is the subtree induced of by all descendants of v in T; here we assume that v is a descendant of itself. The *level* of a node v in T, denoted by level(v), is the *height* of $T[v]$. Thus, whenever we traverse nodes of a phylogenetic tree T in their *increasing* levels ordering, we ensure that the descendants of a node v have already been visited before v.

It is easily seen that Step 1 of ALL-PAIR can be computed in $O(n)$ time by a bottom up computation. A commonly used post order nodes traversal of a tree suffices. Let v be the parent of $\{v_1, \ldots, v_m\}$ in a tree T. It follows that $|L(v)| = |L(v_1)| + \cdots + |L(v_m)|$ with the initial condition that $|L(v)| = 1$ when v is a leaf. Further, level(v) = $\max\{$level(v_1), $\ldots$, level(v_m)$\} + 1$ with the initial condition that level(v) = 1 when v is a leaf. These computation can be done in time proportional to the number of edges plus the number vertices in T, i.e., $O(n)$ time.

Also, it is clear that the total works for the inner loop of Step 3 to Step 9 take time proportional to the number of edges plus the number vertices in T, i.e., $O(n)$ time. Since there are exactly $O(n)$ number of iterations for the outer loop (Step 2), it follows that ALL-PAIR(T_1, T_2) finishes in $O(n^2)$ time. $\quad \square$

3   Nearest Subtrees

The *lowest common ancestor* (LCA) between two nodes u and v in a tree is the furthest node from the root node that exists on both paths from the root to u and v. Harel and Tarjan [18] have shown that any n-node tree can be preprocessed in $O(n)$ time such that subsequently LCA queries can be answered in constant time.

3.1   Confluent Subtrees

Let T be a phylogenetic tree with leaf nodes L. Given $S \subset L$, let set $\Lambda(S) = \{\text{LCA}(x, y) \mid x \neq y \in S\}$ denote the collection of all (proper) lowest common ancestors defined over S.

Definition 5 (confluent subtree). *Let T be a phylogenetic tree with leaf nodes S. Given $S \subset L$, the confluent subtree of S in T is a phylogenetic tree, denoted by $T_{\uparrow S}$, with leaf nodes S and internal nodes $\Lambda(S)$. Further, $u \in \Lambda(S)$ is a parent of v in $T_{\uparrow S}$ if and only if u is the lowest ancestor of v in T comparing to any other node in $\Lambda(S)$.*

Our notation of confluent subtree is called *induced subtrees* in the literature [8]. Let T be a phylogenetic tree with leaf nodes L. A post-order (pre-order, or in-order) traversal of nodes of L within T defines a *tree ordering* of nodes on L. The following results is a generalization of the section 8 of [8].

Lemma 2. *Let T be an n-node phylogenetic tree with leaf nodes L. The following subsequent operation can be done efficiently after an $O(n)$ time preprocessing. Given a query set $A \subset L$, the confluent subtree $T_{\uparrow A}$ can be constructed in $O(|A|)$ time if A is given in sorted tree ordering; otherwise, $T_{\uparrow A}$ can be constructed in $O(|A| \log \log |A|)$ time.*

Proof. We propose an $O(|A|)$ time algorithm, CONFLUENT(T, A), shown in Figure 2. The algorithm requires $O(n)$ time preprocessing phase for building up the tree ordering of L on T, and perform the LCA constant time queries preprocessing [18]. Further, the input $A \subset L$ is assumed to be listed according to the tree ordering of L; otherwise, we can use the data structure of van Emde Boas [28] for sorting these finite ranged integers in $O(|A| \log \log |A|)$ time.

The correctness and the time analysis of the proof is omitted for most of the details are similiar to the arguments presented [8].   □

3.2   Nearest Subtrees

Here we discuss the problem of finding the nearest descendent subtree within a phylogenetic tree given a subset of leaf nodes.

Definition 6 (nearest subtree). *Let T be a phylogenetic tree with leaf nodes L. Given $A \subset L$, a node (internal or leaf) $v \in T$ (inducing $T[v]$) is the nearest subtree of A in T if $(\forall x \in T)\, (d(L(v), A) \leq d(L(x), A))$.*

CONFLUENT(T, A)

Input: A phylogenetic trees T with leaves $L = \{1, 2, \ldots, n\}$, $A \subset L$.
Output: The confluent subtree of A in T, $T_{\uparrow A}$.

Preprocessing: Compute the tree ordering of L on T, and perform the LCA constant time queries preprocessing [18].
Notations: $p[\cdot, T'], left[\cdot, T'], right[\cdot, T']$: parent, left, right children links.

1 Let $A = \langle v_1, v_2, \ldots, v_k \rangle$ be nodes of A in the tree ordering.
2 Create a dummy node λ and let $level[T, \lambda] \leftarrow +\infty$; PUSH(S, λ)
3 **for** $i \leftarrow 1$ **to** $k - 1$ **do** $\triangleright$ visit each v_i's.
4      $x \leftarrow$ LCA(v_i, v_{i+1}) ; $y \leftarrow v_i$
5   **while** $level[x, T] > level[top[S], T]$ **do** $y \leftarrow$ POP(S)
6   PUSH(S, x) ; $p[v_{i+1}, T'] \leftarrow x$; $p[y, T'] \leftarrow x$; $p[x, T'] \leftarrow top[S]$
7      $left[x, T'] \leftarrow y$; $right[x, T'] \leftarrow v_{i+1}$; $right[top[S], T'] \leftarrow x$
8 $root[T'] \leftarrow right[\lambda, T']$; **return** T' as $T_{\uparrow A}$;

Fig. 2. Computing the confluent subtree.

By utilizing Lemma 2, we can efficiently solve the nearest subtrees problem.

Theorem 2. *Let T be an n-leaf phylogenetic tree with leaf nodes L. Given a collection of pairwise disjoint subsets of L, $S = \{A_1, A_2, \ldots, A_j\}$, the nearest subtrees of all A_i's on T can be found in totally $O(n)$ time.*

NEAREST(T, S)

Input: A phylogenetic trees T with leaves L, $S = \{A_1, A_2, \ldots, A_j\}, A_i \subset L$.
Output: The nearest subtrees of A_i's in T.

1 Compute the tree ordering of L on T and the LCA queries preprocessing.
2 Sort nodes of A_i's in the tree ordering.
3 Compute the subtree sum $s[v, T]$'s for each $v \in T$; $Q \leftarrow \emptyset$
4 **for** $i \leftarrow 1$ **to** $|S|$ **do** $\triangleright$ visit each A_i's.
5      $T_i \leftarrow$ CONFLUENT(T, A_i)
6   Compute the subtree sum $s[v, T_i]$'s for each $v \in T_i$.
7      $\triangleright$ Find the node v in T_i with the maximum $d(A_i, L(v))$.
       $v_i \leftarrow \arg\max\{d(A_i, L(v)) = 1 - 2s[v, T_i]/(s[v, T] + |A_i|) \mid v \in T_i\}$
8   Add v_i into output queue Q
9 **return** Q, the nearest subtrees of A_i's in T

Fig. 3. Computing the nearest subtrees.

Proof. We propose an $O(n)$ time algorithm, NEAREST(T, S), shown in Figure 3. For each A_i, the algorithm essentially computes all values of $d(A_i, L(v))$'s and find one with the smallest value.

The correctness of the algorithm follows from the fact that any node $v \notin \Lambda(A_i)$ of T can not have the smallest cluster distance to A_i. The reason is that, if $v \notin \Lambda(A_i)$, one of subtrees of $T[v]$ (with parent v) contains leaves that are completely disjointed with A_i. That is, one of other subtrees shall have a smaller distance. Thus, it suffices to consider only nodes of $\Lambda(A_i)$ or $\text{CONFLUENT}(T, A_i)$. The time complexity analysis appears at the full paper, and is omitted here due to the page limit. $\square$

With slight modifications of the algorithm, $\text{NEAREST}(T, S)$, we can rephrase the result of Theorem 2 and obtain the following:

Theorem 3. *Let T be an n-node phylogenetic tree with leaf nodes L. The following subsequent operation can be done efficiently after an $O(n)$ time preprocessing. Given a query set $A \subset L$, the nearest subtree of A can be constructed in $O(|A|)$ time if A is given in sorted tree ordering; otherwise, some extra $O(|A| \log \log |A|)$ time is needed for sorting A.*

4   Leaf-Agree Subtrees and Isomorphic Subtrees

The definitions of leaf-agree subtrees and leaf-agree isomorphic subtrees can be found in Section 1. Interestingly, using the idea of the LCA sub-merging we can solve the leaf-agree descendent subtrees problem and the isomorphic subtrees problem in linear time. First we present our results for finding the leaf-agree descendent subtrees of two phylogenetic trees.

Lemma 3 (leaf-agree-subtree/two trees). *Given two n-leaf phylogenetic trees T_1 and T_2, finding all paired subtrees of T_1 and subtrees of T_2 with same set of leaves can be done in $O(n)$ time.*

Proof. Given a phylogenetic tree T with leaf nodes L and $S \subset L$, we use the notation $\text{LCA}_T(S)$ to denote *the* lowest common ancestor defined over S; i.e., $\text{LCA}_T(S) = \text{argmax}_v \{\text{level}(v) \mid v \in \Lambda(S)\}$. In other words, suppose $v^* = \text{LCA}_T(S) \in \Lambda(S)$, we must have $\text{LCA}_T(v^*, x) = v^*$ for any vertex $x \in \Lambda(S)$.

Given T_1, T_2, we define a function $\psi[T_1, T_2](\cdot)$, or just $\psi(\cdot)$ in short, such that for each vertex $x \in T_1$ find the corresponding vertex $y \in T_2$ such that $y = \psi(x) = \text{LCA}_{T_2}(L_{T_1}(x))$. By using LCA queries, it is easy to calculate all $\psi(x)$'s totally in $O(n)$ time for every node $x \in T_1$. This can be done by a computation ordering that lists nodes of T_1 from the leaf nodes and steps up toward the root. That is, let x be the parent of $\{x_1, \ldots, x_m\}$. We have:

$$\psi(x) = \text{LCA}_{T_2}(\{\psi(x_1), \ldots, \psi(x_m)\})$$

Note that $A \subseteq L_T(\text{LCA}_T(A))$ in general; thus we have $A = L_T(\text{LCA}_T(A))$ whenever $|A| = |L_T(\text{LCA}_T(A))|$. It follows that $L_{T_1}(x) \subseteq L_{T_2}(\psi(x))$, and $L_{T_1}(x) = L_{T_2}(\psi(x))$ whenever $|L_{T_1}(x)| = |L_{T_2}(\psi(x))|$. We conclude that

a node $x \in T_1$ is agree with the node $\psi(x) \in T_2$

if and only if

$$|L_{T_1}(x)| = |L_{T_2}(\psi(x))|$$

Now that, by Theorem 2, the subtree sums for nodes of T_1 and T_2 can calculated in $O(n)$ time. It follows that the all-agreement problem can be solved in $O(n)$ by checking the constant time LCA queries and the subtree sizes information. □

We can easily extend the result of Lemma 3 to obtain the linear time algorithm for finding all leaf-agree descendent subtrees of more than two phylogenetic trees.

Theorem 4 (leaf-agree-subtree/k trees). *Given a set of n-leaf phylogenetic trees $\{T_1, \ldots, T_k\}$, finding all k-tuple $(v_1, \ldots, v_k)$'s such that $L_{T_1}(v_1) = L_{T_2}(v_2) = \cdots = L_{T_k}(v_k)$ can be done in $O(kn)$ time.*

Proof. By extending the $\psi[T_1, T_2](\cdot)$ function, defined in the proof of Lemma 3, we define the function $\eta(x, i)$ such that for each vertex $x \in T_1$ find the corresponding vertex $y \in T_i$ such that $\eta(x, 1) = x$ and $\eta(x, i+1) = \psi[T_i, T_{i+1}](\eta(x, i))$ defined recursively.

By the discussions in proof of Lemma 3, we can precomputed tables of all $\psi[T_i, T_{i+1}](\cdot)$'s totally in $O(kn)$ time. Furthermore, the tables of all $\eta(x, i)$'s can thus be obtained from $\psi[T_i, T_{i+1}](\cdot)$'s also in $O(kn)$ time. By similar arguments used in proof of Lemma 3, we conclude that

$$L_{T_1}(x) = L_{T_2}(\eta(x, 2)) = \cdots = L_{T_k}(\eta(x, k))$$

if and only if

$$|L_{T_1}(x)| = |L_{T_2}(\eta(x, 2))| = \cdots = |L_{T_k}(\eta(x, k))|$$

Since all the conditions' checking can be done in again $O(kn)$ time, it follows that the leaf-agree subtrees problem can be correctly solved in $O(kn)$ time.   □

Here we show that finding all isomorphic descendent subtrees of phylogenetic trees can be done in linear time as well.

Theorem 5 (isomorphic-subtree). *Given a set of n-leaf phylogenetic trees $\{T_1, \ldots, T_k\}$, finding all k-tuple $(v_1, \ldots, v_k)$'s such that $T_1[v_1] \cong T_2[v_2] \cong \cdots \cong T_k[v_k]$ can be done in $O(kn)$ time.*

Proof. We use the $\eta(x, i)$ function, defined in the proof of Theorem 4, as the basics of testing isomorphism. Let $x \in T_1, y \in T_2$, it is clear that $T_1[x] \cong T_2[y]$ implies $L_{T_1}(x) = L_{T_2}(y)$. To report all possible k-tuple $(v_1, \ldots, v_k)$'s such that $T_1[v_1] \cong T_2[v_2] \cong \cdots \cong T_k[v_k]$, it suffices to consider only those leaf-agree subtrees. That is, tuples of the form $(\eta(x, 1), \eta(x, 2), \ldots, \eta(x, k))$ such as $L_{T_1}(x) = L_{T_2}(\eta(x, 2)) = \cdots = L_{T_k}(\eta(x, k))$. Note that these tuples are obtainable in $O(kn)$ time by Theorem 4.

We say a vertex $x \in T_1$ is a *good start* if and only if $T_1[x] \cong T_2[\eta(x, 2)] \cong \cdots \cong T_k[\eta(x, k)]$. Let x be the parent of $\{x_1, \ldots, x_m\}$. Note that x is a good start implies that each of $\{x_1, \ldots, x_m\}$ is a good start, although the converse is not true. To establish the sufficient and necessary condition, we associate with each vertex $v \in T$ with a unique label and let $\lambda(v) = \min L_T(v)$. Furthermore, for each vertex x being the parent of a set of vertices $\{x_1, \ldots, x_m\}$ in a tree T, we use the *ordered list* $\langle x_1, \ldots, x_m \rangle$ to arrange these k subtrees in their *increasing* $\lambda(\cdot)$ *order*; i.e., $\lambda(x_1) < \cdots < \lambda(x_m)$. It is not hard to see that the calculation of $\lambda(\cdot)$'s and the arrangement of subtrees ordering can be done for all phylogenetic trees in linear, $O(kn)$, time. In the following, we use $\lambda^+(x) = \langle \lambda(x_1), \ldots, \lambda(x_m) \rangle$ to denote the labels sequence for children of x. Now it shall be clear to see that:

$$T_1[x] \cong T_2[\eta(x,2)] \cong \cdots \cong T_k[\eta(x,k)] \text{ or } x \text{ is a good start}$$

if and only if

each child of $\{x_1, \ldots, x_m\}$ is a good start, and

$$\lambda^+(x) = \lambda^+(\eta(x,2)) = \cdots = \lambda^+(\eta(x,k))$$

Note that the total works for checking labels of $\lambda^+(\cdot)$'s are basically equal to visiting the descendent edges of the trees. Since no edge will be visited twice, the total works can not be greater than $O(kn)$, the upper bound for the total number of edges in these trees. It follows that the problem of finding all isomorphic descendent subtrees can be correctly solved in $O(kn)$ time.   □

5   Applications to Bacterial 2CS Sequence Analysis

Rapid adaptation to environmental challenge is essential for bacterial survival. To orchestrate their adaptive responses to changes in their surroundings, bacteria mainly use so-called *two-component regulatory systems* (2CS) [20]. These systems are usually composed of a sensor kinase, which is able to detect one or several environmental stimuli, and a response regulator, which is phosphorylated by the sensor kinase and which, in turn, activates the expression of genes necessary for the appropriate physiological response. Sensor kinases (or histidine kinases) usually possess two domains: an input domain, which monitors environmental stimuli, and a transmitter domain, which auto-phosphorylates following stimulus detection. A classical response regulator contains an amino-terminally located conserved receiver domain that is phosphorylated by the sensor kinase at a strictly conserved aspartate residue, leading to activation of the carboxy-terminal effector or output domain [22,25].

The identification of the function of these 2CS would greatly facilitate not only our understanding on the basic physiology and regulatory networks of bacteria but also designing a way to prevent from causing disease in humans. It is therefore interesting to know whether the gene encoding regulatory protein and the gene encoding the sensor kinase in a 2CS were derived by duplication from an existing 2CS (the *co-evolution*) or they were evolved independently and were assembled by recombination event later. Furthermore, one way of extracting the useful clustering information that might later lead to functional classifications of these 2CS from the regulator tree and the sensor tree is to incorporate the evolutionary information from both trees. To address these questions, we collect regulatory protein encoding genes and sensor-encoding genes of the 63 2CS within P. aeruginosa [25], and construct the evolutionary distances as well as the sensor and regulator gene trees as our model of co-evolutionary clusterings. Based on these obtained data, we have developed a web-based system, mostly consists of a list of PHP programs, for visualizing and integration of sensor and regulator gene trees; the web system is freely accessible at `http://alzoo.cs.pu.edu.tw/two_component.htm`. Currently the system exhibits several distinct relationships of the 2CS within P. aeruginosa, and part of our results can also be found in [21]. In this case, the integration of the two trees has provided biologists bioinformatic evidences toward the key to reveal the secret of 2CS co-evolutionary process.

6   Concluding Remarks

Due to the known algorithmic difficulties of MAST problem concerning the unbounded degree or more than two trees [12,3,19,5], here in this paper we restrict our attention to the problem of comparing the descendent subtrees within a set of unbounded degree phylogenetic trees. In this paper, we present algorithmic results concerning the the descendent subtrees comparison problems with bioinformatic applications in functional analysis and classifications on bacterial genome.

We show that computing all pairs normalized cluster distances between all paired subtrees of two trees can be computationally optimally done in $O(n^2)$ time in Theorem 1. By using the concept of confluent subtree, we are able to show that finding nearest subtrees for a collection of pairwise disjointed subsets of leaves can be done in $O(n)$ time in Theorem 2. Furthermore, we present linear time algorithms for finding all leaf-agree descendent subtrees as well as all isomorphic descendent subtrees in Theorem 4 and Theorem 5.

Finally, we thank Ming-Tat Ko of Academia Sinica for the constructive discussions and good points of ideas. Most of the results presented in the paper are obtained during the first author's visiting in Institute of Information Science Academia Sinica at the summer of 2002.

References

1. A. V. Aho, Y. Sagiv, T. G. Szymanski, and J. D. Ullman. Inferring a tree from lowest common ancestors with an application to the optimization of relational expressions. *SIAM Journal on Computing*, 10(3):405–421, 1981.
2. B. L. Allen and M. Steel. Subtree transfer operations and their induced metrics on evolutionary trees. *Annals of Combinatorics*, 5:1–13, 2001.
3. A. Amir and D. Keselman. Maximum agreement subtree in a set of evolutionary trees: Metrics and efficient algorithms. *SIAM Journal on Computing*, 26(6):1656–1669, 1997.

4. V. Berry and O. Gascuel. Inferring evolutionary trees with strong combinatorial evidence. *Theoretical Computer Science*, 240(2):271–298, 2000.
5. P. Bonizzoni, G. Della Vedova, and G. Mauri. Approximating the maximum isomorphic agreement subtree is hard. In R. Giancarlo and D. Sankoff, editors, *Proceedings of the 11th Annual Symposium on Combinatorial Pattern Matching*, Lecture Notes in Computer Science 1848, pages 119–128, Montréal, Canada, 2000.
6. G.S. Brodal, R. Fagerberg, and C.N. Pedersen. Computing the quartet distance between evolutionary trees in time $O(n \log^2 n)$. *ISAAC, Lecture Notes in Computer Science*, 2223:731–742, 2001.
7. D. Bryant. *Building Trees, Hunting for Trees, and Comparing Trees*. PhD thesis, University of Canterbury, Christchurch, New Zealand, 1997.
8. R. Cole, M. Farach, R. Hariharan, T. Przytycka, and M. Thorup. An $O(n \log n)$ algorithm for the maximum agreement subtree problem for binary trees. *SIAM Journal on Computing*, 30(5):1385–1404, 2002.
9. DasGupta, He, Jiang, Li, Tromp, and Zhang. On distances between phylogenetic trees. In *Proceedings of the 8th ACM-SIAM Symposium on Discrete Algorithms (SODA)*, pages 427–436, 1997.
10. W.H.E. Day. Optimal algorithms for comparing trees with labelled leaves. *Journal of Classification*, 2:7–28, 1985.
11. G. Estabrook, F. McMorris, and C. Meacham. Comparison of undirected phylogenetic trees based on subtrees of four evolutionary units. *Systematic Zoology*, 34(2):193–200, 1985.
12. M. Farach, T.M. Przytycka, and M. Thorup. On the agreement of many trees. *Information Processing Letters*, 55(6):297–301, 1995.
13. M. Farach and M. Thorup. Sparse dynamic programming for evolutionary-tree comparison. *SIAM Journal on Computing*, 26(1):210–230, 1997.
14. J. Felsenstein. Numerical methods for inferring evolutionary trees. *Quarterly Review on Biology*, 57(4):379–404, 1982.
15. W. M. Fitch. Toward defining the course of evolution: Minimal change for a specific tree topology. *Systematic Zoology*, 20:406–441, 1971.
16. D. Gilbert, D. Westhead, N. Nagano, and J. Thornton. Motif–based searching in tops protein topology databases, 1999.
17. D. Gusfield. Efficient algorithms for inferring evolutionary trees. *Networks*, 21:19–28, 1991.
18. D. Harel and R. E. Tarjan. Fast algorithms for finding nearest common ancestors. *SIAM Journal on Computing*, 13(2):338–355, 1984.
19. J. Hein, T. Jiang, L. Wang, and K. Zhang. On the complexity of comparing evolutionary trees. *Discrete Applied Mathematics*, 71:153–169, 1996.
20. J.A. Hoch and T.J. Silhavy. *Two-Component Signal Transduction*. ASM Press, 1995.
21. Y.L. Lin. Two component systems sequence characteristics identification in bacterial genome. In *Sixth Proceedings World Multiconference on Systemics, Cybernetics and Informatics (SCI'2002)*, pages 445–449, Orlando, Florida, 2002.
22. J.S. Parkinson and E.C. Kofoid. Communication modules in bacterial signalling proteins. *Annu. Rev. Genet.*, 26:71–112, 1992.
23. D. F. Robinson and L. R. Foulds. Comparison of weighted labelled trees. In *Combinatorial mathematics, VI (Proc. Sixth Austral. Conf., Univ. New England, Armidale)*, Lecture Notes in Mathematics 748, pages 119–126. Springer-Verlag, Berlin, 1979.
24. D. F. Robinson and L. R. Foulds. Comparison of phylogenetic trees. *Math. Biosci*, 53(1-2):131–147, 1981.

25. A. Rodrigue, Y. Quentin, A. Lazdunski, V. Méjean, and M. Foglino. Two-component systems in pseudomonas aeruginosa: why so many? *Trends Microbiol.*, 8:498–504, 2000.
26. N. Saitou and M. Nei. The neighbor-joining method: a new method for reconstructing phylogenetic trees. *Molecular Biology Evolution*, 4:406–425, 1987.
27. K. Strimmer and A. von Haeseler. Quartet puzzling: a quartet maximum-likelihood method for reconstructing tree topologies. *Molecular Biology and Evolution*, 13(7):964–969, 1996.
28. P. van Emde Boas. Preserving order in a forest in less than logarithmic time and linear space. *Information Processing Letters*, 6:80–82, 1977.
29. M. S. Waterman and T. F. Smith. On the similarity of dendrograms. *Journal of Theoretical Biology*, 73:789–800, 1978.

Settling the Intractability of Multiple Alignment

Isaac Elias

Dept. of Numerical Analysis and Computer Science,
Royal Institute of Technology, Stockholm, Sweden
isaac@nada.kth.se

Abstract. In this paper some of the most fundamental problems in computational biology are proved intractable. The following problems are shown NP-hard for all binary or larger alphabets under all fixed metrics: MULTIPLE ALIGNMENT with SP-score, STAR ALIGNMENT, and TREE ALIGNMENT (for a given phylogeny). Earlier these problems have only been shown intractable for sporadic alphabets and distances, here the intractability is settled. Moreover, the construction can be extended to prove NP-hardness results for CONSENSUS PATTERNS and SUBSTRING PARSIMONY.

1   Introduction

Multiple sequence alignment is at the very core of many computational problems in molecular biology. Different variations of multiple sequence alignment occur in areas such as protein structure prediction, phylogeny (inference of evolutionary history among species), and localization of functionally important units in biological sequences. As the field of bioinformatics grows these problems, and several of their variations, become increasingly important. Although the results in this paper are not surprising, the significance of the problems make the results both interesting and important.

The evolutionary process is driven by mutation and natural selection. DNA sequence similarity is therefore a good indication of common evolutionary origin and function. With *pairwise alignment* two sequences are aligned while allowing errors such as substitutions, insertions and deletions of symbols. The idea is that these errors model the mutations occurring in DNA sequence replication.

Multiple alignment is the natural extension of pairwise alignment, and also a much more powerful tool. Typically, when sequence similarity is weak, multiple alignment may find similarities which pairwise alignments would not. However, pairwise alignment is solvable in polynomial time and multiple alignment is "not".

Many scoring schemes have been suggested to measure the cost of a multiple alignment. In this paper the focus is on the sum-of-pairs score (SP-score), STAR ALIGNMENT, and TREE ALIGNMENT. The three scoring schemes are in many aspects different and are therefore considered as separate problems.

In [1] Wang and Jiang gave a short NP-hardness proof for the SP-score under a non-metric distance measure over a 4 symbol alphabet. This result was then

T. Ibaraki, N. Katoh, and H. Ono (Eds.): ISAAC 2003, LNCS 2906, pp. 352–363, 2003.

improved by Bonizzoni and Vedova [2], who showed that the problem is NP-hard
for the binary alphabet and a specific metric. The result was extended further by
Just [3] to cover many metrics, and also under some non-metrics the problem was
proved APX-complete. However, all metrics were not covered and in particular
not the unit metric. We build on some of the ideas developed by Bonizzoni and
Vedova to show that the problem is intractable for all binary or larger alphabets
under any metric.

In [1] STAR ALIGNMENT was proved to be APX-complete over a 7 symbol
alphabet, however the symbol distance did not have the property of identity nor
that of triangle inequality. In [4] Li et al. gave a PTAS and an NP-hardness result
under the unit metric for a version of STAR ALIGNMENT in which there was a
restriction on the number of gaps. Moreover, in [5] the problem was proved NP-
hard for a 6 symbol metric. Wang and Jiang also proved that TREE ALIGNMENT
is NP-hard for a specific metric over a 4 symbol alphabet. Later in two companion
papers [6,7] they gave a couple of nice PTASs working for all metrics. In this
paper both problems are proved intractable for all binary or larger alphabets
under any metric, thereby settling the complexity[1] of TREE ALIGNMENT. We
emphasize that hardness results for non-metrics are easier to come by and that
these do not cover the problems considered in practice. Moreover, by considering
metrics in general, this paper covers most, if not all, variations occurring in
practice.

Rather than finding a consensus for the strings as a whole it is sometimes
of biological interest to focus on the consensus of well conserved regions, e.g.
in gene regulation. A well conserved region in biological sequences relates to
a functionally important unit. CONSENSUS PATTERNS and SUBSTRING PARSI-
MONY are natural formalizations of the problem of finding the most conserved
region. While our NP-hardness result for SUBSTRING PARSIMONY is new, CON-
SENSUS PATTERNS has earlier been proved NP-hard [8,9,10] and W[1]-hard in
[11]. The constructions in both proofs are similar to that of STAR ALIGNMENT
and can be found in [12].

In the following section MULTIPLE ALIGNMENT with SP-score is proved to be
NP-hard for binary or larger alphabets under the unit metric, the result for all
metrics is achieved by a slight modification and is given in [12]. Then in Sect. 3
STAR ALIGNMENT and TREE ALIGNMENT are proved to be NP-hard for binary
or larger alphabets under any metric.

2   Multiple Alignment with SP-Score Is NP-Hard

In this paper a *string* is a sequence of symbols from an alphabet Σ, typically $\Sigma = \{0, 1\}$. A *pairwise alignment* of two strings s_1 and s_2 is a $2 \times l$
matrix A, where row one and two contain strings s_1 and s_2 interleaved by
spaces, respectively. The spaces are represented by the symbol $'-' \notin \Sigma$. By
the cost of A we mean $d_A(s_1, s_2) = \sum_{i=1}^{l} \mu(r_1[i], r_2[i])$, where r_1 and r_2 are the

---

[1] All problems considered in this paper have polynomially bounded optimal solutions
and therefore an FPTAS can not exist unless P=NP.

rows in A and μ a predefined metric for symbols from the extended alphabet $\Sigma \cup \{-\}$. We call the least such cost, denoted $d(s_1, s_2)$, the *evolutionary distance*.
The most simple of metrics, the *unit metric*, is the met-
ric in which all non-zero distances are exactly 1. The cost
of the minimum pairwise alignment under the unit metric
is also referred to as the *edit distance* for strings. The edit
distance is simply the minimum number of edit operations
(substitutions, insertions, and deletions) needed to transform
one of the strings into the other. In Table 1 the metric for
the extended binary alphabet is depicted (the variables will
reappear later).

Table 1.

	0	1	–
0	0	α	β
1	α	0	γ
–	β	γ	0

Definition 1 (Multiple Alignment with SP-score). *A multiple alignment of a set S of k strings, is a $k \times l$ matrix A where row i contains string s_i interleaved by spaces. The SP-score (sum-of-pairs) for a multiple alignment is the sum of all pairwise distances between rows in the alignment; $\sum_{i=1}^{k} \sum_{j=i}^{k} d_A(s_i, s_j)$. MULTIPLE ALIGNMENT with SP-score is the problem of finding a minimum alignment under the SP-score.*

The main theorem of this section is Theorem 1 which states that MULTIPLE ALIGNMENT with SP-score is NP-hard under all metrics. However, to convey the proof, a restricted case of the problem is shown NP-hard, Corollary 1. The full proof requires only a slight modification and is given in [12]. Some of the ideas in the construction[2] is by Bonizzoni and Vedova [2].

Theorem 1. *The decision version of MULTIPLE ALIGNMENT with SP-score is NP-complete for the binary alphabet under each metric. (Proof in [12])*

Corollary 1. *The decision version of MULTIPLE ALIGNMENT with SP-score is NP-complete for the binary alphabet under the unit metric. (Proof below)*

First the reduction is presented and on page 356 its correctness is proved. The reduction is from INDEPENDENT SET in 3-regular graphs: INDEPENDENT R3 SET[3]. Let $V = \{v_1, \ldots, v_n\}$ be the vertices of the graph and $E \subseteq \{(v_i, v_j) : 1 \le i < j \le n\}$ the edges. From now on we reserve n for $|V|$, m for $|E|$, and c for the decision limit of the INDEPENDENT R3 SET instance.

The decision version of the MULTIPLE ALIGNMENT instance has a set of strings $S = \mathcal{T} \cup \mathcal{P} \cup \mathcal{C}$ and a decision limit K. It will be shown that there is an independent set of size c if and only if there is an alignment of S of cost K.

Let $b = 6nm^2$; a number chosen big enough to have a dominating effect in the alignment. In S there are b *template strings* $\mathcal{T}$, which force every optimum alignment to have a canonical structure, illustrated in Table 2. All template

---

[2] Bonizzoni and Vedova made a similar reduction from VERTEX COVER. Although they conjectured that it could be improved to cover an *ultra metric*, they did not consider the unit metric or, more importantly, metrics in general.

[3] In [13,14] INDEPENDENT SET is shown to be NP-complete even for graphs with degree bounded by 3. It is a simple matter to extend the result to 3-regular graphs.

strings are identical to $T = (10^b)^{n-1}1$. Since they are identical, they are also aligned identically in every optimum alignment. In the canonical alignment the 1's in column $(b+1)(i-1)+1$ play the role of vertex v_i in the graph. For this reason we refer to the column as the i'th vertex column.

In $\mathcal{S}$ there are also $b = |\mathcal{P}|$ identical pick strings $P = 1^c$. For the same reason as for the template strings, these are aligned identically. Moreover, in any optimum alignment the 1's in the pick strings are aligned in those columns with the most 1's, which are the vertex columns. Thus the pick strings pick c of the n vertices to be part of the independent set (in Table 2 vertex v_2 is picked).

Table 2. A canonical alignment for the complete graph with four vertices. Since v_2 is the only vertex column containing three 1's from the constraint strings, the pick strings are aligned to pick v_2.

		v_1		v_2		v_3		v_4	
$\|T\| = b$		1	0...0...	1	0...0...	1	0...0...	1	
		⋮	⋮	⋮	⋮	⋮	⋮	⋮	
		1	0...0...	1	0...0...	1	0...0...	1	
$\|P\| - b$				1					
				⋮					
				1					
C_{12}		0	0...10...	1	0...0...	0	0...0...	0	0...
C_{13}	0...	1	0...0...	0	0...10...	0	0...0...	0	
C_{14}		0	0...10...	0	0...0...	0	0...0...	1	0...
C_{23}	0...	0	0...0...	1	0...10	0	0...0...	0	
C_{24}	0...	0	0...0...	1	0...0...	0	0...10...	0	
C_{34}	0...	0	0...0...	0	0...0...	1	0...10...	0	
	$\underbrace{\quad}_{4n\ 0's}$							$\underbrace{\quad}_{4n\ 0's}$	

There are also m constraint strings C in $\mathcal{S}$, one for each edge. The constraint string for edge $(v_i, v_j) \in E$ is the string

$$C_{ij} = 0^{4n}(00^b)^{i-1}10^{b-4n}(00^b)^{j-i-1}10^b(00^b)^{n-j-1}00^{4n}.$$

That is, C_{ij} has two 1's and is $4n$ longer than the template strings ($|C_{ij}| = 5n + b(n-1)$). The string C_{ij} can be constructed from T by setting all but the i'th and j'th vertex positions to 0, adding $4n$ 0's to the beginning and end and removing $4n$ 0's from in between the i'th and j'th vertex position. This structure ensures that only one of the two 1's can be aligned in its associated vertex column. The 1 that is not aligned in its vertex column is not part of the independent set. (In Table 2 vertex v_1 is selected not to be part of the independent set by both the alignment of rows C_{12} and C_{14}.)

We now formally define the canononical alignment illustrated in Table 2.

Definition 2 (Canonical Alignment). *A canonical alignment is an alignment in which; (1) the template strings are aligned identically, (2) the pick strings are aligned identically and their 1's are in vertex columns, (3) each constraint string is aligned with the template strings so that $4n$ of its first or last 0's are matched with spaces and the rest with symbols of the template strings.*

We use $d(\mathcal{T}, \mathcal{P})$ to denote the sum of pairwise distances between rows (the alignment matrix is implicit) associated with strings in $\mathcal{T}$ and $\mathcal{P}$, i.e. $d(\mathcal{T}, \mathcal{P}) = \sum_{t \in \mathcal{T}} \sum_{p \in \mathcal{P}} d(t, p)$. With this notation the total cost of the alignment is $\frac{1}{2} d(\mathcal{S}, \mathcal{S})$.

Since $\mathcal{S} = \mathcal{T} \cup \mathcal{P} \cup \mathcal{C}$ the cost of any alignment is

$$\frac{1}{2} d(\mathcal{S}, \mathcal{S}) = \frac{1}{2} d(\mathcal{T}, \mathcal{T}) + d(\mathcal{T}, \mathcal{P}) + d(\mathcal{T}, \mathcal{C}) + \frac{1}{2} d(\mathcal{P}, \mathcal{P}) + d(\mathcal{P}, \mathcal{C}) + \frac{1}{2} d(\mathcal{C}, \mathcal{C}).$$

Below we consider each pairwise distance to get the value of the decision limit K. That is, K is chosen so that there is an alignment of cost K if and only if there is an independent set of size c.

A1. $d(\mathcal{T}, \mathcal{T}) = 0$ in any optimum alignment and in any canonical alignment.

A2. $d(\mathcal{T}, \mathcal{P}) = (n - c + b(n - 1))b^2$ in any optimum alignment and in any canonical alignment. All 0's and $n - c$ 1's are matched with spaces for each pair of template and pick strings.

A3. $d(\mathcal{T}, \mathcal{C}) \geq (4n + n)bm$ is the sum of minimum pairwise costs and also the cost in any canonical alignment. One of the two 1's in each constraint string is aligned in its associated vertex column. Thus $4n$ 0's are matched with spaces and n 1's are matched with 0's for each pair of template and constraint string.

A4. $d(\mathcal{P}, \mathcal{P}) = 0$ in any optimum alignment and in any canonical alignment.

A5. $d(\mathcal{P}, \mathcal{C}) \geq (5n + b(n - 1))bm - c3b$ gives a lower bound for all canonical alignments. Remember, the graph is 3-regular and hence there can at most be three 1's from the constraint strings in the columns picked by the strings in $\mathcal{P}$. It is clear that if there is an independent set of size c then there also is a canonical alignment for which equality holds. Moreover, the minimum possible cost of $d(\mathcal{P}, \mathcal{C})$ in any alignment is $(5n + b(n - 1))bm - 2bm$, which happens if both 1's of each constraint string are aligned with a 1 from the pick strings.

A6. $\frac{1}{2} d(\mathcal{C}, \mathcal{C}) < (8n + 4)m(m - 1)/2 < 5nm^2$ in any canonical alignment. In a canonical alignment at most $8n$ 0's are matched with spaces and at most 4 1's are matched with 0's for each pair of constraint strings.

Summing all these we get the value for the decision limit;

$$K = (n - c + b(n - 1))b^2 + (4n + n)bm + (5n + b(n - 1))bm - c3b + 5nm^2.$$

Note that the equalities in A1-A4 are achieved by every canonical alignment. Equality in A5 is achieved by every canonical alignment describing an independent set of size c. A6 provides an upper bound for the constraint strings in every canonical alignment.

Proof (Corollary 1). Clearly MULTIPLE ALIGNMENT $\in$ NP. Moreover, K was chosen in such a manner that if there is an independent set of size c then there is an alignment of cost K. Below the opposite is proved; if there is no independent set of size c then there is no alignment of cost K.

Assume that there is no independent set of size c. We first show that there can not be a canonical alignment with cost K. Consider a canonical alignment, since there is no independent set of size c, there has to be at least one column, selected by the pick strings, which does not contain three 1's from the constraint strings. Thus, the cost of $d(\mathcal{P},\mathcal{C}) \geq (5n + b(n-1))bm - c3b + b$, i.e. compared to the lower bound in A5 there is an additional cost of at least b. Thereby the cost of the alignment is at least $K - 5nm^2 + b > K$. Notice that we have disregarded the cost of $\frac{1}{2}d(\mathcal{C},\mathcal{C}) \geq 0$ and only considered A1-A5. Therefore, the cost of any canonical alignment is more than K.

The proof is completed by showing that there is no alignment of cost K. Recall that the equalities in A1, A2, and A4 are achieved by any optimum alignment and that the contribution of $d(\mathcal{T},\mathcal{C})$ can be no less than in A3. Thus for an optimum alignment to have cost $\leq K$ the contribution of $d(\mathcal{P},\mathcal{C})$ has to be made smaller. There are two cases in which this is possible and in each case we show that there exists a better canonical alignment, a contradiction. Essentially; aligning the constraint strings in a non-canonical fashion to improve $d(\mathcal{P},\mathcal{C})$ is penalized by $d(\mathcal{T},\mathcal{C})$.

(i) Assume that there are r constraint strings aligned such that one of their 1's is in an unassociated vertex column. That is, if C_{ij} is such a string then one of its 1's is in the k'th vertex column for $k \neq i, j$. Then the cost of $d(\mathcal{P},\mathcal{C}) + \frac{1}{2}d(\mathcal{C},\mathcal{C})$ can be at most $2br + 5nm^2$ **less than** in a canonical alignment. However, the cost of $d(\mathcal{T},\mathcal{C})$ is at least $2(b - 4n - 1)br$ **more than** in a canonical alignment; due to a gap of $\geq b - 4n$. Since $2(b - 4n - 1)br > 2br + 5nm^2$ the alignment is not optimum.

(ii) Assume that there are r constraint strings aligned such that both of their 1's are in associated vertex columns. That is, if C_{ij} is such a string then the first of its 1's is in the i'th vertex column and the other in the j'th. As above $d(\mathcal{P},\mathcal{C}) + \frac{1}{2}d(\mathcal{C},\mathcal{C})$ is at most $2br + 5nm^2$ less than in a canonical alignment. However, the cost of $d(\mathcal{T},\mathcal{C})$ becomes $\geq (8n - 2)br$ more than in a canonical alignment; due to a gap of $4n$ positions. Since $(8n - 2)br > 2br + 5nm^2$ the alignment is not optimum. $\qquad\square$

3   Star Alignment and Tree Alignment Are NP-Hard

In this section STAR ALIGNMENT and TREE ALIGNMENT are proved NP-hard for all binary or larger alphabets under any metric. Both reductions are from VERTEX COVER and have very similar constructions. The metric is depicted in Table 1. We assume w.l.o.g. that $\beta \leq \gamma$ and that $1 \leq \min(\alpha,\beta)$. Due to space limitations we have, in this version of the paper, omitted the proof of the special case $\alpha = \beta + \gamma$. From now on we assume that $\alpha < \beta + \gamma$. Moreover, we have omitted the proofs of several technical lemmas, these can be found in [12].

Lemma 1 (Triangle inequality for strings). *If the symbol distance, μ, is a metric then the distance for strings defined by the cost of pairwise alignments w.r.t. μ satisfies the triangle inequality.*

3.1   Star Alignment Is NP-Hard

Below we formally define the problem. The reader should notice the relation to Steiner trees and that the Steiner tree is restricted to be a star.

Definition 3 (Star Alignment). *Given a set of strings $\mathcal{S}$,* Star Alignment *is the problem of finding a string c (called a Steiner string) minimizing the sum of pairwise alignments between c and the strings in $\mathcal{S}$, i.e. $\sum_{s \in \mathcal{S}} d(c, s)$.*

The reduction is from Vertex Cover and the construction, given in Table 3 and Fig. 1, has three types of components; *base components, selection components,* and one *ground component.* A general outline of the construction is given below (see 1-3). Let $G = (V, E)$ be the graph of the Vertex Cover instance, $n = |V|$, and $m = |E|$.

(1) There are r base components, definition below, ensuring that the optimum Steiner string is a string in which there are n vertex positions. A 1 in vertex position i corresponds to the i'th vertex being part of the vertex cover. That is, the optimum Steiner string corresponds to a subset V' of the vertices.

(2) There are m selection components, definition below, one for each edge. These components ensure that there for each edge (v_i, v_j) is a 1 in either the i'th or the j'th vertex position of the Steiner string. That is, the optimum Steiner string corresponds to a vertex cover V'.

(3) The ground component, definition below, minimizes the number of 1's in vertex positions. That is, the optimum Steiner string corresponds to a minimum vertex cover V'.

Fig. 1. Construction for Star Alignment. See 1-3 above for an outline of the components. The strings are from Table 3.

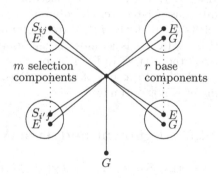

Base Components. The optimum Steiner string is *base string* and is of the form $DDCDD$; where C is a *cover string* and the D's are *delimiter strings*, see Table 3. A cover string consists of n consecutive blocks, each being B_0 or B_1. If the i'th block is B_1 then this corresponds to the i'th vertex being part of the cover. In $B_0 = P0P$ and $B_1 = P1P$ the 0 and 1, respectively, are in the so called *vertex position*. For the construction to work for all metrics the size of the paddings, denoted by P, depends on the metric. Let

$$s \geq (n+1) \cdot \left\lceil \frac{\max(\alpha, \gamma)}{\min(\alpha, \beta)} \right\rceil, \tag{1}$$

and let $P = 0^s 1^s 0^s$. The delimiter strings consists of $|C|$ 1's: $D = 1^{|C|}$.

In the construction there are sufficiently many special pairs of base strings, called *base components*, to ensure that the optimum Steiner string is a base

Table 3. An overview of the strings in the construction (s is from Eq. 1). Each string is formally introduced below. The general idea though is that there is a one-to-one correspondance between the optimum vertex covers and the optimum Steiner strings which are base strings.

Name	Notation	Form	Length
Padding	P	$0^s 1^s 0^s$	$3s$
1-Block	B_1	$P1P$	$2|P| + 1$
0-Block	B_0	$P0P$	$2|P| + 1$
Vertex string	V_i	$B_0^{i-1} B_1 B_0^{n-i}$	$|B_0|n$
Delimiter string	D	$1^{|V_i|}$	$|B_0|n$
Cover string	C	$(B_1|B_0)^n$	$|D|$
Selection string	S_{ij}	$V_i D V_j$	$3|D|$
Enforcer string	E	$DD\ B_1^n\ DD$	$5|D|$
Ground string	G	$DD\ B_0^n\ DD$	$5|D|$
Base string		$DDCDD$	$5|D|$

string. The string pair in a base component consists of one *enforcer string* and one *ground string*, defined by $E = DDB_1^n DD$ and $G = DDB_0^n DD$, respectively. The important properties of the base components are given in the lemma below.

Lemma 2 (Base components). (1) *The only optimum alignment of an enforcer string and a ground string is the direct match. That is, in the direct match the i'th symbol of E is aligned with the i'th symbol of G, thus* $d(F, G) = na$.

(2) *If* $d(E, x) + d(G, x) < d(E, G) + \min(\alpha, \beta, \beta + \gamma - \alpha)$ *and* $\alpha < \beta + \gamma$, *then* x *is a base string.*

Selection Components. Each edge (v_i, v_j) in the vertex cover instance is represented by a selection component. A selection component for the edge (v_i, v_j) consists of two strings, one enforcer string E and one *selection string* $S_{ij} = V_i D V_j$, where $V_i = B_0^{i-1} B_1 B_0^{n-i}$. The important properties of the component are given in the lemma below. According to the lemma $d(E, x) + d(S_{ij}, x)$ is minimized if and only if x is a base string in which block i or j is B_1. Correspondingly, for each edge (v_i, v_j) in the VERTEX COVER instance vertex v_i or v_j have to be part of the cover.

Lemma 3 (Selection component). (1) *The cost of an optimum alignment of an enforcer string and a selection string is* $d(E, S_{ij}) = 2|D|\gamma + (4ns + 2n - 2)\alpha$.

(2) *If x is a base string and* $d(E, x) + d(S_{ij}, x) = d(E, S_{ij})$, *then the i'th or j'th block of x is B_1. Moreover, if x is a base string in which both block i and j are B_0 then* $d(E, x) + d(S_{ij}, x) = d(E, S_{ij}) + 2\alpha$.

Ground Component. The ground component is simply one single ground string. For each B_1 block in the Steiner string the ground component adds an additional cost to the alignment. In other words, the fewer vertices that are selected the smaller the cost.

Lemma 4. *If x is a base string and z the number of B_1 blocks in x, then* $d(G, x) = z\alpha$.

The Completeness Proof.

Theorem 2. *The decision version of* STAR ALIGNMENT *is NP-complete for the binary alphabet under all metrics in which* $\alpha < \beta + \gamma$.

Proof. Clearly STAR ALIGNMENT $\in$ NP. As Fig. 1 indicates, the alignment instance has $2m + 2r + 1$ strings; one selection component per edge, r base components, and one ground component. Let

$$r = n \left\lceil \frac{\max(\alpha, \gamma)}{\min(\alpha, \beta, \beta + \gamma - \alpha)} \right\rceil \tag{2}$$

and the decision limit

$$K = m \cdot \left(2|D|\gamma + (4ns + 2n - 2)\alpha \right) + r \cdot \alpha n + \alpha c,$$

where c is the decision limit of the VERTEX COVER instance.

We now show that an optimum Steiner string corresponds to a minimum vertex cover, and vice versa. If the Steiner string is a base string corresponding to the cover V' then the cost of the star alignment is

$$\underbrace{m \cdot d(E, S_{ij})}_{\text{selection comp., Lem. 3}} + \underbrace{r \cdot d(E, G)}_{\text{base comp., Lem. 2}} + \underbrace{\alpha|V'|}_{\text{ground}}, \tag{3}$$

which is strictly decreasing in the size of the cover, $|V'|$. Clearly, by lemmas 2, 3, and 4, if there exists a cover of size c then there is alignment of cost K. In particular, there is always an alignment of the same cost as above with $|V'| = n - 1$.

Let s^* be an optimum Steiner string.

(i) *Assume that s^* is not a base string.* By Lemma 2 the cost of the base components is $r(d(E, s^*) + d(G, s^*)) \geq r\alpha n + n \max(\alpha, \gamma)$. Moreover, the cost of the selection components is at least $m \cdot d(E, S_{ij})$. Since this is more than the upper limit of (3) this contradicts the optimality of s^*.

(ii) *Assume that s^* does not correspond to a cover.* Then there is a selection string S_{ij} such that both block i and j of s^* is B_0. By Lemmas 2, 3, and 4, we could exchange block i or j for B_1 and thereby improve the cost, contradicting the optimality of s^*.

Since (3) is strictly decreasing in the size of the cover we have shown that the optimum Steiner string corresponds to a minimum vertex cover. Clearly, the reduction is polynomial. Hence STAR ALIGNMENT is NP-hard for the binary alphabet under metrics in which $\alpha < \beta + \gamma$. $\square$

3.2   Tree Alignment Is NP-Hard

A *full labeling* of a tree is a function assigning strings to all vertices of the tree. Similarly a *leaf labeling* is a function assigning labels to the leafs. The *length* of an edge (u, v) in a labeled tree is the cost of the minimum pairwise alignment of the labels at u and v.

Definition 4 (Tree Alignment). *For a leaf labeled tree of bounded degree a tree alignment is a full labeling of the tree, such that the leafs are labeled according to the leaf labeling. Given a leaf labeled tree,* TREE ALIGNMENT *is the problem of finding a minimum cost full labeling, where the cost is the sum of all edge lengths.*

The construction for TREE ALIGNMENT (Fig. 2) is very similar to that of STAR ALIGNMENT. Only some additional arguments to handle the tree structure are required.

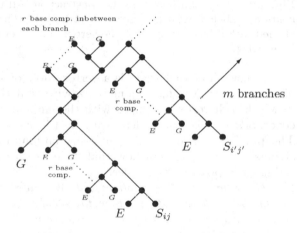

Fig. 2. Construction for TREE ALIGNMENT. There are m branches (one for each edge), each branch has r base components and one selection component. Moreover, in between each branch there are r base components.

Theorem 3. *The decision version of* TREE ALIGNMENT *is NP-complete for the binary alphabet under all metrics in which* $\alpha < \beta + \gamma$.

Proof. Clearly TREE ALIGNMENT $\in$ NP. As Fig. 2 indicates, the alignment instance consists of a tree with $2m + 2r(2m - 1) + 1$ leaves. Let r be as in (2) in the previous proof. For each edge, in the vertex cover instance, there is a branch with one selection component and r base components (see the figure for details). Moreover, each such branch is separated by r base components. As in the proof for STAR ALIGNMENT there is also one ground component. Moreover, the alignment instance has a decision limit

$$K = m\Big(2|D|\gamma + (4ns + 2n - 2)\alpha\Big) + r(2m - 1)\alpha n + \alpha c,$$

where c is the decision limit of the VERTEX COVER instance.

362   I. Elias

If x is a base string corresponding to a cover V', then the cost of the alignment in which all internal vertices are labeled with x is

$$\underbrace{m \cdot \mathsf{d}(E, S_{ij})}_{\text{selection comp.}} + \underbrace{r(2m-1) \cdot \mathsf{d}(E, G)}_{\text{base comp.}} + \underbrace{\alpha|V'|}_{\text{ground}} . \tag{4}$$

If $|V'| \leq c$ then the alignment has cost $\leq K$ (follows from lemmas 2,3, and 4).

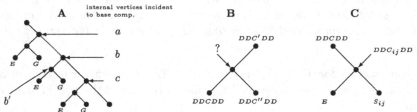

Fig. 3. (A) Part of a branch in the construction. All vertices incident to base components are labeled with the same base string. (B) The vertex connecting a branch is labeled with a base string. (C) The vertex in a selection component is labeled with a base string.

We now show that there is a vertex cover of size c if there is an alignment of cost at most K. This is done by proving that there is an optimum alignment in which each vertex is labeled with the same base string x, corresponding to a cover. Since (4) is strictly decreasing in $|V'|$, x corresponds to a minimum cover. The proof is in two steps: (i) in every optimum alignment all labels are base strings, (ii) using (i) we show that there is an optimum labeling with a base string corresponding to a cover.

(i) *Consider an optimum alignment. We show that if not all internal vertices are labeled with base strings then the alignment is not optimum.* According to Lem. 2, if a vertex incident (e.g. vertex c in Fig. 3A) to a base component is not labeled with a base string, then the cost of that base component is at least $\mathsf{d}(E, G) + \min(\alpha, \beta, \beta + \gamma - \alpha)$. There are r base components on each branch. Thus at least one of the vertices incident to the base components is labeled with a base string. Otherwise, since the contribution of these components is

$$r(\mathsf{d}(E, G) + \min(\alpha, \beta, \beta + \gamma - \alpha)) > r\mathsf{d}(E, G) + n\alpha,$$

the alignment is not optimum, i.e. $n\alpha$ more than in (4).

Let the vertices a,b,c, and b', in Fig. 3A be labeled with the strings s_a, s_b, s_c, and $s_{b'}$, respectively. We show that if s_c is a base string then so is s_b, which inductively implies the claim. Assume that s_b is not a base string. Then by exchanging the label at both b and b' for s_c we achieve a better alignment, a contradiction. This is a direct consequence of the triangle inequality (Lem. 1) and the properties of the base component (Lem. 2).

It remains to show that the vertices connecting the branches and the vertices connected with the leafs of a selection component are labeled with base strings, i.e. the vertices in Fig 3B and 3C. A detailed proof of this fact is given in [12].

(ii) *We show that there is an optimum alignment in which all internal vertices are labeled with a base string* x, *corresponding to a cover.* Consider an optimum alignment in which all labels are base strings. Then x is created so that $\forall i \in [1, n]$ if the i'th block is B_1 in any of the labels in the optimum alignment then the i'th block in x is also B_1. The labeling with x is still optimum because: (1) base strings are aligned symbol by symbol, (2) triangle inequality holds for symbols, and (3) only the cost at the ground is effected by B_1 blocks. Thus with the labeling with x all missmatches occuring in vertex positions have been transfered to the edge incident to the ground. Moreover, for each selection string S_{ij} the i'th or j'th block of x is B_1, hence x corresponds to a cover.

Clearly, the reduction is polynomial. Consequently, TREE ALIGNMENT is NP-hard for the binary alphabet under any metric in which $\alpha < \beta + \gamma$.   □

Acknowledgments. I am very grateful for the help and support that I have received from my supervisor Prof. Jens Lagergren. Without him this paper would not have been written. Moreover, I would like to thank an anonymous referee of an earlier version of this paper for many valuable comments.

References

1. L. Wang and T. Jiang. On the complexity of multiple sequence alignment. *J. Comput. Bio.*, 1:337–348, 1994.
2. P. Bonizzoni and G. D. Vedova. The complexity of multiple sequence alignment with SP-score that is a metric. *TCS*, 259(1–2):63–79, 2001.
3. W. Just. Computational complexity of multiple sequence alignment with sp-score. *Journal of Computational Biology*, 8(6):615–623, 2001.
4. M. Li, B. Ma, and L. Wang. Finding similar regions in many strings. In *Proceedings of the Thirty-First Annual ACM Symposium on Theory of Computing (STOC'99)*, pages 473–482, New York, May 1999. Association for Computing Machinery.
5. J. S. Sim and K. Park. The consensus string problem for a metric is np-complete. *Journal of Discrete Algorithms*, 2(1), 2001.
6. L. Wang, T. Jiang, and E. L. Lawler. Approximation algorithms for tree alignment with a given phylogeny. *Algorithmica*, 16(3):302–315, September 1996.
7. L. Wang, T. Jiang, and D. Gusfield. A more efficient approximation scheme for tree alignment. *SIAM Journal on Computing*, 30(1):283–299, February 2001.
8. M. Li, B. Ma, and L. Wang. Finding similar regions in many sequences. *accepted by Journal of Computer and System Sciences*, July 2001.
9. M. Blanchette, B. Schwikowski, and M. Tompa. Algorithms for phylogenetic footprinting. *J. Comput. Bio.*, 9(2):211–223, 2002.
10. T. Akutsu. Hardness results on gapless local multiple sequence alignment. Technical Report 98-MPS-24-2, 1998.
11. M. Fellows, J. Gramm, and R. Niedermeier. On the parameterized intractability of CLOSEST SUBSTRING and related problems. In *STACS*, 2002.
12. I. Elias. Settling the intractability of multiple alignment. Technical Report TRITA-NA-0316, Nada, KTH, 2003.
13. C. H. Papadimitriou and M. Yannakakis. Optimization, approximation, and complexity classes. *Journal of Computer and System Sciences*, 43(3):425–440, 1991.
14. P. Berman and T. Fujito. On approximation properties of the independent set problem in degree 3 graphs. *Lecture Notes in Computer Science*, 955:449ff, 1995.

Efficient Algorithms for Optimizing Whole Genome Alignment with Noise

T.W. Lam*, N. Lu, H.F. Ting, Prudence W.H. Wong, and S.M. Yiu

Department of Computer Science,
University of Hong Kong, Hong Kong
{twlam,nlu,hfting,whwong,smyiu}@cs.hku.hk

Abstract. Given the genomes (DNA) of two related species, the whole genome alignment problem is to locate regions on the genomes that possibly contain genes conserved over the two species. Motivated by existing heuristic-based software tools, we initiate the study of optimization problems that attempt to uncover conserved genes with a global concern. Another interesting feature in our formulation is the tolerance of noise. Yet this makes the optimization problems more complicated; a brute-force approach takes time exponential in the noise level. In this paper we show how an insight into the problem structure can lead to a drastic improvement in the time and space requirement (precisely, to $O(k^2 n^2)$ and $O(k^2 n)$, respectively, where n is the size of the input and k is the noise level). The reduced space requirement allows us to implement the new algorithms on a PC. It is exciting to see that when compared with the most popular whole genome alignment software (MUMMER) on real data sets, the new algorithms consistently uncover more conserved genes (that have been published by GenBank), while preserving the preciseness of the output.

1 Introduction

Given the genomes (DNA) of two related species, the whole genome alignment problem[2,6,9] is to identify potential regions that contain genes conserved over the two species. This problem has attracted a lot of attention in the past few years and a number of software tools have been developed [1,3,4,5,7,8,10,11].

Related species (such as mouse and human) often have a lot of genes conserved, i.e., having the same functionality. Though a pair of conserved genes rarely contain the same entire sequence (probably due to mutations), they share a lot of short common substrings and some of these substrings are indeed unique to this pair of genes. Thus, the first step to align two genomes would be to identify pairs of maximal substrings that appear uniquely in both genomes. This can be done in linear time using suffix trees. Of course, not every pair of matched substrings correspond to a pair of conserved genes; in fact, most matched substrings in the input are "noise" and many of them actually originate from intergenic regions. Extracting the right pairs is not a trivial problem. See Figure 1 for an example.

---

* This research was supported in part by Hong Kong RGC Grant HKU-7042/02E.

T. Ibaraki, N. Katoh, and H. Ono (Eds.): ISAAC 2003, LNCS 2906, pp. 364–374, 2003.

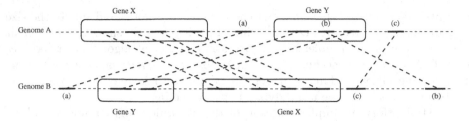

Fig. 1. Among all pairs of matched substrings, a number of them do not originate from conserved gene pairs. See (a), (b), (c) for examples.

Matched substrings that are noise are usually short and isolated. In other words, a pair of conserved genes are likely corresponding to a sequence of matched substrings that are consecutive and close in both genomes and have sufficient length. We call such a sequence a *cluster* and a maximal collection of clusters an *alignment*. At first glance, the problem of finding conserved genes is a simple clustering problem. Such a clustering approach has been used in practice [5], yet the success is limited. There are two major concerns.

- Some conserved genes do not induce clusters of sufficient size; the primary reason is the presence of noise (which separates the actual matched substrings). To uncover such genes, we have to relax the definition of a cluster to allow the presence of noise.
- To report an alignment, one can simply use some ad hoc or greedy approach to cluster the pairs, but does not have much control over the quality of the alignment. It is more desirable to find an alignment that satisfies some instinctive criterion, say, maximizing the size of the smallest cluster. Such a criterion could possibly improve the overall quality of the alignment as we avoid reporting relatively small clusters, which are less likely to be conserved genes. But imposing such a criterion increases drastically the time and space requirement for finding an alignment.

In this paper we introduce the notion of k-noisy clusters, which allows us to ignore up to k pairs of matched substrings in considering a cluster (see the formal definition below). We expect that k is a small integer; otherwise, some clusters reported may be of very poor quality. Based on k-noisy clusters, we first investigate the optimization problem of finding an alignment that maximizes the size of the smallest cluster. Another optimization problem we have studied is finding an alignment that minimizes the number of clusters. Intuitively, both criteria do not favor small clusters, which are less likely to be conserved genes. We believe that the tolerance of noise would enable more conserved genes to be uncovered and the global selection criterion would trim away those small clusters, retaining the preciseness of the output.

The bottleneck in solving these optimization problems is on checking whether two regions on the two genomes contain a k-noisy cluster. A brute-force approach is to examine all possible combinations of at most k substrings within the regions, then check whether throwing these substrings away would leave two sequences of matched substrings that are consecutive on each genome and satisfy the size requirement. This requires $O(n^{k+1})$ time. In this paper we show how to exploit the structure of the problems to devise a more efficient algorithm; it requires only $O(k^2)$ time for checking a pair of regions on average, and $O(k^2n^2)$ time for checking all pairs. This improvement allows us to solve either optimization problem in $O(k^2n^2)$ time using dynamic programming.

A straightforward implementation of the dynamic programming would require $O(kn^2)$ space. This is actually too demanding. For example, in a pair of human and mouse chromosomes, there can be up to a hundred thousand pairs of matched substrings. Assuming $k = 3$, we already need more than ten Gigabytes of memory to implement these algorithms, which far exceeds the capacity of ordinary workstations. Fortunately, we are able to reduce the space requirement of the algorithm to $O(k^2n)$, while maintaining the same time complexity.

We have implemented the new algorithms on a PC and compared them with a heuristic-based software called MUMMER (which is the most popular whole genome alignment software) on seven different sets of human and mouse chromosomes. It is encouraging to see that the new algorithms consistently achieve better coverage while preserving preciseness. They are able to uncover 10% to 25% more conserved genes (that are currently known to the biological community) in each case. See Table 2 in Section 4 for details. It is worth-mentioning that both selection criteria show improvement even if the noisy level is kept to zero.

1.1   Problem Definition

The input is a sequence $M = (m_1, m_2, \ldots, m_n)$, where each m_i denotes a pair of uniquely matched substrings on two given genomes A and B. More precisely, each m_i is represented as a 4-tuple $(a_i, b_i, \ell_i, \sigma_i)$ where a_i and b_i are respectively the starting positions on A and B, ℓ_i the length of the substrings, and σ_i the orientation of the substrings. A pair of matched substrings on two genomes can originate from two strands of the same orientation or opposite orientations. If m_i is of same orientation, we set $\sigma_i = 1$; if m_i is of opposite orientations, we set $\sigma_i = -1$. Intuitively, same orientation means that the a_i-th character of the sense strand of A matches the b_i-th character of the sense strand of B, the $(a_i + 1)$-th matches the $(b_i + 1)$-th and so on; while opposite orientations mean that the a_i-th character of the sense strand of A matches the $(b_i + \ell_i - 1)$-th character of the antisense strand of B, the $(a_i + 1)$-th matches the $(b_i + \ell_i - 2)$-th and so on. We assume that $a_1 < a_2 < \cdots < a_n$. Let Gap and MinSize be two predefined positive constants.

Noisy clusters: A segment C of M is a subsequence in the form $(m_i, m_{i+1}, \ldots, m_{i+t})$. Let k be a positive integer. We say that a segment C of M is a k-noisy cluster if we can remove at most k elements from C, denoted by X, such that the resulting subsequence S satisfies the following conditions:

1. The σ_i's of all m_i's in S are the same.
2. If $\sigma_i = 1$, both the a_i's and b_i's of S are increasing; otherwise, the a_i's are increasing while the b_i's are decreasing.

3. For any two consecutive elements m_p and m_q in S, we have $|a_p - a_q| \leq$ Gap and $|b_p - b_q| \leq$ Gap. This is called the distance requirement.
4. Size(S), defined to be $\sum_{m_i \in S} \ell_i$, is at least MinSize. This is called the size requirement.

Intuitively, X corresponds to the noise.

Alignment: An alignment of M, denoted A below, is a maximal collection of disjoint k-noisy clusters, i.e.,

- clusters in A are mutually disjoint;
- there does not exist another k-noisy cluster which is disjoint with all clusters in A (i.e., we cannot add more clusters to A);
- there does not exist another k-noisy cluster which includes some cluster(s) in A and is disjoint with all other clusters in A (i.e., we cannot replace some cluster(s) in A with a bigger cluster).

Max-min alignment problem: We define the weight of a k-noisy cluster C as follows. Note that there may be more than one subset X that makes C qualified as a k-noisy cluster. Among all such X's, let X_o be the one with the smallest size. Define $w(C)$, the weight of C, to be Size($C - X_o$).

The max-min alignment problem is defined as follows. Given a set M of pairs of matched substrings, we want to find an alignment A^* of M such that $\min_{C \in A^*} w(C) = \max_{A \in \Sigma} \min_{C \in A} w(C)$, where Σ denotes the set of all possible alignments of M. We call A^* a max-min optimal alignment of M and $\min_{C \in A^*} w(C)$ the weight of A^*.

Min-cardinality alignment problem: Given a set M of pairs of matched substrings, we want to find an alignment A^* of M such that $|A^*| = \min_{A \in \Sigma} |A|$, where $|A|$ denotes the number of clusters in the alignment A and Σ denotes the set of all alignments of M. We call A^* a min-cardinality optimal alignment of M.

2   The Max-Min Alignment Problem

2.1   The Dynamic Programming Algorithm

In this section, we describe a dynamic programming algorithm for the max-min alignment problem. Recall that the input is a sequence $M = (m_1, m_2, \ldots, m_n)$ and Σ denotes the set of all alignments of M. We want to find a max-min optimal alignment A^* of M, i.e., $\min_{C \in A^*} w(C) = \max_{A \in \Sigma} \min_{C \in A} w(C)$. The dynamic programming algorithm computes A^* incrementally, by considering the sequences (m_1), (m_1, m_2), $\ldots$, $(m_1, m_2, \ldots, m_j)$ and so on. For $1 \leq j \leq n$, let Φ_j be the set of all possible k-noisy clusters of M whose elements are in $(m_1, m_2, \ldots, m_j)$. Let Σ_j be set of all maximal collections of disjoint k-noisy clusters in Φ_j. Define $\mathtt{W}(j) = \max_{A \in \Sigma_j} \min_{C \in A} w(C)$. Note that $\Phi_n = \Phi$ and $\Sigma_n = \Sigma$. Thus, $\mathtt{W}(n)$ is the weight of the max-min optimal alignment of M. To find $\mathtt{W}(j)$, we consider two cases according to whether m_j is included in some cluster in the alignment. Let $\Gamma_j \subseteq \Sigma_j$ be the set of those maximal collections each of which has a k-noisy cluster containing m_j. We define

$\mathtt{WI}(j) = \max_{A \in \Gamma_j} (\min_{C \in A} w(C))$, and $\mathtt{WE}(j) = \max_{A \in \Sigma_j - \Gamma_j} (\min_{C \in A} w(C))$. Obviously, $\mathtt{W}(j) = \max\{\mathtt{WI}(j), \mathtt{WE}(j)\}$.

The computation of $\mathtt{WI}(j)$ and $\mathtt{WE}(j)$ requires us to determine whether a segment of M in the form $(m_i, m_{i+1}, \ldots, m_j)$ is a k-noisy cluster, for all $1 \le i \le j$. To ease our discussion, we denote the segment $(m_i, m_{i+1}, \ldots, m_j)$ as M_{ij}. Let S_j be the set of the starting positions of all segments which end at position j and which form a k-noisy cluster. Let i^* be the largest position in S_j. The following lemma gives a recurrence formula for $\mathtt{WI}(j)$ and $\mathtt{WE}(j)$ in terms of $\mathtt{W}(j')$ and $\mathtt{WI}(j')$ with $j' < j$.

Lemma 1. *Assume* $\mathtt{W}(0) = \mathtt{WI}(0) = \mathtt{WE}(0) = 0$. *For any* $j \ge 1$,

1. $\mathtt{WI}(j) = \max \left\{ \begin{array}{l} \max_{i \in S_j, \mathtt{W}(i-1) \ne 0} (\min(\mathtt{W}(i-1), w(M_{ij}))), \\ \max_{i \in S_j, \mathtt{W}(i-1) = 0} w(M_{ij}) \end{array} \right\}$.

2. $\mathtt{WE}(j) = \begin{cases} \max_{h \in [i^*, j-1]} \mathtt{WI}(h) & \text{if } S_j \ne \varnothing, \\ \mathtt{W}(j-1) & \text{otherwise.} \end{cases}$

Proof. (1) For every $i \in S_j$, we want to determine the best alignment $A^* \in \Sigma_j$ that contains M_{ij}, i.e., the minimum weight of the clusters in A^* is the maximum among all such alignments. This alignment is the union of $\{M_{ij}\}$ and the best alignment in Σ_{i-1}. If $\mathtt{W}(i-1) \ne 0$, $\min_{C \in A^*} w(C) = \min(\mathtt{W}(i-1), w(M_{ij}))$. If $\mathtt{W}(i-1) = 0$, $\min_{C \in A^*} w(C) = w(M_{ij})$. Therefore, Statement (1) follows.

(2) Suppose $S_j \ne \varnothing$. Let A be any alignment in $\Sigma_j - \Gamma_j$, and h be the largest index of the matched substring pair that is contained in the clusters of A. Notice that we must have $i^* \le h \le j - 1$, otherwise, $A \cup \{M_{i^*j}\}$ is an alignment which contradicts that A is maximal. Therefore, we have $\mathtt{WE}(j) = \max_{i^* \le h \le j-1} \mathtt{WI}(h)$. Suppose $S_j = \varnothing$. Then $\Gamma_j = \varnothing$. Therefore, $\mathtt{WE}(j) = \mathtt{W}(j-1)$.

Based on Lemma 1, we can solve the max-min alignment problem using dynamic programming (see Algorithm 1).

Time complexity: Suppose that we have a preprocessing to find all k-noisy clusters and their weights (i.e., Step 1 of Algorithm 1) in $f(n)$ time so that we can answer in $O(1)$ time whether a particular segment is a k-noisy cluster. Consider each iteration of Step 3 of Algorithm 1. Computing $\mathtt{WI}(j)$ and $\mathtt{WE}(j)$ takes $O(j)$ time. Then $\mathtt{W}(j)$ can be computed in $O(1)$ time. Therefore, Step 3 of Algorithm 1 takes $O(n^2)$ time and the whole algorithm takes $O(n^2 + f(n))$ time.

The preprocessing, i.e., finding all k-noisy clusters, is non-trivial and indeed the bottleneck. In the next section, we give an algorithm to find all k-noisy clusters with time $f(n) = O(k^2 n^2)$. In other words, the whole algorithm runs in $O(k^2 n^2)$ time.

2.2   Finding the k-Noisy Clusters

In this section, we show how to find all k-noisy clusters and determine their weights in $O(k^2 n^2)$ time. A brute-force approach is to determine whether a particular segment M_{ij} is a k-noisy cluster by examining all possible combinations

Algorithm 1 The dynamic programming algorithm for the max-min alignment problem.

---

1. For each subsequence M_{ij} of M with $1 \leq i \leq j \leq n$, determine whether it is a k-noisy clusters and compute its weight if so. For any $1 \leq j \leq n$, let S_j be the set of all i values such that M_{ij} is a k-noisy cluster, and i^* be the largest such value.
2. Set $\mathtt{W}(0) = \mathtt{WI}(0) = \mathtt{WE}(0) = 0$.
3. For $j = 1$ to n
   a) For each $M_{ij} \in S_j$, compute the value according to Lemma 1 part (1) in terms of $\mathtt{W}(i-1)$ and $w(M_{ij})$, and set $\mathtt{WI}(j)$ to be the maximum of these values.
   b) Compute $\mathtt{WE}(j)$ according to Lemma 1 part (2) in terms of $\mathtt{W}(j-1)$ and $\mathtt{WI}(h)$ for $i^* \leq h \leq j-1$.
   c) Set $\mathtt{W}(j) = \max\{\mathtt{WI}(j), \mathtt{WE}(j)\}$.

---

of up to k elements in the segment, and checking whether throwing these elements away would leave a sequence satisfying the k-noisy cluster requirement. This requires $O(n^{k+1})$ time. Hence, computing all k-noisy clusters and their weights takes $O(n^{k+3})$ time. Below we show how to improve the time complexity to $O(k^2 n^2)$. The main observation is that we are able to determine whether a segment M_{ij} is a k-noisy cluster by examining a small number of $M_{ij'}$ for some $j' < j$ that have already been considered. Details are given below.

Consider any $1 \leq i \leq j \leq n$. To determine whether a segment M_{ij} is a k-noisy cluster, we try every $M_{ij'}$ with $j' < j$ to check whether it is possible to obtain a k-noisy cluster by extending $M_{ij'}$ to include m_j while satisfying the three requirements of a k-noisy cluster. We observe that the first two requirements of a k-noisy cluster are local concerns while the third requirement (i.e., the size requirement) is a global concern in the following sense. If the segment $M_{ij'}$ does not satisfy the first two requirements, it is impossible to extend it such that M_{ij} satisfies these requirements. On the other hand, even if $M_{ij'}$ does not satisfy the size requirement, it is still possible to extend $M_{ij'}$ such that M_{ij} is a k-noisy cluster because adding more matched substring pairs may make the extended segment to be of sufficient size. Based on this observation, we exclude the size requirement when we describe the sub-problem.

Now we describe how to find k-noisy clusters. Recall that $\mathtt{Gap}$ and $\mathtt{MinSize}$ are two predefined positive constants. A set $H \subset \{m_i, m_{i+1}, \ldots, m_j\}$ is said to be a set of noise in M_{ij} if $M_{ij} - H$ satisfies the first two requirements of a noisy cluster (i.e., the size requirement is excluded) and the elements in $M_{ij} - H$ are either all of the same orientation or all of the opposite orientations (i.e., the value of σ's are all the same). Notice that $\varnothing$ is also a candidate for H. Let N_{ij}^+ (N_{ij}^-, resp.) be the set of noise H in M_{ij} such that all elements in $M_{ij} - H$ have $\sigma = 1$ ($\sigma = -1$, resp.).

Lemma 2. M_{ij} is a k-noisy cluster if and only if the expression

$$\max \left\{ \begin{array}{l} \max_{H \in N_{ij}^+, |H| \leq k}\{\mathtt{Size}(M_{ij} - H)\}, \\ \max_{H \in N_{ij}^-, |H| \leq k}\{\mathtt{Size}(M_{ij} - H)\} \end{array} \right\}$$

is at least $\mathtt{MinSize}$.

Proof. The lemma follows from definition.

Thus, to find all k-noisy clusters, it suffices to compute the expression in Lemma 2 for all $1 \leq i \leq j \leq n$. In the rest of this section, we show how to compute the expression

$$\max_{H \in N_{ij}^+, |H| \leq k} \{\text{Size}(M_{ij} - H)\} \tag{1}$$

for all $1 \leq i \leq j \leq n$. The counterpart can be computed similarly. Define, for all $1 \leq i \leq j \leq n$ and $0 \leq x \leq k$,

$$\text{V}(i, j, x) = \max_{H \in N_{ij}^+, |H| \leq x} \{\text{Size}(M_{ij} - H)\}.$$

Thus, Expression (1) equals $\text{V}(i, j, k)$. Let

$$\overline{\text{V}}(i, j, x) = \max_{H \in N_{ij}^+, |H| \leq x, m_j \notin H} \{\text{Size}(M_{ij} - H)\}.$$

To take care of the boundary conditions, for any $i, j < 1$ and $x < 0$, we set $\text{V}(i, j, x) = \overline{\text{V}}(i, j, x) = 0$. Then, $\text{V}(i, j, x) = \max\{\overline{\text{V}}(i, j, x), \text{V}(i, j-1, x-1)\}$.

Now we show how to compute $\overline{\text{V}}(i, j, x)$. If m_j is of opposite orientations, $\overline{\text{V}}(i, j, x) = 0$. Suppose m_j is of the same orientation. Let P be the set of matched substring pairs $m_p = (a_p, b_p, \ell_p)$ such that the following properties are satisfied: (i) m_p is of same orientation, (ii) $\max(i, j-x-1) \leq p \leq j-1$, (iii) $b_p < b_j$, (iv) m_p and m_j satisfy the distance requirement, and (v) m_p and m_j satisfy the consecutive requirement. Then we have the following lemma.

Lemma 3. $\overline{\text{V}}(i, j, x)$ *can be computed recursively as follows in terms of* $\overline{\text{V}}(i, j', x')$ *for some $j' < j$ and $x' \leq x$.*

$$\overline{\text{V}}(i, j, x) = \begin{cases} \max_{m_p \in P} \overline{\text{V}}(i, p, x-j+p+1) + \text{Size}((m_j)) & \text{if } P \neq \varnothing, \\ 0 & \text{otherwise.} \end{cases}$$

Proof. For any $m_p \in P$, the number of matched substring pairs in between m_p and m_j is $j - p - 1$. If there is a set X such that $|X| \leq x - (j - p - 1)$ and $M_{ip} - X$ satisfies the first two requirements of noisy cluster, then we can throw away a set X' with at most x matched substring pairs from M_{ij}, where $X' = (m_{p+1}, m_{p+2}, \ldots, m_{j-1}) \cup X$ so that $M_{ij} - X'$ also satisfies the first two requirements of noisy cluster. Therefore, $\overline{\text{V}}(i, j, x) = \max_{m_p \in P} \overline{\text{V}}(i, p, x - j + p + 1) + \text{Size}((m_j))$. On the other hand, if $P = \varnothing$, $\overline{\text{V}}(i, j, x) = 0$.

Time and space complexity: Both the V and $\overline{\text{V}}$ tables have kn^2 entries. Each $\overline{\text{V}}$ entry is the maximum of at most k precomputed values. Therefore, computing the $\overline{\text{V}}$ table takes $O(k^2 n^2)$ time. Each V entry is the maximum of two precomputed values. Therefore, computing the V table takes $O(kn^2)$ time. With the computed V values, we can determine whether a given subsequence of M is a k-noisy cluster in constant time. Together with the discussion in Section 2.1, we have a dynamic programming algorithm for the max-min alignment problem which takes $O(k^2 n^2)$ time.

For the space requirement, a straightforward implementation of the dynamic programming requires $O(kn^2)$ space. We can reduce the requirement to $O(k^2n)$ space. Consider the computation of $\text{WI}(j)$ for some $1 \leq j \leq n$. We need to examine the values $\text{V}(i, j, k)$ with $1 \leq i \leq j$. Computing $\text{V}(i, j, k)$ requires the computation of $\overline{\text{V}}(i, p, x)$ for some $0 \leq x \leq k$ and some p with $\max(i, j - x - 1) \leq p < j$. There are at most $(k + 1)$ such x values and at most $(k + 1)$ such p values. In other words, the computation of $\text{WI}(j)$ requires $O(k^2n)$ precomputed values, so only $O(k^2n)$ space is needed to store these values.

3   The Min-Cardinality Alignment Problem

In this section, we describe a dynamic programming algorithm for the min-cardinality alignment problem. This algorithm makes use of the algorithm described in Section 2.2 to determine whether a subsequence of M is a k-noisy cluster. Recall the definition Σ_j, Γ_j and $\Sigma_j - \Gamma_j$ in the previous section. For any alignment A, let $|A|$ denote the number of clusters in A. For $1 \leq j \leq n$, let $\text{U}(j) = \min_{A \in \Sigma_j} |A|$. To take care of the boundary conditions, we set $\text{U}(0) = \text{UI}(0) = \text{UE}(0) = \infty$. Note that $\text{U}(n)$ is the number of clusters in the min-cardinality optimal alignment of M. To find $\text{U}(j)$, we consider two cases according to whether m_j is included in some clusters in the alignment. We define $\text{UI}(j) = \min_{A \in \Gamma_j} |A|$, and $\text{UE}(j) = \min_{A \in \Sigma_j - \Gamma_j} |A|$. Then, we have $\text{U}(j) = \min\{\text{UI}(j), \text{UE}(j)\}$. The following lemma gives a recursive formula for $\text{UI}(j)$ and $\text{UE}(j)$.

Lemma 4. *Let i' be the smallest value such that $M_{i'j}$ is a k-noisy cluster, and let i^* be the largest such value.*

1. $\text{UI}(j) = \begin{cases} \infty & \text{if there is no such } i', \\ \text{U}(i' - 1) + 1 & \text{if } \text{U}(i' - 1) \neq \infty, \\ 1 & \text{if } \text{U}(i' - 1) = \infty. \end{cases}$

2. $\text{UE}(j) = \begin{cases} \text{UE}(j) = \min_{h \in [i^*, j-1]} \text{UI}(h) & \text{if } i^* \text{ exists}, \\ \text{U}(j - 1) & \text{otherwise}. \end{cases}$

Proof. The proof is similar to Lemma 1 and will be given in the full paper.

Similar to the Max-min algorithm, we can show that the Min-cardinality algorithm takes $O(k^2n^2)$ time and $O(k^2n)$ space.

4   Experiments

We have implemented the Max-min and the Min-cardinality algorithms in a PC with 512M memory and a 2.4GHz CPU. The actual running time of the programs depend on the noise level k and the number of input pairs n. We have tested the programs on some real data sets with n ranging from 30,000 to 70,000 and with $k = 0$ and $k = 3$. The running times are reasonable and range from one hour to several hours.

We compare the quality of the output of our algorithms with that of MUMMER[5], the most popular whole genome alignment software. We have chosen 7 pairs of mouse and human chromosomes as our testing data. For each pair of chromosomes, the biological community has already identified a number of conserved genes; details are published in GenBank[1]. The chromosomes we used in the experiments are of length about 30 million. For each pair of chromosomes, we identify the set of uniquely matched substring pairs with length at least 20 as input to the algorithms. Substring pairs with length less than 20 are likely to be noise [4]. The details of the data sets are given in Table 1.

Table 1. Details of Data Sets

Experiment No.	Mouse Chr No.	Human Chr No.	# of Input Pairs	# of Published Conserved Gene Pairs
1	7	19	52,394	192
2	15	22	71,613	72
3	16	16	66,536	31
4	16	22	61,200	30
5	17	16	29,001	46
6	17	19	56,236	30
7	19	11	29,814	93

Table 2. Coverage of Output of Different Algorithms (In the experiments, we set Gap = 2000, MinSize = 65 for all programs including MUMMER. We have tried the default parameters of MUMMER, but the coverage of the output is much poorer.)

Experiment No.	MUMMER	Max-min $(k = 0)$	Max-min $(k = 3)$	Min-cardinality $(k = 0)$	Min-cardinality $(k = 3)$
1	137	148	157	148	157
2	52	59	62	59	62
3	21	22	24	22	24
4	24	25	28	25	28
5	30	38	38	38	38
6	18	18	21	18	21
7	73	79	79	79	79

We measure the quality of output from two perspectives: the coverage and the preciseness. For coverage, we count the number of published gene pairs that are covered by the clusters reported by the algorithms. However, high coverage alone may not imply a high quality in the output as one can simply output every matched substring pair as a single cluster, thus achieving the highest possible coverage. Therefore, we also consider the percentage of output clusters that

---

[1] GenBank is the largest public database of DNA sequences and is maintained by the National Center for Biotechnology Information (NCBI),
http://www.ncbi.nlm.nih.gov/Homology.

Table 3. The Preciseness of Output of Different Algorithms

Experiment No.	MUMMER	Max-min $(k = 0)$	Max-min $(k = 3)$	Min-cardinality $(k = 0)$	Min-cardinality $(k = 3)$
1	25.7%	24.3%	25.8%	24.3%	26.8%
2	23.3%	24.8%	24.4%	24.8%	24.5%
3	10.1%	12.2%	12.5%	12.2%	12.7%
4	22.9%	25.3%	25.4%	25.3%	22.8%
5	20.4%	24.1%	25.0%	24.1%	23.6%
6	12.5%	13.2%	14.9%	13.2%	14.3%
7	27.5%	27.9%	27.4%	27.9%	28.5%

actually cover the conserved gene pairs. This percentage is referred to as the preciseness of the output. In other words, a good algorithm should produce a set of output clusters with high coverage and high preciseness.

Table 2 shows the coverage of the output from different algorithms in different test cases. In general, both the Max-min and Min-cardinality algorithms have a higher coverage than MUMMER even for $k = 0$. It implies that the global selection criteria are effective. If the noise level increases to 3, the coverage of the output from our algorithms has visible improvement. It shows that the noise tolerance feature does enable more conserved gene pairs to be uncovered. Combining the global selection criteria and the noise tolerance feature can increase the coverage of the output by 10% to 25% compared with that for MUMMER. Also, the set of gene pairs uncovered by the Max-min and the Min-cardinality algorithms (for both $k = 0$ and $k = 3$) is the superset of that uncovered by MUMMER. On the other hand, the output produced by the Max-min and the Min-cardinality algorithms have exactly the same coverage in all cases.

Table 3 shows the preciseness of the output from different algorithms in the test cases. In most cases, the output from the Max-min and Min-cardinality algorithms show a slightly higher preciseness than that of MUMMER. Again, the output from the Max-min and Min-cardinality algorithms show very similar preciseness.

To conclude, based on the global selection criteria and the noise tolerance feature, both of our algorithms are able to produce a set of higher quality output clusters (ie, with higher coverage and similar preciseness) than MUMMER.

References

1. David L. Baillie and Ann M. Rose. Waba success: A tool for sequence comparison between large genomes. *Genome Research*, 10(8):1071–1073, 2000.
2. S. Batzoglou, L. Pachter, J.P. Mesirov, B. Berger, and E.S. Lander. Human and mouse gene structure: Comparative analysis and application to exon prediction. *Genome Research*, 10:950–958, 2000.
3. Jeremy Buhler. Efficient large-scale sequence comparison by locality-sensitive hashing. *Bioinformatics*, 17(5):419–428, 2001.

4. Arthur L. Delcher, Simon Kasif, Robert D. Fleischmann, Jeremy Peterson, Owen White, and Steven L. Salzberg. Alignment of whole genomes. *Nucleic Acids Research*, 27(11):2369–2376, 1999.

5. Arthur L. Delcher, Adam Phillippy, Jane Carlton, and Steven L. Salzberg. Fast algorithms for large-scale genome alignment and comparison. *Nucleic Acids Research*, 30(11):2478–2483, 2002.

6. Kelly A. Frazer, Laura Elnitski, Deanna M. Church, Inna Dubchak, and Ross C. Hardison. Cross-species sequence comparisons: A review of methods and available resources. *Genome Research*, 13:1–12, 2003.

7. B. Morgenstern. Dialign 2: Improvement of the segment-to-segment approach to multiple sequence alignment. *Bioinformatics*, 15:211–218, 1999.

8. B. Morgenstern, K. Frech, D. Dress, and T. Werner. Dialign: Finding local similarities by multiple sequence alignment. *Bioinformatics*, 14:290–294, 1998.

9. Conrad A Nieduszynski, James Murray, and Mark Carrington. Whole-genome analysis of animal a- and b-type cyclins. *Genome Biology*, 3(12), 2002.

10. Scott Schwartz, Zheng Zhang, Kelly A. Frazer, Arian Smit, Cathy Riemer, John Bouck, Richard Gibbs, Ross Hardison, and Webb Miller. Pipmaker - a web server for aligning two genomic dna sequences. *Genome Research*, 10(4):577–586, 2000.

11. P. Vincens, L. Buffat, C. Andre, J.P. Chevrolat, J.F. Boisvieux, and S. Hazout. A strategy for finding regions of similarity in complete genome sequences. *Bioinformatics*, 14:715–725, 1998.

Segmenting Doughnut-Shaped Objects in Medical Images*

Xiaodong Wu

Department of Computer Science
The University of Texas – Pan American
1201 West University Drive
Edinburg, Texas 78539-2999, USA
xwu@cs.panam.edu

Abstract. Image segmentation with specific constraints has found applications in several areas such as biomedical image analysis and data mining. In this paper, we study the problem of segmenting doughnut-shaped and smooth objects in 2-D medical images. Image objects of these shapes are often studied in medical applications. We present an $O(IJU(U-L)\log J\log(U-L))$ time algorithm, where the size of the input 2-D image is $I \times J$, M is the smoothness parameter with $1 \le M \le J$, and L and U are the thickness parameters specifying the thickness between two border contours of a doughnut-shaped object. Previous approaches for solving this segmentation problem are computationally expensive and/or need a lot of user interference. Our algorithm improves the straightforward dynamic programming algorithm by a factor of $O(\frac{J(U-L)M^2}{U\log J\log(U-L)})$. We explore some interesting observations, which make possible to apply the divide-and-conquer strategy combined with dynamic programming. Our algorithm is also based on computing optimal paths in an implicitly represented graph.

1 Introduction

One of the biggest challenges in medical image analysis is accurate image segmentation, which is a key to solving problems in numerous applications such as medical diagnosis, surgical treatment planning, and brain mapping. As a central problem in processing and analyzing image data, image segmentation is to define accurate boundaries between the objects or regions of interest represented by the images. This task is in practice quite often performed by human manual tracing. While manual tracing is robust, it is tedious, time-consuming, and can have a significant inter-observer and intra-observer variability. Hence, efficient and effective automated segmentation methods are highly desirable for many applications [6,10,2,1]. However, due to the inherent visual complexity, efficient and

* This research was supported in part by a grant from the University of Texas – Pan American Faculty Research Council and a grant from the Computing and Information Technology Center at the University of Texas – Pan American, Edinburg, TX 78539, USA.

T. Ibaraki, N. Katoh, and H. Ono (Eds.): ISAAC 2003, LNCS 2906, pp. 375–384, 2003.
© Springer-Verlag Berlin Heidelberg 2003

accurate segmentation poses one of the most notoriously hard problems in image understanding. In some applications, it makes image segmentation much easier to use additional shape information because the target objects are expected to have certain topological or geometric structures or satisfy specific constraints.

In this paper, we study image segmentation for doughnut-shaped and smooth objects in two dimensions. Doughnut-like shape and smoothness capture the properties of abundant objects in medical images, such as vessels, left ventricles, bones, ducts, and vertebrae. As illustrated in Figure 1(a), a doughnut-shaped object consists of an inner and an outer boundaries (called *coupled contours*). Conventional segmentation approaches treat such two boundaries independently and the contours are extracted separately, which ignore the relevant information of the coupled borders. Those methods sometimes fail to accurately identify the target contours, especially with the presence of poor contrast, noise, or adjacent structures near the target object [6,9]. This paper investigates simultaneous detection of coupled contours in 2-D medical images. This approach, intended to mimic the boundary detection strategy of a human observer who will use the position of one contour to create and/or confirm hypotheses about the position of the other contour, has attracted considerable research efforts [7,9,4,11,6]. There are two major methods for simultaneous detection of coupled contours: graph searching and variants of active contour models [5]. Sonka *et al.* [7,6] developed a method for simultaneous detection of both coronary borders in an $n \times n$ image. Their approach is based on searching an optimal path in a 3-D lattice graph with $O(n^3)$ vertices and edges. Unfortunately, it relies on users to define an approximate centerline between the coupled borders to construct the 3-D graph. Very recently, Spreeuwers and Breeuwer [9] extended the active contour method by imposing the geometric properties of coupled boundaries and proposed a so-called *coupled active contour* model to detect the left ventricular epi- and endo-cardinal borders simultaneously. However, this approach suffers the same shortcoming as the active contour model and is computationally intensive. In this paper, we develop a new efficient algorithm based on graph searching for extracting the coupled contours simultaneously with much less user interference.

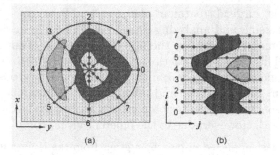

Fig. 1. (a) Illustrating a doughnut-shaped object. (b) Transforming the circular region indicated by the circle in (a), including the doughnut-shaped object,

In general, an original 2-D image can be described by a function $\mathcal{I}(\mathbf{x}, \mathbf{y})$ that defines the intensity of each pixel (x, y) in the image. As was done in [3,6,8,10], we perform a polar coordinate transformation on $\mathcal{I}(\mathbf{x}, \mathbf{y})$ to obtain its corresponding image $\mathcal{P}(\mathbf{i}, \mathbf{j})$. Then, the doughnut-shaped object in $\mathcal{I}(\mathbf{x}, \mathbf{y})$ corresponds to a "strip" in $\mathcal{P}(\mathbf{i}, \mathbf{j})$ as shown in Figure 1. In this paper, we view $\mathcal{P}(\mathbf{i}, \mathbf{j})$ as the input which is a 2-D image of size $I \times J$ (i.e., $\mathcal{P}(\mathbf{i}, \mathbf{j}) = \{(i, j) \mid i = 1, 2, \ldots, I, \ j = 1, 2, \ldots, J\}$). Let w_{ij} be the intensity level of a pixel (i, j) of $\mathcal{P}(\mathbf{i}, \mathbf{j})$. We focus on computing an optimal smooth strip in $\mathcal{P}(\mathbf{i}, \mathbf{j})$.

A 2-D object Q is said to be *stripped* with respect to a line l if for every line l' that is orthogonal to l, the intersection $Q \cap l'$ is a connected component (possibly an empty set). A 2-D object is said to be *x-stripped* if the line l is the x-axis. We define the *thickness* of an x-stripped object Q at $x = x_0$ as the length of the intersection between Q and the line $l : x = x_0$. For an x-stripped object in medical images, we assume its thickness ranges from L to U with $0 < L < U$ (e.g., the wall thickness of vessels changes in a certain range). Roughly speaking, the smoothness constraint means that two distinct pixels (i, j) and (i', j') of a 2-D image can be adjacent to each other on the boundary of a segmented object if the i-th and i'-th rows are neighboring to each other (i.e., $|i - i'| = 1$) and j is "close" enough to j' (i.e., $|j - j'| < M$, where M is an input parameter with $1 \leq M \leq J$). A 2-D image $\mathcal{P}(\mathbf{i}, \mathbf{j})$ can be viewed as representing a setting on a doughnut-shaped object, with the last row of $\mathcal{P}(\mathbf{i}, \mathbf{j})$ being treated as being adjacent to the first row (i.e., $\mathcal{P}(\mathbf{i}, \mathbf{j})$ is "bended" to form a 2-D torus). A smooth strip in $\mathcal{P}(\mathbf{i}, \mathbf{j})$ consists of two non-crossing *smooth contours* C_M's (i.e., coupled contours) in such a "torial" image, with each defined as follows: (1) C_M starts at a pixel $(0, j_0)$ in the first row of $\mathcal{P}(\mathbf{i}, \mathbf{j})$), for some $j_0 \in \{0, \ldots, J - 1\}$. (2) C_M consists of a sequence of I pixels $(0, j_0), (1, j_1), \ldots, (I - 1, j_{I-1})$, one from each row of $\mathcal{P}(\mathbf{i}, \mathbf{j})$), such that for every $k = 0, 1, \ldots, I - 1$, $|j_k - j_{(k+1) \bmod I}| < M$ (i.e., C_M satisfies the monotonicity and smoothness constraints).

Note that the contour C_M is really a closed path in the "torial" $\mathcal{P}(\mathbf{i}, \mathbf{j})$ that is monotone and smooth. The boundaries of some medical objects in 2-D images can be modeled as such coupled contours [8,9,6,10], and it is natural that one would like to find the "best" contours (i.e., ones with maximum total likelihood of pixels on the contours) to bound a sought object.

We present an $O(IJU(U - L) \log J \log(U - L))$ time algorithm for segmenting a smooth strip in image $\mathcal{P}(\mathbf{i}, \mathbf{j})$. Note that our time bound is independent of the smoothness parameter M, which could be as large as J. Our algorithm improves the straightforward dynamic programming algorithm by a factor of $O(\frac{J(U-L)M^2}{U \log J \log(U-L)})$. We model this segmentation problem as searching two optimal non-crossing paths in a graph. The size of the graph built from the input image of size $I \times J$ is $O(IJM)$. Our algorithm is based on an interesting observation which enables us to apply divide-and-conquer strategy, and on computing the optimal non-crossing paths in an implicitly represented graph by dynamic programming.

Image segmentation with specific shape constraints arises in various applications. Certain medical image analysis (e.g., cardiac MRI and intravascular ultrasound imaging) is based on segmenting star-shaped and smooth objects [3,6,8, 10,2]. Asano et al. [1] presented an $O(I^2J^2)$ time algorithm for segmenting an x-monotone and connected object in a 2-D image based on optimizing the interclass variance criterion and by using computational geometry techniques. Segmenting star-shaped/stripped/monotone and connected objects (which is seemingly quite restricted) can be used as an important step in image segmentation for more general settings [1]. For instance, the primary difficulty with the active contour models is finding a good starting point for complicated objects; perhaps our algorithms could be used to get an approximation of the boundary and used to initialize the active contour model.

We omit the proofs of the lemmas due to the space limit.

2   Detecting Smooth Strips in 2-D Images

This section presents our $O(IJU(U - L)\log J\log(U - L))$ time algorithm for segmenting a smooth stripped object in a 2-D medical image. We start with our modeling the segmentation problem as searching optimal two "non-crossing" paths in a graph, and then present our algorithms for the problem.

2.1   The Graph Model of the Problem

Let $G_M = (V, E)$ be a lattice graph, where $V = \{(i, j) \mid 0 \leq i < I, 0 \leq j < J\}$ and M is a given integer with $1 \leq M \leq J$. Each vertex (i, j) of G_M has a real valued weight w_{ij}. We define the M-neighborhood of an vertex $(i, j) \in V$, denoted by $\mathcal{N}_M(i, j)$, as a set of vertices on the same row with distance less than M away from (i, j), i.e., $\mathcal{N}_M(i, j) = \{(i, k) \mid \max\{0, j - M + 1\} \leq k < \min\{j + M, J\}\}$. For each vertex $(i, j) \in V$, there is a directed edge going from (i, j) to every vertex in $\mathcal{N}_M((i+1) \bmod I, j)$. Besides these edges, there is no other edge in the graph G_M. We call such a graph an M-smoothness lattice graph (e.g., see Figure 2(a)). Note that G_M is in fact a directed acyclic graph with vertex weights and has I rows and J columns. For a $j \in \{0, 1, \ldots, J - 1\}$, let p_j be a path in G_M from the vertex $(0, j)$ to a vertex in $\mathcal{N}_M(I - 1, j)$. Such a path is called a c_path. We define the weight of a path p in G_M, $w(p)$, as the total weights of vertices on p, i.e., $\sum_{(i,j)\in p} w_{ij}$. We use $p(i)$ to denote the column index of the vertex on the path p at the i-th row. Given two integers $0 < L < U < J$, two c_paths p_j and $p_{j'}$ $(j < j')$ are called a dual path of G_M, denoted by $p(j, j')$, if for any i $(0 \leq i < I)$, we have $L \leq p_{j'}(i) - p_j(i) \leq U$ (called thickness constraint). For a dual path $p(j, j')$, if $j < j'$, we call c_path p_j (resp., $p_{j'}$) the left path (resp., right path) of $p(j, j')$ (e.g., see Figure 2(a)). The weight of the dual path $p(j, j')$ is the sum of the weights of p_j and $p_{j'}$. For any $j = 0, 1, \ldots, J - 1$, let $p(j, *)$ be a minimum-weight dual path in G_M that starts at the vertex $(0, j)$ (i.e., either the left path or the right path of $p(j, *)$ starts at the vertex $(0, j)$). Our goal is to compute a dual path p^*, whose weight is the minimum among all dual paths in G_M, i.e., $w(p^*) = \min\{w(p(0, *)), w(p(1, *)), \ldots, w(p(J - 1, *))\}$.

The problem of computing an optimal dual path p^* in G_M is well motivated by the need of detecting the coupled contours of smooth stripped objects in 2-D biomedical images $\mathcal{P}(\mathbf{i},\mathbf{j})$ (i.e., smooth doughnut-shaped objects in $\mathcal{I}(\mathbf{x},\mathbf{y})$). We model an input 2-D image $\mathcal{P}(\mathbf{i},\mathbf{j})$ as a directed acyclic graph $G_M = (V,E)$ with vertex weights, such that each pixel of $\mathcal{P}(\mathbf{i},\mathbf{j})$ corresponds to a vertex in V, and the edges of E represent the connections among the pixels to form feasible object borders, which, in fact, enforce the monotonicity and smoothness constraints. The weight of a vertex in V is inversely related to the likelihood that it may be present at the desired border contour, which is usually determined by using simple low-level image features [10,8,6]. An optimal dual path p^* of the minimum total vertex weight in G_M corresponds to the desired coupled borders of certain objects (e.g., doughnut-shaped objects) in medical images, since such a path captures both the local and global information in determining optimal contours in the image.

Chen *et al.* [3] developed an $O(IJ \log J)$ time algorithm for computing an optimal c-path in G_M. Actually, computing an optimal dual path in G_M is to seek two c-paths that satisfy the thickness constraint. One may consider the following greedy algorithm: Compute a minimum-weight c-path p^* in G_M by using Chen *et al.*'s algorithm; and then "remove" p^* from G_M and compute an optimal c-path p'^* in the resulting graph. Unfortunately, this heuristic does not work well since p^* and p'^* may violate the thickness constraint. Thus, we need to consider the left and right paths of a dual path simultaneously, which is the main difficulty in generalizing the algorithm in [3]. Another simple strategy is to consider all possible pairs of vertices $(0,j)$ and $(0,j')$ such that $L \leq |j - j'| \leq U$. For each pair $(0,j)$ and $(0,j')$, we compute a minimum-weight dual path $p^*(j,j')$ in $O(IJ(U - L)M^2)$ time using dynamic programming. Thus, the running time of this algorithm is $O(IJ^2(U - L)^2M^2)$. However, we can do much better. Our algorithm improves this solution by a factor of $O(\frac{JM^2(U-L)}{U \log J \log(U-L)})$ time by exploiting the intrinsic structures of dual paths.

2.2   The Structures of Dual Paths

In this section, we explore the structures of dual paths in G_M, which enables us to apply the divide-and-conquer paradigm. To simplify the discussion of dual paths, as in [3], we modify G_M in the following way: Duplicate the first row of G_M, append it after the last row of G_M, let the vertices of the appended row all have a weight zero, and add directed edges from the vertices of the last row of G_M to the vertices of the appended row based on the M-smoothness constraint. We denote the appended row as row I and the modified graph as G_M^a. A 2-smoothness lattice graph G_M^a is shown in Figure 2(a), where the appended vertices are dashed circles. Note that any dual path $p(j,j')$ in G_M can be viewed as a dual path $p^a(j,j')$ in G_M^a that starts at the vertices $(0,j)$ and $(0,j')$ and ends at the vertices (I,j) and (I,j'), respectively. In Figure 2(a), the dual path $p(r,r')$ consists of two c-paths p_r (i.e., left path) and $p_{r'}$ (i.e., right path) indicated by solid thick edges. Henceforth, our focus will be on G_M^a and its dual paths, and we simply denote G_M^a by G_M and its dual paths by $p(j,j')$.

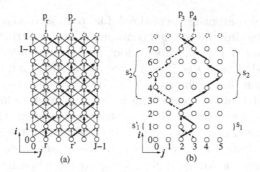

Fig. 2. (a) A 2-smoothness lattice graph, in which dual path $p(r, r')$ consisting of two c_paths p_r and $p_{r'}$ is a dual path with $L = 1$ and $U = 3$. (b) Two c_paths crossing each other and their crossed pairs.

To exploit the intrinsic structures of dual paths, first let us see some useful observations of c_paths. Let p_j and $p_{j'}$ be two c_paths in G_M starting at vertices $(0, j)$ and $(0, j')$, respectively, with $0 \le j < j' < J$. We say that each vertex $(i, p_j(i))$ on p_j has a *corresponding vertex* $(i, p_{j'}(i))$ on $p_{j'}$ at the i-th row. In a similar way, we define the *corresponding subpath* $s' = \{(i, p_{j'}(i)), \ldots, (i', p_{j'}(i'))\}$ on $p_{j'}$, denoted by $p_{j'}[i..i']$, for each subpath $s = \{(i, p_j(i)), \ldots, (i', p_j(i'))\}$ on p_j, denoted by $p_j[i..i']$, with $0 < i \le i' < I$. A vertex $(i, p_j(i))$ on p_j is said to be strictly to the *left* (resp., *right*) of $p_{j'}$ if its corresponding vertex $(i, p_{j'}(i))$ on $p_{j'}$ has a larger (resp., smaller) column index, i.e., $p_{j'}(i) > p_j(i)$ (resp., $p_{j'}(i) < p_j(i)$). Two c_paths p_j and $p_{j'}$ are said to *cross each other* if a vertex on p_j is strictly to the left of $p_{j'}$ and another vertex on p_j is strictly to the right of $p_{j'}$. Given a subpath $s = p_j[i..i']$ on p_j and its corresponding subpath $s' = p_{j'}[i..i']$ on $p_{j'}$, with $0 < i \le i' < I$, s and s' are said to form a *crossed pair* if $p_j(i-1) \le p_{j'}(i-1), p_j(k) > p_{j'}(k)$ for $k = i, 1, \ldots, i'$, and $p_j(i'+1) \le p_{j'}(i'+1)$. If p_j and $p_{j'}$ cross each other, then there exists certainly at least one crossed pair between p_j and $p_{j'}$. Figure 2(b) illustrates two c_paths p_3 and p_4 crossing each other. For simplicity, we only show the edges on the paths.

Now, let us consider a minimum-weight dual path $p(r, *)$. Recall that either the left path or the right path of $p(r, *)$ starts at the vertex $(0, r)$. WLOG, we assume that the left path of $p(r, *)$ starts at $(0, r)$ and the right path is $p_{r'}$ with $r < r'$. The next lemma is a key to our algorithm for computing the optimal dual path p^*.

Lemma 1. *Given a minimum-weight dual path $p(r, *)$ in G_M, for any $0 \le j \le r' - U$ (resp., $r + U \le j < J$), there exists an optimal dual path $p(j, *)$ whose right path (resp., left path) does not cross $p_{r'}$ (resp., p_r), where $p_{r'}$ (resp., p_r) is the right path (resp., left path) of $p(r, *)$.*

Lemma 1 provides a basis for a divide-and-conquer solution for computing the optimal dual path in G_M. Given an optimal dual path $p(r, *)$ consisting of two c_paths p_r and $p_{r'}$ with $r < r'$, we can decompose G_M into two "smaller" subgraphs along $p(r, *)$, and then compute the optimal dual paths in such "smaller" graphs. Before go into details on the decomposition of G_M, we present how to compute an optimal dual path $p(r, *)$ first.

2.3   Computing Optimal Dual Path $p(r, \blacksquare)$

This section shows how to efficiently compute one minimum-weight dual path in G_M, say, $p(r, *)$ that starts at the vertex $(0, r)$ for any $r \in \{0, 1, \ldots, J - 1\}$.

Let $p^*(j, j')$ denote the minimum-weight dual path whose left path starts at vertex $(0, j)$ and right path starts at vertex $(0, j')$. Obviously, one of the c_path in $p(r, *)$ starts at $(0, r)$. Due to the thickness constraint, the possible vertices that the other c_path in $p(r, *)$ may starts at are only a subset of vertices in row 0 whose column indice are in $S_1 = \{r + L \leq k \leq \min\{r + U, J - 1\}\} \bigcup S_2 = \{\min\{r - U, 0\} \leq k \leq r - L\}$. Of course, the optimal dual path $p(r, *)$ can be obtained by computing minimum-weight dual paths $p^*(r, k)$ for all $k \in S_1$ and $p^*(k, r)$ for all $k \in S_2$. However, we can do better by judiciously explore the structures of $p(r, *)$.

Given two c_paths, p_j and $p_{j'}$, we say p_j is to the *left* (resp., *right*) of $p_{j'}$ if for any $0 \leq i \leq I$, $p_j(i) \leq p_{j'}(i)$ (resp., $p_j(i) \geq p_{j'}(i)$). The following lemma makes possible to apply the divide-and-conquer strategy to compute $p(r, *)$.

Lemma 2. *(1) Given an optimal dual path $p^*(r, u)$ ($u \in S_1$), for any $k \in S_1$ and $k > u$ (resp., $k < u$), there exists a minimum-weight dual path $p^*(r, k)$ such that its right path p'_k and its left path p'_r is to the right (resp., left) of p_u and p_r, respectively.*

(2) Given an optimal dual path $p^*(u, r)$ ($u \in S_2$), for any $k \in S_2$ and $k > u$ (resp., $k < u$), there exists a minimum-weight dual path $p^*(k, r)$ such that its left path p'_k and its right path p'_r is to the right (resp., left) of p_u and p_r, respectively.

In terms of Lemma 2, we compute the optimal dual paths $p^*(r, k)$ for every $k \in S_1$, as follows. First, the minimum-weight dual path $p^*(r, u)$ is computed, where $u = r + \lceil (L + U)/2 \rceil$. Using $p^*(r, u)$, we define four sets $J_i^L = \{0, 1, \ldots, p_r(i)\}$, $J_i^R = \{p_r(i), p_r(i) + 1, \ldots, J - 1\}$, $J'^L_i = \{0, 1, \ldots, p_u(i)\}$, and $J'^R_i = \{p_u(i), p_u(i) + 1, \ldots, J - 1\}$, for every $i = 0, 1, \ldots, I$. Then along each c_path of the dual path $p^*(r, u)$, we decompose the graph G_M into two sub-graphs. $G_1 = (V_1, E_1)$ and $G_2 = (V_2, E_2)$ are obtained by decomposing G_M along p_r, where $V_1 = \{(i, j) \mid i \in \{0, 1, \ldots, I\}, j \in J_i^L\}, E_1 = \{e \in E \mid$ both vertices of e are in $V_1\}, V_2 = \{(i, j) \mid i \in \{0, 1, \ldots, I\}, j \in J_i^R\}$, and $E_2 = \{e \in E \mid$ both vertices of e are in $V_2\}$; $G'_1 = (V'_1, E'_1)$ and $G'_2 = (V'_2, E'_2)$ are obtained by decomposing G_M along p_u, where $V'_1 = \{(i, j) \mid i \in \{0, 1, \ldots, I\}, j \in J'^L_i\}, E'_1 = \{e \in E \mid$ both vertices of e are in $V'_1\}, V'_2 = \{(i, j) \mid i \in \{0, 1, \ldots, I\}, j \in J'^R_i\}$, and $E'_2 = \{e \in E \mid$ both vertices of e are in $V'_2\}$. Based on Lemma 2, for any $k \in S_1$ and $k < r + \lceil (L + U)/2 \rceil$ (resp., $k > r + \lceil (L + U)/2 \rceil$), there exists a minimum-weight dual path $p^*(r, k)$ in G_M such that its right path lies in G'_1 (resp., G'_2) and its left path lies in G_1 (resp., G_2). Note that G_1 is a subgraph of G'_1 and G'_2 is a subgraph of G_2. Therefore, we recursively compute optimal dual paths

$p^*(r, k)$ for $k \in S_1$ and $k < r + \lceil (L+U)/2 \rceil$ (resp., $k > r + \lceil (L+U)/2 \rceil$) in G_1 and G_1' (resp., G_2 and G_2').

Similarly, we can compute the minimum-weight dual path $p^*(k, r)$ for every $k \in S_2$. Thus, the following lemma holds.

Lemma 3. *For any given* r *(*$r \in \{0, 1, \ldots, J-1\}$*), the minimum-weight dual path* $p(r, *)$ *can be computed in* $O(T \log(U - L))$ *time, where* T *is the time for computing an optimal dual path* $p^*(j, j')$ *in* G_M *whose c_paths start at vertices* $(0, j)$ *and* $(0, j')$.

2.4   Computing Minimum-Weight Dual Path $p^*(r, r')$

In this section, we present our efficient algorithm for computing an optimal dual path $p^*(r, r')$ whose left and right paths start at vertices $(0, r)$ and $(0, r')$, respectively.

We begin with a less efficient dynamic programming algorithm for computing $p^*(r, r')$ in G_M. First, note that the edges of G_M can be represented *implicitly*. That is, without explicitly storing its edges, we can determine for every vertex of G_M the set of its incoming and outgoing neighbors in $O(1)$ time. Our algorithm uses this implicit representation of G_M. To help our presentation, we say two paths in G_M to be a *twin path* if they start at two vertices of row 0 and satisfy the thickness constraint. The weight of a twin path is the total weights of vertices on both paths. We denote by $m_i[j, k]$ the weight of the optimal twin path in G_M starting from the vertices $(0, r)$ and $(0, r')$ to vertices (i, j) and (i, k), respectively. Due to the smoothness constraint, vertex (i, j) (resp., (i, k)) can be reached from any vertex of row $i-1$ in $\{(i-1, j') \mid \max\{0, j-M+1\} \le j' \le \min\{J-1, j+M-1\}\}$ (resp., $\{(i-1, k') \mid \max\{0, k-M+1\} \le k' \le \min\{J-1, k+M-1\}\}$). But, the thickness constraint restricts our choices of the pair of vertices on row $i-1$. Actually, for any j' such that $\max\{0, j-M+1\} \le j' \le \min\{J-1, j+M-1\}$, we have $\max\{j'+L, k-M+1\} \le k' \le \min\{j'+U, k+M-1\}$. Hence,

$$m_i[j, k] = \min_{j'=\max\{0, j-M+1\}}^{\min\{J-1, j+M-1\}} \min_{k'=\max\{j'+L, k-M+1\}}^{\min\{j'+U, k+M-1\}} m_{i-1}[j', k'] + w(i, j) + w(i, k), \quad (*)$$

when $i > 0$ and $L \le k - j \le U$. One can certainly apply a dynamic programming technique to compute the minimum-weight path $p^*(r, r')$. For each possible pair of j and k, we need to compute the minimum of $O(M^2)$ values; and there are $O(J(U-L))$ such pairs on each row i. Hence, a straightforward dynamic programming algorithm takes $O(IJ(U-L)M^2)$ time to compute $p^*(r, r')$.

Interestingly, we are able to extend the technique developed in [3] to get rid of the M^2 factor for the time complexity.

Suppose that all the optimal twin paths to vertices on rwo $i-1$ have been computed and the weights of these paths, $m_{i-1}[j', k']$ for $0 \le j' < J$ and $j+L \le k' \le \min\{J-1, j+U\}$, are stored (e.g., see Figure 3(a)). Based on equation $(*)$, in order to compute $m_i[j, k]$, we need to know the minimum of $m_{i-1}[j', k']$'s which define a rectangular region centered at the column index pair $< j, k >$ and of size $(2M-1) \times (2M-1)$ in m_{i-1}.

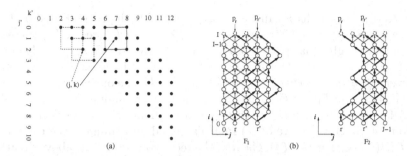

Fig. 3. (a) Incrementally computing the minimum of elements in m_{i-1} that are covered by a rectangle of size of $(2M - 1) \times (2M - 1)$. Herein, $M = 2$, $L = 2$, and $U = 8$. The dots indicate the index pairs $< j', k' >$ that correspond to a twin path. (b) Illustrating the divide-and-conquer algorithm for computing the optimal dual paths $p(j, *)$.

Given an array A of n real numbers and an integer M with $1 \leq M \leq n$, the *min-M-neighbor* of $A[i]$ is defined as $\min\{A[k] \mid \max\{0, i - M + 1\} \leq k \leq \min\{n - 1, i + M - 1\}\}$. Chen *et al.* [3] developed a simple linear time algorithm for computing the min-M-neighbors for all elements in A. Now, we compute the minima for all $< j, k >$ pairs, as follows. For each row $m_{i-1}[j']$ of m_{i-1}, compute the min-M-neighbor for every element in $m_{i-1}[j']$ in $O(U - L)$ time, since each row has at most $(U - L + 1)$ elements. The resulting min-M-neighbors are kept in another 2-D array m'_{i-1}. Then, for each column $m'_{i-1}[k']$ of m'_{i-1}, compute the min-M-neighbor for every element in $m'_{i-1}[k']$ in $O(U - L)$ time. Thus, the minima for all $< j, k >$ pairs can be computed in $O(J(U - L))$ time. Therefore, the minimum-weight dual path $p^*(r, r')$ can be computed in $O(IJ(U - L))$ time. Based on Lemma 3, we have the following lemma.

Lemma 4. *For any given r ($r \in \{0, 1, \ldots, J - 1\}$), the minimum-weight dual path $p(r, *)$ can be computed in $O(IJ(U - L) \log(U - L))$ time.*

2.5   Our Algorithm

Now, we are ready to present our $O(IJU(U - L) \log J \log(U - L))$ time algorithm for computing an optimal dual path p^* in G_M.

Note that the optimal dual path p^* of G_M can be obtained from $p(0, *)$, $p(1, *), \ldots, p(J - 1, *)$. To compute all dual paths $p(0, *)$, $p(1, *), \ldots, p(J - 1, *)$ in G_M, we first compute the minimum-weight dual path $p(\lceil (J - 1)/2 \rceil, *)$ using our algorithm in Section 2.3 and Section 2.4. WLOG, assume the left path of $p(\lceil (J-1)/2 \rceil, *)$ is p_r with $r = \lceil (J-1)/2 \rceil$ and the right path is $p_{r'}$. Using $p(\lceil (J-1)/2 \rceil, *)$, we define two sets $J_i^L = \{0, 1, \ldots, p_{r'}(i)\}$ and $J_i^R = \{p_r(i), p_r(i) + 1, \ldots, J - 1\}$, for every $i = 0, 1, \ldots, I$. Then along the dual path $p(r, *)$, we decompose the graph G_M into two subgraphs $F_1 = (V_1, E_1)$ and $F_2 = (V_2, E_2)$, where $V_1 = \{(i, j) \mid i \in \{0, 1, \ldots, I\}, j \in J_i^L\}, E_1 = \{e \in E \mid$ both vertices of e are in $V_1\}$, $V_2 = \{(i, j) \mid i \in \{0, 1, \ldots, I\}, j \in J_i^R\}$, and $E_2 = \{e \in E \mid$ both vertices of e are in $V_2\}$. Figure 3(b) illustrates the decomposition of the graph

G_M into two subgraphs F_1 and F_2 along the dual path $p(r, *)$. Based on Lemma 1, for any $0 \leq j \leq r' - U$ (resp., $r + U \leq j < J$), in F_1 (resp., F_2) there exists a minimum-weight dual path $p(j, *)$ of G_M. Therefore, we recursively compute $p(j, *)$ for $0 \leq j \leq r' - U$ and for $r + U \leq j < J$) in F_1 and F_2, respectively. However, for every j such that $r' - U < j < r + U$, the optimal dual path $p(j, *)$ may be neither in F_1 nor F_2. Thus, we compute every minimum-weight dual path $p(j, *)$ for $r' - U < j < r + U$ in G_M using our algorithms in Section 2.3 and Section 2.4. Since there are $O(U)$ such j's, based on Lemma 4, the running time is $O(IJU(U - L) \log(U - L))$. Clearly, the recursion tree of our above divide-and-conquer algorithm has $O(\log J)$ levels. At each level, a subset of optimal dual paths $p(j, *)$ is computed (in certain subgraphs of G_M). Due to our construction of the subgraphs, it is easy to see that the total time of each recursion level of our divide-and-conquer algorithm is $O(IJU(U - L) \log(U - L))$. Hence, the total time of the overall divide-and-conquer algorithm is $O(IJU(U - L) \log J \log(U - L))$.

Theorem 1. *Given an implicitly represented M-smoothness lattice graph G_M, a minimum-weight dual path p^* in G_M can be computed in $O(IJU(U - L) \log J \log(U - L))$ time.*

References

1. T. Asano, D. Chen, N. Katoh, and T. Tokuyama, Efficient algorithms for optimization-based image segmentation, *Int J Comp Geom & App.*, 11(2001), pp. 145–166.
2. J. F. Brinkley, A flexible, generic model for anatomic shape: Application to interactive two-dimensional medical image segmentation and matching, *Computers and Biomedical Research*, 26(1993), pp. 121–142.
3. D.Z. Chen, J. Wang, and X. Wu, Image Segmentation with Asteroidality/Tubularity and Smoothness Constraints, *Int J Comp Geom & App.*, 12(2002), pp. 413–428.
4. R. Goldenberg, R. Kimmel, E. Rivlin, and M. Rudzsky, Cortex Segmentation: A Fast Variational Geometric Approach, *IEEE T Med Imag*, 21(2002), pp. 1544-1551.
5. M. Kass, A. Witkin, and D. Terzopoulos, Snakes: Active Contour Models, *Int. J. Comput. Vision*, 1(4)(1988), pp. 321–331.
6. M. Sonka, V. Hlavac, and R. Boyle, *Image Processing, Analysis, and Machine Vision*, 2nd edition, Brooks/Cole Publishing Company, CA, 1999, pp. 199–205.
7. M. Sonka, M.D. Winniford, and S.M. Collins, Robust Simultaneous Detection of Coronary Borders in Complex Images, *IEEE T Med Imag.*, 14(1995), pp. 151–161.
8. M. Sonka, X. Zhang, M. Siebs, M. S. Bissing, S. DeJong, S. M. Collins, and C. R. McKay, Segmentation of Intravascular Ultrasound Images: A Knowledge-Based Approach, *IEEE T Med Imag.*, 14(1995), pp. 719–732.
9. L. Spreeuwers and M. Breeuwer, Detection of Left Ventricular Epi- and Endocardial Borders Using Coupled Active Contours, *Comp. Assisted Radio. & Surgery*, 2003.
10. D.R. Thedens, D.J. Skorton, and S.R. Fleagle, Methods of graph searching for border detection in image sequences with applications to cardiac magnetic resonance imaging, *IEEE T Med Imag.*, 14 (1) (1995), pp. 42–55.
11. X. Zeng, L.H. Staib, R.T. Schultz, and J.S. Duncan, Segmentaion and Measurement of the Cortex from 3-D MR Images Using Coupled Sufaces Propagation, *IEEE T Med Imag.*, 18(1999), pp. 927–937.

On the Locality Properties of Space-Filling Curves

H.K. Dai and H.C. Su*

Computer Science Department, Oklahoma State University
Stillwater, Oklahoma 74078, U. S. A.
{dai, suh}@cs.okstate.edu

Abstract. A discrete space-filling curve provides a linear traversal or indexing of a multi-dimensional grid space. We present an analytical study of the locality properties of the m-dimensional k-order discrete Hilbert and z-order curve families, $\{H_k^m \mid k = 1, 2, \ldots\}$ and $\{Z_k^m \mid k = 1, 2, \ldots\}$, respectively, based on the locality measure L_δ that cumulates all index-differences of point-pairs at a common 1-normed distance δ. We derive the exact formulas for $L_\delta(H_k^m)$ and $L_\delta(Z_k^m)$ for $m = 2$ and arbitrary δ that is an integral power of 2, and $m = 3$ and $\delta = 1$. The results yield a constant asymptotic ratio $\lim_{k \to \infty} \frac{L_\delta(H_k^m)}{L_\delta(Z_k^m)} > 1$, which suggests that the z-order curve family performs better than the Hilbert curve family over the considered parameter ranges.

1 Preliminaries

Space-filling curves have many applications in algorithms, databases, and parallel computation, in which linearization techniques of multi-dimensional arrays or grids are needed. Sample applications include heuristics for Hamiltonian traversals, multi-dimensional space-filling indexing methods, image compression, and dynamic unstructured mesh partitioning.

For positive integer n, denote $[n] = \{1, 2, \ldots, n\}$. An m-dimensional (discrete) space-filling curve of length n^m is a bijective mapping $C : [n^m] \to [n]^m$, thus providing a linear indexing/traversal or total ordering of all grid points in $[n]^m$. An m-dimensional grid is said to be of order k if it has side-length $n = 2^k$; a space-filling curve has order k if its codomain is a grid of order k. The generation of a sequence of multi-dimensional space-filling curves of successive orders usually follows a recursive framework (on the dimensionality and order), which results in a few classical families, such as Gray-coded curves, Hilbert curves, Peano curves, and z-order curves (see, for examples, [AN00] and [MJFS01]).

Denote by H_k^m and Z_k^m an m-dimensional Hilbert and z-order, respectively, space-filling curve of order k. Figure 1 illustrates the recursive constructions of H_k^2 and Z_k^2 for $m = 2$ and $k = 1, 2$, and $m = 3$ and $k = 1$.

---

* Current address: Department of Computer Science, Arkansas State University, State University, Arkansas 72467, U.S.A.

T. Ibaraki, N. Katoh, and H. Ono (Eds.): ISAAC 2003, LNCS 2906, pp. 385–394, 2003.
© Springer-Verlag Berlin Heidelberg 2003

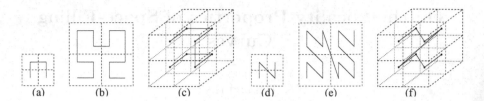

Fig. 1. Recursive constructions of Hilbert and z-order curves of higher order (H_k^m and Z_k^m, respectively) by interconnecting symmetric subcurves, via reflection and rotation, of lower order (H_{k-1}^m and Z_{k-1}^m, respectively): (a) H_1^2; (b) H_2^2; (c) H_1^3; (d) Z_1^2; (e) Z_2^2; (f) Z_1^3.

We measure the applicability of a family of space-filling curves based on their common structural characteristics, which are informally described as follows. Locality preservation reflects proximity between the grid points of $[n]^m$, that is, close-by points in $[n]^m$ are mapped to close-by indices/numbers in $[n^m]$, or vice versa. Clustering performance measures the distribution of continuous runs of grid points (clusters) over identically shaped subspaces of $[n]^m$, which can be characterized by the average number of clusters and the average inter-cluster distance (in $[n^m]$) within a subspace.

Empirical and analytical studies of clustering and inter-clustering performances of various low-dimensional space-filling curves have been reported in the literature (see [MJFS01] for details). Generally, the Hilbert and z-order curve families exhibit good performance in this respect.

Jagadish [Jag97] derives exact formulas for the mean numbers of clusters over all rectangular 2×2 and 3×3 subgrids of an H_k^2-structural grid space. Moon, Jagadish, Faloutsos, and Saltz [MJFS01] prove that in a sufficiently large m-dimensional H_k^m-structural grid space, the mean number of clusters over all rectilinear polyhedral queries with surface area $S_{m,k}$ approaches $\frac{1}{2}\frac{S_{m,k}}{m}$ as k approaches ∞. They also extend the work in [Jag97] to obtain the exact formula for the mean number of clusters over all rectangular $2^q \times 2^q$ subgrids of an H_k^2-structural grid space.

The space-filling index structure can support efficient query processing (such as range queries) provided that we minimize the average number of external fetch/seek operations, which is related to the clustering statistics. Asano, Ranjan, Roos, Welzl, and Widmayer [ARR+97] study the optimization of range queries over space-filling index structures, which aims at minimizing the number of seek operations (not the number of block accesses) — tradeoff between seek time to proper block (cluster) and latency/transfer time for unnecessary blocks (inter-cluster gap). Good bounds on inter-clustering statistics translate into good bounds on the average tolerance of unnecessary block transfers.

Dai and Su [DS03] obtain the exact formulas for the following three statistics for H_k^2 and Z_k^2: (1) the summation of all inter-cluster distances over all $2^q \times 2^q$ query subgrids, (2) the universe mean inter-cluster distance over all inter-cluster gaps from all $2^q \times 2^q$ subgrids, and (3) the mean total inter-cluster distance over all $2^q \times 2^q$ subgrids.

A few locality measures have been proposed and analyzed for space-filling curves in the literature. Generally, Hilbert and z-order curve families achieve good locality performances.

Denote by d and d_p the Euclidean and p-normed metric (Manhattan ($p = 1$), Euclidean ($p = 2$), and maximum metric ($p = \infty$)), respectively. Let C denote a family of m-dimensional curves of successive orders. For quantifying the proximity preservation of close-by points in the m-dimensional space $[n]^m$, Pérez, Kamata, and Kawaguchi [PKK92] employ an average locality measure:

$$L_{\text{PKK}}(C) = \sum_{i,j \in [n^m] | i < j} \frac{|i - j|}{d(C(i), C(j))} \text{ for } C \in \mathcal{C},$$

and provide a hierarchical construction for a 2-dimensional C with good but suboptimal locality with respect to this measure.

Mitchison and Durbin [MD86] use a more restrictive locality measure parameterized by q:

$$L_{\text{MD},q}(C) = \sum_{i,j \in [n^m] | i < j \text{ and } d(C(i), C(j)) = 1} |i - j|^q \text{ for } C \in \mathcal{C}$$

to study optimal 2-dimensional mappings for $q \in [0, 1]$. For the case $q = 1$, the optimal mapping with respect to $L_{\text{MD},1}$ is very different from that in [PKK92]. For the case $q < 1$, they prove a lower bound for arbitrary 2-dimensional curve C:

$$L_{\text{MD},q}(C) \geq \frac{1}{1 + 2q} n^{1+2q} + O(n^{2q}),$$

and provide an explicit construction for a 2-dimensional C with good but suboptimal locality. They conjecture that the space-filling curves with optimal locality (with respect to $L_{\text{MD},q}$ with $q < 1$) must exhibit a "fractal" character.

For measuring the proximity preservation of close-by points in the indexing space $[n^m]$, Gotsman and Lindenbaum [GL96] approximate the locality measures:

$$L_{\text{GL,min}}(C) = \min_{i,j \in [n^m] | i < j} \frac{d(C(i), C(j))^m}{|i - j|}, \text{ and}$$

$$L_{\text{GL,max}}(C) = \max_{i,j \in [n^m] | i < j} \frac{d(C(i), C(j))^m}{|i - j|},$$

for arbitrary m-dimensional curve C, and obtain good bounds for Hilbert curve family. Alber and Niedermeier [AN00] generalize $L_{\text{GL,max}}$ to $L_{\text{AN},p}$ by employing the p-normed metric d_p, in place of the Euclidean metric d. They improve and extend the tight bounds for the 2-dimensional Hilbert curve family in [GL96] for $p = 1$, 2, and ∞.

The focus of this paper provides an analytical study of locality properties of the Hilbert and z-order curve families. The underlying locality measure is similar to $L_{\text{MD},1}$ conditional on a 1-normed distance of δ between points in $[n]^m$:

$$L_\delta(C) = \sum_{i,j \in [n^m] | i < j \text{ and } d_1(C(i), C(j)) = \delta} |i - j|.$$

The locality statistics $L_\delta(C)$ cumulates all index-differences of point-pairs (distances traversed in the sequential index space) at a common 1-normed distance δ (local operation in the C-structural grid space). Note that for the three statistics: $L_\delta(C)$, $L_{[\delta]}(C) = \sum_{i=1}^{\delta} L_i(C)$, and the mean absolute index-difference over all point-pairs at a common 1-normed distance δ, the knowledge of one statistics for all δ yields the other two.

We derive exact formulas for L_δ for the Hilbert curve family $\{H_k^m \mid k = 1, 2, \ldots\}$ and z-order curve family $\{Z_k^m \mid k = 1, 2, \ldots\}$ for $m = 2$ and arbitrary δ that is an integral power of 2, and $m = 3$ and $\delta = 1$. Note that we present the skeletons for proving the main results without the lengthly derivations. Complete proofs and verifying programs are available from the authors.

2   Locality Measures of Hilbert and z-Order Curves

One of the salient characteristics of Hilbert curves is their "self-similarity" — a Hilbert curve can be generated by interconnecting identical subcurves via reflection and rotation (see Figure 1). For 2-dimensional Hilbert curves, this self-similar structural property guides us to decompose H_k^2 into four identical H_{k-1}^2-subcurves (via reflection and rotation), which are amalgamated together by an H_1^2-curve. Following the linear order along this H_1^2-curve, we denote the four H_{k-1}^2-subcurves as $Q_1(H_k^2)$, $Q_2(H_k^2)$, $Q_3(H_k^2)$, and $Q_4(H_k^2)$.

For a 2-dimensional grid, the "orientation" of H_k^2 uniquely determines that of $Q_\alpha(H_k^2)$ for $\alpha = 1, 2, 3, 4$, and thus only one H_k^2 exists modulo symmetry (whereas there are 1536 structurally different 3-dimensional Hilbert curves [AN00]). For a 2-dimensional Hilbert curve H_k^2 indexing the grid $[2^k]^2$, with a canonical orientation shown in Figure 2(a), we denote by $\partial_1(H_k^2)$ and $\partial_2(H_k^2)$ the entry and exit, respectively, grid point in $[2^k]^2$ (with respect to the canonical orientation). Figure 2 depicts the decomposition of H_k^2 and the ∂_1- and ∂_2-labels of four H_{k-1}^2-subcurves.

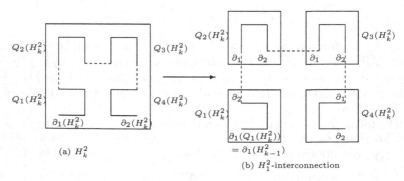

(a) H_k^2

(b) H_1^2-interconnection

Fig. 2. Generation of H_k^2 from a H_1^2-interconnection of four H_{k-1}^2-subcurves.

We derive the exact formula for $L_\delta(H_k^2)$ as follows (similarly for $L_\delta(Z_k^2)$). The recursive decomposition (in k) of H_k^2 gives that

$$L_\delta(H_k^2) = 4L_\delta(H_{k-1}^2) + \sum_{\alpha,\beta \in \{1,2,3,4\} | \alpha < \beta} \Delta_\delta(Q_\alpha(H_k^2), Q_\beta(H_k^2)),$$

where $\Delta_\delta(Q_\alpha(H_k^2), Q_\beta(H_k^2))$ denotes the cumulative contribution of $|i - j|$ from the two subcurves $Q_\alpha(H_k^2)$ and $Q_\beta(H_k^2)$, that is, for all $i, j \in [2^{2k}]$ such that $i < j$, $d_1(H_k^2(i), H_k^2(j)) = \delta$, and i and j appear in (the index ranges of) $Q_\alpha(H_k^2)$ and $Q_\beta(H_k^2)$, respectively. In order to compute the closed-form solution for $L_\delta(H_k^2)$, we develop a suite of lemmas (Lemmas 4, 5, and 6) to compute $\Delta_\delta(Q_\alpha(H_k^2), Q_\beta(H_k^2))$ for all $\alpha, \beta \in \{1, 2, 3, 4\}$ with $\alpha < \beta$, in which we establish a recurrence system (in k — when $2^k > \delta$) of summations with a basis system of summations computed in Lemmas 1, 2, and 3. The following denotations illustrate the geometrical structures (rows, columns, and diagonals) involved in the computations.

With respect to the canonical orientation of H_k^2 shown in Figure 2(a), we cover the 2-dimensional k-order grid with:

1. 2^k rows $(R_{k,1}, R_{k,2}, \ldots, R_{k,2^k})$, indexed from the bottom,
2. 2^k columns $(C_{k,1}, C_{k,2}, \ldots, C_{k,2^k})$, indexed from the left,
3. $2^{k+1} - 1$ main diagonals $(D_{k,1}, D_{k,2}, \ldots, D_{k,2^k} = D'_{k,2^k}, D'_{k,2^k-1}, \ldots, D'_{k,1})$, indexed from the lower-right corner, and
4. $2^{k+1} - 1$ auxiliary diagonals $(A_{k,1}, A_{k,2}, \ldots, A_{k,2^k} = A'_{k,2^k}, A'_{k,2^k-1}, \ldots, A'_{k,1})$, indexed from the lower-left corner.

For $\alpha \in [2^k]$ and a grid point $p \in [2^k]^2$, we denote:

1. $\hbar_k(v, v') = |(H_k^2)^{-1}(v) - (H_k^2)^{-1}(v')|$, the index-difference between two grid points $v, v' \in [2^k]^2$.
2. $\Delta(X_{k,\alpha}, p) = \sum_{v \in X_{k,\alpha}} \hbar_k(v, p)$, where the symbol X denotes R, C, D, D', A, or A' (for example, $\Delta(R_{k,\alpha}, p) = \sum_{v \in R_{k,\alpha}} \hbar_k(v, p)$). That is, $\Delta(X_{k,\alpha}, p)$ cumulates all index-differences of all grid points in the structure $X_{k,\alpha}$ with respect to p; when $p = \partial_1(H_k^2)$, $\Delta(X_{k,\alpha}, p)$ is the index-cumulation of all grid points in $X_{k,\alpha}$.
3. $\mathcal{X}_{k,\alpha} = \sum_{\beta=1}^{\alpha} \sum_{v \in X_{k,\beta}} (\alpha + 1 - \beta)\hbar_k(v, \partial_1(H_k^2))$, where the symbol-pair $(\mathcal{X}, X)$ denotes $(\mathcal{R}, R)$, $(\mathcal{C}, C)$, $(\mathcal{D}, D)$, $(\mathcal{D}', D')$, $(\mathcal{A}, A)$, or $(\mathcal{A}', A')$ (for example, $\mathcal{R}_{k,\alpha} = \sum_{\beta=1}^{\alpha} \sum_{v \in R_{k,\beta}} (\alpha + 1 - \beta)\hbar_k(v, \partial_1(H_k^2))$);
$\mathcal{N}_{k,\alpha} = \sum_{\beta=1}^{\alpha} \sum_{v \in X_{k,\beta}} (\alpha + 1 - \beta)$, when X denotes D, D', A, or A' (independent of the choice); that is, $\mathcal{N}_{k,\alpha}$ cumulates the number of index (grid point v) references in the summation of $\mathcal{X}_{k,\alpha}$ (that is, $\mathcal{D}_{k,\alpha}, \mathcal{D}'_{k,\alpha}, \mathcal{A}_{k,\alpha}$, or $\mathcal{A}'_{k,\alpha}$).
Note that when $\alpha = 0$, all cumulations degenerate to 0, that is, $\mathcal{X}_{k,0} = \mathcal{X}'_{k,0} = \mathcal{N}_{k,0} = 0$.
4. $\overline{\mathcal{X}}_{k,\alpha} = \sum_{\beta=1}^{\alpha} \sum_{v \in X_{k,\beta}} \hbar_k(v, \partial_1(H_k^2)) = \sum_{\beta=1}^{\alpha} \Delta(X_{k,\beta}, \partial_1(H_k^2))$, where the symbol-pair $(\overline{\mathcal{X}}, X)$ denotes $(\overline{\mathcal{R}}, R)$, $(\overline{\mathcal{C}}, C)$, $(\overline{\mathcal{D}}, D)$, $(\overline{\mathcal{D}'}, D')$, $(\overline{\mathcal{A}}, A)$, or $(\overline{\mathcal{A}'}, A')$;

$\overline{\mathcal{N}}_{k,\alpha} = \sum_{\beta=1}^{\alpha} \sum_{v \in X_{k,\beta}} 1$, when the symbol X denotes D, D', A, or A' (independent of the choice); that is, $\overline{\mathcal{N}}_{k,\alpha}$ cumulates the number of index (grid point v) references in the summation of $\overline{\mathcal{X}}_{k,\alpha}$ (that is, $\overline{\mathcal{D}}_{k,\alpha}$, $\overline{\mathcal{D}'}_{k,\alpha}$, $\overline{\mathcal{A}}_{k,\alpha}$, or $\overline{\mathcal{A}'}_{k,\alpha}$).

Note that $\mathcal{X}_{k,\alpha} = \mathcal{X}_{k,\alpha-1} + \overline{\mathcal{X}}_{k,\alpha}$ for $\alpha \in \{2, 3, \ldots, 2^k\}$, where the symbol $\mathcal{X}$ denotes $\mathcal{R}$, $\mathcal{C}$, $\mathcal{D}$, $\mathcal{D}'$, $\mathcal{A}$, or $\mathcal{A}'$.

5. $\overline{\mathcal{W}}_k = \sum_{v \in H_k^2} \hbar_k(v, \partial_1(H_k^2))$, which cumulates the indices of all grid points of H_k^2 relative to $\partial_1(H_k^2)$. (For a grid point v, the membership "$v \in H_k^2$" abbreviates "$v \in H_k^2([2^{2k}])$".)

Figure 3 illustrates the organization of a 2-dimensional grid into the row, column, main-diagonal, auxiliary-diagonal structures and the coverages for $\mathcal{D}_{k,\alpha}$, $\mathcal{D}'_{k,\alpha}$, $\mathcal{A}_{k,\alpha}$, and $\mathcal{A}'_{k,\alpha}$.

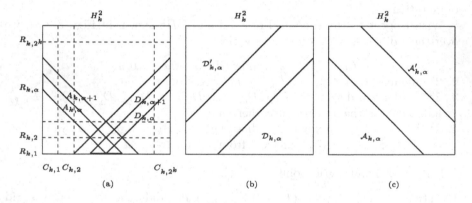

Fig. 3. (a) Organize a 2-dimensional grid $[2^k]^2$ into the row, column, main-diagonal, and auxiliary-diagonal structures; (b) coverages of $\mathcal{D}_{k,\alpha}$ and $\mathcal{D}'_{k,\alpha}$; (c) coverages of $\mathcal{A}_{k,\alpha}$ and $\mathcal{A}'_{k,\alpha}$.

The following three lemmas study the cumulation of indices of grid points in the row, column, diagonal, and auxiliary-diagonal structures of H_k^2.

Lemma 1. *The index-cumulation of a row structure of H_k^2 is independent of its row-number: for all $\alpha \in [2^k]$,*

$$\Delta(R_{k,\alpha}, \partial_1(H_k^2)) = \Delta(R_{k,\alpha}, \partial_2(H_k^2)) = \frac{1}{2} \cdot 2^{3k} - \frac{1}{2} \cdot 2^k \quad \text{(independent of α).}$$

Lemma 2. *The binary representation of the column-number of a column structure of H_k^2 helps compute its index-cumulation as follows:*

1. *For all $\alpha \in [2^{k-1}]$, a recurrence for $\Delta(C_{k,\alpha}, \partial_1(H_k^2))$ is:*

$$\Delta(C_{k,\alpha}, \partial_1(H_k^2)) = \Delta(R_{k-1,\alpha}, \partial_1(H_{k-1}^2)) + \Delta(C_{k-1,\alpha}, \partial_1(H_{k-1}^2)) + \frac{1}{2^3} \cdot 2^{3k}.$$

For $\alpha = 1$, a closed-form solution for $\Delta(C_{k,1}, \partial_1(H_k^2))$ from the recurrence above (in k) is:

$$\frac{3}{2 \cdot 7} \cdot 2^{3k} - \frac{1}{2} \cdot 2^k + \frac{2}{7}.$$

For those α satisfying $2^{q-1} < \alpha \le 2^q$ for some integer $q \in [k-1]$ (that is, $q = \lceil \log \alpha \rceil$), the recurrence above (in k) yields a recurrence:

$$\Delta(C_{k,\alpha}, \partial_1(H_k^2)) = \Delta(C_{q,\alpha}, \partial_1(H_q^2)) + \sum_{\eta=q+1}^{k} (\frac{3}{2^4} \cdot 2^{3\eta} - \frac{1}{2^2} \cdot 2^{\eta}),$$

where the summation is:

$$\frac{3}{2 \cdot 7}(2^{3k} - 2^{3q}) - \frac{1}{2}(2^k - 2^q) = \frac{3}{2 \cdot 7} \cdot 2^{3k} - \frac{1}{2} \cdot 2^k - \frac{3}{2 \cdot 7} \cdot 2^{3\lceil \log \alpha \rceil} + \frac{1}{2} \cdot 2^{\lceil \log \alpha \rceil}.$$

2. *For all $\alpha, \beta \in [2^k]$ such that $\alpha < \beta$ and the binary representations of $\alpha - 1$ and $\beta - 1$ differ only at the i-th low-order bit, where $i \in \{0, 1, \ldots, k-1\}$ (that is, $(\alpha - 1) \oplus (\beta - 1) = 2^i$, where $\oplus$ denotes the binary exclusive-or operator),*

$$\Delta(C_{k,\beta}, \partial_1(H_k^2)) = \Delta(C_{k,\alpha}, \partial_1(H_k^2)) + 2^2 \cdot 2^{3i}.$$

Lemma 3. *For $k \ge 1$,*

1. $\Delta(A_{k,2^k}, \partial_1(H_k^2)) + \Delta(D_{k,2^k}, \partial_1(H_k^2)) = 2^{3k} - 2^k$, *and*
2. $\Delta(A_{k,2^k}, \partial_1(H_k^2)) = \frac{2}{3} \cdot 2^{3k} - \frac{2}{3} \cdot 2^k$.

Now we partition the summation $\sum_{\alpha,\beta \in \{1,2,3,4\} | \alpha < \beta} \Delta_\delta(Q_\alpha(H_k^2), Q_\beta(H_k^2))$ according to the two cases: for $\alpha, \beta \in \{1, 2, 3, 4\}$, contiguous subcurves ($\alpha+1 \equiv \beta$ (mod 4)) with four similar subcases, and diagonal subcurves ($\alpha + 2 \equiv \beta$ (mod 4)) with two similar subcases. The summations resulting from restricting to these six subcases are investigated in the following lemma. A common thread to the computations in the six subcases is to express $\Delta_\delta(Q_\alpha(H_k^2), Q_\beta(H_k^2))$ as summations of index-cumulations of neighboring geometrical structures in $Q_\alpha(H_k^2)$ and $Q_\beta(H_k^2)$. For the case of contiguous subcurves, the boundary rows/columns and the boundary corners (of main- and auxiliary-diagonals) are involved; and for the case of diagonal subcurves, the boundary corners (of main- and auxiliary-diagonals) are involved.

Lemma 4. *For δ that is an integral power of 2, and $1 \le \delta < 2^k$,*

$$\Delta_\delta(Q_1(H_k^2), Q_4(H_k^2)) = 2(\overline{\mathcal{R}}_{k-1,\delta} + 2\mathcal{R}_{k-1,\delta-1} - \mathcal{D}'_{k-1,\delta-1} - \mathcal{A}'_{k-1,\delta-1})$$
$$+(\frac{1}{2} \cdot 2^{2k} + 1)(2^{k-1}\delta^2 - 2\mathcal{N}_{k-1,\delta-1}),$$

$$\Delta_\delta(Q_1(H_k^2), Q_2(H_k^2)) = \Delta_\delta(Q_3(H_k^2), Q_4(H_k^2))$$
$$= (\overline{\mathcal{C}}_{k-1,\delta} + 2\mathcal{C}_{k-1,\delta-1} - \mathcal{D}'_{k-1,\delta-1} - \mathcal{A}_{k-1,\delta-1}) + (\overline{\mathcal{R}}_{k-1,\delta}$$
$$+2\mathcal{R}_{k-1,\delta-1} - \mathcal{A}_{k-1,\delta-1} - \mathcal{D}_{k-1,\delta-1}) + (2^{k-1}\delta^2 - 2\mathcal{N}_{k-1,\delta-1}),$$

$$\Delta_\delta(Q_2(H_k^2), Q_3(H_k^2)) = 2(\overline{\mathcal{C}}_{k-1,\delta} + 2\mathcal{C}_{k-1,\delta-1} - \mathcal{D}'_{k-1,\delta-1} - \mathcal{A}_{k-1,\delta-1})$$
$$+(2^{k-1}\delta^2 - 2\mathcal{N}_{k-1,\delta-1}), \text{ and}$$

$$\Delta_\delta(Q_1(H_k^2), Q_3(H_k^2)) = \Delta_\delta(Q_2(H_k^2), Q_4(H_k^2))$$
$$= (\frac{1}{2^2} \cdot 2^{2k} + 1)\mathcal{N}_{k-1,\delta-1} + \mathcal{D}'_{k-1,\delta-1} + \mathcal{A}_{k-1,\delta-1}.$$

The following two lemmas allow us to simplify the overall summation of $L_\delta(H_k^2)$.

Lemma 5. *For all integers q with $0 \le q \le k$,*

1. $\overline{W}_k = \frac{1}{2} \cdot 2^{4k} - \frac{1}{2} \cdot 2^{2k}$,

2. $\overline{N}_{k,2^q} = \frac{1}{2} \cdot 2^{2q} + \frac{1}{2} \cdot 2^q$,

3. $\overline{R}_{k,2^q} = 2^q \Delta(R_{k,1}, \partial_1(H_k^2))$,

4. $\overline{C}_{k,2^q} = 2^q \Delta(C_{k,1}, \partial_1(H_k^2)) + \frac{2}{7}(2^{4q} - 2^q)$,

5. $\overline{A}_{k,2^k} + \overline{A'}_{k,2^k} = \overline{W}_k + \Delta(A_{k,2^k}, \partial_1(H_k^2))$,

6. $\overline{A}_{k,2^k} = 2\overline{W}_{k-1} + \Delta(A_{k-1,2^{k-1}}, \partial_1(H_{k-1}^2)) + 2^{2k}\overline{N}_{k-1,2^{k-1}}$,
7. *Each of the pairs: $(\overline{D}_{k,2^q}, \overline{A}_{k,2^q})$ and $(\overline{D'}_{k,2^q}, \overline{A'}_{k,2^q})$ are related via $\overline{N}_{k,2^q}$ as follows:*
$$\overline{D}_{k,2^q} + \overline{A}_{k,2^q} = \overline{D'}_{k,2^q} + \overline{A'}_{k,2^q} = (2^{2k} - 1)\overline{N}_{k,2^q},$$

and
8. $\overline{D'}_{k,2^q} = \frac{1}{3}(2^{2k} - 2^{2q})\overline{N}_{k,2^q} + \overline{D'}_{q,2^q}$.

Computations of various $\mathcal{X}_{k,2^q}$ are similar to those for $\overline{\mathcal{X}}_{k,2^q}$.

Lemma 6. *For all integers q with $0 \le q \le k$,*

1. $\mathcal{N}_{k,2^q} = \frac{1}{2 \cdot 3} \cdot 2^{3q} + \frac{1}{2} \cdot 2^{2q} + \frac{1}{3} \cdot 2^q$,
2. $\mathcal{R}_{k,2^q} = \Delta(R_{k,1}, \partial_1(H_k^2)) \sum_{\beta=1}^{2^q} \beta$,
3. $\mathcal{C}_{k,2^q} = \frac{3}{2^2 \cdot 7} \cdot 2^{3k+2q} + \frac{3}{2^2 \cdot 7} \cdot 2^{3k+q} - \frac{1}{2^2} \cdot 2^{k+2q} - \frac{1}{2^2} \cdot 2^{k+q} + \frac{2^3}{3 \cdot 5 \cdot 7} \cdot 2^{5q} + \frac{1}{7} \cdot 2^{4q} + \frac{1}{3 \cdot 5} \cdot 2^q$,
4. *Each of the pairs: $(\mathcal{D}_{k,2^q}, \mathcal{A}_{k,2^q})$ and $(\mathcal{D'}_{k,2^q}, \mathcal{A'}_{k,2^q})$ are related via $\mathcal{N}_{k,2^q}$ as follows:*
$$\mathcal{D}_{k,2^q} + \mathcal{A}_{k,2^q} = \mathcal{D'}_{k,2^q} + \mathcal{A'}_{k,2^q} = (2^{2k} - 1)\mathcal{N}_{k,2^q},$$
5.
$$\mathcal{A}_{k,2^k} = \begin{cases} 0 & \text{if } k = 0 \\ \frac{7}{2^2 \cdot 3^2 \cdot 5} \cdot 2^{5k} + \frac{3}{2^4} \cdot 2^{4k} + \frac{5}{2^2 \cdot 3^2} \cdot 2^{3k} - \frac{1}{2^2} \cdot 2^{2k} - \frac{2^3}{3^2 \cdot 5} \cdot 2^k & \text{otherwise} \end{cases}$$

6. $\mathcal{A}_{k,2^q} = \mathcal{A}_{q,2^q}$,
7.
$$\mathcal{D'}_{k,2^k} = \begin{cases} 0 & \text{if } k = 0 \\ \frac{11}{2^2 \cdot 3^2 \cdot 5} \cdot 2^{5k} + \frac{3}{2^4} \cdot 2^{4k} + \frac{1}{2^2 \cdot 3^2} \cdot 2^{3k} - \frac{1}{2^2} \cdot 2^{2k} - \frac{2^2}{3^2 \cdot 5} \cdot 2^k & \text{otherwise} \end{cases}$$
8. $\mathcal{D'}_{k,2^q} = \frac{1}{3}(2^{2k} - 2^{2q})\mathcal{N}_{k,2^q} + \mathcal{D'}_{q,2^q}$.

Theorem 1. *For $\delta \in [2^k]$ that is an integral power of 2,*

$$L_\delta(H_k^2) = \begin{cases} \frac{17}{2 \cdot 7} \cdot 2^{3k} - \frac{5}{2 \cdot 3} \cdot 2^{2k} - \frac{2^3}{3 \cdot 7} & \text{if } \delta = 1 \\ \frac{17}{2 \cdot 7} \cdot 2^{3k+2\log\delta} - \frac{2^3 \cdot 3 \cdot 5^2 \cdot 7(k - \log\delta) + 5 \cdot 7 \cdot 383}{2^4 \cdot 3^3 \cdot 5 \cdot 7} \cdot 2^{2k+3\log\delta} \\ \quad + \frac{2 \cdot 3 \cdot 5(k - \log\delta) - 1}{2^2 \cdot 3^3} \cdot 2^{2k+\log\delta} - \frac{2^2 \cdot 41}{3^3 \cdot 5 \cdot 7} \cdot 2^{5\log\delta} - \frac{2}{3^3} \cdot 2^{3\log\delta} \\ \quad - \frac{2}{3 \cdot 5} \cdot 2^{\log\delta} & \text{otherwise.} \end{cases}$$

For the z-order curve family, we follow a similar approach to develop a suite of lemmas to establish the following formula for its locality measure.

Theorem 2. *For $\delta \in [2^k]$ that is an integral power of 2,*

$$
L_\delta(Z_k^2) = \begin{cases}
2^{3k} - 2^k & \text{if } \delta = 1 \\
2^{3k+2\log\delta} - \left(\frac{2}{3^2}(k - \log\delta) + \frac{1949}{2^5 \cdot 3^3 \cdot 7}\right)2^{2k+3\log\delta} \\
\quad + \left(\frac{2}{3^2}(k - \log\delta) + \frac{7}{2^2 \cdot 3^3}\right)2^{2k+\log\delta} + \frac{19}{2^2 \cdot 3 \cdot 7} \cdot 2^{2k} - \frac{2^2}{7} \cdot 2^{k+4\log\delta} \\
\quad - \frac{3}{7} \cdot 2^{k+\log\delta} + \frac{2 \cdot 5}{3^3 \cdot 7} \cdot 2^{5\log\delta} - \frac{2^2}{3^3} \cdot 2^{3\log\delta} + \frac{2}{3 \cdot 7} \cdot 2^{2\log\delta} & \text{otherwise.}
\end{cases}
$$

For the 2-dimensional Hilbert and z-order curve families, the complexity of deriving $L_\delta(H_k^2)$ and $L_\delta(Z_k^2)$ lies in the parameterized 1-normed distance δ. For the case of dimensionality 3, we are able to derive exact formulas for $L_\delta(H_k^2)$ and $L_\delta(Z_k^2)$ for $\delta = 1$ (each for one of many structurally different curve families).

Theorem 3. *For a 3-dimensional Hilbert curve family,*

$$
L_1(H_k^3) = \frac{67}{2 \cdot 31} \cdot 2^{5k} - \frac{11}{2 \cdot 7} \cdot 2^{3k} - \frac{2^6}{7 \cdot 31}.
$$

Theorem 4. *For a 3-dimensional z-order curve family,*

$$
L_1(Z_k^3) = 2^{5k} - 2^{2k}.
$$

3   Comparison, Verification, and Conclusion

For sufficiently large k and $\delta \ll 2^k$,

$$
\frac{L_\delta(H_k^m)}{L_\delta(Z_k^m)} \approx \begin{cases}
\frac{17}{2 \cdot 7} \approx 1.2143 & \text{for } m = 2 \text{ and } \delta \text{ an integral power of 2} \\
\frac{67}{2 \cdot 31} \approx 1.0806 & \text{for } m = 3.
\end{cases}
$$

With respect to the locality measure L_δ and for sufficiently large k and $\delta \ll 2^k$, the z-order curve family performs better than the Hilbert curve family for $m = 2$ and over the δ-spectrum of integral powers of 2.

When $\delta = 2^k$, the domination reverses as:

$$
L_\delta(H_k^2) = \frac{37}{240} \cdot 2^{5k} - \frac{1}{12} \cdot 2^{3k} - \frac{2}{15} \cdot 2^k, \text{ and}
$$

$$
L_\delta(Z_k^2) = \frac{107}{672} \cdot 2^{5k} - \frac{1}{12} \cdot 2^{3k} - \frac{3}{28} \cdot 2^{2k}.
$$

These give that

$$
\frac{L_\delta(H_k^m)}{L_\delta(Z_k^m)} \approx \frac{2 \cdot 7 \cdot 37}{5 \cdot 107} \approx 0.9682.
$$

The superiority of the z-order curve family persists but declines for $m = 3$ with unit 1-normed distance for L_δ.

For the extreme case $m = 2$ and $\delta = 1$, the locality measure L_δ in our study degenerates to $L_{MD,1}$ in [MD86]. Their analysis shows that for a 2-dimensional curve C for the grid $[n]^2$, $L_{\text{MD},1}$ attains its minimum $\frac{4-\sqrt{2}}{3}n^3 + O(n^2)$ ($\approx 0.8619n^2 + O(n^2)$) when C and its equivalent variants assume the following characteristics: (1) Within the four $(1-\frac{1}{\sqrt{2}})n \times (1-\frac{1}{\sqrt{2}})n$ corner-subgrids, the sequence of 1-normed distances between adjacent points in $[n]^2$, $d_1(C(i), C(i+1))$, incrementally increases and/or decreases in the range $[1, (1-\frac{1}{\sqrt{2}})n]$ (while interleaving with segments of 1s), and (2) Within the central region interconnecting the corner-subgrids, the 1-normed distances are in $\{(1-\frac{1}{\sqrt{2}})n, n\}$ (while interleaving with segments of 1s). As the z-order curve family shares some of these characteristics, the asymptotic ratios (constants greater than 1) obtained above are not surprising.

We have verified all the exact formulas (intermediate and final) involved in the derivations with computer programs over various grid-orders and 1-normed distances: ($m = 2$, $k \in \{1,2,3,4,5,6,7\}$, and $\delta \in \{1,2^1,2^2,2^3,\ldots,2^k\}$), and ($m = 3$, $k \in \{1,2,3,4,5,6\}$, and $\delta = 1$).

A similar study with dimensions greater than 3 appears to be much more difficult due to the loss of geometric intuition. Alber and Niedermeier [AN00] provide a simple mathematical mechanism to describe and analyze the combinatorial properties of continuous curves such as Hilbert curves and non-continuous ones such as z-order curves in arbitrary dimensions. This structure-theoretic viewpoint may shed some light on our current study with arbitrary dimensions and unit distance.

References

[AN00]   J. Alber and R. Niedermeier. On multi-dimensional curves with Hilbert property. *Theory of Computing Systems*, 33(4):295–312, 2000.

[ARR+97]   T. Asano, D. Ranjan, T. Roos, E. Welzl, and P. Widmayer. Space-filling curves and their use in the design of geometric data structures. *Theoretical Computer Science*, 181(1):3–15, 1997.

[DS03]   H. K. Dai and H. C. Su. Approximation and analytical studies of inter-clustering performances. To appear in *Proceedings of the 2003 Discrete Random Walks Conference*, September 2003.

[GL96]   C. Gotsman and M. Lindenbaum. On the metric properties of discrete space-filling curves. *IEEE Transactions on Image Processing*, 5(5):794–797, 1996.

[Jag97]   H. V. Jagadish. Analysis of the Hilbert curve for representing two-dimensional space. *Information Processing Letters*, 62(1):17–22, 1997.

[MD86]   G. Mitchison and R. Durbin. Optimal numberings of an $N \times N$ array. *SIAM Journal on Algebraic and Discrete Methods*, 7(4):571–582, 1986.

[MJFS01]   B. Moon, H. V. Jagadish, C. Faloutsos, and J. H. Saltz. Analysis of the clustering properties of the Hilbert space-filling curve. *IEEE Transactions on Knowledge and Data Engineering*, 13(1):124–141, 2001.

[PKK92]   A. Pérez, S. Kamata, and E. Kawaguchi. Peano scanning of arbitrary size images. In *Proceedings of the International Conference on Pattern Recognition*, pages 565–568. IEEE Computer Society, 1992.

Geometric Restrictions on Producible Polygonal Protein Chains

Erik D. Demaine[1], Stefan Langerman[2]*, and Joseph O'Rourke[3]**

[1] MIT Laboratory for Computer Science, 200 Technology Square,
Cambridge, MA 02139, USA, edemaine@mit.edu
[2] Université Libre de Bruxelles, Département d'informatique,
ULB CP212, Bruxelles, Belgium, Stefan.Langerman@ulb.ac.be
[3] Department of Computer Science, Smith College,
Northampton, MA 01063, USA, orourke@cs.smith.edu

Abstract. Fixed-angle polygonal chains in 3D serve as an interesting model of protein backbones. Here we consider such chains produced inside a "machine" modeled crudely as a cone, and examine the constraints this model places on the producible chains. We call this notion α-*producible*, and prove as our main result that a chain is α-producible if and only if it is flattenable, that is, it can be reconfigured without self-intersection to lie flat in a plane. This result establishes that two seemingly disparate classes of chains are in fact identical. Along the way, we discover that all α-producible configurations of a chain can be moved to a canonical configuration resembling a helix. One consequence is an algorithm that reconfigures between any two flat states of a nonacute chain in $O(n)$ "moves," improving the $O(n^2)$-move algorithm in [ADD+02].
Finally, we prove that the α-producible chains are rare in the following technical sense. A random chain of n links is defined by drawing the lengths and angles from any "regular" (e.g., uniform) distribution on any subset of the possible values. A random configuration of a chain embeds into $\mathbb{R}^3$ by in addition drawing the dihedral angles from any regular distribution. If a class of chains has a locked configuration (and we know of no nontrivial class that avoids locked configurations), then the probability that a random configuration of a random chain is α-producible approaches zero geometrically as $n \to \infty$.

1   Introduction

The backbone of a protein molecule may be modeled as a 3D polygonal chain, with fixed link (edge) lengths. The joints are not universal; rather the bonds between residues form nearly fixed angles in space. The motions at the joints are then called *dihedral* motions. The study of such *fixed-angle* chains was initiated in [ST00] and continued in [ADM+02] and [BDD+02]. These papers identified *flat states* of a chain—embeddings into a plane without self-intersection—as

---

* Chargé de recherches du FNRS.
** Supported by NSF Distinguished Teaching Scholars award DUE-0123154.

T. Ibaraki, N. Katoh, and H. Ono (Eds.): ISAAC 2003, LNCS 2906, pp. 395–404, 2003.
© Springer-Verlag Berlin Heidelberg 2003

geometrically interesting. A chain that can reconfigure in $\mathbb{R}^3$ via dihedral motions between any two of its flat states is called *flat-state connected*. A chain that has a flat state but is in a configuration that cannot reach that state (via dihedral motions, without self-intersection) is called *unflattenable* or simply *locked*.[1]

We look here at a particularly simple but natural constraint on the "production" of a fixed-angle chain. Our inspiration derives from the ribosome, which is the "machine" that creates protein chains in biological cells. However, we quickly deviate from reality and replace the ribosome by a simple geometric constraint: the chains are produced inside a cone of half-angle $\alpha \leq \pi/2$, emerging through its apex.

We show in Section 3 that this simple constraint guarantees that all producible chains are flattenable and furthermore mutually reachable. There are several interesting aspects to this result. First, cones with $\alpha > \pi/2$ (concave cones) permit the production of locked chains, as shown in Section 4, so the $\leq \pi/2$ constraint is needed. Second, we are naturally led in our proof to a canonical form, called α-CCC, which bears a resemblance to the helical form preferred by many proteins. Third, we show in Section 5 that long "random" chains are locked with probability approaching 1, implying that producible protein chains are rather special.

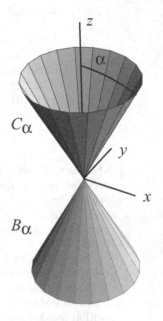

Fig. 1. The chain is produced in C_α, and emerges at the origin into the complimentary cone B_α below the xy-plane.

2   Definitions

2.1   Chains and Motions

The fixed-angle polygonal chain P has $n+1$ vertices $V = \langle v_0, \ldots, v_n \rangle$ and is specified by the fixed turn angle θ_i at each vertex v_i, $i = 1, \ldots, n-1$, and by the edge length d_i between v_i and v_{i+1}, $i = 0, \ldots, n-1$. When all angles $\theta_i \leq \alpha$ for some $0 < \alpha \leq \pi/2$, P is called a $(\leq\alpha)$-*chain*. We write $P[i, j]$, $i \leq j$, for the polygonal subchain composed of vertices $v_i, \ldots, v_j$.

A *configuration* $Q = \langle q_0, \ldots, q_n \rangle$ of the chain P (see Fig. 2) is an embedding of P into $\mathbb{R}^3$, i.e., a mapping of each vertex v_i to a point $q_i \in \mathbb{R}^3$, satisfying the constraints that the angle between vectors $q_{i-1}q_i$ and q_iq_{i+1} is θ_i, and the distance between q_i and q_{i+1} is d_i. The points q_i and q_{i+1} are connected by a straight line segment e_i. Thus, a configuration can be specified by the position of e_0 and dihedral angles δ_i, $i = 1, \ldots, n-2$, where δ_i is the angle between planes $e_{i-1}e_i$ and e_ie_{i+1}. The configuration is *simple* if no two nonadjacent segments intersect.

---

[1] In fact, this definition is slightly more specific than the usual notion of "locked," which says that there are two arbitrary configurations of the linkage that are mutually unreachable.

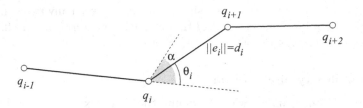

Fig. 2. Notation for a configuration Q.

A *motion* $M = \langle m_0, \ldots, m_n \rangle$ of a chain P is a list of $n + 1$ continuous functions $m_i : [0, \infty] \to \mathbb{R}^3$, $i = 0, \ldots, n$, such that $M(t) = \langle m_0(t), \ldots, m_n(t) \rangle$ is a configuration of P for all $t \in [0, \infty]$. The motion is said to be *simple* if all such configurations $M(t)$ are simple. We normally assume that the motion is *finite* in the sense that, after some time T, M becomes independent of t.

2.2   Chain Production

As mentioned above, our model is that the chain is produced inside an infinite open cone C_α with apex at the origin, axis on the z axis, and half-angle (to the positive z-axis) $\alpha \leq \pi/2$; see Fig. 1. Let $\overline{C}_\alpha$ be the corresponding closed cone. We similarly define the cone B_α, the mirror image of C_α with respect to the xy-plane.

The vertices and edges are created inside $\overline{C}_\alpha$ and exit the machine at the apex of $\overline{C}_\alpha$. The portion of the chain already produced is allowed to move freely as long as it stays simple and never meets C_α. At time $t_0 = 0$, the machine creates v_0 at the apex of C_α, v_1 inside $\overline{C}_\alpha$, and the segment e_0 connecting them. In general, at time t_i, vertex v_i reaches the apex of $\overline{C}_\alpha$, and v_{i+1} and e_i are created inside $\overline{C}_\alpha$. The vertex v_i stays in $\overline{C}_\alpha$ between times t_{i-1} and t_i and $0 = t_0 < t_1 < \cdots < t_n$.

Formally, an α-*production* F is a set of $n + 1$ continuous functions $f_i : [t_{i-1}, \infty] \to \mathbb{R}^3$, $i = 0, \ldots, n$, such that, for all $t \in [t_{j-1}, t_j]$, $f_j(t) \in \overline{C}_\alpha$, $F(t) = \langle f_0(t), \ldots, f_j(t) \rangle$ is a simple configuration of $P[0, j]$, and no segment e_i intersects C_α, $i < j$. A configuration Q is said to be α-*producible* if there exists an α-production F with $F(\infty) = Q$.

One consequence of this model is the following:

Lemma 1. *An $(\leq \alpha)$-chain can be produced only in a cone $C_{\alpha/2}$ or larger.*

Proof. Suppose $\theta_i = \alpha$. At time t_i, when v_{i+1} is created inside the cone, v_i is at the apex, and v_{i-1} is outside. Because we stipulate continuous motion, v_{i-1} must be inside the cone $\overline{B}_{\alpha/2}$ below the xy-plane, for it must have been there throughout $t \in [t_{i-1}, t_i)$. If e_{i-1} is on that cone surface, then v_{i+1} can just barely be inside $\overline{C}_{\alpha/2}$, on its surface, with turn angle α at v_i. Note that, for $t > t_i$, v_{i-1} need no longer remain in $\overline{B}_{\alpha/2}$. $\square$

We will prove that there exists a simple motion between any two α-producible configurations of the same chain, and that all such configurations are flattenable. Next we define the notion of a "simple" motion.

2.3   Complexity of a Motion

There are of course many ways to define the complexity of a motion M. As a first approximation, we could assume that each dihedral angle $\delta_i^M(t)$ of the segment e_i is a piecewise-linear function of time t, and the complexity $T(M)$ of the motion M is the total number of linear pieces over all functions $\delta_i^M(t)$. That is, $T(M) = \sum_{i=1}^{n-2} T(\delta_i^M)$, where $T(\delta_i^M)$ is the number of linear pieces in the function δ_i^M. Unfortunately, this definition is not acceptable, as it restricts the range of possible motions M. The definition can be generalized to allow arbitrary functions $\delta_i^M(t)$, given some corresponding measure of complexity $T(\delta_i^M)$, with the added restriction that for every time range $t \in [r, s]$ during which $\delta_i^M(t)$ is a linear function, that time range contributes at most 1 to the complexity $T(\delta_i^M)$. For example, if $\delta_i^M(t)$ is a piecewise-polynomial function, $T(\delta_i^M)$ could be defined as the sum of the degrees of the polynomial pieces; or more generally $T(\delta_i^M(t))$ might measure the number of inflection points or monotonic pieces of $\delta_i^M(t)$.

The complexity of a production F can be defined in an analoguous way, where $\delta_i^F(t)$ is defined only for the time range $t \geq t_{i+1}$. The resulting value will only account for the dihedral motions outside the cone C_α. We still need to add the complexity of the movement of point $f_{i+1}(t)$ before it exits the cone for all i, i.e., at time $t \in [t_i, t_{i+1})$. If we assume that the chain exits the cone at a constant rate, we only need to consider the vector $u^F(t) = (0, f_{i+1}(t))$ for $t \in [t_i, t_{i+1})$, described in polar coordinates by the angle $\rho^F(t)$ of $u^F(t)$ with the z-axis, and the angle $\gamma^F(t)$ of the projection of $u^F(t)$ onto the xy-plane with the x-axis. The complexity will be expressed by $T(\gamma^F)$ and $T(\rho^F)$, with the restriction that $T(\rho^F)$ be at least the number of connected components in $\{t : \rho^F(t) = 0\}$. For example, the number of pieces in a piecewise-linear function, or the sum of degrees in a piecewise-polynomial function, would qualify. No restrictions are imposed on $T(\gamma^F)$. The total complexity of the production is then $T(F) = \sum_{i=1}^{n-2} T(\delta_i^F) + T(\rho^F) + T(\gamma^F)$.

3   Producible ◻ Flattenable

Key to our main theorem is showing that every α-producible configuration can be moved to a canonical configuration, and therefore to every other α-producible configuration.

3.1   Canonical Configuration

We begin by defining the canonical configuration of α-producible chains, called the α-*cone canonical configuration* or α-CCC. To better understand the constraints of a configuration Q, consider normalizing all edge vectors $q_i q_{i+1}$ to unit vectors $u_i = (q_{i+1} - q_i)/\|q_{i+1} - q_i\|$ which lie on the unit sphere. The α-CCC is constructed to have the property that all such vectors lie along a circle of radius $\alpha/2$ on that sphere. In other words, the vectors u_i lie on the boundary of a cone with half-angle $\alpha/2$.

To ease the description, we use the cone $\overline{C}_{\alpha/2}$ (not C_α) to define α-CCC, but note that the cone and the chain could be rotated and translated. By convention, we place u_0 on the boundary of $\overline{C}_{\alpha/2}$ in the positive quadrant of the yz-plane. Because Q is a configuration of P, the angle between u_{i-1} and u_i is θ_i and so, on the sphere, u_i lies on the circle of radius θ_i centered at u_{i-1}. Because $\theta_i \leq \alpha$, this circle intersects the boundary of $\overline{C}_{\alpha/2}$. We set u_i to be the first intersection counterclockwise from u_{i-1} on the boundary of $\overline{C}_{\alpha/2}$ (where counterclockwise is viewed from the origin). See Fig. 3 for an example.

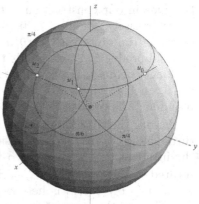

Fig. 3. u_0 lies on the cone $C_{\pi/4}$. $(\theta_1, \theta_2, \theta_3) = (\pi/4, \pi/6, \pi/5)$, respectively.

The position of the u_i's on the unit sphere as described above, along with the position of q_0, uniquely determine the position of the α-CCC of the chain. Because the u_i vectors all have positive z coordinates, we know that the resulting configuration is simple. We can also show that the α-CCC is completely contained in $\overline{C}_{\alpha/2}$:

Lemma 2. *If all unit edge vectors u_i are contained in a cone $\overline{C}_\beta$ for some half-angle $\beta > 0$, then the configuration Q is inside $q_0 + \overline{C}_\beta$, the cone translated so its apex is at q_0. Furthermore, if $u_0 \neq u_1$, then only the first bar of the chain can touch the boundary of $q_0 + \overline{C}_\beta$.*

Proof. The proof is by induction on n. The claim holds for the 1-point chain $Q[n, n]$. Assume $Q[1, n]$ is contained in a cone with apex q_1. Now q_1 is on the boundary of the cone with apex q_0, so the cone with apex at q_1 is contained in the one with apex at q_0. Furthermore, the boundary of these cones intersect only at the line of support q_0q_1. □

In the α-CCC, u_i is always different from u_{i+1}.

3.2 Canonicalization

Next we show how to find a motion from any α-producible configuration of an α-producible chain to the corresponding α-CCC.

Theorem 1. *If a configuration Q of a $(\leq \alpha)$-chain P is α-producible by a production F, then there is a motion M from Q to the α-CCC, with $T(M) \leq T(F) + 3n$.*

Proof. Because Q is α-producible, there exists an α-production F with $F(\infty) = Q$. By scaling time appropriately, we can arrange that $t_i = i$, and the configuration freezes at time $n + 1$, i.e., $F(t) = F(n + 1)$ for $t > n + 1$.

We construct a motion M from Q to the α-CCC, constructed inside $\overline{C}_\alpha$. A key idea in our construction is to play the production movements backwards. More precisely, for all $i = 0, \ldots, n$, we define $m_i(t) = f_i(n + 1 - t)$ for the (reverse) time interval $t \in [0, n + 2 - i]$. (Beyond reverse time $n + 2 - i$, the original production time is less than $n + 1 - (n + 2 - i) = i - 1$ and thus f_i is no longer defined.) To complete the construction, we just have to define $m_i(t)$ for $t > n + 2 - i$, that is, the motion of the part of the chain that has already re-entered the cone $\overline{C}_\alpha$.

During the time interval $(n - i, n + 1 - i)$, the edge e_i is entering the cone $\overline{C}_\alpha$ through the origin, $P[0, i]$ is outside C_α, and $P[i+1, n]$ is inside C_α. We maintain the invariant that $P[i, n]$ is in α-CCC, contained in a cone $\overline{C}_{\alpha/2}$ translated and rotated to some position $\overline{C}'_{\alpha/2}$. So the dihedral angle of e_j does not change for $j > i$, i.e., $P[i + 1, n]$ is held rigid. Because $P[0, i]$ moves freely outside of C_α according to the reversed movements of the α-production, we can only control the dihedral angle of e_i in order to maintain that $\overline{C}'_{\alpha/2}$ (and so $P[i+1, n]$) stays inside $\overline{C}_\alpha$.

Again, consider the vectors u_j. The invariant means that all u_j, $j = i, \ldots, n - 1$, touch the boundary of some circle σ of radius $\alpha/2$ on the unit sphere centered on the apex of the cone, and σ must be inside $\overline{C}_\alpha$. The last condition will be true whenever σ contains the unit vector u_{+z} along the z-axis, because we selected σ to have radius $\alpha/2$, so it has diameter α, which is the angle between u_{+z} and the side of C_α. Thus, for any position u_i, we place σ so that its diameter from u_i contains u_{+z}. As long as $u_i \neq u_{+z}$, this position is unique and the resulting motion is continuous because the production is continuous. When $u_i = u_{+z}$, a discontinuity might be introduced, but these discontinuities can easily be removed by stretching the moment of time at which a discontinuity occurs and filling in a continuous motion between the two desired states.

At time $t = n+1-i$, vertex i enters $\overline{C}_\alpha$ and the invariant needs to be restored for the next phase. At that time, the vector u_{i-1} lies in $\overline{C}_\alpha$, and u_i is on a circle τ of radius θ_i centered at u_{i-1}. Let σ' be the desired new position for σ, that is, the circle whose diameter is α, passes through u_{i-1}, and contains u_{+z}. We know that σ' and τ intersect and all intersections are inside $\overline{C}_\alpha$ because σ' is in $\overline{C}_\alpha$. We first move u_i to the first intersection between σ' and τ counterclockwise from u_{i-1} on σ' by changing the dihedral angle of e_{i-1}, and simultaneously moving σ accordingly as described above by changing the dihedral angle of e_i. We then rotate σ about u_i to the position σ' by changing the dihedral angle of e_i. This motion can be done in such a way that σ always contains u_{+z}, because the set of dihedral angles of e_i for which σ contains u_{+z} is connected.

The complexity of all dihedral motions outside of C_α is $\sum_{i=1}^{n-2} T(\delta_i^F)$. The dihedral motions of e_i during times $t \in (n-i, n+1-i)$ mirror exactly $\gamma^F(n+1-t)$, except at discontinuities, which correspond to times for which $u_i = u_{+z}$, which is exactly when $\rho^F(n+1-t) = 0$, so the total complexity of these dihedral motions is bounded by $C(\rho^F) + C(\gamma^F)$. Finally, whenever a vertex attains the apex of the cone, we perform three dihedral rotations (linear functions of time) to restore the invariant. Summing it all, we obtain $C(M) \leq \sum_{i=1}^{n-2} T(\delta_i^F) + C(\rho^F) + C(\gamma^F) + 3n = C(F) + 3n$. □

Corollary 1. *For any two simple α-producible configurations Q_1 and Q_2 of a common chain, with respective productions F_1 and F_2, there is a simple motion M from Q_1 to Q_2—that is, $M(0) = Q_1$ and $M(\infty) = Q_2$—for which $T(M) \leq T(F_1) + T(F_2) + 6n$.*

Proof. Because Q_1 and Q_2 are α-producible, the previous theorem gives us two motions M_1 and M_2 with $M_1(0) = Q_1$, $M_1(\infty) = \alpha$-CCC, $M_2(0) = Q_2$, and $M_2(\infty) = \alpha$-CCC. By rescaling time, we can arrange that $M_1(t) = M_2(t) = \alpha$-CCC for t beyond some time T. Then define $M(t) = M_1(t)$ for $0 \leq t \leq T$, $M(t) = M_2(2T - t)$ for $T < t \leq 2T$, and $M(t) = Q_2$ for $t > 2T$. □

3.3   Connection to Flat States

Finally, we relate flat configurations to productions and prove our main result that flattenability is equivalent to producibility.

Lemma 3. *All flat configurations of a $(\leq \alpha)$-chain have an α-production F for $\alpha \leq \pi/2$. Furthermore, $T(F) \leq n$.*

Proof. Assume the configuration is in the xy-plane. Any such flat configuration can be created using the following process. First, draw e_0 in the xy-plane. Then, for all consecutive edges e_i, create e_i in the vertical plane through e_{i-1} at angle θ_{i-1} with the xy-plane, then rotate it to the desired position in the xy-plane by moving the dihedral angle of e_{i-1}. During the creation and motion of e_i, it is possible to enclose it in some continuously moving cone C of half-angle α whose interior never intersects the xy-plane: at the creation of e_i, C is tangent to the xy plane on the support line of e_{i-1} and with its apex at p_i. During the rotation of e_i, e_i will eventually touch the boundary of C. We then move C along with e_i so that both e_i and the xy-plane are tangent to C. When e_i reaches the xy plane, we translate C along e_i until its apex is p_{i+1}. Viewing the construction relative to C and placing C on C_α gives the desired α-production. □

Corollary 2. *$(\leq \pi/2)$-chains are flat-state connected. The motion between any two flat configurations uses at most $8n$ dihedral motions.*

Proof. Consider two flat configurations Q and Q' of a $(\leq \pi/2)$-chain. By Lemma 3, Q and Q' are both $(\pi/2)$-producible, and so by Corollary 1, there exists a motion M such that $M(0) = Q$ and $M(+\infty) = Q'$. □

Corollary 3. *All α-producible configurations are flattenable, provided $\alpha \leq \pi/2$. For a production F, the flattening motion M has complexity $T(M) \leq T(F) + 7n$.*

Proof. Consider an α-producible configuration Q of an $(\leq \alpha)$-chain P. Because $\alpha \leq \pi/2$, the chain P also has a flat configuration Q' [ADD+02]. By Lemma 3, Q' is producible, and so by Corollary 1, there exists a motion M such that $M(0) = Q$ and $M(+\infty) = Q'$. □

4   A More Powerful Machine

We now show that, under a different model, our result does not hold. Suppose that v_{i+1} is not created at t_i, but rather imagine the time instant t_i stretched into a positive-length interval $[t_i, t_i']$, allowing time for $v_i v_{i-1}$ to rotate exterior to the cone prior to the creation of v_{i+1} (at time t_i'). This flexibility would remove the connection in Lemma 1 between the half-angle of the cone and the turn angles produced, permitting chains of large turn angle to be produced. Indeed, the sequence of motions depicted in Fig. 4 exploits this large-angle freedom to emit a 4-link fixed-angle chain that is locked.

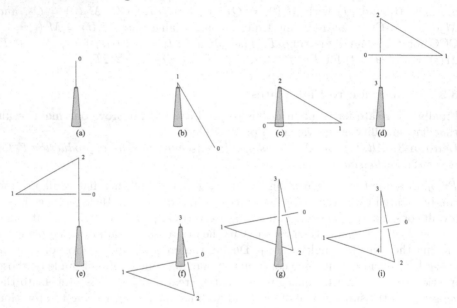

Fig. 4. Production of a locked chain under a model that permits large turning angles to be created. For clarity, the cone is reflected to aim upward. (a) $e_0 = (q_0, q_1)$ emerges; (b) turn at q_1; (c) turn at q_2 and dihedral motion at q_1 places e_1 in front of cone; (d) e_2 nearly fully produced; (e) chain spun about e_2 (or viewpoint changed); (f) rotation at q_3 away from viewer places chain behind cone; (g) e_3 emerges; (i) final locked chain shown loose; the turn angle θ_3 at q_3 can be made arbitrarily close to π.

It is possible to view this model as the same as the previous, but with an $\alpha > \pi/2$, so that the chain inside C_α can form angles at the apex as large as 2α, which could approach 2π.

5   Random Chains

This section proves that the producible/flattenable configurations are a vanishingly small subset of all possible configurations of a chain, for almost any chain. Essentially, the results below say that, if there is one configuration of one chain in a class that is unflattenable, then a randomly chosen configuration of a randomly chosen chain from that class is unflattenable with probability approaching 1 geometrically as the number of links in the chain grows. Furthermore, this result holds for any "reasonable" probability distribution on chains and their configurations.

To define probability distributions, it is useful to embed chains and their configurations into Euclidean space. A chain $P = \langle \theta_1, \ldots, \theta_{n-1}; d_0, \ldots, d_{n-1} \rangle \in [0, \pi/2]^{n-1} \times [0, \infty)^n$ is specified by its turn angles θ_i and edge lengths d_i. A configuration $Q = \langle \delta_1, \ldots, \delta_{n-2} \rangle \in [0, 2\pi)^{n-2}$ of P is specified by its dihedral angles. We also need to be precise about our use of the term "unflattenable" for chains vs. configurations. A simple configuration Q is *unflattenable* or simply *locked* if it cannot reach a flat configuration; a chain P is *lockable* if it has a locked configuration.

We consider the following general model of random chains of size n. Call a probability distribution *regular* if it has positive probability on any positive-measure subset of some open set called the *domain*, and has zero probability density outside that domain.[2] For Euclidean d-space $\mathbb{R}^d$, a probability distribution is regular if it has positive probability on any positive-radius ball inside the domain. Uniform distributions are always regular.

For chains of k links, we emphasize the regular probability distribution $\mathcal{P}_k^{\Theta, \mathcal{D}}$ obtained by drawing each turn angle θ_i independently from a regular distribution Θ, and drawing each edge length d_i independently from a regular distribution $\mathcal{D}$. Similarly, for not-necessarily-simple configurations of a fixed chain P, we emphasize the regular probability distribution obtained by drawing each dihedral angle δ_i independently from a regular distribution Δ. We can modify this probability distribution to have a domain of all simple configurations of P instead of all configurations of P, by zeroing out the probability density of nonsimple configurations, and rescaling so that the total probability is 1. The resulting distribution is denoted $\mathcal{Q}^{P, \Delta}$, and it is regular because the subspace of simple configurations of a chain P is open.

First we show that individual locked examples immediately lead to positive probabilities of being locked. The next lemma establishes this property for configurations of chains, and the following lemma establishes it for chains.

Lemma 4. *For any regular probability distribution $\mathcal{Q}$ on simple configurations of a lockable chain P, if there is a locked simple configuration in the domain of $\mathcal{Q}$, then the probability of a random simple configuration Q of P being locked is at least a constant $c > 0$.*

Lemma 5. *For any regular probability distribution $\mathcal{P}$ on chains, if there is a lockable chain in the domain of $\mathcal{P}$, then the probability of a random chain P being lockable is at least a constant $\rho > 0$.*

Next we show that these positive-probability examples of being locked lead to increasing high probabilities of being locked as we consider larger chains.

---

[2] A closely related but more specific notion of regular probability distributions in 1D was introduced by Willard [Wil85] in his extensions to interpolation search.

Theorem 2. *Let P_n be a random chain drawn from the regular distribution $\mathcal{P}_n^{\Theta,\mathcal{D}}$. If there is a lockable chain in the domain of $\mathcal{P}_n^{\Theta,\mathcal{D}}$ for at least one value of n, then $\lim_{n\to\infty} Pr[P_n$ is lockable] = 1. Furthermore, if Q_n is a random simple configuration drawn from the regular distribution $\mathcal{Q}^{P_n}$, then $\lim_{n\to\infty} Pr[Q_n$ is flattenable] = $\lim_{n\to\infty} Pr[Q_n$ is producible] = 0. Both limits converge geometrically.*

Proof. Suppose there is a lockable chain of k links. By Lemma 5, $Pr[P_k$ is lockable] $> \rho > 0$. Break P_n into $\lfloor n/k \rfloor$ subchains of length k. Each of these subchains is chosen independently from $\mathcal{P}_k^{\Theta,\mathcal{D}}$ and is not lockable with probability $< 1 - \rho$. Now P_n is lockable (in particular) if any of the subchains are lockable, so the probability that P_n is not lockable is $< (1 - \rho)^{\lfloor n/k \rfloor}$ which approaches 0 geometrically as n grows. Likewise, by Lemma 4, the probability that Q_k is locked is $> c\rho$ for some constant $0 < c < 1$, and so the probability that Q_n is flattenable is $< (1 - c\rho)^{\lfloor n/k \rfloor}$ which approaches 0 as n grows.   □

Thus, producible configurations of chains become rare as soon as one chain in the domain of the distribution is lockable. Surprisingly, we do not know of any nontrivial regular probability distributions $\mathcal{P}_n^{\Theta,\mathcal{D}}$ that have no lockable chains in their domain. For example, if $\mathcal{D}$ always picks unit edge lengths, and Θ always picks turn angles $\geq \pi/2$, then we do not know whether any lockable equilateral ($\geq \pi/2$)-chains result.

Acknowledgements. Much of this work was completed at the *Workshop on Geometric Aspects of Molecular Reconfiguration* organized by Godfried Toussaint at the Bellairs Research Institute of McGill University in Barbados, February 2002. We appreciate the helpful discussions with the other participants: Greg Aloupis, Prosenjit Bose, David Bremner, Vida Dujmović, Herbert Edelsbrunner, Jeff Erickson, Ferran Hurtado, Henk Meijer, Pat Morin, Mark Overmars, Suneeta Ramaswami, Ileana Streinu, Godfried Toussaint, and especially Yusu Wang.

References

[ADD+02] G. Aloupis, E. Demaine, V. Dujmović, J. Erickson, S. Langerman, H. Meijer, I. Streinu, J. O'Rourke, M. Overmars, M. Soss, and G. Toussaint. Flat-state connectivity of linkages under dihedral motions. In *Proc. 13th Annu. Internat. Sympos. Alg. Comput.*, volume 2518 of *Lecture Notes in Comput. Sci.*, pages 369–380. Springer, 2002.

[ADM+02] Greg Aloupis, Erik D. Demaine, Henk Meijer, Joseph O'Rourke, Ileana Streinu, and Godfried Toussaint. Flat-state connectedness of fixed-angle chains: Special acute chains. In *Proc. 14th Canad. Conf. Comp. Geom.*, pages 27–30, 2002.

[BDD+02] T. Biedl, E. Demaine, M. Demaine, A. Lubiw, J. O'Rourke, M. Overmars, S. Robbins, I. Streinu, G. T. Toussaint, and S. Whitesides. On reconfiguring tree linkages: Trees can lock. *Discrete Mathematics*, 117:293–297, 2002.

[ST00] M. Soss and G. T. Toussaint. Geometric and computational aspects of polymer reconfiguration. *J. Math. Chemistry*, 27(4):303–318, 2000.

[Wil85] D. E. Willard. Searching unindexed and nonuniformly generated files in $\log \log N$ time. *SIAM J. Comput.*, 14:1013–1029, 1985.

Symmetric Layout of Disconnected Graphs*

Seok-Hee Hong and Peter Eades

School of information Technologies,
University of Sydney, Australia.
{shhong, peter}@it.usyd.edu.au

Abstract. We present a linear time algorithm for drawing disconnected planar graphs with maximum number of symmetries. Our algorithm can be generalized to making symmetric arrangements of bounded disjoint objects in the plane.

1 Introduction

Most graph drawing algorithms focus on connected graphs. However, it has been pointed out [6], that disconnected graph layout problems occur frequently in real world applications. The problem of disconnected graph layout to achieve minimum drawing area was discussed in [6]. In this paper, we address the problem of disconnected graph layout with a different aesthetic criterion: to maximize the symmetry of the drawing. Symmetry is one of the most important aesthetic criteria that represent the structure and properties of a graph visually.

To construct a drawing that displays as much symmetry as possible, we use two steps. The first step, called the *symmetry finding step*, is to find *geometric automorphisms*, which is defined in Section 2.2. The second step, called the *drawing step*, is to construct a drawing that displays these automorphisms.

We should note that although the problem of finding geometric automorphisms is related to, but not equivalent to, the problem of finding automorphisms. The problem of determining whether a graph has a nontrivial automorphism is *isomorphism-complete*. However, the problem of determining whether a graph has a nontrivial *geometric* automorphism is *NP-complete* [13]; it is probably strictly harder than graph isomorphism. Nevertheless, heuristics [5] and exact algorithms [1,2] are devised. For restricted classes of graphs such as trees, outerplanar graphs, plane graphs and series-parallel digraphs, there are linear time algorithms [7,13].

This paper is the last in a series that gives symmetric drawing algorithms for planar graphs. *Triconnected* planar graphs are dealt with in [8] and *biconnected* planar graphs are dealt with in [9]. *One-connected* planar graphs are dealt with in [10]. This paper presents a linear time algorithm for drawing *disconnected* planar graphs with maximum number of symmetries. The following theorem summarizes our main result.

* This research has been supported by a grant from the Australian Research Council. In this extended abstract, proofs are omitted.

T. Ibaraki, N. Katoh, and H. Ono (Eds.): ISAAC 2003, LNCS 2906, pp. 405–414, 2003.

Theorem 1. *There is a linear time algorithm that constructs a maximally symmetric planar drawings of disconnected planar graphs.*

In the next section, we review the background. We present a symmetry finding algorithm in Section 3, and discuss its extension to the more general problem of making symmetric arrangements of bounded disjoint objects in the plane in Section 4.

2   Background

2.1   Automorphisms and Isomorphism Partitions

An *isomorphism* between two graphs $G_1 = (V_1, E_1)$ and $G_2 = (V_2, E_2)$ is an one-one function α from V_1 onto V_2 which preserves adjacency; that is, $(u, v) \in E_1$ if and only if $(\alpha(u), \alpha(v)) \in E_2$. If $G_1 = G_2$ then α is an *automorphism*. The set of automorphisms of a graph forms *automorphism group*. The *isomorphism problem* is to determine all isomorphisms between two given graphs G_1 and G_2.

Automorphisms of a graph are permutations of the vertices, and some of the terminology of permutation groups is helpful. The group generated by $\phi_1, \phi_2, \ldots, \phi_k$ is denoted by $< \phi_1, \phi_2, \ldots, \phi_k >$. Suppose that a permutation group A acts on a set V. We say that $\phi \in A$ *fixes* $v \in V$ if $\phi(v) = v$.

The method from [11] can be used to produce "isomorphism partitions" as follows: suppose that $\mathcal{G} = \{G_1, G_2, \ldots, G_k\}$ is a set of planar graphs. Then we can partition $\mathcal{G}$ into sets of isomorphic graphs in linear time [11]. The isomorphism partition is useful for drawing graphs symmetrically; intuitively, if G_i and G_j are subgraphs of G such that G_i is isomorphic to G_j, then we can draw G_i congruently to G_j.

2.2   Symmetries and Geometric Automorphisms

A symmetry σ of a drawing D of a graph G *induces* a *geometric* automorphism of G, in that the restriction of σ to the points representing vertices of G is an automorphism of G [4]. A drawing D of a graph G *displays* an automorphism ϕ of G if there is symmetry σ of D which induces ϕ. The symmetry group of a graph drawing induces an automorphism group of the graph. An automorphism group A of a graph G is a *geometric automorphism group* if there is a drawing of G which displays every element of A [4].

Figure 1(a) shows a drawing of the graph $K_{2,3}$. The permutation $(123)(45)$ is an automorphism but not a geometric automorphism; in fact the automorphism group of $K_{2,3}$ has size 12, but the only non-trivial geometric automorphism is the one displayed in Figure 1(a), that is, $(13)(45)$.

A geometric automorphism is a *rotational automorphism* (respectively *axial automorphism*) if it is induced by a rotation (respectively reflection). One can deduce (see [4]) that a nontrivial geometric automorphism group is one of three kinds:

Fig. 1. Three drawings with different symmetries.

1. a group of size 2 generated by an axial automorphism;
2. a cyclic group of size k generated by a rotational automorphism;
3. a dihedral group of size $2k$ generated by a rotational automorphism of order k and an axial automorphism.

Thus the problem in drawing graphs with a maximum number of symmetries can be defined formally as follows.

Geometric Automorphism Problem
Input: A graph G.
Output: A maximum size geometric automorphism group of G.

It has been shown that the Geometric Automorphism Problem is NP-hard [13].

2.3   Planar Automorphisms

The concepts in Section 2.2 can be extended to planar drawings: a geometric automorphism ϕ of a graph G is *planar* if there is a planar drawing D of G which displays ϕ, and an automorphism group A is a *planar automorphism group* if there is a planar drawing which displays A. Not every geometric automorphism is planar. For example, the rotational automorphism displayed in Figure 1(b) is not planar; the largest planar automorphism group of K_4, displayed in Figure 1(c), has size 6.

The following problem motivates this paper:

Planar Automorphism Problem
Input: A planar graph G.
Output: A maximum size planar automorphism group of G.

Previous research on the Planar Automorphism Problem has concentrated on subclasses of planar graphs such as trees [13] and series-parallel graphs [7]. Our aim is to give a *linear time* algorithm for planar graphs in general. For this, we use connectivity to divide the Planar Automorphism Problem into cases.

1. Triconnected graphs: a linear time algorithm is presented in [8].
2. Biconnected graphs: a linear time algorithm is presented in [9].
3. One-connected graphs: a linear time algorithm is presented in [10].
4. Disconnected graphs: a linear time algorithm is presented in this paper.

Note that each of these cases relies on the result of the previous (higher connectivity) case. This paper uses the result of [8,9,10].

3   Symmetry Finding Algorithm

In this section, we present an algorithm for finding a largest planar automorphism group of a disconnected graph G. In fact we give algorithms for finding the maximum size planar automorphism group for each of the three types of geometric automorphism groups mentioned in Section 2.2, in subsections 3.2, 3.3, and 3.4. Before describing the algorithm, we need a preprocessing step to compute some parameters of the input graph.

3.1   Preprocessing

First we divide G into connected components $G_1, G_2, \ldots, G_m$. Next, we partition $G_1, G_2, \ldots, G_m$ into isomorphism classes $I_1, I_2, \ldots, I_k$ using the algorithm [11]. Suppose that $n_j = |I_j|$ and $G_\ell \in I_j$ has x_j vertices. Then we use the algorithms of [8,9,10] to compute two sets for each $G_\ell \in I_j$.

- The set C_j of integers g such that $G_\ell \in I_j$ has a cyclic planar automorphism group of size g.
- The set D_j of integers g such that $G_\ell \in I_j$ has a dihedral planar automorphism group of size $2g$.

Throughout the remainder of this paper, we assume that G be a disconnected planar graph and use the notation G_ℓ, for $\ell = 1, 2, \ldots, m$ and I_j, n_j, x_j, C_j, D_j, for $j = 1, 2, \ldots, k$, as defined above. Further, for each positive integer g, we denote the remainder when n_j is divided by g by $r_j(g)$.

There is a small detail here that needs some attention. The algorithms described in [8,9,10] compute a *maximum* size planar automorphism group for the input graph. However, we can modify the algorithms to compute C_j and D_j, because of the following lemma. We say that an element g of a set M of integers is *maximal* if there is no element $h \in M$ with $g|h$.

Lemma 1.   *1. If $g \in C_j$ and $h|g$ then $h \in C_j$. If $g \in D_j$ and $h|g$ then $h \in C_j$.*
2. There are at most 3 maximal elements of C_j, and at most 3 maximal elements of D_j.

Proof. The first part is trivial. For the second part, we give a proof sketch. First suppose that $G_\ell \in I_j$ is triconnected. From Mani's theorem [12], all automorphisms of triconnected planar graphs can be displayed as symmetries of a drawing in three dimensions. Consider a symmetric drawing of triconnected planar graph in three dimension. The projection of the drawing into two dimensions using each of the rotation axis give a symmetric drawing in two dimensions. If the resulting drawing is planar, then it is a planar automorphism group in two dimensions. There are at most three rotation axes. Hence, the size of maximal planar automorphism group is at most 3.

Now suppose that G_ℓ is connected. Note that we can augment G_ℓ with edges and vertices to make it triconnected, preserving both planarity and planar automorphism groups; see [9,10] for details. Thus the lemma holds for connected graphs.

We can deduce the following theorem from Lemma 1 as well as [8,9,10].

Theorem 2. *The sets C_j and D_j, $1 \leq j \leq k$, can be computed in linear time.*

Further, we need to characterize the fixed vertices and faces of a connected graph. Figure 2(a) displays an example of a planar automorphism group which has two fixed faces and Figure 2(b) displays an example of a planar automorphism group which has only one fixed face.

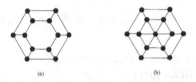

(a)   (b)

Fig. 2. Example of the number of fixed faces.

The following Lemma shows that the examples in Figure 2 represent all possibilities; effectively the lemma gives a unit-time algorithm for deciding whether a planar automorphism group fixes a vertex or two faces.

Lemma 2. *Suppose that G_j has a cyclic planar automorphism group A of size g. Then either:*

- *$g|x_j$ and A fixes two faces of G_j, or*
- *$g|(x_j - 1)$ and A fixes one vertex and one face of G_j.*

Proof. Suppose that D is a drawing of G_j that displays A. Note that the outside face and the barycenter of D are fixed. Note that for each fixed face f, there is circle c_f centered at the barycenter that lies strictly within f. Further, either all of D is inside c_f or all of D is outside c_f, since G_j is connected. It is clear that there can be at most two such circles, and thus A fixes at most two faces. The lemma follows immediately.

A similar result holds for dihedral groups, since a dihedral group has cyclic subgroup. To keep this information, we need one more variable. For each $g \in C_j$ (respectively D_j), we define a boolean value $C_j(g)$ (respectively $D_j(g)$) which is true if and only if G_j has a cyclic (respectively dihedral) planar automorphism group of size g (respectively $2g$) that fixes precisely one face of G_j. Thus we have the following parameters for each isomorphism class I_j:

- n_j and x_j.
- C_j and $C_j(g)$, for each $g \in C_j$.
- D_j and $D_j(g)$, for each $g \in D_j$.

All this information can be computed in linear time.

3.2   Cyclic Case

First we characterize the connected components which are fixed by a cyclic planar automorphism group of size g.

Lemma 3. *Suppose that D is a drawing of G that displays a rotational planar automorphism ρ of order g. Suppose that $G_1, G_2, \ldots, G_a$ are the connected components of G that are fixed by ρ. Then:*

1. *for each i, the restriction ρ_i of ρ to G_i is a rotational planar automorphism of order g; and*
2. *for at most one component G_i, the number of faces fixed by ρ_i is less than two.*

We now characterize the connected components which are not fixed by a cyclic planar automorphism group.

Lemma 4. *Suppose that D is a drawing of G that displays a rotational planar automorphism ρ of order g. Suppose that $G_{a+1}, G_{a+2}, \ldots, G_m$ are the connected components of G that are not fixed by ρ. Let $M = \{j : \text{for some } i, 1 \leq i \leq m-a\}$ and $G_{a+i} \in I_j$. Then $g | n_j$ for all $j \in M$, where $n_j = |I_j|$.*

An example is illustrated in Figure 3(a). Here A, B and C are fixed by the cyclic group.

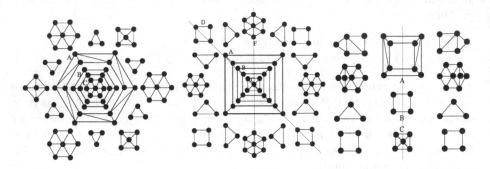

Fig. 3. (a) example of cyclic case (b) example of dihedral case (c) example of one axial case.

Lemmas 3 and 4 lead to the following theorem to compute the set of sizes of the cyclic planar automorphism groups of G.

Theorem 3. *There is a cyclic planar automorphism group of G of size g if and only if for each $j \in \{1, 2, \ldots, k\}$, either*

(a) $r_j(g) = 0$, or
(b) $g \in C_j$ and $C_j(g) = false$, or
(c) $g \in C_j$, $C_j(g) = true$, and $r_j(g) = 1$,

and (c) holds for at most one value of j.

Note that if g is the size of a cyclic planar automorphism group of G, then from Theorem 3 we can deduce that for every j either $g|n_j$ or $g \in C_j$. In the first case, it follows that $g \leq n_j$ and in the second case $g \leq x_j$. Thus $g \leq \min_{1 \leq i \leq k}(\max(n_i, x_i))$, and we need not check values of g greater than this. Based on Theorem 3, we now present an algorithm to compute a maximum size cyclic group of disconnected planar graphs.

Algorithm Cyclic
1. $C_G := \emptyset$
2. For $g = \min_{1 \leq i \leq k}(\max(n_i, x_i))$ down to 2
    a) *fixed_face_chosen* := *false*
    b) For $j = 1$ to k
        i. $gOK := false$
        ii. Compute $r_j(g)$
        iii. if $r_j(g) = 0$ then $gOK := true$
        iv. elseif $g \in C_j$ and $C_j(g) = false$ then $gOK := true$
        v. elseif $g \in C_j$ and $r_j(g) = 1$ and $C_j(g) = true$ and not
         fixed_face_chosen then
            $gOK := true$
            fixed_face_chosen := *true*
    c) If gOK then add g to C_G
3. Return the maximum element of C_G.

We now analyze the time complexity of the algorithm.

Theorem 4. *The maximum size cyclic planar automorphism group of a disconnected planar graph G can be computed in linear time.*

Proof. We have two loops, one from $g = \min_{1 \leq i \leq k}(\max(n_i, x_i))$ down to 2, and the other from $j = 1$ to k. This takes time $O(k \min_{1 \leq i \leq k}(\max(n_i, x_i)))$. But $k \min_{1 \leq i \leq k}(\max(n_i, x_i)) \leq k \min_{1 \leq i \leq k} n_i x_i \leq \sum_{1 \leq i \leq k} n_i x_i = n$. Hence the algorithm is linear.

3.3 Dihedral Case

The dihedral case is more complicated than the cyclic case since there are two types of fixed connected components: fixed by the whole dihedral group or fixed by an axial symmetry. An example is illustrated in Figure 3(b). Here A, B and C are fixed by the whole dihedral group. However, D is fixed by an axial symmetry and F is fixed by another axial symmetry.

As in the cyclic case, at most one connected component with one fixed face and possibly many connected components with two fixed faces can be fixed by the whole dihedral group, and each should display $2g$ dihedral symmetry. Further, g isomorphic components can be fixed by an axial symmetry; if so, then each should display one axial symmetry. The fixed components for the dihedral case are characterized in the following Lemma.

Lemma 5. *Suppose that D is a drawing of G that displays a dihedral planar automorphism group A of size $2g$. Let $G_1, G_2, \ldots, G_a$ be the connected components of G that are fixed by A. Then:*

1. *for each i, the restriction of A to G_i is a dihedral group of size $2g$; and*
2. *for at most one component G_i, the number of faces fixed by A is less than two.*

Now suppose that $G_{a+1}, G_{a+2}, \ldots, G_{a+f}$ are the connected components of G that are fixed by an axial symmetry in A. Then:

1. *for each i, the restriction of the dihedral group to G_i is an axial symmetry.*
2. *Let $I_1, I_2, \ldots, I_\ell$ be the isomorphism classes of $G_{a+1}, G_{a+2}, \ldots, G_{a+f}$. Then $g \mid n_i$ for $i = 1, 2, \ldots, \ell$, where $n_i = |I_i|$.*

We now characterize the connected components which are not fixed by a dihedral planar automorphism group.

Lemma 6. *Suppose that D is a drawing of G that displays a dihedral planar automorphism group A of size $2g$. Let $G_{a+f+1}, G_{a+f+2}, \ldots, G_m$ be the connected components of G that are not fixed by any element of A. Suppose that $I_{\ell+1}, I_{\ell+2}, \ldots, I_k$ denote the isomorphism classes of $G_{a+f+1}, G_{a+f+2}, \ldots, G_m$. Then $2g$ divides n_j for each $j = \ell+1, \ell+2, \ldots, k$, where $n_j = |I_j|$.*

Lemma 5 and Lemma 6 lead to the following theorem, which forms the basis of the algorithm to compute the set of sizes of the dihedral planar automorphism groups of G.

Theorem 5. *For each positive integer g, denote the remainder when n_j is divided by g by $r_j(g)$ and denote the quotient of n_j divided by g by $q_j(g)$. Then there is a dihedral planar automorphism group of G of size $2g$ if and only if for each $j = 1, 2, \ldots, k$, either*

(a) $r_j(g) = 0$ and $q_j(g)$ is even, or
(b) $r_j(g) = 0$ and $q_j(g)$ is odd and $1 \in D_j$, or
(c) $g \in D_j$ and $D_j(g) = false$, or
(d) $g \in D_j$, $r_j(g) = 1$, and $D_j(g) = true$,

and (d) occurs for at most one value of j.

We now present the algorithm.

Algorithm Dihedral
1. $D_G := \emptyset$.
2. For $g = \min_{1 \le i \le k}(\max(n_i, x_i))$ down to 1
    a) $fixed\_face\_chosen := false$
    b) For $j = 1$ to k
        i. $gOK := false$;
        ii. Compute $r_j(g)$ and $q_j(g)$
        iii. if $r_j(g) = 0$

then
   if $q_j(g)$ is even
   then $gOK := true$
   elseif $1 \in D_j$ then $gOK := true$
iv. elseif $g \in D_j$ and $D_j(g) = false$ then $gOK := true$
v. elseif $g \in D_j$ and $r_j(g) = 1$ and $D_j(g) = true$ and not $fixed\_face\_chosen$ then
        $gOK := true$
        $fixed\_face\_chosen := true$
   c) If gOK then add g to D_G
3. Return the maximum element of D_G.

We now summarize the result of this section.

Theorem 6. *The maximum size dihedral planar automorphism group of a disconnected graph G can be computed in linear time.*

3.4   One Axial Symmetry

Finally, we describe how to test whether a disconnected graph has a single axial symmetry. An example is illustrated in Figure 3(c). Here A, B and C are fixed by the axial automorphism. This case is much simpler than previous two cases, and we just give the main theorems.

Theorem 7. *G has an axial planar automorphism group if and only if for every j, either n_j is even or if a component in I_j has an axial planar automorphism group.*

Using Theorem 7, one can easily construct a linear time algorithm to test whether a disconnected graph has one axial symmetry. We now summarize the result of this section.

Theorem 8. *There is a linear time algorithm to test whether a disconnected planar graph G has an axial planar automorphism group.*

4   The Symmetric Arrangement Problem

In this section, we briefly discuss an extension of the algorithm in Section 3 to cover a more general problem. We can define the *Symmetric Arrangement Problem* as follows: given a set of geometric objects, find an arrangement of the set with maximum number of symmetries without overlapping. For simplicity, we allow translation, rotation and scaling. The algorithm presented in Section 3 can be used for constructing such an arrangement as follows.

   Algorithm Symmetric Arrangement
1. Compute the isomorphism classes of the objects in the set, using appropriate isomorphism testing algorithm.

2. For each object in each isomorphism class, detect symmetries of the given geometric object using appropriate symmetry detection algorithm.
3. Apply three algorithms in Section 3 to compute an arrangement of the objects with maximum number of symmetries.

For the isomorphism testing algorithm in Step 1 and the symmetry detection algorithm in Step 2, see a survey of symmetry finding algorithm [3]. Note that the time complexity of **Algorithm Symmetric Arrangement** depends on the algorithms in Steps 1 and 2. For example, consider the case of polygons: the algorithms in Steps 1 and 2 run in linear time[3], and thus the Symmetric Arrangement Problem for polygons can be solved in linear time. For the case of point sets, or a polygon with holes, the algorithms in Steps 1 and 2 run in $O(n \log n)$ time[3], and thus for these cases the Symmetric Arrangement Problem can be solved in time $O(n \log n)$.

References

1. D. Abelson, S. Hong and D. E. Taylor, A Group-Theoretic Method for Drawing Graphs Symmetrically, *Graph Drawing 2002*, LNCS, Springer Verlag, pp. 86–97, 2002.
2. C. Buchheim and M. Junger, Detecting Symmetries by Branch and Cut, *Graph Drawing 2001*, LNCS, Springer Verlag, pp. 178–188, 2001.
3. P. Eades, Symmetry Finding Algorithms, *Computational Morphology*, Machine Intelligence and Pattern Recognition, North Holland, pp. 41–51, 1988.
4. P. Eades and X. Lin, Spring Algorithms and Symmetries, *Theoretical Computer Science*, 240, pp. 379–405, 2000.
5. H. de Fraysseix, An Heuristic for Graph Symmetry Detection, *Graph Drawing'99*, LNCS 1731, pp. 276–285, Springer Verlag, 1999.
6. K. Freivalds, U. Dogrusoz, and P. Kikusts, Disconnected Graph Layout and the Polyomino Packing Approach, *Graph Drawing 2001*, LNCS, 2265, pp. 378–391, Springer Verlag, 2002.
7. S. Hong, P. Eades and S. Lee, Drawing Series Parallel Digraphs Symmetrically, *Computational Geometry: Theory and Applicatons*, 17(3-4), pp. 165–188, 2000.
8. S. Hong, B. McKay and P. Eades, Symmetric Drawings of Triconnected Planar Graphs, *Proc. of SODA 2002*, pp. 356–365, 2002.
9. S. Hong and P. Eades, Drawing Planar Graphs Symmetrically II: Biconnected Graphs, Technical Report CS-IVG-2001-01, School of IT, University of Sydney, 2001.
10. S. Hong and P. Eades, Drawing Planar Graphs Symmetrically III: One-connected Graphs, Technical Report CS-IVG-2001-02, School of IT, University of Sydney, 2001.
11. J. E. Hopcroft and J. K. Wong, Linear Time Algorithm for Isomorphism of Planar Graphs, *Proc. of STOC*, pp. 172–184, 1974.
12. P. Mani, Automorphismen von Polyedrischen Graphen, *Math. Annalen*, 192, pp. 279–303, 1971.
13. J. Manning, *Geometric Symmetry in Graphs*, Ph.D. Thesis, Purdue Univ., 1990.

Approximation Hardness of Minimum Edge Dominating Set and Minimum Maximal Matching

Miroslav Chlebík[1] and Janka Chlebíková[2]*

[1] Max Planck Institute for Mathematics in the Sciences
Inselstraße 22-26, D-04103 Leipzig, Germany
chlebik@mis.mpg.de
[2] Christian-Albrechts-Universität zu Kiel
Institut für Informatik und Praktische Mathematik
Olshausenstraße 40, D-24098 Kiel, Germany
jch@informatik.uni-kiel.de

Abstract. We provide the first interesting explicit lower bounds on efficient approximability for two closely related optimization problems in graphs, MINIMUM EDGE DOMINATING SET and MINIMUM MAXIMAL MATCHING. We show that it is NP-hard to approximate the solution of both problems to within any constant factor smaller than $\frac{7}{6}$. The result extends with negligible loss to bounded degree graphs and to everywhere dense graphs.

1 Introduction

We consider two NP-hard optimization problems MINIMUM EDGE DOMINATING SET and MINIMUM MAXIMAL MATCHING. The problems are motivated by their important applications in areas such as telephone switching networking.

An *edge dominating set* for a simple graph $G = (V, E)$ is a subset D of E such that for all $e \in E \setminus D$ there is an edge $f \in D$ such that e and f are adjacent. The MINIMUM EDGE DOMINATING SET problem (MIN-EDS) asks to find an edge dominating set of minimum cardinality, $eds(G)$ (resp. minimum total weight in weighted case). The decision version of MIN-EDS was shown by Yannakakis and Gavril to be NP-complete even on graphs which are planar (or bipartite) of maximum degree 3 [14]. Later Horton and Kilakos extended their results showing that NP-completeness holds also for planar bipartite graphs, line graphs, total graphs, perfect claw-free graphs, and planar cubic graphs [10]. On the other hand, the problem admits polynomial-time approximation scheme (PTAS) for planar graphs [1] or λ-precision unit disk graphs [11]. Some special classes of graphs for which the problem is polynomially solvable have been discovered, e.g. trees [12], claw-free chordal graphs, locally connected claw-free graphs, the

---

* The author has been supported by EU-Project ARACNE, Approximation and Randomized Algorithms in Communication Networks, HPRN-CT-1999-00112.

T. Ibaraki, N. Katoh, and H. Ono (Eds.): ISAAC 2003, LNCS 2906, pp. 415–424, 2003.

line graphs of total graphs, the line graphs of chordal graphs [10], bipartite permutation graphs, cotriangulated graphs [13].

An edge dominating set of minimum cardinality has close relationship with minimum maximal matchings. A *matching* $M \subseteq E$ in a graph $G = (V, E)$ is *maximal* if no other matching in G properly contains it (or, equivalently, if a matching is an edge dominating set). The MINIMUM MAXIMAL MATCHING problem (MIN-MAXL-MATCH) asks to find a maximal matching of minimum cardinality. The fact that in G there are much more edge dominating sets than maximal matchings does not distinguish the optimization problems MIN-EDS and MIN-MAXL-MATCH significantly. In fact, the minimum cardinality of edge dominating sets in G is achieved also on maximal matchings in G. Even more interestingly, there is a simple polynomial-time algorithm to transform any given edge dominating set D in G to a maximal matching M in G with size $|M| \leq |D|$ (see e.g. [14]). This fact makes MIN-EDS and MIN-MAXL-MATCH equivalent. Any polynomial time ρ-approximation algorithm for MIN-EDS can be easily transformed to the one for MIN-MAXL-MATCH with the same performance ratio; the converse relation being trivial. It is easy to observe that no matching in a graph G can be more than twice larger than any maximal matching. Therefore constructing any maximal matching (which is possible in $O(|E|)$ time) suffices to approximate even the search version of MIN-EDS and MIN-MAXL-MATCH problems to within a factor of 2. Recently, also weighted MIN-EDS was shown to be approximable efficiently to within 2 ([8]).

It is quite straightforward via simple reduction (see [2]) that weighted MIN-EDS is at least as hard to approximate as MINIMUM NODE COVER (MIN-NC), hence any inapproximability result for MIN-NC applies directly to weighted MIN-EDS. In particular, the result of Dinur and Safra [7] implies that it is NP-hard to approximate weighted MIN-EDS to within any constant factor smaller than $10\sqrt{5} - 21 \approx 1.36067$.

In (unweighted) MIN-EDS, or equivalently, MIN-MAXL-MATCH, the gap between the upper bound 2 and the known lower bound on approximability, is much wider. The transformation of Yannakakis and Gavril ([14]) showing NP-completeness of MIN-MAXL-MATCH reducing 3-MIN-NC (the restriction of MIN-NC to cubic graphs) to it, may be regarded as an L-reduction and hence gives APX-completeness for problems we are interested in. This implies NP-hardness to approximate MIN-MAXL-MATCH to within a factor $1 + \delta$ for some $\delta > 0$. But lower estimates on δ obtained from inapproximability results for 3-MIN-NC, and from parameters of that L-reductions are only about $\frac{1}{500}$.

In Section 2 we prove that it is NP-hard to approximate the problem MIN-EDS (and hence also MIN-MAXL-MATCH) to within any factor smaller than $\frac{7}{6}$. We present two approaches how to achieve this lower bound. The first relates the problem to parameters in PCP characterization of NP class, the second one capitalizes on inapproximability result for linear equations systems. The lower bound $\frac{7}{6} - \delta$ holds also for graphs with maximum degree B (reffered to as B-instances in the table), where the value B depends on δ. We have slightly better lower bounds for sparse bipartite graphs with all nodes but one of degree

B (reffered to as B^*-instances in the table); namely we prove NP-hardness factors of $1 + \frac{1}{390}$ and $1 + \frac{1}{250}$ for $B = 4$ and $B = 5$ respectively. The following table summarizes results from this contribution. The upper bound for all problems is 2, except MAXIMUM TOTAL MATCHING with upper bound of $\frac{3}{2}$.

Problem	Lower bound
MIN-EDS or MIN-MAXL-MATCH	$\frac{7}{6} - \delta$
B-MIN-EDS or B-MIN-MAXL-MATCH	$\frac{7}{6} - \frac{24 \log B}{B}$
MIN-EDS or MIN-MAXL-MATCH on everywhere θ-dense graphs	$\frac{7+\theta}{6+2\theta} - \delta$
3-MIN-EDS	$1 + \frac{1}{487}$
4*-MIN-EDS	$1 + \frac{1}{390}$
5*-MIN-EDS	$1 + \frac{1}{250}$
MAXIMUM TOTAL MATCHING	$\frac{10}{9} - \delta$

Definitions. In a graph $G = (V, E)$ a set $C \subseteq V$ is a *node cover*, if every $e \in E$ is incident to some node in C. The MINIMUM NODE COVER problem asks to find a node cover of minimum cardinality, $nc(G)$. A *matching* in a graph G is a set of edges with no shared endpoints. A matching in G is *perfect* if each node of G is incident to an edge of this matching. For a constant $\theta \in (0, 1)$, *everywhere θ-dense* graph is a graph $G = (V, E)$ of minimum degree at least $\theta |V|$.

2   General, Bounded, and Dense Instances

Combinatorial analysis. It is easy to see that a set of edges $F \subseteq E$ is an edge dominating set of $G = (V, E)$ if and only if $V(F)$, the set of end nodes of edges in F, is a node cover of G. In particular, any maximal matching M of G (which is also an edge dominating set) satisfies

$$2|M| = |V(M)| \geq nc(G). \tag{1}$$

Consequently, $nc(G) \leq 2eds(G)$ holds for every graph G. Those graphs G, for which the theoretical bound $nc(G) = 2eds(G)$ is achieved, will be of our main interest in what follows.

Let us denote by $\mathcal{G}$ the class of graphs $G = (V, E)$ for which a minimum cardinality node cover $C \subseteq V$ of G exists such that the subgraph induced by C has a perfect matching. Clearly, any perfect matching M' in that subgraph is a maximal matching of G (as its node set $V(M') = C$ is a node cover of G). Moreover, as $2|M'| = |V(M')| = |C| = nc(G)$, M' is a minimum maximal matching of G (due to (1)). Hence, we have just verified that $nc(G) = 2eds(G)$ for every $G \in \mathcal{G}$.

Due to this simple relation between $eds(G)$ and $nc(G)$ in the class $\mathcal{G}$, our goal is to prove suitable NP-hard gap results for MIN-NC problem restricted to $\mathcal{G}$. For this purpose we have to show first that $\mathcal{G}$ is rich enough. In fact, we will deal with even more restricted class $\mathcal{G}_0 \subseteq \mathcal{G}$ of graphs $G = (V, E)$ for which every minimal (on inclusion) node cover $C \subseteq V$ of G induces a subgraph with a perfect matching.

We start with some combinatorial notions:

Definition 1. *A graph $G[s] = (V[s], E[s])$ is an s-padding (s being a positive integer) of a graph $G = (V, E)$, if $G[s]$ is obtained from G by replacing every node $v \in V$ by a set $v[s]$ of distinct nodes, $v[s] = \{v_1, v_2, \ldots, v_s\}$ and $E[s] := \{\{u_i, v_j\} : \{u, v\} \in E, i, j \in \{1, 2, \ldots, s\}\}$.*

This graph operation has been frequently used and many of its basic properties are well known. Clearly, whenever $C \subseteq V$ is a node cover of G, then $C[s] := \cup_{v \in C} v[s]$ is a node cover of $G[s]$. Moreover, every minimal (on inclusion) node cover of $G[s]$ is of the form $C[s]$ for some (necessarily minimal) node cover C of G. In particular, $nc(G[s]) = s \cdot nc(G)$.

A graph whose s-padding has a perfect matching will be called s-*matchable*. Notice that any graph that admits covering of its node set by (pairwise) node disjoint subgraphs that are either copies of K_2 or (odd) cycles, is 2-matchable. A (nonempty) graph $G = (V, E)$ is said to be s-*safe* in what follows if for every node cover C of G the subgraph induced by C is s-matchable. Clearly, this makes sense only for even positive integer s; for s odd either V, or V without any node, is a node cover with odd number of nodes, and it cannot induce s-matchable subgraph. Example of 2-safe graphs trivially are cliques K_r with $r \geq 3$, and K_r without any edge with $r \geq 5$ as well.

Theorem 1. *Let s be an even positive integer, and $G = (V, E)$ be a graph with the following property: there is a partition $V_1 \cup V_2 \cup \cdots \cup V_p$ of the node set V such that for each $i \in \{1, 2, \ldots, p\}$ the induced subgraph $G_i = (V_i, E_i)$ of G is s-safe. Then the s-padding of G, the graph $G[s]$, has the following property: every minimal node cover of $G[s]$ induces a subgraph in $G[s]$ with a perfect matching. Hence $G[s] \in \mathcal{G}_0 \subseteq \mathcal{G}$, and $eds(G[s]) = \frac{1}{2}nc(G[s]) = \frac{s}{2}nc(G)$.*

The special case of Theorem 1, when $s = 2$ and all those graphs G_i $(i = 1, 2, \ldots, p)$ are cliques of size at least 3, is enough to consider to prove the main Theorem 3 of this paper. Such graphs naturally appear in a general reduction (so called FGLSS-reduction) from languages having efficient PCP (Probabilistic Checking of Proof) systems to approximation versions of MAXIMUM INDEPENDENT SET (or MAXIMUM CLIQUE) and MINIMUM NODE COVER.

PCP Based Proof

We will show that the problem MIN-EDS relates in a straightforward way to parameters of PCP systems. We assume that the reader is familiar with the standard PCP terminology. Recall some notation for verifiers and the parametric complexity classes: Verifier V is called (r, q)-restricted if on input x it generates a random string R tossing $r(|x|)$ coins and queries to an alleged membership proof π via oracle access $q(|x|)$ times. Then it outputs $V^{\pi}(x, R) \in \{$accept $= 1$, reject $= 0\}$.

A language L belongs to the class $\mathrm{PCP}_{c,s}[r, q]$, where c, s are *completeness* and *soundness* probabilities, if there exists an (r, q)-restricted verifier V that given an input x and oracle access to π has the following properties: for $x \in L$ there is a membership proof π such that the verifier accepts π with probability $\geq c$ (over all random strings $R \in \{0, 1\}^{r(|x|)}$); for $x \notin L$ and each membership proof π the probability that the verifier V accepts π is $< s$.

For a verifier V and an input x the graph G_x (more precisely $G_{V,x}$), the FGLSS graph corresponding to V and x, is defined as follows: Every node in G_x corresponds to an *accepting configuration* $(R, Q) \in \{0, 1\}^{r(|x|)} \times \{0, 1\}^q$ of V's computation. That means, for each random string R we enumerate the 2^q possible binary sequences that represent possible sequence of answers to V's oracle queries. For each such sequence Q, we include the pair (R, Q) as a node of G_x if V accepts the sequence Q on random string R. The edges of G_x correspond to inconsistencies among these configurations. That is, there is an edge between (R, Q) and (R', Q') if there is a query $\pi[i]$ that will be asked by V on both (x, R) and (x, R'), and it has different responses in Q and Q'.

The accepting configurations of the form $(R, \cdot)$ for a fixed random string R form a *layer*. Each layer clearly induces a clique in G_x. A verifier has *average free bit complexity* $f_{av} := f_{av}(|x|)$ if the sum of sizes of layers is $2^{r(|x|)+f_{av}(|x|)}$. Notice, that this is the number of nodes of the graph G_x.

For application to problems like MIN-NC it is important that f_{av} is bounded above by small constant, f_*, independent of $|x|$. For our application to MIN-EDS it is further important that we can work with verifiers for which all layers have size at least 3. Then clearly 2-padding of G_x satisfies, due to Theorem 1, $eds(G_x[2]) = nc(G_x)$.

An independent set in G_x corresponds to a proof for x and the size of this set is 2^r times the probability that V accepts this proof. Thus if $x \in L$ there is an independent set of size $c2^r$ (hence $nc(G_x) \leq 2^r(2^{f_{av}} - c)$), whereas if $x \notin L$ the size of any independent set in G_x is less than $s2^r$ (and hence $nc(G_x) > 2^r(2^{f_{av}} - s)$). As $\frac{2^{f_{av}} - s}{2^{f_{av}} - c} = 1 + \frac{c-s}{2^{f_{av}} - c} \geq 1 + \frac{c-s}{2^{f_*} - c}$, any algorithm that approximates eds (on graphs $G_x[2]$) to within $1 + \frac{c-s}{2^{f_*} - c}$ would be sufficient to decide if $x \in L$.

The reduction above has polynomial time complexity if $r(x) = O(\log |x|)$ and q is a constant. Hence if for some NP-complete language L there is a proof that $L \in \mathrm{PCP}_{c,s}[O(\log |x|), q]$ using verifier V with average free bit complexity $\leq f_*$ (f_* being constant) and with at least 3 accepting configurations for any random string R, then approximation of eds to within $1 + \frac{c-s}{2^{f_*} - c}$ is NP-hard. Applying Håstad's result [9] that for every $\varepsilon \in (0, \frac{1}{4})$ NP $\subseteq \mathrm{PCP}_{1-\varepsilon, 0.5+\varepsilon}[O(\log x), 3]$ using verifier with $q = 3$ queries, and exactly 4 accepting configurations for any random string R (hence $f_{av} = f_* = 2$), we obtain inapproximability of MIN-EDS to within any constant smaller than $\frac{7}{6}$.

Reduction from Linear Equation Systems

Definition 2. MAX-E3-LIN-2 *is the following optimization problem: Given a system I of linear equations over $\mathbb{Z}_2$, with exactly 3 (distinct) variables in each equation. The goal is to maximize, over all assignments φ to the variables, the ratio $\frac{sat(\varphi)}{|I|}$, where $sat(\varphi)$ is the number of equations of I satisfied by φ. Ek-MAX-E3-LIN-2 denote the same maximization problem, where each variable occurs exactly k times.*

Let $Q(\varepsilon, k)$ be the following partial decision subproblem of MAX-E3-LIN-2: for given instance of Ek-MAX-E3-LIN-2 the problem is to decide if the fraction of more than $(1-\varepsilon)$ or less than $(\frac{1}{2}+\varepsilon)$ of all equations is satisfied by the optimal (i.e. maximizing) assignment. The following result follows from Håstad results [9] and the proof can be found in [4]

Theorem 2. *For every $\varepsilon \in \left(0, \frac{1}{4}\right)$ there is a constant $k(\varepsilon)$ such that for every $k \geq k(\varepsilon)$ the partial decision subproblem $Q(\varepsilon, k)$ of MAX-E3-LIN-2 is NP-hard.*

Notation. Denote $F(x) := -x \log x - (1 - x) \log(1 - x)$, $x \in (0, 1)$, where log means the natural logarithm. Further, $G(c, t) := (F(t) + F(ct))/(F(t) - ctF(\frac{1}{c}))$ for $0 < t < \frac{1}{c} < 1$, $g(t) := G(\frac{1-t}{t}, t)$ for $t \in (0, \frac{1}{2})$. More explicitly, $g(t) = 2[-t \log t - (1 - t) \log(1 - t)]/[-2(1 - t) \log(1 - t) + (1 - 2t) \log(1 - 2t)]$. Using Taylor series of the logarithm near 1 we see that the denominator here is $t^2 \cdot \sum_{k=0}^{\infty} \frac{2^{k+2}-2}{(k+1)(k+2)} t^k > t^2$, and $-(1-t)\log(1-t) = t - t^2 \sum_{k=0}^{\infty} \frac{1}{(k+1)(k+2)} t^k < t$, consequently $g(t) < \frac{2}{t}(1 + \log \frac{1}{t})$.

For large enough B we look for $\delta \in (0, \frac{1}{6})$ such that $6\lfloor g(\frac{\delta}{2})\rfloor + 12 \leq B$. As $g(\frac{1}{12}) \approx 75.62$ and g is decreasing in $(0, \frac{1}{12})$, we can see that for $B \geq 462$ any $\delta > \delta(B) := 2g^{-1}(\lfloor \frac{B}{6} \rfloor - 1)$ will do. Trivial estimates on $\delta(B)$ (using $g(t) < \frac{2}{t}(1 + \log \frac{1}{t})$) are $\delta(B) < \frac{24}{B-12}(\log(B - 12) + 1 - \log 12) < \frac{24 \log B}{B}$.

We will need the following lemma (based on Theorem 6.6 in [3]) about regular bipartite expanders to prove the main Theorem 3.

Lemma 1. *Let $t \in (0, \frac{1}{2})$ and d be an integer for which $d > g(t)$. For every sufficiently large positive integer n there is a d-regular n by n bipartite graph H with bipartition (V_0, V_1), such that for each independent set J in H either $|J \cap V_0| \leq tn$, or $|J \cap V_1| \leq tn$.*

Theorem 3. *For every $\delta \in (0, \frac{1}{6})$ it is NP-hard to approximate MIN-EDS (MIN-MAXL-MATCH) to within $\frac{7}{6} - \delta$, even in graphs of degree at most $6\lfloor g(\frac{\delta}{2})\rfloor + 12 \leq 6\lceil \frac{4}{\delta}(1 + \log \frac{2}{\delta})\rceil + 6$. Consequently, for any $B \geq 462$ it is NP-hard to approximate B-MIN-EDS (B-MIN-MAXL-MATCH) to within any constant smaller than $\frac{7}{6} - \delta(B)$, where $\delta(B) := 2g^{-1}(\lfloor \frac{B}{6} \rfloor - 1) < \frac{24}{B-12}(\log(B - 12) + 1 - \log 12) < \frac{24 \log B}{B}$. Further, for any $\theta \in (0, 1)$, it is NP-hard to approximate MIN-EDS (MIN-MAXL-MATCH) on everywhere θ-dense graphs to within any constant smaller than $\frac{7+\theta}{6+2\theta}$.*

Sketch of the proof. (a) We first prove the result for graphs without restriction on degrees. Fix $\delta \in (0, \frac{1}{6})$, choose $\varepsilon \in (0, \frac{1}{4})$ such that $\frac{7}{6} - \delta < \frac{7-2\varepsilon}{6+2\varepsilon}$, and then k for which $Q(\varepsilon, k)$ is NP-hard. We describe simple reduction f from Ek-MAX-E3-LIN-2 to graphs and check how the NP-hard gap of $Q(\varepsilon, k)$ is preserved for the value of *eds* or *nc*.

Let I be an instance of Ek-MAX-E3-LIN-2, $\mathcal{V}(I)$ be the set of variables of I, and $m := |\mathcal{V}(I)|$. Clearly the system I has $\frac{mk}{3}$ equations. For each equation we take simple gadget, a 4-clique. More precisely, if the equation reads as $x + y + z = j$ ($j \in \{0, 1\}$) we take a 4-clique whose nodes has labels $\boxed{xyz = 00j}$, $\boxed{xyz = 01(1-j)}$, $\boxed{xyz = 10(1-j)}$ and $\boxed{xyz = 11j}$. Notice, that nodes correspond to partial assignments to variables making the equation satisfied. Now we add an edge for each pair of inconsistently labeled nodes. The pair of nodes is inconsistent if a variable $u \in \mathcal{V}(I)$ exists that is assigned differently in their labels. Let us denote the graph we obtained by G_I, $f(I) := G_I[2]$ its 2-padding.

Clearly G_I has $\frac{4}{3}mk$ nodes. By Theorem 1, $G_I[2] \in \mathcal{G}$, hence $eds(G_I[2]) = \frac{1}{2}nc(G_I[2]) = nc(G_I)$. Denote by $\alpha(G_I)$ cardinality of the maximum independent set in G_I. We show that $\alpha(G_I) = \frac{mk}{3} \cdot \text{OPT}(I)$, where $\text{OPT}(I)$ is the fraction of maximum cardinality of satisfiable equations over all assignment.

Given any assignment $\varphi : \mathcal{V}(I) \to \{0, 1\}$, let J_φ consists of all nodes whose partial assignment is the restriction of φ. J_φ is an independent set and $|J_\varphi|$ is just the number of equations from I that are satisfied by φ. Hence $|J_\varphi| \leq \frac{mk}{3}\text{OPT}(I)$ for each assignment, and there is an assignment for which the equality holds. Moreover, for any independent set J in G_I there is an assignment φ such that $J \subseteq J_\varphi$. Hence the union of those partial assignments is the restriction of some assignment $\varphi : \mathcal{V}(I) \to \{0, 1\}$. Now $\alpha(G_I) = \frac{mk}{3}\text{OPT}(I)$ easily follows. Further, $nc(G_I) = \frac{4}{3}mk - \alpha(G_I) = \frac{mk}{3}(4 - \text{OPT}(I))$. Hence the NP-hard question of whether $\text{OPT}(I)$ is greater than $(1-\varepsilon)$, or in the interval $\langle \frac{1}{2}, \frac{1}{2}+\varepsilon \rangle$ is transformed to NP-hard partial decision problem of whether $nc(G_I) = eds(G_I[2])$ is less than $\frac{mk}{3}(3 + \varepsilon)$, or it is in the interval $(\frac{mk}{3}(\frac{7}{2} - \varepsilon), \frac{mk}{3} \cdot \frac{7}{2}\rangle$.

(b) To prove inapproximability within $\frac{7}{6} - \delta$ for bounded degree graphs one can use the idea already used in [6]: to replace graph G_I of all inconsistencies by its lower degree subgraph with suitable expanding properties.

Let $\delta \in (0, \frac{1}{6})$ be given, put $d := \lfloor g(\frac{\delta}{2}) \rfloor + 1$ ($\leq \lceil \frac{4}{\delta}(1 + \log \frac{2}{\delta}) \rceil$). Then we choose $t \in (0, \frac{\delta}{2})$, close enough to $\frac{\delta}{2}$, so that $d > g(t)$. Further we choose $\varepsilon \in (0, \frac{1}{4})$ such that $(\frac{7}{2} - \varepsilon - 6t)/(3 + \varepsilon) > \frac{7}{6} - \delta$. Then a positive integer k is chosen so that (i) $Q(\varepsilon, k)$ is NP-hard (see Theorem 2), and (ii) there is a d-regular $2k$ by $2k$ bipartite graph H with bipartition (V_0, V_1), such that for each independent set J in H either $|J \cap V_0| \leq 2kt$, or $|J \cap V_1| \leq 2kt$ (see Lemma 1). Keep one such H fixed from now on.

Now we start with an instance I of Ek-MAX-E3-LIN-2, with $m := |\mathcal{V}(I)|$. We take the same equation gadget as in part (a). Consider a variable $u \in \mathcal{V}(I)$. Let $V_j(u)$ ($j \in \{0, 1\}$) be the set of all $2k$ nodes in which u has assigned bit j. Now we create a graph G_I^H on the same set of nodes as G_I (from the part (a)) but with maximum degree at most $3d + 3$, as follows: For each $u \in \mathcal{V}(I)$ we take edges between $V_0(u)$ and $V_1(u)$ exactly as prescribed by our fixed expander H.

Having this done, one after another, for each $u \in \mathcal{V}(I)$, we get the graph G_I^H. Let $h(I) := G_I^H[2]$ be its 2-padding.

Clearly, the transformation h is polynomial, G_I^H is of degree at most $3d+3$, and $h(I)$ is of degree at most $6d+6$. Again, by Theorem 1, $G_I^H[2] \in \mathcal{G}$, hence $eds(G_I^H[2]) = \frac{1}{2}nc(G_I^H[2]) = nc(G_I^H)$. Clearly, any independent set in G_I is also an independent set in G_I^H, hence $\alpha(G_I^H) \geq \alpha(G_I) = \frac{mk}{3}\mathrm{OPT}(I)$ and $nc(G_I^H) \leq nc(G_I) = \frac{mk}{3}(4 - \mathrm{OPT}(I))$.

On the other hand, we can show that $\alpha(G_I^H) \leq \alpha(G_I) + 2kmt = \frac{mk}{3}(\mathrm{OPT}(I)+6t)$ and $nc(G_I^H) \geq \frac{mk}{3}(4-\mathrm{OPT}(I)-6t)$. Hence NP-hard question of whether $\mathrm{OPT}(I)$ is greater than $(1-\varepsilon)$, or less than $\frac{1}{2}+\varepsilon$, is transformed to NP-hard partial decision problem of whether $eds(G_I^H[2]) = nc(G_I^H)$ is less than $\frac{mk}{3}(3+\varepsilon)$, or greater than $\frac{mk}{3}(\frac{7}{2} - \varepsilon - 6t)$.

(c) Let $\theta \in (0,1)$ be fixed and $r \in (1, \frac{7+\theta}{6+2\theta})$. To prove inapproximability to within r on everywhere θ-dense graphs, we choose $\varepsilon > 0$ and $\omega > \frac{\theta}{1-\theta}$ such that $(7 - 2\varepsilon + 8\omega)/(6 + 2\varepsilon + 8\omega) > r$.

Now, as in part (a) starting from an instance I create graph G_I. Consider the graph G_I' obtained from G_I by adding a clique with $\lfloor \frac{4}{3}mk\omega \rfloor$ nodes and connecting any node of the clique to any node of G_I. It is easy to check that G_I' and $G_I'[2]$ are everywhere θ-dense (assuming mk is large enough). By Theorem 1, $G_I'[2] \in \mathcal{G}$, hence $eds(G_I'[2]) = nc(G_I')$. Moreover, $nc(G_I') = nc(G_I) + \lfloor \frac{4}{3}mk\omega \rfloor = \frac{mk}{3}(4-\mathrm{OPT}(I)) + \lfloor \frac{4}{3}mk\omega \rfloor$. Hence, $\mathrm{OPT}(I) > 1-\varepsilon$ implies $eds(G_I'[2]) < \frac{mk}{6}(6+2\varepsilon + 8\omega)$, and $\mathrm{OPT}(I) < \frac{1}{2} + \varepsilon$ implies $eds(G_I'[2]) > \frac{mk}{6}(7 - 2\varepsilon + 8\omega) - 1$.

3   Sparse and Small Degree Instances

One of reductions of [14] starts with a cubic graph G with n nodes and produces a graph $f(G)$ with $10n$ nodes and $\frac{21n}{2}$ edges that is of maximal degree 3 and for which $eds(f(G)) = 2n + nc(G)$. Using our (currently the best) inapproximability results for MIN-NC problem on cubic graphs ([5]) one easily finds that it is NP-hard to distinguish the case of $eds(f(G))$ being larger than $2.51549586n$ from that of being smaller than $2.5103305n$. Hence inapproximability to within $1 + \frac{1}{487}$ follows, even on instances produced by f.

Slightly better results can be obtained for sparse graphs for which one node is allowed to be of large degree and all the others have small degree. The following simple transformation g from MIN-NC problem is universal. Given a graph $G = (V, E)$ with n nodes and m edges, add one new special node 0, connect 0 with every $u \in V$ by an edge, and replace every $e = \{u, v\} \in E$ by a simple gadget G_e depicted on the following figure:

The bipartite graph $g(G)$ constructed in this way has $(n+4m+1)$ nodes and $n+5m$ edges. The important fact is that $eds(g(G))$ is easily related to $nc(G)$. It can be proved that $eds(g(G)) = m + nc(G)$.

Applying the reduction above to a cubic graph G with n nodes produces the bipartite graph $g(G)$ with $7n+1$ nodes, $\frac{17}{2}n$ edges, and all nodes but one of degree ≤ 4. On those instances the corresponding NP-hard question is to decide of whether $eds(g(G))$ is larger than $2.01549586n$, or smaller than $2.0103305n$, hence to approximate eds on such instances to within $1 + \frac{1}{390}$ is NP-hard.

The results are slightly better starting with 4-regular graphs and using our NP-hard gap results [5] for them. For generic 4-regular graph G with n nodes the bipartite graph $g(G)$ has $9n+1$ nodes, $11n$ edges, and all nodes but one of degree ≤ 5. Now it is NP-hard to decide of whether $eds(g(G))$ is larger than $2.53036437246n$, or smaller than $2.52024291497n$, hence to approximate eds on such instances to within $1 + \frac{1}{250}$ is NP-hard.

Remarks. 1. MIN-EDS is equivalent to the MINIMUM (NODE) DOMINATING SET problem (MIN-DS) restricted to line graphs. Hence this restricted version of MIN-DS is APX-complete, has simple 2-approximation algorithm, but it is NP-hard to approximate to within $\frac{7}{6} - \delta$ for any $\delta > 0$. Let us mention that for general graphs MIN-DS is not in APX; it is as hard to approximate as the set cover problem.

2. Recall that if $G = (V, E)$ then the *total graph* of G, denoted by $T(G)$, is defined as $T(G) = (V \cup E, E \cup E' \cup E'')$, where $E' = \{(e,v): e \in E, v \in V$ and v is incident with $e\}$, and $E'' = \{(e,f): e, f \in E$ are adjacent edges$\}$. One can prove that $\alpha(T(G)) = |V(G)| - eds(G)$ (see e.g. [14]). In the proof of Theorem 3 we produced instances $G = (V, E)$ with $n := \frac{8}{3}mk$ nodes for which it was NP-hard to distinguish between the case of $eds(G) < \frac{n}{16}(6 + 2\varepsilon)$ and the one of $eds(G) > \frac{n}{16}(7 - 2\varepsilon)$. For the problem MAX-IS in total graphs they translate as $\alpha(T(G)) > \frac{n}{16}(10 - 2\varepsilon)$ and $\alpha(T(G)) < \frac{n}{16}(9 + 2\varepsilon)$, respectively. Hence it is NP-hard to approximate MAXIMUM INDEPENDENT SET (MAX-IS) in total graphs (MAXIMUM TOTAL MATCHING problem for G) to within any constant smaller than $\frac{10}{9}$. On the other hand, it is easy to design $\frac{3}{2}$-approximation algorithm for MAX-IS in $T(G)$, assuming the graph $G = (V, E)$ is given as an input. It suffices to find any maximal matching M of G and return $M \cup (V \setminus V(M))$; it is an independent set in $T(G)$ of size at least $\frac{2}{3}\alpha(T(G))$.

3. Passing to the complementary problem MIN-NC in Remark 2 one gets $nc(T(G)) = |E(G)| + eds(G)$. To obtain an interesting explicit lower bound on approximability of MIN-NC in total graphs, one can use our NP-hard gap result for MIN-EDS in sparse graphs. For example, NP-hard gap of 5*-MIN-EDS transforms to the one showing that to approximate MIN-NC in total graphs within $1 + \frac{1}{1336}$ is NP-hard. The NP-hard gap with the same inapproximability applies to MIN-EDS (MIN-MAXL-MATCH) in total graphs as well. This is due to the fact that in $T(G)$ any node cover with even number of nodes induces the graph with a perfect matching, assuming that G was connected (see e.g. [10]). It implies that for a connected graph G, $eds(T(G)) = \lceil \frac{nc(T(G))}{2} \rceil$.

We can go even further. Having NP-hard gap result for MIN-EDS in total graphs, we can use Remark 2 for the graph $T(G)$ in place of G to show the NP-hard gap result for MAX-IS of 2-iterated total graph of G, $T(T(G))$.

Using mathematical induction, for any positive integer r we can derive explicit NP-hard gap result for each of problems MAX-IS, MIN-NC, MIN-EDS, MIN-MAXL-MATCH restricted to the r-iterated total graphs.

The fact, that the lower bounds for polynomial time approximability of these problems converge very rapidly to 1 with increasing r, does not necessarily mean that those results are weak. In fact, one can show the upper bounds of the form $1 + \delta^{r^2}$, for some constant $\delta \in (0,1)$, for these problems on the r-iterated total graphs.

References

1. B. S. Baker: *Approximation algorithms for* NP-*complete problems on planar graphs*, Journal of ACM **41**(1994), 153–180.
2. R. Carr, T. Fujito, G. Konjevod and O. Parekh: *A* $2\frac{1}{10}$-*approximation algorithm for a generalization of the weighted edge-dominating set problem*, Journal of Combinatorial Optimization **5**(2001), 317–326.
3. F. R. K. Chung: *Spectral Graph Theory*, CBMS Regional Conference Series in Mathematics, American Mathematical Society, 1997, ISBN 0-8218-0315-8.
4. M. Chlebík and J. Chlebíková: *Approximation hardness for small occurrence instances of NP-hard problems*, Proc. of the 5th CIAC, LNCS **2653**, 2003, Springer, 152–164 (also ECCC Report TR02-73, 2002).
5. M. Chlebík and J. Chlebíková: *Inapproximability results for bounded variants of optimization problems*, Proc. of the 14th Inter. Symp. on Fundamentals of Computation Theory (FCT), Malmö, Sweden, August 12-15, 2003, LNCS 2751, 2003, Springer (also ECCC Report TR03-26, 2003).
6. A. Clementi and L. Trevisan: *Improved non-approximability results for vertex cover with density constraints*, Theor. Computer Science **225**(1999), 113–128.
7. I. Dinur and S. Safra: *The importance of being biased*, ECCC Report TR02-104, 2001.
8. T. Fujito and H. Nagamochi: *A 2-approximation algorithm for the minimum weight edge dominating set problem*, Discrete Appl. Math. **118**(2002), 199–207.
9. J. Håstad: *Some optimal inapproximability results*, Journal of ACM **48**(2001), 798–859.
10. J. D. Horton and K. Kilakos: *Minimum edge dominating sets*, SIAM J. Discrete Math. **6**(1993), 375–387.
11. H. B. Hunt III, M. V. Marathe, V. Radhakrishnan, S. S. Ravi, D. J. Rosenkrantz and R. E. Stearns: *A unified approach to approximation schemes for NP- and PSPACE-hard problems for geometric graphs*, Proc. of the 2nd ESA, LNCS **855**, 1994, 424–435.
12. S. Mitchell and S. Hedetniemi: *Edge domination in trees*, Proc. of the 8th Southearn Conf. on Combinatorics, Graph Theory, and Computing, 1977, 489–509.
13. A. Srinivasan, K. Madhukar, P. Nagavamsi, C. Pandu Rangan and M.-S. Chang: *Edge domination on bipartite permutation graphs and cotriangulated graphs*, Inf. Proc. Letters **56**(1995), 165–171.
14. M. Yannakakis and F. Gavril: *Edge dominating sets in graphs*, SIAM J. Appl. Math. **38**(1980), 364–372.

Enumerating Global Roundings of an Outerplanar Graph

Nadia Takki-Chebihi and Takeshi Tokuyama

Graduate School of Information Sciences, Tohoku University,
{nadia,tokuyama}@dais.is.tohoku.ac.jp

Abstract. Given a connected weighted graph $G = (V, E)$, we consider a hypergraph $\mathcal{H}_G = (V, \mathcal{P}_G)$ corresponding to the set of all shortest paths in G. For a given real assignment $\mathbf{a}$ on V satisfying $0 \leq \mathbf{a}(v) \leq 1$, a global rounding α with respect to $\mathcal{H}_G$ is a binary assignment satisfying that $|\sum_{v \in F} \mathbf{a}(v) - \alpha(v)| < 1$ for every $F \in \mathcal{P}_G$. Asano et al [1] conjectured that there are at most $|V| + 1$ global roundings for $\mathcal{H}_G$. In this paper, we prove that the conjecture holds if G is an outerplanar graph. Moreover, we give a polynomial time algorithm for enumerating all the global roundings of an outerplanar graph.

1 Introduction

Given a real number a, an integer k is a *rounding* of a if the difference between a and k is strictly less than 1, or equivalently, if k is the floor $\lfloor a \rfloor$ or the ceiling $\lceil a \rceil$ of a. We extend this usual notion of rounding into that of *global rounding* on hypergraphs as follows. Let $\mathcal{H} = (V, \mathcal{F})$, where $\mathcal{F} \subset 2^V$, be a hypergraph on a set V of n nodes. Given a real valued function (often called an *input assignment*) $\mathbf{a}$ on V, we say that an integer valued function α on V is a *rounding* of $\mathbf{a}$ if, for each $v \in V$, $\alpha(v)$ is a rounding of $\mathbf{a}(v)$. A rounding α is a *global rounding* of $\mathbf{a}$ with respect to $\mathcal{H}$ if $w_F(\alpha)$ is a rounding of $w_F(\mathbf{a})$ for each $F \in \mathcal{F}$, where $w_F(f)$ denotes $\sum_{v \in F} f(v)$. Since α is a global rounding of $\mathbf{a}$ if and only if $\mathbf{a} - \lfloor \mathbf{a} \rfloor$ is a global rounding of $\alpha - \lfloor \mathbf{a} \rfloor$, where $\lfloor \mathbf{a} \rfloor$ is defined by $\lfloor \mathbf{a} \rfloor(v) = \lfloor \mathbf{a}(v) \rfloor$ for each $v \in V$, we restrict our attention to the case where the ranges of $\mathbf{a}$ and α are $[0, 1]$ and $\{0, 1\}$ respectively.

This notion of global roundings on hypergraphs is closely related to that of *linear* or *inhomogeneous discrepancy* of hypergraphs[5,7]. Given $\mathbf{a} \in [0, 1]^V$ and its rounding $\alpha \in \{0, 1\}^V$, define the *discrepancy* $D_{\mathcal{H}}(\mathbf{a}, \alpha)$ of α with respect to $\mathbf{a}$ on $\mathcal{H}$ by

$$D_{\mathcal{H}}(\mathbf{a}, \alpha) = \max_{F \in \mathcal{F}} |w_F(\mathbf{a}) - w_F(\alpha)|.$$

Then, the linear discrepancy of $\mathcal{H}$ is defined as

$$\sup_{\mathbf{a} \in [0,1]^V} \min_{\alpha \in \{0,1\}^V} D_{\mathcal{H}}(\mathbf{a}, \alpha).$$

In this terminology, α is a global rounding of $\mathbf{a}$ on $\mathcal{H}$ if and only if $D_{\mathcal{H}}(\mathbf{a}, \alpha)$ is strictly smaller than 1: In other words, a global rounding is an integral point in

T. Ibaraki, N. Katoh, and H. Ono (Eds.): ISAAC 2003, LNCS 2906, pp. 425–433, 2003.

the open unit ball about $\mathbf{a}$ by considering $D_{\mathcal{H}}$ as the distance. Every $\mathbf{a} \in [0,1]^v$ has a global rounding on $\mathcal{H}$ if and only if the linear discrepancy of $\mathcal{H}$ is strictly smaller than 1. It is known that unimodularity is the necessary and sufficient condition for this [5].

The algorithmic question of how to obtain a low-discrepancy rounding of given $\mathbf{a}$ is important. For example, consider the problem of digital halftoning in image processing, where the gray-scale value of each pixel has to be rounded into a binary value. This problem is formulated as that of obtaining a low-discrepancy rounding, in which the hypergraph is a family of certain local sets of pixels, and several methods have been proposed[2,3,8]. However, this is an NP-hard problem in general, and a practical approach is to consider a special hypergraph for which we can compute a low-discrepancy rounding efficiently. In the literature [2,3,6], unimodular hypergraphs are mainly considered. However, unimodularity condition is often too strong.

We give in this paper a class of non-unimodular hypergraphs for which all the global rounding can be enumerated in polynomial time. For the purpose, we first consider the number of global roundings, since enumeration is expensive if the output size is large. Given $\mathbf{a} \in [0,1]^V$, we are interested in the number $\nu(\mathcal{H}, \mathbf{a})$ of all global roundings of given $\mathbf{a}$ on $\mathcal{H}$ and its maximum value $\nu(\mathcal{H}) = \max_{\mathbf{a} \in [0,1]^V} \nu(\mathcal{H}, \mathbf{a})$ over all possible inputs $\mathbf{a}$. In other words, this is the upper bound of the number of integer points within a unit (open) ball by using the discrepancy as the distance. Note that a unit ball under the n-dimensional Euclidean distance has at most eight integral points, whereas a unit ball with respect to the n-dimensional L_∞ distance (this is $D_{\mathcal{H}}$ where $\mathcal{H}$ has no hyperedge) may contain 2^n points.

This direction of research was initiated by Sadakane et al.[9] where the authors discovered a somewhat surprising fact that $\nu(\mathcal{I}_n) \leq n+1$ where $\mathcal{I}_n$ is a hypergraph on $V = \{1, 2, .., n\}$ with edge set $\{[i,j]; 1 \leq i \leq j \leq n\}$ consisting of all subintervals of V; moreover, they give an efficient algorithm to enumerate all the global roundings of a given input on $\mathcal{I}_n$. Note that if we slightly change the definition of global roundings and allow the discrepancy of the rounding to be equal to 1, then the number of global roundings on this hypergraph becomes exponential. If we consider the hypergraph $\mathcal{I}_{k,n}$ (denoted by $\mathcal{I}_k$ in [9]) on V consisting of all subintervals of length less than k, the number of global roundings becomes exponentially large in n/k. Nevertheless, based on the structure of global roundings of $\mathcal{I}_n$, Sadakane et al. succeeded to design an efficient system for outputting global roundings of $\mathcal{I}_{k,n}$ in a uniformly random fashion.

The upper bound $n+1$ of $\nu(\mathcal{H})$ is best possible for any hypergraph $\mathcal{H}$: if we let $\mathbf{a}(v) = \epsilon$ for every v, where $\epsilon < 1/n$, then any binary assignment on V that assigns 1 to at most one vertex is a global rounding of $\mathcal{H}$, and hence $\nu(\mathcal{H}) \geq n+1$. Given this discovery, it is natural to ask for which class of hypergraphs this property $\nu(\mathcal{H}) = n+1$ holds.

Given a connected G in which edges are possibly weighted by a positive value, we define a *shortest-path hypergraph* $\mathcal{H}_G$ generated by G as follows: a set F of vertices of G is an edge of $\mathcal{H}_G$ if and only if F is the set of vertices of some shortest path in G with respect to the given edge weights. We permit more than one shortest path between a pair of nodes if they have the same length. $\mathcal{H}_G$ is non-unimodular if G is not a path. Asano et al. [1] proposed the following conjecture:

Conjecture 1 ([1]). $\nu(\mathcal{H}_G) = n + 1$ for any connected graph G with n nodes.

Sadakane et al.'s result implies that the conjecture holds for a path, and Asano et al. [1] proved it for special graphs including trees and cycles. Moreover, if we consider the hypergraph corresponding to the set of all (simple) paths in G, instead of shortest paths, it is easy to see that it has at most $n + 1$ global roundings.

It is convenient for our argument to consider a unit diameter set defined below instead of a unit ball around a given input **a**.

Definition 1. *A set A of binary functions on V is called $\mathcal{H}$-compatible if, for each pair α and β in A, $|w_F(\alpha) - w_F(\beta)| \leq 1$ holds for every hyperedge F of $\mathcal{H}$.*

Given two different global roundings α and β of an input **a** with respect to a hypergraph $\mathcal{H}$, we have $|w_F(\alpha) - w_F(\beta)| \leq |w_F(\mathbf{a}) - w_F(\alpha)| + |w_F(\mathbf{a}) - w_F(\beta)| < 2$. Since the value must be integral, the condition is written as $|w_F(\alpha) - w_F(\beta)| \leq 1$. Thus, a set of global roundings of **a** is $\mathcal{H}$-compatible.

The definition of an $\mathcal{H}$-compatible set does not include the input vector **a**, and facilitates the combinatorial analysis. Let $\mu(\mathcal{H})$ be the maximum cardinality of an $\mathcal{H}$-compatible set. Instead of Conjecture 1, we consider the following (possibly stronger) variants:

Conjecture 2. $\mu(\mathcal{H}_G) = n + 1$ for any connected graph G with n nodes.

Since $\mu(\mathcal{H}) \geq \nu(\mathcal{H})$, it is clear that Conjecture 2 implies Conjecture 1. In this paper, we prove it for outerplanar graphs:

Theorem 1. $\mu(\mathcal{H}_G) = n + 1$ *holds for the shortest-path hypergraph $\mathcal{H}_G$, if G is an outerplanar graph.*

We then investigate the structure of global roundings, and give an algorithm to enumerate all the global roundings of an outerplanar graph G for an input assignment **a** in polynomial time.

2   Preliminaries

We list some necessary results given by Asano et al. [1]. We start with the following easy observations:

Lemma 1. *For hypergraphs $\mathcal{H} = (V, \mathcal{F})$ and $\mathcal{H}' = (V, \mathcal{F}')$ such that $\mathcal{F} \subset \mathcal{F}'$, $\mu(\mathcal{H}) \geq \mu(\mathcal{H}')$.*

For a binary assignment α on V and a subset X of V, $\alpha|_X$ denotes the restriction of α on X. Let $V = X \cup Y$ be a partition of V into nonintersecting subsets X and Y of vertices. For binary assignments α on X and β on Y, $\alpha \oplus \beta$ is a binary assignment on V obtained by concatenating α and β: That is, $\alpha \oplus \beta(v) = \alpha(v)$ if $v \in X$, otherwise it is $\beta(v)$.

Lemma 2. *Let $G = (V, E)$ be a connected graph, and let $V = X \cup Y$ be a partition of V. Let α_1 and α_2 be different assignments on X and let β_1 and β_2 be different assignments on Y. Then, the set $\{\, \alpha_1 \oplus \beta_1,\, \alpha_1 \oplus \beta_2,\, \alpha_2 \oplus \beta_1,\, \alpha_2 \oplus \beta_2 \,\}$ cannot be $\mathcal{H}_G$-compatible.*

A graph G is *series connection* of two graphs G_1 and G_2 if $G = G_1 \cup G_2$ and $G_1 \cap G_2 = \{v\}$ (implying that they share no edge), where v is called the *separator*.

Proposition 1. *Suppose that a graph G is a series connection of two connected graphs G_1 and G_2. Then, $\mu(G) \le \mu(G_1) + \mu(G_2) - 2$.*

3   The Structure of a Compatible Set for a Cycle

Let C_n be a directed cycle on n vertices $V = \{1, 2, \ldots, n\}$ with edge set $\{e_1, \ldots, e_n\}$ where $e_i = (i, i+1)$, $1 \le i \le n$. The arithmetic on vertices are cyclic, i.e., $n + 1 = 1$. For an assignment α, we define $w(\alpha) = w_V(\alpha) = \sum_{v \in C_n} \alpha(v)$ to be the weight of α over all vertices in C_n. The following three results are given by Asano et al. [1].

Lemma 3. *Let α and β be $\mathcal{H}_{C_n}$-compatible assignments on C_n. Then, $w(\alpha)$ and $w(\beta)$ differ by at most 1.*

Lemma 4. *Suppose $w(\alpha) = w(\beta)$ for assignments α and β. Then, if α and β are $\mathcal{H}_{C_n}$-compatible they are compatible on every path of C_n.*

Theorem 2. *$\mu(\mathcal{H}_{C_n}) = n + 1$.*

In order to investigate global roundings with respect to outer planar graphs, we sharpen Theorem 2 slightly. Let A be an $\mathcal{H}_{C_n}$-compatible set. Let w be the minimum of $w_V(\alpha)$ for $\alpha \in A$, where V is the vertex set of C_n. Thus, because of Lemma 3, either $w(\alpha) = w$ or $w(\alpha) = w + 1$ for each $\alpha \in A$.

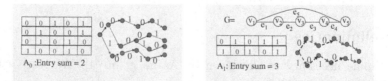

Fig. 1. A compatible set for C_5

Let $A_0 = \{\alpha \in A | w(\alpha) = w\}$ and $A_1 = \{\alpha \in A | w(\alpha) = w + 1\}$. A_0 and A_1 are sets of binary arrays, and each of which can be represented by a tree (Figure 1).

An ordered pair of edges (e_i, e_j) of C_n is called a *binding* pair if the path **P** between the end vertex v_{i+1} of e_i and the starting vertex v_j of e_j has the properties that (1) $w_\mathbf{P}(\alpha)$ has a same value for all $\alpha \in A_0$ and (2) $w_\mathbf{P}(\alpha)$ has a same value for all $\alpha \in A_1$. We can easily see that (e_j, e_i) is binding if (e_i, e_j) is binding, and (e_i, e_k) is binding if both (e_i, e_j) and (e_j, e_k) are binding ;thus, the set of binding pairs gives an equivalence relation on the edge set E of C_n. Let $r(A)$ be the number of equivalence classes of the above relation in E. In Figure 1, (e_1, e_3) is the only binding pair, and hence $r(A) = 5 - 1 = 4$.

Lemma 5. $|A| \le r(A) + 1$.

Proof This lemma is given by modifying the argument of Asano *et al.* [1]. We omit details.   □

We investigate basic structure of an $\mathcal{H}_{C_n}$-compatible set. Let $V_k = \{v_1, v_2, \ldots, v_k\}$, and let $A(V_k)$ be the set of prefixes of A on V_k (i.e., restrictions of roundings to V_k). Similarly, we define $A_0(V_k)$ and $A_1(V_k)$ to be the set of prefixes of A_0 and A_1 on V_k. We set $V_0 = \emptyset$, and $A(V_0) = \{\emptyset\}$; thus, $|A(V_0)| = 1$. Note that a prefix in $A(V_k)$ need not be a global rounding of the spanning subgraph G_k of V_k in the cycle C_n, since the shortest path in G_k between a pair of vertices may be different from that in G between the same pair. Also, a global rounding of G_k is not always in $A(V_k)$.

A prefix $\alpha \in A(V_k)$ is called *double* if $\alpha \in A_0(V_k) \cap A_1(V_k)$. It is called *large* and *small* if $\alpha \in A_1(V_k) \setminus A_0(V_k)$ and $\alpha \in A_0(V_k) \setminus A_1(V_k)$, respectively.

We form a tree T (Figure 2) of depth n each of whose node $v(\alpha)$ correspond to a prefix α of a global rounding: Precisely speaking, its root corresponds to the unique element $\emptyset$ in $A(V_0)$, and a depth k node corresponds to an element in $A(V_k)$. A node $v(\alpha)$ corresponding to $\alpha \in A(V_k)$ is a son of $v(\beta)$ $(\beta \in A(V_{k-1}))$ if β is the prefix of α of length $k - 1$. Clearly, T is a binary tree.

If $v(\alpha)$ is a branching node in T, we call α a branching prefix; In other words, α is a branching prefix if and only if both $\alpha \oplus 0$ and $\alpha \oplus 1$ are prefixes of global roundings. If one branch is large and the other is small, we say that the branching node (and prefix) *split*. If one of the branches is double, we say the branching prefix *multiple*. Other branching prefixes are called *normal*.

By definition, T has $|A(V_n)| \le \mu(\mathcal{H}_{C_n}) = n + 1$ leaves, and hence it has at most n branching nodes. Thus, there are at most n branching prefixes for the $\mathcal{H}_{C_n}$ compatible set A.

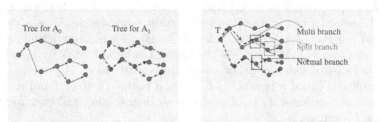

Fig. 2. Three kinds of branching nodes in the tree T

4   Outerplanar Graph

A graph G is an outerplanar graph if and only if it has a planar embedding where all of its vertices lie on the boundary of its outer face. Since series connection has been already considered, we can assume that G is 2-connected. Thus, every edge is either on the cycle C bounding the outer face or a chord of the cycle.

We can assume that every edge e is the shortest path between its endpoints in G; otherwise, we can simply remove it from our consideration. Furthermore, we can assume that e is the unique shortest path between its endpoints. Indeed, if there is another shortest path in G, adding e makes the condition of the global rounding more strict, and hence does not increase the number of global roundings.

Suppose we are given an outerplanar graph G and consider an $\mathcal{H}_G$-compatible set Γ. A face cycle X of G consisting of a part of C and a chord edge e is called an *ear*. Let Y be the graph removing all vertices and edges of X from G except $e = (x, y)$ and its endpoint. Thus, $V(X) \cap V(Y) = \{x, y\}$. Clearly, Y is an outerplanar graph.

Let $n = |V(X)|$. It suffices to prove that $\mu(G) \le \mu(Y) + n - 2$, since by induction we can show that $\mu(G) \le |V(G)| + 1$ from that.

For improving readability, we first give a weaker result that $\mu(G) \le \mu(Y) + 2(n-2)$, from which we can obtain $\mu(G) \le 2|V(G)| + 1$.

Lemma 6. *Given $\gamma \in \Gamma$, consider its restricted assignments γ_X and γ_Y to X and Y, respectively. Then, $A = \{\gamma_X | \gamma \in \Gamma\}$ and $B = \{\gamma_Y | \gamma \in \Gamma\}$ are $\mathcal{H}_X$-compatible and $\mathcal{H}_Y$-compatible sets, respectively.*

Proof For any two vertices u and v in Y, the shortest path $\mathbf{p}$ between u and v in G must be in Y, since otherwise $\mathbf{p}$ contains a path (which is not e) between x and y in X, and we can reduce the length by replacing it with e. Thus, B is a compatible set. Similarly, we can prove that A is a compatible set.   □

If α and β are binary assignments on X and Y respectively such that α and β have the same value at each of x and y, they define a binary assignment on G, denoted by $\alpha \odot \beta$. The previous lemma implies that an element in Γ is always written as $\alpha \odot \beta$ for $\alpha \in A$ and $\beta \in B$.

We consider prefixes of elements of A if we set $V_i = \{v_1, v_2, \ldots, v_i\}$, where $v_1 = x$ and $v_2 = y$. We often call them A-prefixes. We also consider $\alpha \odot \beta$ for an A-prefix α a member β of B.

Let $\Gamma_0 = \{\alpha \odot \beta \in \Gamma | \alpha \in A_0\}$ and $\Gamma_1 = \{\alpha \odot \beta \in \Gamma | \alpha \in A_1\}$, where A_0 and A_1 are the sets defined in the previous section (considering X as a cycle). An assignment $\alpha \odot \beta$ on $V_i \cup V(Y)$ is called a Γ-prefix if it is a restriction of a global rounding of G on $V_i \cup V(Y)$. G_i is the induced subgraph of G by $V_i \cup V(Y)$. A Γ-prefix is called *double, large,* or *small* analogously to an A-prefix.

A Γ-prefix is called a *branching* Γ-prefix if both $(\alpha \oplus 0) \odot \beta$ and $(\alpha \oplus 1) \odot \beta$ are Γ-prefixes. Analogously to A-prefixes, we define *split, multiple,* and *normal* branching Γ-prefixes.

Lemma 7. *Given a branching A-prefix α of length $k \ge 2$, there is at most one $\beta \in B$ such that $\alpha \odot \beta$ is a normal (or multiple) branching Γ-prefix.*

Proof   It suffices to consider normal branching Γ-prefixes, since multiple branching Γ-prefixes are easier to handle. Suppose that both β and β' give normal branching Γ-prefixes combined with α, and let q be one of nearest nodes from v_{k+1} in Y such that $\beta(q) \neq \beta(q')$. Let $\delta_1 = (\alpha \oplus 0) \odot \beta$, $\delta_2 = (\alpha \oplus 1) \odot \beta$, $\delta_3 = (\alpha \oplus 0) \odot \beta'$, and $\delta_4 = (\alpha \oplus 1) \odot \beta'$. Let $\gamma_i \in \Gamma$ has δ_i as its prefix ($i = 1, 2, 3, 4$). Without loss of generality, we assume that δ_1 and δ_2 are small. If δ_3 and δ_4 are large, comparing δ_2 and δ_3, the path $v_{k+2}, v_{k+3}, \ldots, v_n$ cannot be a shortest path. Thus, the shortest path between q and v_{k+1} must be in G_i, and we derive contradiction from the argument given in the proof of Lemma 2.

We thus can assume that δ_3 and δ_4 are small. By symmetry, we can assume that $\beta(q) = 0$ and $\beta(q') = 1$. If the shortest path **P** between v_{k+1} and q contains $v_2, \ldots, v_{k+1}$, we can see that $\gamma_4(\mathbf{P}) - \gamma_1(\mathbf{P}) = 2$ to have a contradiction. For the other case, we consider the shortest path $\mathbf{P}'$ from v_{k+2} to q, and can see that $\gamma_3(\mathbf{P}') - \gamma_2(\mathbf{P}') = 2$.   □

Henceforce, we omit proofs of lemmas analogous to the above one to save space.

Lemma 8. *Given a branching A-prefix α of length $k \geq 2$, there is at most one β such that $\alpha \odot \beta$ is a split (or multiple) branching Γ-prefix.*

Corollary 1. $\mu(G) \leq \mu(Y) + 2(n - 2)$

Proof   For each branching A-prefix, we have shown that there are at most two (one normal and one split) branching Γ-prefixes. This, together with Lemma 5, gives the corollary (we omit details).   □

Now, consider the situation that α is an A-prefix of length k and there are $\beta \neq \beta'$ such that $\alpha \odot \beta$ is a normal Γ-branching and simultaneously that $\alpha \odot \beta'$ is a split Γ-branching. Without loss of generality, we can assume that both $(\alpha \oplus 0) \odot \beta$, $(\alpha \oplus 1) \odot \beta$ are small. We can also assume that $(\alpha \oplus 0) \odot \beta'$ is small and $(\alpha \oplus 1) \odot \beta'$ is large, since it is easy to show that the other case cannot happen. Let γ and γ' are members of Γ obtained by extending $(\alpha \oplus 1) \odot \beta$ and $(\alpha \oplus 1) \odot \beta'$. Let K be the largest index such that $\gamma(v_K) = \gamma'(v_K)$. Since γ is small and γ' is large, $K \neq n$. Let $\tilde{\alpha}$ be the corresponding A-prefix of length K. Then, $\tilde{\alpha}$ gives a split A-branching in T.

Lemma 9. *In the above situation, there is no β'' such that $\tilde{\alpha} \odot \beta''$ is a split branching Γ-prefix.*

Theorem 3. $\mu(G) \leq \mu(Y) + n - 2$.

Proof   An A-prefix α is extended to a split branching Γ-prefix $\alpha \odot \beta$ only if α gives a split or multiple branching node in the prefix tree T of A. On the other hand, α is extended to a normal/multiple branching Γ-prefix only if α gives a non-split (i.e. normal or multiple) branching node in T.

By definition, a multiple branching node in T must have a split branching node as its descendent. Consider any path **P** from a leaf to the root in T. The previous lemma means that among all α corresponding to the nodes of the path **P** at most one α corresponds to a split branching Γ-prefix. Thus, the number of split branching Γ-prefixes is bounded by the number of split branching nodes of T. On the other hand, the number of normal or multiple branching Γ-prefixes is bounded by the number of non-split branching nodes. Thus, the total number of branching Γ-prefixes is bounded by the number of branching nodes of T. $\square$

Thus, we conclude that $\mu(G) \le |V(G)| + 1$ if G is an outerplanar graph.

4.1   Algorithm for Enumerating Global Roundings

Since the number of global roundings of an outerplanar graph G is bounded by $n + 1$, we have hope to enumerate all of them in polynomial time. Indeed, the proof in the previous section leads us to such an algorithm.

Theorem 4. *The set Γ of all global roundings of an input assignment **a** for an outerplanar graph G can be computed in $O(n^3)$ time.*

Proof   Let $|X| = n_0$ and $|Y| = n_1 = n - n_0 + 2$. Given a Γ-prefix $\alpha \odot \beta$ on $V_i \cup V(Y)$, we want to check its extensions $(\alpha \oplus 0) \odot \beta$ and $(\alpha \oplus 1) \odot \beta$ whether they are extendable to members of Γ or not.

It is expensive to check the extendibility exactly, since there are exponential number of possible extensions. Instead, we check whether they satisfy the global rounding conditions for the shortest paths between pairs of nodes in $V_i \cup V(Y)$ for each case where it is small or large (i.e., the node sum on X is w or $w + 1$). Note that the shortest paths may go through vertices in $V \setminus (V_i \cup V(Y))$ A prefix is called a *weak Γ-prefix* if it satisfies this check. From our argument in the previous section, the number of weak Γ prefixes on $V_i \cup V(Y)$ is at most $|Y| + 2(n_0 - 2)$ for each i, and a weak Γ-prefix of $V_{n-1} \cup V(Y)$ is a global rounding of G by definition.

The check is done as follows. We first compute the shortest path tree T_v from $v = v_{i+1}$ in G, and then check for each extension of weak Γ-prefix using paths in the shortest path tree. The sum of entries on a path of T_v can be queried in $O(1)$ time after $O(n)$ time preprocessing. Thus, the set of global roundings of G can be computed in $O(n^2 n_0)$ time from that of Y. This gives the time complexity. $\square$

5   Concluding Remarks

Although the main focus of this paper is theory, our enumeration algorithm for the outerplanar graph has a potential application to digital halftoning if we consider a graph whose nodes are pixels of a digital plane. Naturally, we have the following two drawbacks: (1) it may happen that no global rounding exists (2) the high time complexity prevent us to execute the algorithm on a digital image (for example if $n = 1024 \times 1024$). (1) can be avoided by restricting the length of shortest paths and make a graph giving the global roundings following the idea for generating global roundings of $\mathcal{I}_{k,n}$ given in [9,10]. (2) is serious, and it will be nice if we can reduce the time complexity.

For a general graph, it is an open question whether $\nu(\mathcal{H}_G)$ is polynomially bounded by the number of vertices. Another interesting question is how small hypergraph attains $\mu(\mathcal{H}) = n+1$. We only know a naive bound that $\mathcal{H}$ must have $\Omega(\frac{n}{\log n})$ hyperedges, although we suspect that $n(n-1)/2$ is the true answer.

References

1. T. Asano, N. Katoh, H. Tamaki, and T. Tokuyama, The Structure and Number of Global Roundings of a Graph, to appear in Proceedings of COCOON03.
2. T. Asano, N. Katoh, K. Obokata, and T. Tokuyama, Matrix Rounding under the L_p-Discrepancy Measure and Its Application to Digital Halftoning, *Proc. 13th ACM-SIAM SODA* (2002) pp. 896–904.
3. T. Asano, T. Matsui, and T. Tokuyama, Optimal Roundings of Sequences and Matrices, *Nordic Journal of Computing* 7 (2000) pp. 241–256. (Preliminary version in SWAT00).
4. T. Asano and T. Tokuyama, How to Color a Checkerboard with a Given Distribution – Matrix Rounding Achieving Low 2 × 2 Discrepancy, *Proc. 12th ISAAC, LNCS 2223*(2001) pp. 636–648.
5. J. Beck and V. T. Sós, *Discrepancy Theory*, in *Handbook of Combinatorics Volume II* (ed. T. Graham, M. Grötshel, and L. Lovász) 1995, Elsevier.
6. B. Doerr, Lattice Approximation and Linear Discrepancy of Totally Unimodular Matrices, *Proc. 12th ACM-SIAM SODA* (2001) pp. 119–125.
7. J. Matoušek, *Geometric Discrepancy*, Algorithms and Combinatorics 18, Springer Verlag 1999.
8. V. Rödl and P. Winkler, Concerning a Matrix Approximation Problem, *Crux Mathmaticorum* 1990, pp. 76–79.
9. K. Sadakane, N. Takki-Chebihi, and T. Tokuyama, Combinatorics and Algorithms on Low-Discrepancy Roundings of a Real Sequence, *Proc. 28th ICALP, LNCS 2076* (2001) pp. 166–177.
10. K. Sadakane, N. Takki-Chebihi, and T. Tokuyama, Discrepancy-Based Digital Halftoning: Automatic Evaluation and Optimization, *Interdisciplinary Information Sciences*, 8 (2002) pp. 219–234.

Augmenting Forests to Meet Odd Diameter Requirements

Toshimasa Ishii[1], Shigeyuki Yamamoto[2], and Hiroshi Nagamochi[1]

[1] Department of Information and Computer Sciences
Toyohashi University of Technology,
Aichi 441-8580, Japan
{ishii,naga}@ics.tut.ac.jp
[2] I FOR COM Co.,Ltd.,
Kanagawa 220-0207, Japan

Abstract. Given a graph $G = (V, E)$ and an integer $D \geq 1$, we consider the problem of augmenting G by the smallest number of new edges so that the diameter becomes at most D. It is known that no constant approximation algorithms to this problem with an arbitrary graph G can be obtained unless $P = NP$. For a forest G and an odd $D \geq 3$, it was open whether the problem is approximable within a constant factor. In this paper, we give the first constant factor approximation algorithm to the problem with a forest G and an odd D; our algorithm delivers an 8-approximate solution in $O(|V|^3)$ time. We also show that a 4-approximate solution to the problem with a forest G and an odd D can be obtained in linear time if an augmented graph is additionally required to be biconnected.

1 Introduction

In communication networks, some transfer delay occurs when we send a message from one node to another node. The least number of links through which the message has to be transmitted is considered as one measurement of such a transfer delay. Therefore, it is desirable that a network has a small diameter, which is defined as the maximum distance between every two nodes in the network. As one of network design problems, the problems of constructing a graph with a small diameter by adding new edges to an initial graph have been studied [1, 5,6,8,12,14]. Among these, there is an application to airplane flights scheduling [6].

Given an undirected graph $G = (V, E)$ and a nonnegative integer D, the *augmentation problem with diameter requirements* (for short, *APD*) asks to augment G by adding the smallest number of new edges that reduces the diameter to at most D. Note that the case of $D = 1$ is trivial, because only the complete graph can have diameter one. In general, Schoone et al. [14] have showed that APD is NP-hard for any fixed $D \geq 3$. Moreover, it has been shown that there is no constant approximation algorithm to APD unless P=NP, by a reduction from DOMINATING SET due to Li et al. [12] for $D \geq 4$, and by a reduction

T. Ibaraki, N. Katoh, and H. Ono (Eds.): ISAAC 2003, LNCS 2906, pp. 434–443, 2003.

from SET COVER due to Dodis and Khanna [7] for $D \in \{2,3\}$. The same results have been shown by Chepoi and Vaxes [5]. Let $OPT_A(G, D)$ denote the optimal value to APD with a graph G and an integer D. Alon et al. [1] have showed that $OPT_A(G, 2) = n - \Delta - 1$ and $OPT_A(G, 3) \geq n - O(\Delta^3)$ hold for any graph G with the maximum degree Δ and a sufficiently large number $n = |V|$ of vertices and that $OPT_A(G, D) \leq n/\lfloor D/2 \rfloor$ holds for any connected graph G. Also for APD with some restricted classes of graphs, several problems have been studied. Erdős et al. [8] have investigated upper and lower bounds on the optimal value to APD in the case where a given graph and an augmented graph are restricted to be triangle-free. Alon et al. [1] have proved that $OPT_A(C_n, D) = n/(2\lfloor D/2 \rfloor - 1) - O(1)$ holds for any cycle C_n of n vertices. Recently Chepoi and Vaxes [5] have showed a 2-approximation algorithm to APD with a forest and an even integer D. They have also proved that their algorithm can be applied to a wider class of graphs G satisfying the following conditions (i) and (ii). (i) G is a Helly graph (see [2] for the definition). (ii) There exists a polynomial time algorithm to the k-DOMINATING SET with G, the problem of finding a smallest set X of vertices such that the distance from each vertex to some vertex in X is at most k. Forests and dually chordal graphs (see [3] for the definition) are included in such a class of graphs. However, it was left open whether APD with an odd diameter is approximable by a constant factor or not, even if G is a forest, while it is also left open whether APD with a forest is NP-hard or not.

As a related problem, we consider APD with an additional requirement that the resulting augmented graph is a biconnected graph, i.e., it has at least two vertex-disjoint paths between every two vertices. This problem is called the *biconnectivity augmentation problem with diameter requirements* (for short, *BAPD*). In communication networks, a graph connectivity can be considered as a fundamental measure of its robustness. Eswaran and Tarjan[9] have shown that the problem of augmenting an initial graph up to biconnectivity can be solved in linear time. For graph connectivities augmentation problems, many problems and algorithms have been studied (see [10,13] for surveys). Chepoi and Vaxes [5] have proved that BAPD is NP-hard even if G is a tree. Let us call a solution (a, b)-approximate solution if the number of edges in the solution is at most b surplus edges over a times the optimal, and an algorithm that delivers such a solution an (a, b)-approximation algorithm. Chepoi and Vaxes [5] have also given a 3-approximation algorithm for an even integer D [5], and a $(7, 3)$-approximation (resp., $(9, 4)$-approximation) algorithm for an odd $D \geq 5$ (resp., $D = 3$) [4], in the case where G is a forest.

In this paper, we consider designing an approximation algorithm to APD and BAPD, in the case where an initial graph G is a forest and D is an odd integer. We partly follow Chepoi and Vaxes' approaches [5] to obtain a 2-approximate solution to APD with forest G and the even integer $D - 1$, which is a relaxation of the original problem instance (G, D). Unfortunately, it is not difficult to see that $OPT_A(G, D - 1)/OPT_A(G, D)$ cannot be bounded from above by any constant. We establish a new lower bound on the optimal value to APD with an odd D. With the 2-approximate solution to the even $D + 1$ and the new lower bound on $OPT_A(G, D)$, we prove that an 8-approximate solution to APD can be constructed in $O(|V|^3)$ time. For BAPD, we propose an $O(|V|)$ time $(4, 2)$-approximation (resp., $(6, 3)$-approximation) algorithm for an odd $D \geq 5$ (resp., $D = 3$). Some of proofs will be omitted from this extended abstract.

2   Preliminaries

Let $G = (V, E)$ stand for an undirected simple graph with a set V of *vertices* and a set E of *edges*. An edge with end vertices u and v is denoted by (u, v). We denote $|V|$ by n and $|E|$ by m. A singleton set $\{x\}$ may be simply written as x, and " $\subset$ " implies proper inclusion while " $\subseteq$ " means " $\subset$ " or " $=$ ". In $G = (V, E)$, its vertex set V and edge set E may be denoted by $V(G)$ and $E(G)$, respectively. For an edge set E' with $E' \cap E = \emptyset$, we denote the augmented graph $(V, E \cup E')$ by $G + E'$. For an edge set E', we denote by $V[E']$ a set of all end vertices of edges in E'. For a vertex set $X \subset V$ in a graph G, we denote by $N_G(X)$ a set of vertices in $V - X$ adjacent to some vertex $v \in X$.

The *length of a path* P is defined by the number of edges in P and is denoted as $|P|$ (i.e., $|P| = |E(P)|$). For two vertices $u, v \in V$ in $G = (V, E)$, the *distance between u and v* is defined as the length of a path between u and v with the shortest length, and it is denoted by $d_G(u, v)$. The *diameter of a graph* G, denoted by $diam(G)$, is defined as the maximum among distances between all pairs of two vertices in G.

A *forest* is a graph with no cycle. For a forest $G = (V, E)$, a vertex $v \in V$ with degree 1 or 0 is called a *leaf*, and we denote a set of all leaves in G by $L(G)$. A graph $G = (V, E)$ with $|V| \geq k + 1$ is called *k-vertex-connected*, if the deletion of any vertex set X with $|X| \leq k - 1$ leaves a connected graph. The *vertex-connectivity* of G, denoted by $\kappa(G)$, is defined as the largest integer k for which G is k-vertex-connected.

In this paper, we consider the following two problems.

Problem 1. Augmentation Problem with Diameter Requirements (APD)
Input: A graph $G = (V, E)$ and a nonnegative integer D.
Output: A set E^* of new edges with the minimum cardinality such that $diam(G + E^*) \leq D$ holds.   □

Problem 2. Biconnectivity Augmentation Problem with Diameter Requirements (BAPD)
Input: A graph $G = (V, E)$ with $|V| \geq 3$ and a nonnegative integer D.
Output: A set E^* of new edges with the minimum cardinality such that $diam(G + E^*) \leq D$ and $\kappa(G + E^*) \geq 2$ hold.   □

Let $OPT_A(G, D)$ and $OPT_B(G, D)$ denote the optimal value to APD and BAPD with G and an integer D, respectively. For these problems, we show the following two theorems.

Theorem 1. *If G is a forest and D is an odd integer, then an 8-approximate feasible solution to APD can be found in $O(n^3)$ time.* □

Theorem 2. *Let G be a forest. Then a $(4,2)$-approximate $((6,3)$-approximate) feasible solution to BAPD can be found in $O(n)$ time if D is an odd ≥ 5 (resp., $D = 3$ holds).* □

3   APD with a Forest

In this section, let $G = (V, E)$ be a forest and $D = 2R + 1$ be an odd integer with $R \geq 1$. We show that APD is 8-approximable in $O(n^3)$ time in the case where G is a forest and D is an odd integer.

Let $P_{u,v}$ denote a path between two vertices u and v in G (note that $P_{u,v}$ is uniquely determined if G is a forest). We first find a 2-approximate solution E_1 to APD with the forest G and the even $D' = D + 1$ by Chepoi and Vaxes' algorithm [5]. Note that $|E_1|/2$ is a lower bound on $OPT_A(G, D)$ since we have $OPT_A(G, D) \geq OPT_A(G, D+1) \geq |E_1|/2$. We then construct an 8-approximate solution to APD with G and D based on E_1. In this section, we first review Chepoi and Vaxes' algorithm [5] in Section 3.1, analyze properties of solutions by their algorithm, derive another lower bound on $OPT_A(G, D)$, and finally propose an 8-approximation algorithm based on these analyses in Section 3.2.

3.1   Even Diameters

For a vertex $u \in V$ in a graph G and an integer k, let $N_G^k(u)$ denote a set of vertices v with $d_G(u, v) = k$. A set $B_G(u, k) = \bigcup_{k' \leq k} N_G^{k'}(u)$ of vertices is called the *ball centered u of radius k*. $B_G(u, k)$ may be simply called an (k)-*ball (with a center u)*. For a subset $V' \subseteq V$ of vertices and a family $\mathcal{B}$ of balls, we say that $\mathcal{B}$ *covers* V' if any vertex in V' is contained in some ball in $\mathcal{B}$.

The following algorithm EVEN-APD is a 2-approximation algorithm to APD with a forest G and an even D' by Chepoi and Vaxes [5].

Algorithm EVEN-APD(G, D')
Input: A forest $G = (V, E)$ and an even integer $D' \geq 2$.
Output: A new edge set E_1 with $diam(G + E_1) \leq D'$ and $|E_1| \leq 2OPT_A(G, D')$.
Step 1: Let $R = \frac{D'-2}{2}$. Choose a center $c^* \in V$ for an $(R + 1)$-ball and a set C_1 of centers for (R)-balls so that a family of these $|C_1| + 1$ balls covers V in G and the number $|C_1| + 1$ of centers is minimized. Halt after outputting a set $E_1 = \{(c^*, c) \mid c \in C_1\}$ of new edges. □

Theorem 3. *[5] An edge set E_1 obtained by algorithm EVEN-APD(G, D') satisfies $|E_1| \leq 2OPT_A(G, D')$, and can be found in $O(nm)$ time.* □

Let $C_2 = N_G(c^*)$. The following lemma holds from the construction of E_1.

Lemma 1. (i) $|C_1| = |E_1| \leq 2OPT_A(G, 2R+2) \leq 2OPT_A(G, 2R+1)$ holds.
(ii) The family of (R)-balls with centers in $C_1 \cup C_2$ covers V.
(iii) In $G + E_1$, every vertex $v \in V$ satisfies $d_{G+E_1}(c^*, v) \leq R+1$.
(iv) Every two vertices $u_1, u_2 \in V$ with $d_{G+E_1}(u_1, u_2) > 2R+1$ satisfy $d_{G+E_1}(u_1, u_2) = 2R+2$ and $d_{G+E_1}(c^*, u_1) = d_{G+E_1}(c^*, u_2) = R+1$; such a vertex u_i satisfies $d_G(u_i, c) = R$ for some $c \in C_1 \cup C_2$. □

3.2   Odd Diameters

For a set X of vertices in a forest G, two vertices x_1 and x_2 in V are called *adjacent with respect to* X if the path P_{x_1, x_2} does not contain any vertex in $X - \{x_1, x_2\}$.

In this section, we propose an algorithm, named ODD-APD(G, D), for constructing a solution to APD with an odd diameter $D = 2R+1$. This algorithm consists of the following three steps. In the first step, we compute a center c^*, a set C_1 of centers and the set $C_2 = N_G(c^*)$ in Lemma 1, and augment G by the new edge set $E_1 = \{(c^*, v) \mid v \in C_1\}$. In $G + E_1$, there may be a vertex $u \in V$ such that $d_{G+E_1}(u, u') > 2R+1$ for some other vertex u'. We call such a vertex u *distant*. By Lemma 1(iv), we see that $d_G(u, u') = 2R+2$ holds. Thus, to make the diameter at most $D = 2R+1$, it suffices to decrease by at least one the distance between those vertices in the second and third steps. In the second step, we compute a set C_3 by choosing at most $2|C_1|$ vertices from $N_G(C_1 \cup C_2)$ and augment $G + E_1$ by the new edge set $E_2 = \{(c^*, v) \mid v \in C_3\}$, by which $d_{G+(E_1 \cup E_2)}(c^*, v) \leq R$ holds for some distant vertex v in $G + E_1$. In the third step, we augment $G + (E_1 \cup E_2)$ by a new edge set E_3 with $|E_3| \leq 2OPT_A(G, D)$ so that every distant vertex u in $G + E_1$ now satisfies $d_{G+(E_1 \cup E_2)}(u, u') \leq 2R+1$ for all vertices $u' \in V$.

More precisely, algorithm ODD-APD(G, D) is described as follows, where E_3 in Step 3 is constructed based on our new lower bound on $OPT_A(G, D)$, and how to choose such E_3 will be described after verifying Step 2.

Algorithm ODD-APD(G, D)
Input: A forest $G = (V, E)$ and an odd integer $D \geq 3$.
Output: An edge set E^* with $diam(G + E^*) \leq D$ and $|E^*| \leq 8OPT_A(G, D)$.
Step 1: Let $R = \frac{D-1}{2}$. Compute a center c^*, a set C_1 of centers, the set $C_2 = N_G(c^*)$ and an edge set E_1 that satisfy Lemma 1.
Step 2: Regard each component G^ℓ of G as a rooted tree by choosing its root c^ℓ as c^* if $c^* \in V(G^\ell)$ and as an arbitrary vertex in $C_1 \cap V(G^\ell)$ otherwise. For each vertex $c \in C_1$, let $Q_c = N_G(\{c, p\}) \cap V(P_{c,p})$ for the nearest ancestor $p \in C_1 \cup C_2 \cup \{c^*\}$ of c in the rooted tree G^ℓ containing c. Let $C_3 = \bigcup_{c \in C_1} Q_c$ and $E_2 = \{(c^*, v) \mid v \in C_3\}$.
Step 3: Compute a set E_3 of edges such that $|E_3| \leq 2OPT_A(G, D)$ and $d_{G+E_3}(u, v) \leq 2R+1$ holds for every two vertices $u, v \in V$ with $d_{G+(E_1 \cup E_2)}(u, v) > 2R+1$. Halt after outputting $E^* = E_1 \cup E_2 \cup E_3$. □

We first prove the correctness of algorithm ODD-APD(G, D) under the assumption that Step 3 works correctly. Let Z denote a set of all distant vertices

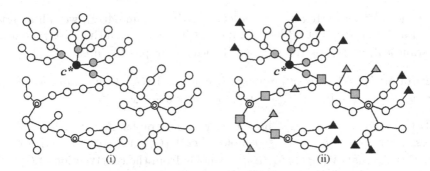

Fig. 1. (i) Illustration of a tree G, a vertex c^* and sets C_1 and C_2 of vertices obtained by applying Step 1 of algorithm ODD-APD$(G, 7)$ to G, where each vertex in C_1 (resp., C_2) is drawn by a double circle (resp., a shaded circle). (ii) Illustration of distant vertices and a set C_3 of vertices, where each distant vertex in Z_1 (resp., Z_2) is drawn by a black (resp., shaded) triangle, and each vertex in C_3 is drawn by a shaded square.

in $G + E_1$ (see Fig. 1 where $D = 7$). Let Z_1 be a set of distant vertices $u \in Z$ such that u has only one vertex in $C_1 \cup C_2$ that is adjacent to u with respect to $C_1 \cup C_2$ in G. Let $Z_2 = Z - Z_1$. For Q_c obtained in Step 2, we have $|Q_c| \leq 2$ for each $c \in C_1$ and $C_3 \subseteq \bigcup_{c \in C_1 \cup C_2} N_G(c)$, and hence we see that the following properties hold.

Lemma 2. (i) $|C_3| \leq 2|C_1|$ holds. (ii) Every distant vertex $u \in Z_2$ satisfies $d_{G+(E_1 \cup E_2)}(u, u') \leq 2R + 1$ for any vertex $u' \in V$.   □

By Lemmas 1(i) and 2(i), we have $|E_1 \cup E_2| \leq 3|C_1| \leq 6OPT_A(G, D)$.

Lemma 3. Assume that such an edge set E_3 in Step 3 can be found. Then an edge set E^* obtained by algorithm ODD-APD(G, D) satisfies $diam(G+E^*) \leq D$ and $|E^*| \leq 8OPT_A(G, D)$.   □

In the rest of this section, we show how to find E_3 in Step 3 of algorithm ODD-APD(G, D). In order to clarify distant vertices in Z_1, we divide G into subgraphs G_i corresponding to $c_i \in C_1 \cup C_2$ in the following manner. Let G_i be a component containing $c_i \in C_1 \cup C_2$ in G' which is obtained from G by removing a set $C_3 \cup \{c^*\}$ of vertices and a set $\{(c, c') \in E \mid c, c' \in C_1 \cup C_2\}$ of edges (see Fig. 2(i)). Then the following properties hold.

Lemma 4. (i) $V(G_i) \cap (C_1 \cup C_2) = \{c_i\}$ holds.
(ii) A vertex $u \in V - (C_1 \cup C_2)$ is contained in G_i if and only if c_i is the only vertex in $C_1 \cup C_2$ that is adjacent to u with respect to $C_1 \cup C_2$.
(iii) Every vertex $v \in V(G_i)$ satisfies $d_G(c_i, v) \leq R$. Moreover, each vertex $v \in V(G_i)$ with $d_G(c_i, v) = R$ is a leaf also in G.
(iv) Every distant vertex $v \in Z_1$ is contained in some G_i, and it is a leaf in G with $d_G(c_i, v) = R$.   □

Since each distant vertex in Z_1 is a leaf in G by Lemma 4(iv), we call a vertex $v \in Z_1$ a *distant leaf*. Let G_i^j be a component in $G_i - c_i$ such that $V(G_i^j)$ contains a distant leaf, and g_i be the number of such subgraphs G_i^j in G_i.

Lemma 5. *Let G_i^j be a subgraph of G_i and $v \in V(G_i^j)$ be a distant leaf in G_i. For any vertex $x \in V - V(G_i^j) - \{c_i\}$, we have $d_G(v,x) > R$.*   □

Let $\mathcal{G} = \{G_1, G_2, \ldots, G_t\}$ be a family of subgraphs G_i which have distant leaves, where $g_1 \geq g_2 \geq \cdots \geq g_t$ holds. Let $V(G_i^j) \cap N_G(c_i) = \{a_i^j\}$ for each $G_i \in \mathcal{G}$ (note that $|V(G_i^j) \cap N_G(c_i)| = 1$ holds from the construction of G_i^j). We here derive a lower bound on $OPT_A(G, 2R+1)$. Let

$$f_1(i,j) = |\{(c_i, c_j)\} - E| + \left\lceil \frac{1}{2} \sum_{\ell \in \{1,2,\ldots,t\}-\{i,j\}} g_\ell \right\rceil, 1 \leq i < j \leq t,$$

$$f_2(i,j,k) = |\{(c_i, c_j), (c_j, c_k), (c_k, c_i)\} - E| + \left\lceil \frac{1}{2} \sum_{\ell \in \{1,2,\ldots,t\}-\{i,j,k\}} g_\ell \right\rceil,$$

$$1 \leq i < j < k \leq t,$$

$$f_3(r) = \frac{r^2}{2} - \frac{3r}{2} + 1 + \left\lceil \frac{1}{2} \sum_{r+1 \leq \ell \leq t} g_\ell \right\rceil, 1 \leq r \leq t.$$

Lemma 6. $OPT_A(G, 2R+1) \geq f(G)$ *holds, where*

$$f(G) = \min\{\min_{1 \leq i < j \leq t} f_1(i,j), \min_{1 \leq i < j < k \leq t} f_2(i,j,k), \min_{r \in \{1,2,\ldots,t\}-\{2,3\}} f_3(r)\}. \quad (1)$$

Proof. Omitted.   □

The following lemma shows that we can find an edge set E_3 with $|E_3| \leq 2f(G)$ and $d_{G+E_3}(u,v) \leq 2R+1$ for every two distant leaves u and v (see Fig. 2(ii)).

Lemma 7. *For an edge set E_3 chosen according to the following (i)–(iii), we have $|E_3| \leq 2f(G)$ and $d_{G+E_3}(u,v) \leq 2R+1$ for every two distant leaves u, v.*
(i) If $f(G) = f_1(i,j)$ holds for some $1 \leq i < j \leq t$, then let $E_3 = \{(c_i, c_j) \notin E\} \cup \{(c_i, a_\ell^h) \mid i \neq \ell \neq j, 1 \leq h \leq g_\ell\}$.
(ii) If $f(G) = f_2(i,j,k)$ holds for some $1 \leq i < j < k \leq t$, then let $E_3 = (\{(c_i, c_j), (c_j, c_k), (c_k, c_i)\} - E) \cup \{(c_i, a_\ell^h) \mid \ell \notin \{i,j,k\}, 1 \leq h \leq g_\ell\}$.
(iii) If $f(G) = f_3(r)$ holds for $r = 1$ or some $4 \leq r \leq t$, then let $E_3 = \{(c_i, c_j) \notin E \mid 1 \leq i < j \leq r\} \cup \{(c_1, a_\ell^h) \mid r+1 \leq \ell \leq t, 1 \leq h \leq g_\ell\}$.   □

The procedure of Step 3 is described as follows.

Step 3: Let G' be the forest obtained from G by removing a set $C_3 \cup \{c^*\}$ of vertices and a set $\{(c, c') \in E \mid c, c' \in C_1 \cup C_2\}$ of edges. Let G_i, $i = 1, 2, \ldots, t$ be a component containing $c_i \in C_1 \cup C_2$ and $N_{G_i}^R(c_i) \neq \emptyset$. Compute a lower bound

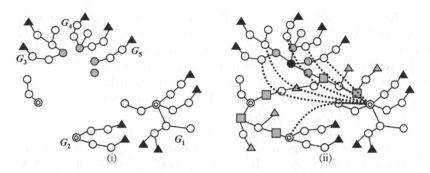

Fig. 2. (i) Illustration of components in G' having a center in $C_1 \cup C_2$, and $\mathcal{G} = \{G_1, G_2, \ldots, G_5\}$, which are obtained from G in Fig. 1, where $g_1 = 3$, $g_2 = g_3 = g_4 = 2$, and $g_5 = 1$ hold. (ii) Illustration of a set E_3 of broken edges based on $f(G)$, where $f(G) = f_1(1, 2) = 4$ holds.

$f(G)$ on $OPT_A(G, D)$ based on $\mathcal{G} = \{G_1, \ldots, G_t\}$. Let E_3 be a set of edges with $|E_3| \leq 2f(G)$ such that $d_{G+E_3}(u, v) \leq 2R + 1$ holds for every two vertices $u, v \in N_{G_1}^R(c_1) \cup N_{G_2}^R(c_2) \cup \cdots \cup N_{G_t}^R(c_t)$. Halt after outputting $E^* = E_1 \cup E_2 \cup E_3$. $\qquad\square$

By Theorem 3 and the property of $f(G)$, it is not difficult to see that Algorithm ODD-APD(G, D) can be implemented to run in $O(n^3)$ time. Summarizing the argument given so far, Theorem 1 is now established.

4   BAPD with a Forest

In this section, we propose an algorithm, named ODD-BAPD(G, D), which delivers a $(4, 2)$-approximate (resp., $(6, 3)$-approximate) solution to BAPD with a forest G and an odd D in $O(n)$ time if $D \geq 5$ (resp., $D = 3$) holds.

Let $G = (V, E)$ be a forest with $|V| \geq 3$ and $I(G)$ be a set of isolated vertices $v \in V$ with $N_G(v) = \emptyset$. Algorithm ODD-BAPD(G, D) consists of slightly modified Steps 1 and 2 of algorithm ODD-APD(G, D), and the final step for biconnectivity. Differently from APD, in BAPD, each leaf (resp., isolated vertex) in G must be incident to at least one added edge (resp., at least two added edges) for the biconnectivity, and so we does not compute $f(G)$ defined in (1) in the algorithm.

Algorithm ODD-BAPD(G, D)
Input: A forest $G = (V, E)$ and an odd integer $D \geq 3$.
Output: An edge set E^* with $diam(G + E^*) \leq D$, $\kappa(G + E^*) \geq 2$, and $|E^*| \leq 4OPT_A(G, D) + 2$ for $D \geq 5$ (resp., $|E^*| \leq 6OPT_A(G, D) + 3$ for $D = 3$).
Step 1: Let $R = \frac{D-1}{2}$. Compute a set C_1 of centers with the minimum cardinality such that $L(G) \subseteq C_1$ holds and a family of (R)-balls with centers in C_1 covers V. Choose two distinct vertices $c_1, c_2 \in C_1$. Let $E_1 = \{(c_1, c_2)\} \cup \{(c_1, c) \mid c \in C_1 - I(G) - \{c_1, c_2\}\} \cup \{\{(c_1, c), (c_2, c)\} \mid c \in I(G) - \{c_1, c_2\}\}$.

Step 2: Regard each component G^ℓ of G as a rooted tree by choosing its root c^ℓ as c_1 if $c_1 \in V(G^\ell)$ and as an arbitrary vertex in $C_1 \cap V(G^\ell)$ otherwise. For each vertex $c_i \in C_1$, let $p(c_i) \in C_1$ be the nearest ancestor of c_i in G^ℓ and let a_i, b_i be vertices in $V(P_{c_i,p(c_i)})$ with $d_G(c_i, a_i) = R$ and $d_G(c_i, b_i) = R+1$ if $d_G(c_i, p(c_i)) \geq R+1$ holds, and $a_i = b_i = \emptyset$ otherwise. Let $Q_i = \{a_i\}$ (resp., $Q_i = \{a_i, b_i\}$) for each vertex $c_i \in C_1 - \{c_1\}$ if $R \geq 2$ (resp., $R = 1$) holds. Let $E_2 = \{(c_1, v) \mid v \in \bigcup_{c_i \in C_1 - \{c_1\}} Q_i\}$.

Step 3: For each component G'_i of G with $\{c_1, c_2\} \cap V(G'_i) = \emptyset$ and $|V(G'_i)| \geq 2$, pick up arbitrarily one edge $(c, c_1) \in E_1$ with $c \in V(G'_i)$ and replace the edge (c, c_1) with a new edge (c, c_2). In the component G' of G with $c_1 \in V(G')$, for the set L_1 of leaves $v \in L(G') - \{c_1\}$ with $c_2 \notin V(P_{v,c_1})$, replace each edge $(c_1, v) \in E_1$ with $v \in L_1$ with a new edge (c_2, v). Let E'_1 be the edge set obtained from E_1 by this procedure. Halt after outputting $E^* = E'_1 \cup E_2$.   □

We prove the correctness of algorithm ODD-BAPD(G, D) by the following lemmas, whose proofs are omitted due to space limitation. The next lemma shows $|E_1| \leq |C_1| + |I(G)| - 1 \leq 2OPT_B(G, 2R+1) + 1$.

Lemma 8. $|C_1| + |I(G)| \leq 2OPT_B(G, 2R+1) + 2$ *holds.*   □

Define a distant vertex v as one in the previous section; $d_{G+E_1}(v, v') > 2R+1$ holds for some $v' \in V - \{v\}$. From the construction of C_1, $G + E_1$ satisfies $d_{G+E_1}(c_1, v) \leq R+1$ for every vertex $v \in V$. Hence any distant vertex $v \in V$ satisfies $d_{G+E_1}(v, c_1) = R+1$. Moreover, by $L(G) \subseteq C_1$, any distant vertex $v \in V$ satisfies $v \notin L(G)$. The following lemma shows that $diam(G+(E_1 \cup E_2)) \leq D-1$ holds.

Lemma 9. $G + (E_1 \cup E_2)$ *satisfies* $d_{G+(E_1 \cup E_2)}(c_1, v) \leq R$ *for all* $v \in V$.   □

Lemma 8 and the following lemmas 10 and 11 indicate that Theorem 2 holds.

Lemma 10. *A set* $E'_1 \cup E_2$ *of edges is feasible to BAPD with a forest G and* $D = 2R+1$ *and satisfies* $|E'_1| = |E_1|$ *and* $|E_2| \leq |C_1| - 1$ *(resp.,* $|E_2| \leq 2|C_1| - 2$*) if* $R \geq 2$ *(resp.,* $R = 1$*) holds.*   □

Lemma 11. *Algorithm ODD-BAPD(G, D) can be implemented to run in $O(n)$ time.*   □

Finally, we remark that Steps 1 and 2 in algorithm ODD-BAPD(G, D) can find a set E' of edges such that we have $diam(G+E') \leq D$ and $|E'|$ is at most four times the optimal (resp., six times the optimal) in the case of $D \geq 5$ (resp., $D = 3$), for any type of problems to which any feasible solution E' satisfies $L(G) \subseteq V[E']$. Now it is known in [15] (resp., [11]) that the problem of augmenting an initial graph up to k-edge-connectivity (resp., k-vertex-connectivity) by adding the minimum number of new edges is polynomially solvable (2-approximable in polynomial time). Therefore, we see the following property.

Corollary 1. *APD with an additional requirement that the resulting augmented graph G' satisfies $\lambda(G') \geq k$ (resp., $\kappa(G') \geq k$) for $k \geq 2$, is 5-approximable (resp., 6-approximable) if D is an odd≥ 5 and 7-approximable (resp., 8-approximable) if $D = 3$ holds, where $\lambda(G)$ denotes the edge-connectivity of G.*   □

5   Conclusion

We have shown that APD with a forest G and an odd D is approximable within a constant in polynomial time, by proposing an $O(n^3)$ time 8-approximation algorithm for the problem. For BAPD with a forest G and an odd D, we have shown that a feasible solution E' with $|E'| \leq 4OPT_B(G, D) + 2$ (resp., $|E'| \leq 6OPT_B(G, 3) + 3$) can be found in $O(n)$ time if $D \geq 5$ (resp., $D = 3$) holds. Both algorithms depend on the performance guarantee of Chepoi and Vaxes' algorithm [5] for APD with an even D. Hence, any better approximation algorithm for APD with an even D improves the performance guarantee of approximating APD with an odd D. Actually, it is still open whether APD with a forest is NP-hard or not, and Chepoi and Vaxes [5] conjectured that a solution obtained by their algorithm for APD with a forest and an even D is optimal when $OPT_A(G, D)$ is sufficiently large.

References

1. N. Alon, A. Gyárfás, and M. Ruszinkó, *Decreasing the diameter of bounded degree graphs*, J. Graph Theory, **35**, (2000), 161–172.
2. C. Berge, Hypergraphs, North-Holland, Amsterdam, (1989).
3. A. Brandstädt, F. Dragan, V. Chepoi, and V. Voloshin, *Dually chordal graphs*, SIAM J. Discrete Math., **11**(3), (1998), 437–455.
4. V. Chepoi, (personal communication), 2002.
5. V. Chepoi and Y. Vaxes, *Augmenting trees to meet biconnectivity and diameter constraints*, Algorithmica, **33**, (2002), 243–262.
6. F. R. K. Chung, *Diameter of graphs: old problems and new results*, Congr Numer, **60**, (1987), 295–317.
7. Y. Dodis and S. Khanna, *Designing networks with bounded pairwise distance*, Proc. 31st Annual ACM Symposium on Theory of Computing, (1999), 750–759.
8. P. Erdős, A. Gyárfás, and M. Ruszinkó, *How to decrease the diameter of triangle-free graphs*, Combinatorica, **18**(4), (1998), 493–501.
9. K. P. Eswaran and R. E. Tarjan, *Augmentation problems*, SIAM J. Comput., Vol.5, 1976, pp. 653–665.
10. A. Frank, *Connectivity augmentation problems in network design*, in Mathematical Programming: State of the Art 1994, J.R. Birge and K.G. Murty (Eds.), The University of Michigan, Ann Arbor, MI, (1994), 34–63.
11. B. Jackson and T. Jordán, *A near optimal algorithm for vertex connectivity augmentation*, Lecture Notes in Computer Science 1969, Algorithms and Computation (Proc. ISAAC '00), (2000), 312–325.
12. C. Li, S. McCormick, and D. Simchi-Levi, *On the minimum-cardinality-bounded-minimum-diameter and the bounded-cardinality-minimum-diameter edge addition problems*, Operations Research Letters, **11**, (1992), 303–308.
13. H. Nagamochi and T. Ibaraki, *Graph connectivity and its augmentation: applications of MA orderings*, Discrete Applied Mathematics, **123**(1), (2002), 447–472.
14. A. A. Schoone, H. L. Bodlaender, and J. van Leeuwen, *Diameter increase caused by edge deletion*, J. Graph Theory, **11**(3), (1987), 409–427.
15. T. Watanabe and A. Nakamura, *Edge-connectivity augmentation problems*, J. Comput. System Sci., **35**, (1987), 96–144.

On the Existence and Determination of Satisfactory Partitions in a Graph

Cristina Bazgan[1], Zsolt Tuza[2], and Daniel Vanderpooten[1]

[1] LAMSADE, Université Paris-Dauphine, France
{`bazgan`,`vdp`}`@lamsade.dauphine.fr`
[2] Computer and Automation Institute, Hungarian Academy of Sciences, Budapest
and Department of Computer Science, University of Veszprém, Hungary

Abstract. The SATISFACTORY PARTITION problem consists in deciding if a given graph has a partition of its vertex set into two nonempty sets V_1, V_2 such that for each vertex v, if $v \in V_i$ then $d_{V_i}(v) \geq s(v)$, where $s(v) \leq d(v)$ is a given integer-valued function. This problem was introduced by Gerber and Kobler [*EJOR* 125 (2000), 283–291] for $s = \lceil \frac{d}{2} \rceil$. In this paper we study the complexity of this problem for different values of s.

Keywords: Satisfactory partition, graph, complexity, polynomial algorithm, NP-complete, degree constraints.

1 Introduction

Gerber and Kobler introduced in [3] the problem of deciding if a given graph has a vertex partition into two nonempty sets such that each vertex has at least as many neighbors in its set as in the other. The complexity of this problem remains open in their paper. They showed the strong NP-hardness of a generalization of this problem where there are weights on the vertices and we ask for a vertex partition into two nonempty sets such that for each vertex the sum of weights of the neighbors in the same set is at least as large as the sum of weights of the neighbors in the other set. The case where edges are weighted was also proved to be strong NP-hard.

For a graph $G = (V, E)$, vertex $v \in V$, and subset $Y \subseteq V$ we denote by $d_Y(v)$ the number of vertices in Y that are adjacent to v; and, as usual, we write $d(v)$ for the degree $d_V(v)$ of v in V. Throughout, the subgraph of graph $G = (V, E)$ induced by $Y \subseteq V$ will be denoted by $G[Y]$. The general problem we are interested in is as follows:

SATISFACTORY PARTITION
Input: A graph $G = (V, E)$, and a function $s : V \to \mathbb{N}$ such that $s(v) \leq d(v)$, for all $v \in V$.
Question: Is there a nontrivial partition (V_1, V_2) of V such that, for every $v \in V$, if $v \in V_i$ then $d_{V_i}(v) \geq s(v)$?

T. Ibaraki, N. Katoh, and H. Ono (Eds.): ISAAC 2003, LNCS 2906, pp. 444–453, 2003.

Considering $A \subset V$, a vertex $v \in A$ is *satisfied* in A if $d_A(v) \geq s(v)$. Moreover A is a *satisfactory subset* if all of its vertices are satisfied in A. If $A, B \subseteq V$ are two disjoint, nonempty vertex subsets such that A and B are satisfactory subsets, we say that (A, B) is a *satisfactory pair*. If, in addition, (A, B) is a vertex partition then it will be called a *satisfactory partition* and a graph admitting such a partition is said to be *partitionable*.

In our statement of the SATISFACTORY PARTITION problem, the function s indicates the level of satisfaction required for the vertices to be satisfied. The problem studied by Gerber and Kobler corresponds to $s = \lceil \frac{d}{2} \rceil$. As remarked in [3], this problem may have no solution. In particular, the following graphs are not partitionable: complete graphs, stars, and complete bipartite graphs with at least one of the two vertex classes having odd size. Some other graphs are easily partitionable: cycles of size at least 4, trees which are not stars, and disconnected graphs.

After stating some preliminary results (Section 2), we study in Sections 3-5 SATISFACTORY PARTITION for different values of s. For $s \leq \lceil \frac{d}{2} \rceil - 1$, a result of Stiebitz [5] indicates that the graph always has such a partition. The original proof is not constructive, and we give here a polynomial-time algorithm that finds such a partition (Section 3). For $s = \lceil \frac{d}{2} \rceil$, we prove that for graphs with maximum degree at most 4, both the decision and search problems are polynomially solvable. This problem on general graphs remains open (Section 4). For $\lceil \frac{d}{2} \rceil + 1 \leq s \leq d - 1$, SATISFACTORY PARTITION is proved to be NP-complete (Section 5). For $s = d$, the problem is trivial since it consists in deciding whether the graph is disconnected.

2 Preliminary Results

Firstly we establish a necessary and sufficient condition to obtain a satisfactory partition.

Proposition 1. *When $s \leq \lceil \frac{d}{2} \rceil$, a graph $G = (V, E)$ is partitionable if and only if it contains a satisfactory pair (A, B). Moreover, if a satisfactory pair (A, B) is given, then a satisfactory partition of G can be determined in polynomial time.*

Proof. The necessary part is obvious. The sufficient part is proved as follows. Let $V_1 = A$ and $V_2 = B$. While there is a vertex v in $V \setminus (V_1 \cup V_2)$ such that $d_{V_1}(v) \geq s(v)$, insert v into V_1. While there is a vertex v in $V \setminus (V_1 \cup V_2)$ such that $d_{V_2}(v) \geq s(v)$, insert v into V_2. At the end, if $C = V \setminus (V_1 \cup V_2) \neq \emptyset$, then $d_{V_1}(v) < s(v)$ and $d_{V_2}(v) < s(v)$ for any $v \in C$. Since $s(v) \leq \lceil \frac{d(v)}{2} \rceil$, we have, for any $v \in C$, $d_{V_1 \cup C}(v) \geq s(v)$ and $d_{V_2 \cup C}(v) \geq s(v)$. Thus we can insert all vertices of C either into V_1 or into V_2, forming a satisfactory partition. $\square$

We show now how to determine satisfactory subsets efficiently.

Proposition 2. *For any $s \leq d$, it is decidable in polynomial time, if a subgraph $G[A]$ of a graph G contains a satisfactory subset.*

Proof. The algorithm iteratively removes from $G[A]$ the vertices v of degree less than $s(v)$, while it is possible.

If at the end of the algorithm we obtain a non-empty subgraph $G[A']$, then $G[A]$ contains a satisfactory subset A' since $d_{A'}(v) \geq s(v)$, for all $v \in A'$.

Conversely, suppose that the algorithm removes all vertices from A and that $G[A]$ would contain a satisfactory subset A'. The first vertex v of A' considered by the algorithm cannot be removed since its current degree is greater than or equal to $d_{A'}(v) \geq s(v)$. In this way no vertex of A' could be removed. Thus, if the entire set A gets deleted, then $G[A]$ does not contain a satisfactory subset.□

A *minimal satisfactory subset* A is a satisfactory subset such that, for every $A' \subset A$, there exists a vertex $u \in A'$ with $d_{A'}(u) \leq s(u) - 1$.

Proposition 3. *For any $s \leq d$, if a graph contains a satisfactory subset, then a minimal satisfactory subset A can be found in polynomial time.*

Proof. Let A_1 be a satisfactory subset of G. We construct a sequence of subgraphs of G, $G[A_1], ..., G[A_t]$ such that $A_{i+1} \subset A_i$ and each A_i is a satisfactory subset:

In step i $(i \geq 1)$, we select a vertex $v \in A_i$, tentatively remove from A_i vertex v and we iteratively remove from $A_i \setminus \{v\}$ the vertices u of degree less than $s(u)$ until we obtain a set X which is either empty or a satisfactory subset. If $X = \emptyset$, then we iterate the previous procedure for vertices $v \in A_i$ until a set $X \neq \emptyset$ is obtained, and in this case we continue the construction with $A_{i+1} = X$. In the other case, i.e. where all the sets X obtained are empty, we stop the algorithm with $t = i$. The set A with the required properties is the set A_t.

It is clear that A is a satisfactory subset. We have to prove that A is minimal. Suppose on the contrary, that there exists a subset $A' \subset A$ such that $d_{A'}(v) \geq s(v)$ for all $v \in A'$. Choose any $u \in A \setminus A'$. Continuing the procedure from $A_t = A$ by removing u, a nonempty set $A_{t+1} \supseteq A'$ would be generated, which contradicts the previous assumption that $A_{t+1} = \emptyset$ holds for all $u \in A$.   □

3   The Case $s \; \square \; \square\frac{d}{2}\square\square \; 1$

Stiebitz [5] proved the following result:

Theorem 1 ([5]). *Let $G = (V, E)$ be a graph, and let $a, b : V \to \mathbb{N}$ be two functions such that $d(x) \geq a(x) + b(x) + 1$ for every $x \in V$. Then, there is a nontrivial vertex partition (A, B) of V such that $d_A(x) \geq a(x)$ for every $x \in A$, and $d_B(x) \geq b(x)$ for every $x \in B$.*

Obviously, if we take $a = b = s$, Stiebitz's result shows the existence of a satisfactory partition for $s \leq \lceil \frac{d}{2} \rceil - 1$. The proof in [5] is not constructive. We show here how to determine such a partition in polynomial time.

Proposition 4. *Algorithm 1 finds in polynomial time a satisfactory pair in any graph for $s \leq \lceil \frac{d}{2} \rceil - 1$.*

Algorithm 1 Determination of a satisfactory pair $(s \leq \lceil \frac{d}{2} \rceil - 1)$

Find a minimal satisfactory subset $A \subseteq V$
$B \leftarrow V \setminus A$
if $G[B]$ contains a satisfactory subset **then**
   $(A, \tilde{B})$ is a satisfactory pair, $\tilde{B}$ being a satisfactory subset of $G[B]$
else
   while $(G[A]$ or $G[B]$ has no satisfactory subset) **do**
      if $G[B]$ has no satisfactory subset **then**
         Let $v \in A$ such that $d_A(v) \leq s(v)$
         $A \leftarrow A \setminus \{v\}; B \leftarrow B \cup \{v\}$
      end if
      if $G[A]$ has no satisfactory subset **then**
         Let $v \in B$ such that $d_B(v) \leq s(v)$
         $A \leftarrow A \cup \{v\}; B \leftarrow B \setminus \{v\}$
      end if
   end while
   $(\tilde{A}, \tilde{B})$ is a satisfactory pair where $\tilde{A}$ and $\tilde{B}$ are satisfactory subsets of $G[A]$ and
   $G[B]$, respectively
end if

Proof. Using Proposition 3, the first step is computable in polynomial time. Using Proposition 2, the **if** and **while** conditions are polynomial-time decidable. We justify that in the **while** loop the selection of a vertex v is always possible. For this, we show that at the beginning of each iteration in the **while** loop, $G[A]$ and $G[B]$ are such that all their subgraphs contain a vertex u of degree at most $s(u)$; and in addition at least one of $G[A]$ and $G[B]$ is such that all their subgraphs contain a vertex u of degree at most $s(u) - 1$. In fact, before entering the **while** loop, each subgraph of $G[A]$ contains a vertex u of degree at most $s(u)$, since A is a minimal satisfactory subset. Also, before entering the **while** loop, $G[B]$ has no satisfactory subset, which means that each of its subgraphs contains a vertex u of degree strictly smaller than $s(u)$. At the end of an iteration of the **while** loop after moving v from A to B for example, the degree of vertices in $G[B \cup \{v\}]$ increases with at most one, so in each subgraph of $G[B \cup \{v\}]$, there is a vertex u of degree at most $s(u)$. Since we are inside the **while** loop only if one of the graphs $G[A]$ and $G[B]$ is such that none of the subgraphs has a satisfactory subset, the corresponding graph has in each subgraph a vertex u of degree at most $s(u) - 1$ that can increase to at most $s(u)$ after moving vertex v into the other vertex class. Hence, the operations inside the loop can always be performed.

We show now that the number of iterations is polynomially bounded. Consider any iteration of the **while** loop. Assume, without loss of generality, that $G[B]$ has no satisfactory subset. By the choice of v, since $d_A(v) \leq s(v)$, we have $d_B(v) \geq s(v) + 1$. Thus, the number of edges between A and B decreases by at least one and thus the algorithm finishes after at most $|E|$ iterations. $\qquad\square$

Theorem 2. SATISFACTORY PARTITION *for* $s \leq \lceil \frac{d}{2} \rceil - 1$ *is polynomial-time solvable.*

Proof. From Propositions 1 and 4.   □

By slightly modifying Algorithm 1 replacing s by a or b in appropriate places we obtain the following result:

Theorem 3. *Let $G = (V, E)$ be a graph, and let $a, b : V \to \mathbb{N}$ be two functions such that $d(x) \geq a(x)+b(x)+1$ for every $x \in V$. Then, we can find in polynomial time a nontrivial vertex partition (A, B) of V such that $d_A(x) \geq a(x)$ for every $x \in A$, and $d_B(x) \geq b(x)$ for every $x \in B$.*

4   The Case $s = \blacksquare\frac{d}{2}\blacksquare$

In this section we show that for graphs G with $\Delta(G) \leq 4$ it is polynomial-time solvable to decide if the graph is (not) partitionable, and also to find a satisfactory partition if it exists. In particular, all cubic graphs except K_4 and $K_{3,3}$ are partitionable and all 4-regular graphs except K_5 are partitionable.

Firstly we prove two propositions.

Proposition 5. *Each cubic graph containing a triangle, except K_4, is partitionable.*

Proof. Let G be a cubic graph, $G \neq K_4$, and let C be a triangle of G with vertices v_1, v_2, v_3. Remark that a vertex outside C cannot have all its neighbors on C since $G \neq K_4$.

If each vertex of $V \setminus V(C)$ has at most one neighbor on C then $V_1 = V(C)$ and $V_2 = V \setminus V(C)$ form a satisfactory partition.

Suppose that there is a vertex v_4 with two neighbors v_1, v_2 on C. If v_3 and v_4 have a common neighbor v_5, then $V_1 = \{v_1, v_2, v_3, v_4, v_5\}$ and $V_2 = V \setminus V_1 \neq \emptyset$ form a satisfactory partition of G. Otherwise $V_1 = \{v_1, v_2, v_3, v_4\}$ and $V_2 = V \setminus V_1 \neq \emptyset$ form a satisfactory partition of G.   □

Proposition 6. *Each cubic graph containing a cycle of size 4, except K_4 and $K_{3,3}$, is partitionable.*

Proof. Let G be a cubic graph other than K_4 and $K_{3,3}$. If G contains a triangle then G is partitionable by Proposition 5. Otherwise let $C = v_1v_2v_3v_4$ be a cycle of size 4. A vertex outside C cannot have more than two neighbors on C since otherwise G contains a cycle shorter than C.

If each vertex of $V \setminus V(C)$ has at most one neighbor on C, then $V_1 = V(C)$ and $V_2 = V \setminus V(C)$ form a satisfactory partition.

Otherwise, suppose that a vertex v_5 has neighbors v_1 and v_3. Since $G \neq K_{3,3}$ there is no vertex of G with the three neighbors v_2, v_4, v_5. Thus, a vertex v_i with $i \geq 6$ has at most two neighbors among $\{v_2, v_4, v_5\}$. If all vertices v_i with

$i \geq 6$ have at most one neighbor among $\{v_2, v_4, v_5\}$ then $V_1 = \{v_1, v_2, v_3, v_4, v_5\}$ and $V_2 = V \setminus V_1 \neq \emptyset$ form a satisfactory partition of G. Otherwise, let v_6 be a vertex that has v_2, v_4 as neighbors. If all vertices v_i with $i \geq 7$ have at most one neighbor among $\{v_5, v_6\}$, then $V_1 = \{v_1, v_2, v_3, v_4, v_5, v_6\}$ and $V_2 = V \setminus V_1 \neq \emptyset$ form a satisfactory partition of G. Otherwise, there is another vertex v_7 with neighbors v_5, v_6. In this case $V_1 = \{v_1, v_2, v_3, v_4, v_5, v_6, v_7\}$ and $V_2 = V \setminus V_1 \neq \emptyset$ form a satisfactory partition of G. □

We show now how to determine a satisfactory partition.

Algorithm 2 Determination of a satisfactory partition for cubic and 4-regular graphs

---

Let G be an $(\ell + 1)$-regular graph ($\ell = 2$ or 3).
Search a shortest cycle C.
if $|C| \geq 5$ **then**
   $V_1 \leftarrow V(C)$; $V_2 \leftarrow V \setminus V(C)$
else
   $V_1 \leftarrow V(C)$
   while there exists a vertex $v \in V \setminus V_1$ with at least ℓ neighbors in V_1 **do**
      $V_1 \leftarrow V_1 \cup \{v\}$
   end while
   $V_2 \leftarrow V \setminus V_1$
end if

Theorem 4. *All cubic graphs except K_4 and $K_{3,3}$ are partitionable in polynomial time.*

Proof. Let G be a cubic graph, $G \neq K_4$ and $K_{3,3}$. Let us verify that Algorithm 2 with $\ell = 2$ is correct.

If $|C| = k \geq 5$, then there are no two vertices on C with a common neighbor v outside C, since otherwise there exists in G a cycle of length at most $\lfloor k/2 \rfloor + 2$. For $k \geq 5$ this would be a cycle shorter than C. So, each vertex outside C has at least two neighbors among $V \setminus V(C)$ and thus $V_1 = V(C)$ and $V_2 = V \setminus V(C) \neq \emptyset$ form a partition where each vertex is satisfied.

If $|C| \leq 4$, then the proofs of the above propositions show that in the partition (V_1, V_2) each vertex is satisfied. □

Theorem 5. *All 4-regular graphs except K_5 are partitionable, in polynomial time.*

Proof. Let us see in the following that Algorithm 2 with $\ell = 3$ is correct.

If $|C| \geq 5$, then as above, $V_1 = V(C)$ and $V_2 = V \setminus V(C) \neq \emptyset$ form a satisfactory partition.

If $|C| = 4$, then there is no vertex outside C with three neighbors on C, and thus $V_1 = V(C)$ and $V_2 = V \setminus V(C) \neq \emptyset$ form a satisfactory partition.

If $|C| = 3$, then denote $C = v_1v_2v_3$. If each vertex of $V \setminus V(C)$ has at most two neighbors on C, then G is partitionable, and $V_1 = V(C)$ and $V_2 = V \setminus V(C)$ form a satisfactory partition. Otherwise let v_4 be a vertex with neighbors v_1, v_2, v_3. If each vertex $v_i, i \geq 5$ has at most two neighbors among v_1, v_2, v_3, v_4 then G is partitionable. Otherwise, since $G \neq K_5$, let v_5 be a vertex with three neighbors among v_1, v_2, v_3, v_4. Then $V_1 = \{v_1, v_2, v_3, v_4, v_5\}$ and $V_2 = V \setminus V_1 \neq \emptyset$ form a satisfactory partition of G. $\square$

Thus, all cubic graphs except K_4 and $K_{3,3}$ are partitionable and all 4-regular graphs except K_5 are partitionable. These results cannot be extended for regular graphs with degree greater than 4 since there are 5-regular graphs, different from K_6 and $K_{5,5}$ that are not partitionable, and there are 6-regular graphs different from K_7 that are not partitionable (see Figure 1).

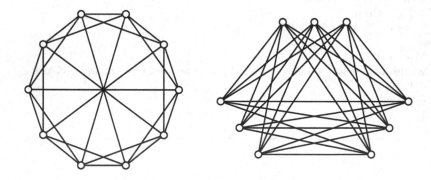

Fig. 1. Non-partitionable 5-regular and 6-regular graphs

We consider now graphs with maximum degree at most 4. As usual, the minimum and maximum degree of G will be denoted by $\delta(G)$ and $\Delta(G)$, respectively.

Proposition 7. *A graph G with $\delta(G) = 3$ and $\Delta(G) \leq 4$ is partitionable if and only if it contains two vertex-disjoint cycles.*

Proof. (If) Immediate from Proposition 1. (Only if) If G is partionable then each vertex has at least two neighbors in its part, so each part contains a cycle. $\square$

Proposition 8. *Let G be a graph with $\Delta(G) \leq 4$. Then G is partitionable if and only if we can add in G at most two disjoint edges between vertices of degrees 1 or 2, such that the resulting multigraph contains two vertex-disjoint cycles.*

Proof. (If) If G contains two disjoint cycles C_1, C_2 then $V(C_1)$ and $V(C_2)$ can be completed to form a satisfactory partition, using Proposition 1.

If G has no two disjoint cycles but adding one edge (v_i, v_j) the graph $G' = (V, E \cup \{(v_i, v_j)\})$ has two disjoint cycles C_1, C_2 then (v_i, v_j) belongs to one of these cycles. Then $V(C_1)$ and $V(C_2)$ form a satisfactory pair once we remove (v_i, v_j) since v_i and v_j have degree at most two.

Assume now that the addition of two non-adjacent edges $(v_i, v_j), (v_k, v_\ell)$ is such that the new graph contains two disjoint cycles. Since these two edges are not adjacent, as above, the two disjoint cycles can be completed to a satisfactory partition.

(Only if) Let (V_1, V_2) be a satisfactory partition of G. If V_i $(i = 1, 2)$ contains no cycle, then we add one edge between two degree-1 vertices of a tree component inside V_i. If the tree in question is just an edge, then we add a parallel edge creating a multiple edge. □

Theorem 6. *Let G be a graph with $\Delta(G) \leq 4$. We can decide in polynomial time if G is (not) partitionable, and find a satisfactory partition of G if it exists.*

Proof. There is a polynomial number of choices to add at most two non-adjacent edges in G. For a fixed choice, we first verify if there are multiple edges. If there are two non-adjacent multiple edges, then we have found two disjoint cycles; if there is one multiple edge, then we search a cycle in the graph obtained by removing the two vertices incident to this edge. The graph is partitionable if and only if such a cycle exists. If the graph has no multiple edges, then we apply a polynomial algorithm that finds two disjoint cycles in a graph if they exist (Bodlaender [1]), to decide if the graph is partitionable. □

5   The Case $\frac{d}{2} + 1 \leq s \leq d - 1$

Chvátal introduced in [2] the decomposition problem of bicoloring the vertices of a graph in such a way that each vertex has at most one neighbor with a different color. He gave a polynomial-time algorithm for this problem for graphs with maximum degree 3. For graphs with vertices of degree 2 and 3 this problem coincides with SATISFACTORY PARTITION when $s = \lceil \frac{d}{2} \rceil$. Theorem 6 contains this result. Chvátal also proved the NP-hardness of this problem for graphs with minimum degree $\delta(G) = 3$ and maximum degree $\Delta(G) = 4$. This result implies the following result for our problem.

Theorem 7. SATISFACTORY PARTITION *is NP-complete when $s = d - 1$, even for graphs with $\delta(G) = 3$ and $\Delta(G) = 4$.*

Observe that Chvátal's problem coincides with SATISFACTORY PARTITION when $s = \lceil \frac{d}{2} \rceil + 1$ or $s = d - 1$ for graphs G with $\delta(G) = 4$ and $\Delta(G) = 5$. In order to prove the NP-hardness of SATISFACTORY PARTITION when $\lceil \frac{d}{2} \rceil + 1 \leq s \leq d - 1$, we just need to adapt Chvátal's construction using a graph with $\delta(G) = 4$ and $\Delta(G) = 5$.

Theorem 8. SATISFACTORY PARTITION *for $\lceil \frac{d}{2} \rceil + 1 \leq s \leq d - 1$ is NP-complete even for graphs G with $\delta(G) = 4$ and $\Delta(G) = 5$.*

Before proving this theorem, we define a problem used in the reduction.

BICOLORING HYPERGRAPHS
Input: A hypergraph $H = (V, E)$.
Question: Is there a coloring with two colors Red and Blue of the vertices such that no hyperedge is monochromatic?

BICOLORING HYPERGRAPHS is NP-hard even if all hyperedges have size 3 ([4]).

Proof. The reduction is from BICOLORING HYPERGRAPHS with hyperedges of size 3. Given an input hypergraph $H = (V, E)$ where $V = \{v_1, \ldots, v_n\}$ and $E = \{e_1, \ldots, e_m\}$, we construct a graph $G = (V', E')$ such that H is bicolorable if and only if G is partitionable. We first briefly describe Chvátal's construction, which uses the following graph Q_d that is a sequence of d triangles (see Figure 2 (a)).

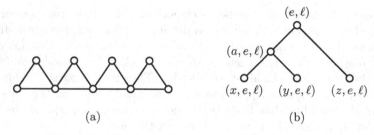

(a)   (b)

Fig. 2. (a) Graph Q_d for $d = 4$;   (b) The gadget $T_{e,\ell}$

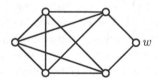

Fig. 3. The gadget $C_{5,w}$

Graph G contains two subgraphs B_0, B_1 and subgraphs A_i for each $v_i \in V$. B_0 and B_1 are graphs Q_{n+m-2} and A_i is Q_{2d_i-1}, where d_i is the number of hyperedges of H containing v_i. In each B_ℓ, $\ell = 0, 1$ the first n consecutive vertices of degree 2 are labeled by $(v_1, \ell), \ldots, (v_n, \ell)$; the remaining m consecutive vertices of degree 2 are labeled by $(e_1, \ell), \ldots, (e_m, \ell)$. The $2d_i + 1$ vertices of degree 2 in A_i are labeled by v_i^* and $(v_i, e_j, 0), (v_i, e_j, 1)$ if v_i belongs to hyperedge e_j. Another gadget used by Chvátal is the graph of Figure 2 (b). For each $\ell = 0, 1$ and for each hyperedge e of H containing vertices x, y, z, we add the graph $T_{e,\ell}$. This graph has the property that if the three vertices of degree 1 are in the same part of a satisfactory partition then the other two vertices of $T_{e,\ell}$ are in the same part. Also, if two of the three vertices of degree 1 are in different parts of a satisfactory partition then the vertex of degree 2 could be in either of the two parts of the partition.

We specify in the following the edges in G that link the subgraphs $A_1, \ldots, A_n$, B_0, B_1. Each v_i^* is joint with $(v_i, 0)$ and $(v_i, 1)$ for $i = 1, \ldots, n$. Subgraphs B_0 and B_1 are joined to subgraphs A_j, $j = 1, \ldots, n$ using gadgets $T_{e,\ell}$, $e \in E$ and $\ell = 0, 1$, by identifying vertices with the same labels. With this construction Chvátal proves the NP-hardness of this decomposition problem.

We introduce the gadget $C_{5,w}$ (see Figure 3) in order to transform any vertex of the graph of Chvátal's construction of degree 2 or 3 to a vertex of degree 4 or 5 while preserving the reduction. The property of this gadget is that its vertices are necessarily in the same part of a satisfactory partition.

We identify vertex w of such a gadget $C_{5,w}$ with vertices $(v_i, 0)$ and $(v_i, 1)$ for $i = 1, \ldots, n$ and with vertices $(v_i, e_j, 0)$ and $(v_i, e_j, 0)$ of the graphs A_i. Also, we identify vertex w of such a gadget $C_{5,w}$ with vertices (a, e, ℓ) of gadgets $T_{e,\ell}$.

We justify in the following that H is bicolorable if and only if G' is partitionable.

Suppose firstly that G' is partitionable. It is easy to see that all vertices in B_0 must belong to the same part of the satisfactory partition. The same property holds for B_1 and also for A_i for $v_i \in V$. Subgraphs B_0 and B_1 must be in the different parts of the satisfactory partition since otherwise all vertices of G would be in the same part. We construct a vertex bicoloring of H from this partition as follows: if A_i is in the same part as B_0 then v_i is colored Red, and if it is in the same part as B_1 then v_i is colored Blue. Given a hyperedge e of H containing vertices x, y, z, it is easy to see using the properties of $T_{e,\ell}$ that e cannot be monochromatic, since otherwise $(e, 0)$ and $(e, 1)$ would be in the same part of the partition.

Suppose that H is bicolorable. All vertices of A_i in G corresponding to vertices v_i in H of the same color belong to the same part. This partition can be extended to a satisfactory partition.   □

References

1. H. L. Bodlaender, *On disjoint cycles*, International Journal of Foundations of Computer Science 5(1) (1994), 59–68.
2. V. Chvátal, *Recognizing decomposable graphs*, Journal of Graph Theory 8 (1984), 51–53.
3. M. Gerber and D. Kobler, *Algorithmic approach to the satisfactory graph partitioning problem*, European Journal of Operation Research, 125 (2000), 283–291.
4. L. Lovász, *Coverings and coloring of hypergraphs*, In Proceedings of 4th Southeastern Conference on Combinatorics, Graph Theory and Computing, Utilitas Mathematica, Winnipeg, 1973, 3–12.
5. M. Stiebitz, *Decomposing graphs under degree constraints*, Journal of Graph Theory 23 (1996), 321–324.

A Turn Function Scheme Realized in the Asynchronous Single-Writer/Multi-reader Shared Memory Model

Tom Altman[1], Yoshihide Igarashi[2], and Michiko Omori[3]

[1] Department of Computer Science and Engineering, University of Colorado at Denver, Denver, CO 80217, USA
taltman@carbon.cudenver.edu
[2] Department of Computer Science, Gunma University, Kiryu, Japan 376-8515
igarashi@comp.cs.gunma-u.ac.jp
[3] Business Networks Division, NEC Corp., Abiko, Chiba, 270-1198, Japan
m-oomori@dc.jp.nec.com

Abstract. We consider a set of users wishing to receive a service in an asynchronous distributed system. Such users declare their wishes and then wait to gain admittance to be served. Except for the initial transient period, at least one user must be waiting to be served, and the system should be as fair as possible for users. A procedure that ensures such a situation is called a *turn* function. It can be easily implemented in the asynchronous multi-writer/reader shared memory model. The *turn* function is useful to solve some problems concerning temporal orders within an asynchronous distributed system (e.g., the mutual exclusion problem and the k-exclusion problem). In this paper we propose an algorithm for the *turn* function that can be implemented in the single-writer/multi-reader shared memory model. Its implementation is simpler than the general method of simulating operations of multi-writer/reader shared variables by using a bounded concurrent time-stamp scheme in the single-writer/multi-reader shared memory model. We show the correctness of our algorithm and discuss its efficiency.

1 Introduction

The shared memory is an abstraction of asynchronous interprocess communication, where the senders and the receivers correspond to the writers and the readers, respectively. Mutual exclusion is a problem of managing access to a single indivisible resource that can only support one user at a time. It is well known as an important and fundamental problem in the area of asynchronous distributed systems. The n-process algorithm by Peterson [12] and the tournament algorithm by Peterson and Fischer [13] are well known lockout free mutual exclusion algorithms. These algorithms use multi-writer/reader shared variables to decide which of the processes is the last arrival. The accelerated version of n-process algorithm by Igarashi and Nishitani [6] also uses multi-writer/reader shared variables.

T. Ibaraki, N. Katoh, and H. Ono (Eds.): ISAAC 2003, LNCS 2906, pp. 454–463, 2003.

The k-exclusion problem is a natural generalization of the mutual exclusion problem. In k-exclusion, some number of processes, specified by the parameter k, are allowed to be concurrently inside the critical region, where corresponding users can use the resource. This generalization was defined and solved by Fischer et al. in the shared memory model [4]. Afek et al.[1] gave a *first-in* and *first-enable* solution to the k-exclusion problem. Their algorithm uses time-stamps. However, bounded concurrent time-stamp schemes known so far contain complicated construction in order to give temporal relations among events in an execution [2,3,5]. We can easily design algorithms for the k-exclusion problem if we are allowed to use multi-writer/reader shared variables as shown in [10,11]. However, the realization of multi-writer/reader shared variables is not easy.

The multi-writer/reader shared variables, named *turn*'s, used in [6,10,11,12, 13] have the same function. If every process can write its identifier in a multi-writer/reader shared variable, by checking the value of the shared variable any process can easily decide which process is the last writer to the shared variable. We call this function a *turn* function. The *turn* function is useful to solve problems in an asynchronous distributed system where a temporal order of events in an execution is required. The mutual exclusion problem and the k-exclusion problem are such problems.

An algorithm for simulating multi-writer/reader shared variables by single-writer/multi-reader variables has been proposed [8]. However, it uses bounded concurrent time-stamps. In this paper we propose an algorithm without using time-stamps for the *turn* function in the single-writer/multi-reader shared memory model. The structure of our algorithm is simple, and it has efficient running cost. By using our algorithm for the *turn* function, the algorithms given in [6, 10,11,12,13] can also be implemented, without using time-stamps, in the single-writer/multi-reader shared memory model. The algorithms in [10,11] for the k-exclusion problem satisfy lockout avoidance (i.e., they are immune to stopping failures of fewer than k processes). Simulation of those algorithms for the k-exclusion problem, by using our *turn* function algorithm, preserves lockout avoidance as well. In Section 3 we describe our algorithm. We prove the correctness of the algorithm and discuss its efficiency in Sections 4 and 5.

2   Preliminaries

The asynchronous single-writer/multi-reader shared memory model is used in this paper. It is a collection of n processes and single-writer/multi-reader shared variables. Each user of the system corresponds to its own process. Interactions between a process and its corresponding user are by input actions from the user to the process and by output actions from the process to the user. A single-writer/multi-reader shared variable can be written by at most one process, but can be read by multiple processes. All communication among the processes is via the shared memory. A full description of an asynchronous shared memory system can be given as such a model [9].

Access to a shared variable has a time duration starting from an invocation and ending with a response. We do not make assumptions about relative speeds of the processes that are communicating via shared variables. Since we only use single-writer/multi-reader shared variables in our algorithm, write operations do not overlap each other. Overlapping read operations are assumed not to affect each other. However, as pointed out by Lamport [7], when a read operation from a shared variable overlaps one or more write operations to the same shared variable, various situations can be considered. Lamport defined three categories for single-writer/multi-reader shared variables according to possible assumptions about what can happen in concurrent cases of read operations and write operations. These are *safe*, *regular*, and *atomic* shared variables [7]. For simplicity, in this paper we assume that all shared variables are atomic. That is, we assume that for any execution in the system, there is some way of totally ordering the read operations and write operations as if the operations are performed in that order without overlapping.

Suppose that a set of users wishing to receive a service is in the system. Such users declare their wishes and then wait to gain admittance to be served. Except for the initial transient period, at least one user must be waiting for the service. A procedure to keep such a situation is called the *turn* function. The system should be as fair as possible.

A user who is receiving the service is modeled as being in the service region. When a user is not involved in the service, he/she is said to be in the remainder region. In order to gain admittance to be in the service region, a process executes a trying protocol. The duration of time from the start of executing the trying protocol to the entrance of the service region is called the waiting time. When a user wishes to leave the service region, he/she sends his/her wish (i.e., the message that he/she wishes to exit from the service region) to the corresponding process. Once the process receives the wish of exit, it sends its corresponding user a message telling that he/she may return to the remainder region. For each user (as well as his/her corresponding process), visits to these regions can be repeated in cyclic order, from the remainder region to the waiting region, then to the service region, and then back again to the remainder region.

We assume that the n processes are numbered $1, \cdots, n$. Each process i corresponds to user U_i ($1 \leq i \leq n$). The inputs to process i from user U_i are $wish_i$ which means a request by user U_i for access to the service region, and $exits_i$ which means an announcement of the end of receiving the service by U_i. The outputs from process i to user U_i are $serve_i$ which means the grant of the service to U_i, and rem_i which tells U_i that it can continue with the rest of its work with no relation to the service. The system to manage the *turn* function should satisfy the following conditions.

(1) Once any process enters the waiting region, at least one process should stay in the waiting region.
(2) If at least two faultless processes are in the waiting region, then at some later point some process enters the service region.
(3) The interaction between users and processes are well formed.

Conditions (1), (2) and (3) above are called non-emptiness of the waiting region, progress for the waiting region, and well formedness between users and processes. Progress for the waiting region is a weaker property than lockout freedom ((4) below), and lockout freedom is a weaker property than lockout avoidance ((5) below).

(4) Any process wishing to be served will eventually enter the service region if every process is faultless, and if a process will enter the waiting region within a finite length of time from any point in time.

(5) Any faultless process wishing to be served will eventually enter the service region if a faultless process will enter the waiting region within a finite length of time after any point in time.

The fairness of the *turn* function can be easily satisfied if we are allowed to use a multi-writer/reader shared variable. Ideally, every process in the waiting region except for the last arrival at the waiting region should be promptly permitted to enter the service region. This property is called the *promptness*. It is straightforward to give a protocol for the *turn* function satisfying fairness and promptness if we are allowed to use a multi-writer/reader shared variable as shown in the following procedure, mw/r-$turn(n)$.

procedure mw/r-turn(n)
shared variable:
    $turn$, initially arbitrary, writable and readable by all processes;

process i $(1 \leq i \leq n)$
    input actions {inputs to process i from user U_i}: $wish_i$, $exit_i$;
    output actions {outputs from process i to user U_i}: $serve_i$, rem_i;

    ** remainder region **

01:    $wish_i$:
02:        $turn := i$;
03:        **waitfor** $turn \neq i$;
04:        $serve_i$;

    ** service region **

05:    $exit_i$:
06:        rem_i;

3   An Algorithm without Using Multi-writers

In this section we give an algorithm, called procedure n-$turn$, for the *turn* function in the single-writer/multi-reader shared memory model, where n is the number of users as well as the number of processes. The algorithm proposed here does not use time-stamps.

The waiting region is essentially divided into six parts/sections. In the $n \times n$ shared array $PView$, each row i is writable by process i and readable by all. The same applies to $WRView[1..n]$. An entry of "1" in position $PView[i, q]$ means that process q was already in the waiting region when process i got there. Other values for the entries will be defined as they are introduced.

Below, we discuss each section in greater detail:

- *Registration section* (lines 02 − 03): Process i checks in.
- *Give Priority section* (lines 04 − 08): Process i checks and writes which processes were originally and/or are currently (to the best of its knowledge) in the waiting region, and it also identifies those processes that asked for priority, as well as those that gave priority to process i during its previous stay in the waiting region. If it finds a process q whose $PView[q, i]$ entry is equal to "3" (a notification by q to process i that q asks for priority), then process i enters a "2" in its $PView[i, q]$ location so that q may eventually proceed to the service region via line 12:b.
- *Prevent Cycle section* (lines 10 − 11): Process i checks if by releasing itself via line 12:d it could produce a cycle of mutually releasing processes, if that is the case, i does not proceed.
- *Decide section* (line 12): Process i checks the $PView$ array, as well as its own local memory $LPView_i$, to determine if it can proceed to the service region. Note that if a process q gave process i prior permission, then, since i has already left the waiting region and came back, process q should now have priority. This is enforced via line 12:c. If two or more processes happened to request priority from each other simultaneously, then all such processes, except the one with the highest identification number (*id* for short) will be allowed to proceed to the service region via line 12:d.
- *Ask for Priority section* (line 13): Getting here indicates that process i could not proceed to the service region and had to stay behind because it was the only one in the waiting region, or it tied with other processes, but it had the highest *id*, it really was the last process to enter the waiting region, or it simply could not make a definite determination. The bookkeeping in line 13 is done so that process i which had to stay behind in the waiting region (for whatever reason) will inform all processes q which did not already give or receive priority to or from i, that next time around they enter the waiting region, they must give priority to i. This section is also used to force a "3 − 3" tie for requests between processes that arrived simultaneously, which will eventually lead to an exit via line 12:d.
- *Check-out section* (lines 15 − 16) Process i exits the waiting region and resets the shared variables as needed.

procedure n-*turn*
shared variables
  $PView[1..n, 1..n]$, each row i $(1 \leq i \leq n)$ writable by process i and
  readable by all, for each (i, j) $(1 \leq i, j \leq n)$ $PView[i, j] \in \{0, 1, 2, 3\}$,
  initially 0;
  $WRView[1..n]$, each entry i writable by process i and readable by all,
  for each i $WRView[i] \in \{0, 1\}$, initially 0;

$Flag[1..n, 1..n]$, each row i ($1 \leq i \leq n$) writable by process i and readable by all, initially **false**;

process i
   input actions {inputs to process i from user U_i}: $wish_i$, $exit_i$;
   output actions {outputs from process i to user U_i}: $serve_i$, rem_i;
   local variables: $LPView_i[1..n]$; $LWRView_i[1..n]$;

** remainder region **

```
01: wishᵢ:
02:    WRView[i] := 1;
03:    for q := 1 to n do begin
          LWRViewᵢ[q]:=WRView[q]; LPViewᵢ[q]:=PView[q,i] end;
04:    for q := 1 to n do if (i ≠ q) then
05:      if (LPViewᵢ[q] = 2) then PView[i,q] := 1
06:        else if (LPViewᵢ[q] = 3) then PView[i,q] := 2
07:          else if (LPViewᵢ[q] = 1) then PView[i,q] := 3
08:            else PView[i,q]:=LWRViewᵢ[q];
09:    while true do begin
10:      for q := i + 1 to n do Flag[i,q] := false;
11:      for q := i + 1 to n do if
            (PView[i,q] = 1 and LPViewᵢ[q] = 0) or
            (PView[i,q] = 2 and LPViewᵢ[q] = 3) or
            (PView[i,q] = 1 and LPViewᵢ[q] = 2)
            then Flag[i,q] := true;
12:      for q := 1 to n do if
  a:        (LPViewᵢ[q] = 1 and PView[i,q] = 0) or
  b:        (LPViewᵢ[q] = 2 and PView[i,q] = 3) or
  c:        (LPViewᵢ[q] = 1 and PView[i,q] = 2) or
  d:        (LPViewᵢ[q] = 3 and PView[i,q] = 3 and i < q and
            ((¬Flag[i,q]∧ ¬Flag[i,q + 1] ∧ ...∧ ¬Flag[i,n]) or
            (∃ (r,s), r,s > i | Flag[i,s] ∧ Flag[r,s])))
            then goto 15;
13:      for q := 1 to n do if
            (LPViewᵢ[q] = 0 and PView[i,q] = 2) or
            (LPViewᵢ[q] ≠ 2 and PView[i,q] ≠ 2) then PView[i,q] := 3;
14:      for q := 1 to n do LPViewᵢ[q]:=PView[q,i]
       end (* while *);

15:    WRView[i] := 0;
16:    for q := 1 to n do begin
          if (PView[i,q] ≠ 1) then PView[i,q] := 0;  Flag[i,q] := false
    end;
17:    serveᵢ;
```

** service region **

```
18: exitᵢ:
19:    remᵢ;
```

4   Correctness of the Algorithm

Let us first informally explain how and why the algorithm n-*turn* works. As stated before, most of the communication between the processes is carried out via the $PView$ array. In fact, since its main diagonal is never used, the $WRView$ array could have been represented there, but for clarity of presentation, we chose to use two separate arrays.

There are four possible values that may be entered into $PView[i, q]$. An entry of "0" means upon entering the waiting region, process i did not encounter process q, whereas an entry of "1" means that it did. Process i will request priority from process q by setting the $PView[i, q]$ entry to "3". This request will be granted by q upon its next visit to the waiting region, which will be indicated with an entry of "2" in $PView$, see line 06.

Each process i uses a local array $LPView_i[1..n]$ to store the contents of the ith column of the (shared) $PView$ array. This approach is used in order to provide (for each process) as consistent a snapshot of $PView$ array's contents as possible.

When deciding if process i may actually leave the waiting region, it must find proof that either one of four conditions (labeled 12: a through d) was met:

(a) A new process q arrived into the waiting region and it had originally not been seen by process i. (case when $PView_i[q] = 1$ and $PView[i, q] = 0$),
(b) i requested priority from q and it was granted (case when $PView_i[q] = 2$ and $PView[i, q] = 3$),
(c) i gave priority to q, but q no longer needs it as it reentered the waiting region (case when $PView_i[q] = 1$ and $PView[i, q] = 2$),
(d) If two or more processes happened to request priority from each other simultaneously, then all such processes, except the one with the highest id number will be allowed to proceed to the service region.

The above exit conditions are mutually exclusive and we will show that, together with the cycle prevention mechanism, implemented via the shared array $Flag$, they guarantee that when process i leaves, at least one process will remain in the waiting region.

Before proving that the waiting region cannot become empty (once it has been occupied by any process), we shall define several terms. For a pair of processes, e.g., i and q, process q is said to *release* process i, written $i <= q$, if the pair satisfies any of the exit conditions a–d. Note that q releasing i does not imply that q has to wait for i to exit the waiting region before q can proceed, i.e., q is not being *blocked* by i. For a pair of processes, i and q, process q is said to *implicitly release* process i, written $i <= *q$, if there exists a sequence of m ($m < n - 1$) unique processes such that $i <= q_1 <= q_2 <= ... <= q_m <= q$. Observe that the concept of implicit release preserves the temporal consistency enforced by the exit conditions. Furthermore, process q need not be present in the waiting region in order for it to release process i. As a process (re)enters the waiting region, and starts to assign its new priorities to other processes (lines 05 - 08), the previously defined release relationships naturally disappear. It follows that no process may appear more than once in any implicit release path.

For any fixed point in time, the release relationship defines a partial temporal order between the processes. In order to show that this order is consistent, we must prove that at no time directed cycles may occur in a precedence graph, called the $<=$-graph, whose nodes correspond to the processes and the directed edges correspond to the release relationships. The absence of cycles in such a $<=$-graph also implies that within any group of processes they cannot all grant releases to each other simultaneously and, thereby, make the waiting region empty.

In order to show that no directed cycles exist in $<=$-graphs, we will prove the existence of transitivity in a weak sense. It is possible for three processes to have the following relationship: $q_i <= q_j <= q_k$, but not the case of $q_i <= q_k$ because process q_i could have already left the waiting region and not even requested priority from q_k. For this reason, we define *pseudo-transitivity* in $<=$-graphs as an existence of a virtual release of process q_i by q_k if q_i would have been released by q_k had process q_j not come along.

Lemma 1. *The $<=$-graphs corresponding to two processes are acyclic.*

Proof. Conditions a–d directly disallow mutual release which makes the graph acyclic. Note that for any (non-failed) process pair, eventually one process would release the other in some finite number of steps. □

Lemma 2. *Pseudo-transitivity is preserved by the $<=$-graphs.*

Proof. Let us take three processes, q_i, q_j, and q_k and let us assume that $q_i <= q_j$ and $q_j <= q_k$. It must be shown that $q_i <= q_k$. We now have $q_i <=_1 q_j <=_2 q_k$, where a suffix of $<=$ shows a release type. There are sixteen possible pairings of release types for $<=_1$ and $<=_2$. They are $\{(a,a), (a,b), ..., (d,d)\}$. In the first fifteen instances, we have direct evidence that process q_k last came in either after q_j or after q_i, or both. This is because for condition (a), the released process was seen in the waiting region when the granting process arrived. For (b), the priority of "2" is given in response to a request of "3" as soon as the granting process *enters* the waiting region (see line 06), so the requesting process was already in the waiting region (and, hypothetically, may have even left it) when the granting process arrived. In case of (c), the process that granted priority "2" was in the waiting region (and, hypothetically, may have even left it) while the recipient left, got service, reentered the waiting region, and reset its entry to "1" in line 05. Note that any potential cycles involving release pairs that contain exactly one $<=_d$ release are prevented by checking the $flag_i$ condition in line 12:d. For the $q_i <=_d q_j <=_d k$ case, the only way it could take place is if $i < j < k$, making $q_k <= q_i$ impossible. Therefore, $q_i <= q_k$. □

Lemma 3. *The $<=$-graphs corresponding to n processes are acyclic.*

Proof. The proof is by induction on n, with the base case already covered by Lemma 1. Let us assume that all $<=$-graphs for up to k processes are always acyclic. We must show that an introduction of process q_{k+1} can not produce a cycle of length $k + 1$. Cycles of shorter length would have been addressed by the inductive hypothesis. Let k processes be present when process q_{k+1} arrives. In order for a $k + 1$ cycle to have a chance to exist, the k processes must have already formed a (directed) path via the release relations, which would have the form $q_1 <= q_2 <= ... <= q_k$. Process q_{k+1} would then have to release q_k and be released by q_1. Since $q_1 <= *q_k$, it follows that process q_k came in after q_1 (or, at least, not before), and by pseudo-transitivity $q_1 <= q_k$, i.e., q_k could have released q_1 directly. Therefore, for the cycle to exist, process q_{k+1} would have to be released by q_1, which cannot take place since by pseudo-transitivity $q_1 <= q_{k+1}$. □

Lemma 4. *Procedure n-turn will not allow the waiting region to become empty.*

Proof. The exits of processes from the waiting region may only take place when the conditions in line 12 are satisfied. For only two processes, conditions in line 12 prevent both from leaving at the same time. The remaining possibility, where three or more processes give mutual release to each other is also impossible because the corresponding $<=$-graph is acyclic. □

Lemma 5. *Procedure n-turn provides lockout avoidance.*

Proof. Let us assume that process i has entered the waiting region and failed to meet any of the conditions given in line 12. In getting to line 13, process i requests from the appropriate processes that it be given priority. Note that the conditions in line 13 will eventually be satisfied once some process q has exited the waiting region and reentered setting its *PView* priorities to "1" or "2" in lines 06 or 07, respectively. Therefore, a process will always eventually be able to write down its priority request and proceed to the service region once one of the conditions in line 12 has been met. □

Theorem 1. *Procedure n-turn correctly implements the turn function.*

Proof. Follows directly from Lemmas 1–5. □

5   Conclusion

The implementation of the algorithm proposed here is much simpler than the general method of simulation required for the multi-writer/reader operations to be carried out using single-writer/multi-reader shared variables. As presented, the algorithm requires $O(n^2)$ bits of memory.

The running time (technically, the waiting time) for each processor in the waiting region is bounded by $O(n)l + c$, where n is the number of processes, l is an upper bound on the time between any two successive atomic steps, and c is an upper bound on time durations between which at least one process enters the waiting region. For all practical purposes, the algorithm is optimal, since each process should perform $O(n)$ operations just to establish the whereabouts of the remaining $n - 1$ processes. The bound of c cannot be overcome as well (e.g., consider a situation such that there is only one process in the waiting region).

The algorithm is robust in that it will operate properly even in the presence of up to $n - 2$ failures of the stopping type, although the algorithm of course cannot guarantee that the process in the waiting region is a non-failed one.

References

1. Y. Afek, D. Dolev. E. Gafni, M. Merritt, and N. Shavit, "A bounded first-in, first-enable solution to the l-exclusion problem", *ACM Transactions on Programming Languages and Systems*, vol.16, pp.939–953, 1994.
2. D. Dolev and N. Shavit, "Bounded concurrent time-stamp systems are constructible", *21st Annual ACM Symposium on the Theory of Computing*, New York, pp. 454–465, 1989.
3. C. Dwork and O. Waarts, "Simple and efficient bounded concurrent timestamping or bounded concurrent timestamp systems are comprehensible", *24th Annual ACM Symposium on the Theory of Computing*, Victoria, B.C., pp. 655–666, 1992.
4. M. J. Fischer, N. A. Lynch, J. E. Burns, and A. Borodin, "Resource allocation with immunity to limited process failure", *20th Annual Symposium on Foundations of Computer Science*, San Juan, Puerto Rico, pp. 234–254, 1979.
5. S. Haldar and P. Vitanyi, "Bounded concurrent timestamps using vector clocks", *J. of the ACM*, vol.49, pp. 101–126, 2002.
6. Y. Igarashi and Y. Nishitani, "Speedup of the n-process mutual exclusion algorithm", *Parallel Processing Letters*, vol.9, pp. 475–485, 1999.
7. L. Lamport, "On interprocess communication, Part II: Algorithms", *Distributed Computing*, vol.1, pp. 86–101, 1986.
8. K. Li, I. Tromp, and P. M. B. Vitanyi, "How to share concurrent wait-free variables", *J. of the ACM*, vol.43, pp. 723–746, 1996.
9. N. A. Lynch, "Distributed Algorithms", Morgan Kaufmann, San Francisco, California, 1996.
10. K. Obokata, M. Omori, K. Motegi, and Y. Igarashi, "A lockout avoidance algorithm without using time-stamps", *7th Annual International Computing and Combinatorics Conference (COCOON 2001)*, Guilin, China, Lecture Notes in Computer Science, vol.2108, pp. 571–575, 2001.
11. M. Omori, K. Obokata, K. Motegi and Y. Igarashi, "Analysis of some lockout avoidance algorithms for the k-exclusion problem", *Interdisciplinary Information Sciences*, vol.8, pp. 187–198, 2003.
12. G. L. Peterson, "Myths about the mutual exclusion problem", *Information Processing Letters*, vol.12, pp. 115–116, 1981.
13. G. L. Peterson and M. J. Fischer, "Economical solutions for the critical section problem in a distributed system", *Proceedings of the 9th Annual ACM Symposium on Theory of Computing*, Boulder, Colorado, pp. 91–97, 1977.

An Optimal Parallel Algorithm for
c-Vertex-Ranking of Trees

Md. Abul Kashem and M. Ziaur Rahman

Department of Computer Science and Engineering
Bangladesh University of Engineering and Technology, Dhaka 1000, Bangladesh
kashem@cse.buet.ac.bd

Abstract. For a positive integer c, a c-vertex-ranking of a graph $G = (V, E)$ is a labeling of the vertices of G with integers such that, for any label i, deletion of all vertices with labels $> i$ leaves connected components, each having at most c vertices with label i. The c-vertex-ranking problem is to find a c-vertex-ranking of a given graph using the minimum number of ranks. In this paper we give an optimal parallel algorithm for solving the c-vertex-ranking problem on trees that takes $O(\log_2 n)$ parallel time using linear number of operations on the EREW PRAM model.

Keywords: Ordered coloring, Parallel algorithm, Separator-tree, Tree, Vertex-ranking.

1 Introduction

An ordinary *vertex-ranking* of a graph G is a labeling (ranking) of the vertices of G with positive integers such that every path between any two vertices with the same label i contains a vertex with label $j > i$ [4]. Clearly a vertex-labeling is a vertex-ranking if and only if, for any label i, deletion of all vertices with labels $> i$ leaves connected components, each having at most one vertex with label i. The integer label of a vertex is called the *rank* of the vertex. A vertex-ranking of G using the minimum number of ranks is called an *optimal vertex-ranking* of G. The *vertex-ranking problem* is to find an optimal vertex-ranking of a given graph.

The vertex-ranking problem has received much attention because of the growing number of applications. The problem of finding an optimal vertex-ranking of a graph G is equivalent to the problem of finding a minimum-height vertex-separator tree of G [8,9]. The vertex-ranking problem plays an important role for the parallel Cholesky factorization of matrices [9]. Yet other applications of the vertex-ranking problem lie in the field of VLSI-layout design [4].

Pothen proved that the vertex-ranking problem is *NP*-hard in general [2,7], while Iyer *et al.* presented an $O(n \log n)$ time sequential algorithm to solve the vertex-ranking problem for trees [4]. Then Schäffer obtained a linear-time sequential algorithm by refining their algorithm and its analysis [8]. Bodlaender *et al.* presented a polynomial-time sequential algorithm to solve the vertex-ranking

T. Ibaraki, N. Katoh, and H. Ono (Eds.): ISAAC 2003, LNCS 2906, pp. 464–473, 2003.

problem for partial k-trees, that is, graphs of treewidth bounded a fixed integer k [2]. On the other hand, de la Torre et $al.$ presented a parallel algorithm to solve the vertex-ranking problem for trees in $O(\log_2 n)$ parallel time using $O(n^2)$ operations on the CREW PRAM model [3].

Generalization of the vertex-ranking problem was introduced in [9]. For a positive integer c, a c-vertex-ranking of a graph G is a labeling of the vertices of G with integers such that, for any label i, deletion of all vertices with labels $> i$ leaves connected components, each having at most c vertices with label i [9]. Clearly an ordinary vertex-ranking is a 1-vertex-ranking. The minimum number of ranks needed for a c-vertex-ranking of G is called the c-$vertex$-$ranking$ $number$, and is denoted by $r_c(G)$. A c-vertex-ranking of G using $r_c(G)$ ranks is called an $optimal$ c-$vertex$-$ranking$ of G. The c-$vertex$-$ranking$ $problem$ is to find an optimal c-vertex-ranking of a given graph. Zhou et $al.$ have obtained a linear-time sequential algorithm to solve the c-vertex-ranking problem for trees [9]. Recently Kashem et $al.$ have presented a polynomial-time sequential algorithm and an $O(\log_2 n)$ time parallel algorithm for partial k-trees [6]. Note that an ordinary tree is a partial 1-tree. Thus putting $k = 1$ in their algorithm we obtain a parallel algorithm to solve the c-vertex-ranking problem for trees in $O(\log_2 n)$ time using $O(n^{61} \log^{32} n)$ operations on the common CRCW PRAM model [6].

In this paper we present an optimal parallel algorithm to solve the c-vertex-ranking problem on trees for any positive integer c in time $O(\log_2 n)$ using linear operations on the EREW PRAM model. Our algorithm uses techniques employed by Torre et $al.$ [3] for the ordinary vertex-ranking problem, and Zhou et $al.$ [9] for c-vertex-ranking problem, as well as new techniques specified to the parallel algorithm to solve c-vertex-ranking problem.

2 Preliminaries

In this section we present some terms and easy observations. Let $T = (V, E)$ be a tree with vertex set V and edge set E. We often denote $V(T)$ as the vertex set of T. Let n be the number of vertices in T. T is a free tree but we regard T as a rooted tree for convenience sake: an arbitrary vertex of tree T is designated as the root of T. The maximal subtree of T rooted at a vertex $w \in V$ is denoted by $T(w)$. We will use notions as: $root$, $internal$ $vertex$, $child$, $leaf$, $ancestor$, and $descendant$ in their usual meaning.

Let φ be a vertex-labeling of a tree $T = (V, E)$ with positive integers. The label (rank) of a vertex $v \in V$ is denoted by $\varphi(v)$. The number of ranks used by a vertex-labeling φ is denoted by $\#\varphi$. One may assume without loss of generality that φ uses the consecutive integers $1, 2, \ldots, \#\varphi$ as the ranks.

For subtree $T' = (V', E')$ of T, we denote by $\varphi|T'$ a restriction of φ to T': let $\eta = \varphi|T'$, then $\eta(v) = \varphi(v)$ for $v \in V(T')$ [9]. Let a vertex $v \in V$ be an ancestor of another vertex $u \in V$ in T. Vertex u is said to be $visible$ from vertex v under φ in T, if every vertex on the path from u to v in T has a rank $\le \varphi(u)$. The rank $\varphi(u)$ of u is also said to be visible from v under φ in T if the vertex u is so. Thus the smallest rank visible from v is equal to $\varphi(v)$.

Zhou *et al.* have shown that the c-vertex-ranking of a tree can be characterized by the number of visible vertices in the following lemma [9].

Lemma 1. *A vertex-labeling φ of T is a c-vertex-ranking of T if and only if*

(a) *$\varphi|T(w)$ is a c-vertex-ranking of $T(w)$ for every child w of the root of T; and*

(b) *at most c vertices of the same rank are visible from the root under φ.* □

Iyer *et al.* introduced the idea of a "critical list" to solve the ordinary vertex-ranking problem for trees [4]. Later similar idea was used to define *visible-list* $L(\varphi)$ as follows [6,9]:

$$L(\varphi) = \{\varphi(v)|v \in V \text{ is visible from the root}\}.$$

The ranks in the list $L(\varphi)$ are sorted in non-increasing order. The list $L(\varphi)$ may contain same ranks with repetition $\leq c$. For an integer l, we denote by $count(L(\varphi), l)$ the number of l's contained in $L(\varphi)$. By Lemma 1, $count(L(\varphi), l) \leq c$ for each rank l.

For a list L and an integer l, we define a sublist $[l \leq L]$ of L as follows [9]:

$$[l \leq L] = \{i \in L|l \leq i\}.$$

Similarly we define sublists $[l < L], [L \geq l], [L > l], [L = l], [l_1 > L > l_2], [l_1 < L < l_2], [l_1 \leq L \leq l_2]$ of L for integers l, l_1, and l_2.

A *critical c-vertex-ranking* [9] of tree T is defined to be a c-vertex-ranking with the lexicographically smallest list of visible ranks. Every critical c-vertex-ranking φ is optimal, because all vertices of the largest rank are visible and hence the topmost rank in $L(\varphi)$ is equal to the number of ranks used by φ.

Let $d(u)$ be the number of children of an internal vertex u in T, and let $v_1, v_2, \ldots, v_{d(u)}$ be the children of u. The idea is to construct a critical c-vertex-ranking of $T(u)$ from critical c-vertex-rankings φ_i of $T(v_i), i = 1, 2, \ldots, d(u)$. By Lemma 1 we have the following lemma [9]

Lemma 2. *Let φ_i be a critical c-vertex-ranking of $T(v_i), i = 1, 2, \ldots, d(u)$. Then $T(u)$ has a critical c-vertex-ranking η such that $\eta|T(v_i) = \varphi_i$ for every $i, 1 \leq i \leq d(u)$.*
□

We now cite the following Lemmas 3 – 5 from [9]. The Lemma 3 tells us about the upper bound of the ranks required to construct a c-vertex-ranking of $T(u)$ from the critical c-vertex-rankings of $T(v_i), 1 \leq i \leq d(u)$. Let m be the maximum rank used by the c-vertex-rankings of $T(v_i)$ for every $i, 1 \leq i \leq d(u)$.

Lemma 3. *$r_c(T(u)) = m$ or $m + 1$.*
□

In order to find a critical c-vertex-ranking η of $T(u)$ from $\varphi_i, 1 \leq i \leq d(u)$, we need the following two lemmas.

Lemma 4. *If $r_c(T(u)) = m + 1$, then*

$$\eta(v) = \begin{cases} m + 1, & \text{if } v = u, \text{ and} \\ \varphi_i(v), & \text{if } v \in V(T(v_i)) \text{ and } 1 \leq i \leq d(u) \end{cases}$$

is a critical c-vertex-ranking of $T(u)$ and $L(\eta) = \{m + 1\}$.
□

Lemma 5. *If $r_c(T(u)) = m$, then*

$$\eta(v) = \begin{cases} \beta, & \text{if } v = u, \text{ and} \\ \varphi_i(v), & \text{if } v \in V(T(v_i)) \text{ and } 1 \le i \le d(u) \end{cases}$$

is a critical c-vertex-ranking of $T(u)$, where β is the minimum rank such that

(a) $\sum_{i=1}^{d(u)} count(L(\varphi_i), \beta) \le c - 1$, and
(b) $\sum_{i=1}^{d(u)} count(L(\varphi_i), \gamma) \le c$ for every rank $\gamma, \beta + 1 \le \gamma \le m$.

Furthermore $L(\eta) = \{\beta\} \cup [\beta \le \cup_{i=1}^{d(u)} L(\varphi_i)]$. □

Let α be the largest integer such that $\sum_{i=1}^{d(u)} count(L(\varphi_i), \alpha) > c$. We assume that $\alpha = 0$ if $\sum_{i=1}^{d(u)} count(L(\varphi_i), l) \le c$ for all $l, l > 0$. From the definition of β it is clear that $\beta > \alpha$.

We then cite the following lemma from [6,9].

Lemma 6. *Every tree T of n vertices satisfies $r_c(T) = O(\log_{c+1} n)$.* □

3   Bottom-up Algebraic Tree Computation

In this paper we use bottom-up algebraic tree computation (B-ATC) technique [1] to develop optimal parallel algorithm of the c-vertex-ranking problem. A *structure* is a triple (S, NF, EF) consisting of a set S, a vertex function set $NF \subseteq \{f | f : S \times S \to S\}$, and an edge function set $EF \subseteq \{g | g : S \to S\}$. A bottom-up algebraic computation tree on (S, NF, EF) is a binary tree T such that each leaf v of T is labeled by a value $VAL(v) \in S$; each internal vertex u of T is labeled by a function $f_u \in NF$; and each edge e of T is labeled by a function $g_e \in EF$.

In order to solve the B-ATC problems in parallel, Abrahamson *et al.* introduced the following *shunt operation* [1]. Let u be a vertex of T with left child v_1, right child v_2 and parent w. Let $e_1 = (v_1, u), e_2 = (v_2, u)$, and $e_0 = (u, w)$. Suppose v_1 is a leaf. A shunt operation on v_1 is as follows: delete v_1 and u from T and make v_2 the left child of w. Let $e' = (v_2, w)$ be the new edge. For the B-ATC problem, assign e' a function $g_{e'}$ defined by

$$g_{e'}(x) = g_{e_0}(f_u(g_{e_1}(VAL(v_1)), g_{e_2}(x))),$$

where x is the value associated with node v_2 that is not calculated yet. If the right child v_2 of u is a leaf, a shunt operation performed on v_2 is defined similarly. Clearly, a shunt operation does not affect subsequent evaluation on T. The following algorithm solves the B-ATC problems [5].

Algorithm *Tree_Contraction*
Input: A rooted binary tree T such that each vertex has exactly two children.
Output: T is converted to a three-node binary tree.
begin

1   label the leaves of T consecutively from the left to the right, excluding the leftmost and the rightmost leaves, and store the labeled leaves in an array A of size n;
2   **for** $\lceil \log(n+1) \rceil$ iterations **do**
3   apply the shunt operation concurrently to all the elements of A_{odd} that are left children;
4   apply the shunt operation to the rest of the elements in A_{odd};
5   set $A := A_{even}$;
  end;

The following theorem has been proved in [5].

Theorem 1. *Algorithm Tree_Contraction correctly contracts the input binary tree into a three-node binary tree. This algorithm can be implemented on the EREW PRAM in $O(\log_2 n)$ time using a linear number of operations, where n is the number of vertices in the input tree.*   □

4   An Optimal Parallel Algorithm

The main result of this paper is the following theorem.

Theorem 2. *An optimal c-vertex-ranking of a tree T can be found in $O(\log_2 n)$ parallel time using $O(n)$ operations on the EREW PRAM model for any positive integer c, where n is the number of vertices in T.*

Before proving the Theorem 2, we have to convert an arbitrary rooted tree into a regular binary tree to solve the c-vertex-ranking problem using B-ATC. We now show how an arbitrary tree T rooted at u can be converted to a regular binary tree T_b [3]. T_b is constructed by replacing every vertex u of T having d children by $d+1$ vertices $u^1, u^2, \ldots, u^{d+1}$. In T_b, u^{i+1} is the right child of u^i. If vertex v is the i-th child of u in T, then v^1 is the left child of u^i in T_b. In binary tree T_b, the nodes with superscript '1' represents a node of tree T, on the other hand nodes with other superscripts are dummy nodes that do not correspond to a node of tree T.

We define the triple (S, NF, EF) for the c-vertex-ranking problem. The set S consists of the lists of visible ranks of the tree T_b. The dummy leaves of T_b are assigned with an empty list. And the leaves of T_b that correspond to leaves of T are assigned rank 1 and a list $\{1\}$.

We define two types of functions in the domain NF. Internal vertices u^i's are assigned with function $f \in NF$ when $i = 1$ (internal vertices of T_b that corresponds to internal vertices of T). Function f calculates the visible list at node u^i, denoted by $L(u^i)$, from the visible lists $L(v^1)$ and $L(v^2)$, where v^1 and v^2 are the children of vertex u^i. The function is denoted by the following equation:

$$f(L(v^1), L(v^2)) = \{\beta\} \cup [\beta \leq L(v^1)] \cup [\beta \leq L(v^2)] = L(u^i). \tag{1}$$

Here β is the minimum rank that can be assigned to the vertex u^i. So, function f needs to calculate $L(u^i)$ as well as to find the minimum rank that can be assigned to u^i.

Internal vertices u^i's are assigned with function $f' \in NF$ when $i \neq 1$ (the dummy internal vertices of T_b). Function f' calculates the visible list $L(u^i)$ for the vertex u^i which is denoted by the following equation:

$$f'(L(v^1), L(v^2)) = L(v^1) \cup L(v^2) = L(u^i), \tag{2}$$

where v^1 and v^2 are the children of vertex u^i.

A function $g \in EF$ is assigned to each edge of T_b which is an identity function. The function g simply returns the visible list $L(v)$ to the vertex u, where u is the parent of v. Function g is denoted by the following equation:

$$g(L(v)) = f'(\phi, L(v)) = \phi \cup L(v) = L(v), \tag{3}$$

where ϕ is an empty visible list.

Then the following parallel algorithm solves c-vertex-ranking on a tree T.

Algorithm *Optimal_c-vertex-ranking*
Input: A tree T.
Output: An optimal c-vertex-ranking of tree T.
begin
1   convert tree T into an ordered regular binary tree T_b;
2   label all dummy leaves of the T_b by rank 0 and an empty visible list;
3   assign all other leaves by rank 1 and a visible list $\{1\}$;
4   label the edges by identity function g;
5   label all dummy internal vertices by function f' ;
6   label all other internal vertices by function f;
7   perform B-ATC on T_b, by calling the tree contraction algorithm, to find a
     rank for the internal vertices of T_b that corresponds a vertex in tree T;
end;

The following lemma proves that the functions f, f', and g associated with the nodes and edges of tree T_b calculate the list of visible ranks correctly.

Lemma 7. *For every vertex u of the tree T rooted at r, the function associated to vertex u^1 of T_b calculates the visible list $L(u)$ in T.*

Proof. We first observe that if $w_1, w_2, \ldots, w_d$ are u's children in T and the minimum rank that can be assigned to u is β, then

$$L(u) = \{\beta\} \cup [\beta \leq L(w_1)] \cup [\beta \leq L(w_2)] \cup \ldots \cup [\beta \leq L(w_d)].$$

Let us consider the case with $d = 3$. Then according to Lemmas 4 and 5, the rank β of vertex u is calculated from the lists $L(w_1), L(w_2)$, and $L(w_3)$, and

$$L(u) = \{\beta\} \cup [\beta \leq L(w_1)] \cup [\beta \leq L(w_2)] \cup [\beta \leq L(w_3)].$$

Now in tree T_b, the visible list $L(u^1)$ is calculated using function f. So by Eqs. (1) – (3), we have

$$
\begin{aligned}
L(u^1) &= f(g(L(w_1^1)), g(L(u^2))) = f(L(w_1^1), f'(g(L(w_2^1)), g(L(u^3)))) \\
&= f(L(w_1^1), f'(L(w_2^1), f'(L(w_3^1), L(u^4)))) \\
&= f(L(w_1^1), f'(L(w_2^1), L(w_3^1))) = f(L(w_1^1), L(w_2^1) \cup L(w_3^1)) \\
&= \{\beta\} \cup [\beta \le L(w_1^1)] \cup [\beta \le L(w_2^1)] \cup [\beta \le L(w_3^1)].
\end{aligned}
\tag{4}
$$

Since $L(w_1) = L(w_1^1)$, $L(w_2) = L(w_2^1)$ and $L(w_3) = L(w_3^1)$, by Eq. (4) we have $L(u^1) = L(u)$.

Thus the functions associated with the vertex u^1 calculates the visible list $L(u)$ correctly which belongs to the list of visible ranks of tree $T(u)$ and in doing this it finds the rank for the vertex u of T which is β. □

We use a bit string to represent the list of visible ranks at the vertices. For every rank we reserve $\lceil \log_2(c+1) \rceil + 1$ bits. Since by Lemma 1, there could be at most c vertices visible from a vertex in a c-vertex-ranking φ of T, $\lceil \log_2(c+1) \rceil$ bits are sufficient to represent $count(L(\varphi), l)$ for each visible rank $l \in L(\varphi)$. We use one more bit to accommodate the value obtained from the addition of two visible lists. According to Lemma 6 the length of this bit string is

$$
\begin{aligned}
&= \lceil \log_{c+1} n \rceil (\lceil \log_2(c+1) \rceil + 1) \text{ bits} \\
&\le \log_2 n + 2 \log_{c+1} n + \log_2(c+1) + 2 \text{ bits} \\
&= \log_2 4(c+1)n^3 \text{ bits}
\end{aligned}
$$

Since the maximum numerical value a bit string can contain is $\le 4(c+1)n^3$, we can treat these bit strings as numbers.

In function f at first we unify two lists obtained from two children. This unification can be done by adding two lists and is shown by the following equation.

$$
L = L^1 + L^2,
\tag{5}
$$

where the lists L^1 and L^2 are the lists obtained from two children. Each of the lists L^1 and L^2 have values at most c at every field i. When we add two lists the result of adding the values in rank i must be at most $2c$. So, the result will be confined within the corresponding field.

Let X be another bit string containing value c in all fields. So, $X_1 = (X - 1)$ has c in all fields except the lowest field which has value $c - 1$. Let $R_1 = X_1 - L$. This is a simple binary subtraction. If L has 0 in one bit then R_1 will have same value in that bit as X_1 has. If both L and X_1 have 1 in the same bit then R_1 will have 0 in that bit. But if L has 1 and X_1 has 0 in the same bit we have to borrow from higher bits of X_1.

If a field in L contains value $\le c$ then this borrow of bits will not cross the boundary of that field. R_1 will have a value $\le c$ in that field and so the MSB of that field will be 0. On the other hand, if a field in L contains a value $> c$ then we have to borrow from higher bits which lay on the next higher field. So, the MSB of the corresponding field in R_1 will have 1.

Let l be a field containing a value $> c$ in L. We have to borrow from $(l+1)$-st field in X. The value of $(l+1)$-st field become $c-1$. Now if L has value $\leq (c-1)$ in $(l+1)$-st field then we donot need to borrow bit from $(l+2)$-nd field of X. So, MSB of $(l+1)$-st field in R_1 will be 0. But if $(l+1)$-st field has value $\geq c$ then we have to borrow from $(l+2)$-nd field of X and as a result MSB of $(l+2)$-nd field in R_1 will be 1. This process will continue for subsequent higher fields.

So, it is clear that for all fields with value $> c$ in L has 1 in MSB of R_1. And also if a field has value $> c$ and its subsequent higher fields contain value $\geq c$ then the MSBs of corresponding fields in R_1 will be 1.

Now, consider a case where all fields of L contains value $\leq c$. Let l be the lowest field containing value $< c$. All fields smaller than l has value c. According to the definition $\alpha = 0$ and $\beta = l$. When $l = 1$, the first field of L contains value $\leq (c-1)$. As X has $(c-1)$ in first field, we donot need to borrow and as a result MSB of the field in R_1 will 0. In that case MSBs of all the fields of R_1 will be 0. Let $l > 1$. Then first field of L contains c and first field of X_1 contains $(c-1)$. So, we have to borrow from second field of X_1 and MSB of first field in R_1 will be 1. As we borrow from second field of X_1, it now contains value $(c-1)$. If 2nd field of L has value c we have to borrow again from next higher field causing a 1 in the MSB of 2nd field of R_1. This process will continue upto field l. As field l in L has value $\leq (c-1)$, there will be no borrow from from next higher field and MSB of field l in R_1 will 0. It is clear that all fields $< l$ in R_1 has 1 in MSB.

According to definition, α be the highest field that contains value $> c$ in L. If all fields has value $\leq c$ then $\alpha = 0$. On the other hand β is the minimum field $> \alpha$ that contains value $< c$. So, all the fields $l, \beta > l > \alpha$ has value c in L. Let, γ be the highest among these fields. Certainly, $\beta = \gamma + 1$. From the above discussion, we know that MSBs of $\alpha(\alpha \neq 0)$ and all fields $l, \beta > l > \alpha$ in R_1 has 1. So, γ will be the highest field that has 1 in MSB.

Let Y be another bit string that has 1 in MSB and 0 in other bit positions of all fields. Let $R_2 = Y\mathbf{AND}\ R_1$, where $\mathbf{AND}$ is bitwise and operation. So, it clears all other bits except MSBs. All bits higher than MSB of field γ has 0 in R_2. Now, γ is the highest field that has a 1 in MSB. To find out γ we have to find the highest bit containing 1. We can find it by using logarithm. Let $R_3 = 2^{\lfloor \log_2 R_2 \rfloor}$. This operation finds the highest bit containing 1 and all other lower bits become 0. So in R_3, only MSB of γ has 1 and all other bits are 0. But MSB of γ has bit position $[(\lceil \log_2(c+1) \rceil + 1)\gamma - 1]$. Since $R_3 = 2^{(\lceil \log_2(c+1) \rceil + 1)\gamma - 1}$, we have

$$2^{\lfloor \log_2 R_2 \rfloor} = 2^{(\lceil \log_2(c+1) \rceil + 1)\gamma - 1}$$

$$\Rightarrow \gamma = \frac{1 + \lfloor \log_2 R_2 \rfloor}{\lceil \log_2(c+1) \rceil + 1} = \frac{1 + \lfloor \log_2(Y\mathbf{AND}\ (X-L-1)) \rfloor}{\lceil \log_2(c+1) \rceil + 1}. \tag{6}$$

In function f, we find β by $\beta = \gamma + 1$. This β is assigned as label to the corresponding node. After assigning the rank, all lower ranks will be hidden and number of visible labels at rank β will increase by 1. Let Z be another bit string containing 1 in all bits. $[2^{(\lceil \log_2(c+1) \rceil + 1)\gamma} - 1]$ is a bit string that has 1 in all bits of the fields $l, \gamma \geq l \geq 1$. So, $(Z - [2^{(\lceil \log_2(c+1) \rceil + 1)\gamma} - 1])$ has 0 in all bits of fields $l, \gamma \geq l \geq 1$ and 1 in all bits of fields $> \gamma$. Let $R_4 = L\ \mathbf{AND}\ (Z - [2^{(\lceil \log_2(c+1) \rceil + 1)\gamma} - 1])$.

All bits of the fields $l, \beta > l > 1$ in R_4 become 0 and other bits remain unchanged. This is equivalent to hide all labels $< \beta$. Again, $2^{(\lceil \log_2(c+1) \rceil + 1)\gamma}$ has only 1 in the LSB of field β and all other bits are 0. Let $R_5 = R_4 + 2^{(\lceil \log_2(c+1) \rceil + 1)\gamma}$. This is equivalent to add 1 in the field β of R_4 and R_5 represents the updated list of visible ranks. So, in function f, we can update the list L after assigning a rank by the following equation.

$$L = (L \textbf{ AND } [Z - \{2^{\gamma(\lceil \log_2(c+1) \rceil + 1)} - 1\}]) + 2^{\gamma(\lceil \log_2(c+1) \rceil + 1)}. \qquad (7)$$

Function f assigns rank β to the vertex and returns L found from Eq. (7).

In function f', we do not find β. So, the list L need not to be updated. Some fields of L may contain values $> c$. If we pass L to its parent then this list will be added to another list. This addition may cause overflow in some fields. But, we assume that addition of two lists does not overflow. So, we have to modify L in function f' so that the updated list L does not cause an overflow in parent node and this overflow will not influence in finding β.

When γ is found in function f' denote it by γ_c. Then clearly γ to be found in function of the parent node, denoted by γ_p, is not less than γ_c, that is, $\gamma_p \geq \gamma_c$. So, number of visible labels in ranks $< \gamma_c$ might be hidden. Again, actual number of visible labels at rank γ_c is not important. We can put 1 in MSB of field γ_c and make all other bits of the field 0. Still γ_p to be found in parent node will not be less than γ_c. On the other hand, it will not cause an overflow in parent, as corresponding field can contain at most $2^{\lceil \log_2(c+1) \rceil} + c \leq 2^{(\lceil \log_2(c+1) \rceil + 1)}$. The update procedure stated above can be done by the following equation.

$$L = (L \textbf{ AND } [Z - \{2^{\gamma(\lceil \log_2(c+1) \rceil + 1)} - 1\}]) + 2^{\gamma(\lceil \log_2(c+1) \rceil + 1) - 1}. \qquad (8)$$

We now give the following algorithms for functions f and f'.

Algorithm *function_f*
Input: Two visible lists denoted by L^1, L^2.
Output: A visible list denoted by L.
Variables: γ and β to hold the corresponding values.
begin
1    $L = L^1 + L^2$;
2   find γ using Eq. (6);
3    $\beta = \gamma + 1$;
4   update L using Eq. (7);
5   **return** L;
end;

Algorithm *function_f'*
Input: Two visible lists denoted by L^1, L^2.
Output: A visible list denoted by L.
Variables: γ to hold the corresponding values.
begin
1    $L = L^1 + L^2$;

2   find γ using Eq. (6);
3   update L using Eq. (8);
4   **return** L;
  end;

Now we are ready to prove Theorem 2. All the operations mentioned in Equations (5) – (8) are arithmetic and logical operations and can be done in $O(1)$ time. Note that although the number of ranks in a list is $O(\log_{c+1} n)$, we process the whole list as a single number. So, functions f, f' and g take $O(1)$ time using $O(1)$ operations on the EREW PRAM model if we can provide every processors a copy of bit strings X, Y and Z.

We have to initialize the bit strings X, Y, and Z for $O(n/\log_2 n)$ processors as $O(n/\log_2 n)$ processors are used in Tree contraction algorithm. Since a visible list contains $O(\log_{c+1} n)$ ranks, we can do this initialization in $O(\log_{c+1} n)$ time using $O(n)$ operations on the EREW PRAM model. Tree conversion can be done in $O(\log_2 n)$ time using $O(n)$ operations on the EREW PRAM model. So, our c-vertex-ranking algorithm takes $O(\log_2 n)$ parallel time using $O(n)$ operations on the EREW PRAM model. Thus we proved Theorem 2.

5 Conclusion

In this paper we present a parallel algorithm for solving the c-vertex-ranking problem on trees. We have used B-ATC to calculate the c-vertex-ranking of a tree that uses tree contraction algorithm. Our algorithm finds an optimal c-vertex-ranking of a given tree T in $O(\log_2 n)$ parallel time using $O(n)$ operations on the EREW PRAM model for any positive integer c, where n is number of vertices in the tree T.

References

1. K. Abrahamson, N. Dadoun, D. G. Kirkpatrick, and T. Przytycka, A simple parallel tree contraction algorithm, *Journal of Algorithms*, **10**(1989), pp. 287–302.
2. H. Bodlaender, J.S. Deogun, K. Jansen, T. Kloks, H. H. Müller, and Zs. Tuza, Rankings of graphs, *SIAM Journal of Discrete Math*, **21**(1998), pp. 168–181.
3. P. de la Torre, R. Greenlaw, and T.M. Przytycka, Optimal tree ranking is in NC, *Parallel Processing Letters*, **2**(1992), pp. 31–41.
4. A.V. Iyer, H.D. Ratliff, and G. Vijayan, Optimal vertex ranking of trees, *Information Processing Letters*, **28**(1988), pp. 225–229.
5. Josheph Já Já. *An Introduction to Parallel Algorithms*, Addison-Wesley, 1992.
6. M. A. Kashem, X. Zhou, and T. Nishizeki, Algorithms for generalized vertex-rankings of partial k-trees, *Theoretical Computer Science*, **240**(2000), pp. 407–427.
7. A. Pothen, The complexity of optimal elimination trees, Technical Report CS-88-13, Pennsylvania State University, U.S.A, 1988.
8. A.A. Schäffer, Optimal vertex ranking of trees in linear time, *Information Processing Letters*, **33**(1989), pp. 91–99.
9. X. Zhou, N. Nagai, and T. Nishizeki, Generalized vertex-rankings of trees, *Information Processing Letters*, **56**(1995), pp. 321–328.

The Student-Project Allocation Problem

David J. Abraham, Robert W. Irving, and David F. Manlove*

Department of Computing Science, University of Glasgow, Glasgow G12 8QQ, UK
{dabraham,rwi,davidm}@dcs.gla.ac.uk, Fax: +44 141 330 4913.

Abstract. We study the *Student-Project Allocation problem* (SPA), a generalisation of the classical Hospitals / Residents problem (HR). An instance of SPA involves a set of students, projects and lecturers. Each project is offered by a unique lecturer, and both projects and lecturers have capacity constraints. Students have preferences over projects, whilst lecturers have preferences over students. We present an optimal linear-time algorithm for allocating students to projects, subject to these preferences and capacities. In particular, the algorithm finds a *stable matching* of students to projects. Here, the concept of stability generalises the stability definition in the HR context. The stable matching produced by our algorithm is simultaneously best-possible for all students. The SPA problem model that we consider is very general and has applications to a range of different contexts besides student-project allocation.

1 Introduction

In many university departments, students seek a project in a given field of speciality as part of the upper level of their degree programme. Usually, a project can be filled by at most one student, though in some cases a project is suitable for more than one student to work on simultaneously. To give students something of a choice, there should be as wide a range of available projects as possible, and in any case the total number of project places should not be less than the total number of students. Typically a lecturer will also offer a range of projects, but does not necessarily expect that all will be taken up.

Each student has preferences over the available projects that he/she finds acceptable, whilst a lecturer will normally have preferences over the students that he/she is willing to supervise. There may also be upper bounds on the number of students that can be assigned to a particular project, and the number of students that a given lecturer is willing to supervise. In this paper we consider the problem of allocating students to projects based on these preference lists and capacity constraints – the so-called *Student-Project Allocation problem* (SPA).

SPA is an example of a *two-sided matching problem* [10], a large and very general class of problems in which the input set of participants can be partitioned into two disjoint sets A and B (in this case A is the set of students and B is the set of projects), and we seek to match members of A to members of B, i.e. to

---

* Supported by award NUF-NAL-02 from the Nuffield Foundation, and grant GR/R84597/01 from the Engineering and Physical Sciences Research Council.

T. Ibaraki, N. Katoh, and H. Ono (Eds.): ISAAC 2003, LNCS 2906, pp. 474–484, 2003.

find a subset of $A \times B$, subject to various criteria. These criteria usually involve capacity constraints, and/or preference lists, for example.

Both historical evidence (see e.g. [4, pp.3-4], [7]) and economic analysis [10] indicate that participants involved in two-sided matching problems should not be allowed to construct an allocation by approaching one another directly in order to make ad hoc arrangements. Instead, the allocation process should be automated by means of a centralised matching scheme. Moreover, it has been convincingly argued [9] that the key property that a matching constructed by such schemes should satisfy is *stability*. A formal definition of stability follows, but informally, a stable matching M guarantees that no two participants who are not matched together in M would rather be matched to one another than remain with their assignment in M. Such a pair of participants would form a private arrangement and would undermine the integrity of the matching.

The National Resident Matching Program (NRMP) [8] in the US is perhaps the largest and best-known example of a centralised matching scheme. It has been in operation since 1952, and currently handles the allocation of some 20,000 graduating medical students, or *residents*, to their first hospital posts, based on the preferences of residents over available hospital posts, and the preferences of hospital consultants over residents. The NRMP employs at its heart an efficient algorithm that essentially solves a variant of the classical Hospitals / Residents problem (HR) [3,4]. The algorithm finds a stable matching of residents to hospitals that is *resident-optimal*, in that each resident obtains the best hospital that he/she could obtain in any stable matching.

There are many other examples of centralised matching schemes, both in educational and vocational contexts. Many university departments in particular seek to automate the allocation of students to projects. However, as we discuss in greater detail later, an optimal linear-time algorithm for this setting cannot be obtained by simply reducing an instance of SPA to an instance of HR. Thus, a specialised algorithm is required for the SPA problem.

In this paper we present a linear-time algorithm for finding a stable matching, given an instance of SPA. This algorithm is *student-oriented*, in that it finds a *student-optimal* stable matching. In this matching, each student obtains the best project that he/she could obtain in any stable matching. Our algorithm is applicable for any context that fits into the SPA model, for example where applicants seek posts at large organisations, each split into several departments.

The remainder of this paper is structured as follows. In Section 2, a formal definition of the SPA problem is given. Then, in Section 3, the algorithm for SPA is presented, together with correctness proofs and an analysis of its complexity. Finally, Section 4 contains some conclusions and open problems.

2   Definition of the Student-Project Allocation Problem

An instance of the *Student-Project Allocation problem* (SPA) may be defined as follows. Let $S = \{s_1, s_2, \ldots, s_n\}$ be a set of *students*, let $P = \{p_1, p_2, \ldots, p_m\}$ be a set of *projects*, and let $L = \{l_1, l_2, \ldots, l_q\}$ be a set of *lecturers*. Each student

Student preferences

$s_1 : p_1 \ p_7$

$s_2 : p_1 \ p_2 \ p_3 \ p_4 \ p_5 \ p_6$

$s_3 : p_2 \ p_1 \ p_4$

$s_4 : p_2$

$s_5 : p_1 \ p_2 \ p_3 \ p_4$

$s_6 : p_2 \ p_3 \ p_4 \ p_5 \ p_6$

$s_7 : p_5 \ p_3 \ p_8$

Lecturer preferences

$l_1 : s_7 \ s_4 \ s_1 \ s_3 \ s_2 \ s_5 \ s_6$

$l_2 : s_3 \ s_2 \ s_6 \ s_7 \ s_5$

$l_3 : s_1 \ s_7$

l_1 offers p_1, p_2, p_3

l_2 offers p_4, p_5, p_6

l_3 offers p_7, p_8

Project capacities: $c_1 = 2$, $c_i = 1$ $(2 \le i \le 8)$

Lecturer capacities: $d_1 = 3$, $d_2 = 2$, $d_3 = 2$

Fig. 1. An instance of the Student-Project Allocation problem.

s_i supplies a preference list, ranking a subset of P in strict order. If project p_j appears on s_i's preference list, we say that s_i finds p_j *acceptable*. Denote by A_i the set of projects that s_i finds acceptable.

Each lecturer l_k *offers* a non-empty set of projects P_k, where $P_1, P_2, \ldots, P_q$ partitions P. Let $B_k = \{s_i \in S : P_k \cap A_i \ne \emptyset\}$ (i.e. B_k is the set of students who find acceptable a project offered by l_k). Lecturer l_k supplies a preference list, denoted by $\mathcal{L}_k$, ranking B_k in strict order. For any $p_j \in P_k$, we denote by $\mathcal{L}_k^j$ the *projected preference list of l_k for p_j* – this is obtained from $\mathcal{L}_k$ by deleting those students who do not find p_j acceptable. In this way, the ranking of $\mathcal{L}_k^j$ is inherited from $\mathcal{L}_k$. Also, l_k has a capacity constraint d_k, indicating the maximum number of students that he/she is willing to supervise. Similarly, each project p_j carries a capacity constraint c_j, indicating the maximum number of students that could be assigned to p_j. We assume that $max\{c_j : p_j \in P_k\} \le d_k$.

An example SPA instance is shown in Figure 1. Here the set of students is $S = \{s_1, s_2, \ldots, s_7\}$, the set of projects is $P = \{p_1, p_2, \ldots, p_8\}$ and the set of lecturers is $L = \{l_1, l_2, l_3\}$. Lecturers offer projects as indicated, and the preference lists and capacity constaints are also shown. As an example, the projected preference list of l_1 for p_1 comprises s_1, s_3, s_2, s_5, ranked in that order.

An *assignment* M is a subset of $S \times P$ such that:

1. $(s_i, p_j) \in M$ implies that $p_j \in A_i$ (i.e. s_i finds p_j acceptable).
2. For each student $s_i \in S$, $|\{(s_i, p_j) \in M : p_j \in P\}| \le 1$.

If $(s_i, p_j) \in M$, we say that s_i is *assigned to* p_j, and p_j is *assigned* s_i. Hence Condition 2 states that each student is assigned to at most one project in M. For notational convenience, if s_i is assigned in M to p_j, we may also say that s_i is assigned to l_k, and l_k is assigned s_i, where $p_j \in P_k$.

For any student $s_i \in S$, if s_i is assigned in M to some project p_j, we let $M(s_i)$ denote p_j; otherwise we say that s_i is *unmatched* in M. For any project $p_j \in P$, we denote by $M(p_j)$ the set of students assigned to p_j in M. Project p_j is *under-subscribed, full* or *over-subscribed* according as $|M(p_j)|$ is less than, equal to, or greater than c_j, respectively. Similarly, for any lecturer $l_k \in L$, we denote by $M(l_k)$ the set of students assigned to l_k in M. Lecturer l_k is *under-subscribed, full* or *over-subscribed* according as $|M(l_k)|$ is less than, equal to, or greater than d_k respectively.

A *matching* M is an assignment such that:

3. For each project $p_j \in P$, $|\{(s_i, p_j) \in M : s_i \in S\}| \leq c_j$.
4. For each lecturer $l_k \in L$, $|\{(s_i, p_j) \in M : s_i \in S \land p_j \in P_k\}| \leq d_k$.

Hence Condition 3 stipulates that p_j is assigned at most c_j students in M, whilst Condition 4 requires that l_k is assigned at most d_k students in M.

A *blocking pair* relative to a matching M is a (student,project) pair $(s_i, p_j) \in (S \times P) \backslash M$ such that:

1. $p_j \in A_i$ (i.e. s_i finds p_j acceptable).
2. Either s_i is unmatched in M, or s_i prefers p_j to $M(s_i)$.
3. Either
   a) p_j is under-subscribed and l_k is under-subscribed, or
   b) p_j is under-subscribed, l_k is full, and either l_k prefers s_i to the worst student s' in $M(l_k)$ or $s_i = s'$, or
   c) p_j is full and l_k prefers s_i to the worst student in $M(p_j)$, where l_k is the lecturer who offers p_j.

A matching is *stable* if it admits no blocking pair. We now give some intuition for the definition of a blocking pair. Suppose that (s_i, p_j) forms a blocking pair with respect to matching M, and let l_k be the lecturer who offers p_j.

In general we assume that s_i prefers to be matched to an acceptable project rather than to remain unmatched. Hence Condition 2 indicates the means by which a student could improve relative to M. Suppose now that this condition is satisfied. To explain Condition 3(a), matching M cannot be stable if each of project p_j and lecturer l_k has a free place to take on s_i (or to let s_i change projects offered by l_k). We now consider Condition 3(b). If p_j is under-subscribed, l_k is full, and s_i was not already matched in M to a project offered by l_k, then l_k cannot take on s_i without first rejecting at least one student. Lecturer l_k would only agree to this switch if he/she prefers s_i to the worst student assigned to l_k in M. In this case, project p_j has room for s_i. Alternatively, if s_i was already matched in M to a project offered by l_k, then the total number of students assigned to l_k remains the same, and l_k agrees to the switch since p_j has room for s_i. Finally, we consider Condition 3(c). If p_j is full, then l_k cannot take on s_i without first rejecting at least one student assigned to p_j. Lecturer l_k would only agree to this switch if he/she prefers s_i to the worst student assigned to p_j in M. Notice that if s_i was already matched in M to a project offered by l_k, then the number of students assigned to l_k would decrease by 1 after the switch. However we argue that this is the "correct" definition of a blocking pair in this case, also having the side-effects of avoiding issues of strategy and maintaining useful structural properties. For a full discussion of this point, we refer the reader to Section 4.1 of [1].

We remark that HR is a special case of SPA in which $m = q$, $c_j = d_j$ and $P_j = \{p_j\}$ $(1 \leq j \leq m)$. Essentially the projects and lecturers are indistinguishable in this case. In the HR setting, lecturers / projects are referred to as *hospitals*, and students are referred to as *residents*. Linear-time algorithms are known for finding a stable matching, given an instance of HR. The *resident-oriented* algorithm [4, Section 1.6.3] finds a *resident-optimal stable matching*. In this stable matching, each matched resident is assigned to the best hospital that he/she could obtain in any stable matching, whilst each unmatched resident is unmatched in every stable matching. On the other hand, the *hospital-oriented* algorithm [4, Section 1.6.2] finds a *hospital-optimal stable matching*. In this stable matching, each full hospital is assigned the best set of residents that it could obtain in any stable matching, whilst each under-subscribed hospital is assigned the same set of residents in every stable matching.

It is worth drawing attention to a special case of HR (and hence of SPA). This is the classical Stable Marriage problem with Incomplete lists (SMI), where $c_j = 1$ $(1 \leq j \leq m)$ [3], [4, Section 1.4.2]. In this setting, residents are referred to as *men* and hospitals are referred to as *women*. There exists a reduction from HR to SMI using the method of 'cloning' hospitals. That is, replace each hospital h_j, of capacity c_j, with c_j women, denoted by $h_j^1, h_j^2, \ldots, h_j^{c_j}$. The preference list of h_j^k is identical to the preference list of h_j. Any occurrence of h_j in a resident's preference list should be replaced by $h_j^1, h_j^2, \ldots, h_j^{c_j}$ in that order. Hence in theory, the Gale / Shapley algorithm for SMI [4, Section 1.4.2] could be used to solve an HR instance. However in practice direct algorithms are applied to HR instances [4, Section 1.6], because the cloning technique increases the number of hospitals (women) in a given HR instance by a potentially significant factor of C/m, where $C = \sum_{j=1}^{j=m} c_j$.

On the other hand there is no straightforward reduction involving cloning from an instance of SPA to an instance of HR, due to the projects and lecturers being distinct entities, each having capacity constraints. Even if such a reduction were possible, again it would typically increase the number of lecturers (hospitals) by a significant factor. This justifies the approach of this paper, in which we consider a direct algorithm for SPA.

The running time of our algorithm is $O(L)$, where L is the total length of the input preference lists, and hence is linear in the size of the problem instance. This algorithm is optimal, since the Stable Marriage problem (SM) – the special case of SMI in which $m = n$ and each student finds every project acceptable – is a special case of SPA. A lower bound of $\Omega(L)$ is known for SM [6], and hence this also applies to SPA.

3   The Algorithm for SPA

3.1   Overview

The algorithm for finding a student-optimal stable matching involves a sequence of *apply* operations (i.e. students *apply* to projects). An apply operation is similar to a *proposal* in the context of the Gale / Shapley algorithm for SM [3]. These operations lead to provisional assignments between students, projects and lecturers; such assignments can subsequently be broken during the algorithm's execution. Also, throughout the execution, entries are possibly deleted from the preference lists of students, and from the projected preference lists of lecturers. We use the abbreviation *delete the pair* (s_i, p_j) to denote the operation of deleting p_j from the preference list of s_i, and deleting s_i from $\mathcal{L}_k^j$, where l_k is the lecturer who offers p_j.

Initially all students are free, and all projects and lecturers are totally unsubscribed. As long as there is some student s_i who is free and who has a non-empty list, s_i applies to the first project p_j on his/her list. We let l_k be the lecturer who offers p_j. Immediately, s_i becomes provisionally assigned to p_j (and to l_k).

If p_j is over-subscribed, then l_k rejects the worst student s_r assigned to p_j. The pair (s_r, p_j) will be deleted by the subsequent conditional that tests for p_j being full. Similarly, if l_k is over-subscribed, then l_k rejects his/her worst assigned student s_r. The pair (s_r, p_t) will be deleted by either of the two subsequent conditionals, where p_t was the project formerly assigned to s_r.

Regardless of whether any rejections occurred as a result of the two situations described in the previous paragraph, we have two further (possibly non-disjoint) cases in which deletions may occur. If p_j is full, we let s_r be the worst student assigned to p_j (according to $\mathcal{L}_k^j$) and delete the pair (s_t, p_j) for each successor s_t of s_r on $\mathcal{L}_k^j$. Similarly if l_k is full, we let s_r be the worst student assigned to l_k, and delete the pair (s_t, p_u) for each successor s_t of s_r on $\mathcal{L}_k$, and for each project p_u offered by l_k that s_t finds acceptable.

The algorithm is described in pseudocode form in Figure 2 as Algorithm SPA-student. We will prove that, once the main loop terminates, the assigned pairs constitute a student-optimal stable matching.

3.2   Correctness of Algorithm SPA-Student

We firstly remark that Algorithm SPA-student terminates with a matching. The correctness of the algorithm, together with the optimality property of the constructed matching, may be established by the following sequence of lemmas.

Lemma 1. *No pair deleted during an execution of Algorithm SPA-student can block the constructed matching.*

Proof. Let E be an arbitrary execution of the algorithm in which some pair (s_i, p_j) is deleted. Suppose for a contradiction that (s_i, p_j) blocks M, the matching generated by E. Now, (s_i, p_j) is deleted in E because either (i) p_j becomes full, or (ii) l_k becomes full, where l_k is the lecturer offering p_j. In Case (i), it turns out that (s_i, p_j) fails (a), (b) and (c) of Condition 3 of a blocking pair, a contradiction. The details for each of these sub-cases are omitted here for space reasons, but may be found in [1]. Case (ii) is easier: (s_i, p_j) cannot block M, since once full, a lecturer never becomes under-subscribed, and is only ever assigned more preferable students.   □

Lemma 2. *Algorithm SPA-student generates a stable matching.*

```
assign each student to be free;
assign each project and lecturer to be totally unsubscribed;
while (some student sᵢ is free) and (sᵢ has a non-empty list) {
    pⱼ = first project on sᵢ's list;
    lₖ = lecturer who offers pⱼ;
    /* sᵢ applies to pⱼ */
    provisionally assign sᵢ to pⱼ;                    /* and to lₖ */
    if (pⱼ is over-subscribed) {
        sᵣ = worst student assigned to pⱼ;     /* according to 𝓛ₖʲ */
        break provisional assignment between sᵣ and pⱼ;
    }
    else if (lₖ is over-subscribed) {
        sᵣ = worst student assigned to lₖ;
        pₜ = project assigned sᵣ;
        break provisional assignment between sᵣ and pₜ;
    }
    if (pⱼ is full) {
        sᵣ = worst student assigned to pⱼ;     /* according to 𝓛ₖʲ */
        for (each successor sₜ of sᵣ on 𝓛ₖʲ)
            delete the pair (sₜ, pⱼ);
    }
    if (lₖ is full) {
        sᵣ = worst student assigned to lₖ;
        for (each successor sₜ of sᵣ on 𝓛ₖ)
            for (each project pᵤ ∈ Pₖ ∩ Aₜ)
                delete the pair (sₜ, pᵤ);
    }
}
```

Fig. 2. Algorithm SPA-student for finding a student-optimal stable matching

Proof. Let M be the matching generated by an arbitrary execution E of the algorithm, and let (s_i, p_j) be any pair blocking M. We will show that (s_i, p_j) must be deleted in E, thereby contradicting Lemma 1. For, suppose not. Then s_i must be matched to some project $M(s_i) \neq p_j$, for otherwise s_i is free with a non-empty preference list (containing p_j), thereby contradicting the fact that the algorithm terminates. Now, when s_i applies to $M(s_i)$, $M(s_i)$ is the first project on his/her list. Hence, (s_i, p_j) must be deleted, since for (s_i, p_j) to block M, s_i must prefer p_j to $M(s_i)$.   □

Lemma 3. *No stable pair (i.e. (student,project) pair belonging to some stable matching) is deleted during an execution of Algorithm SPA-student.*

Proof. Suppose for a contradiction that (s_i, p_j) is the first stable pair deleted during an arbitrary execution E of the algorithm. Let M be the matching immediately after the deletion in E, and let M' be any stable matching containing (s_i, p_j). Now, (s_i, p_j) is deleted in E because either (i) p_j becomes full, or (ii) l_k becomes full, where l_k is the lecturer offering p_j. We consider each case in turn.

(i) Suppose (s_i, p_j) is deleted because p_j becomes full during E. Immediately after the deletion, p_j is full, and l_k prefers all students in $M(p_j)$ to s_i. Now, $s_i \in M'(p_j) \backslash M(p_j)$, and since p_j is full in M, there must be some $s \in M(p_j) \backslash M'(p_j)$. We will show that (s, p_j) forms a blocking pair, contradicting the stability of M'.

Firstly, since (s_i, p_j) is the first stable pair deleted in E, s prefers p_j to any of his/her stable partners (except possibly for p_j itself). Additionally, since $(s_i, p_j) \in M'$ and l_k prefers s to s_i, it follows that l_k prefers s to both the worst student in $M'(p_j)$ and $M'(l_k)$. Clearly then, for any combination of l_k and p_j being full or under-subscribed, (s, p_j) satisfies all the conditions to block M'.

(ii) Suppose that (s_i, p_j) is deleted because l_k becomes full during E. Immediately after the deletion, l_k is full, and l_k prefers all students in $M(l_k)$ to s_i. We consider two cases: $|M'(p_j)| > |M(p_j)|$ and $|M'(p_j)| \leq |M(p_j)|$.

Suppose firstly $|M'(p_j)| > |M(p_j)|$. Since l_k is full in M, and $(s_i, p_j) \notin M$, there must be some project $p \in P_k \backslash \{p_j\}$ such that $|M'(p)| < |M(p)|$. We remark that p is therefore under-subscribed in M'. Now, let s be any student in $M(p) \backslash M'(p)$. Since (s_i, p_j) is the first stable pair deleted, s prefers p to any of his/her stable partners (except possibly for p itself). Also, l_k prefers s to s_i, and hence to the worst student in $M'(l_k)$. So, in either case that l_k is full or under-subscribed, (s, p) blocks M'.

Now suppose $|M'(p_j)| \leq |M(p_j)|$. Then there is some $s \neq s_i \in M(p_j) \backslash M'(p_j)$. Now, p_j is under-subscribed in M, for otherwise (s_i, p_j) is deleted because p_j becomes full, contradicting the assumption that deletion occurs because l_k becomes full. Therefore, p_j is under-subscribed in M'. As above, s prefers p_j to any of his/her stable partners (except possibly for p_j itself), since (s_i, p_j) is the first stable pair deleted. Also, l_k prefers s to s_i, and hence to the worst pair in $M'(l_k)$. So, in either case that l_k is full or under-subscribed, (s, p_j) blocks M'.   □

The following theorem collects together Lemmas 1-3.

Theorem 1. *For a given instance of SPA, any execution of Algorithm SPA-student constructs the student-optimal stable matching.*

Proof. Let M be a matching generated by an arbitrary execution E of the algorithm. In M, each student is assigned to the first project on his/her reduced preference list, if any. By Lemma 2, M is stable, and so each of these (student, project) pairs is stable. Also, by Lemma 3, no stable pair is deleted during E. It follows then that in M, each student is assigned to the best project that he/she can obtain in any stable matching.   □

For example, in the SPA instance given by Figure 1, the student-optimal stable matching is $\{(s_1, p_1), (s_2, p_5), (s_3, p_4), (s_4, p_2), (s_7, p_3)\}$.

We now state a result similar to the 'Rural Hospitals Theorem' for HR [4, Theorem 1.6.3]. In particular, the following theorem indicates that, in no other stable matching could we match a different set of students than that matched by

Algorithm SPA-student. The proof is omitted here for space reasons, but may be found in [1].

Theorem 2. *For a given SPA instance:*

(i)   each lecturer has the same number of students in all stable matchings;
(ii)   exactly the same students are unmatched in all stable matchings;
(iii) a project offered by an under-subscribed lecturer has the same number of students in all stable matchings.

However it turns out that an under-subscribed lecturer need not obtain the same set of students in all stable matchings, and in addition, a project offered by a full lecturer need not obtain the same number of students in all stable matchings. Example SPA instances illustrating these remarks are given in [1].

3.3   Analysis of Algorithm SPA-Student

The algorithm's time complexity depends on how efficiently we can execute 'apply' operations and deletions, each of which occur at most once for any (student, project) pair. It turns out that both operations can be implemented to run in constant time, giving an overall time complexity of $\Theta(L)$, where L is the total length of all the preference lists. We briefly outline the non-trivial aspects of such an implementation.

For each student s_i, build an array, $rank_{s_i}$, where $rank_{s_i}(p_j)$ is the index of project p_j in s_i's preference list. Represent s_i's preference list by embedding doubly linked lists in an array, $preference_{s_i}$. For each project $p_j \in A_i$, $preference_{s_i}(rank_{s_i}(p_j))$ stores the list node containing p_j. This node contains two next pointers (and two previous pointers) – one to the next project in s_i's list (after deletions, this project may not located at the next array position), and another pointer to the next project p' in s_i's list, where p' and p_j are both offered by the same lecturer. Construct this list by traversing through s_i's preference list, using a temporary array to record the last project in the list offered by each lecturer. Use virtual initialisation (described in [2, p.149]) for these arrays, since the overall $\Theta(nq)$ initialisation cost may be super-linear in L. Clearly, using these data structures, we can find and delete a project from a given student in constant time, as well as efficiently delete all projects offered by a given lecturer.

Represent each lecturer l_k's preference list $\mathcal{L}_k$ by an array $preference_{l_k}$, with an additional pointer, $last_{l_k}$. Initially, $last_{l_k}$ stores the index of the last position in $preference_{l_k}$. However, once l_k is full, make $last_{l_k}$ equivalent to l_k's worst assigned student through the following method. Perform a backwards linear traversal through $preference_{l_k}$, starting at $last_{l_k}$, and continuing until l_k's worst assigned student is encountered (each student stores a pointer to their assigned project, or a special null value if unassigned). All but the last student on this traversal must be deleted, and so the cost of the traversal may be attributed to the cost of the deletions in the student preference lists.

For each project p_j offered by l_k, construct a preference array corresponding to $\mathcal{L}_k^j$. These project preference arrays are used in much the same way as the lecturer preference array, with one exception. When a lecturer l_k becomes over-subscribed, the algorithm frees l_k's worst assigned student s_i and breaks the assignment of s_i to some project p_j. If p_j was full, then it is now under-subscribed, and $last_{p_j}$ is no longer equivalent to p_j's worst assigned student. Rather than update $last_{p_j}$ immediately, which could be expensive, wait until p_j is full again. The update then involves the same backwards linear traversal described above for l_k, although we must be careful not to delete pairs already deleted in one of l_k's traversals. Since we only visit a student at most twice during these backwards traversals, once for the lecturer and once for the project, the asymptotic running time remains linear.

The implementation issues discussed above lead to the following conclusion.

Theorem 3. *Algorithm SPA-student may be implemented to use $\Theta(L)$ time and space, where L is the total length of the preference lists in a given SPA instance.*

4   Conclusions and Open Problems

In this paper we have presented a student-oriented algorithm for a SPA instance. This produces the student-optimal stable matching, in which each student obtains the best project that he/she could obtain in any stable matching. We remark that we have also formulated a lecturer-oriented counterpart, which we omit for space reasons. This second algorithm produces the lecturer-optimal stable matching, in which each lecturer obtains the best set of students that he/she could obtain in any stable matching.

A number of interesting open problems remain. These include:

- The SPA model may be extended to the case where lecturers have preferences over (student,project) pairs. However in this setting it is an open problem to formulate an acceptable stability definition that avoids issues of strategy. For example, a student could deliberately shorten his/her preference list in order to obtain a better project, rather than submitting his/her true preferences. These strategic issues are described in more detail in [1].

- If we allow ties in the preference lists of students and lecturers, different stability definitions are possible. These can be obtained by extending stability definitions that have been applied to the Hospitals / Residents problem with Ties [5]. It remains open to construct algorithms for SPA where preference lists contain ties, under each of these stability criteria.

References

1. D.J. Abraham, R.W. Irving, and D.F. Manlove. *The Student-Project Allocation Problem*. Technical Report TR-2003-141 of the Computing Science Department of Glasgow University, 2003.
2. G. Brassard and P. Bratley. *Fundamentals of Algorithmics*. Prentice-Hall, 1996.
3. D. Gale and L.S. Shapley. College admissions and the stability of marriage. *American Mathematical Monthly*, 69:9–15, 1962.

4. D. Gusfield and R.W. Irving. *The Stable Marriage Problem: Structure and Algorithms.* MIT Press, 1989.
5. R.W. Irving, D.F. Manlove, and S. Scott.   Strong stability in the Hospitals/Residents problem. In *Proceedings of STACS 2003: the 20th International Symposium on Theoretical Aspects of Computer Science*, volume 2607 of *Lecture Notes in Computer Science*, pages 439–450. Springer-Verlag, 2003.
6. C. Ng and D.S. Hirschberg. Lower bounds for the stable marriage problem and its variants. *SIAM Journal on Computing*, 19:71–77, 1990.
7. National Resident Matching Program. About the NRMP. Web document available at `http://www.nrmp.org/about_nrmp/how.html`.
8. National Resident Matching Program. Why the Match? Web document available at `http://www.nrmp.org/whythematch.pdf`.
9. A.E. Roth. The evolution of the labor market for medical interns and residents: a case study in game theory. *Journal of Political Economy*, 92(6):991–1016, 1984.
10. A.E. Roth and M.A.O. Sotomayor. *Two-sided matching: a study in game-theoretic modeling and analysis*, volume 18 of *Econometric Society Monographs*. Cambridge University Press, 1990.

Algorithms for Enumerating Circuits in Matroids*

Endre Boros[1], Khaled Elbassioni[1], Vladimir Gurvich[1], and Leonid Khachiyan[2]

[1] RUTCOR, Rutgers University, 640 Bartholomew Road, Piscataway NJ 08854-8003;
{boros,elbassio,gurvich}@rutcor.rutgers.edu
[2] Department of Computer Science, Rutgers University, 110 Frelinghuysen Road,
Piscataway NJ 08854-8003; leonid@cs.rutgers.edu

Abstract. We present an incremental polynomial-time algorithm for enumerating all circuits of a matroid or, more generally, all minimal spanning sets for a flat. This result implies, in particular, that for a given infeasible system of linear equations, all its maximal feasible subsystems, as well as all minimal infeasible subsystems, can be enumerated in incremental polynomial time. We also show the NP-hardness of several related enumeration problems.

1 Introduction

Let M be a matroid on ground set S of cardinality $|S| = n$, i.e. a collection of subsets of S satisfying (i) $\emptyset \in M$, (ii) if $X \in M$ and $Y \subseteq X$ then $Y \in M$, and (iii) if $X, Y \in M$ and $|Y| > |X|$ then there exists an element $y \in Y \setminus X$ such that $X \cup \{y\} \in M$. Elements of M are called the *independent sets* of M. We assume throughout the paper that M is defined by an *independence oracle*, i.e. an algorithm $\mathcal{I}$ which, given a subset X of S, can determine in unit time whether or not X is independent in M. This assumption implies that the rank of any set $X \subseteq S$, $r(X) = \max\{|I| \; : \; I \text{ independent subset of } X\}$, and in particular, the rank of the matroid $r(M) \overset{\text{def}}{=} r(S)$ can be determined in $O(n)$ time by the well-known greedy algorithm. Hence the rank of X in the dual matroid M^* (that is, the matroid whose maximal independent sets are the complements of the maximal independent sets of M) $r^*(X) = r(S \setminus X) + |X| - r(M)$, can also be computed in $O(n)$ time. In particular, $\mathcal{I}$ can be used as an independence oracle for the dual matroid.

Let $\mathcal{C}(M)$ be the family of all circuits of M, i.e. the family of all minimal dependent subsets of S, and let $\mathcal{B}(M)$ be the family of all bases of M, i.e., the collection of all maximal independent sets. By definition, $\mathcal{C}(M)$ and the family

* This research was supported in part by the National Science Foundation Grant IIS-0118635. The research of the first and third authors was also supported in part by the Office of Naval Research Grant N00014-92-J-1375. The second and third authors are also grateful for the partial support by DIMACS, the National Science Foundation's Center for Discrete Mathematics and Theoretical Computer Science.

$\mathcal{B}(M^*) = \{X : S \setminus X \in \mathcal{B}(M)\}$ of bases of the dual matroid M^* are mutually transversal hypergraphs.

It is a folklore result that all bases of a matroid M can be enumerated with polynomial delay, i.e. in $poly(n)$ time per each generated base. This can be done by traversing the connected "metagraph" $\mathcal{G} = (\mathcal{B}(M), \mathcal{E})$ in which two "vertices" $B, B' \in \mathcal{B}(M)$ are connected by an edge in $\mathcal{E}$ iff B and B' can be obtained from each other by exchanging a pair of elements, i.e. when $|B \setminus B'| = |B' \setminus B| = 1$. The connectivity of $\mathcal{G}$ then follows from the well-known *base axiom*:

If $B, B' \in \mathcal{B}(M)$ and $x \in B' \setminus B$ then $(B \cup y) \setminus x \in \mathcal{B}(M)$ for some $y \in B \setminus B'$.

When M is the cycle matroid of a given graph $G = (V, E)$ and $\mathcal{C}(M)$ is the family of all simple cycles of G, all elements of $\mathcal{C}(M)$ can also be enumerated with polynomial delay (see e.g. [9]). This is also true for M^*, the cocycle matroid of G, when each element of $\mathcal{C}(M^*)$ is a minimal set of edges whose removal increases the number of connected components of G (see e.g. [8]). In general, however, we are not aware of any polynomial-delay algorithm for enumerating all circuits of an arbitrary matroid M. Intuitively, the circuit enumeration problem seems to be harder than the base enumeration due to the fact that $|C(M)| \leq (n - r(M))|\mathcal{B}(M)|$, whereas in general, $|\mathcal{B}(M)|$ cannot be bounded by a polynomial in n and $|\mathcal{C}(M)|$. In addition, there is a combinatorial reduction which reduces the enumeration of all bases of a matroid to the enumeration of all circuits of another matroid (see Section 5).

In this paper we present a simple algorithm for enumerating all circuits of an arbitrary matroid M in *incremental polynomial time*, i.e. show that for each $k \leq |\mathcal{C}(M)|$, one can compute k circuits of M in $poly(n, k)$ time. This is done in Section 2. By duality, this result also gives an incremental polynomial time algorithm for enumerating all hyperplanes or, more generally, all flats of a given rank in M or M^*. Thus, any level of the lattice of flats of M can be produced in incremental polynomial time.

In Section 3 we consider the enumeration of all circuits of M which contain a given element $a \in S$. Again, we show that all circuits through a can be enumerated in incremental polynomial time, and discuss some dual formulations of this result. We are not aware of any efficient algorithm for enumerating all circuits containing $t \geq 2$ elements of a given matroid M. In Section 4 we argue that this problem can be solved with polynomial delay for each fixed t when M is the cycle or cocycle matroid of a given graph, but becomes NP-hard when t is part of the input. Section 5 deals with the enumeration of all minimal subsets X of a given set $D \subseteq S$ such that X spans a given flat A of M. Examples of such spanning sets include generalized Steiner trees and multiway cuts in graphs. We reduce the enumeration problem for minimal A-spanning sets to the generation of all circuits through a given element in some extended matroid, and hence obtain an incremental polynomial-time algorithm. All maximal subsets of a given set D which do not span A can also be enumerated in incremental polynomial time.

Finally, Section 6 discusses some variants of the circuit enumeration problem for two matroids on S. We also discuss generalized circuits whose definition is obtained by replacing some singletons of S by subsets, i.e., by performing the parallel extension of the rank function $r(X)$ for some sets $A_1, ..., A_n \subseteq S$. We show that the enumeration problems corresponding to these variants and generalizations of circuits are all NP-hard already for graphic and cographic matroids. By duality, this is also true for analogous problems stated in terms of generalized hyperplanes.

2   Enumeration of All Circuits of a Matroid

Let M be a matroid defined by an independence oracle on ground set S of size n, and let $\mathcal{C}(M) \subseteq 2^S$ be the family of all circuits of M.

Theorem 1. *For each $k \leq |\mathcal{C}(M)|$, computing k circuits of M can be carried out in $poly(n, k)$ time.*

Proof. If B is a base of M and $x \in S \setminus B$ then there exists a unique circuit $C = C(B, x)$ such that $x \in C \subseteq B \cup x$. This circuit $C(B, x)$, called the fundamental circuit of x in the base B, can be computed by querying the independence oracle on at most $|B|$ subsets of $B \cup x$. We start by constructing a base B^o of M and the system $\mathcal{F}(B^o) = \{C(B^o, x) \mid x \in S \setminus B^o\}$ of $n - r(M)$ fundamental circuits for B^o. This can be done in $poly(n)$ time. Next, the family $\mathcal{C}(M)$ of circuits of any matroid satisfies the *circuit axiom*:

If C_1 and C_2 are distinct circuits of M and $e \in C_1 \cap C_2$ there exists a circuit C_3 such that $C_3 \subseteq (C_1 \cup C_2) \setminus e$.

Given an arbitrary collection $\mathcal{C}'$ of k circuits of M we can check in $poly(n, k)$ time whether or not $\mathcal{C}'$ is closed with respect to the circuit axiom, i.e., for any two distinct circuits $C_1, C_2 \in \mathcal{C}'$ with a common element $e \in C_1 \cap C_2$ the given collection $\mathcal{C}'$ also contains a circuit $C_3 \subseteq (C_1 \cup C_2) \setminus e$. To enumerate all circuits in M we start with the fundamental system of circuits $\mathcal{C}' = \mathcal{F}(B^o)$ and repeatedly check whether $\mathcal{C}'$ is closed with respect to the circuit axiom. Since each violation of the circuit axiom produces a new circuit, it remains to show that if some system $\mathcal{C}'$ of circuits is closed with respect to the circuit axiom and $\mathcal{F}(B^o) \subseteq \mathcal{C}'$ then $\mathcal{C}' = \mathcal{C}(M)$. This follows from the fact that any set system $\mathcal{C}' \subseteq 2^S$ satisfying the circuit axiom and the Sperner condition $C_1, C_2 \in \mathcal{C}'$, $C_1 \neq C_2 \implies C_1 \not\subseteq C_2$ defines a matroid M' on S, see [6,11]. By definition, the bases of M' are all maximal independent sets for $\mathcal{C}'$, i.e. all those maximal subsets of S which contain no set in $\mathcal{C}'$. In our case $\mathcal{C}' \subseteq \mathcal{C}(M)$ and hence $\mathcal{C}'$ is Sperner by definition. Furthermore, since $\mathcal{C}'$ contains the fundamental system of circuits for $B^o \in \mathcal{B}(M)$, it follows that B^o is also a base of M', implying that the ranks of M and M' are equal. Let $C \in \mathcal{C}(M)$ be an arbitrary circuit of M, then C is the fundamental circuit for some base $B \in \mathcal{B}(M)$ and some element $x \in S \setminus B$, i.e. $C = C(B, x)$. Since B is independent in M' and $|B| = r(M) = r(M')$, we conclude that $B \in \mathcal{B}(M')$. Now M' must also contain a unique fundamental circuit $C' = C'(B, x)$. Since any circuit of M' is also a circuit of M, we conclude that $C = C(B, x) = C'(B, x)$, which shows that $C \in C' = C(M')$. $\quad\square$

Let $\mathcal{H}_t(M) = \{X : X \text{ maximal subset of } S \text{ such that } r(X) \leq t\}$ be the family of all flats of rank t in M, where t is an integer threshold. In particular, when $t = rank(M) - 1$ the family $\mathcal{H}_t(M)$ consists of all hyperplanes of M. Let also $\mathcal{C}_t(M) = \{X : X \text{ minimal subset of } S \text{ such that } r(X) \leq |X| - t\}$, so that $\mathcal{C}_1(M) = \mathcal{C}(M)$ is exactly the family of all circuits of M.

Corollary 1. *Given an integer parameter t, all flats in $\mathcal{H}_t(M)$ can be enumerated in incremental polynomial time. Similarly, all elements of $\mathcal{C}_t(M)$ can also be enumerated in incremental polynomial time.*

Proof. Since each hyperplane of M is the complement of a cocircuit of M and vice versa, the enumeration of all hyperplanes of M is equivalent with the circuit enumeration for the dual matroid M^*. Hence by Theorem 1 all hyperplanes of M can be enumerated in incremental polynomial time. Furthermore, the corollary also holds for the family $\mathcal{H}_t(M)$ of all flats of rank t, because $\mathcal{H}_t(M)$ consists of all hyperplanes of the truncated matroid M_{t+1} whose rank function is defined by $r_{t+1}(X) = \min\{r(X), t+1\}$. Finally, let $\tau = |S| - r(M) - t$ then enumerating all flats of rank τ for M^* is equivalent with the enumeration of all maximal solutions $Y \subseteq S$ to the inequality $r^*(Y) = r(S \setminus Y) + |Y| - r(M) \leq \tau$. The latter problem is in turn equivalent with the enumeration of all minimal solutions $X = S \setminus Y$ to the inequality $r(X) \leq |X| - t$. $\quad\square$

By Corollary 1 the lattice $\mathcal{L}(M)$ of flats of any matroid M can be computed in incremental polynomial time. It is known [5] that $|\mathcal{L}(M)| \geq 2^{r(M)}$.

3 Circuits through a Given Element

An important open question in linear programming is whether there exists an efficient way to enumerate all vertices of a given polytope

$$P = \{x = (x_1, \ldots, x_n) \in \Re^n : \sum_{i=1}^{n} a_i x_i = a, \quad x_1, \ldots, x_n \geq 0 \},$$

where $a, a_1, \ldots, a_n$ are given d-dimensional vectors. Each vertex of P can be identified with a minimal supporting set I of coordinates $[n] = \{1, \ldots, n\}$ for which the system of linear equations

$$\sum_{i \in I} a_i x_i = a \tag{1}$$

has a positive real solution. Dropping the non-negativity conditions we arrive at the problem of enumerating all minimal sets $I \subseteq [n]$ for which (1) has a real solution. This is equivalent with the enumeration of all those circuits of the vectorial matroid $M = \{a, a_1, \ldots, a_n\} \subseteq \Re^d$ that contain a. When M is the cycle or cocycle matroid of some connected graph $G = (V, E)$ and $a = (uv) \in E$ is an edge with endpoints $u, v \in V$, enumerating all circuits through a calls for computing all simple uv-paths or all minimal uv-cuts in G, which can be done with polynomial delay [9]. The following result indicates that all circuits through a given element a can be efficiently enumerated for any matroid M.

Theorem 2. *Let M be a matroid with ground set S, let $a \in S$, and let $\mathcal{C}(M, a)$ the set of circuits C of M such that $a \in C$. Assuming that M is defined by an independence oracle, all elements of $\mathcal{C}(M, a)$ can be enumerated in incremental polynomial time.*

Proof. Two elements $x, y \in S$ are said to be *connected* in M if either $x = y$ or there is a circuit $C \in \mathcal{C}(M)$ containing both x and y. We may assume w.l.o.g. that M is connected. Given a set $X \subseteq S$, let $D(X) = X \setminus \bigcap \{C \in \mathcal{C}(M, a) : C \subseteq X\}$, where as before $\mathcal{C}(M, a)$ denotes the set of all circuits containing a. Lehman's theorem [6,11] asserts that for any connected matroid M the circuits of M not containing a are precisely the minimal sets of the form $D(C_1 \cup C_2)$ where C_1 and C_2 are distinct members of $\mathcal{C}(M, a)$. Hence for any connected matroid M:

$$|\mathcal{C}(M)| \leq |\mathcal{C}(M, a)|(|\mathcal{C}(M, a)| + 1)/2.$$

This bound and Theorem 1 readily imply that all circuits in $\mathcal{C}(M, a)$ can be enumerated in output polynomial time $poly(|\mathcal{C}(M, a)|)$ by simply generating all circuits in $\mathcal{C}(M)$ and discarding those of them that do not pass through a. In fact, since our enumeration problem is self-reducible, the above bound also implies an incremental polynomial-time algorithm. To see this, assume that we wish to enumerate a given number k of circuits in $\mathcal{C}(M, a)$, or list all of them if $k \geq |\mathcal{C}(M, a)|$. Since for each integer $k' \leq |\mathcal{C}(M)|$ we can obtain k' circuits in $\mathcal{C}(M)$ in $poly(n, k')$ time, we can decide whether or not $k \geq |\mathcal{C}(M, a)|$ by attempting to generate $k' = k(k + 1)/2$ circuits in $\mathcal{C}(M)$, in time bounded by a polynomial in n and k. If we discover that $|\mathcal{C}(M)| \leq k(k + 1)/2$ by producing all circuits in $\mathcal{C}(M)$ then we also have the entire set $\mathcal{C}(M, a)$. Suppose now that we have computed $k(k + 1)/2$ circuits in $\mathcal{C}(M)$ but fewer than k of them pass through a. Let $b \neq a$ be another element of S. Delete b and compute the connected component S' which contains a in the matroid M restricted to $S \setminus b$. Note that any circuit of $\mathcal{C}(M, a)$ which does not contain b must belong to S'. So we may apply the same procedure to the connected matroid M' obtained by restricting M on S', and either obtain all circuits of $\mathcal{C}(M, a)$ which avoid b, or conclude that the number of such circuits exceeds k. Since in the latter case we can reduce the size of S by removing b for good (as long as we are not required to produce more than k circuits of $\mathcal{C}(M, a)$), we may now assume w.l.o.g. that for each element $b \neq a$ we have obtained all the circuits in $\mathcal{C}(M, a)$ which avoid b. This means that in time polynomial in n and k we can produce all circuits in $\mathcal{C}(M, a)$ which skip some element of S. Unless S itself is the only element of $\mathcal{C}(M, a)$, this gives the entire set $\mathcal{C}(M, a)$.   □

By duality, Theorem 2 gives an incremental polynomial-time algorithm for enumerating all hyperplanes (or, more generally, all flats of a given rank t) which *do not contain a*. Needless to say that all hyperplanes (or flats of rank t) which *contain* an arbitrary set of elements $A \subseteq S$ can be enumerated in incremental polynomial time because this is equivalent with enumerating all circuits of the (truncated) matroid M restricted to $S \setminus A$.

It is also worth mentioning that $\{C \setminus \{a\} \mid C \in \mathcal{C}(M, a)\}$ and $\{C' \setminus \{a\} \mid C' \in \mathcal{C}(M^*, a)\}$ form a pair of mutually transversal Sperner hypergraphs. For instance, these hypergraphs consist of all uv-paths and all uv-cuts respectively, when M is a cycle matroid of a connected graph $G = (V, E)$ in which edge $a = (uv)$ connects vertices $u, v \in V$.

4   Circuits through t Elements

It is natural to ask what is the complexity of enumerating all circuits of M which contain a given set $A = \{a_1, \dots, a_t\}$ of $t \geq 2$ elements of S. As we argue below, this problem is NP-hard when t is part of the input but can be solved with polynomial delay if $t = |A|$ is fixed and M is the cycle or cocycle matroid of a given graph $G = (V, E)$. However, we are not aware of an efficient algorithm for listing all circuits through $t = const \geq 2$ elements of arbitrary matroids.

Let M be the cycle matroid of G so that the circuits of M are the simple cycles of G. An edge set A may be contained in a simple cycle only if A itself is a simple cycle or A is a union of k pairwise vertex disjoint simple paths $P_1, \dots, P_k$ for some integer positive $k \leq t$. All simple cycles containing $P_1, \dots, P_k$ can be enumerated with polynomial delay via lexicographic backtracking [9] by growing and merging these partial paths (so that their number continually decreases). Hence backtracking listing algorithms reduce the enumeration of simple cycles containing $a_1, \dots, a_t$ to the following decision problem:

> Does there exist a simple cycle in G which contains k given disjoint paths $P_1, \dots, P_k$?

When k is fixed, by considering all possible permutations and reversals of $P_1, ..., P_k$ the latter problem can in turn be polynomially reduced to the well-known *disjoint-path problem*:

> Given k pairs of vertices $\{u_i, v_i\}$, $i = 1, \dots, k$ of a graph, can these pairs be connected by k pairwise vertex disjoint paths?

Even though the disjoint path problem is NP-complete when k is part of the input (see [4]), it is known [10] to be solvable in polynomial time for each fixed k. Hence all simple cycles through $t = const$ edges can be enumerated with delay bounded by a polynomial in the size of the input graph.

As we mentioned earlier, if $t = |A|$ is part of the input then the problem of enumerating all simple cycles through t edges of a graph becomes NP-complete. In fact, given a graph $G = (V, E)$ and a (large) matching $A \subset E$ it is NP-hard to decide whether G has *any* simple cycle containing A. This can be seen from the following argument. Given a graph $H = (U, E)$, substitute an edge e_u for each vertex $u \in U$. Then, unless G consists of a single edge, the resulting graph

$G = P_2 \times H$ has a simple cycle through the matching $A = \{e_u : u \in U\}$ iff the original graph H is Hamiltonian, a condition which is NP-complete to verify.

Now, let M be the cocycle matroid of a connected graph $G = (V, E)$ and accordingly, let the circuits of M be the minimal cuts of G. It is well-known and easy to see that an edge set $C \subseteq E$ forms a minimal cut in G iff there is a partition $V = U \cup W$ such that C is the set of all edges between U and W and the induced subgraphs $G[U]$ and $G[W]$ are both connected. In particular, this means that C (and each subset of C) must form a bipartite graph. Given an edge set $A = \{a_1, \dots, a_t\} \subseteq E$ which forms a bipartite graph $G_A = (V_A, A)$, let us split G_A into connected components $G_{A_i} = (V_{A_i}, A_i)$, $i = 1, \dots, k$ for some $k \leq t$. Then the problem of enumerating all minimal cuts containing A can be solved with polynomial delay via lexicographic backtracking [9] by growing and merging these connected components in all possible ways (so that their number can only decrease). Specifically, backtracking listing algorithms reduce the enumeration of minimal cuts containing $a_1, \dots, a_t$ to the following decision problem:

> Given two disjoint vertex sets $U', W' \subseteq V$, can they be extended to a partition U, W which defines a minimal cut, that is $U' \subseteq U$, $W' \subseteq W$, $U \cap W = \emptyset$, $U \cup W = V$, and the induced subgraphs $G[U]$, $G[W]$ are both connected ?

If t, and hence $|U'| + |W'|$, is bounded this problem can be solved in polynomial time. In fact, this is true for the following more general problem:

> Given a graph $G = (V, E)$ and r pairwise disjoint vertex sets $U'_1, \dots U'_r \subseteq V$, are there vertex sets $U_1 \dots U_r \subseteq V$ which are still pairwise disjoint, $U'_i \subseteq U_i$ and the induced subgraph $G[U_i]$ is connected (i.e. spans U_i) for each $i = 1, \dots, r$?

Robertson and Seymour [10] proved that for bounded $|U'_1| + \dots + |U'_r|$ the above problem can be solved in polynomial time. Obviously, w.l.o.g. one can assume that the extended sets $U_1 \dots U_r$ form a partition of V and hence for $r = 2$ the above problem includes the previous one.

Finally, similarly to minimal cycles, the enumeration of all minimal cuts through t edges becomes NP-hard when t is part of the input. Indeed, given a graph $G = (V, E)$ and a matching $A = \{a_1 = (u_1, w_1), \dots, a_t = (u_t, w_t)\} \subseteq E$, it may be NP-hard to tell whether G has a minimal cut containing A. This claim can be shown as follows. Let $U' = \{u_1, \dots, u_t\}$, $W' = \{w_1, \dots, w_t\}$, and $V' = V \setminus (U' \cup W')$. Consider the set $\mathcal{G}$ of all graphs $G = (V, E)$ such that (i) the induced subgraph $G[V']$ is complete, (ii) $G[U']$ and $G[W']$ are edge-free, (iii) there are no edges between U' and W' except A, and (iv) the edges between V' and U' and between V' and W' are symmetric in the sense that $(v, u_i) \in E \Leftrightarrow (v, w_i) \in E$ for all $v \in V'$ and all $i = 1, \dots, t$. Note that condition (iv) makes irrelevant any reversals in A, and that the decision problem:

> Given a graph $G \in \mathcal{G}$, is it possible to split V' between U' and W' to obtain two connected induced subgraphs ?

is polynomially equivalent with the special case of the CNF satisfiability problem in which all clauses are either strictly positive or strictly negative, and the clauses in the positive and negative halves are symmetric. It remains to notice that this special case of the satisfiability problem is NP-complete since it is equivalent to the identification of *self-compliment saturated hypergraphs*, a problem whose NP-completeness was shown in [3].

We mention in closing that the results of this section also indicate that it may be NP-complete to decide whether a cycle or cocycle matroid M has a hyperplane avoiding a given set A of elements.

5   Minimal Spanning Sets for a Flat

Let M be a matroid on S. Each circuit C containing a given element $a \in S$ can be identified with a minimal (independent) set I such that $a \in Span(I)$, where

$$Span(I) = \{x \in S \ : \ r(I \cup x) = r(I)\}$$

is the closure operator. In this section we consider the problem of enumerating all minimal sets I spanning a given collection of elements $A \subseteq S$. In fact, we will consider a slightly more general problem of generating all minimal subsets $I \subseteq D$ which span A, where D and A are two given nonempty (and not necessarily disjoint) sets of elements of M. We denote the family of all such minimal spanning sets I by $SPAN(D, A)$. Note that since $A \subseteq Span(I)$ implies $Span(A) \subseteq Span(I)$, we could assume that A is a flat, i.e. $A = Span(A)$.

Example 1 (Generalized Steiner trees and point-to-point connections) Let $G = (V, E)$ be a graph with k given disjoint vertex sets $V_1, \ldots, V_k \subseteq V$. A *generalized Steiner tree* is a minimal set of edges $I \subseteq E$ connecting all vertices within each set V_i, i.e., for each $i = 1, \ldots, k$, all vertices of V_i must belong to a single connected component of (V, I). In particular, for $k = 1$ we obtain the usual definition of Steiner trees. When each set V_i consists of two vertices $\{u_i, v_i\}$, generalized Steiner trees are called *point-to-point* connections. Let $T_1, \ldots, T_k$ be arbitrary spanning trees on $V_1, \ldots, V_k$ composed of "new" edges, and let M the cycle matroid of the multigraph $(V, E \cup T_1 \cup \ldots \cup T_k)$ with a total of $|E| + |V_1| + \ldots + |V_k| - k$ edges. Then $SPAN(E, T_1 \cup \ldots \cup T_k)$ is the family of all generalized Steiner trees for $V_1, \ldots, V_k$.

Example 2 (Multiway cuts) For a connected graph $G = (V, E)$ with k pairs of vertices $\{u_i, v_i\}$, $i = 1, \ldots, k$, a *multiway cut* is a minimal collection of edges whose removal disconnects each u_i from v_i. Letting $A = \{(u_i v_i) \ : \ i = 1, \ldots, t\}$ and assuming w.l.o.g. that $A \cap E = \emptyset$, the family of all multicuts of G can be identified with the family $SPAN(E, A)$ for the cocycle matroid of $(V, E \cup A)$.

Theorem 3. *Given a matroid M with ground set S and two non-empty sets $D, A \subseteq V$, all elements of $SPAN(D, A)$ can be enumerated in incremental polynomial time. All maximal subsets of D which do not span A can also be enumerated in incremental polynomial time.*

Proof. Let α be a new element representing A, and let M_α be the matroid on $D \cup \alpha$ with the following rank function:

$$\rho(X) = \begin{cases} r(X), & \text{if } \alpha \notin X \\ \max\{r((X \setminus \alpha) \cup a) \ : \ a \in A\}, & \text{otherwise.} \end{cases} \qquad (2)$$

It is easy to check that M_α is indeed a matroid. When M is a vectorial matroid over a large field, α can be interpreted as the "general linear combination" of all elements of A; in general, $\rho(X)$ is the so-called *principal extension of $r(X)$ on A with value* 1 (see e.g. [7]).

When $I \in \mathcal{SPAN}(D, A)$ then $I \cup \alpha$ is a circuit in M_α and conversely, for any circuit C in M_α containing α, the set $C \setminus \alpha$ belongs to $\mathcal{SPAN}(D, A)$. Hence the enumeration problem for $\mathcal{SPAN}(D, A)$ is equivalent with that for the set of all circuits through α in M_α. Given an independence oracle for M, the rank function (2) of the extended matroid can be trivially evaluated in oracle-polynomial time. Therefore the first claim of Theorem 3 directly follows from Theorem 2. To see the second claim note that the maximal subsets of D which do not span A are in one-to-one correspondence with the hyperplanes of M_α which avoid α.   □

Finally, let us note that since $\mathcal{SPAN}(S, S)$ is the set of bases of M, the proofs of Theorems 2 and 3 show that the enumeration of all bases of a matroid can be reduced to the enumeration of all circuits of another matroid.

6   Circuits in Two Matroids, Generalized Circuits

Let M_1 and M_2 be two matroids on S, with rank functions $r_1(X)$ and $r_2(X)$. It is known that the minimum of the submodular function $r_1(X) + r_2(S \setminus X)$ for all $X \subseteq S$ gives the maximum cardinality of a set I independent in both M_1 and M_2, and that this minimum can be computed in polynomial time [2]. In particular, when the ranks of M_1 and M_2 are equal one can determine in polynomial time whether M_1 and M_2 share a common base, i.e. $\mathcal{B}(M_1) \cap \mathcal{B}(M_2) \neq \emptyset$. In fact, using this as a subroutine for backtracking on matroids obtained by deleting and contracting elements of S, all bases in $\mathcal{B}(M_1) \cap \mathcal{B}(M_2)$ can be enumerated with polynomial delay.

In contrast to this result, deciding whether M_1 and M_2 contain a common circuit is NP-hard already when M_1 is the cycle matroid of some graph $G = (V, E)$ and M_2 is the uniform matroid on E whose bases are all subsets of size $r = |V| - 1$. In this case, $\mathcal{C}(M_1) \cap \mathcal{C}(M_2) \neq \emptyset$ iff G is Hamiltonian. A similar argument for the NP-complete maximum cut problem shows that testing if $\mathcal{C}(M_1) \cap \mathcal{C}(M_2) \neq \emptyset$ remains NP-hard when M_1 is the cocycle matroid of a graph $G = (V, E)$ and M_2 is again a uniform matroid on E.

Of course, given two matroids M_1 and M_2 on S one can always enumerate all elements of $\mathcal{C}(M_1) \cup \mathcal{C}(M_2)$ in incremental polynomial time due to Theorem 1. Note, however, that deciding whether a given set $C \in \mathcal{C}(M_1) \cup \mathcal{C}(M_2)$ is inclusion-wise *maximal* in $\mathcal{C}(M_1) \cup \mathcal{C}(M_2)$ may be NP-hard. This is because for any set $A \subseteq S$ we may choose M_2 to be the matroids for which A is the only circuit, and then deciding whether A is maximal becomes equivalent with determining if M_1

has a circuit containing A (see Section 4). Perhaps more surprisingly, for two matroids M_1 and M_2 on S enumerating all *minimal* elements of $\mathcal{C}(M_1) \cup \mathcal{C}(M_2)$ may also be hard.

Proposition 1. *Let M_1 and M_2 be the cycle matroids of two graphs $G_1 = (V_1, E)$ and $G_2 = (V_2, E)$ with identical sets of edges, and let $\mathcal{MIN}\{\mathcal{C}(M_1) \cup \mathcal{C}(M_2)\}$ be the collection of all minimal edge sets which form a cycle in G_1 or G_2. Then, given a set family $\mathcal{M} \subseteq \mathcal{MIN}\{\mathcal{C}(M_1) \cup \mathcal{C}(M_2)\}$, it is NP-complete to tell whether $\mathcal{M}$ can be extended, i.e. $\mathcal{M} \neq \mathcal{MIN}\{\mathcal{C}(M_1) \cup \mathcal{C}(M_2)\}$.*

We conclude with yet another generalization of the notion of circuit in a matroid. Let M be a matroid defined by an independence oracle on some ground set U, and let $A_1, \ldots, A_n$ be given (not necessarily disjoint) subsets of U. We define a *generalized circuit* as a minimal subset X of $S = [n]$ such that $\bigcup_{i \in X} A_i$ is a dependent set in M.

Proposition 2. *Enumerating all generalized circuits for the cycle matroid of a graph is NP-hard when $A_1, \ldots, A_n$ are disjoint sets of edges of size 2 each.*

It is easy to see that in Propositions 1 and 2 the cycle matroids of G_1 and G_2 can be replaced by the cocycle matroids of some graphs (e.g., the planar duals of G_1 and G_2). Also, by matroid duality, Proposition 1 shows that it may be NP-hard to enumerate all *generalized hyperplanes* of M, i.e., all those maximal subsets X of $S = [n]$ for which $Span(\cup_{i \in X} A_i) \neq S$.

In contrast to Proposition 2, all *generalized bases* of M, i.e. all minimal sets $X \subseteq [n]$ for which $Span(\cup_{i \in X} A_i) = S$ can be generated in incremental quasi-polynomial time regardless of the sizes of $A_1, \ldots, A_n$, see [1] for more detail.

References

1. E. Boros, K. Elbassioni, V. Gurvich and L. Khachiyan, Matroid intersections, poly-matroid inequalities, and related problems, in *Proc. 27th Intl. Symp. on Mathematical Foundations of Computer Science, (MFCS) 2002*, LNCS 2420, pp. 143–154.
2. J. Edmonds, Submodular functions, matroids, and certain polyhedra, in *Combinatorial structures and their applications*, Gordon and Breach, 69–87.
3. T. Eiter and G. Gottlob, Identifying the minimal transversals of a hypergraph and related problems, *SIAM J. Comput.*, 24 (1995) 1278–1304.
4. R. Karp, On the complexity of combinatorial problems, *Networks* 5 (1975) 45–68.
5. T. Lazarson, Independence functions in algebra, (Thesis), Univ. London (1957).
6. A. Lehman, A solution of the Shannon switching game, *J. Soc. Indust. Appl. Math.* 12 (1964) 687–725.
7. L. Lovász, Submodular functions and convexity, in *Mathematical Programming: The State of the Art*, Bonn 1982, pp. 235–257, (Springer Verlag, 1983).
8. J. S. Provan and D. R. Shier, A paradigm for listing (s, t)-cuts in graphs, *Algorithmica*, 15(4) (1996) 357–372.
9. R. C. Read and R. E. Tarjan, Bounds on backtrack algorithms for listing cycles, paths, and spanning trees, *Networks*, 5 (1975) 237–252.
10. N. Robertson and P. D. Seymour, Graph minors, XIII, The disjoint path problem, *J. Comb. Th.*, Ser. B 63 (1995) 65–110.
11. D.J.A. Welsh, Matroid Theory, Academic Press, 1976.

A Generalized Gale-Shapley Algorithm for a Discrete-Concave Stable-Marriage Model*

Akinobu Eguchi[1], Satoru Fujishige[2], and Akihisa Tamura[2]

[1] Panasonic Mobile Communications Co., Ltd.
[2] Research Institute for Mathematical Sciences, Kyoto University,
Kyoto 606-8502, Japan,
{fujishig,tamura}@kurims.kyoto-u.ac.jp

Abstract. The stable marriage model due to Gale and Shapley is one of the most fundamental two-sided matching models. Recently, Fleiner generalized the model in terms of matroids, and Eguchi and Fujishige extended the matroidal model to the framework of discrete convex analysis. In this paper, we extend their model to a vector version in which indifference on preferences is allowed, and show the existence of a stable solution by a generalization of the Gale-Shapley algorithm.

1 Introduction

The stable marriage model due to Gale and Shapley [7] is one of the most fundamental two-sided matching models. In the original stable marriage model, there are two sets of n men and n women, and each person arbitrarily gives a strict preference order on persons of the opposite gender. A matching is a set of n disjoint pairs of men and women, and is called stable if there is no pair whose members prefer each other to their partners in the matching. Gale and Shapley [7] gave a constructive proof of existence of a stable matching in 1962. Since the advent of their paper a lot of variations and extensions have been proposed in the literature. Recently, a remarkable extension has been made by Fleiner [3,5] (also see [4]). Fleiner [3] extended the stable marriage model to the framework of matroids, showed existence of a stable solution, and examined a lattice structure and a polyhedral characterization of stable solutions in his matroidal model. Fleiner [4] also gave a strong framework to show existence of a stable solution and a lattice structure of stable solutions by utilizing the Knaster-Tarski fixed point theorem. While in the model of Fleiner [3] preference of each person is described by a linear utility function on a matroidal domain, Eguchi and Fujishige [2] extended the matroidal model [3] to the framework of discrete convex analysis which was recently developed by Murota [8,9,10] as a unified framework of discrete optimization. In their model, each agent can express his/her preference by a discrete concave function, called an $M^{\natural}$-concave function.

* This work is supported by a Grant-in-Aid of the Ministry of Education, Culture, Sports, Science and Technology of Japan.

T. Ibaraki, N. Katoh, and H. Ono (Eds.): ISAAC 2003, LNCS 2906, pp. 495–504, 2003.

In this paper, we provide a general two-sided model including the Eguchi-Fujishige model as a special case (see Section 3). Our model has the following features (also see a model in Remark 1 in Section 2):

- the preference of agents on each side over the agents on the other side is expressed by an M$^\natural$-concave function, and indifference on preferences is allowed,
- each pair is permitted to form multiple partnerships.

We propose a generalization of the Gale-Shapley algorithm to show our main theorem claiming that there always exists a stable solution in our model.

This paper is organized as follows. Section 2 explains M$^\natural$-concavity together with its properties and describes our model based on discrete convex analysis. Section 3 gives several existing models that are special cases of our model. In Section 4 we propose an algorithm for finding a stable solution and prove its correctness, which shows our main theorem on existence of a stable solution in our general model. Section 5 gives remarks on time complexity.

2   A General Model

2.1   Preliminaries

We first introduce an M$^\natural$-concave function. Let V be a nonempty finite set, and $\mathbf{Z}$ and $\mathbf{R}$ be the sets of integers and reals, respectively. We define the positive support and the negative support of $x = (x(v) : v \in V) \in \mathbf{Z}^V$, respectively, by

$$\text{supp}^+(x) = \{v \in V \mid x(v) > 0\}, \quad \text{supp}^-(x) = \{v \in V \mid x(v) < 0\}. \tag{1}$$

For any $x, y \in \mathbf{Z}^V$, the vectors $x \wedge y$ and $x \vee y$ in $\mathbf{Z}^V$ are defined by

$$x \wedge y(v) = \min\{x(v), y(v)\}, \quad x \vee y(v) = \max\{x(v), y(v)\} \quad (v \in V). \tag{2}$$

For each $S \subseteq V$, we denote by χ_S the characteristic vector of S defined by $\chi_S(v) = 1$ if $v \in S$; otherwise 0, and simply write χ_u instead of $\chi_{\{u\}}$ for each $u \in V$. For a function $f : \mathbf{Z}^V \to \mathbf{R} \cup \{-\infty\}$, we define the set of maximizers of f on $U \subseteq \mathbf{Z}^V$ by

$$\arg\max\{f(y) \mid y \in U\} = \{x \in U \mid \forall y \in U : f(x) \geq f(y)\}, \tag{3}$$

and the *effective domain* of f by

$$\text{dom} f = \{x \in \mathbf{Z}^V \mid f(x) > -\infty\}. \tag{4}$$

A function $f : \mathbf{Z}^V \to \mathbf{R} \cup \{-\infty\}$ with $\text{dom} f \neq \emptyset$ is called M$^\natural$-*concave* [11] if it satisfies

$(-\text{M}^\natural\text{-EXC}) \; \forall x, y \in \text{dom} f, \; \forall u \in \text{supp}^+(x - y), \; \exists v \in \text{supp}^-(x - y) \cup \{0\} :$

$$f(x) + f(y) \leq f(x - \chi_u + \chi_v) + f(y + \chi_u - \chi_v), \tag{5}$$

where χ_0 is a zero vector.

A simple example of an $M^\natural$-concave function is given as follows.

Example 1. Let $\mathcal{I}$ be the family of independent sets of a matroid on V and $w \in \mathbf{R}^V$. Then, a function $f : \mathbf{Z}^V \to \mathbf{R} \cup \{-\infty\}$ defined by

$$f(x) = \begin{cases} \sum_{v \in I} w(v) & \text{(if } x = \chi_I \text{ for } I \in \mathcal{I}) \\ -\infty & \text{(otherwise)} \end{cases} \quad (x \in \mathbf{Z}^V) \tag{6}$$

is $M^\natural$-concave.

An $M^\natural$-concave function has nice features as a utility function from the point of view of mathematical economics. A utility function is usually assumed to be concave in mathematical economics. For any $M^\natural$-concave function $f : \mathbf{Z}^V \to \mathbf{R} \cup \{-\infty\}$, there exists a concave function $\bar{f} : \mathbf{R}^V \to \mathbf{R} \cup \{-\infty\}$ with $\bar{f}(x) = f(x)$ for any $x \in \mathbf{Z}^V$ [8], that is, any $M^\natural$-concave function on $\mathbf{Z}^V$ has a concave extension on $\mathbf{R}^V$. A utility function usually has decreasing marginal returns, which is equivalent to submodularity in the discrete case. This is also the case for $M^\natural$-concave functions [12], i.e., any $M^\natural$-concave function f on $\mathbf{Z}^V$ satisfies

$$f(x) + f(y) \geq f(x \vee y) + f(x \wedge y) \quad (x, y \in \operatorname{dom} f). \tag{7}$$

$M^\natural$-concave functions enjoy some other combinatorially nice properties (see [6, 13]).

2.2   Model Description and the Main Theorem

Now we introduce our model. Let M and W denote two disjoint sets of agents and V be a finite set. In our model, utilities of M and W over V are described by $M^\natural$-concave functions $f_M, f_W : \mathbf{Z}^V \to \mathbf{R} \cup \{-\infty\}$, respectively. In the exemplary models described in Section 3, M and W denote disjoint sets of agents, and we have $V = M \times W$, where f_M and f_W can be regarded as aggregations of utilities of M-agents and W-agents in these models, respectively (see Remark 1 given below). Furthermore, we assume that f_M and f_W satisfy the following condition:

(A) Effective domains $\operatorname{dom} f_M$ and $\operatorname{dom} f_W$ are bounded and hereditary, and have a common minimum point $\mathbf{0}$,

where the heredity means that $\mathbf{0} \leq x_1 \leq x_2 \in \operatorname{dom} f_M$ (respectively $\operatorname{dom} f_W$) implies $x_1 \in \operatorname{dom} f_M$ (respectively $\operatorname{dom} f_W$).

We say that $x \in \operatorname{dom} f_M \cap \operatorname{dom} f_W$ is an $f_M f_W$-*stable solution* if there exist disjoint subsets V_M and V_W of V and vectors $z_M \in \mathbf{Z}^{V_M}$ and $z_W \in \mathbf{Z}^{V_W}$ such that

$$x \in \arg\max\{f_M(y) \mid y \in \mathbf{Z}^V, \ y|_{V_M} \leq z_M\}, \tag{8}$$
$$x \in \arg\max\{f_W(y) \mid y \in \mathbf{Z}^V, \ y|_{V_W} \leq z_W\}, \tag{9}$$

where $y|_{V_M}$ (resp. $y|_{V_W}$) denotes the restriction of y on V_M (resp. V_W). Since $\operatorname{dom} f_M$ and $\operatorname{dom} f_W$ are bounded due to Assumption (A), there exists $z \in \mathbf{Z}^V$

such that $y \leq z$ for all $y \in \mathrm{dom}\, f_M \cap \mathrm{dom}\, f_W$. We see that $x \in \mathrm{dom}\, f_M \cap \mathrm{dom}\, f_W$ is an $f_M f_W$-stable solution if and only if there exist $z_M, z_W \in \mathbf{Z}^V$ satisfying the following (10)$\sim$(12):

$$z = z_M \vee z_W, \tag{10}$$
$$x \in \arg\max\{f_M(y) \mid y \in \mathbf{Z}^V,\ y \leq z_M\}, \tag{11}$$
$$x \in \arg\max\{f_W(y) \mid y \in \mathbf{Z}^V,\ y \leq z_W\}. \tag{12}$$

In the sequel we will use (10)$\sim$(12) instead of (8) and (9).

Our main result claims nonemptiness of the set of $f_M f_W$-stable solutions of our model.

Theorem 1 (Main Theorem). *For any $M^\natural$-concave functions $f_M, f_W : \mathbf{Z}^V \to \mathbf{R} \cup \{-\infty\}$ satisfying* (A), *there always exists an $f_M f_W$-stable solution.*

A constructive proof of the main theorem will be given in Section 4 by using a generalized Gale-Shapley algorithm.

Remark 1. In our model given above each of M and W is regarded as a single aggregate agent but it can be interpreted as a set of agents as follows. Let $M = \{1, \cdots, m\}$, $W = \{1, \cdots, w\}$, and $V = M \times W$. Also define $V_i = \{i\} \times W$ ($i \in M$) and $V_j = M \times \{j\}$ ($j \in W$). Suppose that each agent $i \in M$ has an $M^\natural$-concave utility function $f_i : \mathbf{Z}^{V_i} \to \mathbf{R} \cup \{-\infty\}$ on V_i and that each agent $j \in W$ has an $M^\natural$-concave utility function $f_j : \mathbf{Z}^{V_j} \to \mathbf{R} \cup \{-\infty\}$ on V_j. Aggregations $f_M(x) = \sum_{i \in M} f_i(x|_{V_i})$ and $f_W(x) = \sum_{j \in W} f_j(x|_{V_j})$ are also $M^\natural$-concave. It should be noted that this modified model is equivalent to our original model. $\square$

3   Existing Special Models

In this section we explain some existing models that are special cases of our model. In these models there are two disjoint sets of agents $M = \{1, \cdots, m\}$ and $W = \{1, \cdots, w\}$. The pairs of agents in M and W may be recognized as those of men and women. We denote by V the set of all pairs of agents of M and W, i.e., $V = M \times W$. For each pair $(i, j) \in V$, a pair (a_{ij}, b_{ij}) is given, where a_{ij} and b_{ij} can be interpreted as utilities (or profits) of i and j, respectively, provided that they are paired. Here, we assume that either $a_{ij} \geq 0$ or $a_{ij} = -\infty$ and we say j is *acceptable* to i if $a_{ij} \geq 0$ and similarly, for b_{ij}.

Although there are several variations of the stable marriage model, we explain one of comprehensive variations. In this model each agent ranks the agents on the opposite side, where unacceptability and indifference are allowed. In our context, agent $i \in M$ *prefers* j_1 to j_2 if $a_{ij_1} > a_{ij_2}$, and j_1 and j_2 are *indifferent* for agent i if $a_{ij_1} = a_{ij_2}$ (similarly, preferences of each $j \in W$ are defined from b_{ij}'s). The model deals with the stability of matchings, where a matching is a subset of V such that every agent appears at most once in the subset. Given a matching X, $i \in M$ (resp. $j \in W$) is called *unmatched in X* if there exists no $j \in W$ (resp. $i \in M$) such that $(i, j) \in X$. A pair $(i, j) \notin X$ is said to be a *blocking pair* for X if i and j prefer each other to their partners or being alone in X. A matching X is called *stable* if each pair (i, j) in X is acceptable for i and j, and if there is no blocking pair for X. It is well-known that any instance of the above model has a stable matching, originally proved by Gale and Shapley [7].

Recently, Fleiner [3] has generalized the above model to matroids. A triple $\mathcal{M} = (V, \mathcal{I}, >)$ is called an *ordered matroid*, if $(V, \mathcal{I})$ is a matroid on ground set V with family $\mathcal{I}$ of independent sets and $>$ is a linear order on V. A subset X of V *dominates* element $v \in V$ if $v \in X$ or there exists an independent set $Y \subseteq X$ such that $\{v\} \cup Y \notin \mathcal{I}$ and $u > v$ for all $u \in Y$. The set of elements dominated by X is denoted by $D_{\mathcal{M}}(X)$. Given two ordered matroids $\mathcal{M}_M = (V, \mathcal{I}_M, >_M)$ and $\mathcal{M}_W = (V, \mathcal{I}_W, >_W)$ on the same ground set V, a subset X of V is called an $\mathcal{M}_M\mathcal{M}_W$-*kernel* if X is a common independent set of $\mathcal{M}_M$ and $\mathcal{M}_W$, and if any element $v \in V$ is dominated by X in $\mathcal{M}_M$ or $\mathcal{M}_W$, that is, if the following condition holds:

$$X \in \mathcal{I}_M \cap \mathcal{I}_W \text{ and } D_{\mathcal{M}_M}(X) \cup D_{\mathcal{M}_W}(X) = V. \tag{13}$$

For example, given a stable marriage instance $(M, W, \{a_{ij}\}, \{b_{ij}\})$ without indifferent preferences, we can construct an equivalent instance in terms of matroids as follows. Let V be the set of pairs (i, j) with $a_{ij}, b_{ij} > -\infty$. Assume that $(V, \mathcal{I}_M)$ is the partition matroid on V defined by disjoint sets $V_i = \{i\} \times W$ $(i \in M)$ and that $(V, \mathcal{I}_W)$ is the partition matroid on V defined by disjoint sets $V_j = M \times \{j\}$ $(j \in W)$. Thus, X is a matching if and only if $X \in \mathcal{I}_M \cap \mathcal{I}_W$. We next define linear orders $>_M$ and $>_W$ on V so that $(i, j_1) >_M (i, j_2)$ whenever $a_{ij_1} > a_{ij_2}$, and that $(i_1, j) >_W (i_2, j)$ whenever $b_{i_1j} > b_{i_2j}$. By the definitions of the linear orders, a matching X is an $\mathcal{M}_M\mathcal{M}_W$-kernel if and only if for each pair $(i, j) \notin X$ there exists (i, j') in X such that $(i, j') >_M (i, j)$, or (i', j) in X such that $(i', j) >_W (i, j)$. Thus, the set of $\mathcal{M}_M\mathcal{M}_W$-kernels coincides with the set of stable matchings. The matroidal model also includes a many-to-many stable matching model, called stable b-matching model. We remark that the matroidal model can easily be modified so that indifference in preferences is admissible. Fleiner [3] showed that any instance of the matroidal model has an $\mathcal{M}_M\mathcal{M}_W$-kernel.

Quite recently, Eguchi and Fujishige [2] proposed a model in terms of M$^\natural$-concavity, which is a set version of our model in which $\text{dom } f_M, \text{dom } f_W \subseteq \{0, 1\}^V$ and for any distinct $x, y \in \text{dom } f_M$ (resp. $x, y \in \text{dom } f_W$) $f_M(x) \neq f_M(y)$ (resp. $f_W(x) \neq f_W(y)$). For convenience, we identify a subset of V with its characteristic vector. The matroidal model described above can be recognized as a special case of this model with linear utility functions. Let $\mathcal{M}_M = (V, \mathcal{I}_M, >_M)$ and $\mathcal{M}_W = (V, \mathcal{I}_W, >_W)$ be an instance of the matroidal model. We define linear orders $>_M$ and $>_W$ by positive numbers $\{a_v\}$ and $\{b_v\}$ as $a_u > a_v \iff u >_M v$ and $b_u > b_v \iff u >_W v$. Also define functions f_M and f_W by

$$f_M(X) = \begin{cases} \sum_{v \in X} a_v & (X \in \mathcal{I}_M) \\ -\infty & (X \notin \mathcal{I}_M), \end{cases} \qquad f_W(X) = \begin{cases} \sum_{v \in X} b_v & (X \in \mathcal{I}_W) \\ -\infty & (X \notin \mathcal{I}_W). \end{cases} \tag{14}$$

Then f_M and f_W are M$^\natural$-concave because these are linear on independence families of matroids. For an independent set X of $\mathcal{M}_M$ and $Z \subseteq V$ with $X \subseteq Z$, we have that $X \in \arg\max\{f_M(Y) \mid Y \subseteq Z\}$ if and only if $Z \subseteq D_{\mathcal{M}_M}(X)$, by the optimality criterion of maximum weight independent sets of a matroid (the same statement for $\mathcal{M}_W$ also holds). Thus, a subset X of V is an $\mathcal{M}_M \mathcal{M}_W$-kernel if and only if it is $f_M f_W$-stable. Eguchi and Fujishige [2] showed that any instance of their model has an $f_M f_W$-stable solution.

Therefore, our model includes all of the above models. Moreover, our model admits multiplicity for each element of V. For example, our model naturally deals with the following problem. The same numbers of men and women attend a dance party at which each person dances a waltz k times and he/she can dance with the same person of the opposite gender time after time. The problem is to find an "agreeable" assignment of dance partners, in which each person is assigned at most k persons of the opposite gender with possible repetition. If preferences of assignments of dance partners for each person can be expressed by an M$^\natural$-concave function (see Remark 1 in Section 2), then our model gives a solution.

4   A Generalized Gale-Shapley Algorithm

In this section we prove our main theorem, Theorem 1, by giving an algorithm for finding $x, z_M, z_W \in \mathbf{Z}^V$ satisfying (10)~(12). This algorithm is a generalization of the Gale-Shapley algorithm.

Before describing the algorithm, we show two fundamental properties of M$^\natural$-concave functions as Lemmas 1 and 2, which hold without Assumption (A).

Lemma 1. *Let $f : \mathbf{Z}^V \to \mathbf{R} \cup \{-\infty\}$ be an M$^\natural$-concave function and $z_1, z_2 \in \mathbf{Z}^V$ be such that $z_1 \geq z_2$, $\arg\max\{f(y) \mid y \leq z_1\} \neq \emptyset$, and $\arg\max\{f(y) \mid y \leq z_2\} \neq \emptyset$.*

(a) *For any $x_1 \in \arg\max\{f(y) \mid y \leq z_1\}$, there exists x_2 such that*

$$x_2 \in \arg\max\{f(y) \mid y \leq z_2\} \quad and \quad z_2 \wedge x_1 \leq x_2. \tag{15}$$

(b) *For any $x_2 \in \arg\max\{f(y) \mid y \leq z_2\}$, there exists x_1 such that*

$$x_1 \in \arg\max\{f(y) \mid y \leq z_1\} \quad and \quad z_2 \wedge x_1 \leq x_2. \tag{16}$$

Proof. (a): Let x_2 be an element in $\arg\max\{f(y) \mid y \leq z_2\}$ that minimizes $\sum\{x_1(v) - x_2(v) \mid v \in \mathrm{supp}^+((z_2 \wedge x_1) - x_2)\}$. We show $z_2 \wedge x_1 \leq x_2$. Suppose, to the contrary, that there exists $u \in V$ with $\min\{z_2(u), x_1(u)\} > x_2(u)$. Then $u \in \mathrm{supp}^+(x_1 - x_2)$. By $(-\mathrm{M}^\natural\text{-EXC})$, there exists $v \in \mathrm{supp}^-(x_1 - x_2) \cup \{0\}$ such that

$$f(x_1) + f(x_2) \leq f(x_1 - \chi_u + \chi_v) + f(x_2 + \chi_u - \chi_v). \tag{17}$$

If $v \neq 0$, then $x_1(v) < x_2(v) \leq z_2(v) \leq z_1(v)$. Hence we have $x_1 - \chi_u + \chi_v \leq z_1$, which implies $f(x_1) \geq f(x_1 - \chi_u + \chi_v)$. This together with (17) yields $f(x_2) \leq f(x_2 + \chi_u - \chi_v)$. Moreover, since $z_2(u) > x_2(u)$, we have $x_2' = x_2 + \chi_u - \chi_v \leq z_2$. It follows that $x_2' \in \arg\max\{f(y) \mid y \leq z_2\}$ and $x_2'(v) \geq \min\{z_2(v), x_1(v)\}$ if $v \neq 0$, which contradicts the minimality condition of x_2.

(b): Let x_1 be an element in $\arg\max\{f(y) \mid y \leq z_1\}$ that minimizes $\sum\{x_1(u) - x_2(u) \mid u \in \text{supp}^+((z_2 \wedge x_1) - x_2)\}$. We show $z_2 \wedge x_1 \leq x_2$. Suppose, to the contrary, that there exists $u \in V$ with $\min\{z_2(u), x_1(u)\} > x_2(u)$. Then $u \in \text{supp}^+(x_1 - x_2)$. By $(-\text{M}^\natural\text{-EXC})$, there exists $v \in \text{supp}^-(x_1 - x_2) \cup \{0\}$ such that

$$f(x_1) + f(x_2) \leq f(x_1 - \chi_u + \chi_v) + f(x_2 + \chi_u - \chi_v). \tag{18}$$

Since $x_2(u) < z_2(u)$, we have $x_2 + \chi_u - \chi_v \leq z_2$, which implies $f(x_2) \geq f(x_2 + \chi_u - \chi_v)$. This together with (18) yields $f(x_1) \leq f(x_1 - \chi_u + \chi_v)$. Obviously $x_1' = x_1 - \chi_u + \chi_v \leq z_1$. However, this contradicts the minimality condition of x_1 because $x_2(v) \geq \min\{z_2(v), x_1'(v)\}$ if $v \neq 0$. $\qquad \square$

Lemma 2. *For an $\text{M}^\natural$-concave function $f : \mathbf{Z}^V \to \mathbf{R} \cup \{-\infty\}$ and a vector $z_1 \in \mathbf{Z}^V$ suppose that $\arg\max\{f(y) \mid y \leq z_1\} \neq \emptyset$. For any $x \in \arg\max\{f(y) \mid y \leq z_1\}$ and any $z_2 \in \mathbf{Z}^V$ such that (1) $z_2 \geq z_1$ and (2) if $x(v) = z_1(v)$, then $z_2(v) = z_1(v)$, we have $x \in \arg\max\{f(y) \mid y \leq z_2\}$.*

Proof. Assume to the contrary that the assertion is not satisfied. Let x' be a point such that $x' \leq z_2$, $f(x') > f(x)$, and x' minimizes $\sum\{x'(v) - z_1(v) \mid v \in \text{supp}^+(x' - z_1)\}$ among such points. By the assumption, there exists $u \in V$ with $x'(u) > z_1(u) > x(u)$. By $(-\text{M}^\natural\text{-EXC})$ for x', x, and u, there exists $v \in \text{supp}^-(x' - x) \cup \{0\}$ such that

$$f(x') + f(x) \leq f(x' - \chi_u + \chi_v) + f(x + \chi_u - \chi_v). \tag{19}$$

Since $x + \chi_u - \chi_v \leq z_1$, we have $f(x) \geq f(x + \chi_u - \chi_v)$, which implies $f(x') \leq f(x' - \chi_u + \chi_v)$. Obviously, $x' - \chi_u + \chi_v \leq z_2$, However, this contradicts the minimality condition of x' because if $v \neq 0$, then $z_1(v) \geq x(v) > x'(v)$. $\qquad \square$

It should be noted that Lemma 2 holds for any function f on $\mathbf{Z}^V$ that has a concave extension on $\mathbf{R}^V$.

To describe an algorithm for finding $x, z_M, z_W \in \mathbf{Z}^V$ satisfying (10)~(12), we assume that we are initially given $x_M, x_W, z_M, z_W \in \mathbf{Z}^V$ satisfying the following:

$$z = z_M \vee z_W, \tag{20}$$

$$x_M \in \arg\max\{f_M(y) \mid y \leq z_M\}, \tag{21}$$

$$x_W \in \arg\max\{f_W(y) \mid y \leq z_W \vee x_M\}, \tag{22}$$

$$x_W \leq x_M. \tag{23}$$

We can easily compute such vectors by setting $z_M = z$, $z_W = \mathbf{0}$, and by finding x_M and x_W such that

$$x_M \in \arg\max\{f_M(y) \mid y \leq z_M\}, \quad x_W \in \arg\max\{f_W(y) \mid y \leq x_M\}. \tag{24}$$

The algorithm is given as follows.

Algorithm_GS$(f_M, f_W, x_M, x_W, z_M, z_W)$
Input: $M^\natural$-concave functions f_M, f_W and
      x_M, x_W, z_M, z_W satisfying (20), (21), (22), (23) ;
   repeat {
      let x_M be any element in $\arg\max\{f_M(y) \mid x_W \le y \le z_M\}$;
      let x_W be any element in $\arg\max\{f_W(y) \mid y \le x_M\}$;
      for each $v \in V$ with $x_M(v) > x_W(v)$ {
         $z_M(v) \leftarrow x_W(v)$;
         $z_W(v) \leftarrow z(v)$;
      } ;
   } **until** $x_M = x_W$;
   return $(x_M, z_M, z_W \vee x_M)$.

It should be noted here that because of Assumption (A) x_M and x_W are well-defined within the effective domains and that Algorithm_GS terminates after at most $\sum_{v \in V} z(v)$ iterations, because $\sum_{v \in V} z_M(v)$ is strictly decreased at each iteration. In order to show that the outputs of Algorithm_GS satisfy (10)~(12), we will show two lemmas, Lemmas 3 and 4.

Let $x_M^{(i)}$, $x_W^{(i)}$, $z_M^{(i)}$, and $z_W^{(i)}$ be x_M, x_W, z_M, and z_W obtained after the ith iteration in Algorithm_GS for $i = 1, 2, \cdots, t$, where t is the last to get the outputs. For convenience, let us assume that $x_M^{(0)}$, $x_W^{(0)}$, $z_M^{(0)}$, and $z_W^{(0)}$ are the input vectors.

Lemma 3. *For each $i = 0, 1, \cdots, t$, we have*

$$x_M^{(i+1)} \in \arg\max\left\{f_M(y) \,\Big|\, y \le z_M^{(i)}\right\}. \tag{25}$$

Proof. We prove (25) by induction on i. For $i = 0$, (25) holds from (21) and (23). We assume that for some l with $0 \le l < t$ (25) holds for any $i \le l$, and we show (25) for $i = l + 1$. Since $x_M^{(l+1)} \in \arg\max\{f_M(y) \mid y \le z_M^{(l)}\}$ and $z_M^{(l)} \ge z_M^{(l+1)}$, Lemma 1 (a) guarantees the existence of an $x \in \arg\max\{f_M(y) \mid y \le z_M^{(l+1)}\}$ with $z_M^{(l+1)} \wedge x_M^{(l+1)} \le x$, which implies (25) for $i = l+1$ because $z_M^{(l+1)} \wedge x_M^{(l+1)} = x_W^{(l+1)}$ by the modification of z_M. $\qquad\square$

Lemma 4. *For each $i = 0, 1, \cdots, t$, we have*

$$x_W^{(i)} \in \arg\max\left\{f_W(y) \,\Big|\, y \le z_W^{(i)} \vee x_M^{(i)}\right\}. \tag{26}$$

Proof. We show (26) by induction on i. For $i = 0$, (26) holds by (22). We assume that for some l with $0 \le l < t$ (26) holds for any $i \le l$, and we show (26) for $i = l + 1$. By the definition of x_M, we have

$$x_M^{(l+1)} \ge x_W^{(l)}. \tag{27}$$

By Lemma 1 (b) and the assumption, there exists x such that

$$x \in \arg\max\left\{f_W(y) \,\Big|\, y \le z_W^{(l)} \vee x_M^{(l)} \vee x_M^{(l+1)}\right\} \tag{28}$$

and

$$\left(z_W^{(l)} \vee x_M^{(l)}\right) \wedge x \le x_W^{(l)}. \tag{29}$$

From (27), (28), and (29), we have $x \le x_M^{(l+1)}$ and hence $f_W(x) = f_W(x_W^{(l+1)})$. If $z_W^{(l+1)} = z_W^{(l)}$, then we immediately obtain (26) for $i = l + 1$. So, we assume that $z_W^{(l+1)} \ne z_W^{(l)}$. By the modification of z_W, we have $x_W^{(l+1)}(v) < x_M^{(l+1)}(v)$ if $z_W^{(l)}(v) < z_W^{(l+1)}(v)$. Hence, by Lemma 2, (26) holds for $i = l + 1$.   □

The correctness of Algorithm_GS follows from Lemmas 3 and 4.

Theorem 2. *The outputs of* Algorithm_GS *satisfy* (10) $\sim$ (12).

Proof. From Lemmas 3 and 4 we have for $i = t$

$$x_M \in \arg\max\left\{ f_M(y) \mid y \le z_M^{(t)} \right\}, \tag{30}$$

$$x_W \in \arg\max\left\{ f_W(y) \mid y \le z_W^{(t)} \vee x_M^{(t)} \right\}, \tag{31}$$

$$x_M = x_W. \tag{32}$$

By the way of modifying z_M, z_W, and x_M, we have

$$z_M^{(t)} \vee \left(z_W^{(t)} \vee x_M^{(t)} \right) = z. \tag{33}$$

This completes the proof of this theorem.   □

Our main result, Theorem 1, is a direct consequence of Theorem 2.

5   Remarks on Time Complexity

We finally discuss the oracle complexities of the problems of finding an $f_M f_W$-stable solution and of checking whether a given point is $f_M f_W$-stable, provided that the function value $f(x)$ of a given M$^{\natural}$-concave function f can be calculated in constant time for each point x.

Algorithm_GS solves the maximization problem of an M$^{\natural}$-concave function in each iteration. It is known that a maximizer of an M$^{\natural}$-concave function f on V can be found in polynomial time in n and $\log L$, where $n = |V|$ and $L = \max\{||x - y||_\infty \mid x, y \in \text{dom } f\}$. For example, O($n^3 \log L$)-time algorithms are proposed in [14,15]. Since Algorithm_GS terminates after at most $\sum_{v \in V} z(v)$ iterations, the oracle time complexity of Algorithm_GS is O(poly(n) · L), where $L = ||z||_\infty$. Unfortunately, there exist a series of examples in which Algorithm_GS requires numbers of iterations proportional to L. While it is known that an $f_M f_W$-stable solution can be found in polynomial time in n for the special case where f_M and f_W are linear on rectangular effective domains [1], it is open whether an $f_M f_W$-stable solution for the general case can be found in polynomial time in n and $\log L$.

On the other hand, the problem of checking whether a given point $x \in \text{dom } f_M \cap \text{dom } f_W$ is $f_M f_W$-stable, can be solved in O(n^2) time by using the following local criterion of the $f_M f_W$-stability.

Lemma 5. *A point $x \in \operatorname{dom} f_M \cap \operatorname{dom} f_W$ is $f_M f_W$-stable if and only if it satisfies the following conditions:*

$$\text{for each } u \in V, \ f_M(x) \geq f_M(x - \chi_u) \quad \text{and} \quad f_W(x) \geq f_W(x - \chi_u), \quad (34)$$

$$\text{for each } u \in V, \ f_M(x) \geq f_M(x + \chi_u - \chi_v) \quad (\forall v \in V \cup \{0\}) \quad \text{or}$$

$$f_W(x) \geq f_W(x + \chi_u - \chi_w) \quad (\forall w \in V \cup \{0\}). \quad (35)$$

References

1. M. Baïou and M. Balinski, Erratum: The stable allocation (or ordinal transportation) problem, *Math. Oper. Res.* **27** (2002) 662–680.
2. A. Eguchi and S. Fujishige, An extension of the Gale-Shapley matching algorithm to a pair of M$^\natural$-concave functions, Discrete Mathematics and Systems Science Research Report 02-05, Osaka University, (2002).
3. T. Fleiner, A matroid generalization of the stable matching polytope, in: B. Gerards and K. Aardal, eds., *Proceedings of the 8th International IPCO Conference*, LNCS **2081** (Springer-Verlag, Berlin, 2001) 105–114.
4. T. Fleiner, Some results on stable matchings and fixed points, EGRES Technical Report 2002-08, (2002), http://www.cs.elte.hu/egres.
5. T. Fleiner, A fixed point approach to stable matchings and some applications, *Math. Oper. Res.* **28** (2003) 103–126.
6. S. Fujishige and Z. Yang, A note on Kelso and Crawford's gross substitutes condition, *Math. Oper. Res.* to appear.
7. D. Gale and L. S. Shapley, College admissions and the stability of marriage, *Amer. Math. Monthly* **69** (1962) 9–15.
8. K. Murota, Convexity and Steinitz's exchange property, *Adv. Math.* **124** (1996) 272–311.
9. K. Murota, Discrete convex analysis, *Math. Programming* **83** (1998) 313–371.
10. K. Murota, *Discrete Convex Analysis*, (Society for Industrial and Applied Mathematics, Philadelphia, 2003).
11. K. Murota and A. Shioura, M-convex function on generalized polymatroid, *Math. Oper. Res.* **24** (1999) 95–105.
12. K. Murota and A. Shioura, Relationship of M-/L-convex functions with discrete convex functions by Miller and by Favati–Tardella, *Discrete Appl. Math.* **115** (2001) 151–176.
13. K. Murota and A. Tamura, New characterizations of M-convex functions and their applications to economic equilibrium models with indivisibilities, *Discrete Appl. Math.* to appear.
14. A. Shioura, Fast scaling algorithms for M-convex function minimization with application to the resource allocation problem, *Discrete Appl. Math.* to appear.
15. A. Tamura, Coordinatewise domain scaling algorithm for M-convex function minimization, in: W. J. Cook and A. S. Schulz, eds., *Proceedings of the 9th International IPCO Conference*, LNCS **2337**, (Springer-Verlag, Berlin, 2002) 21–35.

Succinct Data Structures for Searchable Partial Sums*

Wing-Kai Hon[1], Kunihiko Sadakane[2], and Wing-Kin Sung[3]

[1] Department of Computer Science and Informations Systems,
The University of Hong Kong, Hong Kong,
{wkhon,twlam}@csis.hku.hk
[2] Department of Computer Science and Communication Engineering,
Kyushu University, Japan, sada@csce.kyushu-u.ac.jp
[3] School of Computing, National University of Singapore, Singapore,
ksung@comp.nus.edu.sg

Abstract. The *Searchable Partial Sums* is a data structure problem that maintains a sequence of n non-negative k-bit integers; in addition, it allows us to modify the entries by the *update* operation, while supporting two types of queries: *sum* and *search*. Recently, researchers focus on the succinct representation of the data structure in $kn + o(kn)$ bits. They study the tradeoff in time between the query and the update operations, under the word RAM with word size $O(\lg U)$ bits. For the special case where $k = 1$ (which is known as *Dynamic Bit Vector* problem), Raman et al. showed that both queries can be supported in $O(\log_b n)$ time, while *update* requires $O(b)$ amortized time for any b with $\lg n / \lg \lg n \le b \le n$. This paper generalizes the study and shows that even for $k = O(\lg \lg n)$, both query and update operations can be maintained using the same time complexities. Also, the time for *update* becomes worst-case time. For the general case when $k = O(\lg U)$, we show a lower bound of $\Omega\left(\sqrt{\lg n / \lg \lg n}\right)$ time for the *search* query. On the other hand, we propose a data structure that supports *sum* in $O(\log_b n)$ time, *search* in $O(\tau \log_b n)$ time, and *update* in $O(b)$ time, where τ denotes the value of $\min\left\{\lg \lg n \lg \lg U / \lg \lg \lg U, \sqrt{\lg n / \lg \lg n}\right\}$. When $b = n^\epsilon$, our data structure achieves optimal time bounds.
This paper also extends the *Searchable Partial Sums* with *insert* and *delete* operations, and provides succinct data structure for some cases.

1 Introduction

The size of electronic data is growing exponentially, whose rate is now exceeding that of computer memory. To battle the information avalanche, the quest for highly space-efficient or *succinct* data structures, which are asymptotically optimal in operation times, is desirable, and has attracted many researchers recently

* This work was supported in part by the Hong Kong RGC Grant HKU-7024/01E; by the Grant-in-Aid of the Ministry of Education, Science, Sports and Culture of Japan; by the NUS Academic Research Grant R-252-000-119-112.

T. Ibaraki, N. Katoh, and H. Ono (Eds.): ISAAC 2003, LNCS 2906, pp. 505–516, 2003.

[4,7,8] (See [7] for more references). In this paper, we revisit a well-studied data structure problem called *Searchable Partial Sums*, and provide succinct solutions to it. We assume a unit-cost word RAM with word size $O(\lg U)$ bits,[1] in which standard arithmetic and bitwise boolean operations on word-sized operands can be performed in constant time [1,5].

Let $A[1], A[2], \ldots, A[n]$ be a sequence of n non-negative k-bit numbers with $n \leq U$. The *Searchable Partial Sums* problem maintains the sequence under two query operations sum and search, and an update operation as follows:

- sum(i): return the value $\sum_{t=1}^{i} A[t]$.
- search(j): return the smallest i such that sum(i) $\geq j$.
- update(i, δ): set $A[i] \leftarrow A[i] + \delta$, for some integer δ such that $0 \leq A[i] + \delta \leq 2^k - 1$ and $-\lg^{O(1)} n \leq \delta \leq \lg^{O(1)} n$.

When $k = 1$, such special case is commonly known as the *Dynamic Bit Vector* problem, which maintains a bit vector of length n under two query operations rank and select, and an update operation flip. These operations are essentially the sum, search and update, respectively. In what follows, we adopt the above common notations when dealing with bit vectors.

The *Searchable Partial Sums* was originated from a related problem called *Partial Sums*, which does not consider the search query. Fredman and Saks [3] showed that, in the *cell probe* model of computation (Yao [9]),[2] an intermixed sequence of n queries and updates requires $\Omega(\lg n / \lg \lg n)$ amortized time per operation. Dietz [2] proposed a data structure of $\Theta(n \lg n)$ bits for the *Partial Sums* that supports sum and update optimally in $O(\lg n / \lg \lg n)$ time, for $k = \Theta(\lg n)$. Raman, Raman and Rao [7] generalized the result to $k = O(\lg U)$, and reduced the space required to $kn + o(kn)$ bits. This space is information-theoretically optimal within a lower-order term. In particular, they gave a trade-off result that supports sum in $O(\log_b n)$ time and update in $O(b)$ time, for any parameter $b \geq \lg n / \lg \lg n$. Note that when $b = \lg n / \lg \lg n$, all operations take $O(\lg n / \lg \lg n)$ time.

For *Searchable Partial Sums*, Raman, Raman and Rao [7] gave a succinct structure that supports all operations in $O(\lg n / \lg \lg n)$ worst-case time. Concerning tradeoff, they can only give a succinct solution with the same tradeoff between query and update times for $k = 1$. (That is, $O(\log_b n)$ time for rank (sum) and select (search), while $O(b)$ time for flip (update).) Moreover, their update time becomes amortized instead of worst-case. There are two open questions: 1. *Can we improve the amortized time to worst-case time for $k = 1$? 2. Can we achieve the same tradeoff for $k > 1$?*

In this paper, we investigate the *Searchable Partial Sums* for different ranges of k, and propose corresponding succinct structures that allow tradeoff between query and update times. The space of the structures are all $kn + o(kn)$ bits.

---

[1] We use the notation $\lg n$ and $\log_b n$ to denote the base-2 and base-b logarithm of n, respectively.

[2] In the cell probe model, the time complexity of a sequential computation is defined to be the number of words of memory that are accessed. The lower bound time complexity derived is stronger than that in the word RAM model.

For $k = 1$, we can support sum and search in $O(\log_b n)$ time, while update in worst-case $O(b)$ time. This improves the previous result which requires amortized update time, and answers affirmatively to the first open question. Furthermore, we extend the same tradeoff for $k = O(\lg \lg n)$, thus answering partly to the second open question.

For the general case when $k = O(\lg U)$, we give a negative example for the second open question, by showing a lower bound of $\Omega\left(\sqrt{\lg n / \lg \lg n}\right)$ time for search. On the other hand, our proposed structure can support sum in $O(\log_b n)$ time, update in $O(b)$ time and search in $O(\tau \log_b n)$ time, where $\tau = \min\left\{\lg \lg n \lg \lg U / \lg \lg \lg U, \sqrt{\lg n / \lg \lg n}\right\}$. Thus, our data structure achieves optimal time bounds when $b = n^\epsilon$ for any fixed $\epsilon > 0$.

Technically speaking, when $k = 1$, our improvement stems from a better solution for the select query. Existing method [7] maintains a weight-balanced B-tree (WBB tree) of Dietz [2], and updating of which can only be done in amortized time. In this paper, we modified the WBB tree so that the relevant information in the internal nodes for efficient query can be stored compactly, and updated efficiently. Consequently, the select time is maintained, while the flip time becomes worst-case time.

When $k > 1$, we observe that search can be supported efficiently by coupling an efficient WBB tree with our new solution to the *Dynamic Bit Vector* problem. The idea is to divide the input array into fixed-sized groups, and use a bit vector to remember those groups whose sum of elements is positive. With select, we can access any *positive-sum* groups easily. Then, we can focus on those *positive-sum* groups, and use our WBB tree to manage them.

We also consider the *Searchable Partial Sums with Indel* problem. This problem extends the *Searchable Partial Sums* problem to consider a resizeable sequence, which supports insert and delete operations as follows:

- insert(i, x): insert a new integer x between $A[i]$ and $A[i + 1]$.
- delete(i): remove the entry $A[i]$ from the sequence.

When the sequence consists of only positive k-bit integers and $k = O(1)$, we provide a $kn + o(kn)$-bit data structure that supports sum and search in $O(\log_b n)$ time, update in $O(b)$ time, while insert and delete in amortized $O(b)$ time for $b \geq \lg^{O(1)} U$, where n is the current size of the sequence. On the other hand, if we are given an extra $O(U^\epsilon)$-bit precomputed table for any fixed $\epsilon > 0$, we can extend k to $O(\lg \lg U)$, and all the three update operations can be supported in worst-case $O(b)$ time.

The paper is organized as follows. The next section introduces some basic lemmas for building our data structures. Section 3 discusses the data structure for *Searchable Partial Sums with Indel*. In Sections 4, 5, and 6, we investigate the *Searchable Partial Sums* for $k = 1$, $O(\lg \lg n)$ and $O(\lg U)$, respectively. Concluding remarks are given in Section 7.

2   Preliminaries

The first two lemmas, which are rephrased from [7], form part of the results in the paper.

Lemma 1. *([7], Corollary 2) Given a bit vector of length n. Together with an auxiliary data structure of $o(n)$ bits of space, we can support* rank *in $O(\log_b n)$ time and* flip *in $O(b)$ time, for any parameter b with $\lg n/\lg\lg n \leq b \leq n$.*

Lemma 2. *([7], Theorem 2 with minor adaptation) Given a sequence of n non-negative k-bit integers that is stored in an array, where $k = O(\lg U)$. Together with an auxiliary data structure of $o(kn)$ bits of space, we can support* sum *and* search *in $O(\log_b n)$ time and* update *in $O(b)$ time for any parameter b with $\lg n/\lg\lg n \leq b \leq \lg^{O(1)} n$.*

Then, the following lemmas provide fundamental tools for our data structure.

Lemma 3. *Given a sequence G of non-negative k-bit integers that is stored in an array, where $|G| = \lg^{O(1)} L$ and $k = O(\lg\lg L)$ for some $L \leq U$. Together with an auxiliary data structure of $o(|G|)$ bits of space and a precomputed table of size $O(L^\epsilon)$ bits for any fixed $\epsilon > 0$, we can support* sum, search *and* update *in $O(1)$ time. Moreover, the auxiliary data structure can be constructed in $O(|G|\lg\lg L/\lg L)$ time.*

Proof. Omitted (deferred to the full paper).   □

Lemma 4. *([7], Lemma 2) Given a sequence of n non-negative k-bit integers, where $k = O(\lg U)$. There is a data structure of size $O(kn)$ bits that supports* sum, search *and* update *in $O(\lg n/\lg\lg n)$ time.*

Lemma 5. *(Rephrased from [6]) Given a bit vector of length n. Together with an auxiliary data structure of $o(n)$ bits of space, we can support* rank *in $O(1)$ time. The construction of the auxiliary data structure takes $o(n)$ time.*

3   Searchable Partial Sums with Indel

This section discusses the problem of *Searchable Partial Sums with Indel*. Firstly, we have the following lemma.

Lemma 6. *Given a sequence of at most L integers $p_1, p_2, p_3, \ldots$, with $x/2 \leq p_i \leq x$ for some x. Then, there is a data structure of size $O(z\lg(bxL))$ bits that supports* sum *and* search *in $O(\max\{\log_b z, 1\})$ time, and* update, insert *and* delete *in $O(b)$ time, for all $b \geq (\log_b z)^2$ where z denotes the current size of the sequence.*

To prove the above lemma, we maintain a weight-balanced B-tree (WBB tree) over the z integers as follows. Each integer represents a leaf, and all the leaves are at the same depth. Define *level* of a node to be the depth of the tree minus the depth of the node, and define *weight* of a node to be the total sum of integers under the node. Each internal node at level i maintains an invariant that its weight is at least $b^i x/2$ and at most $b^i x$.

For each internal node at level i, we store:

- the LW-value, which is the sum of integers under all its left siblings. (Note: the LW-value is stored using $(i + 1)\lg(bx)$ bits.)
- the LN-value, which is the number of integers under all its left siblings. (Note: the LN-value is stored using $(i + 1)\lg(b)$ bits.)
- an auxiliary data structure $\mathcal{D}_1$ that returns the leftmost child such that its LW-value is at least j, for any j, in $O(1)$ time. The data structure occupies $O(b)$ bits, and can be constructed in $O(b)$ time.
- an auxiliary data structure $\mathcal{D}_2$ that returns the leftmost child such that its LN-value is at least j, for any j, in $O(1)$ time. The data structure occupies $O(b)$ bits, and can be constructed in $O(b)$ time.
- pointers to its children, each using $O(\lg L)$ bits.

For each leaf node, we simply store the LW-value and the LN-value. Both of them are stored using $\lg(bx)$ bits.

Suppose the auxiliary data structures $\mathcal{D}_1$ and $\mathcal{D}_2$ work with the claimed bounds. Immediately, we have the following propositions.

Proposition 1. *The space occupied by the above B-tree is $O(z\lg(bxL))$ bits.*

Proof. (sketch.) By straightforward calculation. $\square$

Proposition 2. *It takes $O(\log_b z)$ time to perform* search *and* sum *operations by the above WBB tree.*

Proof. (sketch.) To support search, we start from the root and descend level by level to the leaf $p_{\mathsf{search}(j)}$ based on the LW-values and $\mathcal{D}_1$ of the traversed nodes. The required answer is the sum of LN-values on the traversal path. Time bound follows as descending each node takes $O(1)$ time and the height of the tree is $O(\log_b n)$. Similar arguments for the sum operation. $\square$

Proposition 3. *It takes $O(b)$ time to support* update, insert *or* delete *in the above WBB tree.*

Proof. (sketch.) To support the update operations, we follow standard procedure for updating a WBB tree. A straightforward calculation yields an update time of $O(b\log_b z)$. Then, we set b to $b^{1/2}$, so that update time becomes $O(b)$ while the other propositions remain correct. $\square$

Now, it remains to describe the auxiliary data structures $\mathcal{D}_1$ and $\mathcal{D}_2$ in the internal node, as shown in the following proposition.

Proposition 4. *Auxiliary data structures $\mathcal{D}_1$ and $\mathcal{D}_2$ can work with the claimed bounds.*

Proof. To implement $\mathcal{D}_1$ for each internal node, one way is to use a bit vector such that the i-th entry is marked as 1, if one of LW-values of its children is i. Together with an auxiliary data structure of Lemma 5 that supports $O(1)$-time

rank operation on this bit vector, the required query on $\mathcal{D}_1$ can be answered by a **rank** query.

Observe that the sum of integers under each level-i node is at least $b^i x/2$ and at most $b^i x$. A brute force approach would require $b^i x(1 + o(1))$ bits for an internal node at level i, which is too spacious. However, the observation also implies the sum under each child of a level-i node is at least $b^{i-1} x/2$, so that when the LW-values of all these children are divided by $b^{i-1} x/2$, each gives a distinct value of at most $2b$. In other words, the LW-values of the children (after dividing by $b^{i-1} x/2$) can be stored in $2b(1 + o(1))$ bits, while we still can answer the required query on $\mathcal{D}_1$ in $O(1)$ time. Moreover, the construction of this data structure takes $O(b)$ time. The auxiliary data structure $\mathcal{D}_2$ can be constructed and stored similarly. □

The proof of Lemma 6 is completed by combining Propositions 1, 2, 3 and 4. Then based on Lemma 6, we can show the main theorem of this section.

Theorem 1. *Given a sequence of at most L positive k-bit integers, where $L \leq U$ and $k = O(\lg \lg L)$. Then, there is a data structure of $kn + o(kn)$ bits of space, together with a precomputed table of $O(L^\epsilon)$ bits for any fixed $\epsilon > 0$, that supports* **sum** *or* **search** *in $O(\max\{\log_b n, 1\})$ time,* **update**, **insert** *or* **delete** *in $O(b)$ time, for any $\lg^{O(1)} L \leq b \leq L^{O(1)}$. The parameter n denotes the current size of the sequence.*

Proof. For ease of discussion, we assume at the moment that $k = o(\lg \lg L)$. We maintain two auxiliary data structures, one for **sum** and and one for **search**.

Assume that the sequence is $s_1, s_2, \ldots$. Firstly, we partition the elements into groups of size at least $(\lg L/ \lg \lg L)^3$ and at most $2(\lg L/ \lg \lg L)^3$, where elements in the same group are stored in consecutive locations. Each group is then maintained by Lemma 3.

Auxiliary data structure for sum: Let G_x denote the x-th group, and n_x denote its size. Then, to support **sum**, we construct a data structure $\mathcal{W}_1$ of Lemma 6 on all the n_x's. Notice that if a **search**(i) query on $\mathcal{W}_1$ returns x, it indicates that the element s_i is located in G_x. In order to support **sum**, we need to augment the WBB of $\mathcal{W}_1$ with the following things. Firstly, each leaf stores a pointer to the corresponding group. Secondly, in each node u, we store a TW-value (true-weight) which is the total sum of elements in those groups such that the corresponding leaves are under the left siblings of u.

To support **sum**(i) among the input sequence, we first perform a **search**(i) query on $\mathcal{W}_1$ to locate the group G_x that contains s_i. Then, the sum (say, y) of the TW-values on the traversal path indicates the total sum of elements in the groups preceeding G_x. Afterwards, a **sum**$(x - 1)$ query on $\mathcal{W}_1$ returns a value i', which is the total number of elements preceeding G_x. To obtain the required answer, it remains to perform a **sum**$(i - i')$ query within G_x by Lemma 3, and add the result to y. The total time used is $O(\log_b n)$ by straightforward calculation.

For the space, $\mathcal{W}_1$ requires $o(n)$ bits (by setting $z = n/(\lg L/ \lg \lg L)^3$ and $x = O((\lg L/ \lg \lg L)^3)$ in Lemma 6), and it requires $o(n)$ bits for the augmented TW-values and the pointers in the leaves. For the groups, they occupy $o(n)$ bits in total. Thus, the auxiliary data structure for **sum** is of $o(n)$ bits.

Auxiliary data structure for search: For each group G, we partition them into units, so that the sum of each unit is at least $(\lg L/\lg \lg L)^3$ and at most $2(\lg L/\lg \lg L)^3$. Notice that each group has at most $2^k = O(\lg L)$ units. Each unit is maintained by Lemma 3.

Let U_x denote the x-th unit, and σ_x be the sum of its elements. Then, to support search, we construct a data structure $\mathcal{W}_2$ of Lemma 6 on all the σ_x's. Notice that if a search(j) query on $\mathcal{W}_2$ returns x, it indicates that the element $s_{\text{search}(j)}$ is located in U_x. In order to support search, we need to augment the WBB of $\mathcal{W}_2$ with the following things. Firstly, each leaf stores a pointer to the corresponding unit. Then, in each node u of $\mathcal{W}_2$, we store a TC-value (true-count) which is the total number of elements in those units such that the corresponding leaves are under the left siblings of u.

Now, to support search(j) among the input sequence, we first perform a search(j) query on $\mathcal{W}_2$ to locate the group U_x that contains $s_{\text{search}(j)}$. Then, the sum (say, y) of the TC-values on the traversal path indicates the total number of elements in the units preceding U_x. Afterwards, a sum($x-1$) query on $\mathcal{W}_2$ returns a value j', which is the total sum of elements preceding U_x. To obtain the required answer, it remains to perform a search($j-j'$) query within U_x by Lemma 3, and add the result to y. The total time used is $O(\log_b n)$ by straightforward calculation.

For the space, $\mathcal{W}_2$ requires $o(n)$ bits (set $z = O(2^k n/(\lg L/\lg \lg L)^3)$ and $x = O(\lg L/\lg \lg L)^3$ in Lemma 6), while the augmented TC-values and the pointers in the leaves occupies $o(n)$ bits. For the units, they occupy $o(n)$ bits in total. Thus, the auxiliary data structure for search takes $o(n)$ bits.

Modification due to update, insert or delete: To modify the auxiliary structures due to insert or delete, we re-construct all the affected groups, and re-construct all the corresponding underlying units, and update $\mathcal{W}_1$ and $\mathcal{W}_2$ accordingly. Note that only constant number of groups are affected. Since construction time for the data structure of Lemma 3 depends on the size of the sequence stored, each group and all its underlying units can be re-constructed in a total of $O((\lg L/\lg \lg L)^2)$ time. For $\mathcal{W}_1$, it can be fixed in $O(b)$ time by Lemma 6. On the other hand, at most $O(\lg L/\lg \lg L)$ units are re-constructed, so that $\mathcal{W}_2$ can be modified in $O(b \lg L/\lg \lg L)$ time. By setting b to $b^{1/2}$, the total update time becomes $O(b)$ without affect the time for sum and search. Thus, the total time for both update operations is $O(b)$. Finally, notice that update can be done by a delete followed by an insert (or vice versa), so it takes $O(b)$ time as well.

When $k = O(\lg \lg n)$: Notice that the above auxiliary data structures also work well for $k = O(\lg \lg L)$, except that the space required may become too large. This can be handled by a slight modification that, elements of A are partitioned into group of size at least $(\lg L/\lg \lg L)^{O(1)}$ and at most $2(\lg L/\lg \lg L)^{O(1)}$ instead.

$\square$

Corollary 1. *Given a sequence of positive k-bit integers, where $k = O(1)$. Then, there is a data structure of size $kn + o(kn)$ bits that supports sum and search in $O(\max\{\log_b n, 1\})$ time, update in $O(b)$ time, while insert and delete in amortized $O(b)$ time, for any $\lg^{O(1)} U \leq b \leq U^{O(1)}$. The parameter n denotes the current size of the sequence.*

Proof. Omitted (deferred to the full paper).   □

4   Dynamic Bit Vector

This section investigates the tradeoff between query and update times for the dynamic bit vector problem. Our target aims at proving the following theorem:

Theorem 2. *Given a bit vector of length n. Together with an auxiliary data structure of $o(n)$ bits, we can support* rank *and* select *in $O(\log_b n)$ time, and* update *in $O(b)$ time, for any parameter b with $\lg n/\lg\lg n \le b \le n$.*

By Lemma 2, we can show that the above theorem is correct for any parameter b that is between $\lg n/\lg\lg n$ and $\lg^2 n$. Then, Lemma 1 implies that we have an auxiliary data structure of $o(n)$ bits that supports rank in $O(\log_b n)$ time and flip in $O(b)$ time, for $\lg^2 n \le b \le n$. To complete the proof of the above theorem, it remains to design an auxiliary data structure on the bit vector, that supports select in $O(\log_b n)$ time and flip in $O(b)$ time, for any $b \ge \lg^{O(1)} n$. The data structure is shown in following lemma.

Lemma 7. *Given a bit vector X of length n. Together with an auxiliary data structure of $o(n)$ bits of space, we can support* select *in $O(\log_b n)$ time and* flip *in $O(b)$ time, for any parameter b with $\lg^2 n \le b \le n$.*

Proof. We use a data structure to maintain all the positions p such that $X[p] = 1$. The positions are first partitioned into groups, where each group maintains its size to be at least $\lg^2 n$ and at most $2\lg^2 n$. The $\Theta(\lg^2 n)$ positions within each group are organised as follows, so that for any j, we can report the j-th smallest position within the group in $O(1)$ time:

- We store sp and lp explicitly, where sp and lp denotes the smallest and the largest positions among the group.
- For the remaining positions,
  - if $lp - sp \ge \lg^4 n$, they are stored explicitly, so that for any j, the j-th smallest position can be returned immediately.
  - otherwise, we use Lemma 3 to store an auxiliary data structure of size $o(lp - sp)$ bits for the bit vector $X[sp..lp]$. Note that the j-th smallest position can be found by selecting the j-th 1 in $X[sp..lp]$.

Now, let G_i be the i-th group and s_i denote its size. Since each value of s_i is between $\lg^2 n$ and $2\lg^2 n$, we can build a data structure $\mathcal{W}$ to maintain all the s_i's using Lemma 6.

To support select(j), we perform search(j) on $\mathcal{W}$. It returns x and indicates that G_x is the group that stores the j-th smallest position. Then, we obtain $j' = \text{sum}(x - 1)$ from $\mathcal{W}$, which represents the number of positions stored in the groups preceeding G_x. We can see that the required position of select(j) is stored as the $(j - j')$-th smallest value in G_x.

For time complexity, as there are $O(n/\lg^2 n)$ values stored in $\mathcal{W}$, search in this part takes $O(\log_b n)$ time. On the other hand, finding the $(j - j')$-th smallest position in G_x takes $O(1)$ time. Thus, the time for select follows.

As for the space, W occupies $O((n/\lg^2 n)\lg(b\lg^2 n)) = o(n)$ bits. For the groups, all the sp and lp values can be stored in $o(n)$ bits. Then, at most $O(n/\lg^4 n)$ of them would store the $\Theta(\lg^2 n)$ in-between positions explicitly. This occupies at most $o(n)$ bits. For the remaining groups, each requires $o(lp - sp)$ bits for the in-between positions. Again, these sum up to $o(n)$ bits. Thus, the space for the data structure follows.

Finally, to `flip` a bit in X, it corresponds to inserting or deleting a position in some group. Since each group contains $\Theta(\lg^2 n)$ positions, the affected group (or affected groups, in case we need to perform group splitting or merging to maintain the group size) can be updated by fixing at most $O(\lg^2 n)$ positions, or performing at most $O(\lg^2 n)$ `flip` in the auxiliary data structure of Lemma 3. Both can be done in $O(\lg^2 n)$ time. On the other hand, at most one s_i value is updated, inserted or deleted, so that W can be maintained in $O(b)$ time. Since $b \geq \lg^2 n$, the time for `flip` follows. This completes the proof of the lemma. $\square$

By combining Lemmas 1, 2 and 7, Theorem 2 is proved.

5 Searchable Partial Sums When $k = O(\lg\lg n)$

This section shows that when $k = O(\lg\lg n)$, we can achieve the same trade-off result as the *Dynamic Bit Vector* problem. Precisely, `sum` and `search` take $O(\log_b n)$ time, while `update` takes $O(b)$ time.

Notice that when $b < \lg^{O(1)} n$, the required tradeoff can be obtained by Lemma 2. In the remaining of this section, we thus focus on the case when $b \geq \lg^{O(1)} n$.

We first describe the data structure for `sum` among the elements of A.

Lemma 8. *Given a sequence of n non-negative k-bit integers that is stored in an array A, where $k = O(\lg\lg n)$. Together with an auxiliary data structure of size $o(n)$ bits, we can support* `sum` *in $O(\log_b n)$ time and* `update` *in $O(b)$ time, for any parameter b with $\lg^2 n \leq b \leq n$.*

Proof. (sketch.) We partition the elements of A into groups of size $\lg^2 n$, and store each group using Lemma 3. We build a complete b-ary tree, with each group represented by a leaf. Each node stores the LW-value, which is the sum of integers of A under all its left siblings.

Let G denote the group that contains $A[i]$. To support `sum`(i), we can first traverse from the root to the leaf that corresponds to G in the b-ary tree. Precisely, G is the $\lceil i/\lg^2 n\rceil$-th leaf in the tree. The sum (say, σ_1) of all the LW-values in the traversal path is thus equal to the total sum of the values in the groups preceeding G. Then, we perform a sum query within G, and obtain the sum (say, σ_2) of elements preceeding $A[i]$ within G. The required answer is thus equal to $\sigma_1 + \sigma_2$, and the total time used is $O(\log_b n)$. For `update`, a straightforward calculation yields $O(b\log_b n)$ time, which can be reduced by setting b to $b^{1/2}$, without affecting other parts of the proof. Finally, the total space used is $o(n)$ bits. $\square$

Next, we show how to support search and its update, as stated in the following lemma.

Lemma 9. *Given a sequence of n non-negative k-bit integers that is stored in an array A, where $k = O(\lg \lg n)$. Together with an auxiliary data structure of $o(n)$ bits of space, we can support* search *in $O(\log_b n)$ time and* update *in $O(b)$ time, for any parameter b with $\lg^{O(1)} n \leq b \leq n$.*

Proof. We partition the elements of A into groups of size $\lg^3 n$, and store each group using Lemma 3. Each group is given an index from 1 to $n/\lg^3 n$. We keep a dynamic bit vector $\mathcal{B}$ of length $n/\lg^3 n$ using Theorem 2 to mark all the *positive-sum* groups. Precisely, the i-th bit is marked 1 if the the sum of the elements in the index-i group is positive.

Let σ_t denote the sum of the elements in the t-th positive-sum group. Note that each value of σ_t is at most $2^k \lg^3 n = O(\lg^{O(1)} n)$, so that it can be stored in $O(\lg \lg n)$ bits of space. By setting $L = n$, we apply the data structure $\mathcal{C}$ of Theorem 1 on all the σ_t values.

Now, suppose that x is the element $A[\text{search}(j)]$. To support search(j) among all the elements of A, we perform a search(j) on $\mathcal{C}$, so that it returns which positive-sum group contains x. Suppose that it is the t-th positive-group. Then, we perform select(t) on $\mathcal{B}$, which returns the index (say, p) of the group that contains x. Finally, a search within the index-p group returns the rank (say, r) of x within the group. Thus, the required answer is $p \lg^3 n + r$. As there are $O(1)$ steps, and each taking at most $O(\log_b n)$ time, the time bound follows.

The update time follows from straightforward calculation.

For the space, the structure $\mathcal{C}$ occupies $o(n)$ bits (since it maintains $n/\lg^3 n$ values, each occupies $O(\lg \lg n)$ bits), the bit vector $\mathcal{B}$ occupies $O(n/\lg^3 n)$ bits, and all the groups can be stored in $o(n)$ bits in addition to the array A. Thus, the total space of the auxiliary data structure is $o(n)$ bits.   □

By combining Lemmas 2, 8 and 9, we have the following theorem:

Theorem 3. *Given a sequence of n non-negative k-bit integers, where $k = O(\lg \lg n)$. There is a data structure of $kn + o(kn)$ bits of space that supports* sum *and* search *in $O(\log_b n)$ time and* update *in $O(b)$ time, for any parameter b with $\lg n / \lg \lg n \leq b \leq n$.*

6   The General Searchable Partial Sums

In this section, we investigate the *Searchable Partial Sums* problem when $k = O(\lg U)$. We first show a lower bound on the time required for search, and then propose a data structure whose tradeoff achieves such a lower bound in the extreme case.

The lower bound is shown by a reduction from the static predecessor problem, which is defined as follows:

Definition 1. *The* Static Predecessor *problem maintains a set S of n integers from a universe $[1, U]$, and supports* pred(x) *query which returns the largest integer in S that is at most x.*

Lemma 10. *In the worst case, any data structure of size $O(kn)$ bits for the Searchable Partial Sums requires $\Omega\left(\sqrt{\lg n/\lg\lg n}\right)$ time for* search *under the word RAM, irrespective of the* update *time.*

Proof. By reduction from the Static Predecessor problem.   □

The above lemma implies that the general *Searchable Partial Sums* problem cannot achieve the same tradeoff result of $O(\log_b n)$ time for sum and search and $O(b)$ time for update, as in the case when $k = O(\lg\lg n)$. (Otherwise, when b is set to n, we get $O(1)$ time for search, which contradicts with Lemma 10.)

Finally, we claim the following result, whose proof is deferred to the full paper.

Theorem 4. *Given a sequence of n non-negative k-bit integers, where $k = O(\lg U)$. Then, there is a data structure of $kn + o(kn)$ bits of space that supports* sum *in $O(\log_b n)$ time and* update *in $O(b)$ time for any parameter b with $\lg n/\lg\lg n \leq b \leq n$. For* search, *the time depends on the range of b as follows:*

1. *$O(\log_b n)$ time when $\lg n/\lg\lg n \leq b \leq \lg^{O(1)} n$,*
2. *$O(\lg n/\lg\lg n)$ time when $\lg^{O(1)} n \leq b \leq \lg^\tau n$,*
3. *$O(\tau\log_b n)$ for $\lg^\tau n \leq b \leq n$,*

where τ denotes the value of $\min\left\{\lg\lg n\lg\lg U/\lg\lg\lg U, \sqrt{\lg n/\lg\lg n}\right\}$.

7   Conclusion

Raman, Raman and Rao [7] have raised the question that, for what value of k can we obtain a succinct data structure that supports sum and search in $O(\log_b n)$ time and update in $O(b)$ time.

In this paper, we are able to answer partly to the question by showing that such a structure is achievable when $k = O(\lg\lg n)$, while giving a negative example that such a structure does not exist in general. A remaining open question is: What is the bound of k for such structure to exist?

References

1. P. Beame and F. E. Fich. Optimal Bounds for the Predecessor Problem. In *Proc. ACM STOC*, pages 295–304, 1999.
2. P. F. Dietz. Optimal Algorithms for List Indexing and Subset Rank. In *Proceedings of Workshop on Algorithms and Data Structures*, pages 39–46, 1989.
3. M. L. Fredman and M. E. Saks. The Cell Probe Complexity of Dynamic Data Structures. In *Proc. ACM STOC*, pages 345–354, 1989.
4. R. Grossi, A. Gupta, and J. S. Vitter. High-Order Entropy-Compressed Text Indexes. In *Proc. ACM-SIAM SODA*, pages 841–850, 2003.
5. T. Hagerup. Sorting and Searching on the Word RAM. In *Proc. STACS*, pages 366–398, 1998.

6. G. Jacobson. Space-efficient Static Trees and Graphs. In *Proc. IEEE FOCS*, pages 549–554, 1989.
7. R. Raman, V. Raman, and S. S. Rao.   Succinct Dynamic Data Structures.   In *Proceedings of Workshop on Algorithms and Data Structures*, pages 426–437, 2001.
8. R. Raman, V. Raman, and S. S. Rao. Succinct Indexable Dictionaries with Applications to Encoding *k*-ary Trees and Multisets. In *Proc. ACM-SIAM SODA*, pages 233–242, 2002.
9. A. C. Yao. Should Tables Be Sorted? *Journal of the ACM*, 28(3):615–628, 1981.

Range Mode and Range Median Queries on Lists and Trees[*]

Danny Krizanc[1], Pat Morin[2], and Michiel Smid[2]

[1] Department of Mathematics and Computer Science, Wesleyan University,
Middletown, CT 06459 USA dkrizanc@wesleyan.edu
[2] School of Computer Science, Carleton University, 1125 Colonel By Drive, Ottawa,
ON K1S 5B6, CANADA {morin,michiel}@cs.carleton.ca

Abstract. We consider algorithms for preprocessing labelled lists and trees so that, for any two nodes u and v we can answer queries of the form: What is the mode or median label in the sequence of labels on the path from u to v.

1 Introduction

Let $A = a_1, \ldots, a_n$ be a list of elements of some data type. Many researchers have considered the problem of preprocessing A to answer *range queries*. These queries take two indices $1 \leq i \leq j \leq n$ and require computing $F(a_i, \ldots a_j)$ where F is some function of interest.

When the elements of A are numbers and F computes the sum of its inputs, this problem is easily solved using linear space and constant query time. We create an array B where b_i is the sum of the first i elements of A. To answer queries, we simply observe that $a_i + \cdots + a_j = b_j - b_{i-1}$. Indeed this approach works even if we replace $+$ with any group operator for which each element x has an easily computable inverse $-x$.

A somewhat more difficult case is when $+$ is only a semigroup operator, so that there is no analagous notion of $-$. In this case, Yao [18] shows how to preprocess a list A using $O(nk)$ space so that queries can be answered in $O(\alpha_k(n))$ time, for any integer $k \geq 1$. Here α_k is a slow growing function at the kth level of the primitive recursion hierarchy. To achieve this result the authors show how to construct a graph G with vertex set $V = \{1, \ldots, n\}$ such that, for any pair of indices $1 \leq i \leq j \leq n$, G contains a path from i to j of length at most $\alpha_k(n)$ that visits nodes in increasing order. By labelling each edge (u, v) of G with the sum of the elements $a_u, \ldots, a_v$, queries are answered by simply summing the edge labels along a path. This result is optimal when F is defined by a general semigroup operator [19].

A special case of a semigroup operator is the min (or max) operator. In this case, the function F is the function that takes the minimum (respectively

[*] This work was partly funded by the Natural Sciences and Engineering Research Council of Canada.

T. Ibaraki, N. Katoh, and H. Ono (Eds.): ISAAC 2003, LNCS 2906, pp. 517–526, 2003.

maximum) of its inputs. By making use of the special properties of the min and max functions several researchers [1,2] have given data structures of size $O(n)$ that can answer range minimum queries in $O(1)$ time. The most recent, and simplest, of these is due to Bender and Farach-Colton [1].

Range queries also have a natural generalization to trees, where they are sometimes call *path queries*. In this setting, the input is a tree T with labels on its nodes and a query consists of two nodes u and v. To answer a query, a data structure must compute $F(l_1, \ldots, l_k)$, where $l_1, \ldots, l_k$ is the set of labels encountered on the path from u to v in T. For group operators, these queries are easily answered by an $O(n)$ space data structure in $O(1)$ time using data structures for lowest-common-ancestor queries. For semi-group operators, these queries can be answered using the same resource bounds as for lists [18,19].

In this paper we consider two new types of range queries that, to the best of our knowledge, have never been studied before. In particular, we consider range queries where F is the function that computes a mode or median of its input. A mode of a multiset S is an element of S that occurs at least as often as any other element of S. A median of S is the element that is greater than or equal to exactly $\lfloor |S|/2 \rfloor$ elements of S. Our results for range mode and range median queries are summarized in Table 1. Note that neither of these queries is easily expressed as a group, semi-group, or min/max query so they require completely new data structures.

The remainder of this paper is organized as follows: In Section 2 we consider range mode queries on lists. In Section 3 we discuss range mode queries on trees. In Section 4 we study range median queries on lists. In Section 5 we present data structures for range median queries on trees.

Because of space constraints, we do not include proofs of any lemmata and only sketch proofs of some theorems. Details are available in the full version of the paper.

2   Range Mode Queries on Lists

In this section, we consider range mode queries on a list $A = a_1, \ldots, a_n$. More precisely, our task is to preprocess A so that, for any indices i and j, $1 \leq i \leq j \leq n$, we can return an element of $a_i, \ldots, a_j$ that occurs at least as frequently as any other element. Our approach is to first preprocess A for *range counting queries* so that, for any i, j and x we can compute the number of occurences of x in $a_i, \ldots, a_j$. Once we have done this, we will show how a range mode query can be answered using a relatively small number of these range counting queries.

To answer range counting queries on A we use a collection of sorted arrays, one for each unique element of A. The array for element x, denoted A_x contains all the indices $1 \leq i \leq n$ such that $a_i = x$, in sorted order. Now, simply observe that if we search for i and j in the array A_x, we find two indices k and l, respectively, such that, the number of occurences of x in $a_i, \ldots, a_j$ is $l - k + 1$. Thus, we can answer range counting queries for x in $O(\log n)$ time. Furthermore, since each position in A contributes exactly one element to one of these arrays,

Table 1. Summary of results in this paper.

Range Mode Queries on Lists			
§ Space	Query Time	Space × Time	Restrictions
2.1 $O(n^{2-2\epsilon})$	$O(n^\epsilon \log n)$	$O(n^{2-\epsilon} \log n)$	$0 < \epsilon \le 1/2$
2.2 $O(n^2 \log\log n / \log n)$	$O(1)$	$O(n^2 \log\log n / \log n)$	–

Range Mode Queries on Trees			
§ Space	Query Time	Space × Time	Restrictions
2.1 $O(n^{2-2\epsilon})$	$O(n^\epsilon \log n)$	$O(n^{2-\epsilon} \log n)$	$0 < \epsilon \le 1/2$

Range Median Queries on Lists			
§ Space	Query Time	Space × Time	Restrictions
4.2 $O(n \log^2 n / \log\log n)$	$O(\log n)$	$O(n \log^3 n / \log\log n)$	–
4.3 $O(n^2 \log\log n / \log n)$	$O(1)$	$O(n^2 \log\log n / \log n)$	–
4.4 $O(n \log_b n)$	$O(b \log^2 n / \log b)$	$O(nb \log^3 n / \log^2 b)$	$2 \le b \le n$
4.4 $O(n)$	$O(n^\epsilon)$	$O(n^{1+\epsilon})$	$\epsilon > 0$

Range Median Queries on Trees			
§ Space	Query Time	Space × Time	Restrictions
5.1 $O(n \log^2 n)$	$O(\log n)$	$O(n \log^3 n)$	–
5.2 $O(n \log_b n)$	$O(b \log^3 n / \log b)$	$O(nb \log^4 n / \log^2 b)$	$2 \le b \le n$
5.2 $O(n)$	$O(n^\epsilon)$	$O(n^{1+\epsilon})$	–

the total size of these arrays is $O(n)$, and they can all be computed easily in $O(n \log n)$ time.

The remainder of our solution is based on the following simple lemma about modes in the union of three sets.

Lemma 1 *Let A, B and C be any multisets. Then, if a mode of $A \cup B \cup C$ is not in A or C then it is a mode of B.*

In the next two subsections we show how to use this observation to obtain efficient data structures for range mode queries. In the first section we show how it can be used to obtain an efficient time-space tradeoff. In the subsequent section we show how to it can be used to obtain a data structure with $O(1)$ query time that uses subquadratic space.

2.1 A Time-Space Tradeoff

To obtain a time-space tradeoff, we partition the list A into b blocks, each of size n/b. We denote the ith block by B_i. For each pair of blocks B_i and B_j, we compute the mode $m_{i,j}$ of $B_{i+1} \cup \cdots \cup B_{j-1}$ and store this value in a lookup table of size $O(b^2)$. At the same time, we convert A into an array so that we can access any element in constant time given its index. This gives us a data structure of size $O(n + b^2)$.

To answer a range mode query (i, j) there are two cases to consider. In the first case, $j - i \leq n/b$, in which case we can easily compute the mode of $a_i, \ldots, a_j$ in $O((n/b) \log n)$ time by, for example, sorting $a_i, \ldots, a_j$ and looking for the longest run of consecutive equal elements.

The second case occurs when $j - i > n/b$, in which case a_i and a_j are in two different blocks (see Fig. 1). Let $B_{i'}$ be the block containing i and let $B_{j'}$ be the block containing j. Lemma 1 tells us that the answer to this query is either an element of $B_{i'}$, an element of $B_{j'}$, or is the mode $m_{i',j'}$ of $B_{i'+1} \cup \cdots \cup B_{j'+1}$. Thus, we have a set of at most $2n/b + 1$ candidates for the mode. Using the range counting arrays we can determine which of these candidates is a mode by performing at most $2n/b + 1$ queries each taking $O(\log n)$ time, for a query time of $O((n/b) \log n)$. By setting $b = n^{1-\epsilon}$, we obtain the following theorem:

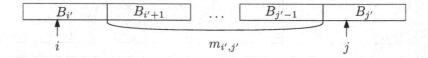

Fig. 1. The mode of $a_i, \ldots, a_j$ is either an element of $B_{i'}$, an element of $B_{j'}$ or is the mode $m_{i',j'}$ of $B_{i'+1}, \ldots, B_{j'+1}$.

Theorem 1 *For any $0 < \epsilon \leq 1/2$, there exists a data structure of size $O(n^{2-2\epsilon})$ that answers range mode queries on lists in time $O(n^\epsilon \log n)$.*[1]

2.2   A Constant Query-Time Subquadratic Space Solution

Initially, one might suspect that any data structure that achieves $O(1)$ query time must use $\Omega(n^2)$ space. However, in the full version of the paper we prove:

Theorem 2 *There exists a data structure of size $O(n^2 \log \log n / \log n)$ that can answer range mode queries on lists in $O(1)$ time.*

3   Range Mode Queries on Trees

In this section we consider the problem of range mode queries on trees. The outline of the data structure is essentially the same as our data structure for

---

[1] The query time of Theorem 1 can be improved by observing that our range counting data structure operates on the universe $1, \ldots, n$ so that using complicated integer searching data structures [15,14,16], the logarithmic term in the query time can be reduced to a doubly-logarithmic term. We observed this but chose not to pursue it because the theoretical improvement is negligible compared to the polynomial factor already in the query time. The same remarks apply to the data structure of Section 3.

lists, but there are some technical difficulties which come from the fact that the underlying graph is a tree.

We begin by observing that we may assume the underlying tree T is a rooted binary tree. To see this, first observe that we can make T rooted by choosing any root. We make T binary by expanding any node with $d > 2$ children into a complete binary tree with d leaves. The root of this little tree will have the original label of the node we expanded and all other nodes that we create are assigned unique labels so that they are never the answer to a range mode query (unless no element in the range occurs more than once, in which case we can correctly return the first element of the range). This transformation does not increase the size of T by more than a small constant factor.

To mimic our data structure for lists we require two ingredients: (1) we should be able to answer range counting queries of the form: Given a label x and two nodes u and v, how many times does the label x occur on the path from u to v? and (2) we must be able to partition our tree into $O(b)$ subtrees each of size approximately n/b.

We begin with the second ingredient, since it is the easier of the two. To partition T into subtrees we make use of the well-known fact (see, e.g., Reference [3]) that every binary tree has an edge whose removal partitions the tree into two subtrees neither of which is more than $2/3$ the size of the original tree. By repeatedly applying this fact, we obtain a set of edges whose removal partitions our tree into $O(b)$ subtrees none of which has size more than n/b. For each pair of these subtrees, we compute the mode of the labels on the path from one subtree to the other and store all these modes in a table of size $O(b^2)$. Also, we give a new data field to each node v of T so that in constant time we can determine the index of the subtree to which v belongs.

Next we need a concise data structure for answering range counting queries. Define the lowest-common-ancestor (LCA) of two nodes u and v in T to be the node on the path from u to v that is closest to the root of T. Let $x(v)$ denote the number of nodes labelled x on the path from the root of T to v, or 0 if v is nil. Suppose w is the LCA of u and v. Then it is easy to verify that the number of nodes labelled x on the path from u to v in T is exactly $x(u) + x(v) - 2x(\text{parent}(w))$, where $\text{parent}(w)$ denotes the parent of w in T or nil if w is the root of T.

There are several data structures for preprocessing T for LCA queries that use linear space and answer queries in $O(1)$ time the simplest of which is due to Bender and Farach-Colton [1]. Thus all that remains is to give a data structure for computing $x(u)$ for any value x and any node u of T. Consider the minimal subtree of T that is connected and contains the root of T as well as all nodes whose label is x. Furthermore, contract all degree 2 vertices in this subtree with the possible exception of the root and call the resulting tree T_x (see Fig. 2). It is clear that the tree T_x has size proportional to the number of nodes labelled x in the original tree. Furthermore, by preprocessing T_x with an LCA data structure and labelling the nodes of T_x with their distance to the root, we can compute, for any nodes u and v in T_x, the number of nodes labelled x on the path from u to v in T.

The difficulty now is that we can only do range counting queries between nodes u and v that occur in T_x and we need to answer these queries for any u and v in T. What we require is a mapping of the nodes of T onto corresponding nodes in T_x. More precisely, for each node v in T we need to be able to identify the first node labelled T_x encountered on the path from v to the root of T. Furthermore, we must be able to do this with a data structure whose size is related to the size of T_x, not T. Omitting the details, which can be found in the full version of the paper, we claim that this mapping can be achieved by performing an interval labelling of the nodes in T [11].

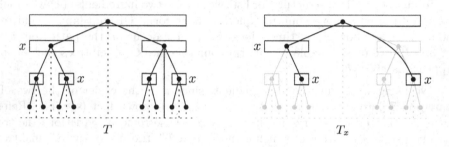

Fig. 2. The trees T and T_x and their interval labelling.

To summarize, we have described all the data structures needed to answer range counting queries in $O(\log n)$ time using a data structure of size $O(n)$. To answer a range mode query (u, v) we first lookup the two subtrees T_u and T_v of T that contain u and v as well as a mode $m_{u,v}$ of all the labels encountered on the path from T_u to T_v. We then perform range counting queries for each of the distinct labels in T_u and T_v as well as $m_{u,v}$ to determine an overall mode. The running time and storage requirements are identical to the data structure for lists.

Theorem 3 *For any $0 < \epsilon \le 1/2$, there exists a data structure of size $O(n^{2-2\epsilon})$ that answers range mode queries on trees in $O(n^\epsilon \log n)$ time.*

4   Range Median Queries on Lists

In this section we consider the problem of answering range median queries on lists. To do this, we take the same general approach used to answer range mode queries. We perform a preprocessing of A so that our range median query reduces to the problem of computing the median of the union of several sets.

4.1   The Median of Several Sorted Sets

In this section we present three basic results that will be used in our range median data structures.

An *augmented* binary search tree is a binary search tree in which each node contains a *size* field that indicates the number of nodes in the subtree rooted at that node. This allows, for example, determining the rank of the root in constant time (it is the size of the left subtree plus 1) and indexing an element by rank in $O(\log n)$ time. Suppose we have three sets A, B, and C, stored in three augmented binary search trees T_A, T_B and T_C, respectively, and we wish find the element of rank i in $A \cup B \cup C$. The following lemma says that we can do this very quickly.

Lemma 2 *Let T_A, T_B, and T_C be three augmented binary search trees on the sets A, B, and C, respectively. There exists an $O(h_A + h_B + h_C)$ time algorithm to find the element with rank i in $A \cup B \cup C$, where h_A, h_B and h_C are the heights of T_A, T_B and T_C, respectively.*

Another tool we will make use of is a method of finding the median in the union of many sorted arrays.

Lemma 3 *Let $A_1, \ldots, A_k$ be sorted arrays whose total size is $O(n)$. There exists an $O(k \log n)$ time algorithm to find the element with rank i in $A_1 \cup \cdots \cup A_k$.*

Finally, we also make use of the following fact which plays a role analogous to that of Lemma 1.

Lemma 4 *Let A, B, and C be three sets such that $|A| = |C| = k$ and $|B| > 4k$. Then the median of $A \cup B \cup C$ is either in A, in C or is an element of B whose rank in B is in the range $[|B|/2 - 2k, |B|/2 + 2k]$.*

4.2   A First Time-Space Tradeoff

To obtain our first data structure for range median queries we proceed in a manner similar to that used for range mode queries. We partition our list A into b blocks $B_1, \ldots, B_b$ each of size n/b. We will create two types of data structures. For each block we will create a data structure that summarizes that block. For each pair of blocks we will create a data structure that summarizes all the elements between that pair of blocks.

To process each block we make use of *persistent augmented binary search trees*. These are search trees in which, every time an item is inserted or deleted, a new *version* of the tree is created. These trees are called persistent because they allow accesses to all previous versions of the tree. The simplest method of implementing persistent augmented binary search trees is by *path-copying* [6,8, 9,10,13]. This results in $O(\log n)$ new nodes being created each time an element is inserted or deleted, so a sequence of n update operations creates a set of n trees that are represented by a data structure of size $O(n \log n)$.[2]

For each block $B_{i'} = b_{i',1}, \ldots, b_{i',n/b}$, we create two persistent augmented search trees $\overrightarrow{T}_{i'}$ and $\overleftarrow{T}_{i'}$. To create $\overrightarrow{T}_{i'}$ we insert the elements $b_{i',1}, b_{i',2}, \ldots, b_{i',n/b}$ in that order. To create $\overleftarrow{T}_{i'}$ we insert the same elements in reverse order, i.e., we insert $b_{i',n/b}, b_{i',n/b-1}, \ldots, b_{i',1}$. Since these trees are persistent, this means that, for any j, $1 \le j \le n/b$, we have access to a search tree $\overrightarrow{T}_{i',j}$ that contains exactly the elements $b_{i',1}, \ldots, b_{i',j}$ and a search tree $\overleftarrow{T}_{i',j}$ that contains exactly the elements $b_{i',j}, \ldots, b_{i',n/b}$.

For each pair of blocks $B_{i'}$ and $B_{j'}$, $1 \le i' < j' \le n$, we sort the elements of $B_{i'+1} \cup \cdots \cup B_{j'-1}$ and store the elements whose ranks are within $2n/b$ of the median in a sorted array $A_{i',j'}$. Observe that, by Lemma 4, the answer to a range median query (i,j) where $i = i'n/b + x$ is in block i' and $j = j'n/b + y$ is in block j', is in one of $\overrightarrow{T}_{i',x}$, $A_{i',j'}$ or $\overleftarrow{T}_{j',y}$. Furthermore, given these two trees and one array, Lemma 2 allows us to find the median in $O(\log n)$ time.

Thus far, we have a data structure that allows us to answer any range median query (i,j) where i and j are in different blocks i' and j'. The size of the data structure for each block is $O((n/b) \log n)$ and the size of the data structure for each pair of blocks is $O(n/b)$. Therefore, the overall size of this data structure is $O(n(b + \log n))$. To obtain a data structure that answers queries for *any* range median query (i,j) including i and j in the same block, we build data structures recursively for each block. The size of all these data structures is given by the recurrence

$$T_n = bT_{n/b} + O(n(b + \log n)) = O(n(b + \log n) \log_b n) .$$

Theorem 4 *For any $1 \le b \le n$, there exists a data structure of size $O(n(b + \log n) \log_b n)$ that answers range median queries on lists in time $O(\log(n/b))$.*

At least asymptotically, the optimal choice of b is $b = \log n$. In this case, we obtain an $O(n \log^2 n / \log \log n)$ space data structure that answers queries in $O(\log n)$ time. In practice, the choice $b = 2$ is probably preferable since it avoids having to compute the $A_{i',j'}$ arrays altogether and only ever requires finding the median in two augmented binary search trees. The cost of this simplification is only an $O(\log \log n)$ factor in the space requirement.

4.3   A Constant Query Time Subquadratic Space Data Structure

In the full version of the paper we prove:

Theorem 5 *There exists a data structure of size $O(n^2 \log \log n / \log n)$ that can answer range median queries on lists in $O(1)$ time.*

---

[2] Although there are persistent binary search trees that require only $O(n)$ space for n operations [5,12], these trees are not *augmented* and thus do not work in our application. In particular, they do not allow us to make use of Lemma 2.

4.4   A Data Structure Based on Range Trees

Using the method of *range trees* [7,17] we can reduce the range median problem to a problem of finding the median of $O(b \log_b n)$ sorted arrays. Applying Lemma 3 we obtain the following theorem (details are in the full paper):

Theorem 6 *For any integer* $1 \leq b \leq n$, *there exists a data structure of size* $O(n \log_b n)$ *size that answers range median queries on lists in* $O(b \log^2 n / \log b)$ *time. In particular, for any constant* $\epsilon > 0$ *there exists a data structure of size* $O(n)$ *that answers range median queries in* $O(n^\epsilon)$ *time.*

5   Range Median Queries on Trees

Next we present two data structures for answering range median queries on trees. As with range mode queries, we may assume that T is a binary tree by doing a small amount of preprocessing on T. Details of this preprocessing are included in the full version.

5.1   More Space, Faster Queries

Our first method is essentially a binary version of the data structure of Section 4.2 modified to work on trees instead of lists. Details are included in the full version.

Theorem 7 *There exists a data structure of size* $O(n \log^2 n)$ *that can answer range median queries in trees in* $O(\log n)$ *time.*

5.2   Less Space, Slower Queries

There exists a method of decomposing a tree T into a set of paths such that the path between any two nodes u and v in T visits $O(\log n)$ of these paths [4]. By treating each of these paths as a list and using the range-tree method of Section 4.4 on each list we are able to obtain the following result (details are in the full version):

Theorem 8 *For any integer* $1 \leq b \leq n$, *there exists a data structure of size* $O(n \log_b n)$ *that can answer range median queries in trees in* $O(b \log^3 n / \log b)$ *time. In particular, for any constant* $\epsilon > 0$, *there exists a data structure of size* $O(n)$ *that answers range median queries in* $O(n^\epsilon)$ *time.*

Acknowledgement. The second author would like to thank Stefan Langerman for helpful discussions.

References

1. M. A. Bender and M. Farach-Colton. The LCA problem revisited. In *Proceedings of Latin American Theoretical Informatics (LATIN 2000)*, pages 88–94, 2000.
2. O. Berkman, D. Breslauer, Z. Galil, B. Schieber, and U. Vishkin. Highly parallelizable problems. In *Proceedings of teh 21st Annual ACM Symposium on the Theory of Computing*, pages 309–319, 1989.
3. B. Chazelle. A theorem on polygon cutting with applications. In *In Proceedings of the IEEE Symposium on Foundations of Computer Science*, pages 339–349, 1982.
4. R. Cole and U. Vishkin. The accelerated centroid decomposition technique for optimal parallel tree evaluation in logarithmic time. *Algorithmica*, 3:329–346, 1988.
5. J. R. Driscoll, N. Sarnak, D. D. Sleator, and R. E. Tarjan. Making data structures persistent. *Journal of Computer and System Sciences*, 38(1):86–124, February 1989.
6. T. Krijnen and L. G. L. T. Meertens. Making B-trees work for B. Technical Report 219/83, The Mathematical Center, Amsterdam, 1983.
7. G. S. Luecker. A data structure for orthogonal range queries. In *Proceedings of the 19th IEEE Symposium on Foundations of Computer Science*, pages 28–34, 1978.
8. E. W. Myers. AVL dags. Technical Report 82-9, Department of Computer Science, University of Arizona, 1982.
9. E. W. Myers. Efficient applicative data structures. In *Conference Record eleventh Annual ACM Symposium on Principles of Programming Languages*, pages 66–75, 1984.
10. T. Reps, T. Teitelbaum, and A. Demers. Incremental context-dependent analysis for language-based editors. *ACM Transactions on Programming Languages and Systems*, 5:449–477, 1983.
11. N. Santoro and R. Khatib. Labelling and implicit routing in networks. *The Computer Journal*, 1:5–8, 1985.
12. N. Sarnak and R. E. Tarjan. Planar point location using persistent search trees. *Communications of the ACM*, 29(7):669–679, July 1986.
13. G. Swart. Efficient algorithms for computing geometric intersections. Technical Report #85-01-02, Department of Computer Science, University of Washington, Seattle, 1985.
14. M. Thorup. On RAM priority queues. In *Proceedings of the 7th ACM-SIAM Symposium on Discrete Algorithms*, pages 59–67, 1996.
15. P. van Emde Boas. Preserving order in a forest in less than logarithmic time and linear space. *Information Processing Letters*, 6:80–82, 1977.
16. D. E. Willard. Log-logarithmic worst-case range queries are possible in space $\theta(n)$. *Information Processing Letters*, 17(2):81–84, 1983.
17. D. E. Willard. New data structures for orthogonal queries. *SIAM Journal on Computing*, pages 232–253, 1985.
18. A. C. Yao. Space-time tradeoff for answering range queries. In *Proceedings of the 14th Annual ACM Symposium on the Theory of Computing*, pages 128–136, 1982.
19. A. C. Yao. On the complexity of maintaining partial sums. *SIAM Journal on Computing*, 14:277–288, 1985.

Quasi-Perfect Minimally Adaptive q-ary Search with Unreliable Tests [*]

Ferdinando Cicalese[1] and Christian Deppe[2]

[1] Dept. of Computer Science and Appl., Univ. of Salerno, 84081 Baronissi (SA), Italy,
cicalese@dia.unisa.it, http://www.dia.unisa.it/~cicalese
[2] Dept. of Mathematics, Univ. of Bielefeld, D-33501 Bielefeld, Germany,
cdeppe@mathematik.uni-bielefeld.de,
http://www.mathematik.uni-bielefeld.de/~cdeppe

Abstract. We consider the problem of determining the minimum number of queries to find an unknown number in a finite set when up to a finite number e of the answers may be erroneous. In the vast literature regarding this problem, the classical case of binary search is mostly considered, that is, when only *yes-no* questions are allowed. In this paper we consider the variant of the problem in which questions with q many possible answers are allowed. We prove that at most one question more than the information theoretic lower bound is sufficient to successfully find the unknown number. Moreover we prove that there are infinitely many cases when the information theoretic lower bound is *exactly* attained and the so called perfect strategies exist. Our strategies have the important feature that they use a minimum amount of adaptiveness, a relevant property in many practical situation.

1 Introduction

We consider the following scenario: Two players, classically called Paul and Carole, first agree on fixing an integer $M \geq 0$ and a search space $S = \{0, \ldots, M-1\}$. Then Carole thinks of a number $x_* \in S$ and Paul must find out x_* by asking q-ary questions, that is multiple choice questions with exactly q choices each. The parameter q is fixed beforehand. It is agreed that Carole is allowed to lie at most e times, where the integer $e \geq 0$ is fixed and known to both players, too.

We are interested in the problem of determining the minimum number of questions Paul has to ask in order to infallibly guess the number x_*.

When $q = 2$ and the questions are asked *adaptively*, i.e., the ith question is asked knowing the answer to the $(i-1)$th question, the problem is generally referred to as the Ulam-Rényi game, [14,17], and is strictly related to Berlekamp's theory of error correcting communication with noiseless feedback [2]. In fact, when the totality of questions is asked at the outset (*non-adaptive search*), before knowing *any* answer, the problem amounts to finding a shortest e error correcting q-ary code with M codewords.

---

[*] This work was partially supported by INTAS 00-738

T. Ibaraki, N. Katoh, and H. Ono (Eds.): ISAAC 2003, LNCS 2906, pp. 527–536, 2003.
© Springer-Verlag Berlin Heidelberg 2003

Let $N_{\min}^{[q]}(M, e)$ denote the smallest integer satisfying $N_{\min}^{[q]}(M, e) = \min\{n \mid M \sum_{i=0}^{e} \binom{n}{i}(q-1)^i \leq q^n\}$. It is known that at least $N_{\min}^{[q]}(M, e)$ questions are *necessary* to find an unknown number in a set of cardinality M when q-ary questions are used and up to e of the answers may be erroneous. Searching strategies that find the unknown number in exactly $N_{\min}^{[q]}(M, e)$ questions are called *perfect* strategies.

In the fully adaptive *binary* case, an important result of Spencer [15] gives conditions for the existence of perfect strategies in terms of the earliest e questions. In particular for $M = 2^m$, Spencer's result implies that $N_{\min}^{[2]} 2^m$ questions are always sufficient, up to finitely many exceptional m's. This result was strengthened in [4] where it is proved that perfect strategies exists which use adaptiveness only once, that is, the questions of the strategies in [4] can be asked in only two batches, and questions in each batch can be asked in completely non-adaptive fashion. It should be remarked that in the fully non-adaptive case perfect strategies are generally not known to exist. In the adaptive case, searching strategies using the minimum number of questions had been previously exhibited by [12], [5], [7], [11],[6], for special values of e.

In this paper we fully generalize the results in both [15] and [4] in the case of q-ary search. We prove that for any number of errors $e > 0$ and $q \geq 2$, q-ary e-error-correcting strategies using the theoretical minimum number of questions always exist up to finitely many exceptions. Moreover these strategy uses adaptiveness only once. This set the critical threshold between the fully adaptive case (where perfect search is always achievable) and the fully non adaptive case where perfect searching strategies with exactly $N_{\min}^{[q]}(M, e)$ questions—or equivalently, e error correcting codes with M codewords of length $N_{\min}^{[q]}(q^m, e)$—are sporadic exceptions already for $e = 2$, and are generally not known to exist for $e > 2$, except in trivial cases. Moreover, a series of negative results culminating in the celebrated papers by Tietäväinen [16] and Zinoviev-Leontiev [18] (also see [8]) shows that if $n = N_{\min}^{[q]}(q^m, e)$, is such that $\sum_{i=0}^{e} \binom{n}{i}(q-1)^i = q^{q-m}$, then e error correcting codes of length n with q^m codewords *do not exist* for all $e > 2$. Thus, in general, adaptiveness in Ulam-Rényi games can be completely eliminated *only by significantly increasing the number of questions in the solution strategy*.

Related work. In its fully adaptive variant the problem of q-ary search with $e \geq 1$ lies was first considered by Malinowski [9] and Aigner [1]. Muthukrishnan [10] provides an algorithm that uses a number of queries at most one question more than the information theoretic bound. However, his algorithm critically depends on the possibility that each question depends on all the previous answers. Conversely, our algorithms, not only attain *exactly* the information theoretic bound for any $e \geq 1$ and for infinitely many values of M (the search space cardinality) but, more importantly, use adaptiveness only once. This is the best possible since the complete elimination of adaptiveness is generally impossible without loosing the perfectness condition on the strategy length [16,18]

2   The q-ary Ulam-Rényi Game

In the Rényi-Ulam game with q-ary search, Paul and Carole first fix integers $q \geq 2, M \geq 1$ and $e \geq 0$. The search space is identified with the set $S = \{0, 1, \ldots, M - 1\}$. Carole chooses a number x_* from S and Paul has to guess it by asking q-ary questions. Typically, a q-ary *question* $\mathbf{T}$ has the form *"Which one of the sets $T_0, T_1, \ldots, T_{q-1}$ does x_* belong to ?"*, where $\mathbf{T} = \{T_0, T_1, \ldots, T_{q-1}\}$ is a q-tuple of (possibly empty) pairwise disjoint subsets of S whose union is S. Carole's answer is an integer $i \in \{0, 1, \ldots, q - 1\}$, telling Paul that x_* belongs to T_i.

If the answer to the question $\mathbf{T}$ is "i", numbers in T_i are said to *satisfy* the answer, while numbers in $S \setminus T_i$ (equivalently, numbers in T_j for each $j = 0, 1, \ldots, i - 1, i + 1, \ldots, q - 1$) *falsify* it. At any stage of the game, a number $y \in S$ must be rejected from consideration if, and only if, it falsifies more than e answers. The remaining numbers of S still are possible candidates for the unknown x_*. This account for the fact that Carole committed to lie at most e times.

At any time during the game, Paul's *state* of knowledge is represented by an e-tuple $\sigma = (A_0, A_1, A_2, \ldots, A_e)$ of pairwise disjoint subsets of S, where A_i is the set of numbers falsifying exactly i answers, $i = 0, 1, 2, \ldots, e$. The *initial* state is naturally given by $(S, \emptyset, \emptyset, \ldots, \emptyset)$. A state $(A_0, A_1, A_2, \ldots, A_e)$ is *final* iff $A_0 \cup A_1 \cup A_2 \cup \cdots \cup A_e$ either has exactly one element, or is empty.

If Paul asks the question $\mathbf{T} = \{T_0, T_1, \ldots, T_{q-1}\}$ when the state is $\sigma = (A_0, A_1, \ldots, A_e)$ and Carole's answer is equal to i, then Paul's state becomes

$$\sigma^i = (A_0 \cap T_i, \ (A_0 \setminus T_i) \cup (A_1 \cap T_i), \ \cdots, \ (A_{e-1} \setminus T_i) \cup (A_e \cap T_i)). \quad (1)$$

Let $\sigma = (A_0, A_1, A_2, \ldots, A_e)$ be a state. For each $i = 0, 1, 2, \ldots, e$ let $a_i = |A_i|$ be the number of elements of A_i. Then the e-tuple $(a_0, a_1, a_2, \ldots, a_e)$ is called the *type* of σ. We shall generally identify a state with its type, tacitly assuming that what holds for a given state also holds for any other state of the same type, up to renaming of the numbers.

Given a state σ, suppose questions $\mathbf{T}_1, \ldots, \mathbf{T}_t$ have been asked and answers $\mathbf{b} = b_1, \ldots, b_t$ have been received (with $b_i \in \{0, 1, \ldots, q-1\}$). Iterated application of (1) yields a sequence of states

$$\sigma_0 = \sigma, \quad \sigma_1 = \sigma_0^{b_1}, \quad \sigma_2 = \sigma_1^{b_2}, \quad \ldots, \quad \sigma_t = \sigma_{t-1}^{b_t} = \sigma^{\mathbf{b}}. \quad (2)$$

By a *strategy* $\mathcal{S}$ *with n questions* we mean the q-ary tree of depth n, where each node ν is mapped into a question $\mathbf{T}_\nu$, and the q edges $\eta_0, \eta_1, \ldots, \eta_{q-1}$ generated by ν are, respectively from left to right, labeled with $0, 1, \ldots, q - 1$, which represent Carole's possible answers to $\mathbf{T}_\nu$. Let $\boldsymbol{\eta} = \eta_1, \ldots, \eta_q$ be a path in $\mathcal{S}$, from the root to a leaf, with respective labels $b_1, \ldots, b_q$, generating nodes $\nu_1, \ldots, \nu_q$ and associated questions $\mathbf{T}_{\nu_1}, \ldots, \mathbf{T}_{\nu_q}$. Fix an arbitrary state σ. Then, according to (2), iterated application of (1) naturally transforms σ into $\sigma^{\boldsymbol{\eta}}$ (where the dependence on the b_j and $\mathbf{T}_j$ is understood). We say that strategy $\mathcal{S}$ is *winning* for σ iff for every path $\boldsymbol{\eta}$ the state $\sigma^{\boldsymbol{\eta}}$ is final. A strategy is said to be *non-adaptive* iff all nodes at the same depth of the tree are mapped into the same question.

We denote with $N^{[q]}(M, e)$ the minimum integer n such that *there exists* a winning strategy with n questions for the Ulam-Rényi game with q-ary search and e-errors, over a search space of cardinality M.

For every integer $q \geq 2$ and state σ of type $(a_0, a_1, \ldots, a_e)$, the *(q-ary) n^{th} Volume of σ* is defined by

$$V_n^{[q]}(\sigma) = \sum_{i=0}^{e} a_i \sum_{j=0}^{e-i} \binom{n}{j} (q-1)^j. \tag{3}$$

Define $\mathrm{ch}^{[q]}(\sigma) = \min\{n = 0, 1, 2, \ldots \mid V_n^{[q]}(\sigma) \leq q^n\}$.

The following basic results are well known in the area. The interested reader will refer to [1,3,9,13] for a more detailed analysis.

Proposition 1. *Let σ be a state and $\mathbf{T}$ a question. Let σ^i be as in (1).*

(i) *For every integer $n \geq 1$ we have* $V_n^{[q]}(\sigma) = \sum_{i=0}^{q-1} V_{n-1}^{[q]}(\sigma^i)$.

(ii) *If σ has a winning q-ary strategy with n questions then $n \geq \mathrm{ch}^{[q]}(\sigma)$.*

We define $N_{\min}^{[q]}(M, e) = \min\{n \mid M \sum_{j=0}^{e} \binom{n}{j} (q-1)^j \leq q^n\}$.
As an immediate corollary of the above proposition we have

$$N^{[q]}(M, e) \geq N_{\min}^{[q]}(M, e) = \mathrm{ch}^{[q]}(M, 0, \ldots, 0),$$

for all $M \geq 1$ and $e \geq 0$.

By a *perfect q-ary strategy* for σ we now mean a winning strategy for σ only requiring $\mathrm{ch}^{[q]}(\sigma)$ questions. Accordingly a winning strategy for σ with $\mathrm{ch}^{[q]}(\sigma)+1$ questions will be called *quasi perfect*.

By the above proposition we immediately have the following monotonicity properties.
For any two states $\sigma' = (A_0', \ldots, A_e')$ and $\sigma'' = (A_0'', \ldots, A_e'')$ respectively of type $(a_0', \ldots, a_e')$ and $(a_0'', \ldots, a_e'')$, if $\sum_{i=0}^{k} a_i' \leq \sum_{i=0}^{k} a_i''$ for all $k = 0, 1, 2, \ldots, e$ then[1]

(i) $\mathrm{ch}^{[q]}(\sigma') \leq \mathrm{ch}^{[q]}(\sigma'')$ and $V_n^{[q]}(\sigma') \leq V_n^{[q]}(\sigma'')$, for each $n \geq 0$

(ii) if, for integer $n \geq 0$, there exists a winning strategy for σ'' with n questions then there exists also a winning strategy for σ' with n questions [3].

Note that $\mathrm{ch}^{[q]}(\sigma) = 0$ iff σ is a final state.

A strategy $\mathcal{S}$ of size n for a state σ is said to be *perfect* if $\mathcal{S}$ is winning for σ and $n = \mathrm{ch}^{[q]}(\sigma)$.

Let $\sigma = (A_0, A_1, A_2, \ldots, A_e)$ be a state. We say that the question $\mathbf{T} = \{T_0, T_1, \ldots, T_{q-1}\}$ is *balanced for σ* iff for each $j = 0, 1, 2, \ldots, e$, we have $|A_j \cap T_i| = |A_j \setminus T_{i+1}| = \frac{1}{q}|A_j|$, for $i = 0, 1, \ldots, q - 2$.

By the definition of a *balanced question* together with (3) and Proposition 1 we have the following.

---

[1] We shall refer to such relationship between states, by saying that σ' is a *substate* of σ'' (or, vice versa that σ'' is a *superstate* of σ').

Lemma 1. *Let* **T** *be a balanced question for a state* $\sigma = (A_0, A_1, A_2, \ldots, A_e)$. *Let* σ^i *be as in (1) above. Then for each* $0 \leq i < j \leq q - 1$,

(i) $V_n^{[q]}(\sigma^i) = V_n^{[q]}(\sigma^j) = V_{n+1}^{[q]}(\sigma)$, *for each integer* $n \geq 0$,
(ii) $\mathrm{ch}^{[q]}(\sigma^i) = \mathrm{ch}^{[q]}(\sigma^j) = \mathrm{ch}^{[q]}(\sigma) - 1$.

3 Optimal Strategies with Minimum Adaptiveness

The first batch of questions.
By Proposition 1(ii), at least $N_{\min}^{[q]}(q^m, e)$ questions are *necessary* to guess the unknown number $x_* \in S = \{0, 1, \ldots, q^m - 1\}$, if up to e answers may be erroneous.

As a first result of this paper we shall now prove that, for all suitably large m, $N_{\min}^{[q]}(q^m, e)$ questions are also *sufficient* under the following constraint: first we use a predetermined non-adaptive batch of m questions $\mathcal{D}_1, \ldots, \mathcal{D}_m$, and then, only depending on the answers, we ask the remaining $N_{\min}^{[q]}(q^m, e) - m$ questions in a second non-adaptive batch.

The *first batch of questions* is as follows:

> For each $j = 1, 2, \ldots, m$, let $\mathcal{D}_j = (D_{j0}, D_{j1}, \ldots, D_{jq-1})$ denote the question "What is the jth (q-ary) digit of x_*?" Thus a number $y \in S$ belongs to D_{ji} iff the jth symbol y_j of its q-ary expansion $\mathbf{y} = y_1 \cdots y_m$ is equal to i.

Let $b_j \in \{0, 1, \ldots, q - 1\}$ be the answer to question $\mathcal{D}_j$. Let $\mathbf{b} = b_1 \cdots b_m$. Beginning with the initial state $\sigma = (S, \emptyset, \ldots, \emptyset)$, and repeatedly applying (1) we have that the state resulting from the answers $b_1 \cdots b_m$, is an $(e + 1)$-tuple $\sigma^{\mathbf{b}} = (A_0, A_1, \ldots, A_e)$, where, denoting with $d_H(\cdot, cdot)$ the Hamming distance between two binary vectors, we have

$$A_i = \{y \in S \mid d_H(\mathbf{y}, \mathbf{b}) = i\} \qquad \text{for all } i = 0, 1, \ldots, e,$$

and it holds that $|A_0| = 1$, $|A_1| = m(q-1), \ldots, |A_e| = \binom{m}{e}(q-1)^e$. Thus $\sigma^{\mathbf{b}}$ has type $(1, m(q-1), \binom{m}{2}(q-1)^2, \ldots, \binom{m}{e}(q-1)^e)$. Let σ_j be the state resulting after the first j answers, beginning with $\sigma_0 = \sigma$. Since each question D_j is *balanced* for σ_{j-1}, an easy induction using Lemma 1 yields $\mathrm{ch}^{[q]}(\sigma^{\mathbf{b}}) = N_{\min}^{[q]}(q^m, e) - m$.

The second batch of questions: strategies and codes.
For each m-tuple $\mathbf{b} \in \{0, 1, \ldots, q - 1\}^m$ of possible answers, we shall now construct a non-adaptive strategy $\mathcal{S}_{\mathbf{b}}$ with $\mathrm{ch}^{[q]}(1, m(q-1), \binom{m}{2}(q-1)^2, \ldots, \binom{m}{e}(q-1)^e)$ questions, which turns out to be winning for the state $\sigma^{\mathbf{b}}$. Thus, let us consider the value of $\mathrm{ch}^{[q]}(1, m(q-1), \binom{m}{2}(q-1)^2, \ldots, \binom{m}{e}(q-1)^e)$ for $m \geq 1$.

Definition 1. *Let* $e \geq 0$ *and* $n \geq 2e$ *be arbitrary integers. The critical index* $m_{n,e}^{[q]}$ *is the largest integer* $m \geq 0$ *such that* $\mathrm{ch}^{[q]}(1, m(q - 1), \binom{m}{2}(q - 1)^2, \ldots, \binom{m}{e}(q - 1)^e) = n$.

The following lemma, whose proof is omitted due to space limits, provides the fundamental bounds on the value of the *critical index.*

Lemma 2. *Let $q \geq 2$, $e \geq 1$ and $n \geq 2e$ be arbitrary integers. Then*

$$\left\lfloor \frac{\sqrt[e]{e! q^{\frac{n}{e}}}}{(q-1)} \right\rfloor - n - e \leq m_{n,e}^{[q]} < \left\lceil \frac{\sqrt[e]{e! } \, q^{\frac{n}{e}}}{q-1} \right\rceil + e. \tag{4}$$

We now prove that for all sufficiently large m there exists a second batch of $n = N_{\min}^{[q]}(q^m, e) - m = \mathrm{ch}^{[q]}(1, m(q-1), \binom{m}{2}(q-1)^2, \ldots, \binom{m}{e}(q-1)^e)$ non-adaptive questions allowing Paul to infallibly guess Carole's secret number.

Intermezzo: Strategies vs. Codes. We refer to [8] for background in error correcting codes. Here we shall only fix a few notions and notations for later use.

By a code we shall mean a q-ary code, in the following sense:

Definition 2. *A (q-ary) code $\mathcal{C}$ of length n is a non-empty subset of $\{0, \ldots, q - 1\}^n$. Its elements are called codewords. The minimum distance of $\mathcal{C}$ is given by $\delta(\mathcal{C}) = \min\{d_H(\boldsymbol{x}, \boldsymbol{y}) \mid \boldsymbol{x}, \boldsymbol{y} \in \mathcal{C}, \boldsymbol{x} \neq \boldsymbol{y}\}$.*
We say that $\mathcal{C}$ is an (n, M, d) code iff $\mathcal{C}$ has length n, $|\mathcal{C}| = M$ and $\delta(\mathcal{C}) = d$. Let $\mathcal{C}_1$ and $\mathcal{C}_2$ be two codes of length n. The minimum distance between $\mathcal{C}_1$ and $\mathcal{C}_2$ is defined by $\Delta(\mathcal{C}_1, \mathcal{C}_2) = \min\{d_H(\boldsymbol{x}, \boldsymbol{y}) \mid \boldsymbol{x} \in \mathcal{C}_1, \boldsymbol{y} \in \mathcal{C}_2\}$.

The following lemma is known as Gilbert's bound [8].

Lemma 3. *Let $n = 2, 3, \ldots$. Then for any two integers $1 \leq d \leq \frac{n}{2}$, and*

$$1 \leq M \leq \frac{q^n}{\sum_{i=0}^{d-1} \binom{n}{i}(q-1)^i},$$

there exists an (n, M, d) q-ary code $\mathcal{C}$.

We now formally state the correspondence between non-adaptive winning strategies and certain special codes. An analogous result can be found in [19]. Due to space limit, the proof of the lemma is omitted here.

Lemma 4. *Fix an integer $e = 1, 2, 3, \ldots$. Let $\sigma = (A_0, A_1, A_2, \ldots A_e)$ be a state of type $(a_0, a_1, a_2, \ldots, a_e)$. Let $n \geq \mathrm{ch}(\sigma)$. Then a non-adaptive winning strategy for σ with n questions exists if and only if for all $i = 0, 1, 2, \ldots, e-1$ there are integers $d_i \geq 2(e - i) + 1$, together with an e-tuple of q-ary codes $\Gamma = (\mathcal{C}_0, \mathcal{C}_1, \mathcal{C}_2, \ldots, \mathcal{C}_{e-1})$, such that each $\mathcal{C}_i$ is an (n, a_i, d_i) q-ary code, and $\Delta(\mathcal{C}_i, \mathcal{C}_j) \geq 2e - (i + j) + 1$, (whenever $0 \leq i < j \leq e - 1$).*

According to this result, the second batch of non-adaptive questions will be given by the family of codes provided in the following Lemma.

Lemma 5. *For any fixed integers $k = 0, 1$ and $e = 1, 2, \ldots$ and for all sufficiently large integers n, there exists an e-tuple of q-ary codes $\Gamma = (\mathcal{C}_0, \ldots, \mathcal{C}_{e-1})$ together with integers $d_i \geq 2(e - i) + 1$ $(i = 0, 1, \ldots, e - 1)$ such that*

(i) Each $\mathcal{C}_i$ is an $(n + 2k, \binom{m_{n,e}^{[q]}}{i}(q-1)^i(q+1)^k, d_i)$ code;

(ii) $\Delta(\mathcal{C}_i, \mathcal{C}_j) \geq 2e - (i+j) + 1$, (whenever $0 \leq i < j \leq e - 1$.)

Proof. Let $n' = n - e^2 + 2k$. First we prove the existence of an $(n', \binom{m_{n,e}^{[q]}}{e-1}(q-1)^{e-1}(q+1)^k, 2e+1)$ code. From Lemma 2 together with the trivial inequality $e! \leq \frac{(e+1)^e}{2^e}$, it follows that, for all sufficiently large n

$$\binom{m_{n,e}^{[q]}}{e-1}(q-1)^{e-1}(q+1)^k < (m_{n,e}^{[q]})^{e-1}(q-1)^{e-1}(q+1)^k$$

$$< (\frac{\sqrt[e]{e!}\, q^{\frac{n}{e}}}{q-1} + e)^{e-1}(q-1)^{e-1}(q+1)^k$$

$$\leq e^{e-1}q^{n-\frac{n}{e}+2k} \leq \frac{q^{n-e^2+2k}}{\sum_{j=0}^{2e}\binom{n-e^2+2k}{j}(q-1)^j},$$

since $\sum_{j=0}^{2e}\binom{n-e^2+2k}{j}(q-1)^j$ is polynomial in n.

The existence of the desired $(n', \binom{m_{n,e}^{[q]}}{e-1}(q-1)^{e-1}(q+1)^k, 2e+1)$ code now follows from Gilbert's Bound. We have proved that, for all sufficiently large n, there exists an $(n - e^2 + 2k, \binom{m_{n,e}^{[q]}}{e-1}(q-1)^{e-1}(q+1)^k, 2e+1)$ code $\mathcal{C}'$. For each $i = 0, 1, \ldots, e-1$ let the e^2-tuple $\boldsymbol{a}_i$ be defined by $\boldsymbol{a}_i = \underbrace{0 \ldots 0}_{ie}\underbrace{1 \ldots 1}_{e}\underbrace{0 \ldots 0}_{e^2-(i+1)e}$. Furthermore, let $\mathcal{C}_i''$ be the code obtained by appending the suffix $\boldsymbol{a}_i$ to the codewords of $\mathcal{C}'$. Trivially, $\mathcal{C}_i''$ is an $(n+2k, \binom{m_{n,e}^{[q]}}{e-1}(q-1)^{e-1}(q+1)^k, 2e+1)$ code for all $i = 0, 1, \ldots, e-1$. Furthermore, we have $\Delta(\mathcal{C}_i'', \mathcal{C}_j'') = 2e \geq 2e - (i+j) + 1$, whenever $0 \leq i < j \leq e - 1$. For each $i = 0, 1, \ldots, e - 1$, pick a subcode $\mathcal{C}_i \subseteq \mathcal{C}_i''$ with $|\mathcal{C}_i| = \binom{m_{n,e}^{[q]}}{i}(q-1)^i(q+1)^k$. Then the new e-tuple of codes $\Gamma = (\mathcal{C}_0, \mathcal{C}_1, \ldots, \mathcal{C}_{e-1})$ satisfies both conditions (i) and (ii), and the proof is complete.

The following corollary implies the existence of minimum adaptiveness perfect searching strategies.

Corollary 1. *Fix an integer $e \geq 0$. Then for all sufficiently large integers m and for every state σ of type $(1, m(q-1), \ldots, \binom{m}{e}(q-1)^e)$ there exists a non-adaptive winning strategy $\mathcal{S}$ such that the number of questions in $\mathcal{S}$ coincides with Berlekamp's lower bound $\mathrm{ch}^{[q]}(\sigma) = N_{\min}^{[q]}(q^m, e) - m$.*

Proof. Skipping all trivialities, assume $e \geq 1$. Let $n = \mathrm{ch}^{[q]}(\sigma)$ and $k = 0$. By definition, $n \to \infty$ as $m \to \infty$. Lemmas 5 and 4 yield a non-adaptive winning strategy with n questions for any state of type $(1, m_{n,e}^{[q]}(q-1), \binom{m_{n,e}^{[q]}}{2}(q-1)^2, \ldots, \binom{m_{n,e}^{[q]}}{e}(q-1)^e)$. By Definition 1, $m \leq m_{n,e}^{[q]}$, and a fortiori, for all sufficiently large m, a non-adaptive winning strategy with n questions exists for any state of type $(1, m(q-1), \ldots, \binom{m}{e}(q-1)^e)$.

We can summarize our finding in the following theorem.

Theorem 1. *Fix an integer $e \geq 0$. Then for all sufficiently large integers m there exists a perfect winning strategy $\mathcal{S}$ for the Ulam-Rényi game with q-ary question and e lies over the search space of cardinality q^m, which uses adaptiveness only once. More precisely $\mathcal{S}$ has exactly size $N_{\min}^{[q]}(q^m, e)$. Therefore,*

$$N^{[q]}(q^m, e) = N_{\min}^{[q]}(q^m, e).$$

4   Quasi-perfect Strategies Always Exist

In this section we remove the constraint that the size of the search space is a power of q. In this case we prove that for any choice of the parameter $q > 2$ and $e \geq 0$ *quasi-perfect* strategies always exist up to finitely many exceptional values of M the search space cardinality.

The following lemma extends the result of the previous section. It implies that for any $e \geq 1$ there are infinitely many values of M (besides $M = q^m$) for which perfect and minimally adaptive searching strategies exist.

Lemma 6. *Fix $q \geq 2$, $e \geq 0$. Then, for all sufficiently large n,*

$$\sigma = \left((q+1)q^{m_{n-1,e}^{[q]}}, 0, \ldots, 0 \right).$$

there exists a perfect strategy using $ch(\sigma) = (m_{n,e}^{[q]} + n + 1)$ questions.

Proof. First we shall prove that $\mathrm{ch}^{[q]}(\sigma) > m_{n,e}^{[q]} + n + 1$. By definition of *character*, it is enough to show that the $n + m_{n,e}^{[q]}$th q-ary volume of σ exceeds $q^{n+m_{n,e}^{[q]}}$, that is $V_{n+m_{n,e}^{[q]}}^{[q]}(\sigma) > q^{n+m_{n,e}^{[q]}}$.

For $i = 0, 1, \ldots, m_{n,e}^{[q]} - 1$, let $\sigma_i = (a_{i0}, a_{i1}, \ldots, a_{ij}, \ldots, a_{ie})$, where $a_{ij} = (q+1)q^{m_{n,e}^{[q]} - 1 - i}\binom{i}{j}(q-1)^j$, It is not hard to verify that for $i = 0, 1, \ldots, m_{n,e}^{[q]} - 2$, the state σ_{i+1} coincides with the one produced by asking an even splitting question in the state σ_i. Hence by Lemma 1 we have $V_{n+m_{n,e}^{[q]}-i}^{[q]}(\sigma_i) = q V_{n+m_{n,e}^{[q]}-i-1}^{[q]}(\sigma_{i+1})$. Let us now consider the state

$$\sigma' = \left((q+1), (q+1)(m_{n,e}^{[q]} - 1)(q-1), \ldots, (q+1)\binom{m_{n,e}^{[q]} - 1}{e}(q-1)^e \right).$$

It holds that

$$
\begin{aligned}
V_{n+1}^{[q]}(\sigma') &= \sum_{j=0}^{e}(q+1)\binom{m_{n,e}^{[q]} - 1}{j}(q-1)^j \sum_{i=0}^{e-j}\binom{n+1}{i}(q-1)^i \\
&\geq \frac{(q+1)(q-1)^e}{e!}(m_{n,e}^{[q]} + n - e)^e \\
&> \frac{(q+1)(q-1)^e}{e!}\left(\frac{\sqrt[e]{e!}q^{\frac{n}{e}}}{(q-1)} - 2e - 1 \right)^e > q^{n+1}.
\end{aligned}
$$

Thus we have the desired result

$$V^{[q]}_{n+m^{[q]}_{n,e}}(\sigma) = V^{[q]}_{n+m^{[q]}_{n,e}}(\sigma_0) = q^{m^{[q]}_{n,e}-1}V^{[q]}_{n+1}\left(\sigma_{m^{[q]}_{n,e}-1}\right) = q^{m^{[q]}_{n,e}-1}V^{[q]}_{n+1}(\sigma')$$
$$> q^{m^{[q]}_{n,e}-1+n+1} = q^{m^{[q]}_{n,e}+n}.$$

It remains to prove that there exists a q-ary winning strategy of length $n + m^{[q]}_{n,e} + 1$ for the state σ. In fact, we already, implicitly proved that there exists a strategy with $m^{[q]}_{n,e} - 1$ questions (the even splitting questions described above) for the state σ which leads Paul into the state σ'. Therefore in order to complete the proof it is enough to show that there exists a winning strategy for the state σ' with $n + 2$ questions. Indeed such a strategy is immediately obtained by Lemma 5 (setting $k = 1$) and Lemma 4. In fact such a strategy is a non-adaptive one.

Proposition 2. *Let* $k \geq 4e^2$, *then it holds that*

$$\sum_{j=0}^{e-1}\left(\binom{k}{j} + \binom{k+1}{j}\right)(q-1)^j \leq \sum_{j=0}^{e}\binom{k}{j}(q-1)^j.$$

Lemma 7. *Let* $N^{[q]}_{\min}(q^m, e) \geq 4e^2$. *The following inequalities hold:*
$$N^{[q]}_{\min}(q^m, e) + 1 \leq N^{[q]}_{\min}(q^{m+1}, e) \leq N^{[q]}_{\min}(q^m, e) + 2.$$

We are now ready to prove that for any $e \geq 1$ and up to finitely many exceptional M, searching strategies with at most $N^{[q]}_{\min}((,e)M) + 1$ questions always exist which use adaptiveness only once.

Theorem 2. *For any fixed* $e \geq 0$ *and* $q \geq 2$ *and for all sufficiently large* M *it holds that:*
$$N^{[q]}_{\min}(M, e) \leq N^{[q]}(M, e) \leq N^{[q]}_{\min}(M, e) + 1.$$

Proof. Let $m = \lfloor \log_q M \rfloor$. Thus $N^{[q]}(q^m, e) \leq N^{[q]}(M, e) \leq N^{[q]}(q^{m+1}, e)$. Fix the smallest integer n such that $m \leq m^{[q]}_{n,e}$. Hence, by definition and Theorem 1 we have $N^{[q]}_{\min}(q^m, e) = m + n = N^{[q]}(q^m, e)$.

We shall argue by cases.

Case 1. $m < m^{[q]}_{n,e}$. Hence $m + 1 \leq m^{[q]}_{n,e}$. Definition 1 and Theorem 1 yield

$$N^{[q]}_{\min}(q^{m+1}, e) = m + 1 + n = N^{[q]}(q^{m+1}, e).$$

Thus we have the desired result

$$N^{[q]}(M, e) \leq N^{[q]}(q^{m+1}, e) = N^{[q]}(q^m, e) + 1 = N^{[q]}_{\min}(q^m, e) + 1 \leq N^{[q]}(M, e) + 1.$$

Case 2. $m = m^{[q]}_{n,e}$. Thus $m + 1 > m^{[q]}_{n,e}$. By definition $N^{[q]}_{\min}(q^{m+1}, e) \geq m + n + 2$. On the other hand, by Lemma 7 we have $N^{[q]}_{\min}(q^{m+1}, e) \leq N^{[q]}_{\min}(q^m, e) + 2 = m + n + 2$. Hence $N^{[q]}_{\min}(q^{m+1}, e) = n + m + 2$, and by Theorem 1, we have $N^{[q]}(q^{m+1}, e) = m + n + 2$.

Recall that $m = m_{n,e}^{[q]}$ and by Lemma 6 we have $N^{[q]}((q-1)q^{m-1}, e) = m + n + 1 = N_{\min}^{[q]}((q-1)q^{m-1}, e)$.

Therefore, for $q^m \le M \le (q-1)q^{m-1}$, we have

$$N^{[q]}(M, e) \le N(q-1)q^{m-1} = m + n + 1 = N_{\min}^{[q]}(q^m, e) + 1 \le N_{\min}^{[q]}(M, e) + 1.$$

On the other hand for $(q-1)q^{m-1} < M < q^{m+1}$, we have the desired result

$$N^{[q]}(M, e) \le N^{[q]}(q^{m+1}, e) = m + n + 2 = N_{\min}^{[q]}((q-1)q^{m-1}, e) + 1 \le N_{\min}^{[q]}(M, e) + 1.$$

References

1. M. Aigner, *Searching with lies*, J. Comb. Theory, Ser. A, **74** (1995), pp. 43–56.

2. E. R. Berlekamp, *Block coding for the binary symmetric channel with noiseless, delayless feedback*, In: Error-correcting Codes, H.B. Mann (Editor), Wiley, New York (1968), pp. 61–88.

3. F. Cicalese, and U. Vaccaro, *Optimal strategies against a liar*, Theoretical Computer Science, **230** (2000), pp. 167–193.

4. F. Cicalese, D. Mundici, and U. Vaccaro, *Least adaptive optimal search with unreliable tests*, Theoretical Computer Science, vol. 270, no. 1–2, pp. 877–893, 2001.

5. J. Czyzowicz, D. Mundici, and A. Pelc, *Ulam's searching game with lies*, J. Comb. Theo., Ser. A, **52** (1989), pp. 62–76.

6. C. Deppe, *Solution of Ulam's searching game with three lies or an optimal adaptive strategy for binary three-error-correcting codes*, Discrete Math., 224, no. 1–3 (2000), pp. 79–98.

7. W. Guzicki, *Ulam's Searching Game with Two Lies*, J. Combin. Theory Ser. A **54** (1990) 1–19.

8. F.J. MacWilliams, and N.J.A. Sloane, *The Theory of Error-Correcting Codes*, North-Holland, Amsterdam, 1977.

9. Malinowski, *K-ary searching with a lie*, Ars Combinatoria, **37**, (1994), pp. 301–308.

10. S. Muthukrishnan, *On optimal strategies for searching in presence of errors*, In: Proc. of the 5th ACM-SIAM SODA, (1994), pp. 680–689.

11. A. Negro, and M. Sereno, *Ulam's searching game with three lies*, Adv. in Appl. Math., **13** (1992), pp. 404–428.

12. A. Pelc, *Solution of Ulam's problem on searching with a lie*, J. Combin. Theory, Ser. A, **44** (1987), pp. 129–142.

13. A. Pelc, *Search games with errors – Fifty years of coping with liars*, Preprint, 2000.

14. A. Rényi, *Napló az információelméletről*, Gondolat, Budapest, 1976. (English translation: *A Diary on Information Theory*, J.Wiley and Sons, New York, 1984).

15. J. Spencer, *Ulam's searching game with a fixed number of lies*, Theoretical Comp. Sci., **95** (1992), pp. 307–321.

16. A. Tietäväinen, *On the nonexistence of perfect codes over finite fields*, SIAM J. Appl. Math., **24**, (1973), pp. 88–96.

17. S.M. Ulam, *Adventures of a Mathematician*, Scribner's, New York, 1976.

18. V.A. Zinoviev, V.K. Leontiev, *The non-existence of perfect codes over Galois fields*, Probl. Contr. Inform. Theory, **2** (1973), pp. 123–132.

19. V.A. Zinoviev, G.L. Katsman, *Universal Code Families*. Information Theory and Coding Theory, **29** (2) (1993), pp. 95–100.

New Ways to Construct Binary Search Trees

Travis Gagie

Department of Computer Science
University of Toronto
travis@cs.toronto.edu

Abstract. We give linear-time algorithms for re-ordering and height-restricting a binary search tree with only a small increase in cost, constructing a nearly optimal binary search tree given the rank by probability of each possible outcome, and height-restricting an optimal binary search tree when the increase in cost is restricted. Whereas most algorithms for constructing good binary search trees need the probabilities of outcomes as input, our algorithms do not.

1 Introduction

Binary search trees are a fundamental and well-studied data structure. There are two complexity metrics commonly associated with them: the maximum number of comparisons made during a search and the expected number of comparisons made during a search. It is interesting to consider how to minimize or nearly minimize both metrics simultaneously. The difficulty of doing this depends on how much information is given.

There are $2n + 1$ possible outcomes of a search in a binary search tree on n nodes: the search target could be less than the smallest node; for each node, the search target could equal that node; for each consecutive pair of nodes, the search target could be strictly between them; or the search target could be greater than the largest node. For a fixed probability distribution over the outcomes, the *cost* of a binary search tree is the expected number of comparisons made during a search.

In this paper, we consider the problem of constructing good binary search trees given incomplete information about the probability distribution over the outcomes. In particular, we do not assume that we are given any of the probabilities. The types of input that we consider instead are: a binary search tree for a different ordering on the nodes; a ranking of the nodes by probability; or an *optimal* binary search tree, that is, one with minimum cost.

There are algorithms for constructing optimal [8] or nearly optimal binary search trees [10,9], and algorithms for constructing optimal binary search trees whose heights are restricted [5,7,12]. The latter are useful because the maximum number of comparisons made during a search cannot be greater than the height plus 1. Thus, height-restriction can be used to produce binary search trees that perform well in both the worst case and the expected case. However, all of the algorithms mentioned above require us to know the probability of each outcome.

T. Ibaraki, N. Katoh, and H. Ono (Eds.): ISAAC 2003, LNCS 2906, pp. 537–543, 2003.

All known algorithms for constructing optimal binary search trees, whether height-restricted or not, use dynamic programming. Knuth's algorithm [8] runs in $O(n^2)$ time, where n is the number of nodes. Itai [7] and Wessner [12] independently improved Garey's algorithm [5] to run in $O(n^2 L)$ time, where L is the height restriction. Their algorithm gives us an optimal binary search tree of height h and its cost, for each h such that $\lfloor \log_2 n \rfloor \le h \le L$. Mehlhorn's and Larmore's algorithms [10,9] can be implemented to run in $o(n^2)$ time, but the trees that they produce are not always optimal.

Recently, Evans and Kirkpatrick [2] presented an algorithm for constructing binary search trees that does not require the probabilities of the outcomes. Given a binary search tree T on n nodes, it constructs another binary search tree T' of height at most $\lfloor \log_2 n \rfloor + 1$ whose cost is at most $\log_2 \log_2(n + 1)$ greater than T's. Thus, if T performs well in the expected case, then T' performs well in both the worst case and the expected case. They also proved tight tradeoffs for the worst-case cost increase as a function of the height restriction.

In Section 2, we consider the problem of re-ordering the nodes in a binary search tree, when all searches are for nodes in the tree. For example, suppose that we have a collection of student records, each with two possible keys: surname and student number. Given a binary search tree storing these records indexed by surname, we might want to construct a binary search tree storing them indexed by student number. We show how, given a binary search tree T on n nodes and a new ordering on those nodes, we can construct a binary search tree T' for the new ordering that is of height at most $\lceil \log_2 n \rceil + 1$ and whose cost is at most $\lceil \log_2 \log_2(n + 1) \rceil + 2$ greater than T's. Notice that, if the new ordering is the same as the old ordering, we get almost the same result as Evans and Kirkpatrick, but with a simpler proof.

Both Evans and Kirkpatrick's result and our result from Section 2 are based on bounding the difference between nodes' depths in the new tree and the original tree. In Section 3, we show how we can do this slightly better. Given a binary search tree T on n nodes, we can construct a binary search tree T' of height $\lceil \log_2 n \rceil + 1$ such that, if a node is the rth node visited in a breadth-first traversal of T, then it is of depth at most $\lfloor \log_2 r \rfloor + \lceil \log_2 \log_2(n + 1) \rceil + 2$ in T'. We also show how, given n nodes and a ranking by probability of the corresponding outcomes, we can construct a binary search tree of height at most $\lceil \log_2(2n + 1) \rceil$ whose cost is within $\lceil \log_2 \log_2(n + 1) \rceil + 3$ of optimal.

Given an optimal binary search tree, which may have poor worst-case performance, we can also construct a binary search tree with reasonable worst-case performance and expected-case performance that is very close to optimal. We show how to do this in Section 4. Specifically, given a optimal binary search tree on n nodes and a positive value $\epsilon < 1$, we can construct a binary search tree of height $O\left(\log n + \log(1/\epsilon)\right)$ whose cost is at most the optimum unrestricted cost plus ϵ.

All of our algorithms take $O(n)$ time, where n is the number of nodes.

2   Re-ordering a Binary Search Tree

Suppose that we have a binary search tree T on n nodes and we want to construct a binary search tree on the same set of nodes, for a different set of keys. Using this new set of keys might result in a different ordering of the nodes. However, each of the nodes has the same probability of being sought. We will show how to construct a binary search tree of height at most $\lceil \log_2 n \rceil + 1$ for the new ordering whose cost is at most $\lceil \log_2 \log_2(n+1) \rceil + 2$ greater than T's, when all searches are for nodes in the tree. This algorithm takes $O(n)$ time and does not need the probabilities of the nodes as input.

We will combine two known results to show that the nodes of a binary search tree can be re-ordered without any node increasing in depth by very much. We do this in such a way that the resulting binary search tree is short. When we refer to the ith node in a tree, we mean the ith node visited in an in-order traversal. In particular, when we write that the nodes of a tree are of depths $l_1, \ldots, l_n$, we mean that, for $1 \leq i \leq n$, the ith node is of depth l_i.

The following lemma, a proof of which is given by Ahlswede and Wegener [1], extends one direction of the better-known Kraft Inequality.

Lemma 1. *Suppose that there exists a binary tree on n nodes of depths $l_1, \ldots, l_n$. Then*

$$\sum_{i=1}^{n} 2^{-l_i} \leq \log_2(n+1) .$$

Mehlhorn [11] gave a constructive proof of the following theorem, which can be implemented in linear time [3]. Notice that the statement of the theorem does not refer to the order of the nodes. A *strict* binary tree is one in which each node has exactly 0 or 2 children.

Theorem 1 (Mehlhorn, 1977). *Let n be odd and suppose that $p_1, \ldots, p_n$ is a probability distribution. Then there exists a strict binary tree of height at most $\lceil - \log_2 (\min_{1 \leq i \leq n} \{p_i\}) \rceil$ on n nodes of depths at most $\lceil - \log_2 p_1 \rceil + 1, \ldots, \lceil - \log_2 p_n \rceil + 1$.*

We now combine Lemma 1 and Theorem 1 to obtain an upper bound on the increase in nodes' depths that is necessary when a binary search tree is re-ordered and height-restricted.

Theorem 2. *Let n be odd and suppose that there exists a binary tree on n nodes of depths $l_1, \ldots, l_n$. Then, for any permutation π of $\{1, \ldots, n\}$, there exists a strict binary tree of height at most $\lceil \log_2 n \rceil + 1$ on n nodes of depths at most $l_{\pi(1)} + \lceil \log_2 \log_2(n+1) \rceil + 2, \ldots, l_{\pi(n)} + \lceil \log_2 \log_2(n+1) \rceil + 2$.*

Proof. By Lemma 1,

$$\sum_{i=1}^{n} 2^{-l_i} \leq \log_2(n+1) .$$

Consider the probability distribution $p_1, \ldots, p_n$, where

$$p_i = \frac{1}{2}\left(\frac{2^{-l_{\pi(i)}}}{\sum_{j=1}^{n} 2^{-l_i}} + \frac{1}{n}\right) \geq \frac{2^{-l_{\pi(i)}-1}}{\log_2(n+1)} + \frac{1}{2n} > \frac{2^{-l_{\pi(i)}-1}}{\log_2(n+1)}.$$

By Theorem 1, since $\min_{1 \leq i \leq n}\{p_i\} \geq 1/2n$, there exists a strict binary tree of height at most $\lceil \log_2 n \rceil + 1$ on n nodes in which, for $1 \leq i \leq n$, the ith node is of depth at most

$$\lceil -\log_2 p_i \rceil + 1 \leq \left\lceil -\log_2\left(\frac{2^{-l_{\pi(i)}-1}}{\log_2(n+1)}\right)\right\rceil + 1 = l_{\pi(i)} + \lceil \log_2 \log_2(n+1)\rceil + 2.\square$$

Since the construction for Theorem 1 can be implemented in linear time, we can re-order and height-restrict a binary search tree on n nodes in $O(n)$ time without any node increasing in depth by more than $\lceil \log_2 \log_2(n+1)\rceil + 2$. The cost also does not increase by more than $\lceil \log_2 \log_2(n+1)\rceil + 2$, when all searches are for nodes in the tree.

3   Constructing a Binary Search Tree from Ranks

Given n nodes, we might have some information about the probability distribution over the corresponding $2n+1$ outcomes, but not the probabilities themselves. In this section, we will show how, given only a ranking of the outcomes by probability, we can construct a nearly optimal binary search tree, of height at most $\lceil \log_2 n \rceil + 1$. This algorithm takes $O(n)$ time. We will also strengthen Theorem 2.

Theorem 3. *Suppose that we are given n nodes and a ranking by probability of the corresponding $2n + 1$ outcomes. Then we can construct a binary search tree of height at most $\lceil \log_2(2n + 1)\rceil$ whose cost is within $\lceil \log_2 \log_2(2n + 1)\rceil + 2$ of the optimum unrestricted cost.*

Proof. Consider the outcomes as $2n+1$ nodes: the successes as the n nodes that we have been given, and the failures as an additional $n + 1$ nodes.

It is easy to construct a binary tree T on these $2n+1$ nodes that has minimum expected depth. To do this, first, we make the node with rank 1 the root. Then, for $1 \leq r \leq \lfloor n/2 \rfloor$, we make the nodes with ranks $2r$ and $2r + 1$ (if they exist) the children of the node with rank r. Notice that this may not preserve the order of the nodes.

By applying Theorem 2 to T, we can obtain a strict binary tree T' on these $2n + 1$ nodes, in order, whose height is at most $\lceil \log_2(2n + 1)\rceil + 1$ and whose expected depth is within $\lceil \log_2 \log_2(n + 1)\rceil + 3$ of minimum.

By removing T''s leaves, we obtain a binary search tree on the n nodes we were originally given, whose height is at most $\lceil \log_2(2n + 1)\rceil$ and whose cost is within $\lceil \log_2 \log_2(n + 1)\rceil + 3$ of the optimum unrestricted cost. $\square$

Using the same proof techniques, we now strengthen Theorem 2.

Theorem 4. *Let n be odd, let T be a binary tree on n nodes, and let π be a permutation of $\{1, \ldots, n\}$. Then there exists a strict binary tree T' of height at most $\lceil \log_2 n \rceil + 1$ on n nodes with the following property: For $1 \leq i \leq n$, if the ith node of T is visited rth in a breadth-first traversal of T, then the ith node of T' is of depth at most $\lfloor \log_2 r \rfloor + \lceil \log_2 \log_2(n+1) \rceil + 2$.*

Proof. It is easy to construct a binary tree T'' on the same n nodes as T such that, for $1 \leq r \leq n$, the rth node visited in a breadth-first traversal of T is of depth exactly $\lfloor \log_2 r \rfloor$ in T''. To do this, first, we make the first node visited in T the root of T''. Then, for $1 \leq r \leq \lfloor n/2 \rfloor$, we make the 2rth and $(2r+1)$st nodes visited in T (if they exist) the children of the rth node visited. Notice that this may not preserve the order of the nodes.

By applying Theorem 2 to T'', we can obtain a strict binary search tree T' of height at most $\lceil \log_2 n \rceil + 1$ on the same n nodes as T and T'' such that: nodes are in the same order in T and T'; and each node's depth is at most $\lceil \log_2 \log_2(n+1) \rceil + 2$ greater in T' than in T''. This means that, for $1 \leq i \leq n$, if the ith node of T is visited rth in a breadth-first traversal, then the ith node of T' is of depth at most $\lfloor \log_2 r \rfloor + \lceil \log_2 \log_2(n+1) \rceil + 2$.   □

4   Height-Restricting an Optimal Binary Search Tree

For some probability distributions over n nodes, every optimal binary search tree is of height much greater than $\log_2 n$. For example, there are cases when there is only one optimal binary search tree and it is of height $n - 1$. It may be that such worst-case performance is unacceptable. We will show how, given an optimal binary search tree T on n nodes and a positive value $\epsilon < 1$, we can construct a binary search tree T' of height $O(\log n + \log(1/\epsilon))$ whose cost is at most the optimum unrestricted cost plus ϵ. This algorithm takes $O(n)$ time and does not need the probabilities of the outcomes as input.

First, we state a theorem due to Hirschberg, Larmore, and Molodowitch [6]. This bounds the total probability of a subtree in an optimal binary search tree, in terms of the depth of its root. A subtree's *total probability* is the probability of a search ending in that subtree. Then, we show that deeply-rooted subtrees of an optimal binary search tree can be height-restricted without significantly increasing the cost of the whole tree.

Theorem 5 (Hirschberg, Larmore, and Molodowitch, 1986). *For any node v of depth l in an optimal binary search tree, the total probability of the subtree rooted at v is at most $2/F_{l+3}$, where F_i is the ith Fibonacci number.*

Using Theorem 5, it is easy to construct a nearly optimal binary search tree of small height.

Theorem 6. *Given an optimal binary search tree T on n nodes and a positive value $\epsilon < 1$, we can construct a binary search tree of height $2.45 \log_2 n + 1.45 \log_2(1/\epsilon) + O(\log \log \log n)$ whose cost is at most the optimum unrestricted cost plus ϵ. This takes $O(n)$ time.*

Proof. First, we truncate T at depth

$$L = \left\lceil \frac{\log_2 n + \log_2(1/\epsilon) + \log_2\left(\lceil \log_2 \log_2(n+1) \rceil + 2\right) + 1}{\log_2 \phi} \right\rceil ,$$

where $\phi = \left(1 + \sqrt{5}\right)/2 \approx 1.62$ is the golden ratio. Notice that L is in $1.45 \log_2 n + 1.45 \log_2(1/\epsilon) + O(\log\log\log n)$.

By Theorem 5, the total probability of each of the removed subtrees is less than

$$\frac{2}{F_{L+3}} = 2^{1-\log_2 F_{L+3}} < 2^{1-L\log_2 \phi} \le \frac{\epsilon}{n\left(\lceil \log_2 \log_2(n+1)\rceil + 2\right)} .$$

Let c be the sum of the total probabilities of all removed subtrees. Since there are at most n of these, $c < \epsilon/\left(\lceil \log_2 \log_2(n+1)\rceil + 2\right)$.

Next, we use Theorem 2 to replace each removed subtree by a subtree on the same nodes, in the same order, but of height at most $\lceil \log_2 n \rceil + 1$. Let T' be the resulting binary search tree. Notice that T' is of height at most $L + \lceil \log_2 n \rceil + 1$, which is in $2.45 \log_2 n + 1.45 \log_2(1/\epsilon) + O(\log\log\log n)$.

For any node v, the depth of v in T' is at most $\lceil \log_2 \log_2(n+1) \rceil + 2$ greater than the depth of v in T. Therefore, the cost of T' is at most the cost of T plus $c\left(\lceil \log_2 \log_2(n+1)\rceil + 2\right) \le \epsilon$.   □

Given n nodes, the probability distribution over the outcomes, and a positive value $\epsilon < 1$, we can efficiently construct a binary search tree whose cost is at most ϵ plus the optimum unrestricted cost U and which has small height. This follows easily from Knuth's algorithm for constructing an optimal binary search tree (with no height restriction) [8] and Theorem 6.

In fact, given this information, we can efficiently construct a binary search tree whose cost is at most $U + \epsilon$ and which has the smallest height of any such tree. To do this, first, we use Knuth's algorithm to find U. Second, we use Theorem 6 to find a height restriction $L \in 2.45 \log_2 n + 1.45 \log_2(1/\epsilon) + O(\log\log\log n)$ such that there exists a binary search tree of height at most L whose cost is at most $U + \epsilon$. Third, we use the dynamic programming algorithm due to Itai [7] and Wessner [12] to obtain an optimal binary search tree of height h and its cost, for each h such that $\lfloor \log_2 n \rfloor \le h \le L$. Finally, from among the resulting trees whose costs are at most $U + \epsilon$, we choose one with smallest height. In total, this takes $O\left(n^2(\log n + \log(1/\epsilon))\right)$ time.

5   Conclusion

We have shown that constructing good binary search trees does not require complete information. In particular, we have given linear-time algorithms for re-ordering and height-restricting a binary search tree with only a small increase in cost, constructing a nearly optimal binary search tree given the rank by probability of each possible outcome, and height-restricting an optimal binary search tree when the increase in cost is restricted. All of these algorithms run in linear time and do not need the probability distribution over the outcomes as input. We leave as future work improving our upper bounds and proving lower bounds for these problems.

In this paper, we use a construction due to Mehlhorn [10], because it is easy to prove upper bounds on the height of the tree produced by this construction, and the depths of the nodes in this tree. However, in practice, it is faster and simpler to use algorithms for constructing alphabetic minimax trees [2,4]. The latter also run in $O(n)$ time, but with smaller coefficients.

Acknowledgments. Many thanks to: Faith Ellen Fich, who supervised this research; Ken Sevcik and Will Evans, for helpful suggestions; and an anonymous referee, who brought Theorem 5 to our attention. This research was supported in part by the Natural Sciences and Engineering Research Council of Canada.

References

1. R. Ahlswede and I. Wegener. *Search Problems*. Wiley, 1987.
2. W. S. Evans and D. G. Kirkpatrick. Restructuring ordered binary trees. In *Proceedings of the 11th Annual Symposium on Discrete Algorithms*, pages 477–486, 2000.
3. M. Fredman. Two applications of a probabilistic search technique: sorting $x + y$ and building balanced search trees. In *Proceeding of the 7th Annual Symposium on Theory of Computing*, pages 240–244, 1975.
4. T. Gagie. Dynamic length-restricted coding. Master's thesis, University of Toronto, 2003.
5. M. R. Garey. Optimal binary search trees with restricted maximal depth. *SIAM Journal on Computing*, 3:101–110, 1974.
6. D. S. Hirschberg, L. L. Larmore, and M. Molodowitch. Subtree weight ratios for optimal binary search trees. Technical report, University of California Irvine, 1986.
7. A. Itai. Optimal alphabetic trees. *SIAM Journal on Computing*, 5:9–18, 1976.
8. D. E. Knuth. Optimum binary search trees. *Acta Informatica*, 1:79–110, 1971.
9. L. L. Larmore. A subquadratic algorithm for constructing approximately optimal binary search trees. *Journal of Algorithms*, 8:579–591, 1987.
10. K. Mehlhorn. Nearly optimal binary search trees. *Acta Informatica*, 5:287–295, 1975.
11. K. Mehlhorn. A best possible bound for the weighted path length of binary search trees. *SIAM Journal on Computing*, 6:235–239, 1977.
12. R. L. Wessner. Optimal alphabetic search trees with restricted maximal height. *Information Processing Letters*, 4:90–94, 1976.

Improved Approximation Algorithms for Optimization Problems in Graphs with Superlogarithmic Treewidth

Artur Czumaj[1], Andrzej Lingas[2], and Johan Nilsson[2]

[1] Department of Computer Science, New Jersey Institute of Technology, Newark, NJ 07102, USA. czumaj@cis.njit.edu.
[2] Department of Computer Science, Lund University, 22100 Lund, Sweden. Andrzej.Lingas@cs.lth.se, f98jn@efd.lth.se.

Abstract. In this paper we present two novel generic schemes for approximation algorithms for optimization $\mathcal{NP}$-hard graph problems constrained to partial k-trees. Our first scheme yields *deterministic polynomial-time algorithms* achieving typically an approximation factor of $k/\log^{1-\epsilon} n$, where $k = \text{polylog}(n)$. The second scheme yields *randomized polynomial-time algorithms* achieving an approximation factor of $k/\log n$ for $k = \Omega(\log n)$. Both our approximation methods lead to the best known approximation guarantees for some basic optimization problems. In particular, we obtain best known polynomial-time approximation guarantees for the classical *maximum independent set* problem in partial trees.

1 Introduction

In this paper we investigate approximation algorithms for several optimization graph problems constrained to partial k-trees. For a natural k, a *partial k-tree* is a subgraph of a k-tree. A *k-tree* is either a k-clique, i.e., a complete graph on k vertices, or a graph which can be obtained from another k-tree by addition of a vertex with k edges connecting it to k pairwise adjacent vertices in the other k-tree [4]. Each partial k-tree admits the so called tree-decomposition of width k and *vice versa*, each graph which has a tree-decomposition of width k is a partial k-tree (see [3,4,8] and Preliminaries).

Shortly after introducing the notion of partial trees, it has been shown that many $\mathcal{NP}$-hard graph problems constrained to partial $O(1)$-trees admit polynomial-time or even linear-time exact algorithmic solutions [3,4,8] (e.g., these definable in extended weak monadic second-order logic [4]). For some of these $\mathcal{NP}$-hard problems (e.g., these in the so called C-ECC class or those in the so called C-LCC class having $O(1)$ maximum degree) analogous, polynomial-time solutions are possible for partial $O(\log n)$-trees [8]; a standard example here is the maximum independent set problem [8].

In this paper, we investigate the approximability status of some of the aforementioned $\mathcal{NP}$-hard problems, where our main interest is on partial k-trees with

T. Ibaraki, N. Katoh, and H. Ono (Eds.): ISAAC 2003, LNCS 2906, pp. 544–553, 2003.
© Springer-Verlag Berlin Heidelberg 2003

$k = \Omega(\log n)$. We focus our study on the maximum independent set and maximum clique problems and further applications of our methods are obtained by extensions of our algorithms for maximum independent set.

The *maximum independent set* problem (or equivalently, the *maximum clique* problem) is a classical $\mathcal{NP}$-hard optimization problem studied intensively for a three decades (these problems were proven to be $\mathcal{NP}$-hard in Karp's original paper on $\mathcal{NP}$-completeness [15]). For general graphs, the best known polynomial-time approximation algorithm for maximum independent set (or, equivalently, maximum clique) achieves solely $n \log \log^2 n / \log^3 n$ factor [12]. On the other hand, it is known that unless $\mathcal{NP} \subseteq \text{ZPTIME}(2^{(\log n)^{O(1)}})$, no polynomial-time algorithm can achieve the approximation guarantee of $n^{1-O(1/(\log n)^\gamma)}$ for some constant γ [16] (see also [11,14] for other results in this theme). Better approximation bounds are achievable for special classes of graphs. For partial trees, one can fairly easily color any partial k-trees with $k + 1$ colors (see Lemma 1 for details) what immediately implies a polynomial-time $(k + 1)$-approximation algorithm for maximum independent set. For $k = O(\log n)$, Bodlaender [8] presented a polynomial-time algorithm that returns an optimal solution. Another known approach, developed for k-clique-free graphs in [1,19], does not yield any non-trivial approximation bounds when $k = \Omega(\log n)$. A partial k-tree is $(k + 2)$-clique-free graph by definition. The technique by Ajtai, Komlós, and Szemerédi [1] treated by Shearer [19] as a *randomized* greedy algorithm can be made deterministic to find an independent set in k-clique-free graphs of size $\Omega(n^{1/(k-1)} \cdot (\log n)^{(k-2)/(k-1)})$ in polynomial time. The latter bound for $k = \Omega(\log n)$ yields merely $O(\log n)$ size independent set for a partial k-tree and therefore it implies only a trivial approximation factor in this case.

1.1   New Contribution

We present two novel generic schemes for approximation algorithms for maximum independent set and other optimization $\mathcal{NP}$-hard graph problems constrained to partial k-trees. Our first scheme leads to *deterministic* polynomial-time algorithms that achieve typically an approximation factor guarantee of $k/\log^{1-\epsilon} n$ for all $k = \text{polylog}(n)$. The second scheme yields *randomized* polynomial-time algorithms achieving an approximation factor of $k/\log n$ for $k = \Omega(\log n)$.

These two generic schemes lead to significantly improved approximation bounds for maximum independent set. Our deterministic algorithm improves the previous approximation guarantees for all $k = \omega(\log n)$ and $k \leq \text{polylog}(n)$, and our randomized algorithm does so for all $k = \omega(\log n)$.

Besides the maximum independent set problem, the first scheme can be also adapted to the maximum induced m-colorable subgraph problem, and simplified to include the maximum clique problem (see Section 4). The second scheme can be applied to induced subgraph with hereditary property Π problems that can be solved exactly in polynomial time on graphs with given tree-decomposition of logarithmic width (e.g., members of the C-ECC class or the C-LCC class having $O(1)$ maximum degree [8]), in particular the so called d-separable problems. All these approximation factors achievable in polynomial time are the best known for the aforementioned problems constrained to partial k-trees where k is polylogarithmic or superlogarithmic, respectively. In case a tree-decomposition of width k is not given, the approximation factors achievable by our methods increase by $O(\log k)$.

1.2 Paper Organization

In Preliminaries, we introduce the notion of tree-decomposition, treewidth, nice tree-decomposition and present several known facts on tree-decomposition construction. We describe also a simple method of approximating maximum independent set in a partial k-tree via graph coloring. In Section 3, we present our first deterministic method by applying it to maximum independent set. In the next section, Section 4, we adapt the method to the maximum induced m-colorable subgraph problem and simplify it to include the maximum clique problem. In Section 5, we exemplify our second randomized method by applying it to maximum independent set. Because of the space considerations, for the extensions of the randomized method to include maximum induced subgraph with hereditary property Π problems (that can be solved exactly in polynomial time on graphs with given tree-decomposition of logarithmic width) the reader is referred to the full version. In the final Section 6, we provide concluding remarks.

2 Preliminaries

The notion of *treewidth* of a graph was originally introduced by Robertson and Seymour [18] as one of the main contributions in their seminal graph minor project. It has turned out to be equivalent to several other interesting graph theoretic notions, e.g., the aforementioned notion of partial k-trees (see Introduction and [3,5]).

Definition 1. *A* tree-decomposition *of a graph* $G = (V, E)$ *is a pair* $(\{X_i \mid i \in I\}, T = (I, F))$, *where* $\{X_i \mid i \in I\}$ *is a collection of subsets of* V, *and* $T = (I, F)$ *is a tree, such that the following conditions hold:*

1. *$\bigcup_{i \in I} X_i = V$,*
2. *for all edges* $(v, w) \in E$, *there exists a node* $i \in I$, *with* $v, w \in X_i$, *and*
3. *for every vertex* $v \in V$, *the subgraph of* T, *induced by the nodes* $\{i \in I \mid v \in X_i\}$ *is connected.*

The size *of* T *is the number of nodes in* T, *that is,* $|I|$. *Each set* $X_i, i \in I$, *is called the* bag *associated with the ith node of the decomposition tree* T. *The width of a tree-decomposition* $(\{X_i \mid i \in I\}, T = (I, F))$ *is* $\max_{i \in I} |X_i| - 1$. *The* treewidth *of a graph is the minimum width of its tree-decomposition taken over all possible tree-decompositions of the graph. A graph which has a tree-decomposition of width* $O(1)$ *is called a* bounded treewidth graph.

Fact 1 [4] *A graph G is a partial k-tree if and only if the treewidth of G is at most k.*

Fact 2 [6] *For a partial k-tree on n vertices, a tree decomposition of width k can be found in time $O(n\,2^{O(k^3)})$.*

Fact 3 [9] *For a partial k-tree on n vertices, a tree decomposition of width $O(k \log n)$ and size $O(n)$ can be found in time polynomial in n.*

Fact 3 has been refined as follows.

Fact 4 [2] *For a partial k-tree on n vertices, a tree decomposition of width $O(k \log k)$ and size $O(n)$ can be found in time polynomial in n.*

For technical reasons, it will be more convenient to use a special form of tree-decomposition termed as a *nice tree-decomposition*.

Definition 2. *A tree-decomposition $T = (I, F)$ of a graph G is nice if it fulfills the following conditions:*

1. *T is a binary rooted tree,*
2. *if a node $i \in I$ has two children j_1 and j_2, then $X_i = X_{j_1} = X_{j_2}$ (i is called a join node),*
3. *if a node $i \in I$ has one child j, then either $X_j \subset X_i$ and $|X_i - X_j| = 1$, or $X_i \subset X_j$ and $|X_j - X_i| = 1$ (i is called an introduce or a forget node, respectively).*

Fact 5 [17] *A tree-decomposition $T = (I, F)$ of a graph G can be transformed without increasing its width into a nice tree-decomposition in time polynomial in $|I|$ and the size of G. The size of the resulting nice decomposition is $O(\ell \cdot |I|)$, where ℓ is the width of the tree-decomposition.*

Note that we may assume w.l.o.g that the leaf bags in the resulting nice tree-decomposition are singletons. For technical reasons, we shall keep this assumption for nice tree-decompositions throughout the paper.

2.1   Simple Algorithm for Coloring Partial Trees

The following simple lemma gives a simple polynomial-time $(k + 1)$-approximation algorithm for maximum independent set in partial k-trees mentioned in Introduction.

Lemma 1. *Any partial k-tree can be colored with $k + 1$ colors in polynomial time. Consequently, in any partial k-tree, an independent set of size at least $\frac{n}{k+1}$ can be found in polynomial time too.*

Proof. It is well known that any partial k-tree and any its subgraph (as a partial ℓ-tree with $\ell \leq k$) has a vertex of degree at most k. Therefore, it is sufficient to pick such a vertex v, remove it from the graph, color the resulting subgraph inductively with $k + 1$ colors, and then color v with one of the $k + 1$ colors different from those of its neighbors. $\square$

3   Deterministic Approximation of Maximum Independent Set

In this section we present a deterministic approximation algorithm for finding maximum independent set in k-partial trees with given nice decomposition-tree of width ℓ. The algorithm traverses the nice decomposition-tree of the input graph bottom-up to collect information about independent sets in the subtrees of the tree. For each node v in the tree with the bag X_v, we would like to collect information about all independent sets induced by the vertices of the input graph that are in the subtree of the decomposition tree rooted at v. Unfortunately, in general, the number of these sets might be too large. Therefore, we consider only the sets having at most $M(n)$ nodes in each bag, where $M = \Theta(\log n / \log\log n)$. For this, with each node v we associate a set S_v containing pairs (b, r) such that $b \subseteq X_v$ and there is an independent set I on the vertices of the subtree rooted at v of size r with $I \cap X_v = b$.

Algorithm 1:

Input: A nice tree-decomposition T of a partial tree G and a parameter M.

Output: An independent set in G.

for each node v of T **do**
    if v is a leaf **then** $S_v = \{(b, 1), (\emptyset, 0)\}$ *where b is the singleton bag of v ($X_v = \{b\}$)*
    else $S_v = \{(\emptyset, 0)\}$

    {Invariant: $(b, r) \in S_v$ *means that there is an independent set I of size r with $X_v \cap I = b$*
    that contains only the vertices from the bags in the subtree rooted at v}

Traverse the tree T bottom-up

    for a join node v of T with children u and w **do**
        for each $(b_u, n_u) \in S_u$ and $(b_w, n_w) \in S_w$, where $b_u = b_w$ **do**
            $S_v = S_v \cup \{(b_u, n_u + n_w - |b_u|)\}$

    for an introduce node v of T with one child u **do**
        begin
            $q \leftarrow$ the vertex in $X_v \setminus X_u$
            for each $(b_u, n_u) \in S_u$ **do**
                $S_v = S_v \cup \{(b_u, n_u)\}$
                if $b_u \cup \{q\}$ is independent and $|b_u| + 1 \leq M$ **then**
                    $S_v = S_v \cup \{(b_u \cup \{q\}, n_u + 1)\}$
        end

    for a forget node v of T with one child u **do**
        begin
            $q \leftarrow$ the vertex in $X_u \setminus X_v$
            for each $(b_u, n_u) \in S_u$ **do**
                $S_v = S_v \cup \{(b_u \setminus \{q\}, n_u)\}$
        end

Let r be the root of T.
Find a pair (b, m) in S_r that maximizes m.
By backtracking, produce an independent set in G on m vertices that includes b.

Theorem 1. *If T has width poly-logarithmic in n and size polynomial in n, and $M = O(\log n / \log \log n)$ then Algorithm 1 runs in polynomial time.*

Proof. Let ℓ be the width of T. The running time of the algorithm is equal to the running time required to traverse the entire nice tree-decomposition T, and thus, it is the sum of the running times the algorithm spends in each node of T. Since the number of nodes in the nice tree-decomposition in T is polynomial, it is enough to show that the time spent in each node is polynomial too. The time spent on a node v with two children u and w is $O(|S_u| \cdot |S_w|)$, and the time spent on a node v with one child u is $O(|S_u|)$. Therefore, to complete the proof, we must show that the size of each S_v is polynomial. This follows from the fact that each element in S_v is of the form (b, r), with $0 \le r \le n$, $b \subseteq X_v$ with $|b| \le M = O(\log n / \log \log n)$. Therefore, since $|X_v| \le \ell \le \log^{O(1)} n$, we have at most $(n+1) \cdot \binom{\ell}{M} \le (n+1)\ell^M \le n^{O(1)}$ sets b associated with S_v and hence the size of each S_v is polynomial in n. $\qquad\square$

Theorem 2. *Suppose that the nice tree-decomposition T of a partial k-tree has width ℓ and the size polynomial in n. Let ϵ be any positive constant satisfying $\ell \ge \log^{1-\epsilon} n$. There is a constant c such that if $M \ge \frac{c \log n}{\epsilon \log \log n}$ then Algorithm 1 returns an independent that is an $(\ell / \log^{1-\epsilon} n)$-approximation of maximum independent set of G.*

Proof. We set the constant c such that T has size upper bounded by n^{c-1}.

Let I be a maximum independent set in G. Let $s = \log^{1-\epsilon} n$ and $r = \ell / \log^{1-\epsilon} n$. It is easy to verify that the invariant in Algorithm 1 is satisfied throughout the entire algorithm and therefore the output is a correct independent set. Furthermore, we observe that Algorithm 1 returns an independent set of G whose size is not less than that of any independent set in G whose intersection with any bag of T is of cardinality not exceeding M. Therefore, to conclude the proof we only must show the *existence* of an independent set whose size is at least $|I|/r$ and whose intersection with any bag of T has at most M vertices.

Let $\lambda = c/\epsilon$. Consider a randomized construction of a smaller independent set $I' \subseteq I$ that is obtained by taking each element from I to I' independently at random with probability $\frac{1}{r}$. We show first that with high probability the intersection of I' with any bag in the nice tree-decomposition T does not exceed M.

For any node v in the tree-decomposition T, let $\mathfrak{Y}_v$ be the random variable that denotes the size of the intersection of I' with the bag X_v of v. Let $q_v = |I \cap X_v|$. Clearly, the random variable $\mathfrak{Y}_v$ has the binomial distribution with parameters q_v and $\frac{1}{r}$. Therefore, $\mathbf{E}[\mathfrak{Y}_v] = \frac{q_v}{r}$. Since $q_v \le |X_v| \le \ell = r \cdot s$, we have $\mathbf{E}[\mathfrak{Y}_v] \le s$. Furthermore, by the Chernoff bound (see, e.g., [10]), for every $t > \mathbf{E}[\mathfrak{Y}_v]$ we have $\mathbf{Pr}[\mathfrak{Y}_v \ge t] \le (e \cdot \mathbf{E}[\mathfrak{Y}_v]/t)^t \le (es/t)^t$. If we set $t = M = \lambda \log n / \log \log n$, then we obtain

$$\mathbf{Pr}[\mathfrak{Y}_v \ge M] \le (es/M)^M = \left(\frac{es}{\lambda \log n / \log \log n} \right)^{\lambda \log n / \log \log n}$$

$$\leq \left(\frac{s}{\log n}\right)^{\lambda \log n / \log \log n} = \left(\log^{-c/\lambda} n\right)^{\lambda \log n / \log \log n}$$

$$= \left(2^{-\frac{c}{\lambda} \cdot \log \log n}\right)^{\lambda \log n / \log \log n} = n^{-c} .$$

In the bound above we use the fact that $s = \log^{1-\epsilon} n = \log^{1-\frac{c}{\lambda}} n$.

Since the number of nodes in T is at most n^{c-1}, the union bound yields

$$\mathbf{Pr}\left[\exists v \mid \mathfrak{Y}_v \geq M\right] \leq \sum_v \mathbf{Pr}\left[\mathfrak{Y}_v \geq M\right] \leq n^{c-1} \cdot n^{-c} \leq n^{-1} .$$

Hence, the intersection of the independent set I' in G with every bag of T is of cardinality not exceeding M with high probability. Furthermore, with a constant probability $|I'| \geq |I|/r$. This implies that in our probabilistic experiment, with probability at least 0.1, the set I' is an independent set of size at least $|I|/r$ that intersects every bag of T in at most M elements. Since this probabilistic experiment makes the random choices at random independently of G and T, the claim above implies that there exists an independent set in G of size at least $|I|/r$ that intersects every bag of T in at most M elements. This yields an r-approximation of a maximum independent set of G.   □

Note that Algorithm 1 yields $\log^{1-\epsilon} n$ times better approximation than that implied by Lemma 1.

Theorem 3. *Let $\ell = O(\log^{O(1)} n)$ and let ϵ be any positive constant. For a partial k-tree given with its nice tree-decomposition of width ℓ having a polynomial size, there exists an $M = \Theta(\log n / \epsilon \log \log n)$ such that Algorithm 1 yields an $(\ell / \log^{1-\epsilon} n)$-approximation of maximum independent set in polynomial time.*

4   Extensions to Other Problems

The deterministic approximation method for independent set presented in the previous section can be adapted to several other $\mathcal{NP}$-hard optimization graph problems constrained to partial polylog-trees.

The following fact yields a straightforward simplification of the method for a *maximum clique* in partial polylog-trees.

Fact 6 *Let $(\{X_i | i \in I\}, T = (I, F))$ be a tree-decomposition of $G = (V, E)$. Suppose that $W \subseteq V$ forms a clique in G. There is $i \in I$ such that $W \subseteq X_i$.*   □

Theorem 4. *Let $\ell = O(\log^{O(1)} n)$. For a partial k-tree given with its tree-decomposition of width ℓ and of polynomial size, an $(\ell \log \log n / \log n)$-approximation of maximum clique can be found in polynomial time.*

Proof. By Fact 6, a maximum clique is contained in one of the bags of the given decomposition tree. Therefore, by checking each subset of size $O(\log n / \log \log n)$ of each bag for whether or not it induces a clique, we can obtain the desired approximation. By straightforward calculations, the number of subsets to check is polynomial.   □

The problem of *maximum induced m-colorable subgraph* for a graph $G = (V, E)$ is to find a maximum cardinality subset of V that induces an m-colorable subgraph of G. The problem is known to be $\mathcal{NP}$-hard already for $m = 2$ (see [13]).

Theorem 5. *Let $\ell = O(\log^{O(1)} n)$, $m \geq 2$ and let ϵ be an arbitrary small positive constant where $\ell \geq \log^{1-\epsilon} n$. For a partial k-tree given with its tree-decomposition of width ℓ and of polynomial size, the problem of maximum induced m-colorable subgraph admits an $(\ell/\log^{1-\epsilon} n)$-approximation in polynomial-time.*

Proof. We use a method analogous to Algorithm 1. For the sake of explanation let us assume $m = 2$ first. The main difference now is that the classes S_v contain triplets (V', V'', n'') where:

- V', V'' are disjoint subsets of $O(\log n / \log \log n)$ vertices in the bag corresponding to v, and
- n'' is the maximum cardinality of the union $V_1 \cup V_2$ where V_1 and V_2 are disjoint subsets of vertices in the subgraph of the input graph induced by the bag corresponding to v and the the bags lying under it in the given tree-decomposition, $V' \subset V_1$ and $V'' \subset V_2$, and the subgraph of the input graph induced by $V_1 \cup V_2$ can be colored with two colors by coloring vertices in V_1 with the first color and vertices in V_2 with the second color.

Note that the number of such pairs V', V'' is polynomial since the bag is of size $O(\log^{O(1)} n)$. A straightforward modification of Algorithm 1 yields the thesis. We replace b_u with pairs b'_u, b''_u and the test of $b_u \cup \{q\}$ for independence with the test of whether or not the subgraph induced by $b'_u \cup \{q\} \cup b''_u$ can be colored with two colors such that vertices in $b'_u \cup \{q\}$ are colored with the first color and vertices in b''_u are colored with the second color, or vertices in b'_u are colored with first color and vertices $b''_u \cup \{q\}$ are colored with the second color, respectively. To prove the approximation factor of our method we proceed along the lines of the proof of Theorem 2. We leave the straightforward details and the straightforward generalization to an arbitrary $m = O(1)$ to the reader.

5   Randomized Approximation of Maximum Independent Set

One drawback of Theorem 3 is that it requires that the width ℓ is polylogarithmic. In this section we overcome this obstacle and describe a *randomized* algorithm that works for arbitrary $\ell = \Omega(\log n)$ and achieves a better approximation than in Theorem 3.

Theorem 6. *Let c be any positive constant. For a partial k-tree G on n vertices given with its tree-decomposition of width $\ell \geq \log n/c$ and of polynomial size, the problem of maximum independent set admits a randomized $(c\ell/\log n)$-approximation algorithm running in polynomial time, with high probability.*

Proof. We assume, without loss of generality and for simplicity of presentation only, that $c\ell/\log n$ and $n \log n/(c\ell)$ are integers.

Let I be an arbitrary maximum independent set in G. Partition the vertices of G into $c\ell/\log n$ sets $V_1, \dots, V_{c\ell/\log n}$ independently and uniformly at random. (That is, for each vertex y of G and for each i, $\mathbf{Pr}[y \in V_i] = \log n/(c\ell)$.) For any i, $1 \le i \le c\ell/\log n$, let G_i be the subgraph of G induced by the vertex set V_i.

Let T be a tree-decomposition of G of width ℓ and let the size of T be $O(n^b)$ for a positive constant b. Let T_i be the tree-decomposition T constrained to the vertices in V_i. We show that for each i, the tree-decomposition T_i has width $O(\log n)$ with probability $1 - o(1)$. Indeed, let us first consider any node v in T and let us estimate the probability that the bag of v, X_v, intersects with more than $O(\log n)$ vertices in V_i. Since for any i, for any vertex $y \in X_v$, $\mathbf{Pr}[y \in V_i] = \log n/(c\ell)$, and since $|X_v| \le \ell$, the size of $X_v \cap V_i$ is (stochastically) upper bounded by a random variable with the binomial distribution with the parameters k and $\log n/(c\ell)$, which we denote by $\mathbb{B}(\ell, \log n/(c\ell))$. That is, for any N, $\mathbf{Pr}[|X_v \cap V_i| \ge N] \le \mathbf{Pr}[\mathbb{B}(\ell, \log n/(c\ell)) \ge N]$. On the other hand, by the Chernoff bound we have for $\lambda = 2e + c(b+1)$,

$$\mathbf{Pr}\left[\mathbb{B}(\ell, \log n/(c\ell)) \ge \tfrac{\lambda \log n}{c}\right] \le \left(\frac{e \log n/c}{\lambda \log n/c}\right)^{\lambda \log n/c} = (e/\lambda)^{\lambda \log n/c}$$

$$\le (1/2)^{c(b+1)\log n/c} = n^{-(b+1)} \ .$$

Since T has $O(n^b)$ nodes and since there are $c\ell/\log n$ sets V_i, this implies that for each V_i, the tree T_i has width $O(\log n)$ with probability at least $1 - O(n^b) \cdot \frac{c\ell}{\log n} \cdot n^{-(b+1)} = 1 - o(1)$. Therefore, conditioned on that, for each i, $1 \le i \le c\ell/\log n$, we can find a maximum independent set in G_i by using the standard dynamic programming method on T_i [8]. By the pigeon hole principle, at least one of these maximum independent sets is of size not less than $|I| \cdot \log n/(c\ell)$, which yields the theorem. The failure probability of the randomized algorithm is $O(\frac{c\ell}{\log n}) = o(1)$. One can easily modify our algorithms and the arguments to amplify the failure probability to less than n^{-c} for any given constant $c > 0$. □

6   Final Remarks

The $\mathcal{NP}$-hard problem of finding a tree decomposition of a graph having minimum treewidth is known to admit logarithmic-factor approximation polynomial-time algorithms (see Fact 3 and 4). Merely, for graphs of constant treewidth, polynomial-time algorithms for tree decomposition of minimum width are known (see Fact 2). On the other, a tree decomposition of a graph can be transformed into its nice tree decomposition without increasing the width (see Fact 5). Therefore, for a partial k-tree on n vertices, in case a tree decomposition of width k is not given, all our upper bounds on approximation factors achievable in polynomial time established in the previous sections have to be increased by a logarithmic factor. Due to the improvement of Fact 3 to Fact 4, the logarithmic factor is of the form $O(\log k)$. Thus, in particular, if k is polylogarithmic in n, the increase is merely by an $O(\log \log n)$ factor.

References

1. M. Ajtai, J. Komlós, and E. Szemerédi. A note on Ramsey numbers. *Journal of Combinatorial Theory, Series A*, 29: 354–360, 1980.
2. E. Amir. Efficient approximation for triangulation of minimum treewidth. *Proceedings of the 17th Conference in Uncertainty in Artificial Intelligence (UAI'01)*, pages 7–15, University of Washington, Seattle, WA, USA, August 2–5, 2001.
3. S. Arnborg. Efficient algorithms for combinatorial problems on graphs with bounded decomposability — A survey. *BIT*, 25(1): 2–23, 1985.
4. S. Arnborg, J. Lagergren, and D. Seese. Easy problems for tree-decomposable graphs. *Journal of Algorithms*, 12(2): 308–340, 1991.
5. H. L. Bodlaender. A tourist guide through treewidth. *Acta Cybernetica*, 11(1-2): 1–22, 1993.
6. H. L. Bodlaender. A linear time algorithm for finding tree-decompositions of small treewidth. *SIAM Journal on Computing*, 25(6): 1305–1317, 1996.
7. H. L. Bodlaender. A partial k-arboretum of graphs with bounded treewidth. *Theoretical Computer Science*, 209(1-2): 1–45, 1998.
8. H. L. Bodlaender. Dynamic programming on graphs with bounded treewidth. Technical Report RUU-CS-87-22, Utrecht University 1987.
9. H. L. Bodlaender, J. R. Gilbert, H. Hafsteinsson, and T. Kloks. Approximating treewidth, pathwidth, and shortest elimination tree height. *Journal of Algorithms*, 18(2): 238–255, 1995.
10. H. Chernoff. A measure of asymptotic efficiency for tests of a hypothesis based on the sum of observations. *The Annals of Mathematical Statistics*, 23:493–507, 1952.
11. L. Engebretsen and J. Holmerin. Clique is hard to approximate within $n^{1-o(1)}$. In *Proc. 27th ICALP*, pages 2–12, 2000.
12. U. Feige. Approximating maximum clique by removing subgraphs. Manuscript, March 2002.
13. M. R. Garey and D. S. Johnson. *Computers and Intractability: A Guide to the Theory of NP-completeness*. Freeman, New York, NY, 1979.
14. J. Håstad. Clique is hard to approximate within $n^{1-\epsilon}$. *Acta Mathematica*, 182(1): 105–142, 1999.
15. R. Karp. Reducibility among combinatorial problems. In R. E. Miller and J. W. Thatcher, eds., *Complexity of Computer Computations*, pages 85–103, Plenum Press, New York, 1972.
16. S. Khot. Improved inapproximability results for MaxClique, chromatic number, and approximate graph coloring. In *Proc. 42nd FOCS*, pages 600–609, 2001.
17. T. Kloks. Treewidth: Computations and Approximations. *Lecture Notes in Computer Science* 842. Springer-Verlag, Heidelberg, 1994.
18. N. Robertson and P. Seymour. Graph minors. II. Algorithmic aspects of tree-width. *Journal of Algorithms*, 7(3): 309–322, 1986.
19. J.B. Shearer. A note on the independence number of triangle-free graphs. *Discrete Mathematics*, 46: 83–87, 1983.

Biconnectivity on Symbolically Represented Graphs: A Linear Solution

Raffaella Gentilini and Alberto Policriti

Università di Udine (DIMI), Via Le Scienze 206, 33100 Udine - Italy.
{gentilini|policriti}@dimi.uniud.it

Abstract. We define an algorithm for determining, in a linear number of symbolic steps, the biconnected components of a graph implicitly
represented with Ordered Binary Decision Diagrams (OBDDs). Working
on symbolically represented data has potential: the standards achieved
in graph sizes (playing a crucial role, for example, in verification, VLSI
design, and CAD) are definitely higher. On the other hand, symbolic algorithm's design generates constraints as well. For example, Depth First
Search is not feasible in the symbolic setting, and our algorithm relies
on the use of *spine-sets*, introduced in [8] for strongly connected components, as its substitute. Our approach suggests a symbolic framework to
tackle those problems which are naturally solved by a DFS-based algorithm in the standard case.

1 Introduction

This paper follows [8] and elaborates on ideas presented there in order to solve
a basic and classical algorithmic graph-theoretic problem, under the assumption
of a symbolic representation of the data. The problem we tackle here is the
determination of the biconnected components of an un-oriented graph and the
main result consists in an algorithm that solves the problem in a linear number
of symbolic steps. In [8] the algorithm presented was a routine to determine
strongly connected components in, again, a linear number of symbolic steps.

The assumption that the data–the graph–is represented *symbolically* (i.e. via
Ordered Binary Decision Diagram, see [5]) is motivated by the new standards
that this kind of representation allows to achieve when really large graphs need
to be represented [6]. Symbolic representation, as opposed to the standard or
explicit one, is based on a binary encoding of any object to be manipulated by the
algorithm: nodes are (encoded as) sequences of 0's and 1's, edges become pairs
of such sequences, and everything is represented as a set of the corresponding
codes via characteristic functions. The important positive drawback of such a
representation mainly consists in the *space sharing* that induces, which is the
basic ingredient allowing the manipulation of extremely large data set (see [11,
6,7]).

Working on a symbolic representation of the data has potential but generates
constraint as well: any flagging or the simple storing of information relative
to each individual piece of data becomes impossible. On the other hand, the

T. Ibaraki, N. Katoh, and H. Ono (Eds.): ISAAC 2003, LNCS 2906, pp. 554–564, 2003.

number of symbolic steps necessary for some of the basic operations changes drastically: in one symbolic steps the set of successors (predecessors) of a given set is computed and hence, for example, a breadth first visit costs a number of symbolic steps bounded by the diameter of the graph.

Our previous result on a symbolic algorithm was centered exactly on a problem which could be solved in linear time by a standard algorithm via an individual manipulation of the data: the algorithm by Tarjan for the determination of the strongly connected components of an oriented graph (see [13]). In [13] depth first visit (DFS-visit) is used to determine an ordering in which the strongly connected components could be produced linearly. The idea that allowed us to establish a linear bound on the number of symbolic steps necessary to solve the strongly connected components problem (improving on previous attempts, see [4,3]) was to use the notion of *spine-set*. A spine-set represents a "maximum length" (*chordless*) path that plays in the symbolic setting the same role that the dfs-ordering plays in the explicit correspondent.

In this paper we reuse the notion of spine-set for the biconnectivity problem. Even though spine-sets alone do not solve the problem, as the reader can check in the rest of the paper they determine (a segment of) the "right" ordering in which a fast computation for biconnected components can take place. Moreover, spine-sets can be computed in a linear amortized (symbolic) cost. Hence, the entire algorithm is based on an alternation of spine-sets' computations and biconnected components' productions.

Altogether, the result we obtain somehow suggests that the notion of spine-sets is a natural substitute for the use of DFS in a symbolic setting. For lack of space we put all the proofs and further material in [9] (available via web).

2   Preliminaries

This preliminary section introduces biconnectivity giving the basic notions, simple results and non-standard definitions that we will use in the following.

From now on let $G = \langle V, E \rangle$ be a connected undirected graph that we assume to have $|E| \geq 1$ and no self loops. A vertex a is said to be an *articulation point* of G if there exist two distinct vertices $v \neq a$ and $w \neq a$ such that every path between v and w contains a. A graph G is *biconnected* if it contains no articulation point. The biconnected components of a graph $G = \langle V, E \rangle$ can be defined upon the following equivalence relation $\circlearrowright$ on E.

Definition 1. *Given $G = \langle V, E \rangle$, consider two edges $(v, u) \in E$ and $(w, z) \in E$. (v, u) and (w, z) are in relation $\circlearrowright$ if and only if either they are the same edge or there is a cycle in G containing both (v, u) and (w, z).*

Definition 2 (Biconnected Components). *Given $G = \langle V, E \rangle$, consider the partition of E induced by $\circlearrowright$: $\langle E_1, \ldots, E_k \rangle$. For each $1 \leq i \leq k$, let V_i be the set of endpoints of the set of edges E_i. The biconnected components of G are the subgraphs $\langle V_1, E_1 \rangle, \ldots \langle V_k, E_k \rangle$.*

Definition 3. *Let $G' = \langle V', E' \rangle$ be a subgraph of $G = \langle V, E \rangle$. G' is said $\circlearrowleft$-closed if and only if for each biconnected component of G, $\langle V_i, E_i \rangle$, it holds that either $E_i \cap E' = \emptyset$ or $E_i \subseteq E'$.*

The following lemma, proved in [1], gives useful information on biconnectivity.

Lemma 1. *For $1 \leq i \leq k$, let $G_i = \langle V_i, E_i \rangle$ be the biconnected components of $G = \langle V, E \rangle$. Then:*

1. *G_i is biconnected;*
2. *For all $i \neq j$, $V_i \cap V_j$ contains at most one vertex;*
3. *a is an articulation point of G if and only if $a \in V_i \cap V_j$ for some $i \neq j$.*

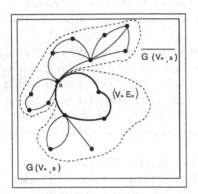

Fig. 1. Graphs $G(V_*, a)$, $\overline{G(V_*, a)}$

Given an articulation point a in G, Definition 4, below, introduces a canonical way of splitting G into two subgraphs: by Lemma 1 there are at least two biconnected components containing a and the splitting takes place around one of them, say $\langle V_*, E_* \rangle$, with $a \in V_*$. As depicted in Figure 1, one of the two subgraphs into which G gets splitted contains $\langle V_*, E_* \rangle$ (and it is called $G(V_*, a)$). The other subgraph includes all the remaining biconnected components containing a (and is called $\overline{G(V_*, a)}$). Definition 4 and Lemma 2 will be central in the design of our symbolic biconnectivity procedure. We denote by $\overset{G}{\rightsquigarrow}$ (the nodes in) a simple path in the graph G.

Definition 4. *Let $\langle V_*, E_* \rangle$ be a biconnected component of $G = \langle V, E \rangle$. If $a \in V_*$ is an articulation point of G, then $G(V_*, a)$ and $\overline{G(V_*, a)}$ are the subgraphs of G induced by the sets of nodes W and $(V \setminus W) \cup \{a\}$, respectively, where:*

$$W = \{a\} \cup \{v \mid \exists \overset{G}{\rightsquigarrow} (a \overset{G}{\rightsquigarrow} v \wedge \overset{G}{\rightsquigarrow} \cap (V_* \setminus \{a\}) \neq \emptyset\}$$

Lemma 2. *Consider a biconnected component $\langle V_*, E_* \rangle$ of $G = \langle V, E \rangle$. If $a \in V_*$ is an articulation point of G, then:*

1. *The two subgraphs $G(V_*, a)$ and $\overline{G(V_*, a)}$ are $\circlearrowleft$-closed;*
2. *$\langle V_*, E_* \rangle$ is a subgraph of $G(V_*, a)$.*

The result in Lemma 3 will be used in in Section 6.

Lemma 3. *Consider the set A_G of articulation points of a graph G. Given $a \in A_G$ let $m_G(a)$ (the multiplicity of the articulation point a) be the number of biconnected components of G containing a. Then, $\sum_{a \in A} m_G(a) \leq 2|V| - 4$.*

3 Symbolic Representation and Manipulation of Graphs

We review here some basics on OBDDs and symbolic algorithms.

Ordered Binary Decision Diagrams (OBDDs) [10,2,5] are a fundamental representation technique originally developed for efficiently storing and manipulating boolean functions. Any boolean function $f(x_1, \ldots, x_k)$ can be naturally represented by a *Binary Decision Tree (BDT)* of height k. In the BDT for $f(x_1, \ldots, x_k)$ each path defines a boolean assignment, $b_1 \ldots b_k$, for the variables of f and the leaves are labelled with the boolean value $f(b_1, \ldots, b_k)$. Collapsing bottom-up a BDT [10,2] we obtain a directed rooted acyclic graph which compactly stores the same information through data-sharing. By introducing an ordering over the node labelling variables in such diagrams, Bryant [5] observed that it was possible to obtain a *canonical* representation and, consequently, a manipulation framework for boolean functions (the OBDDs).

The way OBDDs are usually employed to represent a graph $G = \langle V, E \rangle$ is based on the following further observations:

- each node is encoded as a binary number i.e. $V = \{0, 1\}^v$. Hence, a set $U \subseteq V$ is a set of binary strings of length $v = \log(|V|)$ whose characteristic (boolean) function, $\chi_U(u_1, \ldots, u_v)$, can be represented by an OBDD;

- $E \subseteq V \times V$ is a set of binary strings of length $2v$ whose characteristic (boolean) function, $\chi_E(x_1, \ldots, x_v, y_1, \ldots, y_v)$, can be represented by an OBDD.

To combine with $\cup, \cap$, and $\setminus$ OBDD-represented vertex sets, it is sufficient to use the corresponding operations of logic composition over boolean functions. These operations, fully specified by Bryant in [5], are particularly efficient in that their cost is linear in the sizes of the input OBDDs. The same cost is achieved by the operation pick(U) that picks an element from the set U [4]. By the canonicity of the OBDD representation, the equality test can be implemented in constant time. Given a vertex set U, the graph operation of successor[1] (succ(U)), computes the (OBDD for the) set of nodes that have an edge to a vertex of U. In practical cases the cost of the operations succ, even thought acceptable, is the crucial one: indeed, its worst-case is exponential in the heights of the OBDDs for χ_U and χ_E [11,12,7]. Thus, in the area of symbolic computation, the operations of succ are referred as *symbolic steps* and symbolic (graph) algorithms are compared in terms of symbolic steps (see [4,7,12]).

4 Spine-Sets: A Counterpart to DFS in Symbolic Setting

We now revise the notion of *spine-set* introduced in [8] and we link it to the biconnected components of a graph. Then, we briefly return on the sense in which spine-sets can be used as a substitute of DFS visit in the symbolic setting.

A path $(v_0, \ldots, v_p)$ in a graph $G = \langle V, E \rangle$ is said a *chordless path* if and only if for all $0 \le i < j \le p$ such that $j - i > 1$, there is no edge from v_i to v_j in G.

---

[1] image computation and pre-image computation for directed graphs (cf. [12])

Definition 5 (Spine-set). *Let $S \subseteq V$ be a set of nodes in $G = \langle V, E \rangle$. The pair $\langle S, v \rangle$ is a* spine-set *of G if and only if G contains a chordless path ending at node v and whose vertex set is S. The node v is said the* spine-anchor *of $\langle S, v \rangle$.*

Lemma 4, below, states that a spine-set is associated to a unique chordless path. On this ground, we use the notation $\overline{v_0 \ldots v_p}$ to express the fact that $\langle \{v_0, \ldots, v_p\}, v_p \rangle$ is a spine-set of $G = \langle V, E \rangle$ associated to the chordless path $(v_0, \ldots, v_p)$. Though simple, Lemma 5 is significant in our context, in that it allows to view a spine-set as an *implicitly ordered set*. Both lemmas are proved in [8].

Lemma 4. *If $\langle S, v \rangle$ is a spine set in G, then there is a unique chordless path in G whose vertex set is S.*

Lemma 5. *If $\overline{v_0 \ldots v_p}$ and $p > 0$, then $E(v_p) \cap \{v_0, \ldots v_p\} = \{v_{p-1}\}$ and $\overline{v_0 \ldots v_{p-1}}$*

Lemma 6 ultimately links spine-sets to the biconnected components of a graph.

Lemma 6. *Consider a spine-set, $\overline{v_0 \ldots v_p}$, in $G = \langle V, E \rangle$ and let V_* be the vertex set of a biconnected component containing v_p. There exists $0 \le t \le p$ such that:*

1. *$V_* \cap \{v_0, \ldots, v_p\} = \{v_t, \ldots, v_p\}$;*
2. *If v_t is an articulation point then $\overline{v_0 \ldots v_t}$ is a spine in $\overline{G(V_*, v_t)}$;*
3. *If $a \ne v_t$, $a \in V_*$ is an articulation point and $\bar{V}_*$ is the vertex set of $\overline{G(V_*, a)}$, then $\bar{V}_* \cap \{v_0, \ldots v_p\} \subseteq \{a\}$.*

Both the biconnectivity algorithm presented here and the strong connectivity algorithm in [8] use spine-sets to *drive* the computation on opportune breadth-first discovered $\circlearrowleft$-closed subgraphs. Thus, despite the vertex set is always explored in a breadth first search manner, globally, the biconnected components (strongly connected components) get produced in a *piecewise depth first order*.

5   Solving the Biconnectivity Problem on Symbolically Represented Graphs

The algorithm we propose uses a rather simple strategy to find the nodes of each biconnected component in an OBDD-represented graph $G = \langle V, E \rangle$. Yet, this strategy would have a quadratic performance (in the number of vertices) if not properly combined with the notion of spine-set.

Given an edge $(u_*, v_*) \in E$, let V_* be the vertex set of the biconnected component containing the edge $(u_*, v_*) \in E$. The strategy for building V_* relies on extending the vertex set B, initialized as $B = \{u_*, v_*\}$, maintaining the invariant below:

$$\forall v \in B(v \in \{u_*, v_*\} \vee \exists \text{ a cycle linking } v, u_*, \text{ and } v_* \text{ in B}) \qquad (1)$$

Invariant (1) ensures that $B(\supseteq \{u_*, v_*\})$ induces a biconnected subgraph i.e. $B \subseteq V_*$. Under the above invariant, a safe increasing of B is obtained by adding to B all nodes on simple paths between two nodes of B (simple paths *reaching back* B). The search for these paths could naturally take place from a node $x \in B$ linked to some node outside B: a sort of *exploration point* for B.

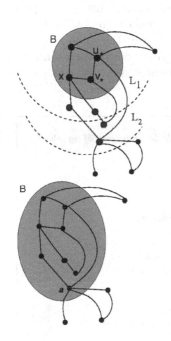

We depict in Figure 2 a successful attempt of augmenting $B \subseteq V_*$ looking for paths that source from the exploration point $x \in B$, cross $V \setminus B$, and terminate at a node in B other than x. The set L_1 containing the successors of $\{x\}$ in $V \setminus B$ is computed and then levels at increasing distance from L_1 are discovered. If a level L_p intersecting $B \setminus \{x\}$ is encountered, this guarantees the existence of some simple paths between two nodes of B.

If the overall process allows discovering only vertices outside B or equal to the exploration point, the attempt of growing $B \supseteq \{u_*, v_*\}$ fails. In this case, invariant (1) ensures that the exploration point involved in the visit is an articulation point of G. This situation is exemplified in Figure 2 on the bottom, when we choose node a as the next exploration point for B. Always in Figure 2, the set of nodes that can be reached using a as exploration point is the set of vertices of the ↻-closed subgraph $\overline{G(V_*, a)}$. This set of nodes can be ignored while extending B to compute V_*, but it can be used used to localize the (recursive) computation of subsequent biconnected components.

Fig. 2. Augmenting B under invariant (1).

Summarizing, the above ideas lead to a recursive procedure in which the process of building the vertex set of each biconnected component $\langle V_*, E_* \rangle$ roughly results in subsequent breadth-first visits from a node of $B \subseteq V_*$. Each visit either augmenting $B \subseteq V_*$ or discovering a ↻-closed subgraph not containing $\langle V_*, E_* \rangle$, on which a recursive call can take place.

The problem with the above approach, is that the symbolic steps performed to discover the subgraph $\overline{G(V_*, a)}$ make the algorithm quadratic in the number of symbolic steps. For example, the procedures may have quadratic performances on a graph simply consisting of a chain of nodes.

The notion of spine-set allows to (piece-wise) drive in a depth-first fashion the order in which biconnected components are discovered so that the global number of symbolic steps becomes linear. The way spines are involved in the strategy described above is the following. Whenever the visit from an exploration point $\{a\}$ of B results in a set of p levels outside B, these levels are used to build a spine-set in the graph $\overline{G(V_*, a)}$ whose vertex set is $\{a\} \cup L_1 \cup \ldots \cup L_p$. This spine, $\overline{av_1 \ldots v_p}$, traverses all levels $L_1 \ldots L_p$ and its length represents the number of symbolic steps necessary to compute $\overline{G(V_*, a)}$. Moreover, the order in which subsequent biconnected components are discovered in $\overline{G(V_*, a)}$ is naturally given by the spine-set: the edge used to initialize B in $\overline{G(V_*, a)}$ is an edge having v_p as one of its end-points.

The linear performance of the full algorithm is a consequence of the following two facts: the spine-driven order in which biconnected components get computed ensures that the global number of symbolic steps necessary to obtain the subgraphs for the recursive calls is $O(|V|)$ (stated another way, the spine-sets generated during the entire algorithm collect at most $O(|V|)$ nodes); each remaining symbolic steps assign (at least) one node to its biconnected component.

```
SYMBOLIC-BCC(⟨V, E⟩, ⟨S, N⟩)
 1    ▷ Initialize a biconnected component vertex set with the endpoints of an edge
 2    if (N ≠ ∅) then B ← N else B ← pick(V)
 3    B ← pick(succ(B)) ∪ B
 4    ▷ ensure that B ∩ S = N
 5    if (B \ S = ∅) then S ← S \ N; N ← succ(N) ∩ S
 6    ▷ Extend the vertex set B
 7    while (∃ an exploration point other then the spine-anchor)
 8    do ▷ Choose an exploration point other than the spine-anchor
 9        X ← pick(succ(succ(B) ∩ (V \ B)) ∩ (B \ N))
10        ▷ Explore outside B. Obtain a set, C, of new nodes for B or
11        ▷ the vertex set V' ⊉ B of a ↻-closed graph and a spine in it, ⟨S', N'⟩
12        ⟨C, V', ⟨S', N'⟩⟩ ← VISIT(⟨V, E⟩, ⟨S, N⟩, B, X)
13        if (V' ≠ ∅)
14            then ▷ X={x} contains an articulation point
15                ▷ Recursive call on G(V_*, x) coupled with a spine-set
16                SYMBOLIC-BCC(⟨V', E(V')⟩, ⟨S', N'⟩)
17                V ← (V \ V') ∪ X;    E ← E(V)
18            else B ← B ∪ C    ▷ Augment B with nodes on paths reaching back B ∪ S
19        ⟨B, ⟨S, N⟩⟩ ← EAT-SPINE(⟨V, E⟩, ⟨S, N⟩, B)    ▷ Extend B with a spine-suffix
20    Output B as the vertex set of a biconnected component in G
21    ▷ Recursive call in case N contains (the unique) articulation point in ⟨V, E⟩
22    if (V \ B ≠ ∅)
23        then V ← (V \ B) ∪ N;    E ← E(V); SYMBOLIC-BCC(⟨V, E⟩, ⟨S, N⟩)
```

Fig. 3. The Biconnected Components Algorithm for Symbolic Graphs

5.1   The Linear Biconnectivity Algorithm

The algorithm SYMBOLIC-BCC in Figure 3 implements the ideas outlined in the previous section and efficiently computes the vertex set of each biconnected component in a symbolically represented graph. SYMBOLIC-BCC is a recursive procedure that takes in input a graph $G = \langle V, E \rangle$ and a pair of sets of nodes $\langle S, N \rangle$. $\langle S, N \rangle$ is either a pair of empty sets or $S = \{v_0, \ldots, v_p\}$ and $N = \{v_p\}$, with $\overline{v_0 \ldots v_p}$ a spine in G. Lines 2-5 initialize the vertex set of a biconnected component, B, to the endpoints of an edge, $\{v_*, u_*\}$. If the spine is not empty, then one of the endpoints of this edge is the spine-anchor. Line 5 updates the spine to $\overline{v_0 \ldots v_{p-1}}$ in the case in which $B = \{v_{p-1}, v_p\}$. This ensures that the spine represents a chordless path sharing with B only its last node (or is empty). Maintaining this property allows to extend B in two phases involving the nodes in the spine-set only to add them to B. The procedure VISIT in Figure 4 is called in the first phase: the detection of paths reaching back $B \cup S$. The procedure EAT-SPINE, always in Figure 4, is called in the second phase.

VISIT($\langle V, E \rangle, \langle S, N \rangle, B, X$)
1   Let $\mathcal{L}$ be an empty stack of vertex sets
2   $F \leftarrow \text{succ}(X) \cap (V \setminus (B \cup S))$ ▷ *Initialize frontier of vertex set discovered from X*
3   if $(F = \emptyset)$
4   then return$\langle \emptyset, \emptyset, \langle \emptyset, \emptyset \rangle \rangle$
5   else $U \leftarrow V \setminus (X \cup F)$ ▷ *Initialize the undiscovered nodes set*
6         $C \leftarrow \emptyset$ ▷ *Initialize nodes on simple paths reaching back $B \cup S$*
7   while $(C = \emptyset \wedge F \neq \emptyset)$
8   do
9   PUSH$(F, \mathcal{L})$; $F \leftarrow \text{succ}(F) \cap U$; $U \leftarrow U \setminus F$ ▷ *Discover a level*
10           $C \leftarrow C \cup (F \cap ((B \cup S) \setminus X))$ ▷ *Check if level intersect $(B \cup S) \setminus X$*
11   if $(C \neq \emptyset)$
12   then while NOTEMPTY$(\mathcal{L})$ ▷ *Collect in C paths reaching back $B \cup S$*
13   do $C \leftarrow \text{succ}(C) \cap \text{POP}(\mathcal{L})$
14   else   ▷ *X is an articulation point*
15              $V' \leftarrow X \cup (V \setminus (B \cup U))$ ▷ *Prepare the next recursive call*
16   ▷ *Build spine in the $\circlearrowleft$-closed subgraph discovered*
17              $S' \leftarrow N' \leftarrow \text{pick}(\text{POP}(\mathcal{L}))$
18   while NOTEMPTY$(\mathcal{L})$
19   do $S' \leftarrow S' \cup \text{pick}(\text{succ}(S') \cap (\text{POP}(\mathcal{L}))$
20   return$(C, V', \langle S' \cup X, N' \rangle)$

EAT-SPINE($\langle V, E \rangle, \langle S, N \rangle, B$)
1   $C \leftarrow (\text{succ}(B \setminus N)) \cap S$
2   while $(C \neq \emptyset)$ ▷ *Update B with maximum spine suffix reaching back B*
3   do $B \leftarrow B \cup (\text{succ}(N) \cap S)$; $C \leftarrow C \setminus N$; $S \leftarrow S \setminus N$; $N \leftarrow \text{succ}(N) \cap S$
4   return$(B, \langle S, N \rangle)$

Fig. 4. The subprocedures VISIT and EAT-SPINE executed within SYMBOLIC-BCC

VISIT gets in input the exploration point $X = \{x\}$ selected at line 9 in SYMBOLIC-BCC, the set B, the graph to explore $\langle V, E \rangle$, and its spine $\langle S, N \rangle$ (collapsing in B). The procedure uses a stack of sets $\mathcal{L}$ to keep trace of levels at increasing distance from the set of nodes outside $B \cup S$ that are linked to the exploration point. Within each iteration of the loop at lines 7-10 of VISIT, a new level is pushed onto $\mathcal{L}$ while either no new node can be discovered or a level intersecting $B \cup S$ is detected. In the first case the vertex set discovered is that of a $\circlearrowright$-closed subgraph that is used for the next recursive call[2]. Lines 15-19 build a spine-set in such a subgraph by suitably selecting a node for each level popped out from $\mathcal{L}$. In the second case, the vertex set discovered contains some simple path between the exploration point and a vertex in $B \cup S$. The while-loop in lines 12-13 detects the vertex sets of those paths containing exactly one node for each level pushed onto $\mathcal{L}$ and whose last node belongs to $B \cup S$. These nodes are assigned to the set C and will be added to B at line 14 of the main routine.

The purpose of the subprocedure EAT-SPINE (see Figure 4) is that of augmenting B with the maximum suffix of the chordless path induced by the spine-set that reaches back B. This ensures invariant (1) upon the termination of each SYMBOLIC-BCC loop iteration.

6   Correctness and Complexity Results

Lemma 7, below, provides four invariants for SYMBOLIC-BCC which essentially ensure its correctness.

Lemma 7. *Let $G^{In} = \langle V^{In}, E^{In} \rangle$ be a graph. In each recursive call to SYMBOLIC-BCC($\langle V, E \rangle, \langle S, N \rangle$) within the execution of SYMBOLIC-BCC($\langle V^{In}, E^{In} \rangle, \langle \emptyset, \emptyset \rangle$), the following items hold upon entering each iteration of the while-loop:*

1. *$\langle V, E \rangle \sqsubseteq \langle V^{In}, E^{In} \rangle$ is connected and $\circlearrowright$-closed;*
2. *$\{v_*, u_*\} \subseteq B \subseteq V_* \subseteq V$ and the subgraph induced by B is biconnected;*
3. *either $|B|$ is increased or $V \setminus V_*$ is decreased;*
4. *$\langle S, N \rangle$ is a spine in $\langle V, E \rangle$ and if $S \neq \emptyset$, then $S \cap B = N$;*

where V_* is the vertex set of the biconnected component of $(v^*, u^*) \in E$.

Theorem 1 (Correctness).   *The   algorithm   SYMBOLIC-BCC($\langle V^{In}, E^{In} \rangle, \langle \emptyset, \emptyset \rangle$) computes the vertex sets of the biconnected components in $G^{In} = \langle V^{In}, E^{In} \rangle$.*

Theorem 2 states that SYMBOLIC-BCC($\langle G^{In} = \langle V^{In}, E^{In} \rangle, \langle \emptyset, \emptyset \rangle$) needs $O(|V^{In}|)$ symbolic steps to compute $\{V_1, \ldots, V_n\}$, where $\{\langle V_1, E_1 \rangle \ldots \langle V_n, E_n \rangle\}$ are the biconnected components in G^{In}. As already anticipated, the complexity result follows from the following considerations. First, the global number of symbolic steps spent to detect simple paths reaching back a partial biconnected component is $O(|V_1| + \ldots + |V_n|)$. Moreover, the global number of symbolic steps spent for obtaining the subgraphs for the recursive calls is proportional to the number of insertions of nodes in a spine. By Lemma 8 also the global number of insertions of nodes into a spine is $O(|V_1| + \ldots + |V_n|)$. Note that $(|V_1| + \ldots + |V_n|) \geq |V|$ because of the articulation points, however, by Lemma 3, $(|V_1| + \ldots + |V_n|) = O(|V^{In}|)$.

---

[2] For the sake of simplicity, the first parameter in input to the recursive calls to SYMBOLIC-BCC is a subgraph of the initial graph, whereas only the vertex set of such a subgraphs would be necessary: successor sets are then obtained combining succ and intersection with the input set of nodes.

Lemma 8. *Let $v \in V^{In}$ belong to m biconnected components of $\langle V^{In}, E^{In} \rangle$. Throughtout the entire execution of* SYMBOLIC-BCC$(\langle V^{In}, E^{In} \rangle, \langle \emptyset, \emptyset \rangle)$, v *is inserted at most m times in a spine.*

Theorem 2 (Complexity). *The algorithm* SYMBOLIC-BCC$(\langle V^{In}, E^{In} \rangle, \langle \emptyset, \emptyset \rangle)$ *runs in* $O(|V^{In}|)$ *symbolic steps.*

Note that also the global number of operations on OBDDs, performed overall SYMBOLIC-BCC, is $O(|V^{In}|)$.

7   Conclusions

We think that a general approach to the design and analysis of efficient symbolic algorithms could benefit from the result presented here. At a general level, we believe that a study of symbolic versions of (weighted) graph algorithms, as well as algorithms operating on different basic data structures, is an interesting and exciting algorithmic field. At a more technical level the question of designing even faster symbolic algorithms for strongly connected/biconnected components (e.g. linear in the number of components) remains open. Moreover, it would be interesting to study special cases of more efficient implementation for the basic symbolic steps.

The positive drawbacks given by the space reuse that is naturally forced by the symbolic representation of data could play a crucial role in any area in which large and loosely structured basic data objects must be manipulated.

References

1. Aho, Hopcroft, and Ullman. *The Design and Analysis of Computer Algorithms.* Addison Wesley, 1974.
2. S. B. Akers. Binary decision diagrams. *IEEE Transaction on Computers*, 27(6):509–516, 1978.
3. P.A. Berel and A. Xie. Implicit enumeration of strongly connected components. *Proceeding of the International Conference on Computer-Aided Design (IC-CAD99)*, pages 37–40, 1999.
4. R. Bloem, H. N. Gabow, and F. Somenzi. An algorithm for strongly connected component analysis in $n \log n$ symbolic steps. In *Proceeding of the International Conference on Formal Methods in Computer-Aided Design (FMCAD'00)*, volume 1954 of *LNCS*, pages 37–54. Springer, 2000.
5. Randal E. Bryant. Symbolic Boolean manipulation with ordered binary-decision diagrams. *ACM Computing Surveys*, 24(3):293–318, 1992.
6. J. R. Burch, E. M. Clarke, K. L. McMillan, D. L. Dill, and L. J. Hwang. Symbolic model checking: 10^{20} states and beyond. *Information and Computation*, 98(2):142–170, 1992.
7. E. M. Clarke, O. Grumberg, and D. A. Peled. *Model checking.* MIT Press, 1999.
8. R. Gentilini, C. Piazza, and A. Policriti. Computing strongly connected components in a linear number of symbolic steps. In *Proceeding of the 14-th ACM-SIAM Symposium on Discrete Algorithms (SODA'03)*, pages 573–582, 2003.

9. R. Gentilini and A. Policriti. Biconnectivity on simbolically represented graphs: a linear solution. RR 13-2003, Dep. of Computer Science, Udine University , Italy.

10. C. Y. Lee. Binary decision programs. *Bell System Technical Journal*, 38(4):985–999, 1959.

11. K. L. McMillan. *Symbolic model checking: an approach to the state explosion problem*. Kluwer Academic Publishers, 1993.

12. F. Somenzi. *Calculational System Design*, volume 173 of *Nato Science Series F: Computer and Systems Sciences*, chapter Binary Decision Diagrams, pages 303–366. IOS Press, 1999.

13. R. E. Tarjan. Depth first search and linear graph algorithms. *SIAM Journal on Computing*, 1(2):146–160, 1972.

A Dynamic Data Structure for Maintaining Disjoint Paths Information in Digraphs

Torsten Tholey

Institut für Informatik
Johann Wolfgang Goethe-Universität Frankfurt
D-60054 Frankfurt am Main, Germany
tholey@ka.informatik.uni-frankfurt.de

Abstract. In this paper we present the first dynamic data structure for testing - in constant time - the existence of two edge- or quasi-internally vertex-disjoint paths p_1 from s to t_1 and p_2 from s to t_2 for any three given vertices s, t_1, and t_2 of a digraph. By quasi-internally vertex-disjoint we mean that no inner vertex of p_1 appears on p_2 and vice versa. Moreover, for two vertices s and t, the data structure supports the output of all vertices and all edges whose removal would disconnect s and t in a time linear in the size of the output. The update operations consist of edge insertions and edge deletions, where the implementation of edge deletions will be given only in the full version of this paper. The update time after an edge deletion is competitive with the reconstruction of a static data structure for testing the existence of disjoint paths in constant time, whereas our data structure performs much better in the case of edge insertions.

1 Introduction

Suppose that in a network represented by a directed graph $G = (V, E)$ we want to send packets from a node v to another node w. Then, for $n \in \mathbb{N}$, it may be useful to know whether there are n edge- or internally vertex-disjoint paths from v to w. This may increase the capacity between the nodes, so that we can send more packets from v to w at the same time. Another aspect is the reliability of the network: If, for $n \geq 2$, there are n edge- (or internally vertex-) disjoint paths from v to w, we can guarantee that w is reachable from v even after the removal of $n-1$ edges (or vertices). Moreover, we can try to check whether some packets are lost by sending the same packets along different routes. Disjoint paths problems also arise in the context of VLSI design.

More generally, given $2k$ vertices $s_1, s_2, \ldots, s_k$ and $t_1, t_2, \ldots, t_k$, one may be interested in testing whether there are k edge-disjoint or quasi-internally vertex-disjoint paths p_i from s_i to t_i $(1 \leq i \leq k)$. By *quasi internally vertex-disjoint* (or for short *q.i.disjoint*) we mean that, for all pairs (i, j) with $i, j \in \{1, \ldots, k\}$ and $i \neq j$, no inner vertex of p_i appears on p_j. If the vertices $s_1, \ldots, s_k, t_1, \ldots, t_k$ are pairwise distinct, the problems above are known as the *(vertex-disjoint) k-paths problem* or the *arc-disjoint k-paths problem*, respectively. Unfortunately, both

T. Ibaraki, N. Katoh, and H. Ono (Eds.): ISAAC 2003, LNCS 2906, pp. 565–574, 2003.

problems are NP-complete [6], even for $k = 2$. Hence, we focus on a special case where $k = 2$ and additionally $s_1 = s_2$. By symmetry, the special case where $t_1 = t_2$ can be handled in the same way.

Previous Results. Using standard network-flow techniques k edge- or q.i.-disjoint paths from a source node s to not necessarily distinct vertices $t_1, \ldots, t_k$ can be computed in $O(|E| + |V|)$ time if $k = O(1)$, and if such paths exist. For a fixed vertex s, Suurballe and Tarjan [12] have shown that, after a preprocessing time of $O(|E| \log_{1 + \lceil |E|/|V| \rceil} |V|)$, one can output a pair of edge-disjoint or q.i.disjoint paths p_1 and p_2 from s to an arbitrary vertex t with minimal total length in time linear in the number of edges of the paths output, if such paths exist. It is implicit that - after the preprocessing - we can test the existence of such paths in $O(1)$ time. Lee and Wu [9] consider the problem of finding k edge-disjoint paths between two vertices s and t that - among all edge-disjoint paths between s and t - have a smallest number of common vertices and that, among all such paths, induce the smallest cost, where, for our purposes, we can assume that the cost is equal to the total number of edges of the paths output. They reduce the problem to a minimum-cost network-flow problem that, if $k = O(1)$, can be solved in $O(|V||E| \log |V|)$ time using the algorithm of Ahuja et al. [1].

Concerning dynamic algorithms, where edges may be inserted or deleted dynamically, there was a great development for undirected graphs, see e.g. [8], [13], and [14]. Much less is known about dynamic algorithms for digraphs. The most important results concerning digraphs are about the maintenance of the transitive closure ([3], [10] and [11]) and of shortest paths ([4], [5], [10] and [11]). These results imply a quadratic or super-quadratic amortized update time, respectively.

New results. In this paper we present the first dynamic algorithm for testing the existence of two edge- or q.i.disjoint paths p_1 from s to t_1 and p_2 from s to t_2, for all possible $\Theta(|V|^3)$ values of (s, t_1, t_2). If no edge- or q.i.disjoint paths between two vertices s and t exist, our data structure can output the set $V_G(s, t)$ of all vertices or the set $E_G(s, t)$ of all edges whose removal would disconnect s and t. More precisely, to avoid ambiguity, $V_G(s, t)$ and $E_G(s, t)$ denote the set of all vertices or edges, respectively, that lie on every path from s to t, i. e. in particular $s, t \in V_G(s, t)$. In more detail, we develop a data structure supporting update operations Initialize, Insert, and Delete, and queries EdgeDis, VertexDis, CEdges, and CVertices defined as follows: Given an $n \in \mathbb{N}$, Initialize(n), initializes the data structure for the graph G with vertex set $V = \{1, \ldots, n\}$ and an empty edge set E. Given two vertices $r, s \in V$ with $r \neq s$, Insert(r, s) adds edge (r, s) to E, Delete(r, s) deletes edge (r, s) from E, CEdges(r, s) returns $E_G(r, s)$, and CVertices(r, s) returns $V_G(r, s)$. Finally, given three vertices s, t_1, t_2, EdgeDis and VertexDis return "yes" if there exist two paths p_1 from s to t_1 and p_2 from s to t_2 that are edge-disjoint or q.i.disjoint, respectively, and "no" otherwise.

Our data structure is *output-linear*. By that we mean that it supports all queries in a time linear in the complexity of the output. For example, the running time of CEdges is linear in the number of edges output. Initialize and Insert require $O(|V|^2)$ time, whereas Delete is supported in $O(\min\{|V|^2|E|, |V|^3\})$ time.

The update time for an edge deletion in our dynamic data structure is competitive with the best known construction time for a static output-linear data structure supporting our four queries (in the full version of this paper we will show that a construction time of $O(\min\{|V|^2|E|, |V|^3\})$ is possible), whereas in the case of insertions the dynamic data structure performs much better.

In the full version of this paper we present an incremental version of our dynamic data structure supporting an additional query MDisPath (see Theorem 11). This operation, given three vertices s, t_1, and t_2, supports the output of two simple paths from s to t_1 and from s to t_2 that are simultaneously *maximally edge-disjoint* and *maximally vertex-disjoint*. By that we mean that the paths, among all pairs of paths leading from s to t_1 and s to t_2, have the smallest number of common vertices or edges, respectively.

2   The Main Idea

As shown later, for two vertices v and w of a digraph $G = (V, E)$, there are two q.i.disjoint paths from v to w if and only if $V_G(v, w) = \{v, w\}$ and $(v, w) \notin E_G(v, w)$. Hence, if we restrict our attention to the special case $t_1 = t_2$, one way to support VertexDis(s, t_1, t_2) in $O(1)$ time is to maintain the sets $V_G(v, w)$ and $E_G(v, w)$ for all pairs of vertices (v, w). But, if we store each such set separately, an edge insertion can add $\Omega(|V|)$ vertices or edges to nearly all such sets so that our update time may exceed the promised performance bound of $O(|V|^2)$.

Fortunately, one can show that all simple directed paths from v to w visit the vertices of $V_G(v, w)$ in the same order and that, for the last vertex $u \in V_G(v, w)$ visited before reaching w, $V_G(v, u) = V_G(v, w) - \{w\}$ holds. For each fixed vertex $v \in V$, we can therefore store the sets $V_G(v, w)$, for all vertices w reachable from v, in one tree T_v such that the nodes on the tree path from v to w are exactly the vertices of $V_G(v, w)$. This reduces the space for representing the sets $V_G(v, w)$ for all pairs (v, w) to $O(|V|^2)$. As we will show later, the time needed for the update of all trees T_v after an edge insertion can be reduced to $O(|V|^2)$ as well.

We will prove that, if we mark all tree arcs (x, y) of T_v with $(x, y) \notin E_G(v, y)$ and x is the father of y, then the set of unmarked tree arcs on the tree path from v to another node w of T_v is exactly $E_G(v, w)$. Moreover, there are two edge-disjoint paths from v to w if and only if all tree arcs on the tree path from v to w are marked. Hence, if we let $a_{T_v}(w)$ be the ancestor of w in T_v with the farthest distance from w that is connected to w by a tree path without any unmarked tree arcs, then $E_G(v, w) = \emptyset$ iff $a_{T_v}(w) = v$. Thus, given the value $a_{T_v}(w)$, we can answer EdgeDis(v, w, w) in constant time. As we will see later, the same is true for all queries of the form VertexDis(v, w_1, w_2) and EdgeDis(v, w_1, w_2).

3   Representing Disjoint Paths Information

We call the tree T_v introduced in the last section the *bottleneck tree* of v or, for short, the *B-tree* of v. In this section we study some basic properties of the

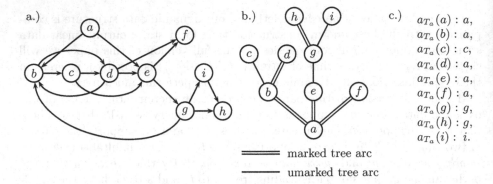

a.)   b.)   c.)
$a_{T_a}(a) : a,$
$a_{T_a}(b) : a,$
$a_{T_a}(c) : c,$
$a_{T_a}(d) : a,$
$a_{T_a}(e) : a,$
$a_{T_a}(f) : a,$
$a_{T_a}(g) : g,$
$a_{T_a}(h) : g,$
$a_{T_a}(i) : i.$

══════ marked tree arc

────── umarked tree arc

Fig. 1. a) a digraph, b) the B-tree T_a of a, c) the function a_{T_v}.

bottleneck tree, and of some special kind of lists that we will call *bottleneck lists*. But first, let us make some further definitions:

Let $G = (V, E)$ be a digraph. A path p in G is *simple* if no vertex appears on p more than once. We use the notation $p : a \to b$ to denote a path p leading from $a \in V$ to $b \in V$. A vertex $w \in V$ is *doubly-edge-reachable* from a vertex $v \in V$ if there are at least two edge-disjoint paths from v to w, and we denote this fact by writing $v \underset{\overline{2}}{\Rightarrow} w$. If there are also at least two different q.i.disjoint paths from v to w, we call w *doubly-vertex-reachable* from v and write $v \underset{\overline{2}}{\Rightarrow} w$. Let us say that $v \underset{\overline{2}}{\Rightarrow} v$ and $v \underset{\overline{2}}{\Rightarrow} v$ hold by definition. In Sect. 2 we mentioned that, if v $\underset{\overline{2}}{\Rightarrow}$ w, i. e. if v and w are the only common vertices of two maximally vertex-disjoint paths from v to w, then we have $V_G(v, w) = \{v, w\}$, and that all simple paths from v to w visit the vertices of $V_G(v, w)$ in the same order. This follows from Lemma 1:

Lemma 1. *The set of common edges of two arbitrary maximally edge-disjoint paths from v to w is exactly $E_G(v, w)$ and, similarly, the set of common vertices of two arbitrary maximally vertex-disjoint paths from v to w is exactly $V_G(v, w)$. Moreover, all simple paths from v to w visit the edges of $E_G(v, w)$, as well as the vertices of $V_G(v, w)$, in the same order.*

We call the list $(v_1, v_2, \ldots)$ of all vertices from $V_G(v, w)$, sorted in the order of their appearance on every simple path from v to w, the *bottleneck list* of (v, w), and we refer to it as $bl(v, w)$ (take $bl(v, v) = (v)$). For the graph in Fig. 1.a we have $bl(a, h) = (a, e, g, h)$. We write $x \in bl(v, w)$ if x is a vertex that appears in the list $bl(v, w)$. By $last(v, w)$ we denote the last vertex in $bl(v, w)$ before w, or w itself if $v = w$. For bottleneck lists the following holds:

Lemma 2. *Let $v, w \in V$ with $v \neq w$ and $(v_1, \ldots, v_k) = bl(v, w)$. Then, for all $i \in \mathbb{N}$ with $0 < i < k$, either $v_i \underset{\overline{2}}{\Rightarrow} v_{i+1}$ or $(v_i, v_{i+1}) \in E_G(v, w)$, but not both.*

In the last section we already mentioned that $V_G(v, last(v, w)) \subseteq V_G(v, w)$. We can show something more:

Lemma 3. *Let v and w be two distinct vertices of V, and $(v_1, \ldots, v_k) = bl(v, w)$. Then, for every vertex u on a simple path from v to v_i with $i \in \{1, \ldots, k\}$,*

- *$(v_i, v_{i+1}, \ldots, v_k)$ is a suffix of $bl(u, w)$,*
- *$E_G(u, w) \supseteq \{(r, s) \in E_G(v, w) \mid r = v_j, i \leq j < k\}$.*

Moreover, if $u = v_i$, then $bl(u, w) = (v_i, \ldots, v_k)$, and the inclusion above for $E_G(u, w)$ holds with equality. By symmetry, if u is a vertex of a simple path from v_i to w for some $i \in \{1, \ldots, k\}$, we have

- *$(v_1, \ldots, v_i)$ is a prefix of $bl(v, u)$,*
- *$E_G(v, u) \supseteq \{(r, s) \in E_G(v, w) \mid r = v_j, 1 \leq j < i\}$,*

and, if $u = v_i$, then $bl(v, u) = (v_1, \ldots, v_i)$, and the inclusion above for $E_G(v, u)$ holds with equality.

The data structure presented in this paper maintains for each $v \in V$ the B-tree T_v of v. Recall that the nodes of T_v are those vertices of G that are reachable from v, its root is v, and the father of an inner node u in T_v, denoted by $f_{T_v}(u)$, is $last(v, u)$. We mark a tree arc $(f_{T_v}(u), u)$ iff $(f_{T_v}(u), u) \notin E_G(v, u)$ which according to Lemma 2 and Lemma 3 is equivalent to $f_{T_v}(u) \Rrightarrow u$. Moreover, we define a function m_{T_v} that maps $(f_{T_v}(u), u)$ to 1 if $(f_{T_v}(u), u)$ is marked, and to 0 otherwise. The B-tree for vertex a of the graph in Fig. 1.a is given in Fig. 1.b. From the B-tree one can read off the sets $V_G(v, w)$ and $E_G(v, w)$:

Lemma 4. *Let u be an ancestor of a node w in the B-tree T_v of v. Then the ordered list of nodes on the tree path from u to w is exactly $bl(u, w)$, and the set of unmarked arcs on this path is exactly $E_G(u, w)$.*

For determining the set $E_G(v, w)$ more efficiently, we store with each node w of the B-tree T_v a value $a_{T_v}(w)$, which we have already defined as the ancestor of w in T_v with the farthest distance from w that is connected to w by a tree path without any unmarked tree arcs (see Fig. 1.c). Then, given an unmarked tree arc (x, y) with $x = f_{T_v}(y)$ and $a_{T_v}(x) \neq v$, the next unmarked tree arc on the tree path from x to v is $(f_{T_v}(a_{T_v}(x)), a_{T_v}(x))$. We can also conclude that in the case $a_{T_v}(x) \neq v$ vertex x is not doubly edge-reachable from v since $(f_{T_v}(a_{T_v}(x)), a_{T_v}(x)) \in E_G(v, x)$. This means that $v \Rrightarrow x$ implies $a_{T_v}(x) = v$. The following lemma shows that the reverse is also true:

Lemma 5. *If x is an ancestor of a node y in the B-tree T_v of v such that all tree arcs on the path from x to y are marked, then $x \Rrightarrow y$. In particular, for all nodes w in tree T_v, we have $a_{T_v}(w) \Rrightarrow w$.*

Another important property of B-trees is given in the following lemma:

Lemma 6. *Let x, y, and z be three distinct nodes of a B-tree T_v such that x is the lowest common ancestor of y and z in T_v. Then there exist two q.i.disjoint paths, one going from x to y, and the other one going from x to z.*

In the following we will use the notation $lca_T(u, v)$ to denote the lowest common ancestor of two nodes u and v in a tree T.

4 The Dynamic Data Structure

Our dynamic data structure maintains, for each vertex $v \in V$, the B-tree T_v of v, (the values of) the functions a_{T_v} and m_{T_v}, and a data structure L_{T_v}, where for a tree T the data structure L_T allows us to compute $lca_T(u, w)$ for all nodes u, w of T in constant time. Such a data structure is given by Harel and Tarjan [7].

For every vertex $v \in V$, Initialize defines T_v to be the tree consisting of only one node, namely v, and lets $a_{T_v}(w) = v$ if $w = v$, and $a_{T_v}(w) = f_{T_v}(w) = nil$ if $w \neq v$. VertexDis(v, w, w) returns "yes" if $f_{T_v}(w) = v$ and the tree arc (v, w) is marked, and "no" in all other cases. If $w_1 \neq w_2$ VertexDis(v, w_1, w_2) outputs "yes" if and only if $lca_{T_v}(w_1, w_2) = v$ (Lemma 4 and 6). EdgeDis(v, w, w) returns "yes" iff w is a node of T_v and $a_{T_v}(w) = v$. As shown in Sect. 3, this is correct. EdgeDis(v, w_1, w_2) outputs "yes" if and only if $a_{T_v}(lca_{T_v}(w_1, w_2)) = v$. See the full version of this paper for the correctness of this step.

CVertices(v, w) returns the set of all nodes on the tree path from v to w in T_v, whereas CEdges(v, w) has to return the set of unmarked tree arcs on this tree path (Lemma 4). It is not hard to see that the implementations above support VertexDis and EdgeDis in constant time, Initialize in $O(|V|^2)$ time, and CVertices and CEdges in a time linear in the number of vertices or edges output, respectively (for supporting CEdges we make use of function a_{T_v}).

We still have to implement Insert, which will be more complicated. Suppose that an edge (r, s) is inserted in G, and we want to update T_v, m_{T_v}, a_{T_v}, and L_{T_v} for an arbitrary, but fixed, vertex $v \in V$ with $bl(v, r) = (v_1, \ldots, v_k)$. Before describing the update in more detail, we will make some further definitions:

For all $x \in V$, we let $R(x)$ be the set of vertices that are reachable from x before the insertion of (r, s). The vertices of $bl(v, r)$ and their descendants in T_s will be handled in a special way[1]. Thus, for brevity, we denote the set of these vertices by S. Finally, we call a vertex $w \in V$ broken if $w \in (R(s) \cap R(v)) - S$ and either $w = s$ or, before the insertion of (r, s), the father of w in T_s does not coincide with the father of w in T_v. The broken vertices will be the only vertices for which we possibly have to "break" a given tree edge in the old B-tree T_v before the update and to connect them to a new father after the update.

Now Insert(r, s) updates T_v, m_{T_v}, a_{T_v}, and L_{T_v} as follows:

If r is not reachable from v, i. e. $r \neq v$ and $f_{T_v}(r) = nil$, Insert(r, s) leaves T_v, m_{T_v}, and a_{T_v} unchanged. Otherwise, Insert(r, s) determines the index $ind(w)$ with $v_{ind(w)} := lca_{T_v}(r, w)$ for all $w \in R(v)$. Then a depth-first search in T_s is started at node s, and for each visited node w, the following is done:

If $w = v_{ind(w)}$ we skip w and its descendants in T_s and continue the depth-first search with the next node of T_s that does not lie in the subtree rooted at w. Otherwise, we compute a vertex u and a value $mark \in \{0, 1\}$ such that

- $u = r$ and $mark = 0$, if $w = s$ and $w \notin R(v)$,
- $u = v_{ind(w)}$ and $mark = 1$, if $w \in R(s) \cap R(v)$ and w is broken,
- $u = f_{T_s}(w)$ and $mark = m_{T_s}(u, w)$ in the remaining cases,

---

[1] For the following, keep in mind that T_s and - for all $w \in V$ - $bl(s, w)$ cannot be changed by the insertion of an edge (r, s).

and then we set $f_{T_v}(w) = u$, and $m_{T_v}(f_{T_v}(w), w) = mark$. Moreover, we define $a_{T_v}(w) = a_{T_v}(u)$, if $mark = 1$, and $a_{T_v}(w) = w$, if $mark = 0$. After this update of T_v, m_{T_v}, and a_{T_v} we recompute L_{T_v}. Using the data structure of Harel and Tarjan [7] or the simpler implementation of Bender and Farach-Colton [2] this takes $O(|V|)$ time.

With the above implementation the update of T_v, m_{T_v}, a_{T_v}, and L_{T_v} takes $O(|V|)$ time, so that Insert(r, s) runs in $O(|V|^2)$ time. We still have to show that, for each vertex $v \in V$, the functions f_{T_v}, m_{T_v}, and a_{T_v} are correctly updated:

The implementation of Insert does not change any of the values $f_{T_v}(w)$, $m_{T_v}(f_{T_v}(w), w)$ and $a_{T_v}(w)$, if $r \notin R(v), w \notin R(s)$, or $w \in S$. In the full version of this paper we show that this is correct. Thus, in the following, let us assume that $r \in R(v), w \in R(s) - S$, and that we have already shown that, for all ancestors u of w in T_s, the values $f_{T_v}(u), m_{T_v}(f_{T_v}(u), u)$, and $a_{T_v}(u)$ were updated correctly.

If $w \in R(s) - (R(v) \cup \{s\})$, it follows from $f_{T_s}(w) \in bl(s, w)$ that, after the insertion of (r, s), every path from v to w visits vertex $f_{T_s}(w)$. Thus, we have $f_{T_s}(w) \in V_G(v, w)$ for the updated graph, and $f_{T_s}(w)$ must be an ancestor of w in the updated B-tree T_v. Moreover, before and hence after the update we have $bl(f_{T_s}(w), w) = (f_{T_s}(w), w)$, and it is easy to see that there are two q.i.disjoint paths from $f_{T_s}(w)$ to w in the updated graph iff this also holds before the update. Hence, the new values of $f_{T_v}(w)$ and $m_{T_v}(f_{T_v}(w), w)$ are correctly defined to be equal to the (old) values of $f_{T_s}(w)$ and $m_{T_s}(f_{T_s}(w), w)$, respectively. Finally, since $a_{T_v}(f_{T_s}(w))$ was already updated correctly, Insert(r, s) correctly lets $a_{T_v}(w)$ be equal to w if $m_{T_v}(f_{T_v}(w), w) = 0$, and equal to $a_{T_v}(f_{T_s}(w))$ if $m_{T_v}(f_{T_v}(w), w) = 1$. Similar arguments show that if for a vertex $w \in R(s) \cap R(v)$ the parents of w in T_s and T_v exist and coincide, the values $f_{T_v}(w), m_{T_v}(f_{T_v}(w), w)$, and $a_{T_v}(w)$ are also correctly updated in the same way.

If $w = s$ and $s \notin R(v)$ it is easy to see that $f_{T_v}(w) = r, m_{T_v}(f_{T_v}(w), w) = 0$, and $a_{T_v}(w) = w$ must hold after the update.

Finally, let w be broken, i. e. $w \in (R(s) \cap R(v)) - S$ and either $w = s$ or the father of w in T_s does not coincide with the father of w in T_v. It is clear that every path from v to w in the updated graph not using edge (r, s) has to visit $lca_{T_v}(w, r)$ - where $lca_{T_v}(w, r)$ should denote the corresponding value before the update - since this was true before the update. But every new path using edge (r, s) has also to visit node $lca_{T_v}(w, r)$, since $lca_{T_v}(w, r) \in bl(v, r)$. Hence, $lca_{T_v}(w, r) \in V_G(v, w)$, and $lca_{T_v}(w, r)$ must be an ancestor of w in the updated B-tree T_v. As we will show, there exist two q.i.disjoint paths from $lca_{T_v}(w, r)$ to w in the updated graph, and thus Insert(r, s) correctly defines $f_{T_v}(w) = lca_{T_v}(w, r), m_{T_v}(f_{T_v}(w), w) = 1$, and $a_{T_v}(w) = a_{T_v}(lca_{T_v}(w, r))$.[2]

It remains to show that there exist indeed two q.i.disjoint paths from $v_{ind(w)}$ $(= lca_{T_v}(w, r))$ to w after the update. Let us consider two different cases:

Case 1. $w \in (R(s) \cap R(v)) - S$, and either $w = s$ or $f_{T_s}(w) \notin R(v)$. In this case, before and hence after the update, there exist two q.i.disjoint paths $p_1 : v_{ind(w)} \to w$ and $p_2 : v_{ind(w)} \to r$ (Lemma 6).

---

[2] Since $lca_{T_v}(w, r) \in bl(v, r)$ the value $a_{T_v}(lca_{T_v}(w, r))$ does not change, so that w.l.o.g. we can assume that $a_{T_v}(lca_{T_v}(w, r))$ is already updated correctly.

If $w \neq s$ we replace p_2 by a new path that follows the old path p_2 between $v_{ind(w)}$ and r, then follows edge (r, s), and finally follows an arbitrary simple path from s to $f_{T_s}(w)$. This new path p_2 is also q.i.disjoint to p_1, since $f_{T_s}(w)$ and therefore all vertices x on the new path between s and $f_{T_s}(w)$ do not belong to $R(v)$.[3] We know that $bl(f_{T_s}(w), w) = (f_{T_s}(w), w)$ before and hence also after the update. According to the following lemma $v_{ind(w)} \underset{2}{\leftrightsquigarrow} w$ holds.

Lemma 7. *Let $q_1 : a \to b$ and $q_2 : a \to c$ be q.i.disjoint paths in a digraph. Then, if $bl(b, c) = (b, c)$, there exist two q.i.disjoint simple paths from a to c.*

Similar considerations show that $v_{ind(w)} \underset{2}{\leftrightsquigarrow} w$ also holds if $w = s$.

Case 2. $w, f_{T_s}(w) \in (R(s) \cap R(v)) - S$ and $f_{T_s}(w) \neq f_{T_v}(w)$ before the insertion of (r, s). Let $t = f_{T_s}(w)$ and z be the first broken node on the tree path from t to s in T_s in this direction. Such a node exists: If there is a node $a \in R(v)$ on the tree path from t to s with $f_{T_s}(a) \notin R(v)$, the first such node is broken, otherwise s is broken. We consider the situation before the insertion of edge (r, s): It follows from the definition of z that node t is a descendant of z in T_v (and T_s) - possibly equal to z - but w cannot be a descendant of z in T_v. There exist two simple q.i.disjoint paths $p_1 : lca_{T_v}(t, w) \to w$ and $q_1 : lca_{T_v}(t, w) \to t$ (Lemma 6). Let r_1 be a third simple path from v to $lca_{T_v}(t, w)$. r_1 is q.i.disjoint to p_1 and q_1. Otherwise, there would be a common vertex x of r_1, and say p_1, with $x \neq lca_{T_v}(t, w)$, and hence a path from v to w not using node $lca_{T_v}(t, w)$, a contradiction to $lca_{T_v}(t, w) \in bl(v, w)$. Figure 2.a shows the different cases that can occur if $ind(w) > ind(t)$, $ind(t) > ind(w)$, or $ind(w) = ind(t)$.

The sub-paths of p_1, q_1 or r_1 between any two consecutive vertices of Fig. 2.a are pairwise q.i.disjoint in all five cases. Thus, we can construct new q.i.disjoint simple paths as indicated in Fig. 2.b. Since z is broken and z is an ancestor of w in T_s we conclude that $f_{T_v}(z) = v_j$ and $v_j \underset{2}{\leftrightsquigarrow} z$ hold for some $j \in \{1, \ldots, k\}$ after the update. $j \leq ind(z)$, since $v_i \notin V_G(v, z)$ for all $i > ind(z)$ before and hence after the update. Moreover, $j \geq ind(w)$. Otherwise, since $w \notin S$, there is a path from z to w that does not visit $v_{ind(w)}$ and hence a path via z from v to w that does not visit $v_{ind(w)}$. But we already know that $v_{ind(w)} \in V_G(v, w)$ after the insertion of (r, s). Altogether, there are two q.i.disjoint paths t_1 and t_2 from some v_j with $ind(w) \leq j \leq ind(z)$ to z. We distinguish between different cases where $ind(w) > j$, or $ind(w) = j$ as shown in Fig. 2.c.

In Case α of Fig. 2.c v_j is a descendant of $v_{ind(w)}$ in T_v. Then, since $j \leq ind(z) = ind(t)$, we are in Case A of Fig. 2.b, and we choose s_1 to be the path following q_3 from $v_{ind(w)}$ to v_j. It follows that p_2, q_2, and s_1 are pairwise q.i.disjoint. In both cases of Fig. 2.c we can apply the following lemma to construct two q.i.disjoint paths $p_w : v_{ind(w)} \to w$ and $p_t : v_{ind(w)} \to t$.

Lemma 8. *Let a, b, c, d, and e be vertices of a digraph G with $b \notin \{c, d\}$. Then, if there exist five paths $p_1 : a \to b$, $p_2 : a \to c$, $p_3 : d \to e$, p_4 and p_5 leading from c to d in G such that p_1 is q.i.disjoint to both p_2 and p_3, and p_4 is q.i.disjoint to p_5 (see Fig. 3), there exist two q.i.disjoint simple paths $p_6 : a \to b$ and $p_7 : a \to e$.*

---

[3] Otherwise, $x \in R(v)$ and $f_{T_s}(w) \in R(x)$ would lead to $f_{T_s}(w) \in R(v)$.

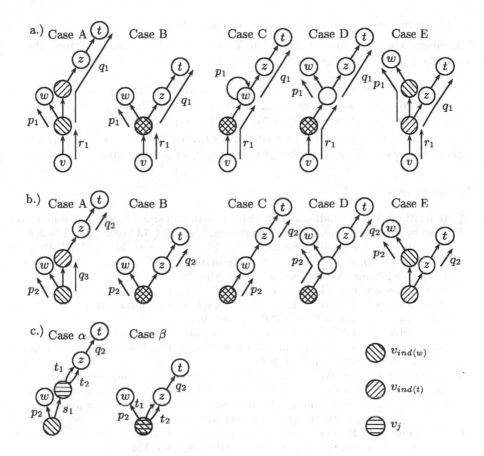

Fig. 2. Construction of disjoint paths in Case 2.

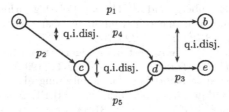

Fig. 3. The paths of Lemma 8.

From $t = f_{T_s}(w)$ it follows that $bl(t, w) = (t, w)$. According to Lemma 7 we can construct two q.i.disjoint paths from $v_{ind(w)}$ to w. This finishes our proof for Case 2. We just have shown:

Theorem 9. *There exists an output-linear data structure using $O(|V|^2)$ space and supporting the operations Initialize, Insert, VertexDis, EdgeDis, CEdges, and CVertices such that Initalize and Insert have a running time of $O(|V|^2)$.*

In the full version of this paper we will also show:

Theorem 10. *The data structure of Theorem 9 can be extended such that it supports Delete in $O(\min\{|V|^2|E|, |V|^3\})$ time.*

Theorem 11. *There exists an output-linear data structure using $O(|V|^3)$ space and supporting the operations Initialize, Insert, VertexDis, EdgeDis, CVertices, CEdges, and MDisPath such that Initialize has a running time of $O(|V|^2)$, and Insert runs in $O(|V|^3)$ worst case time and $O(\min\{|V|^4/m + |V|^2, |V|^3\})$ amortized time, where m denotes the total number of edge insertions.*

References

1. R. K. Ahuja, A. V. Goldberg, J. B. Orlin, and R. E. Tarjan, Finding minimum-cost flows by double scaling. *Math. Programming, Series A* **53** (1992), pp. 243–266.
2. M. A. Bender, and M. Farach-Colton, The LCA problem revisited. Proc. 4th Latin American Theoretical Informatics Symposium (LATIN 2000), Lecture Notes in Computer Science, Vol. 1776, Springer, Berlin, 2000, pp. 88–94.
3. C. Demetrescu, and G. F. Italiano, Fully dynamic transitive closure: Breaking through the $O(n^2)$ barrier. Proc. 41st Annual IEEE Symposium on Foundations of Computer Science (FOCS 2000), pp. 381-389.
4. C. Demetrescu, and G. F. Italiano, Fully dynamic all pairs shortest paths with real edge weights. Proc. 42nd Annual IEEE Symposium on Foundations of Computer Science (FOCS 2001), pp. 260–267.
5. C. Demetrescu, and G. F. Italiano, Improved bounds and new trade-offs for dynamic all pairs shortest paths. Proc. 29th International Colloquium on Automata, Languages, and Programming (ICALP 2002), Lecture Notes in Computer Science, Vol. 2380, Springer, Berlin, 2002, pp. 633–643.
6. S. Fortune, J. E. Hopcroft, and J. Wyllie, The directed subgraph homeomorphism problem. *Theoretical Computer Science* **10** (1980), pp. 111–121.
7. D. Harel, and R. E. Tarjan, Fast algorithms for finding nearest common ancestors. *SIAM J. Comput.* **13** (1984), pp. 338–355.
8. J. Holm, K. de Lichtenberg, and M. Thorup, Poly-logarithmic deterministic fully-dynamic algorithms for connectivity, minimum spanning tree, 2-edge, and biconnectivity. *J. ACM* **48** (2001), pp. 723–760.
9. S.-W. Lee, and C.-S. Wu, A K-best paths algorithm for highly reliable communication networks. *IEICE Trans. Commun.* **E82-B** (1999), pp. 586–590.
10. V. King, Fully dynamic algorithms for maintaining all-pairs shortest paths and transitive closure in digraphs. Proc. 40th Annual IEEE Symposium on Foundations of Computer Science (FOCS 1999), pp. 81-89.
11. V. King, and M. Thorup, A space saving trick for directed dynamic transitive closure and shortest path algorithms. 7th Annual International Computing and Combinatorics Conference (COCOON 2001), Lecture Notes in Computer Science, Vol. 2108, Springer, Berlin, 2001, pp. 268–277.
12. J. W. Suurballe, and R. E. Tarjan, A quick method for finding shortest pairs of disjoint paths. *Networks* **14** (1984), pp. 325-336.
13. M. Thorup, Near-optimal fully-dynamic graph connectivity. Proc. 32nd Annual ACM Symposium on Theory of Computing (STOC 2000), pp. 343–350.
14. M. Thorup, Fully-dynamic min-cut. Proc. 33rd Annual ACM Symposium on Theory of Computing (STOC 2001), pp. 224–230.

Deterministic Algorithm for the t-Threshold Set Problem

Jérémy Barbay[1] and Claire Kenyon[2]

[1] Department of Computer Science,
University of British Columbia,
201-2366 Main Mall, Vancouver, B.C.
V6T 1Z4 Canada
[2] Laboratoire d'Informatique (LIX),
École Polytechnique,
91128 Palaiseau Cedex - France

Abstract. Given k sorted arrays, the t-*Threshold* problem, which is motivated by indexed search engines, consists of finding the elements which are present in at least t of the arrays. We present a new deterministic algorithm for it and prove that, asymptotically in the sizes of the arrays, it is optimal in the alternation model used to study adaptive algorithms. We define the *Opt-Threshold* problem as finding the smallest non empty t-threshold set, which is equivalent to find the largest t such that the t-threshold set is non empty, and propose a naive algorithm to solve it.

Keywords: Adaptive algorithm, t-threshold-set, opt-threshold set.

1 Introduction

We consider search engines where *queries* are composed of k keywords, and where each keyword is associated to a sorted array of references to entries in some database. The answer to a t-threshold query is the set of references which appear in at least t of the k arrays [3]. The answer to an opt-threshold query is the non-empty set of references maximizing the number of arrays they appears in. The algorithms studied are in the *comparison model*, where comparisons are the only operations permitted on references.

The analysis of the complexity of those problems in the worst case, when only the number of arrays k and their sizes $n_1, \ldots, n_k$ are fixed, is trivial and does not permit to distinguish between most algorithms. We propose a *finer analysis* using a difficulty measure δ on the instances: we analyze the complexity of the problem in the worst case among instances of same number of arrays, size of arrays, and difficulty. This type of analysis was already performed on adaptive algorithms for the union problem [6], intersection problem [3,6], several sorting problems [5,8,11], and for the computation of the convex hull [9].

The t-threshold problem has been studied before, as a generalization of the intersection problem, but the algorithm was complicated and of complexity

T. Ibaraki, N. Katoh, and H. Ono (Eds.): ISAAC 2003, LNCS 2906, pp. 575–584, 2003.

$O(t\delta \log k \log \sum_i n_i)$, which is not optimal because of the $\log k$ factor, and because when the arrays are of very different sizes the complexity increases more quickly than the lower bound [3]. Moreover this type of query is a parametrized relaxation of the intersection, and is not quite practical for general purpose search engines.

To answer those problems, in section 2, we give a simpler and better deterministic algorithm for t-Threshold, with time complexity $O(\delta \sum_{i=1}^{k} \log(n_i/\delta+1) + \delta k \log(k-t+1))$, which is, asymptotically in the sizes of the arrays, optimal for $t \geq k/2$ (no lower bound is known for $t < k/2$). We also discuss the notion of the *opt-threshold* set of an instance, defined as the smallest non-empty threshold set, or identically as the non empty t-threshold set with maximal t. This would permit opt-threshold queries, which seem more practical than conjunctive or even t-threshold queries for a search engine. Finally in section 3, we present some perspectives for the domain, and especially address the issue of the practical testing of those algorithms.

2 t-Threshold

Let $\mathcal{U}$ be a totally ordered space. Let $-\infty$ and $+\infty$ be such that all elements of $\mathcal{U}$ are strictly larger than $-\infty$ and strictly smaller than $+\infty$.

Definition 1 (Instance, Signature, t-Threshold Set [3, definition 4.1]).
An instance *consists of k sorted arrays $A_1, \ldots, A_k$ of sizes $n_1, \ldots, n_k$, whose elements come from $\mathcal{U}$. Its* signature *is $(k, n_1, \ldots, n_k)$. An instance has signature* at most *$(k, n_1, \ldots, n_k)$ if it has signature $(k', n'_1, \ldots, n'_{k'})$ with $k' \leq k$ and $n'_i \leq n_i$ for all $i \leq k'$. The output of the t-Threshold* problem *is the set $T_t(A_1, \ldots, A_k)$ containing exactly the elements present in at least t arrays.*

Note that the 1-threshold set is the union of the arrays and that the k-threshold set is their intersection.

Example 1. For instance the following set of arrays forms an instance of signature $(4, 5, 7, 6, 5)$ where the first number corresponds to the number of arrays, and the following numbers correspond to the sizes of those arrays. The 1-threshold set is the union of all the arrays; the 2-threshold set is $\{3, 4, 5, 7, 10, 11\}$; the 3-threshold set is $\{5\}$; and the 4-threshold set is the intersection and is empty.

$$A = \boxed{3\;4\;5\;6\;7}$$
$$B = \boxed{5\;6\;7\;10\;11\;12\;13}$$
$$C = \boxed{0\;1\;2\;10\;11\;14}$$
$$D = \boxed{3\;4\;5\;8\;9}$$

2.1   Algorithm

The algorithm that we propose here for the t-threshold set uses an **unbounded search** algorithm, which looks for an element x in a sorted array A of unknown size, starting at position *init*. It returns a value p such that $A[p-1] < x \leq A[p]$, called the *insertion point* of x in A. This algorithm has already been studied before, it can be implemented using the doubling search and binary search algorithms [1,3,6,7,10], and is then of complexity $2\lceil \log_2(p-init)\rceil$, and can be implemented directly [4] to improve the complexity by a constant factor of less than 2.

In [3, algorithm 3], we gave an algorithm to compute the t-threshold set which performed unbounded searches in parallel in all arrays. Its complexity was close to the lower bound in the worst case for $n = \sum_i n_i$ and k fixed, but not in the worst case for an arbitrary signature $(k, n_1, \ldots, n_k)$. Here, we give a different algorithm which performs unbounded searches one at a time, whose complexity is better for an arbitrary signature $(k, n_1, \ldots, n_k)$ fixed.

Given $t \in \{1, \ldots, k\}$, and k non-empty sorted sets $A_1, \ldots, A_k$ of sizes $n_1, \ldots, n_k$, algorithm 1 computes the t-threshold set $T = T_t(A_1, \ldots, A_k)$. For simplicity, we assume that all arrays contain the element $-\infty$ at position 0 and the element $+\infty$ at position $n_i + 1$.

The algorithm has two nested loops. The outer loop goes through potential elements of T (in variable m) in increasing order. Given a candidate element m, for each array i, the variable $contain_i \in \{\texttt{MAYBE}, \texttt{YES}, \texttt{NO}\}$ expresses the current knowledge of the algorithm regarding the question: "does m belong to A_i?". To answer the question "does m belong to T?", the algorithm looks for m in arrays marked $\texttt{MAYBE}$ until either t arrays are marked $\texttt{YES}$, in which case we can conclude that $m \in T$, or $k - t + 1$ arrays are marked $\texttt{NO}$, in which case we can conclude that $m \notin T$. In each pass in the inner loop the algorithms searches for m in one array A_s which potentially contains m.

Invariant: at the start of the inner loop, for every i, p_i denotes the first potential position for m in A_i, i.e. it is known that $A_i[p_i - 1] < m$. To decide if m is present in an array A_s, the algorithm effects an unbounded search for m from the position p_s. The position returned is the *insertion* position of m: in particular all elements before this position are smaller than m, and so p_i is updated to this position, thus maintaining the invariant.

The algorithm updates m each time it enters the outer loop, at which point the goal is to compute t-threshold on the sets $A_i[p_i \ldots n_i]$. It would seem natural to take the next candidate m as $\min_i A_i[p_i]$, but one can do better than that to gain efficiency: observe that if m is in T, then any set of $k - t + 1$ arrays must contain at least one copy of m; hence it is enough to define m as $\min_{i \in H} A_i[p_i]$, where H is any set of arrays of size $k - t + 1$. A heap data structure is appropriate for H, as it permits to maintain $\min_{i \in H} A_i[p_i]$ with a minimum of comparisons[1].

Once m is defined, the arrays whose index are not in the heap, which potentially contain m, are marked $\texttt{MAYBE}$, the arrays in the heap whose first element is equal to m are marked $\texttt{YES}$ and removed from the heap, and the arrays still left in the heap, which cannot contain m, are marked $\texttt{NO}$.

Example 2. On the following set of arrays for instance, if $t = 3$ and $m = 5$, when the algorithm found it in B and D, looked for it but didn't find it in C, and will

---

[1] See remark 1 page 581 for a comment on the use of an array instead of a heap.

look for it in A, the internal state looks like this:

MAYBE	$A =$	3	4	5	6	7		$p_A = 1$
YES	$B =$	5	6	7	10	11	12	13	$p_B = 1$
NO	$C =$	0̸	1̸	2̸	10	11	14	$p_C = 4$
→ YES	$D =$	3̸	4̸	5	8	9		$p_D = 3$

The arrow indicates the array whose marking has just been updated, the first column gives the markings and the last column the positions.

After finding $m = 5$ in A the algorithm will get out from the inner loop deciding that 5 is in the 3-threshold set. It will then increment p_A, p_B and p_D, and will choose another value for m:

- it will complete the heap to 2 indexes (here with D hence $H = \{C, D\}$),
- will set m to the smallest first element of those arrays (here $m=D_4 = 8$),
- will mark arrays out of the heap with MAYBE (here A and B),
- will mark D with YES and take it out from the heap,
- and finally will mark C with NO.

→ MAYBE	$A =$	3̸	4̸	5̸	6	7		$p_A = 4$
→ MAYBE	$B =$	5̸	6	7	10	11	12	13	$p_B = 2$
→ NO	$C =$	0̸	1̸	2̸	10	11	14	$p_C = 4$
→ YES	$D =$	3̸	4̸	5̸	8	9		$p_D = 4$

Algorithm 1 Threshold Set $(t, A_1, \ldots, A_k)$

Given k, $t \in \{1, \ldots, k\}$, and k sorted sets $A_1, \ldots, A_k$, all of which contain $+\infty$, the algorithm computes the t-threshold set $T = T_t(A_1, \ldots, A_k)$.

---

for all i **do** $p_i \leftarrow 1$ **end for**
$T \leftarrow \emptyset; H \leftarrow \emptyset; s \leftarrow 1$
repeat
    Complete H so that it contains $k - t + 1$ indices of arrays.
    $m \leftarrow \min\{A_i[p_i] \text{ s.t. } i \in H\}$
    for all $i \notin H$ **do** $contain_i \leftarrow$ MAYBE **end for**
    for all $i \in H$ s.t. $A_i[p_i] = m$ **do** $contain_i \leftarrow$ YES; remove i from H **end for**
    for all $i \in H$ s.t. $A_i[p_i] \neq m$ **do** $contain_i \leftarrow$ NO **end for**
    while #YES $< t$ **and** #NO $< k - t + 1$ **do**
        Let A_s be the next array marked MAYBE in the cyclic order.
        $p_s \leftarrow$ Unbounded Search(m, A_s, p_s)
        if $A_s[p_s] \neq m$ **then** $contain_s \leftarrow$ NO **else** $contain_s \leftarrow$ YES **end if**
    end while
    if #YES $\geq t$ **then** $T \leftarrow T \cup \{m\}$ **end if**
    for all i such that $contain_i =$ YES **do** $p_i \leftarrow p_i + 1$ **end for**
until $m = +\infty$
return T

2.2   Analysis

Any instance can be decomposed into blocks of consecutive elements, in order to put in perspective its structure and capture some aspect of its difficulty. We present here one way to do it with the t-partition certificate. This permits to analyze the complexity of the algorithm (Theorem 1), and to prove that, asymptotically in the sizes of the arrays, no other algorithm can perform better on instances of similar structures (see the lower bound in [3], improved in [1, chap. 4]).

Definition 2 (t-Partition-Certificate). *A t-partition-certificate is a partition of $\mathcal{U}$ into intervals such that each singleton interval is an element of T_t, and all other intervals have an empty intersection with at least $k - t + 1$ arrays.*

The *non-deterministic complexity* is the minimal number of comparisons needed by a non-deterministic algorithm to check the result of the instance. It is a weak lower bound on the complexity of a randomized or deterministic algorithm. For $t = k$, the t-threshold set is exactly the intersection, and the minimal size of a t-partition-certificate is exactly the non-deterministic complexity of the instance plus one [3], which forms a natural measure of difficulty.

Imagine a function which indicates, for each element $x \in \mathcal{U}$, either the indices of t arrays containing x (if x is in the t-threshold set) or the indices of $k - t + 1$ arrays not containing x (if x is *not* in the t-threshold set). For each element several answers are acceptable, but elements in the same interval of a partition-certificate of the instance will have common answers. The minimal number of times such a function *alternates* answers, for x scanning $\mathcal{U}$ in increasing order, is also the minimal size of a partition-certificate of the instance (minus one), which is called t-*alternation*.

Definition 3 (t-Alternation δ_t). *The t-alternation $\delta_t(A_1, \ldots, A_k)$ of an instance $(A_1, \ldots, A_k)$ is the minimal number of intervals composing a t-partition-certificate of this instance.*

For general values of t the non-deterministic complexity nd does not correspond exactly to the minimum size δ of a t-partition certificate, but the values are still related:

- To any comparison-based proof, one can associate a t-partition-certificate, and the size of this partition-certificate is at most the size of the proof plus one, hence $\delta - 1 \leq nd$;
- conversely, from any t-partition-certificate, one can deduce a comparison-based proof whose length (number of comparisons) is at most $(k - t + 1)$ times the t-alternation minus 1, hence $nd \leq (k - t + 1)(delta - 1)$.

Example 3. The partition-certificates are easier to see if we represent each array by a line where elements of value x are drawn at abscissa x:

$$
\begin{array}{ll}
A = & 3\ 4\ 5\ 6\ 7 \\
B = & \quad\ \ 5\ 6\ 7 \quad\ \ 10\ 11\ 12\ 13 \\
C = 0\ 1\ 2 & \quad\quad\quad\quad\ \ 10\ 11 \quad\quad 14 \\
D = & \quad 3\ 4\ 5 \quad\ 8\ 9
\end{array}
$$

For instance, the 4-threshold set of the last instance (A, B, C, D) is empty, and the 3-threshold set is $T_3(A, B, C, D) = \{5\}$:

- the partition $\{(-\infty, 3), [3, 10), [10, +\infty)\}$ is a 4-partition-certificate of minimal size for this instance, hence its 4-alternation is $\delta_4(A, B, C, D) = 3$;
- the partition $\{(-\infty, 3), [3, 5), \{5\}, (5, 8), [8, 10), [10, +\infty)\}$ is a 3-partition-certificate of minimal size for this instance, hence the 3-alternation of this instance is $\delta_3(A, B, C, D)=6$, and its 3-threshold set is $T_3(A, B, C, D)=\{5\}$.

Note that a t-partition certificate of minimal size can be generated by a greedy algorithm, but that it is not needed in an efficient algorithm to compute the t-threshold set. Algorithm 1 and its analysis improve the previous upper bound $O(\delta t \log k \log \sum_i n_i)$ [3] for the t-threshold set computational complexity. This is partly due to the algorithm, which performs one unbounded search at a time instead of performing several in parallel; and partly due to a better analysis.

Theorem 1. *Algorithm 1 performs* $O(\delta \sum_i \log(n_i/\delta+1) + \delta k \log(k-t+1))$ *comparisons on an instance of signature* $(k, n_1, \ldots, n_k)$ *and t-alternation δ.*

This upper bound has to be compared to the lower bound $\Omega(\delta \sum_{i=2}^{k} \log n_i/\delta)$ (see [3, Corollary 3.1] improved in [1, chap. 4]), valid when $t \geq k/2$. The ratio is then of $1 + k \log(k-t+1)/\sum_{i=2}^{k} \log n_i/\delta$. This is equal to 1 if $t = k$, and smaller than 2 in most cases, in particular as long as $\forall_i n_i \geq \delta(k-t+1)$. Otherwise it is $O(\log(k-t+1))$, which is reasonably small for queries to search engines on the web, where k is the number of keywords input by the user.

Proof. Consider an instance $(A_1, \ldots, A_k)$ of signature $(k, n_1, \ldots, n_k)$ and of t-alternation δ. Let $(I_j)_{1 \leq j \leq \delta}$ be a corresponding t-partition-certificate. We call *search comparisons* the comparisons performed during an unbounded search, and *heap comparisons* the other comparisons.

During the execution of algorithm 1, the sequence of values taken by m is strictly increasing. For $j = 1, \ldots, \delta$ we say that a comparison is performed during *phase j* if $m \in I_j$ when the comparison is performed.

For each phase $j = 1, \ldots, \delta$, by definition either I_j is a singleton whose element is present in at least t arrays or there is at least $k - t + 1$ arrays which do not intersect I_j. As the algorithm searches the arrays in a fixed order, it performs at most one search in each array before to update m to a value not in I_j, and move to the next phase. Hence in each phase at most one search is performed for each array.

For each phase $j = 1, \ldots, \delta$ and each array A_i, let g_j^i be the increment of p_i between the instants before and after the unbounded search during phase j in array A_i. The algorithm performs $2 \log_2(g_j^i + 1)$ search comparisons in array A_i during phase j, and a total of $2 \sum_j \log_2(g_j^i + 1)$ during the execution of the algorithm. This is smaller than $2\delta \log_2(\sum_j g_j^i/\delta+1)$ by concavity of the function $\log_2(x + 1)$. These g_j^i elements are "jumped" by the algorithm and will not be compared anymore: so $\sum_j g_j^i \leq n_i$ and the algorithm performs less than $2\delta \log_2(n_i/\delta + 1)$ search comparisons in array A_i. Summing over all arrays gives the upper bound $2\delta \sum_i \log_2(n_i/\delta + 1)$ of the number of search comparisons performed by the algorithm.

The heap H contains at most $k - t + 1$ elements, so each action on H costs at most $\log_2(k - t + 1)$ comparisons. During a positive phase (when $m \in T_t$) there is only one iteration of the outer loop, hence a maximum of $k - t + 1$ additions, of total cost at most $(k - t + 1)\log_2(k - t + 1)$, accounting for $2(k - t + 1)\log_2(k - t + 1)$ comparisons for additions and removals.

During a negative phase, there can be several iterations of the outer loop, each such that $\#\texttt{NO} = k - t + 1$. Let's note $\#H$ the number of indexes in H during an iteration of the outer loop: it is the value of $\#NO$ before it enters the inner loop. At the next iteration of the main loop the algorithm must add $k - t + 1 - \#H$ indexes to complement the heap, which is exactly the number of negative unbounded searches it performed to obtain $\#\texttt{NO} = k - t + 1$. As the algorithm performs at most $k - 1$ unbounded searches per phase, the number of addition to the heap during such a phase is at most $k - 1$, of total cost including removals at most $2(k - 1)\log_2(k - t + 1)$. Hence the algorithm performs in total less than $2\delta(k - 1)\log_2(k - t + 1)$ heap comparisons.

The total number of search and heap comparisons performed by the algorithm is smaller than $2\delta \sum_i \log_2(n_i/\delta + 1) + 2\delta(k - 1)\log_2(k - t + 1)$, which is in $O(\delta \sum_i \log(n_i/\delta + 1) + \delta(k - 1)\log(k - t + 1))$. $\qquad\square$

Remark 1. Note that the use of an array instead of a heap for H would permit to save comparisons in many cases, in particular in positive phases where computing the min would cost only $k - t$ comparisons. But during a negative phase, there can be up to $k - 1$ iterations of the external loop, each with only one unbounded search but also one min computation. In this case an array costs $(k-1)(k-t+1)$ comparisons while the heap costs only $2(k - 1)\log_2(k - t + 1)$. Hence the choice of a heap to implement H.

2.3   From t-Threshold to Opt-Threshold

The t-threshold set is a relaxation of the intersection: it is less constrained as t is getting smaller. By definition, the sets are then increasing and $T_k \subset \ldots \subset T_1$. For conjunctive queries whose corresponding intersection is empty, the $(k - 1)$-threshold set would be a more informative answer. The same reasoning can be applied to any t-threshold query for $t > 1$: if the answer to the query is empty then the $(t - 1)$-threshold query answer is more informative.

We define the opt-threshold set as the smallest non empty threshold set. It is always defined, as the 1-threshold set is never empty because it is the union of the arrays, whose sizes are required to be positive. The multiplicity of the instance is simply the value of t for which the opt-threshold set is the t-threshold set.

Definition 4 (Opt-Threshold Set). *The multiplicity $opt(A_1, \ldots, A_k)$ of an instance is the maximum number of arrays with non-empty intersection. The* Opt-Threshold Set *of an instance of multiplicity t is the sorted array $T_t(A_1, .., A_k)$.*

The opt-threshold set is the most adequate answer to a simple query composed of k words on an indexed search engine. When some elements of the database match all the words of the query then it corresponds to an intersection, otherwise it corresponds to the set of elements maximizing the number of words matched.

Example 4. The multiplicity of example 1 is $opt(A, B, C, D) = 3$, and the opt-threshold set is $T_3 = \{5\}$ (see example 3 for the proof).

A naive algorithm to solve this problem would be to use algorithm 1 to compute iteratively the t-threshold set for t decreasing from k to 2 till a non-empty threshold set is computed. This is better than performing a binary search or a doubling search on the optimal value of t, as the t-alternation can vary widely from one value of t to the next, and hence the complexity of algorithm 1.

Proposition 1. *The naive algorithm performs* $O(\delta(k - t + 1) \sum_i \log(n_i/\delta+1))$ *comparisons on an instance of signature* $(k, n_1, \ldots, n_k)$, *multiplicity* t *and* t-*alternation* δ.

A more sophisticated algorithm would compute each t-partition certificate recursively from a $t+1$-partition certificate, till obtaining a non-empty threshold set, but this saves only a constant factor in the worst case complexity: such an algorithm can still be forced to search $k - t + 1$ times in the same array for elements of the same interval of a partition certificate.

The algorithm is optimal if $t = k$. Otherwise its complexity is at a factor of $O(k - t + 1)$ of the lower bound, which can be considered small for queries to search engines on the web.

3   Perspectives

An obvious perspective concerns the opt-threshold set problem: is the naive algorithm optimal ? Is the t-alternation for an optimal value of t an adequate measure of difficulty for this problem ? We thought for a while that there was an algorithm solving this problem with the same complexity than for the t-threshold set, but were proved wrong: the problem is still open...

The worst instances used in the lower bounds [3] are pathological: δ_t elements are in a number of arrays maximizing the number of comparisons needed to find it ($k-1$ for the intersection, and $t-1$ in general for the t-threshold set). A measure taking into account the *multiplicity* of each element would be more precise. For the intersection the optimal algorithm has to be randomized: for instance if an element is present in exactly half of the arrays, a randomized algorithm will look for it in 2 arrays on average before concluding, while a deterministic algorithm will look for it in $k/2$ arrays [2]. Those results do not apply to the t-threshold directly, whose analysis needs a more sophisticated generalization of the measure of difficulty.

Jason Hartline suggested an interesting extension of the t-threshold and opt-threshold problems, in which a weight is associated to each array, and a score is defined for each reference by summing the weights of the arrays containing it. The problems consist then in returning references scoring above the threshold t, or the maximum score attained by a reference. It is easy to extend the algorithms to solve those new problems, and extending their analysis and lower bounds seems feasible.

More complex queries can be defined by combining t-threshold functions. We recursively define a *concept* as a t-threshold or an opt-threshold function on concepts or keywords. We define in turn a *concept query* by a concept, and we define the answer to such a query as the set of references matching this concept. Preliminary work shows that the lower bounds and algorithms studied on the t-threshold set problem can be generalized to those more complex queries.

Testing algorithms for the intersection is feasible on data from any actual search engine (see [7]). On the other hand, testing accurately algorithms for the t-threshold set or for opt-threshold set won't be so easy. With usual search engines which perform only intersections, users restrict their queries to a small number of keywords, in order to limit the risk to obtain an empty answer. A realistic test would require the implementation of a search engine using an opt-threshold set algorithm, and real testing by users.

Acknowledgements. Thanks to the anonymous reviewers for helping to point out a mistake concerning the opt-threshold set problem. Jérémy Barbay wishes also to thank the "Institut National de Recherche en Informatique et Automatisme" of France for funding his postdoctoral position, and Joël Friedman for inviting him at UBC.

References

1. J. Barbay. *Analyse fine: bornes inférieures et algorithmes de calculs d'intersection pour moteurs de recherche.* PhD thesis, Université Paris-Sud, Laboratoire de Recherche en Informatique, Septembre 2002.
2. J. Barbay. Optimality of randomized algorithms for the intersection problem. In *2nd Symposium on Stochastic Algorithms, Foundations and applications.* LNCS, Springer-Verlag, 2003.
3. J. Barbay and C. Kenyon. Adaptive intersection and t-threshold problems. In *Proceedings of the 13th ACM-SIAM Symposium On Discrete Algorithms (SODA),* pages 390–399. ACM-SIAM, ACM, January 2002.
4. J. L. Bentley and A. C.-C. Yao. An almost optimal algorithm for unbounded searching. *Information processing letters,* 5(3):82–87, 1976.
5. C. Cool and D. Kim. Best sorting algorithm for nearly sorted lists. *Communication of ACM,* 23:620–624, 1980.
6. E. D. Demaine, A. López-Ortiz, and J. I. Munro. Adaptive set intersections, unions, and differences. In *Proceedings of the 11th ACM-SIAM Symposium on Discrete Algorithms (SODA),* pages 743–752, 2000.
7. E. D. Demaine, A. López-Ortiz, and J. I. Munro. Experiments on adaptive set intersections for text retrieval systems. In *Proceedings of the 3rd Workshop on Algorithm Engineering and Experiments, Lecture Notes in Computer Science,* pages 5–6, Washington DC, January 2001.

8. V. Estivill-Castro and D. Wood. A survey of adaptive sorting algorithms. ACM Computing Surveys, 1992. 24(4):441–476.
9. D. G. Kirkpatrick and R. Seidel. The ultimate planar convex hull algorithm? *SIAM J. Comput.*, 1986. 15(1):287–299.
10. K. Mehlhorn. *Data Structures and Algorithms 1: Sorting and Searching*, chapter 4.2 Nearly Optimal Binary Search Tree, pages 184–185. Springer-Verlag, 1984.
11. O. Petersson and A. Moffat. A framework for adaptive sorting. *Discrete Applied Mathematics*, 59:153–179, 1995.

Energy-Efficient Wireless Network Design*

Ioannis Caragiannis, Christos Kaklamanis, and Panagiotis Kanellopoulos

Computer Technology Institute and
Dept. of Computer Engineering and Informatics
University of Patras, 26500 Rio, Greece

Abstract. A crucial issue in *ad hoc wireless networks* is to efficiently support communication patterns that are typical in traditional (wired) networks. These include broadcasting, multicasting, and gossiping (all-to-all communication). Since, in ad hoc networks energy is a scarce resource, the important engineering question to be solved is to guarantee a desired communication pattern minimizing the total energy consumption. Motivated by this question, we study a series of *wireless network design problems* and present new approximation algorithms and inapproximability results.

1 Introduction

Wireless networks have received significant attention during the recent years. Especially, *ad hoc wireless networks* emerged due to their potential applications in battlefield, emergency disaster relief, etc. [16]. Unlike traditional wired networks or cellular wireless networks, no wired backbone infrastructure is installed for ad hoc wireless networks.

A node in these networks is equipped with an omnidirectional antenna which is responsible for sending and receiving signals. Communication is established by assigning to each station a transmitting power. In the most common power attenuation model [16], the signal power falls as $1/r^\alpha$, where r is the distance from the transmitter and α is a constant which depends on the wireless environment (typical values of α are between 1 and 6). So, a transmitter can send a signal to a receiver if $\frac{P_s}{d(s,t)^\alpha} \geq \gamma$ where P_s is the power of the transmitting signal, $d(s,t)$ is the Euclidean distance between the transmitter and the receiver, and γ is the receiver's power threshold for signal detection.

So, communication from a node s to another node t may be established either directly if the two nodes are close enough and s uses adequate transmitting power, or by using intermediate nodes. Observe that due to the nonlinear power attenuation, relaying the signal between intermediate nodes may result in energy conservation.

A crucial issue in ad hoc wireless networks is to support communication patterns that are typical in traditional networks. These include broadcasting, multicasting, and gossiping (all-to-all communication). Since establishing a communication pattern strongly depends on the use of energy, the important engineering

---

* This work was partially supported by the European Union under IST FET Project ALCOM–FT, IST FET Project CRESCCO, and RTN Project ARACNE.

T. Ibaraki, N. Katoh, and H. Ono (Eds.): ISAAC 2003, LNCS 2906, pp. 585–594, 2003.
© Springer-Verlag Berlin Heidelberg 2003

question to be solved is to guarantee a desired communication pattern minimizing the total energy consumption. In this work, we consider a series of wireless network design problems which we formulate below.

Consider a complete directed graph $G = (V, E)$, where $|V| = n$, with a non-negative edge cost function $c : E \to R^+$. Given a non-negative node weight assignment $w : V \to R^+$, the *transmission graph* G_w is the directed graph defined as follows. It has the same set of nodes as G and a directed edge (u, v) belongs to G_w if the weight assigned to node u is at least the cost of the edge (u, v), i.e., $w(u) \geq c(u, v)$. Intuitively, the weight assignment corresponds to the energy levels at which each node operates (i.e., transmits messages) while the cost between two nodes indicates the minimum energy level necessary to send messages from one node to the other. Usually, the edge cost function is symmetric (i.e., $c(u, v) = c(v, u)$). Asymmetric edge cost functions can be used to model medium abnormalities or batteries with different energy levels [14].

The problems we study can be stated as follows. Given a complete directed graph $G = (V, E)$ with $|V| = n$, with non-negative edge costs $c : E \to R^+$, find a non-negative node weight assignment $w : V \to R^+$ such that the transmission graph G_w maintains a connectivity property and the sum of weights is minimized. Such a property is defined by a requirement matrix $R = (r_{ij}) \in \{0, 1\}$ where r_{ij} is the number of directed paths required in the transmission graph from node v_i to node v_j. Depending on the connectivity property for the transmission graph, we may define the following problems.

In MINIMUM ENERGY STEINER SUBGRAPH (MESS), the requirement matrix is symmetric. Alternatively, we may define the problem by a set of nodes $D \subseteq V$ partitioned into p disjoint subsets $D_1, D_2, ..., D_p$. The entries of the requirement matrix are now defined as $r_{ij} = 1$ if $v_i, v_j \in D_k$ for some k and $r_{ij} = 0$, otherwise. The MINIMUM ENERGY SUBSET STRONGLY CONNECTED SUBGRAPH (MESSCS) is the special case of MESS with $p = 1$ while the MINIMUM ENERGY STRONGLY CONNECTED SUBGRAPH (MESCS) is the special case of MESSCS with $D = V$ (i.e., the transmission graph is required to span all nodes of V and to be strongly connected). The authors of [1] study MESCS under the extra requirement that the transmission graph contains a bidirected subgraph which maintains the connectivity requirements of MESCS. By adding this extra requirement to MESS and MESSCS, we obtain the bidirected MESS and bidirected MESSCS, respectively. For bidirected MESCS, [1] shows a constant approximation algorithm in symmetric graphs and a logarithmic inapproximability result in asymmetric graphs. The same reduction used to prove this inapproximability result can be used for proving a logarithmic inapproximability result for MESCS in asymmetric graphs as well. MESCS in symmetric graphs is studied by Kirousis et al. [13] who present (among other results) a 2-approximation algorithm. Clementi et al. [8] study geometric versions of the problem and show approximation-preserving reductions from VERTEX COVER on bounded-degree graphs to geometric instances of MESCS. By adapting the reduction of [8] and using the hardness results of [2], we can obtain an inapproximability factor of 313/312 for MESCS in symmetric graphs. As observed in [1], this result holds for bidirected MESCS as well.

In MINIMUM ENERGY MULTICAST TREE (MEMT), the connectivity property is defined by a root node v_0 and a set of nodes $D \subseteq V - \{v_0\}$ such that $r_{ij} = 1$ if $i = 0$ and $v_j \in D$ and $r_{ij} = 0$, otherwise. The MINIMUM ENERGY BROADCAST TREE (MEBT) is the special case of MEMT with $D = V - \{v_0\}$. Liang [14] shows an $O(|D|^\epsilon)-$ and an $O(n^\epsilon)$–approximation algorithm for MEMT and MEBT, respectively, for any constant $\epsilon > 0$. These results follow by using an intuitive reduction of any instance of MEMT to an instance of DIRECTED STEINER TREE and then applying the algorithm of Charikar et al. [5] for computing an approximate directed Steiner tree which gives an approximate solution to MEMT. Note that the work of Liang does not answer the question whether MEMT and MEBT are strictly easier to approximate than DIRECTED STEINER TREE or not. For MEMT in symmetric graphs, Liang [14] shows an $O(\ln^3 |D|)$-approximation algorithm while, for MEBT in symmetric graphs, we show in [4] a $10.8 \ln n$-approximation algorithm by reducing instances of the problem to instances of NODE-WEIGHTED CONNECTED DOMINATING SET and using the algorithm of [11] for computing an approximate connected dominating set which gives an approximate solution to MEBT. Constant approximation algorithms for geometric versions of MEBT are presented in [7,16].

By inverting the connectivity requirements, we obtain the MINIMUM ENERGY INVERSE MULTICAST TREE (MEIMT) where the connectivity property is defined by a root node v_0 and a set of nodes $D \subseteq V - \{v_0\}$ such that $r_{ij} = 1$ if $v_i \in D$ and $j = 0$ and $r_{ij} = 0$, otherwise, and the MINIMUM ENERGY INVERSE BROADCAST TREE (MEIBT) which is the special case of MEIMT with $D = V - \{v_0\}$.

In the paper, we usually refer to classical combinatorial optimization problems. For completeness, we present their definitions here. The STEINER FOREST (SF) problem is defined as follows. Given an undirected graph $G = (V, E)$ with an edge cost function $c : E \to R^+$ and a set of nodes $D \subseteq V$ partitioned into p disjoint sets $D_1, ..., D_p$, compute a subgraph H of G of minimum total cost such that any two nodes v_i, v_j belonging to the same set D_k for some k are connected through a path in H. STEINER TREE (ST) is the special case of SF with $p = 1$. An instance of the DIRECTED STEINER TREE (DST) is defined by a directed graph $G = (V, E)$ with an edge cost function $c : E \to R^+$, a root node $v_0 \in V$, and a set of terminals $D \subseteq V - \{v_0\}$. Its objective is to compute a tree of minimum cost which is directed out of v_0 and spans all nodes of D. The NODE–WEIGHTED STEINER FOREST (NWSF) problem is defined as follows. Given an undirected graph $G = (V, E)$ with a node cost function $c : V \to R^+$ and a set of nodes $D \subseteq V$ partitioned into p disjoint sets $D_1, ..., D_p$, compute a subgraph H of G of minimum total cost such that any two nodes v_i, v_j belonging to the same set D_k for some k are connected through a path in H. NODE–WEIGHTED STEINER TREE (NWST) is the special case of NWSF with $p = 1$.

In the rest of this section we summarize our results. In Section 2, we present constant approximation algorithms for MESS, MESSCS, bidirected MESS and bidirected MESSCS in symmetric graphs (i.e., input instances with symmetric edge cost functions) exploiting known efficient approximation algorithms for SF and ST. For bidirected MESSCS, we also give a simple inapproximability result.

We also present approximation algorithms for MEMT and MEBT in symmetric graphs (Section 3) with logarithmic approximation ratios by using a new reduction of instances of MEMT and MEBT to instances of NWST. These results are asymptotically optimal since MEBT in symmetric graphs has been proved to be inapproximable within a sublogarithmic factor [7]. Our result for MEMT improves the polylogarithmic approximation algorithm of Liang [14] while the result for MEBT improves the result of [4] by a multiplicative factor of 4.

In Section 4, we observe that MEIMT is equivalent to DST, while in Section 5 we show that, in asymmetric graphs, MEMT and MESSCS are at least as hard to approximate as DST. Using a recent inapproximability result for DST due to Halperin and Krauthgamer [12] we obtain polylogarithmic inapproximability results for these problems. On the positive side, we show that MESSCS in asymmetric graphs can be solved by solving an instance of MEMT and an instance of MEIMT.

For MEBT and MESCS in asymmetric graphs, we present logarithmic approximation algorithms exploiting a recent result of Zosin and Khuller [17]. These results are asymptotically optimal. In particular, the result for MEBT significantly improves the $O(n^\epsilon)$-approximation algorithm due to Liang [14]. These results are presented in Section 6. In Section 7 we present logarithmic approximation algorithm for bidirected MESS, bidirected MESSCS and bidirected MESCS in asymmetric graphs by using a new reduction of instances of these problems to instances of NWSF. These results asymptotically match the inapproximability result for bidirected MESCS of Althaus et al. [1]. Very recently, Gruia Calinescu informed us that logarithmic approximation algorithms for MEBT, MESCS and bidirected MESCS in asymmetric graphs were independently obtained in [3] using different techniques.

Due to lack of space, formal proofs have been omitted from this extended abstract.

2   Symmetric Graphs and Connectivity Requirements

In this section, we first show constant approximation algorithms for MESS, MESSCS, bidirected MESS, and bidirected MESSCS, extending the algorithm of Kirousis et al. [13] for MESCS in symmetric graphs. Then, we show an inapproximability result for bidirected MESSCS.

Consider an instance I_{MESS} of MESS which consists of a complete directed graph $G = (V, E)$, a symmetric edge cost function $c : E \to R^+$ and a set of terminals $D \subseteq V$ partitioned into p disjoint subsets $D_1, ..., D_p$. We construct the instance I_{SF} of SF which consists of the complete undirected graph $H = (V, E')$, the edge cost function $c' : E' \to R^+$ defined as $c'(u, v) = c(u, v) = c(v, u)$ on the undirected edges of E', and the set of terminals D together with its partition into the sets $D_1, ..., D_p$. Consider a solution for I_{SF} that consists of a subgraph $F = (V, A)$ of H. We construct the weight assignment w to the nodes of V by setting $w(u) = 0$ if there is no edge touching u in A and $w(u) = \max_{v:(u,v)\in A}\{c'(u, v)\}$, otherwise. We can prove that if F is a ρ–approximate solution for I_{SF} then w is a 2ρ–approximate solution for I_{MESS}.

We can solve I_{SF} using the 2-approximation algorithm of Goemans and Williamson [10] for SF. When $p = 1$ (i.e., when I_{MESS} is actually an instance of MESSCS), the instance I_{SF} is actually an instance of ST which can be approximated within 1.55 using an algorithm from [15]. We obtain the following.

Theorem 1. *There exist a 4- and a 3.1-approximation algorithm for MESS and MESSCS in symmetric graphs, respectively.*

Note that the transmission graph constructed by the technique in this section contains a bidirected subgraph that maintains the connectivity requirements of MESS and, thus, our algorithms for MESS and MESSCS provide solutions to bidirected MESS and bidirected MESSCS, respectively. It can be easily seen that the analysis still holds if we consider instances of bidirected MESS and bidirected MESSCS instead of instances of MESS and MESSCS, respectively. Thus, the approximation guarantees of Theorem 1 hold for bidirected MESS and bidirected MESSCS in symmetric graphs as well.

The inapproximability result of 313/312 for MESCS mentioned in the introduction holds for bidirected MESCS in symmetric graphs as well, and, hence, it holds for bidirected MESSCS. We can show a simple approximation-preserving reduction from ST to bidirected MESSCS in symmetric graphs and, using the inapproximability result of [6], we obtain the following.

Theorem 2. *For any $\epsilon > 0$, bidirected MESSCS is not approximable within $96/95 - \epsilon$, unless $P = NP$.*

3   Multicasting and Broadcasting in Symmetric Graphs

In this section we present logarithmic approximation algorithms for MEMT and MEBT in symmetric graphs.

Consider an instance I_{MEMT} of MEMT which consists of a complete directed graph $G = (V, E)$, a symmetric edge cost function $c : E \to R^+$, a root node $v_0 \in V$ and a set of terminals $D \subseteq V - \{v_0\}$.

We construct an instance I_{NWST} of NWST, which consists of an undirected graph $H = (U, A)$, a node weight function $c' : U \to R^+$ and a set of terminals $D' \subseteq U$. For a node $v \in V$, we denote by n_v the number of different edge costs in the edges directed out of v, and, for $i = 1, ..., n_v$, we denote by $X_i(v)$ the i-th smallest edge cost among the edges directed out of v. The set of nodes U consists of n disjoint sets of nodes called *supernodes*. Each supernode corresponds to a node of V. The supernode Z_v corresponding to node $v \in V$ has the following $n_v + 1$ nodes: an *input node* $Z_{v,0}$ and n_v *output nodes* $Z_{v,1}, ..., Z_{v,n_v}$. For each pair of nodes $u, v \in V$, the set of edges A contains an edge between the output node $Z_{u,i}$ and the input node $Z_{v,0}$ such that $X_i(u) \geq c(u, v)$. Also, for each node $v \in V$, A contains an edge between the input node $Z_{v,0}$ and each output node $Z_{v,i}$, for $i = 1, ..., n_v$. The cost function c' is defined as $c'(Z_{v,0}) = 0$ for the input nodes and as $c'(Z_{v,i}) = X_i(v)$ for $i = 1, ..., n_v$, for the output nodes. The set of terminals D' is defined as $D' = \{Z_{v,0} \in U | v \in D \cup \{v_0\}\}$.

Consider a subgraph $F = (S, A')$ of H which is a solution for I_{NWST}. We compute a spanning tree $T' = (S, A'')$ of F and, starting from $Z_{v_0,0}$, we compute a Breadth First Search (BFS) numbering of the nodes of T'. For each $v \in S$, we denote by $m(v)$ the BFS number of v. We construct a tree $T = (V, E')$ which, for each edge of F between a node $Z_{u,i}$ of supernode Z_u and a node $Z_{v,j}$ of another supernode Z_v such that $m(Z_{u,i}) < m(Z_{v,j})$, contains a directed edge from u to v. The output of our algorithm is the weight assignment w defined as $w(u) = \max_{(u,v) \in T} c(u, v)$ if u has at least one outgoing edge in T, and $w(u) = 0$, otherwise. We can prove that if F is a ρ–approximate solution to I_{NWST}, then w is a 2ρ–approximate solution to I_{MEMT}.

In [11], Guha and Khuller present a $1.35 \ln k$–approximation algorithm for NWST, where k is the number of terminals in the instance of NWST. Given an instance I_{MEMT} of MEMT with a set of terminals D, the corresponding instance I_{NWST} has $|D| + 1$ terminals. Thus, the cost of the solution of I_{MEMT} is within $2.7 \ln(|D| + 1)$ of the optimal solution. The next theorem summarizes the discussion of this section. Note that MEBT is the special case of MEMT with $D = V - \{v_0\}$.

Theorem 3. *There exists a $2.7 \ln(|D| + 1)$– and a $2.7 \ln n$–approximation algorithm for MEMT and MEBT in symmetric graphs, respectively.*

4   Approximating MEIMT and MEIBT

In this section, we first show that MEIMT is equivalent to DST. Assume we have an instance I_{MEIMT} of MEIMT defined by a complete directed graph $G = (V, E)$, an edge cost function $c : E \to R^+$, a root node $v_0 \in V$ and a set of terminals $D \subseteq V - \{v_0\}$. Consider the instance I_{DST} of DST that consists of G, the edge cost function $c' : E \to R^+$ defined as $c'(u, v) = c(v, u)$ for any edge $(u, v) \in E$, the set of terminals D and the root node v_0. Also, we may start by an instance I_{DST} of DST and construct I_{MEIMT} in the same way. We can prove that a ρ-approximate solution for I_{DST} reduces in polynomial time to a ρ-approximate solution for I_{MEIMT} and a ρ-approximate solution for I_{MEIMT} reduces in polynomial time to a ρ-approximate solution for I_{DST}.

Thus, using the results of [5] and [12], we obtain that MEIMT is approximable within $O(|D|^\epsilon)$ and inapproximable within $O(\ln^{2-\epsilon} n)$, for any constant $\epsilon > 0$. Notice that DST in symmetric graphs is equivalent to ST. Thus, using the approximability and inapproximability results of [15] and [6], we obtain that MEIMT in symmetric graphs is approximable within 1.55 and inapproximable within $96/95 - \epsilon$ for any $\epsilon > 0$. Also, instances of DST having all non-root nodes as terminals are actually instances of MINIMUM SPANNING ARBORESCENCE which is known to be computable in polynomial time [9]. Thus, MEIBT can be solved in polynomial time (even in asymmetric graphs).

5   Approximating MEMT and MESSCS

In this section, we first show that MEMT and MESSCS are as hard to approximate as DST. Then, we present a method for approximating MESSCS.

Consider an instance I_{DST} of DST that consists of a directed graph $G = (V, E)$ with an edge cost function $c : E \to R^+$, a root node v_0 and a set of terminals $D \subseteq V - \{v_0\}$. Without loss of generality, we may assume that G is a complete directed graph with some of its edges having infinite cost.

We construct the instance I_{MEMT} of MEMT which consists of a complete directed graph $H = (U, A)$ with edge cost function $c' : A \to R^+$, a root node $v_0' \in U$ and a set of terminals $D' \subseteq U - \{v_0'\}$. The set of nodes U has a node h_v for each node $v \in V$ and a node $h_{(u,v)}$ for each directed edge (u, v) of E. For each directed edge (u, v) of E, the directed edge $(h_u, h_{(u,v)})$ of A has zero cost and the directed edge $(h_{(u,v)}, h_v)$ of A has cost $c'(h_{(u,v)}, h_v) = c(u, v)$, while all other edges of A have infinite cost. The set of terminals is defined as $D' = \{h_u \in U | u \in D\}$, while $v_0' = h_{v_0}$. We can show that a ρ-approximate solution to I_{MEMT} reduces in polynomial time to a ρ-approximate solution to I_{DST}.

We construct the instance I_{MESSCS} of MESSCS which consists of the graph G, the set of terminals D, the root node v_0, and an edge cost function $c'' : E \to R^+$ defined as follows. For each directed edge (u, v) of E such that $u \neq v_0$, it is $c''(u, v) = c(v, u)$, while all edges of E directed out of v_0 have zero cost. We can show that a ρ-approximate solution to I_{MESSCS} reduces in polynomial time to a ρ-approximate solution to I_{DST}.

Using the inapproximability result for DST [12], we obtain the following.

Theorem 4. *For any $\epsilon > 0$, MEMT and MESSCS are not approximable within $O(\ln^{2-\epsilon} n)$, unless $NP \subseteq ZTIME(n^{polylog(n)})$.*

We now present a method for approximating MESSCS. Let I_{MESSCS} be an instance of I_{MESSCS} that consists of a complete directed graph $G = (V, E)$ with edge cost function $c : E \to R^+$ and a set of terminals $D \subseteq V$. Pick an arbitrary node $v_0 \in V$ and let I_{MEMT} and I_{MEIMT} be the instances of MEMT and MEIMT, respectively, consisting of the graph G with edge cost function c, the root node v_0 and the set of terminals $D - \{v_0\}$.

Assume we have weight assignments w_1 and w_2 to the nodes of V which are solutions for I_{MEMT} and I_{MEIMT}, respectively. Construct the weight assignment w_3 defined as $w_3(u) = \max\{w_1(u), w_2(u)\}$ for every $u \in V$. We can prove that if the weight assignments w_1 and w_2 are ρ_1- and ρ_2- approximate solutions for I_{MEMT} and I_{MEIMT} respectively, then the weight assignment w_3 is a $(\rho_1 + \rho_2)$-approximate solution to I_{MESSCS}.

We can solve I_{MEMT} and I_{MEIMT} using the $O(|D|^\epsilon)$-approximation algorithm of Liang [14] and the $O(|D|^\epsilon)$-approximation algorithm of [5] for DST. In this way we obtain the following.

Theorem 5. *For any $\epsilon > 0$, there exists an $O(|D|^\epsilon)$-approximation algorithm for MESSCS.*

6   Logarithmic Approximations for MEBT and MESCS

In this section we show that MEBT and MESCS can be approximated within a logarithmic factor. These results are optimal within constant factors.

Liang in [14] presents an intuitive reduction for transforming an instance I_{MEBT} of MEBT into an instance I_{DST} of DST in such a way that a ρ-approximate solution for I_{DST} implies a ρ-approximate solution for I_{MEBT}.

We describe this reduction here. Assume that I_{MEBT} consists of a complete directed graph $G = (V, E)$ with an edge cost function $c : E \to R^+$ and a root node $r \in V$. Then, the instance I_{DST} consists of a directed graph $H = (U, A)$ with an edge cost function $c' : A \to R^+$, a root node $r' \in U$ and a set of terminals $D \subseteq U - \{r'\}$. For a node $v \in V$, we denote by n_v the number of different edge costs in the edges directed out of v, and, for $i = 1, ..., n_v$, we denote by $X_i(v)$ the i-th smallest edge cost among the edges directed out of v. For each node $v \in V$, the set of nodes U contains $n_v + 1$ nodes $Z_{v,0}, Z_{v,1}, ..., Z_{v,n_v}$. For each directed edge $(v, u) \in E$ and for $i = 1, ..., n_v$, the set of edges A contains a directed edge of zero cost from $Z_{v,i}$ to $Z_{u,0}$ if $X_i(v) \geq c(v, u)$. Also, for each node $v \in V$, and $i = 1, ..., n_v$, the set of edges A contains a directed edge from $Z_{v,0}$ to $Z_{v,i}$ of cost $c'(Z_{v,0}, Z_{v,i}) = X_i(v)$. The set of terminals is defined by $D = \{Z_{v,0}|v \in V - \{r\}\}$ and $r' = Z_{r,0}$.

We use an algorithm proposed by Zosin and Khuller [17] to approximate I_{DST} by repeatedly solving instances of the MINIMUM DENSITY DIRECTED TREE (MDDT) problem. An instance of MDDT is defined in the same way as instances of DST and the objective is to compute a tree directed out of the root node such that the ratio of the cost of the tree over the number of terminals it spans is minimized. The algorithm of [17] repeatedly solves instances I_{MDDT}^i of MDDT derived by the instance I_{DST}. The instance I_{MDDT}^1 is defined by the graph H with edge cost function c, the set of terminals $D_1 = D$ and the root node $r_1 = r'$. Initially, the algorithm sets $i = 1$. While $D_i \neq \emptyset$, it repeats the following. It finds a solution T to I_{MDDT}^i that consists of a tree $T_i = (V(T_i), E(T_i))$, defines the instance I_{MDDT}^{i+1} by contracting the nodes of T_i into the root node r_{i+1} and by setting $D_{i+1} = D_i \backslash V(T_i)$, and increments i by 1.

Zosin and Khuller [17] show that if the solution T_i is a ρ-approximate solution for I_{MDDT}^i in each iteration i, then the union of the trees T_i computed in all iterations is an $O(\rho \ln n)$-approximate solution for I_{DST}. They also show how to find a $(d + 1)$-approximate solution for I_{MDDT}^i if the graph obtained when removing the terminals from G has depth d. Observe that, given an instance I_{MEBT} of MEBT, the graph H obtained by applying the reduction of Liang is bipartite, since there is no edge between nodes of $D \cup \{r'\}$ and between nodes of $V - (D \cup \{r'\})$. Thus, the graph obtained by removing the terminals of D from H has depth 1. Following the reasoning of [17], we obtain the following result.

Theorem 6. *There exists an $O(\ln n)$-approximation algorithm for MEBT.*

Now, following a similar technique with the one we used in section 5 for approximating MESSCS, we can solve any instance of MESCS by solving an instance of MEBT and an instance of MEIBT and then merging the two solutions. In this way we obtain an $O(\ln n)$-approximation algorithm for MESCS.

7 Approximating Bidirected MESS and Related Problems

In the following, we present a logarithmic approximation algorithm for bidirected MESS. The algorithm uses a reduction from instances of bidirected MESS to instances of NWSF.

Consider an instance I_{bMESS} of bidirected MESS which consists of a complete directed graph $G = (V, E)$, an edge cost function $c : E \to R^+$ and a set of terminals $D \subseteq V$ partitioned into p disjoint subsets $D_1, D_2, ..., D_p$.

We construct an instance I_{NWSF} of NWSF consisting of an undirected graph $H = (U, A)$, a node weight function $c' : U \to R^+$ and a set of terminals $D' \subseteq U$ partitioned into p disjoint sets $D'_1, D'_2, ..., D'_p$. For a node $v \in V$, we denote by n_v the number of different edge costs in the edges directed out of v, and, for $i = 1, ..., n_v$, we denote by $X_i(v)$ the i–th smallest edge cost among the edges directed out of v. The set of nodes U consists of n disjoint sets of nodes called *supernodes*. Each supernode corresponds to a node of V. The supernode Z_v corresponding to node $v \in V$ has the following $n_v + 1$ nodes: a *hub node* $Z_{v,0}$ and n_v *bridge nodes* $Z_{v,1}, ..., Z_{v,n_v}$. For each pair of nodes $u, v \subset V$, the set of edges A contains an edge between the bridge nodes $Z_{v,i}$ and $Z_{u,j}$ such that $X_i(u) \geq c(u, v)$ and $X_j(v) \geq c(v, u)$. Also, for each node $v \in V$, A contains an edge between the hub node $Z_{v,0}$ and each bridge node $Z_{v,i}$, for $i = 1, ..., n_v$. The cost function c' is defined as $c'(Z_{v,0}) = 0$ for the hub nodes and as $c'(Z_{v,i}) = X_i(v)$ for $i = 1, ..., n_v$, for the bridge nodes. The set of terminals D' is defined as $D' = \cup_i D'_i$ where $D'_i = \{Z_{v,0} \in U | v \in D_i\}$.

Consider a subgraph $F = (S, A')$ of H which is a solution for I_{NWSF}. We construct a weight assignment w on the nodes of G by setting $w(v) = 0$ if S contains no node from supernode Z_v, and $w(v) = \max_{u \in (Z_v \cap S)} c'(u)$, otherwise. We can prove that if F is a ρ–approximate solution to I_{NWSF}, then w is a ρ–approximate solution to I_{bMESS}.

In [11], Guha and Khuller present a $1.61 \ln k$–approximation algorithm for NWSF, where k is the number of terminals in the graph. Using this algorithm for solving I_{NWSF}, we obtain a solution of I_{bMESS} which is within $1.61 \ln |D|$ of optimal. Moreover, when $p = 1$ (i.e., when I_{bMESS} is actually an instance of bidirected MESSCS), the instance I_{NWSF} is actually an instance of NWST which can be approximated within $1.35 \ln k$, where k is the number of terminals in the graph [11]. The next theorem summarizes the discussion of this section.

Theorem 7. *There exist an $1.61 \ln |D|$-, an $1.35 \ln |D|$-, and an $1.35 \ln n$-approximation algorithm for bidirected MESS, bidirected MESSCS, and bidirected MESCS.*

References

1. E. Althaus, G. Călinescu, I. Măndoiu, S. Prasad, N. Tchervenski, and A. Zelikovsky. Power Efficient Range Assignment in Ad-Hoc Wireless Networks. In *Proc. of the IEEE Wireless Communications and Networking Conference (WCNC '03)*, IEEE Computer Society Press, pp. 1889–1894, 2003.

2. P. Berman and M. Karpinski. On Some Tighter Inapproximability Results. In *Proc. of the 26th International Colloquium on Automata, Languages, and Programming (ICALP '99)*, LNCS 1644, Springer, pp. 200–209, 1999.
3. G. Călinescu, S. Kapoor, A. Olshevsky and A. Zelikovsky. Network Lifetime and Power Assignment in Ad-Hoc Wireless Networks. In *Proc. of the 11th Annual European Symposium on Algorithms (ESA '03)*, 2003, to appear.
4. I. Caragiannis, C. Kaklamanis and P. Kanellopoulos. New Results for Energy-Efficient Broadcasting in Wireless Networks. *In Proc. of the 13th Annual International Symposium on Algorithms and Computation (ISAAC '02)*, LNCS 2518, Springer, pp. 332–343, 2002.
5. M. Charikar, C. Chekuri, T.-Y. Cheung, Z. Dai, A. Goel, S. Guha and M. Li. Approximation Algorithms for Directed Steiner Problems. *Journal of Algorithms*, 33(1):73–91, 1999.
6. M. Chlebík and J. Chlebíková. Approximation Hardness of the Steiner Tree Problem on Graphs. In *Proc of the 8th Scandinavian Workshop on Algorithm Theory (SWAT '02)*, LNCS 2368, Springer, pp. 170–179, 2002.
7. A. E. F. Clementi, P. Crescenzi, P. Penna, G. Rossi, and P. Vocca. On the Complexity of Computing Minimum Energy Consumption Broadcast Subgraphs. In *Proc. of the 18th Annual Symposium on Theoretical Aspects of Computer Science (STACS '01)*, LNCS 2010, Springer, pp. 121–131, 2001.
8. A. E. F. Clementi, P. Penna, and R. Silvestri. Hardness Results for the Power Range Assignment Problem in Packet Radio Networks. In *Proc. of Randomization, Approximation, and Combinatorial Optimization (RANDOM/APPROX '99)*, LNCS 1671, Springer, pp. 197–208, 1999.
9. J. Edmonds. Optimum Branchings. *Journal of Research of the National Bureau of Standards*, 71B:233–240, 1967.
10. M. X. Goemans and D. P. Williamson. A General Approximation Technique for Constrained Forest Problems. *SIAM Journal on Computing*, 24:296–317, 1995.
11. S. Guha and S. Khuller. Improved Methods for Approximating Node Weighted Steiner Trees and Connected Dominating Sets. *Information and Computation*, 150(1):57–74, 1999.
12. E. Halperin and R. Krauthgamer. Polylogarithmic Inapproximability. In *Proc. of the 35th Annual ACM Symposium on Theory of Computing (STOC '03)*, pp. 585–594, 2003.
13. L. M. Kirousis, E. Kranakis, D. Krizanc, and A. Pelc. Power Consumption in Packet Radio Networks. *Theoretical Computer Science*, 243(1–2):289–305, 2000.
14. W. Liang. Constructing Minimum-Energy Broadcast Trees in Wireless Ad Hoc Networks. In *Proc. of 3rd ACM International Symposium on Mobile Ad Hoc Networking and Computing (MOBIHOC '02)*, pp. 112–122, 2002.
15. G. Robins and A. Zelikovsky. Improved Steiner Tree Approximations in Graphs. In *Proc. of the 11th Annual ACM-SIAM Symposium on Discrete Algorithms (SODA '00)*, pp. 770–779, 2000.
16. P.-J. Wan, G. Călinescu, X.-Y. Li, and O. Frieder. Minimum-Energy Broadcasting in Static Ad Hoc Wireless Networks. *Wireless Networks*, 8(6):607–617, 2002.
17. L. Zosin and S. Khuller. On Directed Steiner Trees. In *Proc. of the 13th Annual ACM/SIAM Symposium on Discrete Algorithms (SODA '02)*, pp. 59–63, 2002.

Wavelength Conversion in Shortest-Path All-Optical Networks*

Thomas Erlebach and Stamatis Stefanakos

Computer Engineering and Networks Laboratory (TIK)
ETH Zürich, CH-8092 Zürich, Switzerland
{erlebach|stefanak}@tik.ee.ethz.ch

Abstract. We consider all-optical networks with shortest-path routing that use wavelength-division multiplexing and employ wavelength conversion at specific nodes in order to maximize their capacity usage. We present efficient algorithms for deciding whether a placement of wavelength converters allows the network to run at maximum capacity, and for finding an optimal wavelength assignment when such a placement of converters is known. Our algorithms apply to both undirected and directed networks. Furthermore, we show that the problem of finding an optimal placement of converters is MAX SNP-hard in both undirected and directed networks. Finally, we give a linear-time algorithm for finding an optimal placement of converters in undirected triangle-free networks, and show that the problem remains $\mathcal{NP}$-hard in bidirected triangle-free planar networks.

1 Introduction

All-optical networks are emerging as a promising solution for meeting the rapidly increasing bandwidth demand. In these networks optical switches are employed to avoid the bottleneck of opto-electronic conversions, and wavelength-division multiplexing is used to partition the optical bandwidth into channels that carry data at rates manageable by electronic network elements. A connection between two nodes must be carried through a single channel that operates on a different wavelength than any other channel with which it shares a fiber. Wavelength converters are being used to fully exploit the available capacity of the network. A converter, when placed at some node of the network, has the ability of altering the operating wavelength of any channel that goes through that node.

Several interesting algorithmic problems arise in such networks. The wavelength assignment problem asks for an assignment of a minimum number of wavelengths to a given set of connections such that no conflicts occur. If wavelength converters are used, the wavelength of a connection can change whenever its route goes through a converter, otherwise each connection must be carried through the same wavelength all the way from sender to receiver. The use of wavelength converters can decrease the number of necessary wavelengths for routing a given number of connections. Ideally, one should be

---

* Research partially supported by the Swiss National Science Foundation under Contract No. 21-63563.00 (Project AAPCN) and the EU Thematic Network APPOL II (IST-2001-32007), with funding provided by the Swiss Federal Office for Education and Science (BBW).

T. Ibaraki, N. Katoh, and H. Ono (Eds.): ISAAC 2003, LNCS 2906, pp. 595–604, 2003.

able to route any set of connections that induce congestion L (i.e., at most L connections share a common fiber) with L wavelengths. This is the case when all the nodes of the network are equipped with converters. However, due to the high cost of such devices one is faced with a network design problem, namely to achieve the optimal capacity usage by placing a minimum number of converters on the network.

In this paper, we study issues related to the design of networks with wavelength converters and to the problem of wavelength assignment in networks that already have conversion capabilities. We restrict ourselves to the practical scenario where shortest-path routing is used in the network; if one does not take into account the specific routing algorithm that will be used, and allows arbitrary routings, the requirements of converters are overly pessimistic.

Preliminaries. We model the network by a graph $G = (V, E)$. We will consider both undirected and directed graph models since both are of interest for optical networks. If the fiber allows two-way communication then we model the network as an undirected graph, while if the fiber allows one-way communication we model the network as a directed graph. A special case of directed graphs that are of particular interest are *bidirected* graphs: In these graphs, for every directed edge the oppositely directed edge also exists. Connections in the network can be seen as paths on G, and wavelengths can be regarded as colors. If the network does not employ wavelength conversion then a *wavelength assignment* or *coloring* for a set $\mathcal{P}$ of paths is an assignment of a color to each path in $\mathcal{P}$. A *valid coloring* is one in which no two paths that use the same edge get assigned the same color. In the presence of wavelength converters, a coloring is an assignment of a color to every edge of each path. If the converters are placed in the vertices in $S \subseteq V$ we say that a coloring is *valid with respect to* S if it satisfies the additional constraint that the color assignments to two consecutive edges of a path differ only if their incident vertex is in S. We denote the *load* or congestion of the network that is induced by a set of paths $\mathcal{P}$ by $L(\mathcal{P}) = \max_{e \in E} L_e(\mathcal{P})$ where $L_e(\mathcal{P})$ is the number of paths in $\mathcal{P}$ that use edge e. We denote the degree of a vertex v by $\deg(v)$, and the maximum degree of G by $\Delta(G)$ (in a directed graph, the degree of a vertex is its degree in the underlying undirected graph). The *diameter* of a graph is the number of edges on the longest shortest path. For any graph-theoretic terms or notation not defined here we refer the reader to [2].

Most networks that do not employ wavelength conversion are destined to waste capacity. Consider an undirected graph with a vertex v of degree at least 3, and assume that only 2 wavelengths are available. The paths between 3 neighbors of v that go through v have load 2, but require 3 colors for a valid coloring if v is not equipped with a converter. Therefore, not all 3 paths can be simultaneously routed, and furthermore, two of the edges incident to v will only use one of the two available wavelengths resulting in a 50% waste of capacity. To avoid this, for a graph $G = (V, E)$ we need a placement of wavelength converters on a subset of its vertices $S \subseteq V$ such that any set of paths $\mathcal{P}$ on G can be colored with $L(\mathcal{P})$ colors with respect to S. A set of vertices S that has this property is a *sufficient set*. If the network uses shortest-path routing, we require that any set $\mathcal{P}$ of shortest paths can be colored with $L(\mathcal{P})$ colors with respect to S. We refer to this kind of sufficient sets for shortest-path routings as *SP-sufficient sets*. Note that an SP-sufficient set might be substantially smaller than a sufficient set. For example, a vertex of degree greater than or equal to 3 might not require a converter if its neighborhood does not contain an independent set of size three. We say that an induced $K_{1,3}$ is a *claw*; the vertex adjacent to the independent set of size three is its *center*.

Previous Work. Wilfong and Winkler [15] showed that the only bidirected graphs that admit the empty sufficient set are spiders, i.e., trees with at most one vertex of degree greater than two, and that rings (cycles) admit a sufficient set of size 1. They provided an efficient way of determining whether a set S is sufficient for a bidirected graph G: One modifies G by "exploding" each node $s \in S$ into degree-of-s-many copies, each of which is made adjacent to one of the old neighbors of s. S is sufficient for G if and only if every component of the graph obtained after this modification is a spider. Concerning the problem of finding a minimum sufficient set (MIN SUFFICIENT SET), they showed that it is $\mathcal{NP}$-hard even for planar bidirected graphs. Kleinberg and Kumar [11] showed how the "exploding" technique from [15] can be extended for arbitrary directed graphs. They also gave a 2-approximation algorithm for arbitrary directed graphs and a polynomial time approximation scheme for directed planar graphs. Their approach can be extended to give a linear time algorithm for MIN SUFFICIENT SET in directed graphs of bounded treewidth [3]. Sufficient sets in undirected graphs were studied in [3]. Therein, it was shown that lines (paths) are the only undirected graphs that do not need converters, and an optimal polynomial-time algorithm for finding a minimum sufficient set was given. Networks with shortest-path routings were considered in [4]. A complete characterization of the undirected graphs which admit the empty SP-sufficient set, as well as efficient optimal coloring algorithms for this class of graphs were given.

The characterization in [4] implies that the restriction to shortest-path routings can reduce the converter requirements of a given network significantly. Furthermore, the known algorithms for MIN SUFFICIENT SET from [3] and [11] indicate that by allowing arbitrary routings we end up with overly pessimistic placements of converters since they can result in picking half or even all vertices of degree greater than 2. Because of the high cost of wavelength converters, and since optical networks typically employ simple fixed-routing strategies, i.e., for every pair of nodes there is a prespecified path through which all traffic between these nodes will be carried (see [16]), it is important to consider the problem of converter placement under such practical scenarios and avoid the traditional worst-case analysis for arbitrary paths. In this paper, we mainly consider networks with shortest-path routing, but as we will see the algorithms we propose can be adapted to work for other fixed routings as well. From the theoretical point of view, it is interesting to observe how the restriction to shortest-path routings changes the nature of the problem thus requiring completely different methods for tackling it than the ones used for MIN SUFFICIENT SET in [3,11,15].

Our Results. In Sect. 2, we give a polynomial-time algorithm for deciding whether for a given graph $G = (V, E)$, a subset $S \subseteq V$ is SP-sufficient, and a polynomial-time algorithm for optimally coloring any set of shortest paths on G with respect to a valid SP-sufficient set. Both results make use of an auxiliary graph that depends only on the shortest paths of length 2 that exist on G and not on G itself, and hence apply to both directed and undirected graphs. This generalizes the result of [4], and also extends it to the directed case. We note that the proof given here, although for a much more general result, is substantially simpler and more elegant than the one given in [4]. In their most general form, our algorithms apply to networks with other routings as well (for example arbitrary routings). The only restriction is that the set of allowed paths on the network must be closed under taking subpaths of length 2 and 3. We are thus able to unify the results for identifying sufficient sets in undirected and directed graphs from [3,11,15].

In Sect. 3, we turn to the problem of finding a minimum SP-sufficient set (MIN SP-SUFFICIENT SET). We show that the problem is MAX SNP-hard for undirected and directed graphs by providing L-reductions from EDGE BIPARTIZATION and VERTEX BI-PARTIZATION respectively, i.e., the problems of deleting a minimum set of edges or vertices in order to make a given graph bipartite. We also show that MIN SP-SUFFICIENT SET can be solved optimally in linear time in undirected triangle-free graphs, but remains $\mathcal{NP}$-hard for bidirected triangle-free planar graphs.

We conclude in Sect. 4 with a discussion on possible directions for future research.

2   Identifying Valid Placements of Converters

Before we present the main result of this section we need to introduce some notation. For a graph $G = (V, E)$ let $\mathcal{P}_G$ be the set of all shortest paths on G. For a set $\mathcal{P}$ of paths on G and a set $S \subseteq V$, let $\mathcal{P}(S)$ be the set of paths obtained from $\mathcal{P}$ after cutting every path at the vertices of S that it contains. Clearly, a coloring of a set $\mathcal{P}$ of paths with respect to $S \subseteq V$ is a coloring of $\mathcal{P}(S)$. For a set $\mathcal{P}$ of shortest paths on G let $T(\mathcal{P})$ be the multigraph on E with one edge for every path of length 2 in $\mathcal{P}$, and one edge for every shortest path of length 2 that is contained in a path of length greater than or equal to 3 in $\mathcal{P}$.

The following theorem characterizes valid SP-sufficient sets.

Theorem 1. *Let $G = (V, E)$ be a (possibly directed) graph. $S \subseteq V$ is SP-sufficient for G if and only if the following two conditions hold:*

(i) $T(\mathcal{P}_G(S))$ is bipartite, and
(ii) not both edges corresponding to a path of length 3 in $\mathcal{P}_G(S)$ lie consecutively on the same cycle in $T(\mathcal{P}_G(S))$.

An example of the construction of $T(\mathcal{P}_G(S))$ is shown in Fig. 1. An efficient algorithm for deciding whether a given subset $S \subseteq V$ is SP-sufficient for a graph $G = (V, E)$ follows easily. Constructing $T(\mathcal{P}_G(S))$ and checking whether it is bipartite can clearly be done in polynomial-time. Verifying condition (ii) can be done by checking for each path of length 3 whether its corresponding edges lie in different biconnected components of $T(\mathcal{P}_G(S))$.

We proceed to prove Theorem 1. It is easy to see that the conditions of the statement are indeed necessary. First assume that $T(\mathcal{P}_G(S))$ is not bipartite. Then, $T(\mathcal{P}_G(S))$ contains an odd cycle whose edges correspond to a set of shortest paths on G with load 2 that require 3 colors for a valid coloring. To see that (ii) is necessary, assume that $T(\mathcal{P}_G(S))$ is bipartite and that there is a shortest path p of length 3 in $\mathcal{P}_G(S)$ whose edges lie on the same (even) cycle C in $T(\mathcal{P}_G(S))$. Let e be the middle edge of p. The paths corresponding to the edges of C that are not incident to e, along with p, form a set of paths of load 2 that require 3 colors for a valid coloring. Sufficiency follows from the following theorem.

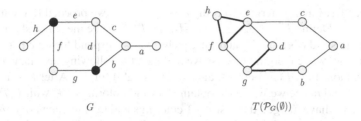

$$G \qquad\qquad T(\mathcal{P}_G(\emptyset))$$

Fig. 1. An example of a graph G along with $T(\mathcal{P}_G(S))$ for $S = \emptyset$. Notice that both conditions of Theorem 1 are violated: $T(\mathcal{P}_G(\emptyset))$ is not bipartite, and both edges of a shortest path of length 3 (e.g., the path using edges a, c, e) lie consecutively on the same cycle. If we let S consist of the two black vertices then $T(\mathcal{P}_G(S))$ is obtained from $T(\mathcal{P}_G(\emptyset))$ by removing the bold edges and S is indeed an SP-sufficient set.

Theorem 2. *Let $G = (V, E)$ be a (possibly directed) graph and $S \subseteq V$ be such that the conditions of Theorem 1 are satisfied. There exists a polynomial-time algorithm for coloring any set $\mathcal{P}$ of shortest paths on G with $L(\mathcal{P})$ colors with respect to S.*

Proof. Let $G = (V, E)$ be a (possibly directed) graph, and let $S \subseteq V$ be such that conditions $(i), (ii)$ hold. We show how to color a set $\mathcal{P}$ of shortest paths on G with $L(\mathcal{P})$ colors with respect to S. For ease of notation we let $\mathcal{P}$ be equal to $\mathcal{P}(S)$. Also, we remove all paths of length one from $\mathcal{P}$ since these can be colored greedily afterwards. The coloring of $\mathcal{P}$ will be obtained by edge-coloring $T(\mathcal{P})$. The edge-coloring of $T(\mathcal{P})$ will be done by computing many local edge-colorings and then merging them in order to obtain a coloring for $T(\mathcal{P})$ with $L(\mathcal{P})$ colors such that edges in $T(\mathcal{P})$ that correspond to the same path in $\mathcal{P}$ get the same color.

We refer to paths in $\mathcal{P}$ of length 2 as *short* paths and to paths in $\mathcal{P}$ of length greater than or equal to 3 as *long* paths. We refer to edges in $T(\mathcal{P})$ that correspond to short paths as *solid* edges and to edges that correspond to paths of length 2 that are contained in some long path as *partial* edges. We call two partial edges that correspond to the same path in $\mathcal{P}$ *relatives*. An edge-coloring of $T(\mathcal{P})$ is *valid* if all edges incident to the same vertex get different colors, except for relative partial edges which are required to have the same color. Let $B_1, \ldots, B_k$ be the blocks (biconnected components) of $T(\mathcal{P})$ ordered according to a depth-first search traversal of the block graph of $T(\mathcal{P})$, i.e., the bipartite graph on $C \cup \mathcal{B}$ and edges cB for $c \in C$, $B \in \mathcal{B}$ if $c \in B$, where C is the set of cut-vertices of $T(\mathcal{P})$ and $\mathcal{B}$ is the set of blocks of $T(\mathcal{P})$. Let H_i be the subgraph of $T(\mathcal{P})$ that contains all edges that are contained in block B_i and all solid edges incident to a cut-vertex of B_i that are not contained in B_i. Let $\mathcal{P}_i \subseteq \mathcal{P}$ be the set of paths that correspond to an edge in H_i. Since condition (i) is satisfied, H_i is bipartite and can be edge-colored with $\Delta(H_i)$ colors in polynomial time [12]. Since condition (ii) is satisfied, H_i may contain only one partial edge from each long path and hence the edge-coloring is valid for H_i. Furthermore, the degree of every vertex of H_i is equal to the load of the corresponding edge in G that is induced by $\mathcal{P}_i$.

Let A_i be a valid edge-coloring for H_i that uses $L(\mathcal{P}_i)$ colors. We will show how we can merge colorings $A_1, \ldots, A_k$ into a valid coloring for $\bigcup_{1 \leq i \leq k} H_i$ that uses $L(\mathcal{P})$ colors. We begin by merging A_1 with A_2. After the merging, A_2 is the new coloring we obtain. After having merged colorings $A_1, \ldots, A_{i-1}$ we proceed to the merging of A_i with A_{i-1}. Define $H_i' := H_1 \cup \ldots \cup H_i$. Let $\mathcal{P}_i' \subseteq \mathcal{P}$ be the set of short paths that correspond to solid edges in H_i' and long paths that correspond to some partial edge in H_i'. During the whole merging process we maintain the following invariants for A_i: (a) A_i uses no more than $L(\mathcal{P}_i')$ colors, and (b) A_i is valid for H_i'. After $k-1$ mergings, $H_k' = T(\mathcal{P})$ and hence we will have obtained a valid coloring of $\mathcal{P}$ with $L(\mathcal{P})$ colors.

Assume we have merged the first $i-1$ colorings and the invariants $(a), (b)$ hold for A_{i-1}. We show how to merge A_{i-1} with A_i such that $(a), (b)$ are maintained. Let x be the common cut-vertex of B_i with a block whose coloring has already been merged. All solid edges incident to x are colored with different colors in both A_{i-1} and A_i. All partial edges incident to x are colored in at most one of the two colorings. In order to merge the two colorings and maintain the invariants we have to ensure that (1) solid edges incident to x have the same color in both A_{i-1} and A_i, (2) partial edges incident to x that correspond to the same path in $\mathcal{P}$ get the same color in A_{i-1} and A_i, and (3) partial edges incident to x that correspond to different paths in $\mathcal{P}$ get different colors in A_{i-1} and A_i.

In order to ensure (1), we permute A_i so that every solid edge incident to x that is colored with different colors in A_{i-1} and A_i gets the color it has in A_{i-1}. In order to ensure (2), we permute A_i so that every partial edge incident to x that is colored in A_i and is relative to a partial edge f colored in A_{i-1}, gets the color that f has in A_{i-1}. We now show how we can ensure (3). Assume there are two partial edges e, colored in A_{i-1}, and f, colored in A_i, that have the same color and correspond to different paths. In H_i', these edges contribute 2 to the degree of x (and their corresponding paths contribute 2 to the load of edge x). However, in each of H_{i-1}', H_i only one of these edges is present. Therefore, there is at least one color among $1, \ldots, L(\mathcal{P}_i')$ that is not used by the edges incident to x in H_i'. Let c be such a color. We assign color c to f and permute coloring A_i so that all edges that were previously assigned color c get the color that f had and vice versa.

Since both colorings were valid, they remain valid after these modifications. Notice that since partial edges are only colored in one coloring it can happen that a partial and a solid edge have the same color in different colorings. However, since solid edges are colored in both colorings, after the permutation both edges will be colored with different colors. After permuting A_i, the two colorings become compatible and can be merged in the obvious way. After $k-1$ such mergings, A_k is a valid coloring for $\mathcal{P}$ that uses $L(\mathcal{P})$ colors. $\qquad\square$

Notice that we have actually proved a stronger result. The fact that we are dealing with shortest paths does not play a role in the proof of Theorem 2. What we need is that $\mathcal{P}_G(S)$ in the conditions of Theorem 1 is closed under taking subpaths of length 2 and 3: These are the paths needed for the necessity of the conditions in Theorem 1 since they provide the routings that witness the non-existence of a coloring with $L(\mathcal{P})$ colors. It is also interesting to observe that we can always find such a witness routing that has load 2 and requires 3 colors for a valid coloring, and that if no such routing exists then we can find a "good" coloring of any set of paths just by merging colorings of paths of length 2.

Therefore, our algorithms for identifying whether a placement of converters allows a network to run at maximum capacity and for finding an optimal wavelength assignment with respect to such a placement of converters can be applied to any network that uses a routing with this property. If, for example, we allow arbitrary routings, we choose $\mathcal{P}_G$ as the set of all simple paths (actually the set of all simple paths of length 2 and 3 would do), thus providing an algorithm to unify the results in [3,11,15] for identifying sufficient sets and finding an optimal wavelength assignment with respect to a valid sufficient set in both undirected and directed networks. Observe that in this case $T(\mathcal{P}_G)$ is simply the line graph of G if we disregard parallel edges.

We also give an alternative formulation of Theorems 1 and 2 that might find applications in other problems as well.

Corollary 1. *There exists a polynomial-time algorithm to decide whether for a given multiset $\mathcal{P}$ of paths, that is closed under taking subpaths of length 2 and 3, all subsets $\mathcal{P}' \subseteq \mathcal{P}$ can be colored with $L(\mathcal{P}')$ colors, and, if the answer is yes, a polynomial-time algorithm to find such a color assignment for any given $\mathcal{P}' \subseteq \mathcal{P}$.*

That is, given a set $\mathcal{P}$ of paths, with the property that for every path $p \in \mathcal{P}$ all its subpaths of length 2 and 3 are also in $\mathcal{P}$, we construct $T(\mathcal{P})$ and check whether the conditions of Theorem 1 are satisfied. If not then there exists some $\mathcal{P}' \subseteq \mathcal{P}$ that can not be colored with $L(\mathcal{P}')$ colors. If the conditions are satisfied, any $\mathcal{P}' \subseteq \mathcal{P}$ can be colored with $L(\mathcal{P}')$ colors using the algorithm described in the proof of Theorem 2.

3   Complexity and Hardness of Placing Converters

We now consider the problem of placing as few converters as possible on a given network in order to optimize its capacity usage. In order to show that this problem is hard even to approximate, we provide L-reductions (see [14]) from already known hard problems. All proofs in this section are omitted from this version; they can be found in [5].

3.1   The Undirected Case

Theorem 3. *There exists an L-reduction from* EDGE BIPARTIZATION *to the undirected* MIN SP-SUFFICIENT SET *problem.*

We give here the main idea of the proof. Given an instance $G = (V, E)$ of EDGE BIPARTIZATION, we construct an undirected instance $G' = (V', E')$ of MIN SP-SUFFICIENT SET. G' is constructed in a way so that odd cycles of G are mapped onto "bad" induced odd cycles in G', i.e., cycles on which the set of all shortest paths of length 2 corresponds to an odd cycle in $T(\mathcal{P}_G(\emptyset))$. Since single triangles do not allow the construction of such a set of shortest paths, but have to be hit by any solution of EDGE BIPARTIZATION, we replace each edge with a long path in order to "blow up" the length of the cycles of G. Moreover, in order to avoid claws in G' we use a special gadget for every vertex of G: each vertex v of degree $\deg(v)$ in G is replaced by a clique on $\deg(v)$ vertices. Finally, we eliminate all shortest paths of length 3 from G' so that no other configuration apart from odd induced cycles of length greater than 3 will need to be hit by a solution for MIN SP-SUFFICIENT SET.

Since EDGE BIPARTIZATION is known to be MAX SNP-hard [14], and since the constructed instance of MIN SP-SUFFICIENT SET has diameter 2, we obtain the following corollary.

Corollary 2. *The undirected* MIN SP-SUFFICIENT SET *problem is MAX SNP-hard even when restricted to graphs of diameter 2.*

We note that the presence of triangles in the proof of Theorem 3 is essential in order to avoid claws. In fact, if we restrict to triangle-free graphs then the problem can be solved optimally in polynomial time as the following theorem illustrates.

Theorem 4. *There exists a linear-time algorithm for finding a minimum SP-sufficient set in undirected triangle-free graphs.*

3.2 The Directed Case

The directed MIN SP-SUFFICIENT SET problem gives us more freedom in designing a reduction since claws do not necessarily require a converter. This is in accord to our expecting the directed case to be more difficult (recall that MIN SUFFICIENT SET is $\mathcal{NP}$-hard in directed graphs but polynomial in undirected). Indeed, in this case we are able to give an approximation preserving reduction from VERTEX BIPARTIZATION, which is likely to be harder than its edge-deletion counterpart (see [13]).

Theorem 5. *There exists an L-reduction from* VERTEX BIPARTIZATION *to the directed* MIN SP-SUFFICIENT SET *problem.*

The complete proof is omitted from this version. The idea behind the reduction is similar as in the reduction given in Theorem 3, but the construction is much simpler. Given an undirected instance of VERTEX BIPARTIZATION, we replace each edge with a bidirected path of length 3, and add a new vertex that is made adjacent to all other ones via two oppositely directed edges. The reason for doing so is because cycles of length 3 do not necessarily need to be hit by an SP-sufficient set, and therefore we need to "blow-up" the size of cycles in our construction. The new vertex is added in order to ensure that no shortest path of length 3 exists, and hence only odd cycles will need to be hit.

Since VERTEX BIPARTIZATION is known to be MAX SNP-hard [13], and our constructed instance of MIN SP-SUFFICIENT SET is bidirected and has diameter 2, Theorem 5 implies the following.

Corollary 3. *The directed* MIN SP-SUFFICIENT SET *problem is MAX SNP-hard even when restricted to bidirected graphs of diameter 2.*

We present here without a proof the following theorem which shows that MIN SP-SUFFICIENT SET is $\mathcal{NP}$-hard even on bidirected triangle-free planar graphs. The reduction is from PLANAR 3-SAT (see [7]) and is similar to the one given in [15] for showing the hardness of MIN SUFFICIENT SET. Our reduction shows that, in contrast to the undirected case, MIN SP-SUFFICIENT SET remains $\mathcal{NP}$-hard even on triangle-free bidirected graphs.

Theorem 6. *The problem of determining whether for a given directed graph G and an integer k there exists an SP-sufficient set for G of size k is $\mathcal{NP}$-complete even when restricted to bidirected triangle-free planar graphs.*

4 Discussion

We presented a polynomial time algorithm for deciding whether for a given graph $G = (V, E)$ a subset $S \subseteq V$ is SP-sufficient, and a polynomial-time algorithm for optimally coloring any set of shortest paths on G with respect to an SP-sufficient set. These algorithms can be extended to address sufficient sets for arbitrary routings in both undirected and directed graphs. We also showed that MIN SP-SUFFICIENT SET is at least as hard to approximate as EDGE BIPARTIZATION in undirected graphs, and at least as hard to approximate as VERTEX BIPARTIZATION in directed graphs (and hence is MAX SNP-hard in both cases). Finally, we gave a linear-time algorithm that solves MIN SP-SUFFICIENT SET optimally in undirected triangle-free graphs and showed that the problem remains $\mathcal{NP}$-hard even for bidirected triangle-free planar graphs.

A challenging remaining open problem is that of designing good approximation algorithms for MIN SP-SUFFICIENT SET. Although we are able to prove only MAX SNP-hardness of MIN SP-SUFFICIENT SET, our results indicate that it is unlikely or at least highly non-trivial to obtain a constant factor approximation algorithm. Indeed, that would imply a constant approximation for EDGE or VERTEX BIPARTIZATION whose approximability status has had a gap of $O(\log n)$ for the last 10 years (an $O(\log n)$ approximation for both problems follows from the multicut algorithm of Garg, Vazirani and Yannakakis [8,9], see also an older polylogarithmic approximation given in [10]). In [13], Lund and Yannakakis conjecture that *for every nontrivial, hereditary property π with an infinite number of minimal forbidden subgraphs the node-deletion problem cannot be approximated with constant ratio.* Although the conjecture has been disproved for π = "acyclic" (by a constant approximation for the undirected feedback vertex set problem [1]) and for properties derived from matroids definable on the edge set of any graph [6], it still remains likely that this is the case for VERTEX BIPARTIZATION.

Therefore, the design of a logarithmic approximation or of a reduction that places MIN SP-SUFFICIENT SET in some higher inapproximability class appears to be the most promising direction for future research. From the algorithmic point of view, MIN SP-SUFFICIENT SET seems similar to EDGE BIPARTIZATION since by placing converters in G we delete certain edges in $T(\mathcal{P}_G(\emptyset))$. We believe however that MIN SP-SUFFICIENT SET is actually harder than EDGE BIPARTIZATION: The reason is that a single converter on some vertex v does not delete one edge from $T(\mathcal{P}_G(\emptyset))$ but all the edges that correspond to the shortest paths of length 2 that go through v in G. If the edge-sets in $T(\mathcal{P}_G(\emptyset))$ that correspond to single vertices in G are connected subgraphs then a logarithmic approximation, at least for bipartizing $T(\mathcal{P}_G(\emptyset))$, can be obtained by a simple adaptation of the multicut-based algorithm given in [9]. Unfortunately, this is not the case in general, in both undirected and directed graphs. Furthermore, solving MIN SP-SUFFICIENT SET requires not only bipartizing $T(\mathcal{P}_G(\emptyset))$, but also hitting all "bad" paths of length 3. In all our reductions we explicitly forced the diameter of the constructed graph to be less than 3 in order to focus on the bipartization phase of the problem and ignored the second condition of Theorem 1. We believe that these additional degrees of complexity that MIN SP-SUFFICIENT SET has, could be exploited in order to place it in some higher inapproximability class. We note finally that an n/k-approximation for any constant k follows trivially from Theorem 1: We search for a valid SP-sufficient set in all subsets up to k vertices; if none is found we place a converter at every vertex.

References

1. V. Bafna, P. Berman, and T. Fujito. A 2-approximation algorithm for the undirected feedback vertex set problem. *SIAM Journal on Discrete Mathematics*, 12(3):289–297, 1999.
2. R. Diestel. *Graph Theory*. Springer-Verlag, 2000.
3. T. Erlebach and S. Stefanakos. Wavelength conversion in networks of bounded treewidth. TIK-Report 132, ETH Zurich, April 2002.
4. T. Erlebach and S. Stefanakos. On shortest-path all-optical networks without wavelength conversion requirements. In *Proceedings of the 20th International Symposium on Theoretical Aspects of Computer Science (STACS'03)*, LNCS 2607, pages 133–144, 2003.
5. T. Erlebach and S. Stefanakos. Wavelength conversion in shortest-path all-optical networks. TIK-Report 177, ETH Zurich, August 2003.
6. T. Fujito. A primal-dual approach to approximation of node-deletion problems for matroidal properties. In *Proccedings of the 24th International Colloquium on Automata, Languages, and Programming (ICALP'97)*, LNCS 1256, pages 749–759, 1997.
7. M. R. Garey and D. S. Johnson. *Computers and Intractability: A Guide to the Theory of NP-completeness*. Freeman, 1979.
8. N. Garg, V. V. Vazirani, and M. Yannakakis. Multiway cuts in directed and node weighted graphs. In *Proccedings of the 21st International Colloquium on Automata, Languages, and Programming (ICALP'94)*, LNCS 820, pages 487–498, 1994.
9. N. Garg, V. V. Vazirani, and M. Yannakakis. Approximate max-flow min-(multi)cut theorems and their applications. *SIAM J. Comput.*, 25(2):235–251, 1996.
10. P. N. Klein, S. Rao, A. Agrawal, and R. Ravi. An approximate max-flow min-cut relation for unidirected multicommodity flow, with applications. *Combinatorica*, 15(2):187–202, 1995.
11. J. Kleinberg and A. Kumar. Wavelength conversion in optical networks. *Journal of Algorithms*, 38(1):25–50, 2001.
12. D. König. Über Graphen und ihre Anwendung auf Determinantentheorie und Mengenlehre. *Math. Ann.*, 77:453–465, 1916.
13. C. Lund and M. Yannakakis. The approximation of maximum subgraph problems. In *Proccedings of the 20th International Colloquium on Automata, Languages, and Programming (ICALP'93)*, LNCS 700, pages 40–51, 1993.
14. C. Papadimitriou and M. Yannakakis. Optimization, approximation, and complexity classes. *Journal of Computer and System Sciences*, 43:425–440, 1991.
15. G. Wilfong and P. Winkler. Ring routing and wavelength translation. In *Proceedings of the 9th Annual ACM-SIAM Symposium on Discrete Algorithms (SODA'98)*, pages 333–341, 1998.
16. H. Zang, J. Jue, and B. Mukherjee. A review of routing and wavelength assignment approaches for wavelength-routed optical WDM networks. *Optical Networks Magazine*, 1(1):47–60, January 2000.

A Heuristic for the Stacker Crane Problem on Trees Which Is Almost Surely Exact

Amin Coja-Oghlan[1]*, Sven O. Krumke[2]**, and Till Nierhoff[1]***

[1] Humboldt-Universität zu Berlin, Institut für Informatik
Unter den Linden 6, 10099 Berlin, Germany
{coja, nierhoff}@informatik.hu-berlin.de
[2] Konrad-Zuse-Zentrum für Informationstechnik Berlin, Department Optimization
Takustr. 7, 14195 Berlin-Dahlem, Germany
krumke@zib.de

Abstract. Given an edge-weighted transportation network G and a list of transportation requests L, the *stacker crane problem* is to find a minimum-cost tour for a server along the edges of G that serves all requests. The server has capacity one, and starts and stops at the same vertex. In this paper, we consider the case that the transportation network G is a tree, and that the requests are chosen randomly according to a certain class of probability distributions. We show that a polynomial time algorithm by Frederickson and Guan [11], which guarantees a 4/3-approximation in the worst case, on almost all inputs finds a minimum-cost tour, along with a certificate of the optimality of its output.

1 Introduction

The Stacker Crane Problem (SCP) is among the classical tour problems that have been studied since the early days of computing [12,17,3]. An illustrating application is scheduling a delivery truck [17]: Given transportation jobs that consist of a pickup and a delivery location, the truck must traverse a certain distance to complete the jobs. This distance depends on the order the truck chooses to serve the jobs, and the goal is to find an order minimizing the distance. In the following precise definition of the SCP, the order of the jobs is not explicit. However, it can be extracted from any Euler tour of $(V, L \cup A)$:

Definition 1 (Stacker Crane Problem SCP). *An instance of the Stacker Crane Problem* SCP *consists of an undirected graph $G = (V, E)$ with edge-lengths $\ell \colon E \to \mathbb{R}_0^+$ and a list L of pairs of vertices, called requests. A solution is a multi-set A of pairs (u, v) where $\{u, v\} \in E$ such that the directed multi-graph $(V, L \cup A)$ is Eulerian after removal of isolated vertices. The cost of A is the total length of an Euler tour in $(V, L \cup A)$, where the length of an arc (u, v) equals the length of a shortest path between u and v in G with respect to ℓ. We denote the cost of an optimum solution by* $\mathrm{SCP}(G, L)$.

* Research supported by the German Science Foundation (DFG, grant FOR 413/1-1)
** Research supported by the German Science Foundation (DFG, grant Gr 883/10)
*** Research supported by the German Science Foundation (DFG, grant PR 296/6-3)

T. Ibaraki, N. Katoh, and H. Ono (Eds.): ISAAC 2003, LNCS 2906, pp. 605–614, 2003.
© Springer-Verlag Berlin Heidelberg 2003

As it is a generalization of the TSP, it is clear that a polynomial time algorithm for the SCP is not likely to exist. There is an important special case of the SCP, where the underlying graph G is a tree. This case arises e.g. in applications to warehouses that are operated by automated item transportation devices (*stacker cranes*) [9,7]. The worst case tractability of the SCP on trees has been investigated thoroughly in [11]. In that paper it is shown that the SCP on trees is hard, and that there is a 5/4-approximation algorithm for it.

However, approximation is only one way to cope with NP-hardness. Another approach is to look for *heuristics* that solve the problem exactly on "all but a few" instances. In fact, one of the reasons to study approximation algorithms is that an algorithm that has a good performance guarantee in the worst case is expected to perform even better on a large number of instances [21, p. IX].

Average case analysis. The approach to solve hard computational problems on all but a few instances is also known as *average case* or *probabilistic analysis*. This approach has been applied successfully, for instance, to the minimum bisection problem [6], to the k-center-problem [19], and to the knapsack problem [5]. Frequently the investigation is motivated by the observation that a certain problem, despite being hard in the worst case, has an algorithm that solves virtually every instance arising from applications.

A more advanced issue is certifiability. Though an algorithm may compute a good or even optimal solution on almost all inputs, this does not necessarily mean that the algorithm also finds an efficiently checkable *certificate* that the solution is indeed reasonable. For instance, it is well-known that a linear-time greedy heuristic approximates the chromatic number of almost all graphs within a factor of 2 (cf. [16]). More precisely, by constructing a coloring of the input graph, the greedy heuristic computes an upper bound that is at most twice the chromatic number almost surely. However, as the greedy procedure does not provide a lower bound on the chromatic number, it fails to certify that the output is a good approximate solution. In contrast, the algorithms given in [6, 19,5] for minimum bisection, knapsack, and k-center provide certificates.

A crucial question in the context of average case analysis concerns the random model being used. To be reasonable and to explain real-world observations, the frequently changing input parameters can be modeled randomly, whereas static parameters, i.e. input parameters that vary not at all or only slightly, should be modeled in worst case fashion, viz. deterministically. For instance, in the above application of the SCP to delivery trucks, the underlying graph models road distances which can be assumed to remain fixed values (for a longer time). Thus, it is not appropriate to model the network itself with a random experiment. On the other hand, the structure of the requests is different. In particular, if the truck has to be rescheduled often (say on a daily basis for the newly arrived demand), then it is reasonable to model the list of requests randomly.

Results. The aim of this paper is to investigate the average case of the SCP in the case where the underlying graph G is a tree. We consider the algorithm

"Use-minspan-tree" by Frederickson and Guan [11, Section 4.2]. We show that this algorithm is optimal on "all but a few" instances, thereby complementing the result of [11] that the algorithm is 4/3-approximative in the worst case. More precisely, our random model of the input assumes that the underlying tree is given deterministically (i.e. worst case-like), and that the list of requests is chosen at random.

Definition 2. *Let $T = (V, E)$ be a tree with arbitrary edge lengths $\ell : E \to \mathbb{R}_0^+$. Moreover, let $(p_v)_{v \in V}$ be an arbitrary probability distribution on the vertices of T, i.e. $p_v \in [0, 1]$ for all $v \in V$ and $\sum_{v \in V} p_v = 1$. Then a random list L of requests of length n is obtained by choosing each of the n requests at random as follows.*

- *The probability of the request $(u, v) \in V^2$ is $p_u \cdot p_v$.*
- *The requests are chosen independently of each other.*

Note that this model entails a wide variety of distributions, including the important special case of the uniform distribution (set $p_v = \#V^{-1}$ for all v). We say that an event A holds *with high probability* or *whp.* if the probability that A occurs tends to 1 as the number n of requests tends to infinity. Thus, the notion "with high probability" formalizes the naïve phrase "on all but a few instances". Note that the relation to the size of the underlying network is *not* relevant. The aim of this paper is to prove the following theorem.

Theorem 3. *The algorithm "Use-minspan-tree" by Frederickson and Guan (Algorithm 9 below) solves instances that are chosen according to the random model given in Definition 2 optimally with high probability. This is certifiable, i.e. whp. a random instance has a certain property which (i) can be checked efficiently and (ii) implies the optimality of the algorithm's solution.*

A detailed description of the algorithm is the content of Section 2. The proof of Theorem 3 starts with some preliminaries in Section 2, and its sketch will be completed in Section 4. In Section 3 we give an alternative description of the random model of Definition 2, which is essential for the proof of Theorem 3.

Related work. Approximation algorithms for the SCP on general graphs can achieve an approximation ratio of 129/128 at the best, if $P \neq NP$ [20]. The best approximation ratio known for the case of general underlying graphs is 9/5 and is achieved by an algorithm of Frederickson, Hecht, and Kim [12]. The complete algorithm by Frederickson and Guan [11] achieves an approximation ratio of 5/4 on trees. On general trees the problem is NP-hard [11,9], but on paths, the problem is in P [2].

Several extensions of the SCP are known as *dial-a-ride problems* or DARP. Of these, the SCP is the special case of a single server with capacity one. Charikar and Rhaghavachari [8] consider the case of the capacitated DARP, i.e., where the server can serve a limited number of jobs simultaneously. This problem is already NP-hard on paths if no preemption is allowed, but solvable in polynomial time in the preemptive case [14]. The paper [15] considers the DARP when additional precedence constraints between the requests are specified. Online variants of the DARP where requests become known to an online algorithm over time have been studied in [10,1,4]. The online scenario, as well as release time constraints are beyond the scope of this paper.

The average case of the SCP on trees has been examined for the special case of caterpillars as underlying graphs in [9]. (This special case is important for the application to the scheduling of elevators with starting and stopping times.) The elevator scheduling problem with capacities but without starting and stopping times has been solved by Karp (see the discussion by Knuth [18, Section 5.4.8]).

2   The Algorithm

In the following we give a rough sketch of the algorithm "Use-minspan-tree" of Frederickson and Guan that is quoted in Theorem 3. It has two main parts that we call *balancing* and *MST*. Balancing adds new requests to the given list of requests in such a way that the optimum cost does not increase. Therefore, an optimum solution with respect to the extended list of requests is also an optimum solution to the original instance.

Algorithm 4 (Balancing).
Input: A tree $T = (V, E)$ and a list of requests $L \subset (V \times V)^*$.
Output: A multiset of additional requests $B \subset (V \times V)^*$.
Each edge $e = \{u, v\} \in E$ corresponds to a cut $(C, V \setminus C)$, where $C \ni u$. Let e_+ be the number of requests starting in C and ending in $V \setminus C$, i.e. in $C \times V \setminus C$. Let e_- be the number of requests in $V \setminus C \times C$. Assume that $e_+ \geq e_-$. For e, B contains $e_+ - e_-$ requests (u, v). B can be computed in linear time [11].

Proposition 5 ([11]). *Let T be a tree, L be a given list of requests, and B be the output of the balancing procedure. Then* $\mathrm{SCP}(T, L) = \mathrm{SCP}(T, L \cup B)$ *and every component of* $(V, L \cup B)$ *is Eulerian.*   □

We call the isolated vertices of $(V, L \cup B)$ the *trivial components* and all other components the *nontrivial components*. Note that the remaining task is to find a minimum cost (multi-)set A of pairs so that $(V, L \cup B \cup A)$ has only one nontrivial, Eulerian component. It is easy to see that such a multiset consists of anti-parallel pairs along a subset of those edges of the tree that are not internal to one of the components of $(V, L \cup B)$.

Definition 6 (star metric). *Let $\mathcal{C}$ be the set of components of $(V, L \cup B)$ (including isolated vertices). For $C_1, C_2 \in \mathcal{C}$ let their distance, $d(C_1, C_2)$, be the length of a shortest path connecting a vertex of C_1 to a vertex of C_2. Then $(\mathcal{C}, d)$ is a metric and we denote the set of nontrivial components by $\mathcal{C}'$. Using somewhat unconventional notation, we call $(\mathcal{C}, d)$ a star metric, if there is a nontrivial component $C^* \in \mathcal{C}'$, such that $d(C_1, C_2) = d(C_1, C^*) + d(C^*, C_2)$ for all $C_1, C_2 \in \mathcal{C}'$.*

The optimum solution A has anti-parallel arcs along a minimum cost tree in $(\mathcal{C}, d)$ that spans all nontrivial components. The problem to find such a tree is known as the Steiner tree problem, and the second part of the algorithm is essentially the well-known *minimum spanning tree heuristic* for that problem.

Algorithm 7 (MST).
Input: The metric $(\mathcal{C}, d)$ with a subset $\mathcal{C}' \subset \mathcal{C}$ of nontrivial components
Output: A set A of anti-parallel arcs along the edges of a tree in $(\mathcal{C}, d)$ that spans $\mathcal{C}'$ and results from the minimum spanning tree heuristic for the Steiner tree problem.

Proposition 8. *The set A output by Algorithm 7 is at most twice as long as a minimum cost set. It is of minimum cost, if the metric $(\mathcal{C}, d)$ is a star metric.*   □

This proposition is a consequence of elementary results on approximation algorithms for the Steiner tree problem in graphs, see e.g. [13]. Then the algorithm of Frederickson and Guan that is quoted in Theorem 3 reads as follows:

Algorithm 9 (Use-minspan-tree [11, Section 4.2]).
Input: A tree T, a list L
Output: The length of an Euler tour in $(V, L \cup B \cup A)$, where
B is the output of Algorithm 4 on input T and L, and
A is the output of Algorithm 7 on the input induced by $(V, L \cup B)$.

As a direct consequence of Proposition 8, this algorithm has a performance ratio of 2 and is optimal (or exact) if the metric $(\mathcal{C}, d)$ is a star metric. This favorable situation can be detected easily in polynomial time. To complete the proof of Theorem 3, we show that it occurs with high probability. Our key to proving Theorem 3 is the following result:

Theorem 10. *Whp. $(\mathcal{C}, d)$ is a star metric.*

The following two sections are devoted to the proof of Theorem 10. First we show that it suffices to consider the case that T is a full binary tree.

3   From General Trees to Binary Trees

In this section we show that we can simplify the situation of a general tree to binary trees. Specifically, given a list of requests L, we shall modify the tree T via some elementary operations so that we obtain a full binary tree with exactly one request starting or ending at each leaf, and without requests incident with internal vertices. Recall that a binary tree is *full*, if each non-leaf node has exactly two children. Indeed, we just apply the following four operations repeatedly until T is of the desired form.

  a. Remove leaves that are not involved in requests.
  b. Introduce a new vertex for each end of a request and append it as a leaf to the original endpoint of the request. The new edge gets $\ell = 0$.

c. Contract vertices of degree 2. If v is a vertex of degree 2 and e, f are the incident edges, then let $\ell(e) \leftarrow \ell(e) + \ell(f)$, $\ell(f) \leftarrow 0$, and identify v with the other endpoint of f.

d. Split vertices of degree $d > 3$ into $d - 2$ vertices of degree 3 each. If v is a vertex of degree $d > 3$ and e, f are two of the incident edges, then let v' be a new vertex, connect it to v with an edge of $\ell = 0$ and replace v in e and f with v'. Proceed until v has degree 3.

Having adapted the tree T via a–d, we place a *root* r in the middle of an edge both of whose endpoints are connected to at least a third of the leaves without using that edge. We call the outcome (T_L, L) of the above procedure the *modified instance*. We emphasize that passing to the modified instance is part of the proof of Theorem 10; the *algorithm* sticks to the original instance.

Lemma 11. *If after applying the balancing operation the non-trivial components of the modified instance (T_L, L) form a star metric, then so do the non-trivial components of the original instance (T, L).*

Let L be a list of requests of length n. For each vertex v of T we let $d_v(L)$ denote the number of occurrences of v in L. Moreover, let $d(L) = (d_v(L))_{v \in V}$. Clearly, the outcome (T_L, L) of the modification procedure a–d depends only on the sequence $d(L)$. Conversely, for each sequence $d = (d_v)_{v \in V}$ such that $\sum_v d_v = 2n$ and $d_v \geq 0$ for all v, we can construct a rooted binary tree T_d via a–d, which has precisely $2n$ leaves $l_1, \ldots, l_{2n}$. Further, fixing d, a random list L of requests conditioned on $d(L) = d$ induces a random set of arcs $R(L) \subset \{l_1, \ldots, l_{2n}\}^2$ in which each leaf occurs precisely once. One could call $R(L)$ a *perfect directed matching* of the leaves $l_1, \ldots, l_{2n}$.

However, fixing d (and thus T_d), we can generate a random perfect directed matching R without referring to transportation requests in the original tree T at all: First, we choose a sequence $x = (x_1, \ldots, x_{2n}) \in \{1, -1\}^{2n}$ such that $\sum_{i=1}^{2n} x_i = 0$ uniformly at random among all $\binom{2n}{n}$ possible sequences. The sequence x specifies which leaves l_j will be heads ($x_j = 1$) and which leaves l_i will be tails ($x_i = -1$) of arcs in R. Then, we choose a permutation $\sigma : \{1, \ldots, n\} \to \{1, \ldots, n\}$ uniformly at random and independently of x. As there are precisely n leaves l_j with $x_j = 1$ and precisely n leaves l_i with $x_i = -1$, the permutation σ induces a bijection $\sigma_x : \{l_i \mid x_i = -1\} \to \{l_j \mid x_j = 1\}$ in the obvious manner. Finally, the perfect directed matching $R(x, \sigma)$ is just $\{(l_i, l_j) \mid \sigma_x(l_i) = l_j\}$. (Note the similarity between $R(x, \sigma)$ and the configuration model of random graphs with a prescribed degree sequence [16].) A tedious counting argument proves the following lemma.

Lemma 12. *Fix d. The probability distribution on perfect directed matchings induced by $R(x, \sigma)$ and by $R(L)$ conditioned on $d(L) = d$ coincide.*

By Lemma 11 and Lemma 12, in order to prove Theorem 10 it suffices to show the following.

Theorem 13. *Let T be any full binary tree with leaves $l_1, \ldots, l_{2n}$. Let $R = R(x, \sigma)$. Let B be the output of the balancing operation on input (T, R). Then* *whp. the non-trivial components of the graph $D(\boldsymbol{x}, \boldsymbol{\sigma}) = (V, R \cup B)$ form a star metric.*

4 Proof of Theorem 13

After introducing some notation and stating some simple lemmas in Section 4.1, we proceed in two steps to prove Theorem 13. First, in Section 4.2 we analyze the number and the size of the components of the graph $D(\boldsymbol{x}, \boldsymbol{\sigma})$. It turns out that though there may be a few "small" components, there is exactly one "large" component whp. Then, in Section 4.3, we show that in the tree T any path connecting two "small" components will pass through the "large" component whp., thereby establishing that the components form a star metric.

4.1 Preliminaries

We let $\log = \log_2$. Throughout, we let $T = (V, E)$ be a full binary tree with root r and leaves $l_1, \ldots, l_{2n}$. We have a canonical partial order $\preceq$ on V, by letting $v \preceq w$ iff w lies on the path from v to r. For each $v \in V \setminus \{r\}$, we let $\rho(v)$ denote the parent of v. We say that a set $S \subset V$ *majorizes* $S' \subset V$ ($S' \preceq S$) if for each $w \in S'$ there is $v \in S$ such that $w \preceq v$. For each $v \in V$, let $b(v)$ denote the number of leaves majorized by v.

As in Section 3, we let $\boldsymbol{x}$ denote a sequence $(\boldsymbol{x}_1, \ldots, \boldsymbol{x}_{2n}) \in \{1, -1\}^{2n}$ such that $\sum_i \boldsymbol{x}_i = 0$ chosen uniformly at random. For each $v \in V$, let $S_v = S_v(\boldsymbol{x}) = \sum_{i:l_i \preceq v} \boldsymbol{x}_i$. We say that v is *balanced* if $S_v = 0$. Set $E_B = E_B(\boldsymbol{x}) = \{\{v, \rho(v)\} \mid v \in V \setminus \{r\}$ is not balanced$\}$, and $B = B(\boldsymbol{x}) = (V, E_B)$. Moreover, let $\boldsymbol{\sigma}$ denote a permutation $\{1, \ldots, n\} \to \{1, \ldots, n\}$ chosen uniformly at random and independently of $\boldsymbol{x}$, and let $\boldsymbol{\sigma}_{\boldsymbol{x}}$ be as in Section 3. Let $E_A = \{\{l_i, l_j\} \mid \boldsymbol{\sigma}_{\boldsymbol{x}}(l_i) = l_j\}$, and $A = A(\boldsymbol{x}, \boldsymbol{\sigma}) = (V, E_A \cup E_B)$. Note that E_B consists of precisely those edges of T that will occur in the output of the balancing operation on input $R(\boldsymbol{x}, \boldsymbol{\sigma})$. Therefore, the non-trivial components of the simple graph A are in one-to-one correspondence with the non-trivial components of the directed multigraph $D(\boldsymbol{x}, \boldsymbol{\sigma})$ (cf. Theorem 13). First, we compute the probability that $S_v = 0$.

Lemma 14. *For all $v \neq r$ we have $\mathrm{P}\,(S_v = 0) = O(b(v)^{-1/2})$.*

Let $\mathcal{C} = \mathcal{C}(\boldsymbol{x})$ denote the set of all non-trivial components of B.

Lemma 15. *Each $C \in \mathcal{C}$ contains at least two leaves and has a unique maximal vertex (w.r.t. the partial order $\preceq$), which is balanced.*

We say that a set $\mathcal{C}_0 \subset \mathcal{C}$ is *separated* in A if there is no edge in E_A that joins a vertex in $\mathcal{C}_0$ with a vertex outside $\mathcal{C}_0$. Let $b(\mathcal{C}_0)$ denote the number of leaves $l_j \in \mathcal{C}_0$ with $\boldsymbol{x}_j = 1$.

Lemma 16. *The probability that $\mathcal{C}_0$ is separated is $\binom{n}{b(\mathcal{C}_0)}^{-1}$.*

It will be useful to partition the set V into sets

$$L_j = \{v \in V \mid 2^j \leq b(v) < 2^{j+1}\} \qquad (j = 0, \ldots, \log(2n)).$$

Then the sets L_j are pairwise disjoint, and their union is V. L_0 is the set of all leaves of T and it may be helpful to think of the sets L_j as "levels" in the tree T. As a convenience we set

$$L_{\leq k} = L_1 \cup \cdots \cup L_k \text{ and } L_{\geq k} = L_k \cup \cdots \cup L_{\log(2n)} \qquad (1 \leq k \leq \log(2n)).$$

Lemma 17. *Let $1 \leq j \leq \log(2n)$. The set L_j contains at most $n2^{1-j}$ maximal (minimal) vertices (w.r.t. the partial order $\preceq$).*

4.2   The Effect of the Balancing Operation

Let us call a non-trivial component of A *small* if it contains at most n leaves of T. Otherwise, we call the non-trivial component *large*.

Proposition 18. *Whp. the graph A enjoys the following properties.*

1. *There is a unique large component, which contains $(2 - o(1))n$ leaves.*
2. *There are $O(\log(n))$ small components.*
3. *All small components are cycles of length $O(\log(n))$.*

The proof of Proposition 18 proceeds in two steps. First, we estimate the number of non-trivial components of the graph $B = B(x) = (V, E_B)$, i.e. we only consider edges included via the balancing operation. Then, we study how the requests E_A connect the non-trivial components of B into larger blocks.

The number of non-trivial components of B. Since each non-trivial component of B contains a unique maximal vertex, we can define $X_j = X_j(x)$ to be the number of non-trivial components of B whose maximal vertex belongs to L_j. Then $\sum_{j \geq 1} X_j$ is the total number of non-trivial components of B.

How large can the probable value of $\sum_{j \geq 1} X_j$ be? If T is a complete binary tree, we see that the expectation of X_1 can be as large as $n/2$. Furthermore, in this case, X_1 is concentrated about its mean, whence $\sum_{j \geq 1} X_j \geq (1 - o(1))n/2$ whp. On the other extreme, in the case where T is a caterpillar, the analogy with a constrained random walk shows that $\sum_{j \geq 1} X_j = O(n^{1/2})$ whp.

As a consequence, we cannot expect that the number of non-trivial components is sublinear in n. Nonetheless, it can be shown, that the number is not more than a constant fraction of n:

Lemma 19. *The number of non-trivial components of B is at most $98n/99$ whp.*

Sketch of proof. First, using a first moment argument, one can show that only very few components reach the high levels of T. More precisely, $\sum_{j_0 < j} X_j(x) = o(n)$ whp., where $j_0 = \log(2n)/3$. Then a careful analysis shows, that the expectation of the number $\sum_{j=1}^{j_0} X_j$ of the other non-trivial components of B, is bounded by $49n/50$. Finally, a martingale argument proves that this number is concentrated about its mean. □

Glueing the non-trivial components of B together. In order to prove Proposition 18, we show that the edges E_A induced by the random permutation σ link most of the non-trivial components of B. We rely on the fact that x and σ are chosen independently.

Lemma 20. *The number of non-trivial components of A is $O(\log n)$ whp.*

Proof. By Lemma 19, we may assume that the number of non-trivial components of $B = B(x)$ is $\leq 98n/99$. Observe that the number of non-trivial components of A is at most twice the number of subsets $\mathcal{C}_0 \subset \mathcal{C}$ that are separated in A and that satisfy $b(\mathcal{C}_0) \leq n/2$. (Actually, the number of separated sets $\mathcal{C}_0$ is exponential in the number of non-trivial components of A, but we don't need that.) Therefore, invoking Lemma 16, we see that the expected number of non-trivial components of A is at most

$$2 \sum_{k=1}^{\#\mathcal{C}-1} \sum_{\mathcal{C}_0 \subset \mathcal{C},\ \#\mathcal{C}_0 = k,\ b(\mathcal{C}_0) \leq n/2} \binom{n}{b(\mathcal{C}_0)}^{-1} \leq 2 \sum_k \binom{98n/99}{k}\binom{n}{k}^{-1} = O(1).$$

Thus, by Markov's inequality, the number of non-trivial components of A is $O(\log n)$ with high probability. $\qquad\square$

Proof of Proposition 18 (sketch). The above lemma already gives the second assertion in Proposition 18. The proof of the third claim uses a similar estimate. Finally, as there are at most $O(\log n)$ small components all of which are cycles whp., at most $O(\log n)^2$ leaves lie in small components. Hence, there must be a large component that contains the remaining $(2 - o(1))n$ leaves. $\qquad\square$

4.3   Completing the Proof of Theorem 13

To prove that the non-trivial components of A form a star metric whp., we show that any path that joins two vertices in different small components of A passes through the large component.

Lemma 21. *There is no vertex $v \in L_{\leq 9\log(2n)/10}$ that majorizes vertices of two different small components of A whp.*

Lemma 22. *Let $j = 9\log(2n)/10$. The graph A enjoys the following property whp. If $u, w \in L_{\geq j}$ are such that $u \preceq w$, and if u majorizes vertices that belong to a small component C_1, and w majorizes vertices that belong to a small component $C_2 \neq C_1$ of A, then there is a vertex s, $u \preceq s \preceq w$, such that $|S_s| > 2$.*

Proof of Theorem 13. We may assume that A enjoys the properties stated in Proposition 18, Lemma 21, and Lemma 22. Let $C_1 \neq C_2$ be small components of A, and let C be the unique large component. We are to show that any path P that connects $v \in C_1$ with $w \in C_2$ passes through C. If $v \in L_{\leq 9\log(2n)/10}$, then by Lemma 21 the path P will pass through $L_{\geq 9\log(2n)/10}$. Thus, let s be the first vertex in $L_{\geq 9\log(2n)/10}$ on P, let q be the last one, and let u be the maximal vertex on P. Then $v \preceq s$, $w \preceq q$, and $q, s \preceq u$. Therefore, by Lemma 22, there exists a vertex t on P such that $|S_t| > 2$. Since by Proposition 18 all small components are cycles, we conclude that $t \in C$. $\qquad\square$

References

1. Ascheuer, N., Krumke, S.O., Rambau, J.: Online dial-a-ride problems: Minimizing the completion time. In: Proceedings of the 17th STACS. Volume 1770 of Lecture Notes in Computer Science., Springer (2000) 639–650
2. Atallah, M.J., Kosaraju, S.R.: Efficient solutions to some transportation problems with applications to minimizing robot arm travel. SIAM Journal on Computing **17** (1988) 849–869
3. Ausiello, G., Crescenzi, P., Gambosi, G., Kann, V., Marchetti-Spaccamela, A., Protasi, M.: Complexity and Approximation. Springer (1999)
4. Ausiello, G., Feuerstein, E., Leonardi, S., Stougie, L., Talamo, M.: Algorithms for the on-line traveling salesman. Algorithmica **29** (2001) 560–581
5. Beier, R., Vöcking, B.: Random knapsack in expected polynomial time. In: Proc 35th SToC. (2003)
6. Boppana, R.B.: Eigenvalues and graph bisection: An average case analysis. In: Proceedings of 28th FoCS. (1987)
7. Burkard, R., Fruhwirth, B., Rote, G.: Vehicle routing in an automated warehouse: Analysis and optimization. Annals of Operations Research **57** (1995) 29–44
8. Charikar, M., Raghavachari, B.: The finite capacity dial-A-ride problem. In: Proceedings of the 39th FoCS. (1998)
9. Coja-Oglan, A., Krumke, S.O., Nierhoff, T.: Scheduling a server on a caterpillar network - a probabilistic analysis. In: Proceedings of the 6th Workshop on Models and Algorithms for Planning and Scheduling Problems (2003)
10. Feuerstein, E., Stougie, L.: On-line single server dial-a-ride problems. Theoretical Computer Science. To appear.
11. Frederickson, G.N., Guan, D.J.: Nonpreemptive ensemble motion planning on a tree. Journal of Algorithms **15** (1993) 29–60
12. Frederickson, G.N., Hecht, M.S., Kim, C.E.: Approximation algorithms for some routing problems. SIAM Journal on Computing **7** (1978) 178–193
13. Gröpl, C., Hougardy, S., Nierhoff, T., Prömel, H.J.: Approximation algorithms for the Steiner tree problem in graphs. In Cheng, X., Du, D.Z., eds.: Steiner Trees in Industry. Kluwer Academic Publishers (2001) 235–279
14. Guan, D.J.: Routing a vehicle of capacity greater than one. Discrete Applied Mathematics **81** (1998) 41–57
15. Hauptmeier, D., Krumke, S.O., Rambau, J., Wirth, H.C.: Euler is standing in line. Discrete Applied Mathematics **113** (2001) 87–107
16. Janson, S., Luczak, T., Ruciński, A.: Random Graphs. John Wiley & Sons (2000)
17. Johnson, D.S., Papadimitriou, C.H.: Performance guarantees for heuristics. In Lawler, E.L., Lenstra, J.K., Kan, A.H.G.R., Shmoys, D.B., eds.: The Travelling Salesman Problem. Wiley (1985) 145–180
18. Knuth, D.E.: The art of computer programming. Volume 3: Sorting and searching. Addison-Wesley, Reading MA (1968)
19. Kreuter, B., Nierhoff, T.: Greedily approximating the r-independent set and k-center problems on random instances. In Rolim, J.D.P., ed.: Randomization and Approximation Techniques in Computer Science. Volume 1269 of LNCS., Springer (1997) 43–53
20. Papadimitriou, C.H., Vempala, S.: On the approximability of the traveling salesman problem. In: Proc. of the 32nd SToC. (2000)
21. Vazirani, V.: Approximation Algorithms. Springer (2001)

Flexible Train Rostering

Stephan Eidenbenz[1], Aris Pagourtzis[2]*, and Peter Widmayer[3]

[1] Basic and Applied Simulation Science (CCS-5),
Los Alamos National Laboratory, `eidenben@lanl.gov`[†]
[2] School of Electrical and Computer Engineering,
National Technical University of Athens, `pagour@cs.ntua.gr`
[3] Institute of Theoretical Computer Science, ETH Zürich, `widmayer@inf.ethz.ch`

Abstract. Determining cost-effective vehicle scheduling is an important optimization issue in mass transportation networks. An interesting question in this context is whether allowing certain flexibility in the departure times of scheduled routes may reduce the number of vehicles needed. We formulate this question as the FLEXIBLE TRAIN ROSTERING[1] problem. We consider two cases that are of practical interest:

- *Unlimited flexibility*: only the durations of routes are given and we are free to determine the most appropriate departure time for each route.
- *Limited flexibility*: initial departure times are given, together with a delay threshold ε; we are asked to determine the most appropriate delay $\leq \varepsilon$ for each route.

We also consider variants where we are allowed to use *empty rides*, (i.e., routes without passengers). We present a variety of results for these problems: polynomial-time algorithms that optimally solve some of them, $\mathcal{NP}$- and $\mathcal{APX}$-hardness proofs for others, as well as approximation algorithms for most of the hard problems.

1 Introduction

The rapid expansion of mass transportation all around the globe and the related financial aspects of running a mass transportation network have dramatically increased the need for systematic study of optimization problems that arise in this context. A central family of questions in this context are known under the general name *vehicle scheduling*. When restricted to railways, other common names are *train assignment* and *rolling stock rostering*. In the basic train rostering problems, periodic routes are given that need to be assigned to trains in such a way that the number of trains needed to implement all routes in each

---

[*] Work partially done while visiting the Institute of Theoretical Computer Science, ETH Zürich, supported by the Human Potential Programme of EU, contract no HPRN-CT-1999-00104 (AMORE).
[†] Los Alamos National Laboratory Publication no. LA-UR:03-3758
[1] Our motivation comes from railway optimization problems. However, our results apply to other mass transportation media as well.

T. Ibaraki, N. Katoh, and H. Ono (Eds.): ISAAC 2003, LNCS 2906, pp. 615–624, 2003.
© Springer-Verlag Berlin Heidelberg 2003

period is minimal. The standard approach, followed by most researchers so far, is to consider routes with specified departure and arrival times. Saving trains is a crucial financial objective for train operators as, for example, owning a locomotive incurs an annual cost in the 6-digit dollar range even if the locomotive is not used at all; thus, train companies are willing to slightly change their fixed time schedules (i.e., set of routes) by allowing certain flexibility in the given departure and arrival times if this promises to reduce the total number of trains needed. We embark on a study, where we model this flexibility into the train rostering problem. Allowing flexibility may prove to be a powerful tool, because it reveals how much a train company can cut costs by trying to modify an existing schedule. We study two situations: (a) *unlimited flexibility*: departure and arrival times are not specified at all and we are called to determine these times as well, always aiming at minimizing the number of necessary trains; we call this problem FLEXIBLE TRAIN ROSTERING (FTR), and (b) *limited flexibility*: departure-arrival times are given together with a parameter $\varepsilon > 0$, and we are allowed to shift the departure time (consequently the arrival time too) of a route by at most ε; we call this problem ε-FLEXIBLE TRAIN ROSTERING (ε-FTR). Notice that FTR is the special case of ε-FTR where ε is equal to the period length; however, FTR is worth studying separately as we will show that the problems differ in their complexity. In some situations, it can be useful to move a train from one station to another without passengers. We call this an *empty ride*. We consider variations of the above problems where empty rides are allowed. We denote the corresponding problems by FTRER and ε-FTRER (where the suffix 'ER' stands for 'EMPTY RIDES').

Our results. We first consider the unlimited flexibility problems: we start by giving a polynomial-time algorithm for FTR; next we study FTRER and show that the complexity of the problem depends on the number of connected components in the *route graph* — the graph that represents stations as nodes and routes as edges. In particular, if the route graph is connected the problem can be solved in polynomial time with an algorithm that uses Eulerian completion, whereas if it is not connected then the problem is $\mathcal{APX}$-hard (by reduction from the TRAVELING SALESPERSON PROBLEM) and cannot be approximated within $2 - \epsilon$, for any $\epsilon > 0$; we also show that the algorithm for the one-component case yields an approximation algorithm for the many-component case, that achieves approximate solutions of cost at most $OPT + m - 1$, where OPT is the cost of an optimal solution and m is the number of components in the route graph.

For the problems with limited flexibility, we show that ε-FTR and ε-FTRER are both $\mathcal{NP}$-hard by a reduction from 3-PARTITION, even if we restrict ε to be $\Theta(t)$, where t is the duration of the shortest route. If we lift this restriction we can prove $\mathcal{APX}$-hardness for ε-FTR by a reduction from PARTITION, which also shows that no polynomial-time algorithm can achieve an approximation ratio strictly less than 3/2, unless $\mathcal{P} = \mathcal{NP}$. For ε-FTRER we strengthen this result by proposing a reduction from TRAVELING SALESPERSON PROBLEM WITH TRIANGLE INEQUALITY: we prove that no approximation algorithm can guarantee a ratio strictly better than 2 — and this holds even if we allow ε to be as large as a fraction of $\frac{2}{9}$ of the period.[2] Finally, we propose an approximation algorithm for the limited flexibility problem with empty rides ε-FTRER that achieves a ratio of $O(\log n)$ by first discretizing the problem and then modeling it as a SET COVER problem. The algorithm only works if the set of potential empty rides is sufficiently large, the distances between stations obey the triangle inequality, and ε is at most a constant times the duration of the shortest route; however, these assumptions are fairly reasonable in practice. This algorithm applies to FTRER as well and can serve as an alternative to the $(OPT + m - 1)$-algorithm mentioned above.

Related work. To the best of our knowledge the concept of flexibility has not been introduced before in the context of train rostering problems. For the non-flexible case there are several results in the literature: the simplest minimization version, also known as MINIMUM FLEET SIZE [2], or ROLLING STOCK ROSTERING [6], can be solved efficiently; Dantzig and Fulkerson [5] give the first known algorithm and Erlebach et al. [6] present a much faster one. Erlebach et al. [6] also study several variations, like allowing empty rides, or requiring that the trains pass through a *maintenance station*, and show the corresponding problems $\mathcal{APX}$-complete. Several other variations have been studied in the literature, with various different objectives and constraints which render the problem quite hard; a number of heuristic approaches have been proposed based on branch and bound, branch and cut, linear programming and relaxation, and simulated annealing [12,11,3,4,7,10,1].

2   Model Description – Problem Definitions

We are given a set of train routes. A train route r is described by a triple $(s_d(r), s_a(r), d(r))$ representing the departure station, the arrival station and the duration of the trip, respectively.

A tuple of routes $R = \langle r_1, \ldots, r_k \rangle$ is called *sequence of routes* if $s_a(r_i) = s_d(r_{i+1}), 1 \le i \le k - 1$; a sequence of routes is called *cycle of routes* if, in addition, $s_a(r_k) = s_d(r_1)$. The duration of a sequence of routes R is denoted by $d(R)$; it holds $d(R) = \sum_{r \in R} d(r)$. A collection of cycles of routes such that each cycle consists of routes in R and each route in R appears exactly once in some cycle is called *schedule of R*.

The cost of a cycle C is defined to be the number of trains needed to execute each route of the cycle in each period. If a cycle is k periods long, k trains will be necessary to execute the cycle in every period; therefore, the cost of a cycle C is equal to $\lceil d(C)/T \rceil$ for period length T; The cost of a schedule is the sum of the costs of the cycles that constitute the schedule.

We define the following problem:

FLEXIBLE TRAIN ROSTERING (FTR)
Input: A set of train routes $R = \{r_1, \ldots, r_n\}$ and a time period T.

---

[2] Note that several proofs are only sketched or completely omitted due to space limitations. A full version of the paper is available from the authors upon request.

Output: A schedule of R, $\mathcal{S} = \{C_1, \ldots, C_m\}$.
Goal: Minimization of the cost of $\mathcal{S}$.

There is an interesting generalization of FTR: sometimes there exists no schedule for the given set of routes (e.g. for routes $A \to B, B \to C$); in such cases we should add some route without passengers, called *empty ride*, in order to be able to find at least one schedule (for example, for routes $A \to B, B \to C$ we may add the empty ride $C \to A$). More formally, given two sets of routes R and Q we define a *schedule of R with empty rides from Q* to be a collection of cycles in which each route of R appears exactly once, and some routes of Q appear one or more times. The above give rise to the following definition:

FLEXIBLE TRAIN ROSTERING WITH EMPTY RIDES (FTRER)
Input: A set of train routes $R = \{r_1, \ldots, r_n\}$, a set of empty rides $Q = \{q_1, \ldots, q_m\}$ and a time period T.
Output: A schedule of R with empty rides from Q, $\mathcal{S} = \{C_1, \ldots, C_m\}$.
Goal: Minimization of the cost of $\mathcal{S}$.

Next we consider the case where each train route r is associated with a departure time $t_d(r)$ (consequently with an arrival time as well, $t_a(r) = (t_d(r) + d(r)) \bmod T$). The waiting times $w(r_i) = (t_d(r_{i+1}) - t_a(r_i)) \bmod T$ are now added to the duration of each cycle of the schedule, thus affecting the cost of the schedule. Here we consider a setting where the departure time can be slightly changed by allowing delays of at most ε time units. We thus define the following two problems:

ε-FLEXIBLE TRAIN ROSTERING (ε-FTR)
Input: A set of train routes $R = \{r_1, \ldots, r_n\}$, where each route r_i is a quadruple $r_i = (s_d(r_i), s_a(r_i), d(r_i), t_d(r_i))$, $1 \le i \le n$, a time period T, and a time-shift threshold ε.
Output: A new set of routes $R' = \{r_1', \ldots, r_n'\}$, such that $\forall\, i \in \{1, \ldots, n\}$, $(t_d(r_i') - t_d(r_i)) \bmod T \le \varepsilon$, and schedule of R', $\mathcal{S} = \{C_1, \ldots, C_m\}$.
Goal: Minimization of the cost of $\mathcal{S}$.

ε-FLEXIBLE TRAIN ROSTERING WITH EMPTY RIDES (ε-FTRER) is defined similarly to ε-FTR, augmenting the input by a set of empty rides Q as in FTRER.

A useful observation is that allowing negative shifts would not make any difference. Indeed, allowing shifts in $[-\varepsilon, \varepsilon]$ is equivalent to initially subtracting ε from the departure times and then allowing shifts in $[0, 2\varepsilon]$.

3 Unlimited Flexibility

We first show that FTR can be solved in polynomial time. We represent stations as nodes of a graph; each route is depicted by a directed edge starting from the route's departure station and ending at the route's arrival station. Each edge has a weight equal to the duration of the corresponding route. We call this graph *route graph*.

Given an instance of FTR it is easy to see that there exists a solution if and only if the route graph is an Euler graph. Clearly, the least expensive solutions are those that cover all edges with a minimum number of cycles because the cost of any two edge-disjoint cycles C_1, C_2 is $\lceil d(C_1)/T \rceil + \lceil d(C_2)/T \rceil \geq \lceil (d(C_1) + d(C_2))/T \rceil$, which is the cost of the cycle consisting of C_1 and C_2 — if such cycle exists (i.e. if C_1 and C_2 share at least one node). So, the solution consists of one Euler cycle for each weakly connected component of the graph (if, of course, for each node v it holds $deg_{in}(v) = deg_{out}(v)$ — otherwise no solution exists). These cycles can be found in polynomial time.

The case where empty rides are allowed can be represented by a graph $G = (V, E_R)$ and a set E_Q of "optional" edges corresponding to Q which can be used one or more times, or not at all, in order to construct cycles that contain all edges in E_R exactly once. There are two cases, depending on the number of weakly connected (connected in the undirected sense) components of the route graph G.

FTRER *in one-component route graphs.* The route graph $G(V, E_R)$ is weakly connected. In this case we can show that the problem can be solved in polynomial time.

Theorem 1. FTRER *is in $\mathcal{P}$ for instances with connected route graph.*

Proof (sketch). The idea of the algorithm is to use Eulerian completion: in contrast to FTR, if the graph is not Eulerian we may attempt to make it such by using empty rides. One way to do this is to find a minimum weight (duration) Eulerian completion; this can be done efficiently by finding a minimum weight perfect matching on a bipartite graph. Nodes of this graph correspond to nodes of G whose indegree is different from their outdegree, and edges represent the existence of a path of empty rides between such nodes; the shortest path between two nodes determines the weight of the corresponding edge.   □

FTRER *in many-component route graphs.* If the route graph G consists of several components, the minimum schedule may consist of one or more cycles. It turns out that this possibility renders the problem $\mathcal{NP}$-hard. In fact, a stronger property holds:

Theorem 2. *There exists no polynomial-time $(2 - \epsilon)$-approximation algorithm for FTRER in instances with unconnected route graph for any $\epsilon > 0$, unless $\mathcal{P} = \mathcal{NP}$.*

Proof (sketch). By reduction from TSP: we map towns to mandatory routes of cost 1 and distances to empty rides of the same cost (in time units); we also set the period $T = n + K$, where K is the given bound for the cost of a tour. It is not hard to see that there is a schedule of cost 1 period for the constructed instance if and only if there is a tour of cost at most K for the initial TSP-instance. Therefore, since the cost of an FTRER-instance is expressed as an integer number of periods, it is $\mathcal{NP}$-complete to decide if the minimum schedule has cost 1 or at least 2; the $(2 - \epsilon)$-inapproximability follows.   □

Remark. We may require that the edge weight between a pair of stations is unique in the sense that all rides (scheduled and empty) connecting the two stations in either direction will take the same amount of time; this is an additional requirement that we call the *unique edge-weight* requirement.

We could let the above reduction be from TSP with triangle inequality. Then, our hardness result would still hold even under the unique edge-weight requirement and even if we required the durations to fulfill the triangle inequality.

We will now show that the algorithm for FTRER with connected route graph yields an approximation algorithm for FTRER with unconnected route graph that computes a solution of cost at most $OPT + m - 1$, where OPT is the optimal cost and m is the number of connected components of the route graph.

Indeed, using the algorithm for one-component route graph, we actually obtain a schedule S the cycles of which contain all routes in R and several empty rides, and the sum of the durations of the cycles (say D) is minimal among all schedules. Cycles that contain nodes from the same connected component can be joined without loss of minimality; hence we end up with at most m cycles. Applying simple properties of ceiling addition it turns out that the total cost is at most $\lceil \frac{D}{T} \rceil + m - 1 \leq OPT + m - 1$. Therefore:

Theorem 3. *There exists an approximation algorithm that produces a solution of cost at most $OPT + m - 1$ for* FTRER *in instances with m-component route graph.*

4   Limited Flexibility

Theorem 4. *(i) ε-*FLEXIBLE TRAIN ROSTERING *(ε-FTR) is $\mathcal{NP}$-hard, even if*
- *the route graph satisfies the unique edge-weight requirement*
- *the route graph satisfies the triangle inequality*
- *it holds $4t \leq \varepsilon \leq \frac{16t}{3}$ where t is the duration of the shortest route.*

(ii) ε-FTR is $\mathcal{APX}$-hard and no polynomial time algorithm can guarantee an approximation ratio strictly less than $\frac{3}{2}$, even if the route graph satisfies the unique edge-weight requirement and the triangle inequality.

Proof (sketch). The basic idea for proving (i) is: Given an instance of 3-PARTITION with $3n$ numbers and bound B, we construct pairs of routes, starting at the same station at time 0, such that the durations of the pairs are the given numbers. Setting appropriate shift-threshold ε and some special long routes, we can guarantee that a solution (schedule) with n trains exists if and only if each train executes exactly 3 pairs of routes from time 0 to time B without waiting for a single time unit; this corresponds to a solution for the 3-PARTITION instance. For (ii) we use a similar reduction from PARTITION, in which the routes of each set of the partition are executed by a single train; an optimum solution will take 2 trains, if the PARTITION instance has a solution, otherwise at least 3 trains will be necessary. However, the conditions are slightly less restrictive as we cannot limit ε to be a constant times the duration of the shortest route.   □

Note that the above results for ε-FTR also hold for ε-FTRER; however, we next show an even stronger result for ε-FTRER. We will prove that ε-FLEXIBLE TRAIN ROSTERING WITH EMPTY RIDES (ε-FTRER) is $\mathcal{NP}$-hard.

Unlike the result for FTRER, this result holds even when the route graph is connected. Similar to the case without empty rides (ε-FTR), we may add the *unique edge-weight* and other requirements. We distinguish between the route graph (consisting only of edges corresponding to scheduled routes) and the *route graph with empty rides* that contains edges for empty rides as well.

Theorem 5. ε-FLEXIBLE TRAIN ROSTERING WITH EMPTY RIDES *(ε-FTRER) is $\mathcal{NP}$-hard to approximate with an approximation ratio of strictly less than 2, even if*

- *we require the route graph to be connected*
- *the route graph with empty rides satisfies the unique edge-weight requirement*
- *the route graph with empty rides satisfies the triangle inequality*
- *ε is restricted to be a fraction $f \leq \frac{2}{9}$ of period T (i.e., $\varepsilon = fT$)*

The proof is based on a reduction from $TSP_{\Delta\neq}$. Details are omitted.

We propose an approximation algorithm for ε-FTRER, where we require the route graph to satisfy the unique edge-weight requirement and the triangle inequality. For ease of presentation, we assume the set of allowed empty rides to be unrestricted (i.e., an empty ride is possible from any station to any other station at any given time). Let t denote the duration of the shortest ride (scheduled or empty) in the instance; we require $\varepsilon < kt$ for some constant k.

Our approximation algorithm will achieve an approximation ratio of $O(\log n)$, where n is the number of routes in the ε-FTRER instance. In order to show this result, we first show that the optimum solution of a discrete version of ε-FTRER, where we allow routes to start only at $8n$ evenly distributed points in their ε time interval (rather than at an infinite number of possible starting points), is at most four times as large as a solution for the same unrestricted ε-FTRER instance. We then show how to compute a sequence for a single train (i.e. one period long) for a discrete ε-FTRER instance that executes a maximum number of routes among all possible sequences. Finally, we iteratively use this algorithm to compute maximum cycles and remove the already executed routes from the instance. We show that this corresponds to the greedy heuristic for the MINIMUM SET COVER problem, which achieves a logarithmic approximation ratio.

Lemma 1. *Let SOL be a solution for a given ε-FTRER instance I with the unique edge-weight requirement, the triangle inequality, and unrestricted empty rides; let $|SOL|$ denote the number of trains needed in the solution. If we consider instance I to be an instance of discrete ε-FTRER, where the potential departure points for a given route with scheduled departure at time t_d are restricted to be at times $t_d + i \cdot \frac{\varepsilon}{8n}$ for $i \in \{0, \dots, 8n\}$, then there exists a solution SOL' for the discrete ε-FTRER instance I with*

$$|SOL'| \leq 4|SOL|.$$

Proof (sketch). Any non-discrete train cycle can be transformed into two train cycles with only discrete departure points, where each cycle needs at most one train more to connect to its beginning across the period jump, thus leading to the factor 4 in the worst case.

The first discrete train cycle covers all routes with delay at most $\frac{\varepsilon}{2}$, the second discrete train cycle covers all routes with delay greater than $\frac{\varepsilon}{2}$. This is possible since the necessary rounding costs at most 2 discrete time units (of $\frac{\varepsilon}{8n}$ time each) for each route and there are at most $2n$ routes (scheduled and empty), hence the total cost is bounded by $\frac{\varepsilon}{2}$. This argument works well for the first train; for the second, we first subtract $\frac{\varepsilon}{2}$ from all the corresponding routes and then apply the above argument again, showing that the delay of each route will never exceed ε.

□

Proposition 1. *Given a discrete ε-FTRER instance I with $\varepsilon < kt$ for some constant $k > 0$, where t is the duration of the shortest route, a maximum (w.r.t. number of routes) sequence that can be executed by a single train within one time period can be found in polynomial time.*

Proof. Let T_I denote the set of all possible departure points for all routes on all stations as induced by the discreteness of I; let $T_I = \{t_1 \dots, t_{8n^2}\}$ be ordered in order of descending time (ties can be broken arbitrarily); i.e., t_1 is the departure point which is closest to the end of the period, t_{8n^2} is closest to the beginning of the period. Let $S = \{s_1, \dots, s_{|S|}\}$ denote the set of stations.

For each t_i, we want to compute the maximum number of routes $R_i^{\max}$ that a train starting at t_i can execute until the end of the period; moreover, we also need to compute for each t_i the last k routes (i.e. those closest to t_i) of every maximum sequence. Beginning with t_1 and working our way through t_{8n^2}, we execute the following for each t_i: Let departure point t_i be from station s_j (there exists a unique route r_i, of which t_i is a possible departure point). We then virtually send a train from point t_i to each station $s_{j'}$ for any j' (including station s_j) with an empty ride. Once arrived at station $s_{j'}$, we find the next possible departure point $t_{i'}$ from station $s_{j'}$ (if there are several departure points at the same time at $s_{j'}$, we will look at all of them). Since $i > i'$, we must have already computed the sequence with a maximum number $R_{i'}^{\max}$ of routes leaving at $t_{i'}$; moreover, we also have a list of the last k routes or empty rides traveled on each sequence that is maximum for point $t_{i'}$. If station $s_{j'}$, is the arrival station of the route r_i uniquely associated with departure point t_i, we scan through these lists: if we find a maximum path in these lists that does not contain route r_i as one of the k last routes traveled, we can add route r_i, which increases the number of routes for the train sequence starting at t_i by one. We let the maximum number of routes $R_i^{\max}$ be the maximum of all $R_{i'}^{\max}$ that we looked at at the stations (plus one if we can add route r_i). We also copy the lists from all visited stations $s_{j''}$ that maximized $R_i^{\max}$, add the ride from station s_j to $s_{j''}$ to the lists and remove the last ride of each list.

Once we have processed departure point t_{8n^2}, we scan through all $R_i^{\max}$ and choose a maximum sequence. This procedure needs polynomial time: we process $O(n^2)$ departure points; at each such point, we look at $O(n^2)$ possible succeeding departure points; the path lists that we copy have at most k entries each such that there can be at most $O(n^k)$ different lists. The procedure is correct since the maximum sequence of routes from a departure point consists of one route together with a sequence that is locally maximum from its departure point; we avoid counting routes twice by looking at the last k routes or empty rides traveled by any maximum sequence, which is the last route that could potentially be a duplicate as the ε interval ends after at most k routes.   □

Theorem 6. *ε-FTRER can be approximated within $O(\log n)$.*

Proof. We prove the claim by establishing a relationship between MINIMUM SET COVER and discrete ε-FTRER that will allow us to iteratively apply the procedure from above to compute an $O(\log n)$-approximate solution for an ε-FTRER instance. A simple greedy heuristic, which iteratively adds to the solution a subset that contains a maximum number of elements not yet covered by other subsets already in the solution, yields a $\log n$-approximate solution for any MINIMUM SET COVER instance (see [8] for details). We can transform a discrete ε-FTRER instance (with unrestricted empty rides) into a MINIMUM SET COVER instance by letting the routes be elements and by letting all valid sequences of routes that a single train can execute in a single period be sets. Such a set may contain a route that crosses a period either at the beginning or at the end. A solution for this MINIMUM SET COVER instance assigns each route to at least one train; if a route is executed by two or more trains, we transform this route into an empty ride for all but one train. This solution may not directly translate into a feasible solution for the ε-FTRER instance as trains need to be connected across period jumps, which may not be feasible, for example if the route going across the period jump was started ε time units after scheduled departure time and the first route starting in the next period was scheduled at its scheduled departure time. However, the optimum MINIMUM SET COVER solution provides a lower bound for the optimum ε-FTRER solution. Moreover, we can transform a MINIMUM SET COVER solution into a feasible ε-FTRER solution by assigning at most three trains to each set in the set cover solution: one train to execute the period jump route, a second train to execute the remaining routes in the set, and a third train to connect the period jump route to the first route (and thus form a cycle across at most three periods). This assumes that no route takes longer than a whole period and it also assumes that any station can be reached from any station within a single period by a single empty ride.

Thus, if we find a $O(\log n)$-approximate solution for the MINIMUM SET COVER instance, we can transform this into a $O(\log n)$-approximate solution for the ε-FTRER instance. However, in the transformation from ε-FTRER to the MINIMUM SET COVER, the number of sets (i.e., the number of valid train cycles) may be exponential. Fortunately, the greedy heuristic for MINIMUM SET COVER only needs to have the set containing a maximum number of routes not yet covered by sets already in the solution. Our procedure for computing a maximum number of routes does exactly this; we iteratively apply this procedure to the discrete ε-FTRER instance, which gives us a $O(\log n)$-approximation that is also a $O(\log n)$-approximation for the ε-FTRER instance.   □

Remark. This approach does not work for ε-FTR, as we require empty rides at several points in the algorithm. Moreover, the approximation algorithm has a running time that is polynomial (essentially $O(n^k)$) but may be prohibitive for a practical setting. On the other hand the algorithm works for FTRER providing an alternative to the m-approximation algorithm discussed in Section 3.

A useful by-product of the constant-ratio approximation algorithm for maximizing one train cycles, is that it can be turned to a constant-ratio approximation algorithm for maximizing the number of routes that can be executed by a fixed number of trains. This is achieved by simple iteration of the algorithm as can be shown by a standard analysis, similar to the one used for the MAXIMUM SET COVERAGE problem [9].

References

1. L. Anderegg, S. Eidenbenz, M. Gantenbein, C. Stamm, D.S. Taylor, B. Weber, and P. Widmayer. Train Routing Algorithms: Concepts, Design Choices, and Practical Considerations. Proceedings of The Fifth Workshop on Algorithm Engineering and Experiments (ALENEX'03), pp. 106–118, 2003.
2. A. Bertossi, P. Carraresi, and G. Gallo. On some matching problems arising in vehicle scheduling models. *Networks*, 17:271–281, 1987.
3. P. Brucker, J.L. Hurink, and T. Rolfes. Routing of railway carriages: a case study. *Memorandum No. 1498, University of Twente, Fac. of Mathematical Sciences*, 1999.
4. G. Carpaneto, M. Dell'Amico, M. Fischetti, and P. Toth. A branch and bound algorithm for the multiple depot vehicle scheduling problem. *Networks*, 19:531–548, 1989.
5. G. Dantzig and D. Fulkerson. Minimizing the number of tankers to meet a fixed schedule. *Nav. Res. Logistics Q.*, 1:217–222, 1954.
6. T. Erlebach, M. Gantenbein, D. Hürlimann, G. Neyer, A. Pagourtzis, P. Penna, K. Schlude, K. Steinhöfel, D.S. Taylor, and P. Widmayer. On the Complexity of Train Assignment Problems. Proc. ISAAC 2001, LNCS 2223, pp. 390–402, Springer-Verlag 2001.
7. R. Freling, J.M.P. Paixão, and A.P.M. Wagelmans. Models and algorithms for vehicle scheduling. Report 9562/A, Econometric Institute, Erasmus University Rotterdam, 1999.
8. D.S. Hochbaum. Approximating Covering and Packing Problems: Set Cover, Vertex Cover, Independent Set, and Related Problems. In Dorit Hochbaum (ed.) *Approximation Algorithms for NP-Hard Problems*, PWS Publishing Company, pp. 94–143, 1996.
9. D.S. Hochbaum. Approximation Algorithms for the Set Covering and Vertex Cover Problems; *SIAM J. Comput.* 11(3):555–556 (1982).
10. A. Löbel. Optimal vehicle scheduling in public transit. *PhD thesis, TU Berlin*, 1998.
11. C. Ribeiro and F. Soumis. A column generation approach to the multiple-depot vehicle scheduling problem. *Operations Research*, 42(1):41–52, 1991.
12. A. Schrijver. Minimum circulation in railway stock. *CWI Quarterly*, 6(3):205–217, 1993.

Counting Complexity Classes over the Reals I: The Additive Case

Peter Bürgisser[1]* and Felipe Cucker[2]**

[1] Faculty of Computer Science, Electrical Engineering, and Mathematics
Paderborn University, D-33095 Paderborn, Germany
pbuerg@upb.de
[2] Department of Mathematics, City University of Hong Kong
83 Tat Chee Avenue, Kowloon, Hong Kong, China
macucker@math.cityu.edu.hk

Abstract. We define a counting class $\#P_{add}$ in the Blum-Shub-Smale-setting of additive computations over the reals. Structural properties of this class are studied, including a characterization in terms of the classical counting class $\#P$ introduced by Valiant. We also establish transfer theorems for both directions between the real additive and the discrete setting. Then we characterize in terms of completeness results the complexity of computing basic topological invariants of semi-linear sets given by additive circuits. It turns out that the computation of the Euler characteristic is $FP_{add}^{\#P_{add}}$-complete, while for fixed k, the computation of the kth Betti number is $FPAR_{add}$-complete. Thus the latter is more difficult under standard complexity theoretic assumptions. We use all the above to prove some analogous completeness results in the classical setting.

1 Introduction

In 1989 Blum, Shub and Smale [4] introduced a theory of computation over the real numbers with the goal of providing numerical computations (as performed e.g., in numerical analysis or computational geometry) the kind of foundations classical complexity theory has provided to discrete computation. This theory describes the difficulty of solving numerical problems and provides a taxonomy of complexity classes capturing different degrees of such a difficulty.

Since its introduction, this BSS-theory has focused mainly on decisional problems. Functional problems attracted attention at the level of analysis of particular algorithms, but structural properties of classes of such problems were hardly studied. So far, the only systematic approach to study the complexity of certain functional problems within a framework of computations over the reals is Valiant's theory of VNP-completeness [6,30,33]. However, the relationship of this theory to the more general BSS-setting is, as of today, poorly understood. A detailed account of the research on complexity of real functions within the classical framework can be found in [14].

* Research supported by DFG grant BU 1371
** Research supported by SRG grant 7001290

T. Ibaraki, N. Katoh, and H. Ono (Eds.): ISAAC 2003, LNCS 2906, pp. 625–634, 2003.
© Springer-Verlag Berlin Heidelberg 2003

A first step in the study of functional properties could focus on complexity classes related to counting problems, i.e., functional problems, whose associated functions count the number of solutions of some decisional problem.

In classical complexity theory, counting classes were introduced by Valiant in his seminal papers [31,32]. Valiant defined #P as the class of functions which count the number of accepting paths of nondeterministic polynomial time machines and proved that the computation of the permanent is #P-complete. This exhibited an unexpected difficulty for the computation of a function, whose definition is only slightly different from that of the determinant, a problem known to be in $\mathsf{FNC}^2 \subseteq \mathsf{FP}$, and thus considered "easy." This difficulty was highlighted by a result of Toda [28] proving that $\mathsf{PH} \subseteq \mathsf{P}^{\#\mathsf{P}}$, i.e., that #P has at least the power of the polynomial hierarchy.

In the continuous setting, i.e., over the reals, the only attempt to define counting classes was made by Meer [17]. He defined a real version of the class #P and studied some of its logical properties in terms of metafinite model theory. Meer did not investigate complete problems for this class.

In this paper we will define and study counting classes in the model of additive BSS-machines [15]. The computation nodes of these machines perform additions and subtractions, but no multiplications and divisions. The corresponding complexity classes are denoted by $\mathrm{P_{add}}$ and $\mathrm{NP_{add}}$[1].

The results in this paper can be seen as a first step towards a better understanding of the power of counting in the unrestricted BSS-model over the reals (allowing also for multiplications and divisions). A sequel to this paper studying this setting is under preparation [8].

Our results can be grouped in two kinds: structural relationships between complexity classes and completeness results. The latter (for whose proofs the former are used) satisfy a driving motivation for this paper: to capture the complexity of computing basic topological invariants of geometric objects in terms of complexity classes and completeness results.

Due to space limitations, proofs had to be omitted in this extended abstract.

2   Counting Classes and Completeness

Recall that #P is the class of functions $f: \{0,1\}^\infty \to \mathbb{N}$ for which there exists a polynomial time Turing machine M and a polynomial p with the property that for all $n \in \mathbb{N}$ and all $x \in \{0,1\}^n$, $f(x)$ counts the number of strings $y \in \{0,1\}^{p(n)}$ such that M accepts (x,y).

By replacing Turing machines with additive BSS-machines in the above definition, we get a class of functions $f : \mathbb{R}^\infty \to \mathbb{N} \cup \{\infty\}$, which we denote by $\#\mathrm{P_{add}}$. Thus $f(x)$ counts the number of vectors $y \in \mathbb{R}^{p(n)}$ such that M accepts (x,y). By counting only the number of "digital" vectors $y \in \{0,1\}^{p(n)}$, we obtain a smaller class of functions $f : \mathbb{R}^\infty \to \mathbb{N}$ denoted by $\mathrm{D}\#\mathrm{P_{add}}$.

---

[1] To distinguish between classical and additive complexity complexity classes, we use the subscript "add" to indicate the latter. Also, to further emphasize this distinction, we write the former in sans serif

Completeness will be studied either with respect to parsimonious reductions or with respect to Turing reductions (see [24] for definitions).

We can prove that there is a wealth of natural complete problems for the class $D\#P_{add}$ with respect to Turing reductions. This follows from the following general principle:

Proposition 1. *Let* $f \colon \mathbb{R}^\infty \to \mathbb{N}$ *belong to* $D\#P_{add}$ *and assume that the restriction of* f *to* $\mathbb{Z}^\infty$ *is* #P*-complete with respect to Turing reductions. Then* f *is* $\#P_{add}$*-complete and thus* $D\#P_{add}$*-complete with respect to Turing reductions.*

The proof is based on the results of Sect. 3 and extends previous results due to Fournier and Koiran [11].

Proposition 1 yields plenty of Turing complete problems in $D\#P_{add}$. We just mention two particularly interesting ones. Assume that we are given a graph G with real weights on the edges and some $w \in \mathbb{R}$. We define the weight of a subgraph as the sum of the weights of its edges.

1. (*Counting Traveling Salesman*) Let $\#TSP_{\mathbb{R}}$ be the problem to count the number of Hamilton cycles of weight at most w in the graph G.
2. (*Counting Weighted Perfect Matchings*) Let $\#PM_{\mathbb{R}}$ be the problem to count the number of perfect matchings of weight at most w in the graph G (here we assume that G is bipartite).

Valiant [31,32] proved the #P-completeness of the problem to count the number of Hamilton cycles of a given graph, and of the problem to count the number of perfect matchings of a given bipartite graph. Together with Proposition 1 this immediately implies the following.

Corollary 1. *The problems* $\#TSP_{\mathbb{R}}$ *and* $\#PM_{\mathbb{R}}$ *are* $D\#P_{add}$*-complete with respect to Turing reductions.*

3   The Power of Discrete Oracles and Boolean Parts

One can assign to any complexity class $\mathcal{C}$ of decision problems a corresponding counting complexity class $\# \cdot \mathcal{C}$ as follows [29]. To a set $A \in \{0,1\}^\infty$ and a polynomial p we assign the function $\#_A^p \colon \{0,1\}^\infty \to \mathbb{N}$, which associates to $x \in \{0,1\}^n$ the number $\#_A^p(x) := |\{y \in \{0,1\}^{p(n)} \mid (x,y) \in A\}|$. To a complexity class $\mathcal{C}$ of decision problems we assign $\# \cdot \mathcal{C} := \{\#_A^p \mid A \in \mathcal{C} \text{ and } p \text{ a polynomial}\}$. Similarly, one assigns $\# \cdot \mathcal{C}$ and $D\# \cdot \mathcal{C}$ to a complexity class $\mathcal{C}$ over $\mathbb{R}$. Note that $\# \cdot P = \#P$, $\# \cdot P_{add} = \#P_{add}$, and $D\# \cdot P_{add} = D\#P_{add}$.

The following result says that for several classical[2] complexity classes $\mathcal{C}$ consisting of decisional problems, the corresponding additive complexity class $\mathcal{C}_{add}$ is contained in, or even equal to, $P_{add}^{\mathcal{C}}$. That is, all problems in $\mathcal{C}_{add}$ can be solved by an additive machine working in polynomial time and having access to

---

[2] All along this paper we use the words *discrete, classical* or *Boolean* to emphasize we are refering to the theory of complexity over a finite alphabet as exposed in, e.g., [1, 24].

a (discrete) oracle in $\mathcal{C}$. Likewise, if $\mathcal{C}$ is a classical complexity class of functions $\{0,1\}^\infty \to \{0,1\}^\infty$, we obtain that $\mathcal{C}_{\text{add}} \subseteq \text{FP}^{\mathcal{C}}_{\text{add}}$.

Theorem 1. *The following statements hold* $(k \geq 0)$:

1. $\Sigma^k_{\text{add}} \subseteq P^{\Sigma^k}_{\text{add}}$, $\Pi^k_{\text{add}} \subseteq P^{\Pi^k}_{\text{add}}$, $\text{PH}_{\text{add}} = P^{\text{PH}}_{\text{add}}$.
2. $\text{D}\# \cdot \Sigma^k_{\text{add}} \subseteq \text{FP}^{\#\cdot\Sigma^k}_{\text{add}}$, $\text{D}\# \cdot \Pi^k_{\text{add}} \subseteq \text{FP}^{\#\cdot\Pi^k}_{\text{add}}$, $\text{D}\# \cdot \text{PH}_{\text{add}} \subseteq \text{FP}^{\#\cdot\text{PH}}_{\text{add}}$.
3. $\text{PAR}_{\text{add}} = P^{\text{PSPACE}}_{\text{add}}$.
4. $\text{FPAR}_{\text{add}} = \text{FP}^{\text{PAR}_{\text{add}}}_{\text{add}} = \text{FP}^{\text{PSPACE}}_{\text{add}}$.

This result was already stated and proved for the class NP_{add} in Fournier and Koiran [11]. Moreover, in [11, Remark 2] it was mentioned that the result for NP_{add} can be extended to the classes of the polynomial hierarchy and to PAR_{add}. So what is new in Theorem 1 is the extension to the counting classes, and to the functional class FPAR_{add}. As in [10,11], the proof relies on Meyer auf der Heide's (nonuniform) construction of small depth linear decision trees for point location in arrangements of hyperplanes [19,20], see also Meiser [18].

An interesting application of the above insights is that Toda's famous result [28], as well as its extension by Toda and Watanabe [29], carries over to the real additive setting.

Corollary 2. *We have* $\text{D}\# \cdot \text{PH}_{\text{add}} \subseteq \text{FP}^{\#\text{P}}_{\text{add}}$.

We use this to prove that the counting class $\#\text{P}_{\text{add}}$ is closely related to its digital variant $\text{D}\#\text{P}_{\text{add}}$, in the sense that a $\#\text{P}_{\text{add}}$-oracle does not give more power to an additive polynomial time Turing machine than a $\text{D}\#\text{P}_{\text{add}}$-oracle

Theorem 2. *We have* $\text{FP}^{\#\text{P}_{\text{add}}}_{\text{add}} = \text{FP}^{\text{D}\#\text{P}_{\text{add}}}_{\text{add}} = \text{FP}^{\#\text{P}}_{\text{add}}$. *In particular, a counting problem in* $\text{D}\#\text{P}_{\text{add}}$ *is* $\text{D}\#\text{P}_{\text{add}}$-*complete with respect to Turing reductions iff it is* $\#\text{P}_{\text{add}}$-*complete with respect to Turing reductions.*

The Boolean part of $\text{D}\#\text{P}_{\text{add}}$ consists of the restrictions of all functions in $\text{D}\#\text{P}_{\text{add}}$ to the set of binary inputs $\{0,1\}^\infty$. The proof of the following proposition is similar to that of [3, Theorem 2, Chap. 22].

Proposition 2. *We have* $\text{BP}(\text{D}\#\text{P}_{\text{add}}) = \#\text{P}/\text{poly}$.

An application of our structural insights is the following transfer result.

Corollary 3. *We have the following transfer results:*

1. $\#\text{P}_{\text{add}} \subseteq \text{FP}_{\text{add}}$ *iff* $\text{D}\#\text{P}_{\text{add}} \subseteq \text{FP}_{\text{add}}$ *iff* $\#\text{P} \subseteq \text{FP}/\text{poly}$.
2. $\text{FPAR}_{\text{add}} \subseteq \text{FP}^{\#\text{P}_{\text{add}}}_{\text{add}}$ *iff* $\text{PSPACE} \subseteq \text{P}^{\#\text{P}}/\text{poly}$.
3. *Similar equivalences hold for additive machines without constants and uniform classical complexity classes, respectively.*

4   Complexity to Compute Topological Invariants

Algebraic topology studies topological spaces X by assigning to X various algebraic objects in a functorial way. In particular, homeomorphic (or even homotopy equivalent) spaces lead to isomorphic algebraic objects. For a general reference in algebraic topology we refer to [13,23].

Typical examples of such algebraic objects studied are the (singular) homology vector spaces $H_k(X; \mathbb{Q})$ over $\mathbb{Q}$, defined for integers $k \in \mathbb{N}$. The dimension $b_k(X)$ of $H_k(X; \mathbb{Q})$ is called the kth *Betti number* of the space X. The zeroth Betti number $b_0(X)$ counts the number of connected components of X, and for $k > 0$, $b_k(X)$ measures a more sophisticated "degree of connectivity". Intuitively speaking, for a three-dimensional space X, $b_1(X)$ counts the number of holes and $b_2(X)$ counts the number of cavities of X. It is known that $b_k(X) = 0$ for $k > n := \dim X$. The Betti numbers modulo a prime p are defined by replacing the coefficient field $\mathbb{Q}$ by the finite field $\mathbb{F}_p$.

The *Euler characteristic* of X defined by $\chi(X) := \sum_{k=0}^{n}(-1)^k b_k(X)$ is an important numerical invariant of X, enjoying several nice properties. For a finite set X, $\chi(X)$ is just the cardinality of X.

The notion of a cell complex [13,23] will be of importance for our algorithm to compute the Euler characteristic and the Betti numbers. For instance, if X is decomposed as a finite cell complex having c_k cells of dimension k, then $\chi(X) := \sum_{k=0}^{n}(-1)^k c_k(X)$.

We remark that the number of connected components, the Euler characteristic, and the Betti numbers lead to interesting lower complexity bounds for semi-algebraic decision problems, see [2,34,35] and the survey [7].

4.1   Semi-linear Sets and Additive Circuits

In this paper, we will confine our investigations to *semi-linear sets* $X \subseteq \mathbb{R}^n$, which are derived from closed halfspaces by taking a finite number of unions, intersections and complements. Moreover, we assume that the closed halfspaces are given by linear inequalities of "mixed type" $a_1 X_1 + \cdots + a_n X_n \le b$ with integer coefficients a_i and real right-hand side b.

We will represent semi-linear sets by a very compact data structure. An *additive circuit* $\mathcal{C}$ is a special arithmetic circuit [12], whose set of arithmetic operations is restricted to additions and subtractions. The circuit may have selection gates and use a finite set of real constants. The set of inputs accepted by an additive circuit is semi-linear, and any semi-linear set can be described this way. (See [3] for details.)

The basic problem $\mathrm{CSAT_{add}}$ to decide whether a given semi-linear set X is nonempty turns out to be $\mathrm{NP_{add}}$-complete [3]. By contrast, the feasibility question for a system of linear inequalities of the above mixed type is solvable in $\mathrm{P_{add}}$. This is just a rephrasing of a well-known result by Tardos [27].

Over the real numbers, space is not as meaningful a resource as it is in the discrete setting [21]. The role of space, however, is satisfactorily played by parallel time formalized by the notion of uniform arithmetic circuits [4,9]. We denote by PAR_{add} the class of decision problems for which there exists a P_{add}-uniform family $(\mathcal{C}_n)$ of additive circuits such that the depth of $\mathcal{C}_n$ grows at most polynomially in n. $FPAR_{add}$ denotes the class of functions f which can be computed with such resources and such that the size of $f(x)$ is polynomially bounded in the size of x. (The size of a vector is defined as its length.)

In the computational problems listed below, it is always assumed that the input is an additive circuit $\mathcal{C}$ and X is the semi-linear set accepted by $\mathcal{C}$. We also say that X is defined or given by $\mathcal{C}$.

4.2   Complexity to Compute the Dimension

Our first results deals with the computation of the dimension. For all $d \geq 0$, the problem $DIM_{add}(d)$ consists of deciding whether the set X given by an additive circuit $\mathcal{C}$ has dimension at least d. We define $\dim \emptyset := -1$ so that we can decide for nonemptyness using the dimension function.

Theorem 3. *For all $d \geq 0$, the problem $DIM_{add}(d)$ is NP_{add}-complete.*

4.3   Counting Connected Components

Consider the *reachability problem* $REACH_{add}$ to decide for a given additive circuit $\mathcal{C}$ and two points s and t, whether these points are in the same connected component of the semi-linear set X defined by $\mathcal{C}$. The corresponding counting problem $\#^{cc}CSAT_{add}$ is the problem of counting the number of connected components of X given by $\mathcal{C}$.

Theorem 4. *The problems $REACH_{add}$ and $\#^{cc}CSAT_{add}$ are PAR_{add}-complete and $FPAR_{add}$-complete with respect to Turing reductions, respectively.*

The lower bound in this result is inspired by an early paper by Reif [25] (see also [26]), which showed the PSPACE-hardness of a generalized movers problem in robotics. Reif's result implies that the analogue of $REACH_{add}$ for semi-algebraic sets given by inequalities of (nonlinear) rational polynomials is PSPACE-hard. We cannot apply this result in our context, since we are dealing here with linear polynomials (of mixed type). However, we borrow from Reif's proof the idea to describe PSPACE by symmetric polynomial space Turing machines [16]. Roughly speaking, this is a nondeterministic Turing machine with the property that its transition relation is symmetric. Thus its configuration digraph is in fact a graph, which is essential for capturing the symmetric reachability relation of $REACH_{add}$.

4.4   Euler Characteristic and Betti Numbers

Let $EULER_{add}$ denote the following problem: given an additive circuit $\mathcal{C}$ defining a closed semi-linear set X, compute the Euler characteristic $\chi(X)$ of X. Hence only circuits defining closed semi-linear sets are considered to be admissible inputs. By convention, we assume that $\chi(\emptyset) := \infty$, so that we can distinguish empty sets from nonempty ones.

The next lemma tells us that both closedness and compactness of a semi-linear set can be checked within the allowed resources.

Lemma 1. *Both closedness and compactness of a set X given by an additive circuit can be decided in* $\mathrm{P}^{\#\mathrm{P}}_{\mathrm{add}}$.

Theorem 5. *The problem* $\mathrm{EULER}_{\mathrm{add}}$ *is* $\mathrm{FP}^{\#\mathrm{P}}_{\mathrm{add}}$-*complete with respect to Turing reductions.*

For $k \in \mathbb{N}$, we define $\mathrm{BETTI}_{\mathrm{add}}(k)$ to be the problem of computing the kth Betti number of a closed semi-linear set given by an additive circuit. The problem of computing the kth Betti number modulo a prime p shall be denoted by $\mathrm{BETTI}_{\mathrm{add}}(k, \mathrm{mod}\, p)$. Note that for $k = 0$, these are just the problems of counting the number of connected components, respectively counting them modulo p.

The following result extends Theorem 4.

Theorem 6. *For any $k \in \mathbb{N}$ and any prime p, the problems* $\mathrm{BETTI}_{\mathrm{add}}(k)$ *and* $\mathrm{BETTI}_{\mathrm{add}}(k, \mathrm{mod}\, p)$ *are* $\mathrm{FPAR}_{\mathrm{add}}$-*complete with respect to Turing reductions.*

The $\mathrm{PAR}_{\mathrm{add}}$-hardness of $\mathrm{BETTI}_{\mathrm{add}}(k)$ is deduced from Theorem 4 by establishing a parsimonious reduction from $\#^{\mathrm{cc}}\mathrm{CSAT}_{\mathrm{add}}$ to $\mathrm{BETTI}_{\mathrm{add}}(k)$. This can be done using the suspension construction of algebraic topology. A short outline of the upper bound proof is given in Sect. 4.6.

These results give a complexity theoretic distinction between the problems to compute the Euler characteristic and to compute Betti numbers. The computation of the Euler characteristic is strictly easier than the computation of the number of connected components, or more generally than the computation of the kth Betti number for any fixed k, unless the unlikely collapse $\mathrm{FPSPACE} = \mathrm{FP}^{\#\mathrm{P}}$ happens. Intuitively, the fact that $\mathrm{EULER}_{\mathrm{add}}$ is easier than $\mathrm{BETTI}_{\mathrm{add}}(k)$ can be explained by the various nice properties satisfied by the Euler characteristic.

4.5   Completeness Results in the Turing Model

Let us now restrict the inputs in the three problems $\mathcal{P}$ studied above to *constant free* additive circuits and denote the resulting computational problem by $\mathcal{P}^0$. Note that constant-free circuits can be encoded over a finite alphabet and thus be handled by (classical) Turing machines.

Corollary 4. *For any $k, d \in \mathbb{N}$ and any prime p,* $\mathrm{DIM}^0_{\mathrm{add}}(d)$ *is* NP-*complete,* $\mathrm{EULER}^0_{\mathrm{add}}$ *is* $\mathrm{FP}^{\#\mathrm{P}}$-*complete, and* $\mathrm{BETTI}^0_{\mathrm{add}}(k)$, $\mathrm{BETTI}^0_{\mathrm{add}}(k, \mathrm{mod}\, p)$ *both are* FPSPACE-*complete.*

4.6   Computing Betti Numbers mod 2 in FPSPACE

We outline the proof of $\mathrm{BETTI}^0_{\mathrm{add}}(k, \mathrm{mod}\, 2) \in \mathrm{FPSPACE}$. Working modulo 2 has the advantage that we do not have to worry about orientations.

For $s, n \in \mathbb{N}$ we define $\mathcal{H}_{s,n}$ to be the set of affine linear polynomials $a_0 + \sum_{i=1}^{n} a_i X_i$ with integer coefficients a_i such that $\sum_{i=0}^{n} |a_i| \leq 2^s$. We denote by $\mathcal{F}_{s,n}$ the set of all non-empty sets $F = \bigcap_{f \in \mathcal{H}_{s,n}} \{x \in \mathbb{R}^n \mid f(x) = \sigma(f)\}$, corresponding to some sign function $\sigma \colon \mathcal{H}_{s,n} \to \{-1, 0, 1\}$. The space $\mathbb{R}^n$ is the disjoint union of all $F \in \mathcal{F}_{s,n}$. We will call this the *universal cell decomposition* for the parameters s, n, and we call the sets $F \in \mathcal{F}_{s,n}$ the corresponding *faces* or *cells*.

It is known [4, Thm. 3, Chapt. 21] that each face $F \in \mathcal{F}_{s,n}$ contains a rational point of bit-size at most $(sn)^c$, for some fixed constant $c > 0$. We shall therefore encode a face $F \in \mathcal{F}_{s,n}$ by a triple $(s, n, x) \in \mathbb{N}^2 \times \mathbb{Q}$ such that $x \in F$ and the bit-size of x is at most $(sn)^c$. (Note that one may need exponentially many inequalities to describe a face F.)

If $X \subseteq \mathbb{R}^n$ is compact and a finite union of faces in $\mathcal{F}_{s,n}$, then the decomposition of X is a finite cell complex. The important thing to check here is that the boundary of a cell in $\mathcal{F}_{s,n}$ is a union of cells in $\mathcal{F}_{s,n}$.

Let $\mathcal{C}$ be an additive circuit of size s that defines a compact semi-linear set $X \subseteq \mathbb{R}^n$. We assume that $\mathcal{C}$ uses only the constants $0, 1$ and that it branches according to the sign of intermediate results in a ternary way ($< 0, = 0, > 0$). The set of inputs in $\mathbb{R}^n$, whose path in the corresponding computation tree ends up with a specific leaf ν, shall be called the *leaf set D_ν* of ν. Note that each nonempty leaf set D_ν of $\mathcal{C}$ is union of faces of $\mathcal{F}_{s,n}$, where s denotes the size of $\mathcal{C}$. Therefore, $\{F \in \mathcal{F}_{s,n} \mid F \subseteq X\}$ is a finite cell complex.

We are going to define the cellular homology of this cell complex with respect to the coefficient field $\mathbb{F}_2$. Two faces F, F' of $\mathcal{F}_{s,n}$ are called *incident* iff F' is contained in the closure of F, and if the dimensions of F and F' differ exactly bye one. Let Φ_k denote the set of the k-cells of the cell complex and $\mathcal{C}_k$ be the $\mathbb{F}_2$-vector space having Φ_k as a basis. The boundary map $\partial_k \colon \mathcal{C}_{k+1} \to \mathcal{C}_k$ is the $\mathbb{F}_2$-linear map defined for $F \in \Phi_{k+1}$ by $\partial_k(F) = \sum_{F'} [F, F'] F'$, where the sum is over all $F' \in \Phi_k$ incident to F. The image $B_k := \operatorname{im} \partial_k$ of ∂_k is called the vector space of k-boundaries, and the kernel $Z_k := \ker \partial_{k-1}$ is called the space of k-cycles. The kth *cellular homology vector space* is defined as the quotient space $H_k := Z_k / B_k$. It is well known [13,23] that H_k is isomorphic to the singular homology vector space $H_k(X; \mathbb{F}_2)$. Therefore, $b_k := \dim H_k$ is the kth Betti number modulo 2, which is independent of the cell decomposition. We have $b_k = \dim Z_k - \dim B_k = c_k - \rho_{k-1} - \rho_k$, where $\rho_k := \operatorname{rank} \partial_k$ and $c_k = |\Phi_k|$.

Lemma 2. *The incidence of faces F, F' in $\mathcal{F}_{s,n}$, $s, n \in \mathbb{N}$, can be decided in* PH.

We make now a short digression on space efficient linear algebra. By a *succinct representation* of an integer matrix $A = (a_{ij})$ we understand a Boolean circuit computing the matrix entry a_{ij} from the index pair (i, j) given in binary.

Combing the results of [22] and [5], we obtain:

Lemma 3. *The rank of an $N \times N$ integer matrix A given in succinct representation by a Boolean circuit B can be computed by a Turing machine with space polynomial in $\log N$, the depth of B, and the log of the maximal bitsize of the elements of A.*

The proof that $\text{BETTI}^0_{\text{add}}(k, \bmod p)$ is contained in FPSPACE follows by combining Lemma 2 with Lemma 3.

5 Open Questions

Problem 1. In this paper, we prove completeness with respect to Turing reductions. Do we also have completeness with respect to parsimonious reductions? For instance, how about the completeness of $\#\text{TSP}_\mathbb{R}$ in $\text{D}\#\text{P}_{\text{add}}$?

Problem 2. What is the complexity to deciding connectedness of a semi-linear set given by an additive circuit?

Problem 3. In this paper we proved that computing the torsion-free part of the homology of semi-linear sets is FPAR_{add}-complete. What is the complexity of computing the torsion part of this homology?

Acknowledgments. We thank Eric Allender and Saugata Basu for helpful discussions. Also, we are grateful to anonymous referees for many valuable comments, which helped to improve the presentation significantly.

References

1. J.L. Balcázar, J. Díaz, and J. Gabarró. *Structural Complexity I.* EATCS Monographs on Theoretical Computer Science, 11. Springer-Verlag, 1988.
2. M. Ben-Or. Lower bounds for algebraic computation trees. In *Proc. 15th ACM STOC, Boston,* pages 80–86, 1983.
3. L. Blum, F. Cucker, M. Shub, and S. Smale. *Complexity and Real Computation.* Springer, 1998.
4. L. Blum, M. Shub, and S. Smale. On a theory of computation and complexity over the real numbers. *Bull. Amer. Math. Soc.,* 21:1–46, 1989.
5. A.B. Borodin. On relating time and space to size and depth. *SIAM J. Comp.,* 6:733–744, 1977.
6. P. Bürgisser. *Completeness and Reduction in Algebraic Complexity Theory,* volume 7 of *Algorithms and Computation in Mathematics.* Springer Verlag, 2000.
7. P. Bürgisser. Lower bounds and real algebraic geometry. In S. Basu and L. Gonzales-Vega, editors, *Algorithmic and Quantitative Real Algebraic Geometry,* volume 60 of *DIMACS Series in Discrete Mathematics and Theoretical Computer Science.* AMS, 2003.
8. P. Bürgisser and F. Cucker. Counting complexity classes over the reals. II: The unrestricted case. In preparation.
9. F. Cucker and P. Koiran. Computing over the reals with addition and order: Higher complexity classes. *J. Compl.,* 11:358–376, 1995.
10. H. Fournier and P. Koiran. Are lower bounds easier over the reals? In *Proc. 30th ACM STOC,* pages 507–513, 1998.
11. H. Fournier and P. Koiran. Lower bounds are not easier over the reals: Inside PH. In *Proc. ICALP 2000,* LNCS 1853, pages 832–843, 2000.

12. J. von zur Gathen. Parallel arithmetic computations: a survey. In *Proc. 12th Symp. Math. Found. Comput. Sci., Bratislava*, number 233 in LNCS, pages 93–112, 1986.
13. Allen Hatcher. *Algebraic topology*. Cambridge University Press, Cambridge, 2002.
14. K.-I. Ko. *Complexity of Real Functions*. Birkhäuser, 1991.
15. P. Koiran. Computing over the reals with addition and order. *Theoret. Comp. Sci.*, 133:35–47, 1994.
16. H.R. Lewis and C.H. Papadimitriou. Symmetric space-bounded computation. *Theoret. Comp. Sci.*, 19:161–187, 1982.
17. K. Meer. Counting problems over the reals. *Theoret. Comp. Sci.*, 242:41–58, 2000.
18. S. Meiser. Point location in arrangements of hyperplanes. *Information and Computation*, 106:286–303, 1993.
19. F. Meyer auf der Heide. A polynomial linear search algorithm for the n-dimensional knapsack problem. *J. ACM*, 31:668–676, 1984.
20. F. Meyer auf der Heide. Fast algorithms for n-dimensional restrictions of hard problems. *J. ACM*, 35:740–747, 1988.
21. C. Michaux. Une remarque à propos des machines sur $\mathbb{R}$ introduites par Blum, Shub et Smale. *C. R. Acad. Sci. Paris*, 309, Série I:435–437, 1989.
22. K. Mulmuley. A fast parallel algorithm to compute the rank of a matrix over an arbitrary field. *Combinatorica*, 7:101–104, 1987.
23. James R. Munkres. *Elements of algebraic topology*. Addison-Wesley Publishing Company, Menlo Park, CA, 1984.
24. C.H. Papadimitriou. *Computational Complexity*. Addison-Wesley, 1994.
25. J.H. Reif. Complexity of the mover's problem and generalizations. In *Proc. 20th FOCS*, pages 421–427, 1979.
26. J.H. Reif. Complexity of the generalized mover's problem. In J.T. Schwartz, M. Sharir, and J. Hopcroft, editors, *Planning, Geometry and Complexity of Robot Motion*, pages 267–281. Ablex Publishing Corporation, 1987.
27. E. Tardos. A strongly polynomial algorithm to solve combinatorial linear programs. *Oper. Res.*, 34:250–256, 1986.
28. S. Toda. PP is as hard as the polynomial-time hierarchy. *SIAM J. Comp.*, 21(2):865–877, 1991.
29. S. Toda and O. Watanabe. Polynomial time 1-Turing reductions from #ph to #p. *Theoret. Comp. Sci.*, 100:205–221, 1992.
30. L.G. Valiant. Completeness classes in algebra. In *Proc. 11th ACM STOC*, pages 249–261, 1979.
31. L.G. Valiant. The complexity of computing the permanent. *Theoret. Comp. Sci.*, 8:189–201, 1979.
32. L.G. Valiant. The complexity of enumeration and reliability problems. *SIAM J. Comp.*, 8:410–421, 1979.
33. L.G. Valiant. Reducibility by algebraic projections. In *Logic and Algorithmic: an International Symposium held in honor of Ernst Specker*, volume 30, pages 365–380. Monogr. No. 30 de l'Enseign. Math., 1982.
34. A.C. Yao. Algebraic decision trees and Euler characteristic. In *Proc. 33rd FOCS*, 1992.
35. A.C. Yao. Decision tree complexity and Betti numbers. In *Proc. 26th ACM STOC*, 1994.

Some Properties of One-Pebble Turing Machines with Sublogarithmic Space

Atsuyuki Inoue[1], Akira Ito[1], Katsushi Inoue[1], and Tokio Okazaki[2]

[1] Department of Computer Science and Systems Engineering,
Faculty of Engineering, Yamaguchi University, Ube, 755-8611 Japan
{ainoue, ito, inoue}@csse.yamaguchi-u.ac.jp
[2] Department of Media and Culture Studies, Faculty of Humanities,
Jousai International University, Togane, Chiba, 283-8555 Japan
okazaki@jiu.ac.jp

Abstract. This paper investigates some aspects of the accepting powers of deterministic, nondeterministic, and alternating one-pebble Turing machines with spaces between $\log \log n$ ang $\log n$. We first investigate a relationship between the accepting powers of two-way deterministic one-counter automata and deterministic (or nondeterministic) one-pebble Turing machines, and show that they are incomparable. Then we investigate a relationship between nondeterminism and alternation, and show that there exists a language accepted by a strongly $\log \log n$ space-bounded alternating one-pebble Turing machine , but not accepted by any weakly $o(\log n)$ space-bounded nondeterministic one-pebble Turing machine. Finally, we investigate a space hierarchy, and show that for any one-pebble fully space constructible function $L(n) \leq \log n$, and any function $L'(n) = o(L(n))$, there exists a language accepted by a strongly $L(n)$ space-bounded deterministic one-pebble Turing machine, but not accepted by any weakly $L'(n)$ space-bounded nondeterministic one-pebble Turing machine.

1 Introduction

A Turing machine (Tm) considered here has a two-way read-only input tape and a semi-infinite (infinite to the right) storage tape [6,8]. A one-pebble Tm [8] is a Tm with the capability of using one-pebble which the finite control can use as a marker on the input tape. During the computation, the device can deposit (retrieve) a pebble on (from) any cell of the tape. The next move depends on the current state, the contents of the cells scanned by the input and storage tape heads, and on the presence of the pebble on the current input tape cell. It is easy to see that the pebble is redundant when the storage tape used is $\log n$ or more, because the storage tape can be used to encode, in binary, the position of the tape cell containing the pebble. Therefore, we are interested in one-pebble Tm's operating in space below $\log n$. Blum and Hewitt [1] showed that one-pebble finite automata accept only regular sets. Chang, Ibarra, Palis and Ravikumar [4] strengthened this result, and showed that $o(\log \log n)$ space-bounded one-pebble Tm's accept only regular sets. Further, they showed in [4]

T. Ibaraki, N. Katoh, and H. Ono (Eds.): ISAAC 2003, LNCS 2906, pp. 635–644, 2003.

that one pebble adds power, even when the input is restricted to a language over a unary alphabet, to Tm's whose space complexity lies between $\log \log n$ and $\log n$. Compared with many investigations of Tm's, there are not so many investigations of one-pebble Tm's. This paper investigates some aspects of the accepting powers of deterministic, nondeterministic and alternating one-pebble Tm's operating in space between $\log \log n$ and $\log n$. Through the proofs of our results, we give a new technique for proving that some languages cannot be accepted by space-bounded nondeterministic one-pebble Tm's.

Section 2 gives definitions and notations necessary for the subsequent sections. It is shown in [7] that the accepting powers of two-way deterministic one-counter automata and L(n) space-bounded one-pebble deterministic Turing machines with $\log \log n \leq L(n) = o(\log n)$ are incomparable. Section 3 investigates a relationship between the accepting powers of two-way deterministic one-counter automata and one-pebble nondeterministic Tm's operating in space between $\log \log n$ and $o(\log n)$, and shows that they are incomparable. It is well known [2,8] that for spaces between $\log \log n$ and $o(\log n)$, alternating Tm's are more powerful than nondeterministic Tm's for both the strong and weak modes of space complexity. Section 4 shows a similar result. More specifically, we show that there exists a language accepted by a strongly $\log \log n$ space-bounded alternating one-pebble Tm, but not accepted by any weakly $o(\log n)$ space-bounded nondeterministic one-pebble Tm. It is also well known [6,8] that there is an infinite space hierarchy of the accepting powers of deterministic (or nondeterministic) Tm's with spaces between $\log \log n$ and $\log n$. Section 5 shows a similar result for one-pebble Tm's. That is, we show that for any one-pebble fully space constructible function $L(n) \leq \log n$, and any function $L'(n) = o(L(n))$, there exists a language accepted by a strongly $L(n)$ space-bounded deterministic one-pebble Tm, but not accepted by any weakly $L'(n)$ space-bounded nondeterministic one-pebble Tm. Section 6 concludes this paper by posing open problems.

2 Preliminaries

Below, we denote a Turing machine by Tm. An *alternating* Tm M is a generalization of the nondeterministic Tm. M has a read-only input tape $\cent w\$$ (where $\cent$ is the left endmarker, $\$$ is the right endarker, and w is an input word) on which the input head can move right or left, and has one semi-infinite (infinite to the right) storage tape equiped with a storage head which can move right or left, and can read or write. All states of M are partitioned into *universal* and *existential* states. A *storage state* of M is a combination of the (i) contents of the storage tape, (ii) position of the storage head within the nonblank portion of the storage tape, and (iii) state of the finite control. A *configuration* of M on an input w is a combination of the (i) storage state, and (ii) position of the input head on $\cent w\$$. We can view the computation of M as a tree whose nodes are labeled by configurations. A configuration is called *universal, existential, accepting* if the state associated with the configuration is universal (existential, accepting). A *computation tree* of M on an input w is a tree such that the root is labelled by the initial configuration and the children of any nonleaf node labelled by a universal (existential) configuration include all (one) of the immediate successors of that configuration. A computation tree is *accepting* if it is finite and all the leaves are labelled by accepting configurations. M accepts an input word w if there is an accepting computation tree of M on w. Note that a nondeterministic Turing machine is an alternating Tm with existential states only. See [3,8] for the more detailed definitions of alternating and nondeterministic Tm's.

A *one-pebble alternating* Tm is an alternating Tm with the capability of using one-pebble which the finite control can use as a marker on the input tape. During the computation, the device can deposit (retrieve) a pebble on (from) any cell of the tape. The next move depends on the current state, the contents of the cells scanned by the input and storage tape heads, and on the presence of the pebble on the current input tape cell. The concepts of "storage state", "computation tree", "accepting computation tree", and "acceptance of an input word" for one-pebble alternating Tm's are defined as in alternating Tm's. A computation tree of a one-pebble alternating Tm M (on some input) is l *space-bounded* if all nodes of the tree are labeled with configurations using at most l cells of the storage tape. Let $L(n) : N \to N$ be a function of the input length n, where N denotes the set of all the positive integers. M is *weakly $L(n)$ space-bounded* if for every input w of length n, $n \geq 1$, that is accepted by M, there exists an $L(n)$ space-bounded accepting computation tree of M on w. M is *strongly $L(n)$ space-bounded* if for every input w of length n (accepted by M or not), $n \geq 1$, any computation tree of M on w is $L(n)$ space-bounded. *One-pebble nondeterministic* and *one-pebble deterministic* Tm's are defined as usual. Let $weak\text{-}ASPACE^{peb}(L(n))$ ($weak\text{-}NSPACE^{peb}(L(n))$, $weak\text{-}DSPACE^{peb}(L(n))$) denote the class of languages accepted by weakly $L(n)$ space-bounded one-pebble alternating (nondeterministic, deterministic) Tm's, and let $strong\text{-}ASPACE^{peb}(L(n))$ ($strong\text{-}NSPACE^{peb}(L(n))$, $strong\text{-}DSPACE^{peb}(L(n))$) denote the class of languages accepted by strongly $L(n)$ space-bounded one-pebble alternating (nondeterministic, deterministic) Tm's.

A function $L : N \to N$ is *one-pebble fully space constructible* if there exists a strongly $L(n)$ space-bounded deterministic one-pebble Tm M such that, for all $n \geq 1$ and for any input word of length n, M will eventually halt having marked exactly $L(n)$ cells of the storage tape. We say that M *fully constructs* $L(n)$.

In Section 5, we will use the following fact which was proved in [4].

Fact 1 $\lceil \log \log n \rceil$ is one-pebble fully space constructible.

A *two-way deterministic one-counter automaton* (2-dc) is a two-way deterministic pushdown automaton [5] which can use only one kind of symbol on the pushdown tape. Let 2-DC denote the class of languages accepted by 2-dc's.

Throughout this paper, we assume that the base of logarithm is 2. For any machine M, let $T(M)$ denote the set of words accepted by M. For any word w, $|w|$ denotes the length of w, and for any set S, $|S|$ denotes the cardinality of S.

For any alphabet Σ and any integer $n \geq 1$, Σ^n denotes the set of all the words of length n over Σ. See [6] for undefined terms..

3   Incomparability with 2-DC

This section investigates a relationship between the accepting powers of 2-dc's and sublogarithmically space-bounded one-pebble nondeterministic Tm's.

The following theorem is proved in [7]:

Theorem 1. $strong\text{-}DSPACE^{peb}(\log \log n) - 2\text{-}DC \neq \phi$.

Theorem 2. $2\text{-}DC - weak\text{-}NSPACE^{peb}(o(\log n)) \neq \phi$.
Proof: Let $T_1 = \{ww | w \in \{0,1\}^+\}$. It is an easy exercise to show that $T_1 \in 2\text{-}DC$. We below show that $T_1 \notin weak\text{-}NSPACE^{peb}(o(\log n))$. We suppose to the contrary that an weakly $L(n)$ space-bounded one-pebble nondeterministic Tm M accepts T_1, where $L(n) = o(\log n)$. Let Q be the set of states of the finite control of M. We divide Q into two disjoint subsets Q^+ and Q^- which correspond to the sets of states when M holds and does not hold the pebble in the finite control, respectively. M starts from the initial state in Q^+ with the input head on the left endmarker ϕ. We assume without loss of generality that M satisfies the following condition (C): "When M accepts an input word in T_1, M enters an accepting state in Q^+ on the right endmarker $\$$, and halts." Below we shall consider the computations of M on words of length $2n$ for large n. Thus M uses at most $L(2n)$ cells of the storage tape. For each $n \geq 1$, let an n-word be a word over $\{0,1\}$ of length n, and $S(n)$ be the set of possible storage states of M using at most $L(2n)$ cells of the storage tape. Let $S^+(n) = \{s \in S(n) \mid$ the state component of s is in $Q^+\}$, $S^-(n) = \{s \in S(n) \mid$ the state component of s is in $Q^-\}$, and thus $S(n) = S^+(n) \bigcup S^-(n)$. Clearly $s^+(n) \stackrel{\triangle}{=} |S^+(n)| = O(t^{L(2n)})$, and $s^-(n) \stackrel{\triangle}{=} |S^-(n)| = O(t^{L(2n)})$ for some constant t depending only on M. Let x be any n-word that is supposed to be a subword of an input to M. Suppose that the pebble of M is not placed on this word x. Then, we define a mapping M_x, which depends on M and x, from $S^-(n) \times \{left, right\}$ to the power set of $S^-(n) \times \{left, right\}$ as follows: $(q', e') \in M_x(q, e) \Leftrightarrow$ when M enters x in storage state q from the e edge of x, there exists a sequence of steps of M in which M eventually exits x in storage state q' from the e' edge of x. We say that two n-words x_1, x_2 are M^--equivalent if $M_{x_1}(q, e) = M_{x_2}(q, e)$ for each $(q, e) \in S^-(n) \times \{left, right\}$ (i.e., if two mappings M_{x_1} and M_{x_2} are equivalent). Clearly, M^--equivalence is an equivalence relation on n-words. There are 2^n n-words. Clearly, there are at most $e(n) = (2^{2s^-(n)})^{2s^-(n)}$ M^--equivalence classes of n-words. Let $P(n)$ be a largest M^--equivalence class of n-words. Then we have $|P(n)| \geq \frac{2^n}{e(n)}$. Note that $|P(n)| \gg 1$ for large n, because $L(n) = o(\log n)$. Let w_1 and w_2 be n-words. For any computation $comp(w_1 w_2)$ of M on $w_1 w_2$, let

- $cross(comp(w_1w_2)) \overset{\triangle}{=}$ the sequence of storage states when M crosses the boundary between w_1 and w_2 from left to right or from righ t to left in $comp(w_1w_2)$, and

- $pebble\text{-}cross(comp(w_1w_2)) \overset{\triangle}{=}$ the sequence of storage states (in $S^+(n)$) when M crosses the boundary between w_1 and w_2 with the pebble in the finite control from left to right or from right to left in $comp(w_1w_2)$.

For each n-word w, ww is in T_1, and so ww is accepted by M, and the length of ww is $2n$. Therefore, there exists an accepting computation of M on ww using at most $L(2n)$ cells of the storage tape. Let "$accomp(ww)$" be such a fixed loop-free accepting computation of M on ww. The following lemma must hold.

Lemma 1. For any two different n-words x and y in $P(n)$,

$$pebble\text{-}cross(accomp(xx)) \neq pebble\text{-}cross(accomp(yy)).$$

[*Proof.* Suppose to the contrary that $pebble\text{-}cross(accomp(xx)) = pebble\text{-}cross$
$(accomp(yy))$. From condition (C) mentioned previously, we can assume without loss of generality that for some *odd* number $k \geq 1$,

(i) $pebble\text{-}cross(accomp(xx)) = pebble\text{-}cross(accomp(yy)) = s_1s_2\dots s_k$
    (each $s_i \in S^+(n)$),

(ii) $cross(accomp(xx)) = s_{01}^x s_{02}^x \dots s_{0i_0}^x s_1 s_{11}^x s_{12}^x \dots s_{1i_1}^x s_2 s_{21}^x s_{22}^x \dots s_{2i_2}^x s_3 \dots s_k$
    $s_{k1}^x s_{k2}^x \dots s_{ki_k}^x$ $(i_0, i_1, \dots, i_k \geq 0$, and each $s_{ij}^x \in S^-(n))$,

(iii) $cross(accomp(yy)) = s_{01}^y s_{02}^y \dots s_{0j_0}^y s_1 s_{11}^y s_{12}^y \dots s_{1j_1}^y s_2 s_{21}^y s_{22}^y \dots s_{2j_2}^y s_3 \dots s_k$
    $s_{k1}^y s_{k2}^y \dots s_{kj_k}^y$ $(j_0, j_1, \dots, j_k \geq 0$, and each $s_{ij}^y \in S^-(n))$, and

(iv) $accomp(yy)$ ends with an accepting state $q_a \in Q^+$ on the right endmarker
    $.

Since x and y are M^--equivalent, it follows that we can construct a computation $comp(xy)$ of M on xy such that:

(i) $cross(comp(xy)) = s_{01}^x s_{02}^x \dots s_{0i_0}^x s_1 s_{11}^y s_{12}^y \dots s_{1j_1}^y s_2 s_{21}^x s_{22}^x \dots s_{2i_2}^x s_3$
    $s_{31}^y s_{32}^y \dots s_{3j_3}^y s_4 \dots s_k s_{k1}^y s_{k2}^y \dots s_{kj_k}^y$, and

(ii) $pebble\text{-}cross(comp(xy)) = s_1s_2\dots s_k$.

Clearly, $comp(xy)$ can end with M entering the accepting state $q_a \in Q^+$ on the right endmarker $. Therefore, xy is also accepted by M, which contradicts the fact that xy is not in T_1. This completes the proof of the lemma.]

For each $w \in P(n)$, $accomp(ww)$ is loop-free. Therefore, it follows that, for each $w \in P(n)$, $pebble\text{-}cross(accomp(ww))$ is such that the same storage state appears at most twice (one is with M crossing the boundary between the left w and the right w from left to right (or from right to left), and the other is with M crossing the boundary from right to left (or from left to right)) in $pebble\text{-}cross(accomp(ww))$. Therefore, for each $w \in P(n)$, the length of $pebble\text{-}cross(accomp(ww))$ is bounded by $2s^+(n)$. For each $n \gg 1$, let $PEBBLE\text{-}CROSS(n) = \{pebble\text{-}cross(accomp(ww)) | w \in P(n)\}$. From the observation above, it follows that $|PEBBLE\text{-}CROSS(n)| \leq (s^+(n))^{2s^+(n)}$. Since

$L(n) = o(\log n)$, by a simple calculation, it follows that $|P(n)| \gg |PEBBLE\text{-}CROSS(n)|$ for large n. Thus, there must be two different n-words x and y in $P(n)$ such that $pebble\text{-}cross(accomp(xx)) = pebble\text{-}cross(accomp(yy))$. This contradicts Lemma 1. This completes the proof of "$T_1 \notin weak\text{-}NSPACE^{peb}(o(\log n))$". $\qquad\square$

From Theorems 1 and 2, we get the following corollary:

Corollary 1. For any $m \in \{strong, weak\}$, any $X \in \{D, N\}$, and any function $L(n)$ such that $\log\log n \leq L(n) = o(\log n)$, $m\text{-}XSPACE^{peb}(L(n))$ is incomparable with 2-DC.

4   Nondeterminism versus Alternation

This section investigates a relationship between the accepting powers of sublogarithmically space-bounded nondeterministic and alternating one-pebble Tm's.

Our main result of this section is :

Theorem 3. $strong\text{-}ASPACE^{peb}(\log\log n) - weak\text{-}NSPACE^{peb}(o(\log n)) \neq \phi$.

Proof: Let

$$T_2 = \{B(1)\#B(2)\# \ldots \#B(n)cw_1cw_2c \ldots cw_k ccu_1cu_2c \ldots cu_rc \in \{0,1,c,\#\}^+$$
$$\mid n \geq 2 \wedge k \geq 1 \wedge r \geq 1 \wedge (\text{each } w_i, u_j \in \{0,1\}^{\lceil \log n \rceil}]) \wedge$$
$$\forall i(1 \leq i \leq k)[\exists j_i(1 \leq j_i \leq r)[w_i = u_{j_i}]]\},$$

where for each positive integer i, $B(i)$ denotes the word over $\{0,1\}$ that represents the integer i in binary notation (with no leading zeros). To prove the theorem, we show that (1) $T_2 \in strong\text{-}ASPACE^{peb}(\log\log n)$, and (2) $T_2 \notin weak\text{-}NSPACE^{peb}(o(\log n))$.

Proof of (1): T_2 is accepted by a strongly $\log\log n$ space-bounded alternating one-pebble Tm M which acts as follows. Suppose that an input string

$$\phi y_1 \# y_2 \# \ldots \# y_n cw_1cw_2c \ldots cw_k ccu_1cu_2c \ldots cu_rc\$$$

(where $n \geq 2, k, r \geq 1$, and $y_i's, w_j's, u_m's$ are all in $\{0,1\}^+$) is presented to M. (Input strings in the form different from the above can easily be rejected by M.) By using the well-known technique (see [6, Problem 10.2]), M first marks off $\log\log n$ cells of the storage tape when $y_i = B(i)$ for each $1 \leq i \leq n$. (Of course, M enters a rejecting state if $y_i \neq B(i)$ for some $1 \leq i \leq n$.) M then checks, by using $\log\log n$ cells of the storage tape, that $|w_1| = \ldots = |w_k| = |u_1| = \ldots = |u_r| = \lceil \log n \rceil$. After that, M universally checks that for all $i(1 \leq i \leq k)$, $w_i = u_{j_i}$ for some $j_i(1 \leq j_i \leq r)$. That is, for example, in ordrer to check that $w_i = u_{j_i}$ for some $j_i(1 \leq j_i \leq r)$, M first places the pebble on the symbol c just before w_i, and then moves to the right to existentially choose u_{j_i}. After that, by universally checking that the lth symbol of w_i is equal to the lth symbol of u_{j_i} for all $l(1 \leq l \leq \lceil \log n \rceil)$, M can check whether $w_i = u_{j_i}$. (For this check, log log n cells of the storage tape are sufficient.) M enters an accepting state only if these checks are all successful. It is obvious that M accepts the language T_2.

Proof of (2): The proof is similar to that of "$T_1 \notin$ *weak-NSPACE$^{peb}(o(\log n))$*" in the proof of Theorem 2. Suppose to the contrary that an $L(n)$ space-bounded nondeterministic one-pebble Tm M accepts T_2, where $L(n) = o(\log n)$. Let Q be the set of states of the finite control of M, and Q^+ and Q^- be defined as in the proof of Theorem 2. We again assume without loss of generality that when M accepts an input word in T_2, M enters an accepting state in Q^+ on the right endmarker $\$$, and halts.

For each $n \geq 2$, let $V(n) = \{cw_1cw_2c\ldots cw_{p(n)}c|\forall i(1 \leq i \leq p(n))[w_i \in \{0,1\}^{\lceil \log n \rceil}]\}$, where $p(n) = 2^{\lceil \log n \rceil}$. For each $x = cw_1cw_2c\ldots cw_{p(n)}c \in V(n)$, let *contents*$(x) = \{u \in \{0,1\}^{\lceil \log n \rceil}| u = w_i$ for some $1 \leq i \leq p(n)\}$. For any two words $x, y \in V(n)$, we say that x and y are *contents-equivalent* if *contents*$(x) = $ *contents*(y). Contents-equivalence is an equivalence relation on $V(n)$. There are *contents*$(n) = \binom{p(n)}{1} + \binom{p(n)}{2} + \ldots + \binom{p(n)}{p(n)} = 2^{p(n)} - 1$ contents-equivalence classes of $V(n)$. (Note that *contents*(n) corresponds to the number of all the nonempty subsets of $\{0,1\}^{\lceil \log n \rceil}$.) We denote by $CONTENTS(n)$ the set of all the representatives, one for each contents-equivalence class, chosen arbitrarily. Of course, $|CONTENTS(n)| = $ *contents*(n). For each $n \geq 2$, let $W(n) = \{B(1)\#B(2)\#\ldots\#B(n)xy| x, y \in CONTENTS(n)\}$. Let $r(n)$ be the length of each word in $W(n)$. Note that $r(n) = O(n \log n)$. Below we consider the computations of M on words in $W(n)$ for large n.. Thus M uses at most $L(r(n))$ cells of the storage tape. For each $n \geq 2$, $S(n)$ be the set of possible storage states of M using at most $L(r(n))$ cells of the storage tape, and let $S^+(n)$ and $S^-(n)$ be defined as in the proof of Theorem 2. Clearly $s^+(n) \overset{\triangle}{=} |S^+(n)| = O(t^{L(r(n))})$, and $s^-(n) \overset{\triangle}{=} |S^-(n)| = O(t^{L(r(n))})$ for some constant t depending only on M. Let x be a word in $CONTENTS(n)$ that is supposed to be a subword of an input word (in $W(n)$) to M. Suppose that the pebble of M is not placed on this word x. Then, as defined in the proof of Theorem 2, we define a mapping M_x, which depends on M and x, from $S^-(n) \times \{left, right\}$ to the power set of $S^-(n) \times \{left, right\}$. We say that two words $x_1, x_2 \in CONTENTS(n)$ are M^--*equivalent* if two mappings M_{x_1} and M_{x_2} are equivalent. Clearly, M^--equivalence is an equivalence relation on $CONTENTS(n)$, and there are at most $e(n) = (2^{2s^-(n)})^{2s^-(n)}$ M^--equivalence classes of $CONTENTS(n)$. Let $P(n)$ be a largest M^--equivalence class of $CONTENTS(n)$. Then we have $|P(n)| \geq \frac{|CONTENTS(n)|}{e(n)} = \frac{contents(n)}{e(n)} \simeq \frac{2^{p(n)}}{e(n)}$. For each $x \in P(n)$, $B(1)\#B(2)\#\ldots\#B(n)xx$ is in $T_2 \cap W(n)$, and so it is accepted by M, and its length is $r(n)$. Therefore, there exists an accepting computation of M on $B(1)\#B(2)\#\ldots\#B(n)xx$ using at most $L(r(n))$ cells of the storage tape. Let "*accomp*(xx)" be such a fixed loop-free accepting computation of M on $B(1)\#B(2)\#\ldots\# B(n)xx$. For each $x \in P(n)$, let *pebble-cross*$(accomp(xx))$ be the sequence of storage states (in $S^+(n)$) when M crosses the boundary between the left x and the right x with the pebble in the finite control from left to right or from right to left in $accomp(xx)$.

Then, the following lemma must hold.

Lemma 2. For any two different words x and y in $P(n)$,

$$pebble\text{-}cross(accomp(xx)) \neq pebble\text{-}cross(accomp(yy)).$$

[*Proof.* Suppose to the contrary that $pebble\text{-}cross(accomp(xx)) = pebble\text{-}cross(accomp(yy))$. We assume without loss of generality that $contents(x) - contents(y) \neq \phi$. By using the same idea as in the proof of Lemma 1, it follows that we can construct an accepting computation of M on $B(1)\#B(2)\#\ldots\#B(n)xy$ using at most $L(r(n))$ cells of the storage tape, and thus $B(1)\#B(2)\#\ldots\#B(n)xy$ would be accepted by M. This contradicts the fact that it is not in T_2. This completes the proof of the lemma.]

For each $x \in P(n)$, $accomp(xx)$ is loop-free. Therefore, it follows that, for each $x \in P(n)$, the same storage state (in $S^+(n)$) appears at most twice in $pebble\text{-}cross(accomp(xx))$. Therefore, for each $x \in P(n)$, the length of $pebble\text{-}cross$ $(accomp(xx))$ is bounded by $2s^+(n)$. For each $n \gg 1$, let $PEBBLE\text{-}CROSS(n) = \{pebble\text{-}cross(accomp(xx))|x \in P(n)\}$. From the observation above, it follows that $|PEBBLE\text{-}CROSS(n)| \leq (s^+(n))^{2s^+(n)}$. Since $L(n) = o(\log n)$, by a simple calculation, it follows that $|P(n)| \gg |PEBBLE\text{-}CROSS(n)|$ for large n. Thus, there must be two different words x and y in $P(n)$ such that $pebble\text{-}cross$ $(accomp(xx)) = pebble\text{-}cross(accomp(yy))$. This contradicts Lemma 2. This completes the proof of "$T_2 \notin weak\text{-}NSPACE^{peb}(o(\log n))$". □

From Theorem 3, we get the following corollary:

Corollary 2. For any $m \in \{strong, weak\}$ and any function $\log\log n \leq L(n) = o(\log n)$, $m\text{-}NSPACE^{peb}(L(n)) \subset m\text{-}ASPACE^{peb}(L(n))$.

5   Space Hierarchy

This section investigates a space hierarchy of the accepting powers of deterministic and nondeterministic one-pebble Tm's.

Our main result of this section is:

Theorem 4. Let $L(n) : N \to N$ be a one-pebble fully space constructible function such that $L(n) \leq \log n$ $(n \geq 1)$ and let $L'(n) : N \to N$ be any function such that $L'(n) = o(L(n))$. Then

$$strong\text{-}DSPACE^{peb}(L(n)) - weak\text{-}NSPACE^{peb}(L'(n)) \neq \phi.$$

proof: Let $T(L)$ be the following set depending on the function $L(n)$ in the theorem: $T(L) = \{wc^iw| \exists n \geq 1[w \in \{0,1\}^+ \wedge |w| = 2^{L(n)} \wedge i = n - 2 \times 2^{L(n)}]\}$. It is easy to show that $T(L)$ is in $strong\text{-}DSPACE^{peb}(L(n))$. So, the proof is omitted here. We below show that $T(L) \notin weak\text{-}NSPACE^{peb}(L'(n))$, where $L'(n) = o(L(n))$. The proof is again similar to that of "$T_1 \notin weak\text{-}NSPACE^{peb}(o(\log n))$" in the proof of Theorem 2. Suppose to the contrary that there exists a weakly $L'(n)$ space-bounded nondeterministic one-pebble Tm M accepting

$T(L)$. Let Q be the set of states of the finite control of M, and Q^+ and Q^- be defined as in the proof of Theorem 2. We again assume without loss of generality that when M accepts an input word in $T(L)$, M enters an accepting state in Q^+ on the right endmarker \$, and halts. Below we consider the computations of M on words of length n for large n. Thus M uses at most $L'(n)$ cells of the storage tape. For each $n \geq 2$, let $S(n)$ be the set of possible storage states of M using at most $L'(n)$ cells of the storage tape, and let $S^+(n)$ and $S^-(n)$ be defined as in the proof of Theorem 2. Clearly, $s^+(n) \overset{\triangle}{=} |S^+(n)| = O(t^{L'(n)})$, and $s^-(n) \overset{\triangle}{=} |S^-(n)| = O(t^{L'(n)})$ for some constant t depending only on M. For each $n \geq 1$, let $V(n) = \{0,1\}^{2^{L(n)}}$. Let x be a word in $V(n)$ that is supposed to be a subword of an input word of length n to M. Suppose that the pebble of M is not placed on this word x. Then, as defined in the proof of Theorem 2, we define a mapping M_x, which depends on M and x, from $S^-(n) \times \{left, right\}$ to the power set of $S^-(n) \times \{left, right\}$. We say that two words $x_1, x_2 \in V(n)$ are M^--equivalent if two mappings M_{x_1} and M_{x_2} are equivalent. M^--equivalence is an equivalence relation on $V(n)$, and there are at most $e(n) = (2^{2s^-(n)})^{2s^-(n)}$ M^--equivalence classes of $V(n)$. Let $P(n)$ be a largest M^--equivalence class of $V(n)$. Then we have $|P(n)| \geq \frac{|V(n)|}{e(n)} = \frac{2^{2^{L(n)}}}{e(n)}$. For each $x \in P(n)$, $xc^i x$ (where $i = n - 2 \times 2^{L(n)}$) is in $T(L)$, and so it is accepted by M, and its length is n. Therefore, there exists an accepting computation of M on $xc^i x$ using at most $L'(n)$ cells of the storage tape. Let "$accomp(xc^i x)$" be such a fixed loop-free accepting computation of M on $xc^i x$. For each $x \in P(n)$, let $pebble\text{-}cross(accomp(xc^i x))$ be the sequence of storage states (in $S^+(n)$) when M crosses the boundary between the left x and the right $c^i x$ with the pebble in the finite control from left to right or from right to left in $accomp(xc^i x)$.

Then, the following lemma must hold.

Lemma 3. For any two different words x and y in $P(n)$,

$$pebble\text{-}cross(accomp(xc^i x)) \neq pebble\text{-}cross(accomp(yc^i y)).$$

[*Proof.* Suppose to the contrary that $pebble\text{-}cross(accomp(xc^i x)) = pebble\text{-}cross(accomp(yc^i y))$. By using the same idea as in the proof of Lemma 1, it follows that we can construct an accepting computation of M on $xc^i y$ using at most $L'(n)$ cells of the storage tape, and thus $xc^i y$ would be accepted by M. This contradicts the fact that it is not in $T(L)$. This completes the proof of the lemma.]

For each $x \in P(n)$, $accomp(xc^i x)$ is loop-free. Therefore, it follows that, for each $x \in P(n)$, the same storage state (in $S^+(n)$) appears at most twice in $pebble\text{-}cross(accomp(xx))$. Therefore, for each $x \in P(n)$, the length of $pebble\text{-}cross$ $(accomp(xc^i x))$ is bounded by $2s^+(n)$. For each $n \gg 1$, let $PEBBLE\text{-}CROSS(n) = \{pebble\text{-}cross(accomp(xc^i x)) | x \in P(n)\}$. From the observation above, it follows that $|PEBBLE\text{-}CROSS(n)| \leq (s^+(n))^{2s^+(n)}$. Since $L'(n) = o(L(n))$, by a simple calculation, it follows that for large n, we have $|P(n)| \gg |PEBBLE\text{-}CROSS(n)|$. Thus, there must be two different words x and y in $P(n)$ such that $pebble\text{-}cross$ $(accomp(xc^i x)) =$

pebble-cross(*accomp*($yc^i y$)). This contradicts Lemma 3. This completes the proof of "$T(L) \notin$ *weak-NSPACE*$^{peb}(L'(n))$". □

From the fact (Fact 1) that $\lceil \log \log n \rceil$ is one-pebble fully space constractible, we can easily see that for any integer $k \geq 1$, $\lceil \log \log n \rceil^k$ is one-pebble fully space constractible. From this and from Theorem 4, we get the following corollary:

Corollary 3. For any $m \in \{strong, weak\}$, any $X \in \{D, N\}$, and any integer $k \geq 1$, m-$XSPACE^{peb}(\lceil \log \log n \rceil^k) \subset m$-$XSPACE^{peb}(\lceil \log \log n \rceil^{k+1})$.

6 Conclusion

We conclude this paper by posing several open problems.

− Let 2-*NC* be the class of languages accepted by two-way nondeterministic counter automata. Then,

$$strong\text{-}DSPACE^{peb}(\log \log n) - 2\text{-}NC \neq \phi\ ?$$

− For any $m \in \{strong, weak\}$, and any function $L(n) \geq \log \log n$,

$$m\text{-}DSPACE^{peb}(L(n)) \subset m\text{-}NSPACE^{peb}(L(n))\ ?$$

− Let $L(n)$ be a one-pebble (fully) space constructible function such that $L(n) \leq \log n$ ($n \geq 1$) and let $L'(n) = o(L(n))$. Then

$$strong\text{-}DSPACE^{peb}(L(n)) - weak\text{-}ASPACE^{peb}(L'(n)) \neq \phi\ ?$$

References

1. M.Blum and C.Hewitt, "Automata on a 2-dimensional tape", IEEE Symp. on Switching and Automata Theory(1967) 155-160
2. B.V.Braunmuhl, R.Gngler, and R.Rettinger, "The alternation hierarchy for sublogarithmic space is infinite", Comput. Complexity, vol.3 (1993) 207–230
3. A.K.Chandra, D.C.Kozen and L.J.Stockmeyer, "Alternation", J.Assoc.Comput.Mach., Vol.28, No.1 (1981) 114–133
4. J.H.Chang, O.H.Ibarra,M.A.Palis and B.Ravikumar, "On pebble automata", Theoret. Comput. Sci. 44 (1986) 111–121
5. Z.Galil, "Some open problems in the theory of computation as questions about two-way deterministic pushdown automata languages", Math.Systems Theory 10 (1977) 211–228
6. J.E.Hopcroft and J.D.Ullman, Introduction to Automata Theory, Languages and Computation, Addison-Wesley, Reading, MA (1979)
7. T.Okazaki, L.Zhang, K.Inoue, A.Ito and Y.Wang, "A relationship between two-way deterministic one-counter automata and one-pebble deterministi Turing machines with sublogarithmic space", IEICE Trans. INF. & SYST., Vol.E82-D, No.5 (1999) 999–1004
8. A.Szepietowski, "Turing machines with sublogarithmic space", Lecture Notes in Computer Science 843 (1994)

Hypergraph Decomposition and Secret Sharing

Giovanni Di Crescenzo[1] and Clemente Galdi[2*]

[1] Telcordia Technologies Inc.,
445 South Street, Morristown, New Jersey, 07960, USA.
`giovanni@research.telcordia.com`
[2] Research Academic Computer Technology Institute and
Department of Computer Engineering and Informatics
University of Patras, 26500, Rio, Greece
`clegal@ceid.upatras.gr`

Abstract. In this paper we investigate the construction of efficient secret sharing schemes by using a technique called *hypergraph decomposition*, extending in a non-trivial way the previously studied graph decomposition technique. A major advantage advantage of hypergraph decomposition is that it applies to *any* access structure, rather than only structures representable as graphs. As a consequence we obtain secret sharing schemes for several classes of access structures with improved efficiency over previous results. We also obtain an elementary characterization of the ideal access structures among the hyperstars, which is of independent interest.

Keywords: Cryptography, Secret Sharing, Algorithms, Hypergraph Decomposition.

1 Introduction

A secret sharing scheme is a pair of efficient algorithms: a distribution algorithm and a reconstruction algorithm, run by a dealer and some parties. The distribution algorithm is executed by a dealer who, given a secret, computes some shares of it and gives them to the parties. The reconstruction algorithm is executed by a qualified subset of parties who, by putting together their own shares, can therefore reconstruct the secret. A secret sharing scheme satisfies the additional property that any non-qualified subset of participants does not obtain any information about the secret. The set of qualified subsets of parties is also called "access structure". The notion of secret sharing was introduced by Blackley [2] and Shamir [11], who considered the important case in which the access structure contains all subsets of size at least k, for some integer k.

Since their introduction, secret sharing schemes have been widely employed in the construction of more elaborated cryptographic primitives and several types

* Work done while visiting Telcordia Technologies. The visit of the author to Telcordia Technologies has been partially supported by DIMACS under grant NSF CCR 99-06105. The work of the second author is partially supported by the European Union under IST FET Project CRESCCO, and RTN Project ARACNE.

T. Ibaraki, N. Katoh, and H. Ono (Eds.): ISAAC 2003, LNCS 2906, pp. 645–654, 2003.

of cryptographic protocols. Being so often employed, central research questions in this area are both the construction of efficient secret sharing schemes for several classes of access structures, and finding bounds on the possible efficiency that any such scheme can achieve for a certain access structure. The efficiency measures studied in the literature, and the ones that we will also consider in this paper, are related to the size of the largest distributed share (typically called "information rate", for its analogy with a so-called coding theory notion), or the sum of the distributed shares (typically called "average information rate"). The importance of these parameters is clear since they are directly related to the storage complexity, the communication complexity and the amount of secret information of the scheme. In the construction of efficient sharing schemes and in the search of bounds on such efficiency, the literature has paid special attention to the so-called "ideal" access structures; namely, access structures for which there exists a secret sharing scheme where the share distributed to each participant has the same size as the secret. (Note that this is well-known to be the best efficiency that one can achieve.) Further studied topics along these lines are: The classification of all access structures according to whether they are ideal or not, and the investigation of the efficiency of non-ideal access structures using ideal ones, using elegant techniques such as "graph decomposition".

In this paper we elaborate along this research direction by studying a non-trivial extension of the graph decomposition technique, which we call "hypergraph decomposition"; by applying this technique so to obtain secret sharing schemes that are dramatically more efficient than what previously known; and by finding novel and elementary characterization of ideal access structures within a large class of them.

Previous results. Secret sharing schemes have been proposed, for instance, in [11,2] for threshold structures, in [13] for all graph-based access structures, in [1] for all monotone circuits, in [12] for homogeneous access structures, rank requirements, in [10] for all access structures. Lower bounds on the size of shares for all secret sharing schemes have been proposed, for instance, in [7,3,4] for certain graph-based access structures, and in [14,9,15] for other classes of access structures. A characterization of ideal access structures in terms of weighted matroids has been presented in [6]. The *graph decomposition* technique [13,5] consists of decomposing a graph into smaller graphs whose union covers the original graph and representing ideal access structure. (We note that graphs can be associated only to access structures including all subsets containing some subsets of size 2.) This technique has been firstly extended in [14,12] for general access structures, where the author describes lower bounds for the information rate and average information rate for general access structure.

Our results. Following this line of research, in this paper we present the *hypergraph decomposition* technique, of decomposing an hypergraph into smaller hypergraphs whose union covers the original hypergraph and representing ideal access structures. A secret sharing scheme for the original hypergraph can then be obtained by composing the schemes for the smaller ones. Applying this technique requires (a) finding small hypergraphs which represent the access structure and (b) finding the optimal decomposition of the input hypergraph into such smaller ones. As for (a), we consider simple structures such as hyperstars, and find a new and elementary condition that characterizes whether a given hyperstar is ideal or not. (This condition being more elementary than the condition in [6] that however characterizes all ideal access structures.) We prove (b) to be an NP-complete problem for general hypergraphs, but we note that it can be solved efficiently for special types of hypergraphs. We then move on to study special classes of access structures to which the hypergraph decomposition technique can be efficiently applied. Specifically, we study hyperpaths, hypercycles, hyperstars and hypertrees (all generalizing their graph-based counterpart) and obtain efficient secret sharing schemes for these structures. More specifically, for these classes of access structures, we give upper and lower bounds on the average information rate that improve on the previous known schemes. We further present optimal secret sharing schemes for hyperpaths and hypercycles.

Due to space constraints, several proofs are omitted from this extended abstract.

2 Definitions and Preliminaries

In this section we review some basic definitions and notations that will be used through the paper. Suppose $\mathcal{P}$ be a set of participants. We denote by $\mathcal{A}$ the set of subsets of parties which we desire to be able to reconstruct the secret, thus $\mathcal{A} \subseteq 2^{\mathcal{P}}$. Each set in $\mathcal{A}$ is said to be an *authorized set* while each set not in $\mathcal{A}$ is called a *forbidden set*. We define the family of *minimal sets* as $\delta^- A = \{A \in \mathcal{A} : \forall A' \in \mathcal{A} \setminus \{A\}, A' \not\subset A\}$. The set $\mathcal{A}$ is called the *access structure* and $\delta^- \mathcal{A}$ is said to be its *basis*. We will deal only with access structures that are *monotone*, i.e., they satisfy the following property: If $B \in \mathcal{A}$ and $B \subseteq C \subseteq \mathcal{P}$ then $C \in \mathcal{A}$. Thus, in order to describe an access structure it is sufficient to describe its basis.

Let $\mathcal{S}$ be a set of size q containing all the possible secrets to be shared. For every participant $P \in \mathcal{P}$ let us denote by $\mathcal{S}_P$ a the set containing all the possible information given to P by a secret sharing scheme. The elements in $\mathcal{S}_P$ are called shares. As done in the literature, we will denote by P both the party in the access structure and the random variable describing shares assigned to him. Similarly, we will denote by S both the secret to be shared and the random variable associated to it. Suppose a *dealer* $D \notin \mathcal{P}$ wants to share a secret $s \in S$ among the participants in $\mathcal{P}$. For each party in $P \in \mathcal{P}$ he selects one element in S_P and gives it to P. Using Shannon's entropy function (see [8] for a complete covering), we say a secret sharing scheme to be *perfect* if the following conditions hold:

1 $H(S|A) = 0, \forall A \in \mathcal{A}$ (Any set $A \in \mathcal{A}$ of participants who pool their shares together can recover the secret s).
2 $H(S|A) = H(S), \forall A \notin \mathcal{A}$ (Any set $A \notin \mathcal{A}$ of participants who pool their share together obtain no information on s.)

We will use two values for measuring the efficiency of a secret sharing schemes, the *information rate* ρ and the *average information rate* $\tilde{\rho}$ defined as follows:

$$\rho = \frac{\log q}{\log \max\{|\mathcal{S}_P| : P \in \mathcal{P}\}} \qquad \tilde{\rho} = \frac{|\mathcal{P}| \log q}{\sum_{P \in \mathcal{P}} \log |\mathcal{S}_P|}$$

It is easy to see that in any perfect secret sharing scheme, $q \leq \max\{|\mathcal{S}_P| : P \in \mathcal{P}\}$ and thus $\rho \leq 1$. A secret sharing scheme in which $\rho = 1$ is said to be *ideal*. An access structure having an ideal secret sharing scheme is also called ideal. Notice that as the (maximum) amount of information distributed to the parties increases, the information rate decreases. Thus the closer the information rate is to one, the more efficient the secret sharing scheme is.

The information rate considers only the "maximum size" among the share distributed to the parties. Sometimes it could be more preferable to consider the average size of the shares distributed by the secret sharing scheme. Since, in any perfect secret sharing scheme, for any $P \in \mathcal{P}$, $q \leq |\mathcal{S}_P|$ it is immediate that $\tilde{\rho} \leq 1$. Moreover it is not hard to see that $\tilde{\rho} \geq \rho$.

A *hypergraph* H is a pair (V, E) where V is a non-empty set of vertices and $E = \{E_1, \ldots, E_m\} \subseteq 2^V$ is a set of hyperedges. The hypergraph is said to be *connected* if for any two vertices $u, v \in V$ there exists a hyperpath from u to v in H. More formally there exists a sequence $E_{i_1}, \ldots, E_{i_s}$ such that $u \in E_{i_1}$, $E_{i_j} \cap E_{i_{j+1}} \neq \emptyset$ for each $j = 1, \ldots, s-1$, and $v \in E_{i_s}$.

Each access structure, $\mathcal{A} \subseteq 2^{\mathcal{P}}$, can be represented as a hypergraph $H = (\mathcal{P}, \mathcal{A})$ by letting each party being a vertex and each authorized set being represented as an hyperedge in the hypergraph.

Let $H = (V, E)$ be a hypergraph and let $W \subseteq V$. We say that the sub-hypergraph $H' = (V', E')$ is *S-induced* by W iff $E' = \{e \in E | e \cap W \neq \emptyset\}$ and $V' = \cup_{e \in E'} e$. For any subset $W \subseteq \mathcal{P}$, the sub-hypergraph S-induced by W represents a minimal sub-access structure containing all the vertices in W and, at the same time, all hyperedges that have non-empty intersection with W. (We note that the definition of S-induced subhypergraph does *not* reduce to the classical definition of *induced* subhypergraph.)

Let I be a set of hyperedges. We say that the *region* determined by the hyperedges in I is the set of vertices that belong to all the hyperedges in I and does not belong to any other hyperedge in the hypergraph. More formally: $R = \texttt{Region}(I) = (\cap_{E_i \in I} E_i) \setminus \cup_{E_i \in (E \setminus I)} E_i$. Moreover we say that R is an *i-region* if $|I| = i$. We also define the $\texttt{Remove}(H, R)$ to be hypergraph $H' = (V', E')$ where $V' = V \setminus R$ and $E' = \{E_i' = E_i \cap V' \neq \emptyset$ for any $E_i \in E\}$.

It is important to notice that $\texttt{Remove}(H, R)$ is no longer a substructure of H. Indeed some forbidden sets for H could be authorized sets for $\texttt{Remove}(H, R)$. It is immediate that the following holds:

Theorem 1. *Let $H = (V, E)$ be a hypergraph, $W \subseteq V$ and let H_W be the sub-hypergraph S-induced by W. Then $\rho(H) \leq \rho(H_W)$.*

We will extensively use some classes of hypergraphs that we are going to define formally. These hypergraphs are a natural generalization of graphs like stars, paths and cycles. More precisely, a hypergraph $H = (V, E)$ is said to be a *hyperstar* if $A = \bigcap_{E_i \in E} E_i \neq \emptyset$. We will call A the *center* of the hyperstar. Notice that this definition is more general than the one of *sunflower* or *delta-system*, where it is required the egdes must have *pairwise* the same intersection. In our case, we simply require that the intersection of *all* the edges of the hypergraph must be non-empty. The hypergraph H is said to be a *hyperpath*, (resp. a *hyper-cycle*) if there exists an permutation $\pi : \{0, \ldots, m-1\} \to \{0, \ldots, m-1\}$ such that for any i, $E_{\pi(i)} \cap E_{\pi(i+1)} \neq \emptyset$ and $E_{\pi(i)} \cap E_{\pi(j)} = \emptyset$ if $j \notin \{i-1, i, i+1\}$ and $2 \leq i \leq m-1$, (resp., $j \notin \{i-1 \bmod m, i, i+1 \bmod m\}$ and $0 \leq i \leq m-1$). We will denote by P_m the hyperpath with m hyperedges and by C_m the hyper-cycle with m hyperedges.

3   Hypergraph Decomposition

In this section we describe the technique of hypergraph decomposition, a generalization of the graph decomposition technique studied in [5,13]. Given an access structure $\mathcal{A}$, we can construct a secret sharing for it as follows. We first represent $\mathcal{A}$ as an hypergraph H. Then we decompose the hypergraph in smaller sub-hypergraphs $H_1, \ldots, H_k$ for which efficient (and possibly ideal) secret sharing schemes are known and such that all the edges in H belong to at least one of the H_i. Thus each participant will receive a certain number of shares by means of each sub-structure H_i. The secret sharing for H is thus obtained as a "union" of the secret sharing of all the H_i's. Indeed since all the hyperedges in H are covered by the decomposition, each authorized set will be able to reconstruct the secret. On the other hand, the security of the secret sharing scheme for H is guaranteed by the security of the secret sharing schemes for the H_i's and by the fact that these schemes are independent. Notice that the performance of the secret sharing scheme not only depends on the performance of the decomposition of $\mathcal{A}$, but also on "how" the sub-structures combine together.

We now define formally a hypergraph decomposition:

Definition 1 (Hypergraph Decomposition). *Let $H = (V, E)$ be a hyper-graph and let $\Delta = \{H_1, \ldots, H_k\}$, where $H_i = (V_i, E_i)$, with $E_i \subseteq E$ and $V_i = \cup_{e \in E_i} e$, be a set of sub-hypergraphs of H. The sequence Δ is said to be a decomposition of H if and only if each hyperedge in H belongs to at least one H_i. The decomposition is said to be ideal if the access structure represented each H_i is ideal. A decomposition $\Delta = \{H_1, \ldots, H_k\}$ of H is said to be a hyperstar decomposition of H if all the subhypergraphs H_i are hyperstars.*

Basic results (omitted here) about hypergraph decomposition include generalizations of two Theorems in [5]. Our first theorem allows to evaluate the information rate and the average information rate that can be achieved by a secret sharing scheme for an access structure $\mathcal{A}$ having a decomposition of the hypergraph representing $\mathcal{A}$. Our second theorem states that, having a number of distinct decompositions of a hypergraph, it is possible to construct secret sharing schemes that improve the average information rate w.r.t. the algorithm that use a single hypergraph decomposition.

In order to apply the hypergraph decomposition construction to a certain class of access structures, we have to solve the following two main problems.

- Define classes of ideal hypergraph-based access structures for which it is possible to construct in polynomial time an ideal secret sharing scheme.
- Represent the class of access structures given as a class of hypergraphs and find in polynomial time the optimal decomposition of these hypergraphs using only the ideal structures previously defined.

4   Hyperstars

In this section we give a complete characterization of the hyperstars having an ideal secret sharing scheme. We will show that it is possible in polynomial time to decide whether a given hyperstar represents an ideal access structure on not. This gives a new (and more elementary than [6]) characterization of ideal structures within this specific class of structures. We further give an algorithm that, on input an access structure $\mathcal{A}$ representable as an ideal hyperstar, realizes an ideal secret sharing scheme for it.

Theorem 2. Let $H = (V, E)$ be a hyperstar with $E = (E_1, \ldots, E_m)$ and let $B_0, \ldots B_p$ be the set of all regions in H. Denote by $I_j \subseteq E$ the set of hyperedges determining B_j. There exists an ideal secret sharing scheme for H if and only if for each pair of sets I_{j_1} and I_{j_2} it holds that either $I_{j_1} \cap I_{j_2} = \emptyset$ or $I_{j_1} \subseteq I_{j_2}$ (or $I_{j_2} \subseteq I_{j_1}$).

The key idea of the characterization is the fact that if a hyperstar H contains a non-ideal sub-hypergraph, than H itself cannot be ideal. On the other hand we need an algorithm that, given an ideal hyperstar, distributes to each party a share of the same size of the secret. We start by giving the condition under which a hyperstar is not ideal (in fact, we prove a stronger statement by quantifying the blowup on the size of the shares).

Lemma 1. Let $H = (V, E)$ be a hyperstar with $|V| = n$, $E = (E_1, \ldots, E_m)$ and let $B_1, \ldots, B_p$ be the set of all regions in H. Denote by $I_j \subseteq E$ the set of hyperedges determining B_j. If there exist two non-empty sets I_{j_1} and I_{j_2} such that $I_{j_1} \cap I_{j_2} \neq \emptyset$, $I_{j_1} \setminus I_{j_2} \neq \emptyset$ and $I_{j_2} \setminus I_{j_1} \neq \emptyset$, then there exist two parties P_i and P_j such that $H(P_i) + H(P_j) \geq 3H(S)$.

In the following lemma we show that if the condition of the previous lemma does not hold, then there exists an ideal secret sharing scheme for hypergraph H.

Lemma 2. Let $H = (V, E)$ be a hyperstar with $|V| = n$, $E = (E_1, \ldots, E_m)$ and let $B_0, \ldots B_p$ be the set of all regions in H with B_0 being the center of H. Denote by $I_j \subseteq E$ the set of hyperedges determining B_j. If for each pair of sets I_{j_1} and I_{j_2} it holds that either $I_{j_1} \cap I_{j_2} = \emptyset$ or $I_{j_1} \subseteq I_{j_2}$ (or $I_{j_2} \subseteq I_{j_1}$), then Remove($H, B_0$) is the union of disjoint ideal hyperstars.

This Lemma immediately suggests an algorithm that allows to construct an ideal secret sharing scheme for an ideal hyperstar. Roughly speaking, given an ideal hyperstar H, the algorithm applies a Remove operation on the center B_0 of H obtaining a set of disjoint (ideal) hyperstars. We write s as $s_1 \oplus s_2$ (the $\oplus$ operation being over GF(2)), and share s_1 among the parties in the center using a $(|B_0|, |B_0|)$-threshold scheme, and s_2 among the remaining parties of H. Since the hypergraph graph obtained is the union of a set of disjoint ideal hyperstars, we can recursively apply the same algorithm to each of these hyperstars by using s_2 as a secret. However, there are two algorithmic problems to be solved in order to realize this algorithm. The first one is how to efficiently partition the parties into disjoint regions. Notice that this problem can be easily solved in polynomial time. A second problem is how to verify that a given hyperstar is ideal. But, given the decomposition in regions of the hyperstar, this problem can be easily solved in polynomial time.

5   Average Information Rate

In this section we will give upper bounds on the average information rate for general access structures. By extending the proofs in [5], we can prove the problem of finding the optimal hyperstar decomposition to be NP-Hard. Moreover we can prove that it is possible to compute in polynomial-time, optimal secret sharing schemes for some classes of hypergraphs, namely hyperpaths, hypercycles and hypertrees. We can show that these schemes improve on the previously known secret sharing schemes. We further present upper bounds on the average information rate for some classes of hypergraphs, namely, hyperpaths, hypercycles and hypertrees.

5.1   Upper Bounds on the Average Information Rate

Given a hypergraph H, we construct a new hypergraph H' we call the *foundation* of H. The idea is to construct a hypergraph that contains all the vertices that will receive a share whose size is strictly greater than the size of the secret. More formally we have:

Definition 2 (Foundation). *Let $H = (V, E)$ be a hypergraph. The foundation of H is a hypergraph $H' = (V', E')$, where $V' = \cup_{E_i \in E'} E_i$ and for any hyperedge $E_i \in E$, $E_i \in E'$ if and only if there exist two hyperedges E_j, E_k such that:*

- $E_i \cap E_j \neq \emptyset$ *and* $E_i \cap E_k \neq \emptyset$
- $E_i \cap E_j \nsubseteq E_k$ *and* $E_i \cap E_k \nsubseteq E_j$

Consider a hyperedge E_i in the foundation hypergraph of H. We denote by $N(E_i)$ the set of hyperedges incident to E_i and satisfying the conditions of Definition 2. Moreover, for each E_i in the foundation hypergraph, there exist at least two regions, say $B_{i,1} = E_i \cap E_j$ and $B_{i,2} = E_i \cap E_k$ with $E_j, E_k \in N(E_i)$. By Lemma 1, some of the parties in these regions will receive shares whose size is strictly greater than the size of the secret. Two possible cases can arise:

- $E_i \cap E_j \cap E_k = \emptyset$. In this case, the three hyperedges form a hyperpath of length three that, by Theorem 2, is not ideal.
- $E_i \cap E_j \cap E_k \neq \emptyset$. In this case the three hyperedges form a hyperstar with three hyperedges and two 2-regions that, by Lemma 1 is not ideal.

Given H, we consider the following linear programming problem $\mathcal{A}(\mathcal{H})$.

$$\text{Minimize } C = \sum_{v \in V} a_v$$
$$a_v \geq 0, v \in V$$
$$a_v + a_w \geq 1, \forall E_i \in E', \forall E_j, E_k \in N(E_i), \forall v \in E_i \cap E_j, w \in E_i \cap E_k, j \neq k$$

Theorem 3. *Let $H = (V, E)$ be a hypergraph with foundation H'. Let C^* the optimal solution for the problem $\mathcal{A}(H)$. Then $\tilde{\rho}^* (H) \leq |V|/(C^* + |V|)$.*

Theorem 3 defines an upper bound on the average information rate for general access structures. In the next sections we are going to give specific upper bounds for particular classes of access structures, namely hyperpaths, hypercycles and hypertrees.

Before going on, we are going to prove a result that will be used in the rest of this section. For any hyperedge $E_j \in E'$ in the foundation hypergraph there are at least two *non-ideal regions* we call $B_{j,1}$ and $B_{j,2}$ with weight $w_{B_{j,1}} = |B_{j,1}|$ and $w_{Bj,2} = |B_{j,2}|$ respectively. Denote by $w_j = \min\{w_{B_{j,1}}, w_{B_{j,2}}\}$, $w_{min} = \min\{w_{B_{j,1}}, w_{B_{j,2}} | j = 1, \ldots |E'|\}$, and $w_{max} = \max\{w_{B_{j,1}}, w_{B_{j,2}} | j = 1, \ldots |E'|\}$.

Theorem 4. *Let H be a hypergraph, let $H' = (V', E')$ be its foundation and let $r = w_{min}/w_{max}$. If the vertices in V' have degree at most d than $C^* \geq r|E'|/d$.*

From this theorem it is possible to derive some interesting results on some classes of hypergraphs.

HyperCycles. The first class of hypergraphs we are going to consider is the class of hypercycles. It is not hard to see that the foundation hypergraph of C_m is the C_m itself. Moreover, the non-ideal regions in C_m are exactly all its 2-regions. Since C_m has maximum degree 2, by Theorem 4 we can obtain the following:

Corollary 1. *Let $C_m = (V, E)$ be a hypercycle, let $B_1, \ldots, B_m$ be its 2-regions and let $w_i =| B_i |$ for $i = 1, \ldots, m$. The it holds that: $\tilde{\rho} \leq |V|/(rm/2 + |V|)$ where $r = \min_{1 \leq j \leq m} w_j / \max_{1 \leq j \leq m} w_j$*

HyperPaths. The next bound we are going to show is the upper bound on the average information rate for hyperpaths. It is not hard to see that the foundation hypergraph of a hyperpath P_m is isomorphic to P_{m-2}. More precisely, given a hyperpath P_m, its foundation hypergraph is obtained by removing the first and the last hyperedge in the hyperpath. Indeed all the other hyperedges in the hyperpath will be the middle-hyperedge of some subpaths of length 3.

Corollary 2. *Let $P_m = (V, E)$ be a hyperpath, and let P_{m-2} be its foundation hypergraph. Moreover let $B_1, \ldots, B_{m-2}$ be the 2-regions of P_{m-2} and let $w_i =| B_i |$ for $i = 1, \ldots, m - 2$. The it holds that: $\tilde{\rho} \leq |V|/(r(m - 2)/2 + |V|)$ where $r = \min_{1 \leq j \leq m-2} w_j / \max_{1 \leq j \leq m-2} w_j$*

Hypertrees. Let H be a hypertree with at least four hyperedges. The foundation hypergraph of a hypertree contains at least all the internal vertices of the tree.

Corollary 3. *Let H be a hypertree with maximum degree d, let H' be its foundation and let $r = w_{min}/w_{max}$. It holds that $C^* \geq r|E'|/d$*

6   Optimal Information Rate

In this section we present a general lower bound on the information rate based on the multiple hypergraph decomposition. We shall show that using this technique it is possible to construct optimal secret sharing schemes for some classes of hypergraphs such as hyperpaths, hypercycles and hyperstars w.r.t. the information rate. For a hypergraph H define

$$\rho^*(H) = \sup\{\rho : \exists \text{ perfect secret sharing scheme for } H \text{ with information rate } \rho\}$$

We are interested in the best information rate we can obtain by multiple hypergraph decomposition. To this aim we define $\rho_M^*(H)$ to be this optimal information rate. It is immediate that $\rho_M^*(H) \leq \rho^*(H)$. We first generalize a result in [5] that allows to compute the value of $\rho_M^*(H)$.

Let $H = (V, E)$ be an hypergraph and assume $\Delta_j = \{H_{j1}, \ldots, H_{jk_j}\}$, with $j = 1, 2$ be two hypergraph decompositions of H. We can define a partial order on the Δ_j's as follows: Let $R_{jv} - |\{i : v \in H_{ji}\}|$. We say that $\Delta_i \leq \Delta_j$ if and only if $R_{iv} \leq R_{jv}$ for any $v \in V$. Define a hypergraph decomposition Δ_i to be *minimal* if there does not exists Δ_j such that $\Delta_j \leq \Delta_i$ and $\Delta_j \neq \Delta_i$. Now assume that $\Delta_j = \{H_{j1}, \ldots, H_{jk_j}\}$, with $j = 1, \ldots, L$ be a complete enumeration of all minimal hypergraph decomposition of H and for every vertex $v \in V$ and for any $j = 1, \ldots, L$ define $R_{jv} = |\{i : v \in H_{ji}\}|$. Consider the following optimization problem $\mathcal{I}(H)$

$$\text{Minimize } R = \max\{\textstyle\sum_{j=1}^{L} a_j R_{jv} : v \in V\}$$
$$\text{Subject to: } \quad a_j \geq 0, 1 \leq j \leq L \text{ such that } \textstyle\sum_{j=1}^{L} a_j = 1,$$

The proof of the following theorem is a straightforward extension of the corresponding theorem in [5].

Theorem 5. *Let R^* be the optimal solution to $\mathcal{I}(H)$. Then $\rho_M^*(H) = 1/R^*$.*

Theorem 6. *Let P_m be the hyperpath with m hyperedges. Then $\rho^*(P_m) = 2/3$.*

Theorem 7. *Let C_m be the hypercycle with $m \geq 3$ hyperedges. Then if m is even $\rho^*(C_m) = 2/3$ otherwise $\rho_M^*(C_m) = (2n + 1)/(3n + 2)$*

Theorem 8. *Let H be a non-ideal hyperstar with three hyperedges. It holds that* $\rho^*(H) = 2/3$.

Corollary 4. *Let H be a non-ideal hyperstar with m hyperedges then* $\rho^*(H) \leq$ $2/3$.

References

1. J. Benaloh and J. Leichter, *Generalized secret sharing and monotone functions*, in Advances in Cryptology – CRYPTO '88, S. Goldwasser, ed., Lecture Notes in Computer Science 403 (1989), 27–35.
2. G. R. Blakley, *Safeguarding cryptographic keys*, in Proceedings of the National Computer Conference, 1979, American Federation of Information Processing Societies Proceedings 48 (1979), 313–317.
3. C. Blundo, A. De Santis, R. De Simone, and U. Vaccaro, *Tight Bounds on the Information Rate of Secret Sharing Schemes*, Design, Codes, and Cryptography, vol. 11, 1997, pp. 107–122.
4. C. Blundo, A. De Santis, L. Gargano and U. Vaccaro, *On the Information Rate of Secret Sharing Schemes,* in Theoretical Computer Science, vol. 154, pp. 283–306, 1996.
5. C. Blundo, A. De Santis, D. R. Stinson, U. Vaccaro, *Graph Decomposition and Secret Sharing Schemes*, Journal of Cryptology, Vol. 8 (1995), pp. 39–64. Preliminary version appeared in EuroCrypt 92.
6. E. F. Brickell, D.M. Davenport, *On the Classification of Ideal Secret Sharing Schemes*, Journal of Cryptology, Vol. 4 (1991), pp. 123–134.
7. R.M. Capocelli, A. De Santis, L. Gargano, U. Vaccaro, *On the Size of Shares for Secret Sharing Schemes*, Journal of Cryptology, vol. 6, n. 3, pp. 157–169, 1993.
8. T.M. Cover and J.A. Thomas, *Elements of Information Theory*, John Wiley & Sons, Singapore, 1991.
9. L. Csirmaz, *The Size of a Share Must be Large,* Journal of Cryptology, Vol. **10**, n. 4, pp. 223–231, 1997.
10. M. Ito, A. Saito and T. Nishizeki, *Secret sharing scheme realizing general access structure*, in Proceedings of the IEEE Global Telecommunications Conference, Globecom '87, IEEE Press, 1987, 99–102.
11. A. Shamir, *How to share a secret*, Communications of the ACM 22 (1979), 612–613.
12. D. R. Stinson, *New General Lower ounds on the Information Rate of Secret Sharing Schemes*, in Advances in Cryptology – CRYPTO '92, Lecture Notes in Computer Science 740 (1993), 170–184.
13. D. R. Stinson, *Decomposition Constructions for Secret Sharing Schemes*, IEEE Transactions on Information Theory, vol. 40, 1994.
14. D. R. Stinson, *An Explication of Secret Sharing Schemes*, Design, Codes and Cryptography, Vol. **2**, pp. 357–390, 1992.
15. M. van Dijk, *On the Information Rate of Perfect Secret Sharing Schemes,* in Design, Codes and Cryptography, vol. 6, pp. 143–169, 1995.

A Promising Key Agreement Protocol

Eun-Kyung Ryu, Kee-Won Kim, and Kee-Young Yoo

Department of Computer Engineering, Kyungpook National University,
Daegu 702-701, Republic of Korea
{ekryu, nirvana}@infosec.knu.ac.kr, yook@knu.ac.kr

Abstract. In 1999, Seo and Sweeney proposed a simple authenticated key agreement protocol(SAKA) that was designed to act as a Diffie-Hellman scheme with user authentication. However, the protocol was subsequently found to have security flaws and enhanced in the literature. Recently, Ku and Wang showed a variant of SAKA. This paper shows that the Ku and Wang's scheme is still vulnerable to an off-line password guessing attack. The attack illustrates that extreme care must be taken when passwords are combined to provide user authentication in the key agreement protocols. This paper also presents a new key agreement protocol that resists the guessing attacks mounted by either passive or active network attackers, allowing low-entropy passwords to be used safely. The protocol has more efficient performance by reducing the number of protocol steps.

1 Introduction

Key agreement protocol is the process in which two communication parties establish a shared secret key using information contributed by both of them. The key may subsequently be used to achieve some cryptographic goal, such as confidentiality or data integrity. Secure authenticated key agreement protocols are important as effective replacements for traditional key establishment achieved using expensive and inefficient couriers[1]. The Diffie-Hellman(DH) scheme[2] is a well-known key agreement protocol whose security is based on the difficulty of computing discrete logarithms over a finite field. Unfortunately, the main problem of the DH key agreement protocol is that it cannot withstand *the man-in-the-middle attack*.

In the literature, a number of techniques[1], [3]-[7] have been shown for solving the problem of Diffie-Hellman key agreement. They can be classified into two principal techniques, symmetric protocols and asymmetric protocols, by information contributed by legitimate parties that is used to derive a shared secret key. In symmetric protocols the two parties possess common secret information in advance, while in asymmetric protocols the two parties share only public information that has been authenticated. In particular, many works have focused on symmetric setting in which the parties only use a pre-shared secret, such as password; no supplementary keys or certificates are required. This paper is concerned with key agreement protocols in the symmetric setting.

T. Ibaraki, N. Katoh, and H. Ono (Eds.): ISAAC 2003, LNCS 2906, pp. 655–662, 2003.

Simple authenticated key algorithm(SAKA) [3] is a symmetric key agreement scheme in which the communication parties use only a pre-shared password. Since the password-based mechanism allows people to choose their own passwords with no assistant device to generate or store, it is the most widely used method for user authentication. SAKA is considered as an efficient one in terms of computational time and exchanged messages[4]. However, the protocol was found to have security flaws, and then was modified to eliminate such problems in [4][5][6]. Recently, Ku and Wang's protocol [6] proposed a variant of SAKA that they claimed their protocol can solve the problems.

In this paper, we will show an off-line password guessing attack on Ku and Wang's protocol whereby an attacker can easily obtain a legitimate communication parties' password. The attack illustrates that extreme care must be taken when passwords are combined to provide user authentication in the key agreement protocols. We also present a new key agreement protocol that resists the guessing attacks mounted by either passive or active network attackers, allowing low-entropy passwords to be used safely. The protocol has more efficient performance by reducing the number of protocol steps.

The remainder of this paper is organized as follows. In section 2, we begin by describing desirable properties for key agreement protocols. Then, briefly review the Ku and Wang's protocol and explain security weaknesses on their protocol. In section 3, we demonstrate a new key agreement protocol that can solve such problems. In section 4, we analyze the security of the new scheme. Finally, conclusion is given in section 5.

2   Background

In this section, we describe some desirable properties for key agreement protocols. Then, briefly review Ku and Wang's protocol and discuss security weaknesses on their protocol.

2.1   Desirable Properties for Key Agreement Protocols

A secure protocol should be able to withstand both *passive* attacks(where an attacker attempts to prevent a protocol from achieving its goals by merely observing honest entities carrying out the protocol) and *active* attacks(where an attacker additionally subverts the communications by injecting, deleting, altering or replaying messages). In addition to implicit key authentication and key confirmation, the following *security properties* of authenticated key agreement protocols should be considered since they are often desirable in some environments. In the following, A and B are honest parties.

1. *Known-key security.* Each run of a key agreement protocol between two entities A and B should produce a unique secret keys; such keys are called *session keys*. A protocol should still achieve its goal in the face of an attacker who has learned some other session keys.

2. *Perfect forward secrecy.* If long-term private keys of one or more entities are compromised, the secrecy of previous session keys established by honest entities is not affected.

Desirable *performance properties* of authenticated key agreement protocols include a minimal number of passes(the number of messages exchanged in a run of the protocol), low communication overhead(total number of bits transmitted), and low computation overhead. Other properties that may be desirable in some circumstances include role-symmetry(the message transmitted between entities have the same structure), non-interactiveness(the messages transmitted between the two entities are independent of each other), and the non-reliance on encryption(to meet possible export requirements), hash functions(since these are notorious hard to design), and timestamping(since it is difficult to implement securely in practice).

2.2 Review of Ku and Wang's Protocol

The system parameters are n and g, where n is a large prime and g is a generator with order $n - 1$ in GF(n) as the original Diffie-Hellman scheme. All exponentiations are performed modulo n. Assume that two communication parties, called Alice and Bob, have a common pre-shared secret password P. Alice and Bob can pre-compute two integers Q and Q^{-1} (mod $n - 1$) from P in any predetermined way before performing the key agreement protocol. In their protocol, two parities exchange two messages to establish a shared secret session key in the protocol. Then, the exchange of two more messages allows the two parties to mutually authenticate. The description of each step in their protocol is as follows:

Key Establishment Phase:

1. Alice selects a random integer a and sends X_1 to Bob, where $X_1 = g^{aQ}$
2. Bob also selects a random integer b and sends Y_1 to Alice, where $Y_1 = g^{bQ}$
3. Alice computes the session key as follows:

$$Y = Y_1^{Q^{-1}} = g^b$$
$$Key_1 = Y^a = g^{ab}$$

4. Bob computes the session key Key_2 as follows:

$$X = X_1^{Q^{-1}} = g^a$$
$$Key_2 = X^b = g^{ab}$$

Key Validation Phase:

1. Alice computes $Y_2 = (Key_1)^Q = g^{abQ}$ and then sends Y_2 to Bob.

2. Bob checks whether $Y_2^{Q^{-1}} = Key_2$ holds or not. If it holds, Bob believes that he has obtained the correct X_1 and Alice has obtained the correct Y_1. That is, Bob is convinced that Key_2 is validated, and then sends X to Alice.
3. Alice checks whether $X = g^a$ holds or not. If it holds, Alice believes that she has obtained the correct Y_1 and Bob has obtained the correct X_1. Alice is convinced that Key_1 is validated.

2.3 Security Weaknesses

Although the Ku and Wang's protocol tried to solve the security problems in SAKA, their scheme is still vulnerable to an off-line password guessing attack. An attacker who captured messages exchanged over network can easily obtain a legitimate communication parties' password P. The attack proceeds as follows: Firstly, an attacker records a pair of information $< X_1, X >$ exchanged in a valid key agreement session. It is not difficult to obtain the information since they all are exposed over the open network. Then, the attacker obtains the password P shared two legitimate parties as follows: (1) The attacker makes a guess at the secret password P' and derives corresponding Q' and Q'^{-1} mod $n - 1$. (2) Computes $X^{Q'}$ and checks if $X_1 = X^{Q'}$ mod n, where X_1 and X are the information that he or she captured. (3) If it is not correct, the attacker repeatedly performs it until $X_1 = X^{Q'}$ mod n.

Unlike typical private keys, the password has limited entropy, constrained by the memory of the user. Roughly speaking, the entropy of human memorable password is about 2 bits per character. Therefore, the goal of obtaining a legitimate communication parties' password by the attacker can be achieved within a reasonable time. Thus, the guessing attack on Ku and Wang's protocol should be considered as the realistic one.

In addition, suppose that the password P is compromised. The secrecy of previous session keys established by the legitimate parties is also affected. Since $Y_2^{Q^{-1}} = Key_1 = Key_2$ (mod n), the attacker can easily recover the previous session keys by computing $Y_2^{Q^{-1}}$, where Y_2 is obtainable information over the network. Therefore, the protocol do not provide the perfect forward secrecy.

The weakness of the Ku and Wang's protocol is due to the two values X_1 and X in their key establishment and key validation phase, respectively. Since the values are publicly visible, an attacker capturing them can easily make a guess at legitimate communication parties' password by judging the correctness of the guess. Thus, the most important requirement to prevent the guessing attack is to eliminate the information that can be used to verify the correctness of the guess. The main idea of our scheme is to isolate such information by using asymmetric structure in the exchanged messages.

3   PKA: A Promising Key Agreement Protocol

In this section we demonstrate a new key agreement protocol resistant to the guessing attacks in which two users Alice and Bob can authenticate each other and establish a common session key $K = h(V||W||g^{r_A r_B})$ for a secure communication.

3.1   System Setup

Two communication parties, called *Alice* and *Bob*, are assumed to share the common secret *password* π in a secure way. In protocol, all computations are performed in a finite field GF(n). In other words, a large prime number n is chosen ahead of time, and all multiplications and exponentiations are performed modulo n. Table 1 shows the notation used in this section. The value n and g are well-known values, agreed to beforehand.

Table 1. Notation

n	A large prime number. All computations are performed modulo n
g	A generator(primitive root) with order $n - 1$
π	The user's password
r_A, r_B	Ephemeral private keys, generated randomly and not publicly revealed
$h()$	One-way hash function
$||$	Concatenation
V, W	Corresponding public keys
K	Session key

3.2   Protocol Run

To establish a session key, Alice and Bob engage in the protocol as shown in Figure 1. The description of each step is as follows:

1. Alice chooses a random integer r_A, $1 < r_A < n$, computes $V = g^{r_A} h(\pi)$, and sends it to Bob.

2. Bob chooses his own random number r_B, $1 < r_B < n$, computes W, α, and X_B, where $W = g^{r_B}$, $\alpha = (V/h(\pi))^{r_B}$ by using the password $h(\pi)$ of Alice, and $X_B = h(\alpha)$. Then, sends W and X_B back to Alice.

3. Alice verifies if X_B is equal to $h(\beta)$, where $\beta = W^{r_A}$. If they match each other, Alice authenticates Bob. Then computes $X_A = h(\beta^{h(\pi)})$ and send it to Bob.

4. Bob verifies if X_A is equal to $h(\alpha^{h(\pi)})$. If they match each other, Bob authenticates Alice.

5. Finally, Alice and Bob agree on the common session key $K = h(V||W||\alpha) = h(V||W||\beta) = h(V||W||g^{r_A r_B})$.

Alice   Bob

$r_A \in_R Z_n^*$

$V = g^{r_A} h(\pi)$ $\qquad\qquad \xrightarrow{\quad V \quad}$

$\qquad\qquad\qquad\qquad\qquad\qquad\qquad\qquad\qquad r_B \in_R Z_n^*$
$\qquad\qquad\qquad\qquad\qquad\qquad\qquad\qquad\qquad W = g^{r_B}$
$\qquad\qquad\qquad\qquad\qquad\qquad\qquad\qquad\qquad \alpha = (V/h(\pi))^{r_B}$
$\qquad\qquad\qquad\qquad\qquad\qquad\qquad\qquad\qquad X_B = h(\alpha)$

$\beta = W^{r_A}$ $\qquad\qquad \xleftarrow{\quad W, X_B \quad}$
Test $X_B = h(\beta)$

$X_A = h(\beta^{h(\pi)})$ $\qquad\qquad \xrightarrow{\quad X_A \quad}$

$K = h(V\|W\|\beta)$ $\qquad\qquad\qquad\qquad\qquad$ Test $X_A = h(\alpha^{h(\pi)})$
$\qquad\qquad\qquad\qquad\qquad\qquad\qquad\qquad\qquad K = h(V\|W\|\alpha)$

Fig. 1. PKA Protocol

Both sides will agree on the session key $K = h(V\|W\|g^{r_A r_B})$ if all steps are executed correctly. Once the protocol run completes successfully, both parties may use K to encrypt subsequent session traffic.

4   Security Analysis

In this section, we discuss the security of the proposed scheme by focusing on how the protocol protects against passive and active attack, to either obtain information about the password, or to obtain a shared session key without using the password.

Passive attack. If an attacker, called *Eve*, who eavesdrops on a successful PKA run can make a guess at the session key using only information obtainable over network and a guessed value of π, she could break a DH key exchange. The reason will be clear. Such a problem can be reduced to compute a keying material $g^{r_A r_B}$ from the value $V = g^{r_A} h(\pi)$ and $W = g^{r_B}$ in Figure 1. Thus, we claim that it is as difficult as to break the DH problem. Without the ability to compute the keying material $g^{r_A r_B}$, the message X_A and X_B leak no information to the passive off-line attacker. Since Alice and Bob do not leak any information either, a passive attacker cannot verify guesses at the user's password. Thus, PKA resists passive password guessing attacks.

Active attack. Active attacks can take many different forms, depending on what information is available to the attacker. An attacker who knows Alice's password π can obviously pretend to be Alice and communicate with Bob. Similarly, an attacker with π can masquerade as Bob when Alice tries to contact him. A man-in-the middle attack, which requires an attacker to fool both sides of a legitimate conversation, cannot be carried out by an attacker who does not know Alice's password. For example, suppose that an attacker, Eve wants to fool Bob into thinking he is talking to Alice. First, she can compute $V' = g^{r_E} h(\pi')$ and send it to Bob. Bob computes $W = g^{r_B}$ and $X_B = h((V'/h(\pi))^{r_B})$ and send them to Eve. When Eve receives W and X_B from Bob, she has to make X_E and send it to Bob. Since the problem is combined with discrete logarithm and a secret password, she can not guess g^{r_B} and $h(\pi)$. Thus, the PKA withstands the man-in-the-middle attack.

Known-key attack. If K is revealed to a passive eavesdropper Eve, she does not learn any new information from combining K with publicly-visible information. This is true because the message X_A or X_B leak no information to the attacker. We have already established that Eve cannot make meaningful guesses at the session key K from guessed passwords, and there does not appear to be any easier way for her to carry out a brute-force attack. It means that the attacker, having obtained some past session keys, cannot compromise the current or future session keys. Thus, it resists the known-key attack.

Perfect forward secrecy. If the user's password itself is compromised, it does not allow the attacker to determine the session key K for past sessions and decrypt them. Since the attacker is still faced with the DH problem. Therefore, the PKA protocol satisfies the property of perfect forward secrecy.

5 Conclusion

In this paper, we presented that the Ku and Wang's protocol is vulnerable to an off-line password guessing attack and do not provide perfect forward secrecy. The attack illustrates that extreme care must be taken when passwords are used to provide user authentication in key agreement protocols. We also proposed a new key agreement protocol that resists the guessing attacks mounted by either passive or active network attackers, allowing low-entropy passwords to be used safely. The protocol has more efficient performance by reducing the number of protocol steps.

Acknowledgement. This work was supported by the Brain Korea 21 Project in 2003.

References

1. S.Blake-Wilson, A. Menezes: Authenticated Diffie-Hellman key agreement protocols. Proceedings of the 5th Annual Workshop on Selected Areas in Cryptography (SAC '98), Lecture Notes in Computer Science, 1556 (1999) 339–361
2. W.Diffie, M.E.Hellman: New directions in cryptography, IEEE Transaction on Information Theory, IT-22 (1976) 644–654

3. Seo D.H, Sweeney, P: Simple authenticated key agreement algorithm. Electronics Letters. Vol. 35 (1999) 1073–1074
4. Yuh-Min Tseng: Weakness in simple authenticated key agreement protocol. Electronics Letters. Vol. 36 (2000) 48–49
5. Iuon-Chang Lin, Chin-Chen Chang, Min-Shiang Hwang: Security enhancement for the simple authentication key agreement algorithm. Computer Software and Applications Conference. (2000) 113–115
6. Wei-Chi Ku, Sheng-De Wang: Cryptanalysis of modified authenticated key agreement protocol. Electronics Letters. Vol. 36 (2000) 1770–1771
7. T. Wu: The secure remote password protocol. In Proceedings of Internet Society Network and Distributed System Security Symposium. (1998) 97–111

Rapid Mixing of Several Markov Chains for a Hard-Core Model

Ravi Kannan[1], Michael W. Mahoney[2], and Ravi Montenegro[3]

[1] Department of Computer Science, Yale University, New Haven, CT 06520
kannan@cs.yale.edu
[2] Department of Mathematics, Yale University, New Haven, CT 06520
mahoney@cs.yale.edu
[3] School of Mathematics, Georgia Institute of Technology, Atlanta, GA 30332
monteneg@math.gatech.edu

Abstract. The mixing properties of several Markov chains to sample from configurations of a hard-core model have been examined. The model is familiar in the statistical physics of the liquid state and consists of a set of n nonoverlapping particle balls of radius r^* in a d-dimensional hypercube. Starting from an initial configuration, standard Markov chain monte carlo methods may be employed to generate a configuration according to a probability distribution of interest by choosing a trial state and accepting or rejecting the trial state as the next configuration of the Markov chain according to the Metropolis filter. Procedures to generate a trial state include moving a single particle globally within the hypercube, moving a single particle locally, and moving multiple particles at once. We prove that (i) in a d-dimensional system a single-particle global-move Markov chain is rapidly mixing as long as the density is sufficiently low, (ii) in a one-dimensional system a single-particle local-move Markov chain is rapidly mixing for arbitrary density as long as the local moves are in a sufficiently small neighborhood of the original particle, and (iii) the one-dimensional system can be related to a convex body, thus establishing that certain multiple-particle local-move Markov chains mix rapidly. Difficulties extending this work are also discussed.

1 Introduction

A very simple model of particle interactions is the hard core model. Consider n points in a d-dimensional unit hypercube distributed uniformly subject to the condition that the distance r between any two particles is greater than some critical distance $2r^*$. Sampling uniformly from the set of such configurations is of interest in statistical physics and in two and three dimensions this hard core model is used as a simple model of liquid state systems.[1,2,20] The Markov chain monte carlo (MCMC) algorithmic procedure is well suited to perform such sampling.[9,10,18] Indeed, MCMC with the Metropolis filter was first applied to the hard core model in two dimensions.[16] Recent work examining the convergence rates of Markov chains has typically examined systems of computer scientific interest or simple models in statistical physics of solid state systems,

T. Ibaraki, N. Katoh, and H. Ono (Eds.): ISAAC 2003, LNCS 2906, pp. 663–675, 2003.

e.g., the Ising model.[6,10,11] In this work, we examine the convergence properties of several Markov chains for sampling from the set of configurations of the n-particle hard-core model of molecular liquids in d dimensions.

Starting from an initial configuration of particles, the MCMC procedure performs the sampling by constructing an irreducible aperiodic Markov chain that converges to the stationary distribution of interest.[9,10,16,18] Each step of the Markov chain consists of a trial move (for which there is much discretion in constructing) of one or more particles followed by an acceptance or rejection (according to the Metropolis rule) of the trial configuration as the next configuration of the Markov chain. One example of a trial move is a single-particle global move in which a single particle is selected and moved to a position that is chosen uniformly from anywhere within the hypercube. Another example is a single-particle local move in which a single particle is selected and moved to a position within the hypercube that is chosen according to a probability distribution that is localized around the original location of the particle. Another example of a trial move is a multiple-particle local move in which some or all of the particles are moved to a new set of positions chosen according to a probability distribution that is localized around the original locations of the particles. Of course, the multiple-particle global move in which every particle is independently randomly moved to any position in the box is a Markov chain which uses no information from the previous configuration.

Single-particle trial moves and multiple-particle trial moves are complementary in that in many cases the former empirically mix rapidly when the system is far from a critical point phase transition while the latter are often superior empirically when the system is near a critical point.[18] Similarly, global trial moves and local trial moves are complementary in that the former appear empirically to mix rapidly at extremely low densities and to mix very slowly at higher densities while the latter often appear empirically to mix rapidly at higher densities.[1] The intuition behind this is that when the density is high, typical configurations of the particles disallow (or more generally make extremely improbable) many of the possible global trial moves; thus these trial moves are typically rejected. On the other hand, by moving a particle to a nearby position, which is often free even at relatively high densities, the trial move is more likely to be accepted. The motivation behind these distinctions is that, as opposed to the Ising model where each spin may adopt only two possible values, for many models each particle may adopt a large number of possible configurations. Trial moves which are local use more information from the previous state of the Markov chain to construct the trial state. The heat-bath algorithm applied to the q-state Potts model is similar in spirit since it too uses local information to boost acceptance probabilities to accelerate the empirically observed mixing.[18] Note that single-particle local moves are often used in practice in statistical physics for the same reason.[1,14,16] See Figure 1 for a summary of the rapid mixing results that are empirically observed for moderately high density liquid state systems in one, two, and three dimensions away from phase transitions and for a summary of

Empirical Results for $d = 1, 2, 3$		
	Local	Global
Single	rapid	slow
Multiple	rarely used	N.A.

Theoretical Results		
	Local	Global
Single	Thm. 3 $(d = 1)$	Thm. 2
Multiple	Thm. 5 $(d = 1)$	N.A.

Fig. 1. Summary of empirically observed and our theoretical rapid mixing results.

our theoretical results;[1] results for both single-particle and multiple-particle local-move and global-move Markov chains are presented.

Despite the widespread use of these methods in statistical physics, dating back to the earliest days of the MCMC method,[16] very little has been rigorously known about the convergence properties of either local-move or global-move Markov chains for this hard-core model. After a review of the hard-core model and of rapidly mixing Markov chains in Section 2 we present several rapid mixing results for this model. In Section 3 we prove that a single-particle global-move Markov chain is rapidly mixing for all dimensions d if the density ρ is sufficiently low. In Section 4 we prove that a single-particle local-move Markov chain is rapidly mixing in one dimension up to density one as long as the moves are within a small enough region around the particles. In Section 5 we relate the n-particle one-dimensional system to a convex body in $\mathbb{R}^n$ and as a corollary show that there exist rapidly mixing multiple-particle local-move Markov chains. In Section 6 we conclude with a discussion of difficulties extending this work to higher densities, other dimensions, and to other energy functions.

2   Background and Preliminaries

2.1   Background on the Hard Core Model

Let Ω_{nd} be the set of all sets of n points in $[0, \ell]^d$, where we let $\ell = 1$ without loss of generality. Thus, if $X_i \in [0, 1]^d$ then $X = (X_1, \cdots, X_n) \in \Omega_{nd}$. Let $U(X)$ be the energy function of the configuration X, where $U(X)$ has the form $U(X) = \sum_{i \neq j} \phi(r_{ij})$, where $r_{ij} = |X_i - X_j|$ and $\phi(r)$ is the two-particle energy function. A two-particle energy function of the form $\phi(r) = 4\epsilon \left[\left(\frac{\sigma}{r} \right)^{12} - \left(\frac{\sigma}{r} \right)^6 \right]$, where ϵ and σ are parameters of the model, is known as the *Lennard-Jones energy function* and is widely used in applications.[1,14] A two-particle energy function of the form

$$\phi(r) = \begin{cases} \infty \text{ if } r \leq 2r^* \\ 0 \ \text{ if } r > 2r^* \end{cases} \tag{1}$$

is known as the *hard-core energy function* and is of interest in the present work.[1, 2,16,20] Note the similarity of this hard-core model to the hard-core Gibbs point process and of this work to related work on that process.[15,19] A two-particle energy function $\phi(r)$ such that $\phi(r) \geq 0$ for all r, e.g., the hard-core energy

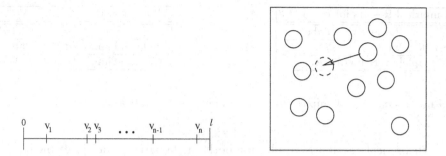

Fig. 2. Illustration of the hard-core model in one and two dimensions

function, is said to be a *purely repulsive energy function*. In the hard-core case, each particle is modeled as a ball of radius r^* and the density of the system is defined to be $\rho = nV_d(B_{r^*})$ where $V_d(B_{r^*})$ is the volume of the d-dimensional ball of radius r^*. We focus attention on ρ (or r^*), d, and n, and let $n \to \infty$, proving results for rapid mixing if ρ assumes certain values. Note that we will also consider the configuration space Ω_{nd}^m, which is a discretized version of Ω_{nd}; more precisely, if $X_i \in \Omega_{1d}^m = \frac{1}{m}\mathcal{Z}_m^d$ then $X = (X_1, \cdots, X_n) \in \Omega_{nd}^m$. Sampling from Ω_{nd}^m followed by a rejection sampling method is then sufficient to sample from Ω_{nd}; see [7]. Let $\pi(X) = \frac{1}{Z} \exp(-\beta U(X))$ be the Boltzmann probability distribution on the configuration space Ω; in this expression β is a parameter known as the inverse temperature and Z is a normalization constant known as the partition function. In statistical mechanics it is often of interest to sample $X \in \Omega$ according to the probability distribution $\pi(X)$ and MCMC is often used as the method to do so. It should be clear that sampling from $\Omega = \Omega_{nd}$ according to π for a system of hard-core particles corresponds to sampling from $X \in \Omega_{nd}$ uniformly subject to the constraint that $r_{ij} > 2r^*$ for all pairs of particles i and j. Particles are assumed to be indistinguishable, although for convenience we may assign them labels. In addition, we will assume either toroidal or truncated boundary conditions, as indicated; see [1] for more detail.

Figure 2 illustrates the system in one and two dimensions for the truncated boundary conditions; in the one-dimensional system the particles are represented as labeled points (with no radius shown) and in the two-dimensional system a single-particle trial move is illustrated.

2.2   Background on Rapid Mixing

Let Ω be a set such as Ω_{nd} or Ω_{nd}^m and let $p^{(0)}$ be an initial probability distribution on Ω, P be the transition kernel of a Markov chain $\mathcal{M}$ on Ω, and $p^{(t)}$ be the t-step distribution; see [9,10,18]. The Markov chains we construct will be time-homogeneous, aperiodic and irreducible and the t-step distribution will converge to a stationary distribution $p^{(\infty)}$, i.e., $p^{(t)} \xrightarrow{t \to \infty} p^{(\infty)}$. Let $X^t = (X_1^t, \cdots, X_n^t) \in \Omega$ be the state at the t-th step of a Markov chain and let X_{TR}^{t+1} be the trial state chosen for the $t + 1$-st step. Since trial moves will be subjected to the Metropolis filter[9,16,18] the trial state is accepted and $X^{t+1} = X_{TR}^{t+1}$ with probability $\min\{1, \pi(X_{TR}^{t+1})/\pi(X^t)\}$, where π is the Boltzmann distribution; otherwise the trial state is rejected and $X^{t+1} = X^t$. In the case of hard-core particles, the Metropolis rule leads to the rejection of any trial states in which two or more particles overlap and the acceptance of all other trial states. With this rule $\pi = p^{(\infty)}$ and since the transition kernel is symmetric for the hard-core model, i.e., $P(A, B) = P(B, A)$ for all appropriately defined $A, B \subset \Omega$, the stationary distribution is uniform subject to the condition that no particles overlap. A trial move is a *single-particle trial move* if the trial state is of the form $X_{TR}^{t+1} = (X_1^t, \cdots, X_{\xi-1}^t, X_\xi', X_{\xi+1}^t, \cdots, X_n^t)$ for some randomly chosen ξ, i.e., if the coordinates of only the single randomly chosen particle ξ are modified. A trial move is a *multiple particle trial move* if $X_{TR}^{t+1} = (X_1', \cdots, X_n')$, where two or more of the $X_i' \neq X_i^t$. A single-particle trial move is a *local trial move* if the chosen particle is moved to a trial state according to a probability distribution that is localized near the previous state and is a *global trial move* otherwise. A similar definition holds for multiple-particle local and global trial moves. In addition, all the Markov chains we consider will have a holding probability of $1/2$, i.e., with probability $1/2$ a trial move is not attempted and $X^{t+1} = X^t$; this is to remove periodicity effects.

   Given any two probability distributions μ and ν on some Ω, the *variation distance* is a measure of how far μ and ν are from each other and is defined to be

$$\|\mu - \nu\|_{TVD} = \sup_{A \subseteq \Omega} |\mu(A) - \nu(A)|. \tag{2}$$

The *mixing time* $\tau(\epsilon)$ is a measure how many steps it takes the Markov chain $\mathcal{M}$ to come close to the uniform distribution and is defined as

$$\tau(\epsilon) = \sup_{p^{(0)}} \min \left\{ t : \|p^{(t)} - \pi\|_{TVD} \leq \epsilon \right\}. \tag{3}$$

We will define $\tau = \tau(1/e)$; since $\tau(\epsilon) \leq 2\tau \log_2(1/\epsilon)$, bounding τ suffices to bound $\tau(\epsilon)$.[10]

   There are several methods that may be used to bound the mixing time of a Markov chain.[10] One is the method of coupling; a coupling is a stochastic process $(X_t, Y_t)_{t \in \mathbb{N}}$ on pairs of states in $\Omega \times \Omega$ such that each of the $(X_t)_{t \in \mathbb{N}}, (Y_t)_{t \in \mathbb{N}}$ considered independently is a faithful copy of the original Markov chain $\mathcal{M}$, and if $X_t = Y_t$ then $X_{t+1} = Y_{t+1}$. A coupling may be used to bound the mixing time of a Markov chain via the coupling inequality,[10] which states that the worst variation distance is bounded by the coupling, i.e., that

$$\sup_{p^{(0)}} \|p^{(t)} - \pi\|_{TVD} \leq \sup_{X_0, Y_0} \mathbf{Pr}\left[X_t \neq Y_t\right]. \tag{4}$$

It is generally quite difficult to construct a coupling for complex Markov chains. The path coupling theorem of Bubley and Dyer simplifies and extends the applicability of coupling.[3] The path coupling theorem states that, given a neighborhood structure on the configuration space that connects every pair of states by some path, it is sufficient to construct a coupling on pairs of neighboring states. We state the theorem in the simplest form necessary for our work.

Theorem 1 (Bubley and Dyer[3]). *Let Ω be given and let $X, Y \in \Omega$. Define a metric $\Phi : \Omega \times \Omega \to \{0, 1, \dots, D\}$ by letting $\Phi(X, Y)$ be the length of the shortest path from X to Y. Suppose there exists a constant ζ and a coupling (X_t, Y_t) of the Markov chain such that when $\Phi(X_t, Y_t) = 1$ then $\mathbf{E}\left[\Phi(X_{t+1}, Y_{t+1})|X_t, Y_t\right] \leq \zeta\Phi(X_t, Y_t)$. If $\zeta < 1$ then the coupling can be extended to $\Omega \times \Omega$ and the mixing time is bounded as $\tau \leq \frac{\log(eD)}{1-\zeta}$. If $\zeta = 1$ and $\mathbf{Pr}\left[\Delta\Phi_{t+1,t} \neq 0\right] \geq \alpha > 0$ for all $X_t, Y_t \in \Omega$ then the mixing time is bounded as $\tau \leq \frac{eD^2}{\alpha}$.*

3   Single Particle Global Moves

In this section we prove that a single-particle global-move Markov chain is rapidly mixing for all dimensions d if the density is sufficiently low. We assume toroidal boundary conditions and have the following theorem.

Theorem 2. *Let Ω_{nd} be the configuration space of n hard-core particles with radius r^* in dimension d. Let the density be ρ and the system have toroidal boundary conditions. Let $\mathcal{M}$ be a Markov chain on Ω_{nd} with the Metropolis filter in which trial moves are single particle global moves and let $\gamma > 0$ be a constant. Then the Markov chain $\mathcal{M}$ is rapidly mixing with mixing time bounded by*

$$\tau \leq \begin{cases} \frac{1+\gamma}{\gamma} 2n\log(2en) & \text{if } \rho \leq 1/(2^{d+1}(1+\gamma)) \\ 2n^2\log(2en) & \text{if } \rho = 1/(2^{d+1}) \end{cases} \tag{5}$$

Proof. The proof will be by path coupling and is a continuous analog of a hard-core result on graphs.[3] Since the n particles can be interpreted as n points (given by the particle centers) such that no two points can be within a distance $2r^*$ of each other, each particle "blocks" other particles from being placed within a ball of radius $2r^*$ around it. If this ball is denoted by B_{2r^*} then the total "blocked" volume is at most $nV_d(B_{2r^*}) = 2^d nV_d(B_r^*) = 2^d\rho$. Two n-particle configurations X and Y are defined to be neighbors if they differ by a single particle; denote the location of this particle in X by p_X and in Y by p_Y.

To bound the diameter, i.e., the maximal value D of the metric, it is necessary to construct paths between every pair of configurations X and Y. Number the particles $1, 2, \dots, n$ in both configurations (any numbering will do). Pick up particle 1 in X and in Y, so that there are $(n-1)$ particles remaining in each. Each particle blocks a neighborhood of size $V_d(B_{2r^*})$ from particle moves, so the $2(n-1)$ particles block at most $2(n-1)V_d(B_{2r^*}) = 2^{d+1}(n-1)V_d(B_r^*) < 2^{d+1}\rho \leq 1$. Since this is a strict inequality there is a spot on the torus that is blocked in neither X nor Y so we can place particle 1 at this spot in both configurations. The same procedure applies to the remaining particles $2, 3, \dots, n$, and gives a common "target" configuration. Thus it requires n steps from X to this target configuration, and n steps from there to return to Y, so the length of the longest path is $D = 2n$.

To define the path coupling, first label the particles in X and Y as follows. Label the particle where X and Y differ as particle 1; the rest of the particles can be labeled such that particle $i > 1$ in X and particle $i > 1$ in Y are at the same location. One step of the Markov chain proceeds as follows:

- Choose particle j.
- Choose trial location P_X for particle j in configuration X.
- If $j = 1$ then chose trial location $P_Y = P_X$ for j in Y.
- If $j \neq 1$ chose:
  - If $P_X \cap [B_{2r^*}(p_X) \cup B_{2r^*}(p_Y)] \neq \emptyset$ then choose $P_Y = p_Y + (p_X - P_X)$, i.e., if the new location overlaps with particle 1 in X or particle 1 in Y then reflect through the midpoint $\frac{1}{2}(p_X + p_Y)$.
  - Otherwise choose $P_Y = P_X$.
- Hold with probability 1/2. Otherwise, attempt the trial move, accepting if it is a valid move.

To analyze the coupling, consider the case that particle $j = 1$ is chosen in X and Y. The coupling was set up such that either the attempted move succeeds and couples ($\Delta \Phi = -1$) in both X and Y, or fails in both in which case both particles return to their initial locations ($\Delta \Phi = 0$). Each of the remaining $(n-1)$ particles prevents a move into a radius $2r^*$ region around them, for a total blocked volume of at most $(n-1)V_d(B_{2r^*}) = 2^d(n-1)V_d(B_{r^*}) = 2^d(1 - 1/n)\rho$. The probability of coupling is the probability of a successful move, which is thus at least $\frac{1}{n}\left(1 - 2^d\left(1 - 1/n\right)\rho\right)$. When a particle $j > 1$ is chosen then there are several cases to consider. If P_X is near p_X then it fails to move in both configurations, so $\Delta \Phi = 0$. If P_X is near p_Y then it might make a move in only one of X or Y and the probability of distance increasing by one ($\Delta \Phi = +1$) may be as high as $V_d(B_{2r*}) = 2^d\rho/n$. Any other location of P_X leads to both configurations moving successfully or both failing to move, so $\Delta \Phi = 0$. This gives

$$\mathbf{E}\left[\Delta \Phi\right] \leq -\frac{1}{2n}\left[1 - (1 - 1/n)2^d \rho\right] + \frac{n-1}{2n}2^d \rho/n$$

$$= \frac{1}{2n}\left[-1 + 2(1 - 1/n)2^d \rho\right]$$

and the theorem follows because $\mathbf{E}\left[\Delta \Phi\right] < 0$ when $\rho \leq 1/2^{d+1}$.

This theorem thus proves rapid mixing in 1-d for $\rho \leq .25$, in 2-d for $\rho \leq .125$, and in 3-d for $\rho \leq .0625$. The corresponding packing densities are 1, $\frac{\pi}{2\sqrt{3}} \approx 0.9$, and $\frac{\pi}{3\sqrt{2}} \approx 0.74$, respectively.[4,17] The slow empirical mixing indicated in Figure 1 for single-particle global-move Markov chains is for typical liquid state densities which are much closer to the packing density than are the densities for which our bounds hold. Although these bounds may thus seem rather weak, the packing density is not the best comparison; it is more appropriate to compare to the lowest density such that no global moves are possible, such as the 2-d square lattice with density $\rho = \frac{\pi}{3\sqrt{3}} \approx 0.78$ and the 3-d cubic lattice with $\rho = \frac{\pi}{6} \approx 0.52$. Alternatively, Rogers showed that $\rho_{max} \geq d\,\zeta(d)/2^{d-1}\,e(1 - e^{-d}) \xrightarrow{d \to \infty} d/2^{d-1}\,e$, where ρ_{max} is the packing density and the Zeta function is $\zeta(d) = \sum_{k=1}^{\infty} k^{-d}$; thus, Theorem 2 proves rapid mixing asymptotically up to a factor of $(ed/4)$ of this lower bound on the packing density.[4,17] Note that even in two and three dimensions the density regime for which we have proven rapid mixing is significantly below densities typically of interest to practitioners simulating liquid state systems.[1]

4   Single Particle Local Moves

In this section we consider a single-particle local-move Markov chain on a discretized version of a one-dimensional n-particle hard-core system. Suppose one is interested in sampling configurations from Ω_{n1} with toroidal boundary conditions, i.e., from on the circle of unit circumference with n particles. If this circle is discretized by placing on it m equally spaced grid points then an acceptable configuration is one in which particle centers are placed on grid points such that adjacent particles are at least a distance $2r^*$ apart; equivalently, the particle centers are at least $\lceil m\rho/n \rceil$ grid points apart. This resulting space Ω_{n1}^m can be sampled with the *grid-walk Markov chain*, which is a single-particle local-move Markov chain in which trial moves are generated by choosing a particle uniformly at random and attempting to move it to either the right or the left one grid point, rejecting the move if this causes two particles to overlap and accepting it otherwise. The original space Ω_{n1} can then be sampled by rejection sampling.[7] Our main result will be the following theorem.

Theorem 3. *Let Ω_{n1}^m be the discretized version of the configuration space of n hard-core particles with radius r^* in dimension 1. Let the density be ρ and the system have toroidal boundary conditions. Let $\mathcal{M}$ be a Markov chain on Ω_{n1}^m with the Metropolis filter in which trial moves are the single-particle local-move grid walk. Then the Markov chain $\mathcal{M}$ is rapidly mixing with mixing time bounded by*

$$\tau \leq \frac{4e}{3} n^3 m^2 (1 - \rho)^2. \tag{6}$$

Proof. The proof will be by path coupling. Let $k = \lceil m\rho/n \rceil$ be the minimal number of grid points between adjacent particle centers. Denote some arbitrary (but fixed) grid point as the origin 0, and number the particles 1, 2, ..., n proceeding counterclockwise from 0. The location of the center of particle j in configuration X will be denoted $p_j^X \in [0 \ldots m - 1]$, counting grid points counterclockwise from the origin 0, and likewise in Y. Two configurations X and Y will be neighbors if they differ by a single particle j, such that the positions of j (p_j^X in X and p_j^Y in Y) are on adjacent grid points, i.e., $p_j^X - p_j^Y \equiv \pm 1$ mod m.

To bound the diameter, first suppose that $p_1^X < p_1^Y$; in this case, move particle 1 in configuration Y down by $p_1^Y - p_1^X$ grid points to reach p_1^X. Likewise, if $p_1^X > p_1^Y$ then move the particle in configuration X instead. Repeat this for the remaining particles, proceeding counterclockwise around the circle (i.e., by increasing index j). Then each particle was moved only once, in either X or Y, and moreover each was moved by at most $m(1 - \rho)$ grid points. Therefore, $D \leq nm(1 - \rho)$.

To define the path coupling, let the origin 0 be set so that under the labeling given above the configurations differ only by particle 1, at locations p_1^X and $p_1^Y \equiv p_X \pm 1$; without loss of generality assume $p_1^X = p_1^Y + 1$. Moves in the Markov chain are defined as follows. First choose particle j in X and trial move to location $P_X \in p_j^X + \{-1, 0, 1\}$. Choose the same particle j in Y and make a move as follows:

- If $j > 1$ then $P_Y = p_j^Y + (P_X - p_j^X)$ (i.e., make the same move in Y as in X)
- If $j = 1$ then $P_Y = p_1^Y + \delta$ where

$$
\delta = \begin{cases}
0 & \text{if } P_X = p_1^X - 1 & \text{(couples and } \Delta\Phi = -1) \\
0 & \text{with probability } 1/2 \text{ if } P_X = p_1^X & \text{(no change and } \Delta\Phi = 0) \\
1 & \text{with probability } 1/2 \text{ if } P_X = p_1^X & \text{(couples and } \Delta\Phi = -1) \\
-1 & \text{if } P_X = p_1^X + 1 & \text{(doesn't couple and } \Delta\Phi = +2)
\end{cases}
$$

To analyze the coupling, first suppose that there are no particles adjacent to particle 1 in either X or Y. Then $\Delta\Phi = 0$ when $j \neq 1$ is chosen, and $\mathbf{E}[\Delta\Phi] = 0$ when particle 1 is chosen. Overall, $\mathbf{E}[\Delta\Phi] = 0$ and $\alpha = 3/4n$. Next, suppose that some particle, say particle 2, is adjacent to particle 1 in X, i.e., $p_2^X = p_1^X + k$. Then, when particle 2 is chosen then $\mathbf{E}[\Delta\Phi] = 1/4$ (when 2 tries to move to $P_X = p_X - 1$), and when 1 is chosen then $\mathbf{E}[\Delta\Phi] = -1/4$. Overall, again $\mathbf{E}[\Delta\Phi] = 0$ and $\alpha = 3/4n$. Likewise when particle 2 is adjacent to 1 in Y instead of in X. Thus, $\mathbf{E}[\Delta\Phi] = 0$, $\zeta = 1$ and $\alpha = \mathbf{Pr}[\Delta\Phi \neq 0] = 3/4n$ in the path coupling theorem. Thus, the result follows from the path coupling theorem.

It might appear that the n^3 term in the mixing time is weak and that one should be able to obtain a bound of $O(n \log n)$, since it takes $O(n \log n)$ steps to choose all of the n particles and most of the particles may have to move $O((m(1 - \rho))^2)$ steps. In fact, one can show that

$$
\tau = O\left((m(1 - \rho))^2 \, n \, (\log n + \log\log m)\right)
$$

by comparing this problem to an n particle exclusion process on the circle with $m(1 - \rho)$ grid points and using a result of Diaconis and Saloff-Coste.[5] Aside from the $\log\log m$ term, this bound is tight. For instance, consider the initial configuration where all the particles are at the "bottom" of the circle. In order to approach the stationary distribution, a significant fraction of the particles will need to become well distributed around the circle. It requires $O((m(1 - \rho))^2)$ steps to move a particle a constant fraction around the circle (consider a random walk on a line). It requires $n \log n$ steps to choose each particle once. Therefore it requires $\Omega((m(1 - \rho))^2 n \log n)$ steps to distribute the particles around the circle. A similar lack of tightness between coupling and the optimal result is seen with a standard random walk on the grid $[m]^n$, where a coupling will yield $\tau = O(m^2 n^3)$, where $D = mn$ and $\alpha = 1/n$, whereas one can obtain a bound of $\tau = O(m^2 n \log n)$ via the method of log-Sobolev constants.[5]

5   Convex Bodies and Multiple Particle Local Moves

Insight into several aspects of the one-dimensional problem may be gained from
the following theorem. It relates an n-particle one-dimensional local-moves problem to the problem of computing the volume of a convex body in n dimensions.

Theorem 4. *Let Ω_{n1} be the configuration space of n hard-core particles with
radius r^* in dimension 1. Let the density be ρ, and the system have truncated
boundary conditions. Let $\mathcal{M}$ be a Markov chain on Ω_{n1} with the Metropolis
filter in which trial moves are generated with the following multiple-particle local
move procedure: for every particle, move that particle to a new position chosen
uniformly from the 1-dimensional ball centered at the initial position of that
particle and of radius less than $4r^*$. Then the set of states reachable by the
Markov chain $\mathcal{M}$ is a convex body in $\mathbb{R}^n$.*

Proof. Consider n particles of radius r^* positioned on a line with initial configuration $0 \le v_1 < v_2 < \ldots < v_n \le \ell = 1$ as in Figure 2. Then if the local moves
are of size less than $4r^*$ then the set of configurations reachable through local
moves is exactly the polytope defined by the following equations.

$$v_1 \ge 0$$
$$v_n \le \ell = 1 \tag{7}$$
$$\forall i < n : v_{i+1} \ge v_i + 2r^*$$

To see this, observe that in the one-dimensional system the particles are ordered
and this order is preserved if the local moves are less that $4r^*$. From the constraints due to the endpoints of the line and since the particles are hard balls
we get (7). Conversely, any values of the v_i that satisfy the $n+1$ conditions (7)
is a valid configuration. Thus, (7) exactly defines the set of valid configurations.

Thus, in one dimension sampling with a local-move Markov chain corresponds
to choosing a random sample from the convex body defined by (7). Sampling with
a global-move Markov chain also corresponds to choosing a random point from
a convex set or one of a large number of (up to particle label) identical convex
sets. This result makes available a great deal of work on various techniques for
sampling from convex bodies.[6,12] As a corollary to Theorem 4, there exist
rapidly mixing Markov chains for multi-particle continuous local-move Markov
chains. For example, continuous moves can be implemented via the *ball walk* of
[12] which in the present context is a multiple-particle local-move Markov chain
in which particle moves are subject to certain conditions.

Theorem 5. *Let Ω_{n1} be the configuration space of n hard-core particles with
radius r^* in dimension 1. Let the density be ρ, and the system have truncated
boundary conditions. Then there exists a multiple-particle local-move Markov
chain $\mathcal{M}$ on Ω_{n1} with the Metropolis filter for which $\tau \le poly(n)$.*

Proof. See [12] and note that the ball walk is a multiple-particle local-move
algorithm.

Due to the identification with the convex body problem, numerous other Markov chains can be seen to mix rapidly. For example, the *King's Moves* of [6] is a single-particle local-move Markov chain that mixes in polynomial time but that has more complex boundary conditions since steps are allowed slightly outside the convex body, i.e., since a small amount of particle overlap is allowed. One Markov chain that is of interest to practitioners involves performing single-particle continuous local moves. In this case the configuration space Ω_{nd} is sampled (not by sampling from Ω_{nd}^m followed by rejection sampling but instead) by performing trial moves in which a single particle is moved to a nearby location chosen from the continuous configuration space and no configurations in which there is any particle overlap are allowed, i.e., the Markov chain must not step outside of the convex body. This Markov chain is not rapidly mixing for general convex bodies, although this does not exclude the possibility that it is rapidly mixing for the convex body of Theorem 4.

6   Discussion and Conclusion

Although it is empirically observed that single-particle global-move Markov chains tend to work best at very low densities and that single-particle local-move Markov chains tend to work best at higher densities, the situation is more complicated for worst case analysis since the configuration space Ω becomes disconnected or weakly connected under local and global moves at relatively low densities. For example, consider the two rigid packings shown in Figure 3. The first has density $\rho \approx 0.6$ but both local and global trial moves will always be rejected; the second has density $\rho \approx 0.39$ and, although global trial moves can be made relatively easily, local trial moves will always be rejected.[4,8] In three dimensions there is even a packing with density $\rho \approx 0.0555$ such that no local trial moves will be accepted.[8] However know from Theorem 2 that a global-move Markov chain at this density mixes in time $\tau \leq 18n \log(2en)$. Note that for configurations such as these, if the particle radius r^* is decreased slightly then the resulting component of Ω will have positive probability but will not communicate or will communicate only weakly, i.e, via a tight "bottleneck", with the remainder of Ω.

One method from physics to construct an initial state that mixes well empirically is to start with the n particles in a dense packing near the packing density and then decrease r^* until the density reaches the desired ρ; this gives a configuration in which the particles are well separated. In one dimension this is equivalent to putting the n particles at locations $\frac{i-0.5}{n}\ell$; from Theorem 4 we see that this is the center of the polytope of one-dimensional configurations. Although constructing such a starting configuration may be easy, determining the mixing rate within the main component is difficult since characterizing the main component is difficult and since methods for rapid mixing require rapid mixing from almost every starting point.

It would be nice to prove a rapid mixing result involving other purely repulsive energy functions or energy functions with both attractive and repulsive

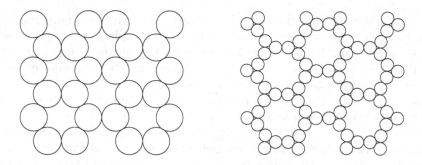

Fig. 3. Two low density rigid packings

terms. One might think that if Theorem 2 holds for hard particles of radius r^*, then it should hold for at least some types of repulsive energy functions that are 0 outside radius r^*. However, even this seems difficult to show. To see why, consider the case in which the differing particle, #1, interacts with many particles in configuration X but with none in configuration Y. This will cause the particles that interact with #1 to have a higher probability of moving in X than in Y, and thus a higher chance of the distance increasing in the coupling. Hence the coupling approach fails. A more extreme example of this phenomenon may be seen by considering energy functions with an attractive term.

Other methods seem equally unlikely to yield positive results. Lovász et. al. have applied conductance methods to the ball walk and Jerrum et. al. have applied coupling and spectral methods to the ball walk.[12,10] These proofs rely on isoperimetric inequalities for convex bodies. By an argument similar to that in the proof of Theorem 4 one can show that if $r^* = 0$ then Ω_{nd} is a convex set. If $r^* > 0$ then if particles i and j overlap then $r_{ij} \leq 2r^*$; this constraint corresponds to the convex region in which one particle is placed anywhere, the second is placed a distance at most $2r^*$ away from it, and the rest of the particles are placed anywhere. Then the configuration space Ω_{nd} for $r^* > 0$ is a convex set with a large number of convex regions removed from it. It does not seem possible to derive isoperimetric inequalities for the non-convex body formed by the configurations of the n particles if $d > 1$.

Related work on the hard-core Gibbs point process and on simulated tempering is of interest.[13,15,19] Simulated tempering is a method which avoids some of the hard-disk problems by running a Markov chain with multiple energy functions or at multiple temperatures. The Markov chain then consists of single-particle moves as well as temperature swaps; it is hoped that the softer energy functions will allow escape from bad configurations. However, analyzing the tempered chain will require knowledge of the mixing times of local-move algorithms with various energy functions and not just the hard-core energy function. In addition, the only mixing bounds currently known for tempered Markov chains establish that the tempered chain mixed no more slowly than the underlying chains; this would not be useful in the present context.

Acknowledgments. The authors sincerely thank Mark Jerrum, Santosh Vempala, and Dana Randall for numerous helpful discussions.

References

1. M.P. ALLEN AND D.J. TILDESLY, *Computer Simulation of Liquids.* (Oxford University Press, Oxford, 1987).
2. B.J. ALDER AND T.E. WAINWRIGHT, *Phase Transition in Elastic Disks.* Physical Review, 127:359–361, 1962.
3. R. BUBLEY AND M. DYER, *Path coupling: A technique for proving rapid mixing in Markov chains.* 38th Annual Symposium on Foundations of Computer Science, pp. 223–231, 1997.
4. J.H. CONWAY AND N.J.A. SLOANE, *Sphere Packings, Lattices and Groups.* (Springer-Verlag, New York, 1988).
5. P. DIACONIS AND L. SALOFF-COSTE, *Logarithmic Sobolev inequalities for finite Markov chains.* Annals of Applied Probability, 6:695–750, 1996.
6. M. DYER, A. FRIEZE AND R. KANNAN, *A random polynomial time algorithm for approximating the volume of convex bodies.* Journal of the ACM, 38:1–17, 1991.
7. G.S. FISHMAN, *Monte Carlo: Concepts, Algorithms, and Applications.* (Springer-Verlag, New York, 1996).
8. M. GARDNER, *Martin Gardner's New Mathematical Diversions from Scientific American.* (Simon and Shuster, CITY, 1966).
9. O. HÄGGSTRÖM, *Finite Markov Chains and Algorithmic Applications.* (Cambridge University Press, Cambridge, 2002).
10. M. JERRUM, *Counting, sampling and integrating: algorithms and complexity.* Lectures in Mathematics, ETH Zürich. (Birkhäuser Verlag, Basel, 2003).
11. M. JERRUM AND A. SINCLAIR, *Polynomial-time approximation algorithms for the Ising model,* SIAM Journal on Computing, 22:1087–1116, 1993.
12. L. LOVÁSZ AND R. KANNAN, *Faster mixing via average conductance.* 31st Annual ACM Symposium on Theory of Computing, pp. 282–287, 1999.
13. N. MADRAS AND D. RANDALL, *Markov chain decomposition for convergence rate analysis.* Annals of Applied Probability, 12:581–606, 2002.
14. M.W. MAHONEY AND W.L. JORGENSEN, *A five-site model for liquid water and the reproduction of the density anomaly by rigid, nonpolarizable potential functions.* Journal of Chemical Physics, 112:8910–8922, 2000.
15. S. MASE, J. MØLLER, D. STOYAN, R.P. WAAGEPETERSEN AND G. DÖGE, *Packing Densities and Simulated Tempering for Hard Core Gibbs Point Processes.* Annals of the Institute of Statistical Mathematics, 53:661–680, 2001.
16. N. METROPOLIS, A.W. ROSENBLUTH, M.N. ROSENBLUTH, A.H. TELLER AND E. TELLER, *Equation of state calculation by fast computing machines.* Journal of Chemical Physics, 21:1087–1092, 1953.
17. http://mathworld.wolfram.com.
18. M.E.J. NEWMAN AND G.T. BARKEMA, *Monte Carlo Methods in Statistical Physics.* (Oxford University Press, Oxford, 1999).
19. D. STOYAN, W.S. KENDALL AND J. MECKE, *Stochastic Geometry and Its Applications, 2nd ed.* (Wiley, New York, 1995).
20. L. TONKS, *The Complete Equation of State of One, Two and Three-Dimensional Gases of Hard Elastic Sphere.* Physical Review, 50:955–963, 1936.

Polynomial Time Approximate Sampler for Discretized Dirichlet Distribution

Tomomi Matsui[1], Mitsuo Motoki[2], and Naoyuki Kamatani[3]

[1] Department of Mathematical Informatics,
Graduate School of Information Science and Technology,
The University of Tokyo, Bunkyo-ku, Tokyo 113-8656, Japan.
http://www.simplex.t.u-tokyo.ac.jp/~/tomomi/
[2] Department of Information Processing,
School of Information Science,
Japan Advanced Institute of Science and Technology,
1-1, Asahidai, Tatsunokuchi, Ishikawa 923-1292, Japan.
mmotoki@jaist.ac.jp
[3] Institute of Rheumatology, Tokyo Women's Medical University,
10-22 Kawada-cho, Shinjuku-ku, Tokyo 162-0054, Japan.

Abstract. In this paper, we propose a Markov chain for sampling a random vector distributed according to a discretized Dirichlet distribution. We show that our Markov chain is rapidly mixing, that is, the mixing time of our chain is bounded by $(1/2)n(n-1)\ln((\Delta-n)\varepsilon^{-1})$ where n is the dimension (the number of parameters), $1/\Delta$ is the grid size for discretization, and ε is the error bound. Thus the obtained bound does not depend on the magnitudes of parameters and linear to the logarithm of the inverse of grid size. We estimate the mixing time by using the path coupling method. We also show the rate of convergence of our chain experimentally.

1 Introduction

Statistical methods are widely studied in bioinformatics since they are powerful tools to discover genes causing a (common) disease from a number of observed data. These methods often use EM algorithm, Markov chain Monte Carlo method, Gibbs sampler, and so on. The Dirichlet distribution is a distribution over vectors of positive numbers in which the sum total is equal to 1. The distribution often appears as prior and posterior distribution for the multinomial distribution in these methods since the Dirichlet distribution is the conjugate prior of parameters of the multinomial distribution [7].

For example, Niu, Qin, Xu, and Liu proposed a Bayesian haplotype inference method [5], which decides phased individual genotypes (diplotype configuration for each subject) probabilistically. This method is based on Gibbs sampler. In their method, the Dirichlet distribution is used to update population haplotype frequencies, i.e., parameters of the multinomial distribution, for each iteration. That is to say, for each iteration starting from the Dirichlet distribution with

T. Ibaraki, N. Katoh, and H. Ono (Eds.): ISAAC 2003, LNCS 2906, pp. 676–685, 2003.

some appropriate parameters, the parameters of the multinomial distribution are updated from the posterior distribution which is the Dirichlet distribution with updated parameters conditional on the "imputed" events.

Another example is a population structure inferring algorithm by Pritchard, Stephens, and Donnely [6]. Their algorithm is based on MCMC method. For each step of MCMC, the Dirichlet distribution with two distinct sets of parameters are used to sample allele frequencies in each population and admixture proportions for each individual. Similar to the first example, these two sets of parameters are updated at each iteration.

In these examples, the Dirichlet distribution appears with various dimensions and various parameters. Thus we need an efficient algorithm for sampling from the Dirichlet distribution with arbitrary dimensions and parameters. One approach of sampling from the Dirichlet distribution is by rejection (see [3] for example). In this way, the number of required samples from the gamma distribution is equal to the size of the dimension of the Dirichlet distribution. Though we can sample from the gamma distribution by using rejection sampling, the ratio of rejection becomes higher as the parameter is smaller. Thus, it does not seems effective way for small parameters.

We employ another approach, the Metropolis algorithm using a Markov chain. This paper deals with the discretized Dirichlet distribution which is obtained by discretizing the domain of the Dirichlet random vector. Discretization of the domain enables us to construct a simple and natural Markov chain and to show that our Markov chain is rapidly mixing. As described later, the mixing time of our Markov chain is linear to the logarithm of the inverse of grid size. Thus, we can simulate the Dirichlet distribution by employing sufficiently small grid size. In the next section, we also discuss the influence of discretization by showing the difference between the (original) Dirichlet distribution and its discretized version.

The mixing time of our chain is bounded by $(1/2)n(n-1)\ln((\Delta - n)\varepsilon^{-1})$ where n is the dimension (the number of parameters), $1/\Delta$ is the grid size for discretization, and ε is the error bound. We note that this mixing time does not depend on the magnitudes of parameters. We also show experimentally that the required number of steps of our Markov chain is much smaller than our theoretical upper bound of the mixing time.

2   Markov Chain for Approximate Sampler

Dirichlet random vector $P = (P_1, P_2, \ldots, P_n)$ with non-negative parameters $u_1, \ldots, u_n$ is a vector of random variables that admits the probability density function

$$\frac{\Gamma(\sum_{i=1}^{n} u_i)}{\prod_{i=1}^{n} \Gamma(u_i)} \prod_{i=1}^{n} p_i^{u_i-1}$$

defined on the set $\{(p_1, p_2, \ldots, p_n) \in \mathrm{R}^n \mid p_1 + \cdots + p_n = 1, p_1, p_2, \ldots, p_n > 0\}$ where $\Gamma(u)$ is the gamma function. Throughout this paper, we assume that $n \geq 2$.

For any integer $\Delta \geq n$, we discretize the domain with grid size $1/\Delta$ and obtain a discrete set of integer vectors Ω defined by

$$\Omega \overset{\text{def.}}{=} \{(p_1, p_2, \ldots, p_n) \in Z^n \mid p_i > 0 \ (\forall i), \ p_1 + \cdots + p_n = \Delta\}.$$

A discretized Dirichlet random vector with non-negative parameters $u_1, \ldots, u_n$ is a random vector $X = (X_1, \ldots, X_n) \in \Omega$ with the distribution

$$\Pr[X = (x_1, \ldots, x_n)] = g(\boldsymbol{x}) \overset{\text{def.}}{=} C_\Delta \prod_{i=1}^{n} (x_i/\Delta)^{u_i - 1}$$

where C_Δ is the partition function (normalizing constant) defined by $(C_\Delta)^{-1} \overset{\text{def.}}{=} \sum_{\boldsymbol{x} \in \Omega} \prod_{i=1}^{n} (x_i/\Delta)^{u_i - 1}$.

For any integer $b \geq 2$, we introduce a set of 2-dimensional integer vectors $\Omega(b) \overset{\text{def.}}{=} \{(Y_1, Y_2) \in Z^2 \mid Y_1, Y_2 > 0, \ Y_1 + Y_2 = b\}$ and a distribution function $f_b(Y_1, Y_2 \mid u_i, u_j) : \Omega(b) \to [0, 1]$ with non-negative parameters u_i, u_j defined by

$$f_b(Y_1, Y_2 \mid u_i, u_j) \overset{\text{def.}}{=} C(u_i, u_j, b) Y_1^{u_i - 1} Y_2^{u_j - 1}$$

where $(C(u_i, u_j, b))^{-1} \overset{\text{def.}}{=} \sum_{(Y_1, Y_2) \in \Omega(b)} Y_1^{u_i - 1} Y_2^{u_j - 1}$ is the partition function.

We describe our Markov chain $\mathcal{M}$ with state space Ω. At each time $t \in \{0, 1, 2, \ldots\}$, transition $X^t \mapsto X^{t+1}$ takes place as follows.

Step 1: Pick a mutually distinct pair of indices $\{i, j\} \subseteq \{1, 2, \ldots, n\}$ uniformly at random.

Step 2: Put $b = X_i^t + X_j^t$. Pick $(Y_1, Y_2) \in \Omega(b)$ according to the distribution function $f_b(Y_1, Y_2 \mid u_i, u_j)$.

Step 3: Put $X_k^{t+1} = \begin{cases} Y_1 & (k = i), \\ Y_2 & (k = j), \\ X_k^t & (\text{otherwise}). \end{cases}$

Clearly, this chain is irreducible and aperiodic. The stationary distribution of the above Markov chain $\mathcal{M}$ is $g(\boldsymbol{x})$, since the detailed balance equations hold as follows. If $(X', X'') \in \Omega^2$ satisfies that $\exists \{i, j\} \subseteq \{1, 2, \ldots, n\}$, $i \neq j$, $x_k' = x_k''$ $(\forall k \in \{1, 2, \ldots, n\} \setminus \{i, j\})$ and $x_i' + x_j' = x_i'' + x_j'' = b$, then

$$\begin{aligned}
&g(X') \Pr[(X^t, X^{t+1}) = (X', X'')] \\
&= (C_\Delta \prod_{k=1}^{n} (x_k'/\Delta)^{u_k - 1})(C(u_i, u_j, b)(x_i'')^{u_i - 1}(x_j'')^{u_j - 1}) \\
&= (C_\Delta \prod_{k=1}^{n} (x_k''/\Delta)^{u_k - 1})(C(u_i, u_j, b)(x_i')^{u_i - 1}(x_j')^{u_j - 1}) \\
&= g(X'') \Pr[(X^t, X^{t+1}) = (X'', X')];
\end{aligned}$$

otherwise, we have $\Pr[(X^t, X^{t+1}) = (X', X'')] = \Pr[(X^t, X^{t+1}) = (X'', X')] = 0$. The following theorem is a main result of this paper, which shows an upper bound of the mixing time of our chain.

Theorem 1 *The mixing time $\tau(\varepsilon)$ of Markov chain $\mathcal{M}$ satisfies*

$$\tau(\varepsilon) \leq (1/2)n(n - 1) \ln((\Delta - n)\varepsilon^{-1}).$$

In the rest of this paper, we prove the above theorem.

Before showing the above, we discuss the influence of discretization. The stationary distribution of our chain is different from the original Dirichlet distribution because of the discretization. The statistics of the Dirichlet distribution with parameters $(u_1, \ldots, u_n)$ are given as follows. For each random variable P_i, $E[P_i] = u_i/u_0$ and $\text{Var}[P_i] = \frac{u_i(u_0 - u_i)}{u_0^2(u_0+1)}$ where $u_0 = \sum_i u_i$. For each pair of random variables P_i and P_j with $(i \neq j)$, $\text{Cov}[P_i, P_j] = \frac{-u_i u_j}{u_0^2(u_0+1)}$. For some discretized Dirichlet distributions, we calculated the statistics, $E_\Delta[P_i]$, $\text{Var}_\Delta[P_i]$, and $\text{Cov}_\Delta[P_i, P_j]$ by a brute force method. Table 1 shows the results.

Table 1. Influence of discretization.

(u_1, u_2, u_3, u_4)	maximum difference of statistic	Δ		
		10	50	100
	$\|E_\Delta[P_i] - E[P_i]\|$	0	0	0
$(1,1,1,1)$	$\|\text{Var}_\Delta[P_i] - \text{Var}[P_i]\|$	0.015	0.003	0.0015
	$\|\text{Cov}_\Delta[P_i, P_j] - \text{Cov}[P_i, P_j]\|$	0.005	0.001	0.0005
	$\max(\|E_\Delta[P_i] - E[P_i]\|)$	0.051	0.0092	0.0046
$(4,3,2,1)$	$\max(\|\text{Var}_\Delta[P_i] - \text{Var}[P_i]\|)$	0.0036	0.00049	0.00023
	$\max(\|\text{Cov}_\Delta[P_i, P_j] - \text{Cov}[P_i, P_j]\|)$	0.0080	0.0074	0.0073
	$\|E_\Delta[P_i] - E[P_i]\|$	0	0	0
$(0.1, 0.1, 0.1, 0.1)$	$\|\text{Var}_\Delta[P_i] - \text{Var}[P_i]\|$	0.11	0.071	0.061
	$\|\text{Cov}_\Delta[P_i, P_j] - \text{Cov}[P_i, P_j]\|$	0.035	0.024	0.020
	$\max(\|E_\Delta[P_i] - E[P_i]\|)$	0.13	0.10	0.092
$(0.4, 0.3, 0.2, 0.1)$	$\max(\|\text{Var}_\Delta[P_i] - \text{Var}[P_i]\|)$	0.090	0.055	0.045
	$\max(\|\text{Cov}_\Delta[P_i, P_j] - \text{Cov}[P_i, P_j]\|)$	0.051	0.042	0.040
	$\max(\|E_\Delta[P_i] - E[P_i]\|)$	0.079	0.029	0.019
$(2, 1.5, 1, 0.5)$	$\max(\|\text{Var}_\Delta[P_i] - \text{Var}[P_i]\|)$	0.014	0.0032	0.0019
	$\max(\|\text{Cov}_\Delta[P_i, P_j] - \text{Cov}[P_i, P_j]\|)$	0.015	0.013	0.013

In the rest of this section, we briefly review the definition of the mixing time and path coupling method. For any probability distribution function π' on Ω, define the *total variation distance* between π' and the stationary distribution function g of $\mathcal{M}$ to be

$$D_{TV}(g, \pi') \overset{\text{def.}}{=} \max_{\Omega' \subseteq \Omega} \left| \sum_{x \in \Omega'} g(x) - \sum_{x \in \Omega'} \pi'(x) \right| = (1/2) \sum_{x \in \Omega} |g(x) - \pi'(x)|.$$

If the initial state of the chain $\mathcal{M}$ is $x \in \Omega$, we denote the distribution of the states at time t by $P_x^t : \Omega \to [0, 1]$, i.e.,

$$P_x^t(y) \overset{\text{def.}}{=} \Pr[X^t = y \mid X^0 = x] \quad (\forall y \in \Omega).$$

The rate of convergence to stationary from the initial state x may be measured by

$$\tau_x(\varepsilon) \overset{\text{def.}}{=} \min\{t \mid D_{TV}(g, P_x^{t'}) \leq \varepsilon \text{ for all } t' \geq t\}$$

where the error bound ε is a given positive constant. The *mixing time* $\tau(\varepsilon)$ of $\mathcal{M}$ is defined by $\tau(\varepsilon) \overset{\text{def.}}{=} \max_{\boldsymbol{x} \in \Omega} \tau_{\boldsymbol{x}}(\varepsilon)$, which is independent of the initial state.

Next, we define a special Markov process with respect to $\mathcal{M}$ called *joint process*. A *joint process* of $\mathcal{M}$ is a Markov chain (X^t, Y^t) defined on $\Omega \times \Omega$ satisfying that each of $(X^t), (Y^t)$, considered marginally, is a faithful copy of the original Markov chain $\mathcal{M}$. More precisely, we require that

$$\Pr[X^{t+1} = \boldsymbol{x}' | (X^t, Y^t) = (\boldsymbol{x}, \boldsymbol{y})] = P_{\mathcal{M}}(\boldsymbol{x}, \boldsymbol{x}'),$$
$$\Pr[Y^{t+1} = \boldsymbol{y}' | (X^t, Y^t) = (\boldsymbol{x}, \boldsymbol{y})] = P_{\mathcal{M}}(\boldsymbol{y}, \boldsymbol{y}'),$$

for all $\boldsymbol{x}, \boldsymbol{y}, \boldsymbol{x}', \boldsymbol{y}' \in \Omega$ where $P_{\mathcal{M}}(\boldsymbol{x}, \boldsymbol{x}')$ and $P_{\mathcal{M}}(\boldsymbol{y}, \boldsymbol{y}')$ denotes the transition probability from $\boldsymbol{x}$ to $\boldsymbol{x}'$ and from $\boldsymbol{y}$ to $\boldsymbol{y}'$ of the original Markov chain $\mathcal{M}$, respectively.

Path coupling lemma [Bubley and Dyer [1]]

Let G be a directed graph with vertex set Ω and arc set $A \subseteq \Omega \times \Omega$. Let $\ell : A \to \mathbb{Z}_{++}$ be a positive integer length function defined on the arc set. We assume that G is strongly connected. For any ordered pair of vertices $(\boldsymbol{x}, \boldsymbol{x}')$ of G, the distance from $\boldsymbol{x}$ to $\boldsymbol{x}'$, denoted by $\mathrm{d}(\boldsymbol{x}, \boldsymbol{x}')$, is the length of a shortest path from $\boldsymbol{x}$ to $\boldsymbol{x}'$, where the length of a path is the sum of the lengths of arcs in the path. Suppose that there exists a joint process $(X, Y) \mapsto (X', Y')$ with respect to $\mathcal{M}$ satisfying that

$$\exists \beta, \ 1 > \beta > 0, \ \forall (X, Y) \in A, \ \mathrm{E}[\mathrm{d}(X', Y')] \le \beta \mathrm{d}(X, Y).$$

Then the mixing time $\tau(\varepsilon)$ of the original Markov chain $\mathcal{M}$ satisfies $\tau(\varepsilon) \le (1 - \beta)^{-1} \ln(D/\varepsilon)$ where D denotes the diameter of G, i.e., the distance of a farthest (ordered) pair of vertices.

3   Analysis of Mixing Time

In this section, we define the joint process and analyze the mixing time by using path coupling method. First, we introduce a directed graph $G = (\Omega, A)$ whose vertex set is equivalent to the state space Ω. There exists a directed arc from a state (vertex) $\boldsymbol{x}$ to $\boldsymbol{y}$ if and only if $||\boldsymbol{x} - \boldsymbol{y}||_1 \overset{\text{def.}}{=} (|x_1 - y_1| + \cdots + |x_n - y_n|) = 2$. Thus the set A of arcs of G is defined by $A \overset{\text{def.}}{=} \{(\boldsymbol{x}, \boldsymbol{y}) \mid \boldsymbol{x}, \boldsymbol{y} \in \Omega, ||\boldsymbol{x} - \boldsymbol{y}||_1 = 2\}$. Clearly, G is strongly connected

Now we define the joint process with state space $\Omega \times \Omega$. For any adjacent pair of states $(\boldsymbol{x}, \boldsymbol{y}) \in A$, the joint process does the following. Without loss of generality, we can assume that $x_1 = y_1 + 1, x_2 = y_2 - 1, x_3 = y_3, \ldots, x_n = y_n$. The transition of the joint process $(\boldsymbol{x}, \boldsymbol{y}) \mapsto (X', Y')$ is defined as follows.

Step 1: Pick a pair of mutually distinct indices $\{i, j\} \in \{1, 2, \ldots, n\}$ at random.
Step 2: For any index $i' \in \{1, 2, \ldots, n\} \setminus \{i, j\}$, set $X'_{i'} = x_{i'}$, $Y'_{i'} = y_{i'}$. Pick $((X'_i, X'_j), (Y'_i, Y'_j))$ from the set $\Omega(x_i + x_j) \times \Omega(y_i + y_j)$ according to the following transition rule.

(Case 1) The pair of indices $\{i, j\}$ picked at Step 1 satisfies $\{1, 2\} \cap \{i, j\} = \emptyset$.

It is easy to see that the equality $x_i + x_j = y_i + y_j$ holds. At Step 2, we pick (X'_i, X'_j) according to the distribution function $f_{(x_i+x_j)}(X'_i, X'_j \mid u_i, u_j)$ and put $(Y'_i, Y'_j) = (X'_i, X'_j)$. Here we note that the pair of states satisfies $(X', Y') \in A$.

(Case 2) The pair of indices $\{i, j\}$ picked at Step 1 satisfies $\{1, 2\} = \{i, j\}$.

At Step 2, we pick (X', Y') in the same way with Case 1. In this case, the pair of states satisfies $X' = Y'$.

(Case 3) The pair of indices $\{i, j\}$ picked at Step 1 satisfies $\{1, 2\} \cap \{i, j\} = \{2\}$.

Without loss of generality, we can assume that $i = 2$. Set $b = x_i + x_j$. Clearly, the equality $y_i + y_j = b + 1$ holds. We introduce the distribution function defined on the set $\Omega(b) \times \Omega(b + 1)$ which is used at Step 2 in this case. We define the set Ω' of states which may have positive probability by

$$\Omega' \overset{\text{def.}}{=} \left\{ \begin{array}{ll} ((1, b-1), (1, b)), & ((2, b-2), (2, b-1)), \cdots, ((b-1, 1), (b-1, 2)), \\ ((1, b-1), (2, b-1)), & ((2, b-2), (3, b-2)), \cdots, ((b-1, 1), (b, 1)) \end{array} \right\}.$$

We set $\Pr[((X'_i, X'_j), (Y'_i, Y'_j)) = ((x'_i, x'_j), (y'_i, y'_j))] = 0, \ \forall ((x'_i, x'_j), (y'_i, y'_j)) \in \Omega(b) \times \Omega(b + 1) \setminus \Omega'$. For each element in Ω', the corresponding probability is defined by

$$\Pr[((X'_i, X'_j), (Y'_i, Y'_j)) = ((k, b-k), (k+1, b-k))]$$
$$= C_b \sum_{l=1}^{k} l^{u_i-1} (b-l)^{u_j-1} - C_{b+1} \sum_{l=1}^{k} l^{u_i-1} (b-l+1)^{u_j-1},$$
$$\Pr[((X'_i, X'_j), (Y'_i, Y'_j)) = ((k, b-k), (k, b-k+1))]$$
$$= C_{b+1} \sum_{l=1}^{k} l^{u_i-1} (b-l+1)^{u_j-1} - C_b \sum_{l=1}^{k-1} l^{u_i-1} (b-l)^{u_j-1},$$

where $k \in \{1, 2, \ldots, b-1\}$ and $C_b = C(u_i, u_j, b)$, $C_{b+1} = C(u_i, u_j, b+1)$. (Here we note that for any sequence of real numbers $\{\kappa_l\}$, we define $\sum_{l=L}^{U} \kappa_l = 0$, if $L > U$.) Each pair of states $(x', y') \in \Omega'$ satisfies that $(x', y') \in A$.

To complete the description of Case 3, we need to show that the above probability is non-negative and the sum total is equal to 1. It is easy to see that the sum total is equal to 1. The following lemma shows the non-negativity.

Lemma 1 *If the parameters u_i and u_j are non-negative, the inequalities*

$$\Pr[((X'_i, X'_j), (Y'_i, Y'_j)) = ((k, b-k), (k+1, b-k))] \geq 0, \tag{1}$$
$$\Pr[((X'_i, X'_j), (Y'_i, Y'_j)) = ((k, b-k), (k, b-k+1))] \geq 0, \tag{2}$$

hold for each $k \in \{1, 2, \ldots, b-1\}$.

The proof of the above lemma is complicated and described in [4]. Here we note that when $u_i, u_j \geq 1$, the corresponding functions have log-concavity, and so we can show the non-negativity in an ordinary way. However, at least one of parameters is less than 1, the function is neither log-concave nor concave. If both parameters are less that 1, the corresponding function is convex and so we cannot apply an ordinary method to show the non-negativity of the transition probability of joint process. See [4] for detail.

Next, we show that marginal distributions of the joint process are faithful copy of the original chain $\mathcal{M}$. Marginal distributions of X', Y' satisfy that

$$\Pr[(X'_i, X'_j) = (k, b - k) \text{ and } (Y'_i, Y'_j) \in \Omega(b+1)]$$
$$= \Pr[((X'_i, X'_j), (Y'_i, Y'_j)) = ((k, b - k), (k + 1, b - k))]$$
$$+ \Pr[((X'_i, X'_j), (Y'_i, Y'_j)) = ((k, b - k), (k, b - k + 1))]$$
$$= C_b \sum_{l=1}^{k} l^{u_i - 1}(b - l)^{u_j - 1} - C_{b+1} \sum_{l=1}^{k} l^{u_i - 1}(b - l + 1)^{u_j - 1}$$
$$+ C_{b+1} \sum_{l=1}^{k} l^{u_i - 1}(b - l + 1)^{u_j - 1} - C_b \sum_{l=1}^{k-1} l^{u_i - 1}(b - l)^{u_j - 1}$$
$$= C_b \sum_{l=1}^{k} l^{u_i - 1}(b - l)^{u_j - 1} - C_b \sum_{l=1}^{k-1} l^{u_i - 1}(b - l)^{u_j - 1} = C_b k^{u_i - 1}(b - k)^{u_j - 1},$$

$$\Pr[(X'_i, X'_j) \in \Omega(b) \text{ and } (Y'_i, Y'_j) = (k, b - k + 1)]$$
$$= \Pr[((X'_i, X'_j), (Y'_i, Y'_j)) = ((k - 1, b - k + 1), (k, b - k + 1))]$$
$$+ \Pr[((X'_i, X'_j), (Y'_i, Y'_j)) = ((k, b - k), (k, b - k + 1))]$$
$$= C_b \sum_{l=1}^{k-1} l^{u_i - 1}(b - l)^{u_j - 1} - C_{b+1} \sum_{l=1}^{k-1} l^{u_i - 1}(b - l + 1)^{u_j - 1}$$
$$+ C_{b+1} \sum_{l=1}^{k} l^{u_i - 1}(b - l + 1)^{u_j - 1} - C_b \sum_{l=1}^{k-1} l^{u_i - 1}(b - l)^{u_j - 1}$$
$$= C_{b+1} \sum_{l=1}^{k} l^{u_i - 1}(b - l + 1)^{u_j - 1} - C_{b+1} \sum_{l=1}^{k-1} l^{u_i - 1}(b - l + 1)^{u_j - 1}$$
$$= C_{b+1} k^{u_i - 1}(b - k + 1)^{u_j - 1}.$$

Lastly, we note that the pair of picked states satisfies that $(X', Y') \in A$.
(Case 4) The pair of indices $\{i, j\}$ picked at Step 1 satisfies $\{1, 2\} \cap \{i, j\} = \{1\}$.

We choose $(X', Y') \in \Omega(b + 1) \times \Omega(b)$ where $b = y_i + y_j$ in a similar way as Case 3. The procedure is obtained by substituting the indices 1 and 2, and states x and y simultaneously in Case 3. In this case, the picked pair of states also satisfies that $(X', Y') \in A$.

Now we completed the description of the transition procedure of joint process. In the rest of this section, we show a proof of the theorem.

Proof of Theorem 1

For any pair of states $(x, y) \in \Omega^2$ adjacent on the graph G define above, i.e., $(x, y) \in A$, we put the length of the edge (x, y) is equal to 1. Then the distance from a state $x' \in \Omega$ to $y' \in \Omega$, denoted by $d(x', y')$, is equal to the length of a shortest path on G from x' to y' where the length of a path is equal to the number of edges contained in the path. For any state $x \in \Omega$, we define $d(x, x) = 0$. It is clear that the diameter of the graph G, the distance between a farthest pair of vertices, is equal to $\Delta - n$.

Next, we estimate the expectation of the distance from X' to Y' obtained by applying the transition procedure of the joint process to an adjacent pair of states $(x, y) \in A$. Without loss of generality, we can assume that the pair (x, y) satisfies that $x_1 = y_1 + 1, x_2 = y_2 - 1, x_3 = y_3, \ldots, x_n = y_n$.

In Cases 1, 3 and 4, the distance from X' to Y' is equal to 1. When Case 2 occurred, the distance from X' to Y' decreases to 0. Since the probability of the event that Case 2 is selected is equal to $2/(n(n-1))$, the expectation of the distance $\mathrm{E}[d(X', Y')]$ becomes $1 - 2/(n(n-1))$. Path coupling theorem [1,2]

shows that the mixing time $\tau(\varepsilon)$ satisfies $\tau(\varepsilon) \leq (1/2)n(n-1)\ln((\Delta - n)\varepsilon^{-1})$.
$\square$

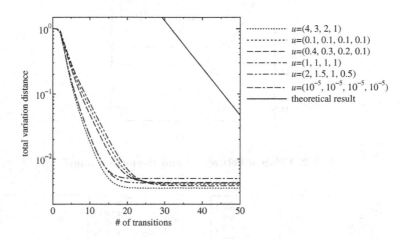

Fig. 1. Relation between mixing time and the magnitude of parameters.

4   Experimental Study

In this section, we show some simulation results. The settings of our simulations are as follows. Through all simulations, we use Mersenne Twister[8] as a pseudo-random generator. We ran these simulations on the PC Linux machine with following specifications.

Machine: Dell Precision 450
CPU: Intel Xeon 2.8GHz (FSB 533MHz) $\times$ 2
OS: RedHat Linux 8.0 (Kernel 2.4.18-14smp)
Memory: Dual channel PC2100 DDR SDRAM 2GByte
Compiler: Intel C++ Compiler 7.0

For each simulation, we ran 10^9 processes of our Markov chain. For each Markov chain process, we chose a random seed deterministically and transitions are executed 50 steps. The initial state is an integer vector in Ω obtained by rounding $(\Delta/n, \cdots, \Delta/n)$. The running time of 10^9 processes, i.e., 5×10^{10} steps, is between 10~30 hours.

First, we show results on the relation between parameters and mixing time. We fixed the dimension n to 4 and the discretizing grid size $1/\Delta$ to $1/100$. We selected parameters from $(1,1,1,1)$, $(4,3,2,1)$, $(2,1.5,1,0.5)$, $(0.1,0.1,0.1,0.1)$, $(0.4,0.3,0.2,0.1)$ and $(10^{-5},10^{-5},10^{-5},10^{-5})$. We note that the case $(1,1,1,1)$ corresponds to the uniform distribution over Ω. In Fig. 1, along the vertical axis we give the total variation distance ε, and the horizontal axis means the number of transitions of chains from the initial state. As Fig. 1 shows, the decrease of

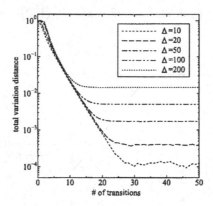

Fig. 2. Relation between Δ and the mixing time.

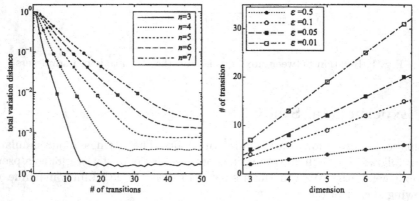

(a): Dimension and total variation distance.   (b): Dimension and mixing time.

Fig. 3. Relation between number of transitions and total variation distance.

total variation distance are saturated at about 0.005, though it must descend constantly. This is caused by the limitation of the number of samples (10^9) from Markov chains, that is, the total variation distance has a positive lower bound for each vector of parameters. Fig. 1 shows that the larger number of executions we run, the smaller the difference will be. Aside from this saturation, we can see that if the value of a parameter is greater than or equal to 1, the mixing time is less than the case that all values of a parameter are less than 1.

Next, we confirm how the discretizing value Δ contribute to the mixing time. We fixed the dimension n to 4 again and the parameter to $(1,1,1,1)$. We chose Δ from 10, 20, 50, 100, and 200. In Fig. 2, we plotted the total variation distance ε for each Δ. This figure shows that Δ will have little contribution to the mixing time. More specifically, until the decrease of ε is saturated, the ratios of decreasing have little difference for each Δ. In the proof of Theorem 1, the term

$(\Delta - n)$ is artificially introduced as the diameter of the graph $G = (\Omega, A)$. These experimental results, however, suggest that the mixing time does not depend on Δ. This property is substantiated by the fact that the diameter of our chain is bounded by n and independent of Δ.

Finally, we checked the relation between the dimension n and the mixing time. Because of restriction of the memory, we fixed the discretizing grid size $1/\Delta$ to $1/20$ and chose the dimension n between 3 and 7. We also fixed each parameter to 1. We show all results in Fig. 3. Since our purpose is to compare the mixing time and dimension, we picked up the first time instance that the total variation distance ε exceeds 0.1, 0.5, 0.05, and/or 0.01. These picked time instances are marked by •, ∘, ∎ and □ respectively in Fig. 3. In Fig. 3(b), we show the results for each ε. Though accurate consideration cannot be made because of the insufficient range of dimension, our results indicate that the mixing time is $\Theta(n)$ rather than $\Theta(n^2)$.

5   Conclusion

In this paper, we proposed a Markov chain whose stationary distribution is a discretized Dirichlet distribution. We showed that our Markov chain is rapidly mixing by using coupling method. Our upper bound of the mixing time does not depend on the magnitudes of parameters. When parameters are less than 1, the corresponding density function is convex and so, ordinary technique related to log-concavity is not applicable. We have shown the required property in [4]. Our computational experiences indicates that the mixing time of the chain is much smaller than our theoretical upper bound.

References

1. Bubley, R., Dyer, M.: Path coupling: A technique for proving rapid mixing in Markov chains, 38th Annual Symposium on Foundations of Computer Science, IEEE, San Alimitos, 1997, 223–231.
2. Bubley, R.: Randomized Algorithms : Approximation, Generation, and Counting, Springer-Verlag, New York, 2001.
3. Durbin, R., Eddy, R., Krogh, A., Mitchison, G.: Biological sequence analysis: probabilistic models of proteins and nucleic acids, Cambridge Univ. Press, 1998.
4. Matsui, T., Motoki, M., and Kamatani, N.: Polynomial time approximate sampler for discretized Dirichlet distribution, technical report METR 2003-10, Department of Mathematical Informatics, the University of Tokyo, 2003 (available from http://www.keisu.t.u-tokyo.ac.jp/Research/techrep.0.html).
5. Niu, T., Qin, Z. S., Xu, X., Liu, J. S.: Bayesian haplotype inference for multiple linked single-nucleotide polymorphisms, Am. J. Hum. Genet., 70 (2002) 157–169.
6. Pritchard, J. K., Stephens, M., Donnely, P.: Inference of population structure using multilocus genotype data, Genetics, 155 (2000) 945–959.
7. Robert, C. P.: The Bayesian Choice, Springer-Verlag, New York, 2001.
8. Mersenne Twister Home Page, http://www.math.keio.ac.jp/~matumoto/mt.html

Fair Cost Allocations under Conflicts
— A Game-Theoretic Point of View —

Yoshio Okamoto[*]

Institute of Theoretical Computer Science, Department of Computer Science,
ETH Zürich, CH-8092, Zürich, Switzerland. okamotoy@inf.ethz.ch

Abstract. We study the cost allocation problem when the players are involved in a conflict situation. More formally, we consider a minimum coloring game, introduced by Deng, Ibaraki & Nagamochi, and provide algorithms for the core, the τ-value, the nucleolus and the Shapley value on some classes of graphs. The investigation gives several insights to the relationship of algorithm theory with cooperative games.

1   Introduction

In cooperative works (projects, or whatever people do in cooperation) we can find two algorithmic problems. First, when people work together, they wish to minimize the cost. This is a focus of optimization theory. Secondly they wish to allocate the minimized total cost in a fair manner. This is a focus of cooperative game theory.

This paper studies fair cost allocations of conflict situations from the viewpoint of cooperative game theory. As a simple model of a conflict, we will use a conflict graph. In a conflict graph, each vertex represents each agent involved in the situation. Two vertices are adjacent through an edge if the corresponding agents are in conflict under the situation. We model the total cost of the conflict simply as it is proportional to the chromatic number of the conflict graph. So we want to divide the chromatic number of the graph and allocate it to each agent. This kind of cooperative games was first introduced by Deng, Ibaraki & Nagamochi [2] by the name of a minimum coloring game. Their paper [2] and a subsequent paper by Deng, Ibaraki, Nagamochi & Zang [3] included some investigations of the core (a sort of fair allocations) of a minimum coloring game.

In this paper, we will study minimum coloring games more thoroughly. Among many kinds of concepts on fair allocations in cooperative game theory, we consider the core (introduced by Gillies [9]), the τ-value (by Tijs [25]), the nucleolus (by Schmeidler [21]) and the Shapley value (by Shapley [23]). For general graphs, it turns out hard to compute any of these fair cost allocations (Proposition 1). Therefore, we will concentrate on a specific class of graphs,

---

[*] Supported by the Berlin-Zürich Joint Graduate Program "Combinatorics, Geometry, and Computation" (CGC), financed by ETH Zürich and the German Science Foundation (DFG).

T. Ibaraki, N. Katoh, and H. Ono (Eds.): ISAAC 2003, LNCS 2906, pp. 686–695, 2003.

namely perfect graphs. This makes sense since perfect graphs give rise to totally balanced minimum coloring games [3]. For perfect graphs, we will show the following theorems.

- The core of the minimum coloring game on a perfect graph is characterized as the convex hull of the characteristic vectors of the maximum cliques of the graph (Theorem 2). This is a generalization of a result by Deng, Ibaraki & Nagamochi [2] for a bipartite graph, and furthermore it implies that we can compute a core allocation in polynomial time and that we can decide whether a given vector belongs to the core or not in polynomial time for perfect graphs (Corollary 3).
- The τ-value for a perfect graph can be computed in polynomial time. This is a consequence of Theorem 4 and a polynomial-time algorithm for computing the chromatic number of a perfect graph [11]. So far, we only knew that this could be done for complete multipartite graphs (since complete multipartite graphs give rise to submodular minimum coloring games [20] and the τ-value of a submodular cost game can be computed in polynomial time by the application of a polynomial-time algorithm for the submodular function minimization [11]).
- The nucleolus is the barycenter of the characteristic vectors of the maximum cliques for some classes of perfect graphs (Theorem 6). This class includes the complete multipartite graphs and the chordal graphs, which appear in some application contexts like scheduling [10] (Proposition 7). As a consequence, for chordal graphs, we obtain a polynomial-time algorithm for computing the nucleoli. We can see that this is much simplified for forests. In addition, for a complete multipartite graph, we can see that the Shapley value and the nucleolus coincide (Corollary 8).
- The Shapley value can be computed efficiently for the minimum coloring game on a forest (Sect. 3.5). However, the same technique cannot be applied to bipartite graphs in general (Proposition 10).

Perhaps, it was Megiddo [17] who first noticed the computational issue on cooperative game theory. Since then, there have been many studies on the computational complexity and algorithms for the core and the nucleolus and a little about the Shapley value (here we omit the vast references). Especially, cooperative games arising from combinatorial optimization problems fit very much into the framework of algorithm theory. These kinds of cooperative games are called "combinatorial optimization games" and some of these cooperative games and their properties are discussed in Curiel's book [1]. However, none of them dealt with minimum coloring games in spite of the importance as a simple model of conflicts, except for a small amount of papers [2,3,20]. Since these works [2, 3,20] only studied the core, this paper provides the first treatment of solution concepts of minimum coloring games other than cores, and will shed more light on relationship of algorithm theory with cooperative games.

The paper is organized as follows. In the next section, we will introduce some graph-theoretic and game-theoretic concepts which we need in the rest of the paper. Sect. 3 is the main part of the paper. Sect. 4 concludes the paper with some open problems. Note that, because of the page limitation, all of the proofs will be omitted in this version. (See the full-paper version for the proofs.)

2   Preliminaries

Throughout the paper, for a vector $x \in \mathbb{R}^N$ and $S \subseteq N$, we write $x(S) := \sum\{x_i : i \in S\}$. When $S = \emptyset$, set $x(S) := 0$. For a subset $S \subseteq N$ of a finite set N, the *characteristic vector* of S is a vector $\mathbb{1}_S \in \{0,1\}^N$ defined as $(\mathbb{1}_S)_i = 1$ if $i \in S$ and $(\mathbb{1}_S)_i = 0$ if not.

A *graph* G is a pair $G = (V, E)$ of a finite set V and a set $E \subseteq \binom{V}{2}$ of 2-element subsets of V. (So, our graph is always simple and finite, and V can be empty.) We assume the familiarity of basic terminology from graph theory. Here we just introduce a perfect graph. A graph is *perfect* if for each of the induced subgraphs the chromatic number is equal to the size of a maximum clique. It is known that bipartite graphs, complete multipartite graphs and chordal graphs are perfect. (A graph is *chordal* if each of the induced cycles has length three.)

A *cooperative game* (or simply a *game*) is a pair (N, γ) of a nonempty finite set N and a function $\gamma : 2^N \to \mathbb{R}$ satisfying $\gamma(\emptyset) = 0$. Often, an element of N is called a *player* of the game, and γ is called the *characteristic function* of the game. Furthermore, each subset $S \subseteq N$ is called a *coalition*. Literally, for $S \subseteq N$ the value $\gamma(S)$ is interpreted as the total profit (or the total cost) for the players in S when they work in cooperation. In particular, $\gamma(N)$ represents the total profit (or cost) for the whole players when they all agree with working together. When γ represents a profit, we call the game a *profit game*. On the other hand, when γ represents a cost, we call the game a *cost game*.[1] In this paper, we will mainly consider a certain class of cost games.

One of the aims of cooperative game theory is to provide a concept of "fairness," namely, how to allocate the total cost (or profit) $\gamma(N)$ to each player in a "fair" manner when we take all the $\gamma(S)$'s into account. In the rest of this section, we will describe some allocation rules which are considered fair in cooperative game theory. Formally, a cost allocation is defined as a preimputation in the terminology of cooperative game theory. A *preimputation* of a cost game (N, γ) is a vector $x \in \mathbb{R}^N$ satisfying $x(N) = \gamma(N)$. Each component x_i expresses how much the player $i \in N$ should owe according to the cost allocation x.

Now we will define some fair allocations, namely a core allocation, the τ-value, the nucleolus and the Shapley value. See Driessen's book [4] for details (why they are seen fair) and other kinds of fair allocation concepts from cooperative game theory. Let (N, γ) be a cost game. A vector $x \in \mathbb{R}^N$ is called a *core allocation* if x satisfies the following conditions: $x(N) = \gamma(N)$ and $x(S) \leq \gamma(S)$ for all $S \subseteq N$. The set of all core allocations of a cost game (N, γ) is called the *core* of (N, γ). The core was introduced by Gillies [9]. Note that a core might be empty. Therefore, a cost game with a nonempty core is especially interesting, and such a cost game is called *balanced*. Moreover, we call a cost game *totally balanced* if each

---

[1] So the terms "profit game" and "cost game" are not mathematically determined. They are just determined by the interpretation of a game.

of the subgames has a nonempty core. (Here, a *subgame* of a cost game (N, γ) is a cost game $(T, \gamma^{(T)})$ for some nonempty $T \subseteq N$ defined as $\gamma^{(T)}(S) = \gamma(S)$ for each $S \subseteq T$.) Naturally, a totally balanced game is also balanced. A special subclass of the totally balanced games consists of submodular games (Shapley [22]), where a cost game (N, γ) is called *submodular* (or *concave*) if it satisfies the following condition: $\gamma(S) + \gamma(T) \geq \gamma(S \cup T) + \gamma(S \cap T)$ for all $S, T \subseteq N$. Therefore, we have a chain of implications: submodularity $\Rightarrow$ total balancedness $\Rightarrow$ balancedness. These implications are fundamental in cooperative game theory.

Here we introduce the τ-value due to Tijs [25]. Let (N, γ) be a cost game. Define two vectors $\underline{m}, \overline{m} \in \mathbb{R}^N$ by $\underline{m}_i := \gamma(N) - \gamma(N \setminus \{i\})$ and $\overline{m}_i := \min\{\gamma(S) - \underline{m}(S \setminus \{i\}) : i \in S \subseteq N\}$ for each $i \in N$. It is known [25] that, if a cost game (N, γ) is balanced, it holds that $\underline{m}_i \leq \overline{m}_i$ for each $i \in N$ and $\underline{m}(N) \leq \gamma(N) \leq \overline{m}(N)$. Then, the τ-*value* of a balanced cost game (N, γ) is defined as a vector $\boldsymbol{x} \in \mathbb{R}^N$ uniquely represented by $\boldsymbol{x} := \lambda \underline{m} + (1 - \lambda)\overline{m}$ where we choose $\lambda \in [0, 1]$ so that $\boldsymbol{x}(N) = \gamma(N)$ is satisfied. From the definition we can see that the τ-value can be computed in polynomial time for submodular games by an algorithm for the submodular function minimization [11].

Next, we will define the nucleolus, which was introduced by Schmeidler [21]. It is known that the nucleolus always belongs to the core if it is not empty. For our purpose, it is better to use an algorithmic definition of the nucleolus due to Peleg (referred by Kopelowitz [12]) than the original one by Schmeidler [21]. In this scheme, we successively solve a series of linear programming problems (P_1), (P_2), and so on. For a cost game (N, γ), the i-th problem (P_i) is described as follows: find $(\boldsymbol{x}, \epsilon) \in \mathbb{R}^N \times \mathbb{R}$ to

(P_i):   maximize ϵ

subject to $\boldsymbol{x}(N) = \gamma(N)$

$\boldsymbol{x}(S) = \gamma(S) - \epsilon_l$ for all $S \in \mathcal{C}_l$

for all $l \in \{1, \ldots, i - 1\}$

$\boldsymbol{x}(S) \leq \gamma(S) - \epsilon$ for all $S \in \mathcal{C}_0 \setminus \bigcup_{l=1}^{i-1} \mathcal{C}_l$,

where $\mathcal{C}_0 = 2^N \setminus \{N, \emptyset\}$, ϵ_j is the optimal value of (P_j), and $\mathcal{C}_j = \{S \in \mathcal{C}_0 \setminus \bigcup_{l=1}^{j-1} \mathcal{C}_l : \boldsymbol{x}(S) = \gamma(S) - \epsilon_j$ for all optimal solutions $(\boldsymbol{x}, \epsilon_j)$ of $(P_j)\}$ for every $j = 1, \ldots, i - 1$. It is known that finally, say, at the t-th step, the problem has a unique optimal solution $(\boldsymbol{x}^*, \epsilon_t)$. (This was essentially shown by Maschler, Peleg & Shapley [15].) Then the vector $\boldsymbol{x}^*$ is called the *nucleolus* of the game. Notice that the procedure above is not a polynomial-time algorithm. Indeed it is NP-hard to compute a nucleolus for a totally balanced game [6]. However, the nucleolus can be computed in polynomial time for a submodular game [7,13].

The Shapley value is another cost allocation we will study. The *Shapley value* of a game (N, γ) is a vector $\boldsymbol{x} \in \mathbb{R}^N$ which is defined as

$$x_i := \sum_{S \subseteq N \setminus \{i\}} \frac{|S|!(|N| - |S| - 1)!}{|N|!} (\gamma(S \cup \{i\}) - \gamma(S)).$$

The Shapley value was first introduced by Shapley [23]. By the definition, the Shapley value always uniquely exists even if the game is not balanced. However, the Shapley value may not be a core allocation. On an algorithmic side, there exists an exponential lower bound for the computation of the Shapley value [5].

3   Minimum Coloring Games

As we saw in Sect. 1, the minimum coloring problem is a simple model of conflicts. The corresponding cost game is called a minimum coloring game. In Sect. 3.1 we will define a minimum coloring game, and subsequently we will investigate the core, the τ-value, the nucleolus and the Shapley value.

3.1   Definition and a Hardness Result

Let $G = (V, E)$ be a graph. The *minimum coloring game* on G is a cost game (V, χ_G) where $\chi_G : 2^V \to \mathbb{R}$ is defined as $\chi_G(S) := \chi(G[S])$ for all $S \subseteq V$. Remember that $G[S]$ represents the subgraph of G induced by S, and $\chi(G)$ is the chromatic number of G.

Deng, Nagamochi & Ibaraki [2] proved that it is NP-complete to decide whether the minimum coloring game on a given graph is balanced. Later, Deng, Ibaraki, Nagamochi & Zang [3] showed that the minimum coloring game on a graph G is totally balanced if and only if G is perfect. So the decision problem on the total balancedness of a minimum coloring game is as hard as recognizing perfect graphs. Furthermore, Okamoto [20] showed that the minimum coloring game on a graph G is submodular if and only if G is complete multipartite. So we can decide whether a given graph yields a submodular minimum coloring game in polynomial time.

In this paper, we are interested in the computation of a core allocation, the τ-value, the nucleolus and the Shapley value of a minimum coloring game. The following observation is important although it is not difficult to show.

Proposition 1. *It is NP-hard to compute a preimputation of the minimum coloring game on a graph given from a class for which the computation of the chromatic number is NP-hard.*

Proposition 1 suggests that, in order to obtain a polynomial-time algorithm to compute a certain preimputation of a minimum coloring game, it would be better to concentrate on a class of graphs for which the chromatic number can be computed in polynomial time. Perfect graphs form such a class. From now on, we will concentrate on perfect graphs, and in Sect. 3.2–3.5, we will investigate the core, the τ-value, the nucleolus and the Shapley value respectively.

3.2   The Core of a Minimum Coloring Game

As described above, the minimum coloring game on a perfect graph is totally balanced [3], which implies that the core is nonempty. Now we characterize the core for a perfect graph in terms of its extreme points.

Theorem 2. *The core of the minimum coloring game on a perfect graph is the convex hull of the characteristic vectors of the maximum cliques of the graph.*

Notice that Theorem 2 generalizes a theorem by Deng, Ibaraki & Nagamochi [2] on bipartite graphs to all perfect graphs.

Making use of a result by Grötschel, Lovász & Schrijver [11] with Theorem 2, we will conclude the following algorithmic consequences.

Corollary 3. *The following problems can be solved in polynomial time. (1) The problem to compute a core allocation of the minimum coloring game on a perfect graph. (2) The problem to decide whether a given vector belongs to the core of the minimum coloring game on a perfect graph.*

3.3 The τ-Value of a Minimum Coloring Game

As we observed before, the τ-value can be computed in polynomial time for a submodular game by an algorithm for the submodular function minimization. However, for minimum coloring games, this only works for complete multipartite graphs. In this subsection, we will describe how to compute the τ-values in polynomial time for perfect graphs. Remark that the τ-value for a perfect graph is well-defined since the minimum coloring game on a perfect graph is totally balanced [3]. The next theorem is crucial.

Theorem 4. *Let $G = (V, E)$ be a perfect graph. Consider the minimum coloring game (V, χ_G) on G. If we denote all the maximum cliques of G by $K_1, ..., K_k$ and $K = K_1 \cap \cdots \cap K_k$, then we have that, for each $v \in V$, $\underline{m}_v = 1$ if $v \in K$ and $\underline{m}_v = 0$ otherwise; $\overline{m}_v = 1$ if $v \in K$ or $K \subseteq N_G(v)$ and $\overline{m}_v = 0$ otherwise.*

Based on Theorem 4, we are able to establish an algorithm to compute the τ-value of the minimum coloring game on every perfect graph. First we will compute $\underline{m}$. To do that, we will just compute $\chi_G(V)$ and $\chi_G(V \setminus \{v\})$ and conclude that $\underline{m}_v = \chi_G(V) - \chi_G(V \setminus \{v\})$ for all $v \in V$. Since the chromatic number of a perfect graph can be computed in polynomial time [11], $\underline{m}$ can also be computed in polynomial time. From $\underline{m}$, we can see what K is, by using Theorem 4, in linear time. Namely, $K = \{v \in V : \underline{m}_v = 1\}$. After we know K, we can immediately compute $\overline{m}$ again with help of Theorem 4. Finally, we can also compute the appropriate λ in a straightforward manner because we have already known $\chi_G(V)$. Thus we have obtained the τ-value and this algorithm runs in polynomial time.

Note that Theorem 4 enables us to compute the τ-value for a complete multipartite graph without using an algorithm for the submodular function minimization. (Actually, we can easily find the explicit formula of the τ-value for such a graph from Theorem 4.)

3.4 The Nucleolus of a Minimum Coloring Game

Now we will investigate the nucleolus. Unfortunately, we are not aware of an efficient algorithm for general perfect graphs. So we restrict to a subclass of the perfect graphs. To do that, we will introduce some terms.

Let $G = (V, E)$ be a perfect graph, $\mathcal{I}_G$ be the family of nonempty independent sets of G, and $K_1, K_2, \ldots, K_k$ be the maximum cliques of G. For every nonempty independent set $I \in \mathcal{I}_G$, define $g(I) := |\{i \in \{1, \ldots, k\} : |I \cap K_i| = 1\}|$. Then consider the set $\Gamma := \{g(I) : I \in \mathcal{I}_G\}$. (Note that Γ is not a multiset.) Let us enumerate the elements of Γ in decreasing order as: $g_1 > g_2 > \cdots > g_{|\Gamma|}$. The following lemma due to Lovász [14] tells us $g_1 = k$.

Lemma 5 ([14]). *For a perfect graph G, there exists an independent set of G which has a nonempty intersection with each of the maximum cliques of G.*

On the other hand, we have less control for g_2 in general. This motivates the definition of O-goodness. A perfect graph G is called *O-good* if $|\Gamma| = 1$ or G satisfies the following condition: for each $j \in \{1, \ldots, k\}$ there exists an independent set $I^{(j)} \in \mathcal{I}_G$ such that $|I^{(j)} \cap K_j| = 0$ and $|\{i \in \{1, \ldots, k\} \setminus \{j\} : |I^{(j)} \cap K_i| = 1\}| = g_2$.

Our theorem on the nucleolus is as follows.

Theorem 6. *The nucleolus of the minimum coloring game on an O-good perfect graph is the barycenter of the characteristic vectors of the maximum cliques of the graph.*

Now we will observe what kind of perfect graphs are O-good.

Proposition 7. *1. A perfect graph with only one maximum clique is O-good. 2. A forest is O-good. 3. A complete multipartite graph is O-good. 4. A chordal graph is O-good.*

Note that there exists a bipartite graph which is not O-good and for which the nucleolus is not given as in Theorem 6.

Now we will describe how to compute the nucleolus for classes of O-good perfect graphs in Proposition 7. First, let us consider a forest, which is O-good by Proposition 7.2. In a forest $G = (V, E)$, the maximum cliques are the edges of G. Let $d_G(v)$ be the degree of $v \in V$ in G. Then, Theorem 6 concludes that the v-th component of the nucleolus for the forest G is $d_G(v)/|E|$. So the nucleolus for a forest can be easily computed.

Next, consider a complete multipartite graph, which is O-good by Proposition 7.3. Let $G = (V, E)$ be a complete r-partite graph in which V is partitioned into $V_1, \ldots, V_r$ and $E = \{\{u, v\} : u \in V_i, v \in V_j, i, j \in \{1, \ldots, r\}, i \neq j\}$. Then a maximum clique K is a vertex subset which satisfies that $|V_i \cap K| = 1$ for all $i \in \{1, \ldots, r\}$. So, with help of Theorem 6, the v-th component of the nucleolus for the complete r-partite graph G can be computed as $1/|V_i|$ if $v \in V_i$. Actually in a past work, the author investigated the Shapley value for a complete multipartite graph [20], and this is exactly the same as the expression above. Thus we immediately obtain the following corollary.

Corollary 8. *For the minimum coloring game on a complete multipartite graph, the Shapley value and the nucleolus coincide.*

Notice that Corollary 8 does not hold for a general submodular game.

For a chordal graph, which is O-good by Proposition 7.4, we are not aware of a closed formula for the nucleolus. However, we can still compute the nucleolus in polynomial time. The strategy is to enumerate all the maximum cliques. A polynomial-time algorithm to enumerate all the maximal cliques of a chordal graph is known (and described in Golumbic's book [10]), which is based on a proposition by Fulkerson & Gross [8]. (Note that the number of the maximal cliques of a chordal graph is bounded by the number of the vertices from above [8].) Therefore, from this enumeration, we are able to obtain the list of all maximum cliques of the chordal graph. In this way, we can compute the nucleolus from this list with Theorem 6.

3.5   The Shapley Value of a Minimum Coloring Game

In the former work [20], the author provided the formula of the Shapley value for a complete multipartite graph (see also Corollary 8). Here we will give a polynomial-time algorithm to compute the Shapley value of a minimum coloring game on a forest. Note that a forest is bipartite. On the Shapley value for a bipartite graph, we have the following lemma.

Lemma 9. *For a bipartite graph $G = (V, E)$, the v-th component of the Shapley value ϕ of the minimum coloring game on G can be written as*

$$\phi_v = \frac{1}{n} + \sum_{k=1}^{n-1} a_v^k(G) \frac{k!(n-k-1)!}{n!}$$

where $n = |V|$ and $a_v^k(G)$ is the number of independent sets I of G such that $v \notin I$, $|I| = k$ and $I \cup \{v\}$ is not independent.

Therefore, if we have a polynomial-time algorithm to compute $a_v^k(G)$ for every $k \in \{1, \ldots, n-1\}$, we are able to obtain the Shapley value in polynomial time. However we are not aware of such a procedure for a general bipartite graph. Actually, we have a hardness result again. (This is just a simple application of the fact that counting the number of independent sets in a bipartite graph is #P-complete [19].)

Proposition 10. *For bipartite graphs G with n vertices and $k \in \{1, \ldots, n-1\}$, it is #P-complete to compute the value $a_v^k(G)$.*

Therefore, we will consider a special case in which G is a forest. As a result, we give a polynomial-time algorithm to compute $a_v^k(G)$ for every $k \in \{1, \ldots, n-1\}$ when G is a forest with n vertices.

Because of the lack of pages, we are not able to give a description of the algorithm here. The idea is as follows. First, we observe that, when G is a forest, we can reduce the computation of the $a_v^k(G)$ to the computation of the number of independent sets of given sizes in G. Then we establish an algorithm to compute these numbers with the dynamic programming technique. Thus, we can obtain a polynomial-time algorithm to compute the Shapley value for a forest.

4   Conclusion

We have investigated some fair cost allocations (the core, the τ-value, the nucleolus, the Shapley value) under conflict situations by modeling them as minimum coloring games. Our investigation on the core and the nucleolus suggests that results from polyhedral combinatorics are really useful in the study of cooperative games arising from combinatorial optimization games. This was indeed true in the work by Deng, Ibaraki & Nagamochi [2]. Furthermore, our approach to the nucleolus gives a viewpoint different from the literature. In the literature, polynomial-time algorithms for nucleoli of special classes of games were based on properties of the classes such as the number of essential coalitions is small (e.g. [24]) or the nucleolus is a unique vector in the intersection of the core and the kernel (e.g. [6]). Furthermore, usually the core is treated as a system of linear inequalities. On the contrary, in our approach we first look at the core as the convex hull of its extreme points (Theorem 2) and represent the nucleolus as a convex combination of them (Theorem 6). This should also be useful for other cooperative games. In addition, our investigation on the Shapley value suggests the use of a recurrence and the dynamic programming technique. Indeed, it is known that for the power indices of a weighted majority game the dynamic programming is quite useful [16]. Since there seemed to exist no application of the dynamic programming to cooperative games other than weighted majority games so far, it should be interesting to investigate more possibility of the dynamic programming technique for the Shapley value.

Finally, we will mention some open questions which this paper raises. First of all, we do not know how to compute the nucleolus and the Shapley value for a general perfect graph or even for a bipartite graph in polynomial time. It could be NP-hard or #P-hard. Another question is the computation of fair cost allocations for the graphs which are not perfect but for which the chromatic number can be computed in polynomial time, like outer-planar graphs. This would be really interesting since the core for an outer-planar graph can be empty.

Acknowledgements. The discussion with Hiroaki Mohri for an article [18] motivated this work. The author thanks him. In addition, the author is grateful to Udo Adamy, Kenji Kashiwabara and Tadashi Sakuma for discussion and/or useful comments and to Emo Welzl for his hospitality.

References

1. I.J. Curiel: Cooperative Game Theory and Applications: Cooperative Games Arising from Combinatorial Optimization Problems. Kluwer Academic Publishers, Dordrecht, 1997.
2. X. Deng, T. Ibaraki and H. Nagamochi: Algorithmic aspects of the core of combinatorial optimization games. Math. Oper. Res. **24** (1999) 751–766.
3. X. Deng, T. Ibaraki, H. Nagamochi and W. Zang: Totally balanced combinatorial optimization games. Math. Program. **87** (2000) 441–452.

4. T. Driessen: Cooperative Games, Solutions and Applications. Kluwer Academic Publishers, Dordrecht, 1988.

5. U. Faigle and W. Kern: The Shapley value for cooperative games under precedence constraints. Internat. J. Game Theory **21** (1992) 249–266.

6. U. Faigle, W. Kern and J. Kuipers: Computing the nucleolus of min-cost spanning tree games is NP-hard. Internat. J. Game Theory **27** (1998) 443–450.

7. U. Faigle, W. Kern and J. Kuipers: On the computation of the nucleolus of a cooperative game. Internat. J. Game Theory **30** (2001) 79–98.

8. D.R. Fulkerson and O.A. Gross: Incidence matrices and interval graphs. Pacific J. Math. **15** (1965) 835–855.

9. D.B. Gillies: Some theorems on n-person games. Ph.D. Thesis, Princeton University, 1953.

10. M.C. Golumbic: Algorithmic Graph Theory and Perfect Graphs. Academic Press, New York, 1980.

11. M. Grötschel, L. Lovász and A. Schrijver: Geometric algorithms and combinatorial optimization. Second edition. Springer-Verlag, Berlin, 1993.

12. A. Kopelowitz: Computation of the kernels of simple games and the nucleolus of n-person games. RM 31, Research Program in Game Theory and Mathematical Economics, The Hebrew University of Jerusalem, 1967.

13. J. Kuipers: A polynomial time algorithm for computing the nucleolus of convex games. Report M 96-12, Maastricht University, 1996.

14. L. Lovász: Normal hypergraphs and the perfect graph conjecture. Discrete Math. **2** (1972) 253–267.

15. M. Maschler, B. Peleg and L.S. Shapley: Geometric properties of the kernel, nucleolus and related solution concepts. Math. Oper. Res. **4** (1979) 303–338.

16. T. Matsui and Y. Matsui: A survey of algorithms for calculating power indices of weighted majority games. J. Oper. Res. Soc. Japan **43** (2000) 71–86.

17. N. Megiddo: Computational complexity and the game theory approach to cost allocation for a tree. Math. Oper. Res. **3** (1978) 189–196.

18. H. Mohri and Y. Okamoto: Discrete optimization and cooperative games (2). (In Japanese.) Comm. Oper. Res. Soc. Japan **48** (2003) 114–120.

19. J.S. Provan and M.O. Ball: The complexity of counting cuts and of computing the probability that a graph is connected. SIAM J. Comput. **12** (1983) 777–788.

20. Y. Okamoto: Submodularity of some classes of the combinatorial optimization games. Math. Methods Oper. Res. **58** (2003), to appear.

21. D. Schmeidler: The nucleolus of a characteristic function game. SIAM J. Appl. Math. **17** (1969) 1163–1170.

22. L.S. Shapley: Cores of convex games. Internat. J. Game Theory **1** (1971) 11–26. Errata is in the same volume, 1972, pp. 199.

23. L.S. Shapley: A value for n-person games. In: H. Kuhn and A.W. Tucker eds., Contributions to the Theory of Games II, Princeton University Press, Princeton, New Jersey, 1953, 307–317.

24. T. Solymosi and T.E.S. Raghavan: An algorithm for finding the nucleolus of assignment games. Internat. J. Game Theory **23** (1994) 119–143.

25. S.H. Tijs: Bounds for the core and the τ-value. In: O. Moeshlin and P. Pallaschke, eds., Game Theory and Mathematical Economics, North Holland, Amsterdam, 1981, 123–132.

Equilibria for Networks with Malicious Users⋆

George Karakostas[1] and Anastasios Viglas[2]

[1] McMaster University, Dept. of Computing and Software, 1280 Main St. West,
Hamilton, Ontario L8S 4K1, Canada, `gk@cas.mcmaster.ca`
[2] University of Toronto, Computer Science Department, 10 King's College Road,
Toronto, ON M5S 3G4, Canada `aviglas@cs.toronto.edu`

Abstract. We consider the problem of characterizing user equilibria and
optimal solutions for selfish routing in a given network. We extend the
known models by considering malicious behaviour. While selfish users
follow a strategy that minimizes their individual cost, a *malicious* user
will use his flow through the network in an effort to cause the maximum
possible damage to this cost. We define a generalized model, present
characterizations of flows at Wardrop equilibrium and prove bounds for
the ratio of the social cost of a flow at Wardrop equilibrium over the cost
when centralized coordination among users is allowed.

1 Introduction

Koutsoupias and Papadimitriou [5] initiated the study of the *coordination ratio*
(also referred to as the price of anarchy): How much worse is the performance of
a network of selfish users where each user optimizes her own cost, compared to
the best possible performance that can be achieved on the same system? This
question has been studied in various different models (e.g. [11], [12]) and bounds
for the coordination ratio have been shown for many interesting cases.

A basic assumption of the models considered so far is that the users are
considered to be selfish and *non-malicious*: the user optimizes her own utility
or payoff, and does not care about the performance of the system or the cost
induced to other users by her strategy. We extend these models by considering
malicious users. A malicious user will choose a strategy that will cause the worst
possible performance for the entire network. Such malicious behaviour can be
found in practice in settings such as the internet (for example in 'denial of service'
attacks, or malicious flow in peer-to-peer networks). While in terms of Wardrop
equilibria, the extension of the selfish model considered before is quite straightforward, the existence of malicious users forces us to a different model for the
'social cost'. We no longer have an objective function that can be minimized by
the centralized coordination among the users, since in our setting some of the
users still can be coordinated to *minimize* it, but at the same time there is a
(malicious) user that tries to *maximize* it. This leads naturally to the formulation
of the 'social cost' objective as a *minimax* problem instead of just a minimization

---

⋆ Extended Abstract. Detailed proofs appear in the full version.

T. Ibaraki, N. Katoh, and H. Ono (Eds.): ISAAC 2003, LNCS 2906, pp. 696–704, 2003.

problem. As a result, we cannot refer to an 'optimal social cost' that is a global minimizer of the social cost objective. Instead, we have to compare the worst Wardrop equilibrium to the *saddle-points* of the minimax problem. We define the 'optimal social cost' as the minimum cost achieved by the set of saddle-points. The fact that this set is (usually) *non-convex* makes the exact characterization of the 'optimal social cost' (and therefore the coordination ratio) more difficult to characterize than the previous models. Nevertheless, in this paper we show that in the very general setting considered by Roughgarden and Tardos [11], their results can be extended to the case of systems with malicious users.

Previous Work: Many of the Game Theoretic tools used for analyzing systems of non-cooperative users derive from results in traffic models and transportation, including work of Dafermos and Sparrow [4], Beckmann, McGuire and Winsten [2] and Aashtiani and Magnanti [1]. More recently, Nash equilibria and their applications were used for routing problems and the internet. Koutsoupias and Papadimitriou [5] considered the coordination ratio for load balancing problems (routing on a network of parallel links). The model they considered allowed multiple equilibria, and the coordination ratio compared the worst case equilibrium cost to the optimal routing cost. Their bounds were improved in subsequent work on the same model by Mavronicolas and Spirakis [6], and Czumaj and Vöcking [3]. Roughgarden and Tardos [11] considered a different model for selfish routing, where there is a unique Wardrop equilibrium and proved bounds for the coordination ratio, including results for the special case of linear utility functions. Other work in this model includes results on the topology of the underlying network [8,10], and algorithms and bounds for Stackelberg scheduling strategies [9].

2   The Model

We are given a directed network $G = (V, E)$ and k source-sink pairs of nodes $(s_i, t_i), i = 1 \ldots k$. There are also two special nodes s_M, t_M connected to G with edges $(s_M, s_i), (t_i, t_M), i = 1 \ldots k$. A commodity i with demand r_i is associated with each pair $(s_i, t_i), i = 1 \ldots k$, and a commodity M of demand F is associated with pair (s_M, t_M). Let $\mathcal{P}_i$ ($\mathcal{P}_M$) be the set of acyclic paths from s_i to t_i (s_M to t_M). A latency function $l_P(\cdot)$ is associated with each path P. For a flow f on G, $l_P(f)$ is the latency (cost) of path P for this particular flow. Notice that in general this latency depends on the whole flow f, and not only on the flow f_e through each edge $e \in P$. In this paper we adopt the *additive model* for the path latencies, i.e. $l_P(f) = \sum_{e \in P} l_e(f_e)$, where l_e is the latency function for edge e and f_e is the amount of flow that goes through e. We also let $\mathcal{P}$ be the set of all available paths in the network and assume that for every source-sink pair there is at least one path joining the source to the sink. We use the shorthand (G, r, F, l) to describe an instance of the model.

Commodities $i = 1 \ldots k$ model selfish, but otherwise 'good' users who want to just use the network in order to satisfy their demands with the smallest possible cost (i.e. latency for every unit of flow routed). Commodity M models a selfish 'malicious' user who wants to use his own flow F in such a way that will do the biggest possible damage to the total cost of the good players.

For our equilibrium model, we use the following general formulation by Aashtiani and Magnanti [1]:

Definition 1 *A flow* $f = \cup_{P \in \mathcal{P}} f_P$ *is at* Wardrop equilibrium *for instance* (G, r, F, l) *iff it satisfies the following constraints:*

$$
\begin{align}
(T_P(f) - u_i)f_P = 0 \quad &\text{for all } P \in \mathcal{P}_i, i = 1 \ldots k \tag{1} \\
(T_P(f) - u_M)f_P = 0 \quad &\text{for all } P \in \mathcal{P}_M \\
T_P(f) - u_i \geq 0 \quad &\text{for all } P \in \mathcal{P}_i, i = 1 \ldots k \\
T_P(f) - u_M \geq 0 \quad &\text{for all } P \in \mathcal{P}_M \\
\sum_{P \in \mathcal{P}_i} f_P - r_i = 0 \quad &\text{for all } i = 1 \ldots k \\
\sum_{P \in \mathcal{P}_M} f_P - F = 0 \\
f \geq 0, \quad u \geq 0
\end{align}
$$

where T_P *is the delay time or general disutility for path* P, f_P *is the flow through path* P, *and* $u = (u_1, \ldots, u_k, u_M)$ *is the vector of shortest travel times (or generalized costs) for the commodities.*

T_P does not need to be the same function for all paths P (it will be a different function for the good and the malicious users). Also we emphasize that T_P is *not* the path latency (the latter is given by function l_P). In what follows we define precisely the functions T_P for all users, and thus we define completely the equilibrium model of Definition 1.

The first four equations are the conditions for the existence of a Wardrop traffic equilibrium. They require that the general disutility for all paths P that carry flow $f_P > 0$ is the same and equal to u for every user, and less or equal to the disutility of any path with zero flow. Any flow that complies with this definition of a Wardrop equilibrium, also satisfies the following alternative characterization:

Lemma 1. *A flow that is feasible for instance* (G, r, F, l) *is a Wardrop equilibrium iff for every commodity* i *(i can be the malicious commodity M) and every pair of paths* $P_1, P_2 \in \mathcal{P}_i$ *with* $f_{P_1} > 0$, $T_{P_1}(f) \leq T_{P_2}(f)$.

2.1 Existence of Wardrop Equilibrium

The model of Definition 1 is very general. It turns out that the existence of a Wardrop equilibrium in this model can also be proved under very general assumptions. More specifically, the following theorem follows immediately from Theorem 5.4 in [1]:

Theorem 1. *Suppose that* T_P *is a positive continuous function for all* $P \in \mathcal{P}$. *Then there is a flow that satisfies the conditions of Definition 1.*

A function is positive if its values are positive. In order to make sure that a Wardrop always exists, from now on we make the following assumption:

Assumption 1 *The disutility function for every path is a* positive *function of the total flow, and that the disutility functions for the* good *users are increasing functions of the flow, i.e. as the congestion increases for a good user's path, its disutility also increases.*

3 Social Cost When Malicious Users Are Present

The existence of a malicious user forces us to redefine the notion of 'social cost' [5]. In addition to a set of users that collectively strive to *minimize* their collective cost (the 'social cost', as defined earlier [5], [11]), we have a user who strives to *maximize* this same cost. Therefore we define the 'socially best' flow in terms of a *minimax* problem. Note that in such a setting the notion of an "optimal flow" is replaced by the notion of a flow "in equilibrium". Therefore our work compares a Wardrop equilibrium to a minimax equilibrium (as opposed to the comparison of a Wardrop equilibrium to an optimal solution of a minimization problem, as in [11]).

In what follows, we denote the flow of the good users by f^G, and the flow of the malicious user by f^M (recall that we denote by f the total flow). We consider the following minimax formulation:

$$\max_{f^M} \min_{f^G} \sum_{e \in E} c_e(f_e^M, f_e^G) \quad \text{subject to:} \qquad \text{(MINMAX)}$$

$$\sum_{P \in \mathcal{P}_i} f_P^G = r_i \qquad \forall i \in \{1, \dots, k\}$$

$$\sum_{P \in \mathcal{P}_M} f_P^M = F$$

$$f_e^G = \sum_{P \in \mathcal{P}: e \in P} f_P^G \quad \forall e \in E$$

$$f_e^M = \sum_{P \in \mathcal{P}: e \in P} f_P^M \quad \forall e \in E$$

$$f_P^G \geq 0 \qquad \forall P \in \mathcal{P}$$

$$f_P^M \geq 0 \qquad \forall P \in \mathcal{P}$$

where $c_e(f_e^M, f_e^G)$ is the cost of flow (f_e^M, f_e^G) passing through edge e. In our case we have

$$c_e(f_e^M, f_e^G) = f_e^G \cdot l_e(f_e^G, f_e^M)$$

We call this minimax formulation (MINMAX), and its objective function $C(f^M, f^G) = \sum_{e \in E} c_e(f_e^M, f_e^G)$. The solution(s) to (MINMAX) are called *saddle-points*, defined as follows:

Definition 2 *A flow* $(\bar{f}^G, \bar{f}^M)$ *is said to be a* saddle-point *of* C *(with respect to maximizing in* f^M *and minimizing in* f^G*) if*

$$C(\bar{f}^G, f^M) \leq C(\bar{f}^G, \bar{f}^M) \leq C(f^G, \bar{f}^M), \quad \forall f^M, \forall f^G. \tag{2}$$

We also refer to (MINMAX) saddle-points as *(MINMAX) equilibria.*

3.1   Existence of Saddle-Points

A saddle-point is not always guaranteed to exist. But under certain assumptions, we can show that (at least one) saddle-point exists. We assume the following for the cost function $C(f^M, f^G)$:

Assumption 2 *The functions* $c_e(f_e^M, f_e^G)$ *are continuous, differentiable, convex with respect to* f^G*, and concave with respect to* f^M *for all* $e \in E$.

Following the methods of Dafermos and Sparrow [4], and under Assumption 2, we can prove the following theorem for the existence and properties of saddle-points for (MINMAX).

Theorem 2. *Under Assumption 2, a feasible flow* $\bar{f} = (\bar{f}^M, \bar{f}^G)$ *is a solution (saddle-point) to the minimax problem (MINMAX) if and only if it has the following properties:*

$$\sum_{e \in P} \frac{\partial c_e}{\partial f_e^G}(\bar{f}) = \sum_{e \in P'} \frac{\partial c_e}{\partial f_e^G}(\bar{f}) = A_i, \quad \forall P, P' \in \mathcal{P}_i, \quad \bar{f}_P^G, \bar{f}_{P'}^G > 0 \tag{3}$$

$$\sum_{e \in P} \frac{\partial c_e}{\partial f_e^M}(\bar{f}) = \sum_{e \in P'} \frac{\partial c_e}{\partial f_e^M}(\bar{f}) = B, \quad \forall P, P' \in \mathcal{P}_M, \quad \bar{f}_P^M, \bar{f}_{P'}^M > 0 \tag{4}$$

The conditions of Theorem 2 are simply the Kuhn-Tucker conditions for problem (MINMAX) [7].

4   Wardrop vs. Minimax Equilibria

We define natural *selfish* behaviors for both the good and malicious users, in accordance with the general model of Definition 1. Our aim will be to estimate how far can selfishness push the total cost from the optimal coordinated one (i.e. the best saddle-point of (MINMAX)). In order to do this, we modify the definition of the *price of anarchy* or *coordination ratio*, defined by Koutsoupias and Papadimitriou [5] and used by Roughgarden and Tardos [11].

Definition 3 (Coordination ratio) *Let* (G, r, F, l) *be an instance of the routing problem on network* G *with latency function* $l_e(\cdot)$ *for every edge* e*, with* k *good users with demands* r_i*,* $i = 1, \ldots, k$ *and a malicious user with flow* F*. Then the* coordination ratio $\rho(G, r, F, l)$ *for this instance is defined as follows:*

$$\rho(G, r, F, l) = \frac{worst\ Wardrop\ equilibrium}{best\ saddle\text{-}point\ of\ (MINMAX)}. \tag{5}$$

According to the model of Definition 1, the selfish users will base their decisions for picking flow paths on their individual notion of general disutility T_P, for every path P. This disutility is very easy to be defined for the 'good' users: it is simply the latency of the path, i.e.

$$T_P(f^G, f^M) := l_P(f^G, f^M) \; (= \sum_{e \in P} l_e(f_e)), \quad \forall i = 1, \dots, k, \; \forall P \in \mathcal{P}_i \quad (6)$$

For the malicious user though, the form of his general disutility in fact determines how powerful or weak this user can be. In this paper we study malicious players that base their decisions exclusively on the costs of *individual paths*. The malicious player exhibits a rather greedy behavior, and does not (or cannot[1]) take into account the impact of his decisions on the whole network (e.g. by solving (MINMAX) so that his allocation of flow will have the worst impact on the 'social cost' he might be able to achieve more damage than looking greedily at the costs of individual paths). Let $M(f^G) = \sum_{e \in E} f_e^G \cdot \frac{\partial l_e}{\partial f_e^M}(f_e^G, 0)$. Then the general disutility for the malicious user paths is defined as follows:

$$T_P(f^G, f^M) := M(f^G) - \sum_{e \in P} f_e^G \cdot \frac{\partial l_e}{\partial f_e^M}(f_e^G, f_e^M), \quad \forall P \in \mathcal{P}_M \quad (7)$$

In other words, the malicious player always tries to send his flow through a path with the biggest possible congestion increase for every unit of flow he allocates to this path, i.e. the malicious player follows a "best value for your money" policy.

The quantity $M(\cdot)$ is introduced so that Assumption 1 holds and therefore Wardrop equilibria exist.

4.1   Bicriteria Bound

As in the case of [11] we can prove a "bicriteria" result that gives an upper bound for the ratio between the cost at Wardrop equilibrium and the cost of the saddle-point solution.

Theorem 3. *If $f = (f^G, f^M)$ is a flow at Wardrop Equilibrium for (G, r, F, l) and $\hat{f} = (\hat{f}^G, \hat{f}^M)$ is a saddle-point of (MINMAX) for $(G, 2r, F, l)$ then $C(f) \leq C(\hat{f})$.*

Proof. The (social) cost of flow f is defined as

$$C(f) = \sum_e f_e^G \cdot l_e(f_e^G + f_e^M).$$

If f is at Wardrop equilibrium, then the total latency along any flow path P for good user i from s_i to t_i, $i = 1 \dots, k$ is the same, denoted by $L_i(f)$, and the total cost can be expressed as $C(f) = \sum_i L_i(f) r_i$. Define a new latency function $\bar{l}_e(x, y)$ as follows:

---

[1] maybe because of lack of resources, e.g. time in an on-line scenario

$$\bar{l}_e(x,y) = \begin{cases} l_e(x,y) & \text{if } x > f_e^G \text{ and } y > f_e^M \\ l_e(x, f_e^M) & x > f_e^G \text{ and } y \le f_e^M \\ l_e(f_e^G, y) & x \le f_e^G \text{ and } y > f_e^M \\ l_e(f_e^G, f_e^M) & x \le f_e^G \text{ and } y \le f_e^M \end{cases} \tag{8}$$

Note that the difference $\bar{l}_e(x, f_e^M) - l_e(x, f_e^M)$ is zero for $x \ge f_e^G$. Therefore the following is true for all $x \ge 0$:

$$x(\bar{l}_e(x, f_e^M) - l_e(x, f_e^M)) \le l_e(f_e^G, f_e^M)f_e^G. \tag{9}$$

The new latency functions give a new cost (cost with respect to $\bar{l}$) that is not too far from the real cost:

$$\sum_e \bar{l}_e(\hat{f}_e^G, f_e^M)\hat{f}_e^G - C(\hat{f}^G, f^M) \le \sum_e \bar{l}_e(\hat{f}_e^G, f_e^M)\hat{f}_e^G - C(\hat{f}^G, f^M) =$$
$$\sum_e \hat{f}_e^G(\bar{l}_e(\hat{f}_e^G, f_e^M) - l_e(\hat{f}_e^G, f_e^M)) \le \sum_e f_e^G l_e(f_e^G, f_e^M) = C(f) \tag{10}$$

The first inequality is due to the fact that $\hat{f} = (\hat{f}^G, \hat{f}^M)$ is a saddle-point for $(G, 2r, F, l)$, i.e. $C(\hat{f}^G, f^M) \le C(\hat{f}^G, \hat{f}^M)$ since $(\hat{f}^G, f^M)$ is a feasible solution for (MINMAX). The second inequality comes from (9) for $x := \hat{f}_e^G$.

Consider any path $P \in \mathcal{P}_i$. From the definition of $\bar{l}_e$ we have that

$$\sum_{e \in P} \bar{l}_e(0, f_e^M) \ge \sum_{e \in P} l_e(f_e^G, f_e^M) = L_i(f).$$

and from the fact that $\bar{l}_e(x, f_e^M)$ is an increasing function of x we get

$$\sum_{e \in P} \bar{l}_e(\hat{f}_e^G, f_e^M) \ge \sum_{e \in P} \bar{l}_e(0, f_e^M).$$

Therefore:

$$\sum_{e \in E} \bar{l}_e(\hat{f}_e^G, f_e^M) \cdot \hat{f}_e^G \ge \sum_i \sum_{P \in \mathcal{P}_i} \hat{f}_P^G \sum_{e \in P} \bar{l}_e(\hat{f}_e^G, f_e^M) \ge$$
$$\sum_i \sum_{P \in \mathcal{P}_i} L_i(f)\hat{f}_P^G = \sum_i 2L_i(f)r_i = 2C(f) \tag{11}$$

By combining (10) with (11) we get $C(f) \le C(\hat{f})$.

The same proof also gives the following result:

Theorem 4. *If $f = (f^G, f^M)$ is a flow at Wardrop Equilibrium for (G, r, F, l) and $\hat{f} = (\hat{f}^G, \hat{f}^M)$ is a saddle-point of (MINMAX) for $(G, (1 + \gamma)r, F, l)$, $\gamma > 0$ then $C(f) \le \frac{1}{\gamma}C(\hat{f})$.*

At a first glance, it seems rather surprising that the bicriteria bounds of [11] are quite robust against the existence of a malicious user. But if we look closer to the quantities compared in the theorems above, we see that while the demands of the good users are increased, the flow quantity at the disposal of the malicious user remained the same. Intuitively, the malicious user has the same power to disrupt the good users in both cases, and therefore if he settles with some strategy to do so for the initial good demands, this strategy should work about as well when the latter demands increase. The same goes for the good users' strategies as well.

4.2   Special Case: Linear Latency Functions

In this section we deal with the special case of linear edge latency functions, i.e. for every edge $e \in E$, $l_e(f_e^G, f_e^M) = a_e(f_e^G + f_e^M) + b_e$ for some $a_e \geq 0, b_e > 0$. Note that we assume that the latency for an edge is positive even if no flow passes through it. This is a quite natural assumption (in all physical systems there is always some delay in moving from point A to point B, even if there is no congestion at all), and allows Theorem 1 to apply in this case. We modify our shorthand notation to (G, r, F, a, b) to include the linear coefficient vectors. In this special case we have

- $T_P(f^G, f^M) := \sum_{e \in P}(a_e f_e^G + a_e f_e^M + b_e), \ \forall i = 1, \ldots, k, \ \forall P \in \mathcal{P}_i$
- $T_P(f^G, f^M) := \sum_{e \in E} a_e f_e^G - \sum_{e \in P} a_e f_e^G, \ \forall P \in \mathcal{P}_M$

Lemma 1 and Theorem 2 take a more specific form for the linear case:

Lemma 2. *Let* $l_e(f_e^G, f_e^M) = a_e(f_e^G + f_e^M) + b_e$ *with* $a_e \geq 0, b_e > 0$ *be the latency function for every edge* $e \in E$ *of* G.

(a) a flow $f = (f^G, f^M)$ *is at Wardrop equilibrium iff*
  - *for all users* $i = 1, \ldots, k$ *and paths* $P, P' \in \mathcal{P}_i$ *with* $f_P > 0$

$$\sum_{e \in P} \left(a_e f_e^G + a_e f_e^M + b_e\right) \leq \sum_{e \in P'} \left(a_e f_e^G + a_e f_e^M + b_e\right)$$

  - *for all paths* $P, P' \in \mathcal{P}_M$ *with* $f_P > 0$: $\sum_{e \in P} a_e f_e^G \geq \sum_{e \in P'} a_e f_e^G$

(b) a flow $\bar{f} = (\bar{f}^G, \bar{f}^M)$ *is an equilibrium for* (MINMAX) *iff*
  - *for all commodities* $i = 1, \ldots, k$ *and paths* $P, P' \in \mathcal{P}_i$ *with* $\bar{f}_P > 0$

$$\sum_{e \in P} \left(2a_e \bar{f}_e^G + a_e \bar{f}_e^M + b_e\right) \leq \sum_{e \in P'} \left(2a_e \bar{f}_e^G + a_e \bar{f}_e^M + b_e\right)$$

  - *for all paths* $P, P' \in \mathcal{P}_M$ *with* $\bar{f}_P > 0$: $\sum_{e \in P} a_e \bar{f}_e^G \geq \sum_{e \in P'} a_e \bar{f}_e^G$

For this special form of the edge latency functions, we can prove that the saddle-point cost for (MINMAX) is unique (proof omitted). In a way similar to [11] we can prove our main theorem for the coordination ratio in the linear case:

Theorem 5. *For instance* (G, r, F, a, b), $1 \leq \rho(G, r, F, a, b) \leq \frac{4}{3}$.

Note that the lower bound for the coordination ratio is tight, since $\rho(G, r, F, a, b) = 1$ if G is just a path with the sources for all users in one end, and all the sinks in the other.

5 Open Problems

The model presented in our work gives rise to many open problems. It would be very interesting to present a result connecting the social cost of an equilibrium point in a network with malicious users and the cost in an equivalent instance without malicious users. This would give a clear characterization of the negative impact of the presence of malicious flow. For the general latency functions, it seems that it is possible to prove more tight results and extend the bicriteria result by proving a lower bound. The model defined in our work gives rise to unique saddle-points and Wardrop equilibria. It would be interesting to consider a more general model that allows multiple equilibria (for example, by adding capacities for the edges in the network [12]) and analyze the performance of the system in the presence of malicious users.

Acknowledgments. We would like to thank Tamás Terlaky and Nicola Galesi for many helpful discussions.

References

1. H. Z. Aashtiani and T. L. Magnanti. Equilibria on a congested transportation network. *SIAM J. on Algebraic and Discrete Methods*, 2(3):213–226, Sept. 1981.
2. M. Beckmann, C. B. McGuire, and C. B. Winsten. Studies in the economics of transportation. *Yale University Press*, 1956.
3. A. Czumaj and B. Vöcking. Tight bounds for worst-case equilibria. In *13th ACM-SIAM Symposium On Discrete Mathematics*, pages 413–420, 2002.
4. S. Dafermos and F. Sparrow. The traffic assignment problem for a general network. *J. of Research of the National Bureau of Standards*, 73B:91–118, 1969.
5. E. Koutsoupias and C. Papadimitriou. Worst-case equilibria. In *16th Symposium on Theoretical Aspects of Computer Science, LNCS 1563*, pages 404–413, 1999.
6. M. Mavronicolas and P. Spirakis. The price of selfish routing. In *33rd Annual ACM Symposium on Theory of Computing*, pages 510–519, 2001.
7. R. T. Rockafellar. *Convex Analysis*. Princeton University Press, 1970.
8. T. Roughgarden. Designing networks for selfish users is hard. In *42nd IEEE Symposium on Foundations of Computer Science*, pages 472–481, 2001.
9. T. Roughgarden. Stackelberg scheduling strategies. In *33rd Annual ACM Symposium on Theory of Computing*, pages 104–113, 2001.
10. T. Roughgarden. The price of anarchy is independent of the network topology. In *34th Annual ACM Symposium on Theory of Computing*, pages 428–437, 2002.
11. T. Roughgarden and É. Tardos. How bad is selfish routing? *J. of the ACM*, 49(2):236–259, Mar. 2002.
12. A. S. Schulz and N. S. Moses. On the performance of user equilibria in traffic networks. In *14th Symposium on Discrete Algorithms*, pages 86–87, 2003.

Quasi-optimal Arithmetic for Quaternion Polynomials

Martin Ziegler*

University of Paderborn, 33095 GERMANY; ziegler@upb.de

Abstract. Fast algorithms for arithmetic on real or complex polynomials are well-known and have proven to be not only asymptotically efficient but also very practical. Based on *Fast Fourier Transform*, they for instance multiply two polynomials of degree up to n or multi-evaluate one at n points simultaneously within quasi-linear time $\mathcal{O}(n \cdot \text{polylog } n)$. An extension to (and in fact the mere definition of) polynomials over fields $\mathbb{R}$ and $\mathbb{C}$ to the *skew*-field $\mathbb{H}$ of quaternions is promising but still missing. The present work proposes three approaches which in the commutative case coincide but for $\mathbb{H}$ turn out to differ, each one satisfying some desirable properties while lacking others. For each notion, we devise algorithms for according arithmetic; these are quasi-optimal in that their running times match lower complexity bounds up to polylogarithmic factors.

1 Motivation

Nearly 40 years after COOLEY and TUKEY [4], their Fast Fourier Transform (FFT) has provided numerous applications, among them

- fast multiplication of polynomials
    Given the coefficients of $p, q \in \mathbb{C}[X]$, $n := \deg(p) + \deg(q)$;
    determine the coefficients of $p \cdot q$.
  which, based on FFT, can be performed in $\mathcal{O}(n \cdot \log n)$ and

- their multi-evaluation
    Given the coefficients of $p \in \mathbb{C}[X]$, $\deg(p) < n$, *and* $x_1, \ldots, x_n \in \mathbb{C}$;
    determine the values $p(x_1), \ldots, p(x_n)$.
  allowing algorithmic solution within $\mathcal{O}(n \cdot \log^2 n)$.

Observe in both cases the significant improvement over naive $\mathcal{O}(n^2)$ approaches. These two examples illustrate a larger class of operations called *Fast Polynomial Arithmetic* [1, 14] with, again, a vast number of applications [7]. For instance, GERASOULIS employed fast polynomial arithmetic to drastically accelerate N-Body Simulations in 2D [8], and PAN, REIF, and TATE did so in 3D [11]. Since systems with up to $N = 10^5$ objects arise quite frequently when simulating biochemical processes, the theoretical benefit of asymptotic growth $\mathcal{O}(N \cdot \text{polylog } N)$ over $\mathcal{O}(N^2)$ pays off in practice as well.

Technically speaking in order to calculate, for each of the N particles, the total force it experiences due to the $N - 1$ others, GERASOULIS identifies the plane $\mathbb{R}^2$ with $\mathbb{C}$; he thus turns Coulomb's potential into a rational complex function which, by means of fast polynomial multiplication and multi-evaluation, can be handled efficiently. [11,13]

---

* Supported by PaSCo, DFG Graduate College no.693

on the other hand exploit fast multi-evaluation of polynomials to *approximate* the total forces in $\mathbb{R}^3$. Whether 3D forces can be obtained *exactly* within subquadratic time is still an open question. One promising approach proceeds by identifying, similarly to [8], $\mathbb{R}^3$ with (a subspace of) HAMILTON's four-dimensional algebra of Quaternions $\mathbb{H}$ and there applying fast polynomial arithmetic of some kind or another. In fact the mere notion of a polynomial becomes ambiguous when passing from fields $\mathbb{K} = \mathbb{R}$ and $\mathbb{K} = \mathbb{C}$ to the skew-field $\mathbb{K} = \mathbb{H}$. We consider three common approaches to define polynomials (Section 2) and, for each induced kind of quaternion polynomials, present quasi-optimal algorithms supporting according arithmetic operations (Section 3).

2 Quaternions

The algebra $\mathbb{H}$ of quaternions was discovered in 1843 by W.R. HAMILTON in an attempt to extend multiplication of 'vectors' from $\mathbb{R}^2 \cong \mathbb{C}$ to $\mathbb{R}^3$. In fact, $\mathbb{H}$ is a *four*-dimensional real vector space whose canonical basis $1, i, j, k$ satisfies the non-commutative multiplicative rule

$$i^2 = j^2 = k^2 = ijk = -1, \qquad ij = -ji = k \qquad \text{+ cyclic interchange} \qquad (1)$$

which, by means of associative and distribute laws, is extended to arbitrary quaternions. $\mathbb{H}$ is easily verified to form a *skew-field*, that is, any non-zero element a possesses a unique two-sided multiplicative inverse a^{-1}. In fact it holds $a^{-1} = \bar{a}/|a|^2$ where $\bar{a} := \text{Re}(a) - i\,\text{Im}_i(a) - j\,\text{Im}_j(a) - k\,\text{Im}_k(a)$ is the analogue of complex conjugation and $|a| := \sqrt{a \cdot \bar{a}} = \sqrt{\bar{a} \cdot a} \in \mathbb{R}_+$ the *norm* satisfying $|a \cdot b| = |a| \cdot |b|$. The *center* of $\mathbb{H}$ is $\mathbb{R}$; in other words: real numbers and only they multiplicatively commute with any quaternion. For further details, please refer to the excellent[1] CHAPTER 7 of [5]. THEOREM 17.32 in [3] determines the (multiplicative algebraic) complexity of quaternion multiplication; [2] does so similarly for quaternion inversion and division. However rather than on single quaternions, our focus shall lie on asymptotics w.r.t. n, the quaternion polynomials' degree, tending to infinity.

It is well-known that commutativity *has* to be abandoned in order to turn $\mathbb{R}^4$ into some sort of a field; in fact, FROBENIUS' Theorem states that $\mathbb{H}$ is the *only* associative division algebra beyond $\mathbb{R}^2 \cong \mathbb{C}$. On the other hand to the author's best knowledge, all notions of polynomials either require the ground ring $\mathcal{R}$ to satisfy commutativity or — such as *skew polynomial rings*, see P.262, CHAPTER 16 of [10] — they lack evaluation homomorphisms. The latter means that any polynomial $p = p(X) \in \mathcal{R}[X]$ should naturally induce a mapping $\hat{p} : \mathcal{R} \to \mathcal{R}, x \mapsto \hat{p}(x)$ such that for all $a, x \in \mathcal{R}$:

$$\hat{X}(x) = x, \quad \hat{a}(x) = a, \quad \widehat{p \cdot q}(x) = \hat{p}(x) \cdot \hat{q}(x), \quad \text{and} \quad \widehat{p + q}(x) = \hat{p}(x) + \hat{q}(x) \ .$$

The distant goal is to find a notion of quaternion polynomials which naturally generalizes from real or complex ones *and* supports efficient arithmetic by means of, say, quasi-linear time algorithms. Our contribution considers three such definitions for $\mathbb{K}[X]$ which, in case $\mathbb{K}$ is an infinite field, are equivalent to the usual notion. In case $\mathbb{K} = \mathbb{H}$

---

[1] wrongly condemned in CHAPTER XXI, P.245 of [12] . . .

however they disagree and give rise to different arithmetic operations. We focus on Multiplication and Multi-Evaluation and present in Section 3, for each of the three notions, according quasi-optimal algorithms.

2.1 Polynomials as Ring of Mappings

The idea pursued in this subsection is that the following objects should be considered polynomials:

- the identity mapping $X := \mathrm{id} : \mathbb{K} \to \mathbb{K}$, $x \mapsto x$,
- any constant mapping $\hat{a} : \mathbb{K} \to \mathbb{K}$, $x \mapsto a$ for $a \in \mathbb{K}$
- the sum of two polynomials   and
- the product of two polynomials.

Formally, let the set $\mathbb{K}^{\mathbb{K}}$ of mappings $f : \mathbb{K} \to \mathbb{K}$ inherit the ring structure of $\mathbb{K}$ by defining pointwise $f + g : x \mapsto f(x) + g(x)$, $f \cdot g : x \mapsto f(x) \cdot g(x)$. Then embed $\mathbb{K}$ into this ring by identifying $a \in \mathbb{K}$ with the constant mapping $\mathbb{K} \ni x \mapsto a \in \mathbb{K}$.

Definition 1. $\mathbb{K}_1[X]$ *is the smallest subring of* $\mathbb{K}^{\mathbb{K}}$ *containing* X *and the constant mappings* $\mathbb{K}$. *For instance,*

$$a_1 + X \cdot a_2 \cdot X \cdot X \cdot a_3 + a_4 \cdot X \cdot X \cdot X \cdot a_5 \in \mathbb{K}_1[X] \ , \qquad a_1, \dots, a_5 \in \mathbb{K} \ fixed. \tag{2}$$

$\mathbb{K}_1[X]$ is closed not only under addition and multiplication but also under composition, i.e., $f + g, f \cdot g, f \circ g \in \mathbb{K}_1[X]$ for $f, g \in \mathbb{K}_1[X]$. Since, in the commutative case, any such polynomial can be brought to the form

$$\sum\nolimits_{\ell=0}^{n-1} a_\ell X^\ell, \qquad n \in \mathbb{N}, \quad a_\ell \in \mathbb{K} \ , \tag{3}$$

Definition 1 there obviously coincides with the classical notion of polynomial rings $\mathbb{R}[X]$ and $\mathbb{C}[X]$. For the skew-field $\mathbb{K} = \mathbb{H}$ of quaternions, the structure of $\mathbb{H}_1[X]$ is not so clear at first sight:

- $a \cdot X \neq X \cdot a$ unless $a \in \mathbb{R}$ i.e., the form (3) in general cannot be attained any more.
- Uniqueness becomes an issue, since

$$X \cdot X \cdot i \cdot X \cdot i + i \cdot X \cdot X \cdot i \cdot X - i \cdot X \cdot i \cdot X \cdot X - X \cdot i \cdot X \cdot X \cdot i \tag{4}$$

  vanishes identically [5, TOP OF P.201];
  in particular, a polynomial can have many more roots than its 'degree' suggests.
- The fundamental theorem of algebra is violated as well: $i \cdot X - X \cdot i + 1$ has no root in $\mathbb{H}$ [5, P.205].
- Lagrange-style polynomials P_m to pairwise distinct points $x_0, \dots, x_{n-1} \in \mathbb{H}$, e.g.,

$$\left(\prod_{\substack{\ell=0 \\ \ell \neq m}}^{n-1} (X - x_\ell) \right) \cdot \left(\prod_{\substack{\ell=0 \\ \ell \neq m}}^{n-1} (x_m - x_\ell) \right)^{-1} \quad \text{or} \quad \prod_{\substack{\ell=0 \\ \ell \neq m}}^{n-1} \left((x_m - x_\ell)^{-1} \cdot (X - x_\ell) \right)$$

  both interpolate $P_m(x_m) = 1, P_m(x_\ell) = 0, m \neq \ell$ but obviously lack uniqueness.
- There is no polynomial division with remainder; e.g. $X \cdot i \cdot X \bmod X^2 = ???$

On the other hand we present in Subsection 3.2 algorithms for addition, multiplication, and multi-evaluation of this kind of quaternion polynomials of degree n in time $\mathcal{O}(n^4 \cdot \text{polylog } n)$. Since it turns out that generic $p \in \mathbb{H}_1[X]$ have roughly n^4 free coefficients, the running time is thus quasi-optimal. Finally, a fast randomized zero-tester for expressions like (2) and (4) comes out easily.

2.2   Polynomials as Sequence of Coefficients

Since the above Definition 1 thus does not *allow* for quaternion polynomial arithmetic as fast as quasi-linear time, the present subsection proposes another approach. The idea is to identify polynomials with their coefficients. Recall that for $p = \sum_{\ell=0}^{n-1} a_\ell X^\ell$ and $q = \sum_{\ell=0}^{m-1} b_\ell X^\ell$ over a commutative field $\mathbb{K}$, the finite sequence of coefficients $c = (c_\ell) \in \mathbb{K}^*$ of $p \cdot q$ is given in terms of $a = (a_\ell) \in \mathbb{K}^*$ and $b = (b_\ell) \in \mathbb{K}^*$ by the convolution product

$$c = a * b, \quad c_\ell = \sum_{t=0}^{\ell} a_t \cdot b_{\ell-t}, \quad \ell = 0, \ldots, n+m-1 \tag{5}$$

with the implicit agreement that $a_\ell = 0$ for $\ell \geq n$ and $b_\ell = 0$ for $\ell \geq m$.

Definition 2. $\mathbb{K}_2[X]$ *is the set* $\mathbb{K}^*$ *of finite sequences of quaternions, equipped with componentwise addition and convolution product according to (5). Let X denote the special sequence* $(0, 1, 0, \ldots, 0) \in \mathbb{K}^*$.

It is easy to see that this turns $\mathbb{K}_2[X]$ into a ring which, in case of fields $\mathbb{K}$ of characteristic zero, again coincides with the usual ring of polynomials $\mathbb{K}[X]$. Here the classical results assert that arithmetic operations + and * can be performed within time $\mathcal{O}(n)$ and $\mathcal{O}(n \cdot \log n)$, respectively. In Subsection 3.1, we show that the same is possible in the non-commutative ring $\mathbb{H}_2[X]$. Dealing with n coefficients, this is trivially quasi-optimal.

Unfortunately fast arithmetic for $\mathbb{H}_2[X]$ does not include multi-evaluation, simply because evaluation (substituting X for some $x \in \mathbb{H}$) makes no sense here: One might be tempted to identify $a \in \mathbb{H}^*$ with the formal expression $\sum_\ell a_\ell X^\ell$ and b with $\sum_\ell b_\ell X^\ell$, but then $c := a * b$ does not agree with

$$\left(\sum a_\ell X^\ell\right) \cdot \left(\sum b_\ell X^\ell\right) = \sum_\ell \sum_{t=0}^{\ell} a_t \cdot \underbrace{X^t \cdot b_{\ell-t}}_{\neq b_{\ell-t} \cdot X^t} \cdot X^{\ell-t} \neq \sum_\ell c_\ell X^\ell$$

because of non-commutativity.

The next subsection considers expressions of the form $\sum a_\ell X^\ell$ as further notion of quaternion polynomials. These lack closure under multiplication; on the other hand, there, multi-evaluation does make sense and turns out to have classical complexity $\mathcal{O}(n \cdot \log^2 n)$.

2.3   One-Sided Polynomials

Roughly speaking, one aims at a subclass of $\mathbb{H}_1[X]$ where polynomials have only $\mathcal{O}(n)$ rather than $\Theta(n^4)$ coefficients and thus give a chance for operations with quasi-linear complexity.

Definition 3. *Let* $X : \mathbb{K} \to \mathbb{K}$ *denote the identity mapping and consider this class of mappings on* $\mathbb{K}$: $\quad \mathbb{K}_3[X] \quad := \quad \{ \sum_{\ell=0}^{n} a_\ell X^\ell : n \in \mathbb{N}_0, a_\ell \in \mathbb{K} \} \quad \subseteq \quad \mathbb{K}^{\mathbb{K}}.$
The **degree** *of* $p \in \mathbb{K}_3[X]$ *is* $\quad \deg(p) = \max_{a_\ell \neq 0} \ell, \quad \deg(0) := -1.$

Again this coincides for fields $\mathbb{K}$ of characteristic zero with the usual notions. For the skew-field of quaternions, the restriction compared to (2) applies that all coefficients a_ℓ must be on the *left* of powers X^ℓ. Unfortunately, this prevents $\mathbb{H}_3[X]$ from being closed under multiplication; fortunately, $\mathbb{H}_3[X]$ has the following other nice properties:
- being a real vector space;   – allows fast multi-evaluation;
- supports interpolation;   – a fundamental theorem of algebra holds;
          – polynomials satisfy uniqueness.   Formally:

Lemma 4. *Consider* $p := \sum_{\ell=0}^{n-1} a_\ell X^\ell, \ a_\ell \in \mathbb{H}.$

a) *Suppose* $p(x) = 0$ *for all* $x \in \mathbb{H}$. *Then* $a_\ell = 0$ *for all* ℓ.
b) *Nevertheless even* $p \neq 0$ *may have an infinite (and in particular unbounded in terms of* p's *degree) number of roots.*
c) *If* $a_\ell \neq 0$ *for some* $\ell \geq 1$, *then* p *has at least one root.*

Proof. a) Follows from Lemma 7b) by choosing $n \geq \deg(p)$ and pairwise distinct
$x_0, \ldots, x_{n-1} \in \mathbb{R}$ since then, no three are automorphically equivalent.
b) All quaternions $x = i\beta + j\gamma + k\delta$ with $\beta, \gamma, \delta \in \mathbb{R}$ and $\beta^2 + \gamma^2 + \delta^2 = 1$ are easily verified zeros of $p := X^2 + 1$.
c) Cf. P.205 in [5] or see, e.g., [6].

Interpolation is the question of existence and uniqueness, given $x_0, \ldots, x_{n-1}$ and $y_0, \ldots, y_{n-1} \in \mathbb{K}$, of a polynomial $p \in \mathbb{K}[X]$ with degree at most $n - 1$ satisfying $p(x_\ell) = y_\ell$ for all $\ell = 0, \ldots, n-1$. In the commutative case, both is asserted for pairwise distinct x_ℓ. Over quaternions, this condition does not suffice neither for uniqueness (Lemma 4b) nor for existence:

Example 5. No $p = aX^2 + bX + c \in \mathbb{H}_3[X]$ satisfies $p(i) = 0 = p(j), p(k) = 1$.

It turns out that here, an additional condition has to be imposed which, in the commutative case, hold trivially for distinct x_ℓ, namely being automorphically inequivalent.

Definition 6. *Call* $a, b \in \mathbb{H}$ **automorphically equivalent** *iff* $a = u \cdot b \cdot u^{-1}$ *for some non-zero* $u \in \mathbb{H}$, *that is, iff* $\quad \mathrm{Re}(a) = \mathrm{Re}(b) \quad \wedge \quad |\mathrm{Im}(a)| = |\mathrm{Im}(b)| \quad$ *where* $\mathrm{Im}(a) := i \, \mathrm{Im}_i(a) + j \, \mathrm{Im}_j(a) + k \, \mathrm{Im}_k(a).$

This obviously *is* an equivalence relation (reflexivity, symmetry, transitivity). The name comes from the fact that mappings $x \mapsto u \cdot x \cdot u^{-1}$ are exactly the $\mathbb{R}$-algebra automorphisms of $\mathbb{H}$; cf. [5, BOTTOM OF P.215]. The central result of [9] now says:

Lemma 7. *For* $x_0, \ldots, x_{n-1} \in \mathbb{H}$, *the following are equivalent*

a) *To any* $y_0, \ldots, y_{n-1} \in \mathbb{H}$, *there exists* $p \in \mathbb{H}_3[X]$ *of* $\deg(p) < n$ *such that* $p(x_\ell) = y_\ell, \ \ell = 0, \ldots, n - 1.$
b) *Whenever* $p = \sum_{\ell=0}^{n-1} a_\ell X^\ell$ *and* $q = \sum_{\ell=0}^{n-1} b_\ell X^\ell$ *satisfy* $p(x_\ell) = q(x_\ell)$ *for* $\ell = 0, \ldots, n - 1$, *it follows* $a_\ell = b_\ell.$

*c) The **Quaternion Vandermonde Matrix** $V := (x_\ell^m)_{\ell,m=0,..,n-1}$ is invertible.*
*d) Its **Double Determinant** $\|V\|$ does not vanish.*
*e) The x_ℓ are pairwise distinct **and** no three of them are automorphically equivalent.*

Concluding this subsection, $\mathbb{H}_3[X]$ has (unfortunately apart from closure under multiplication) several nice structural properties. In 3.3 we will furthermore show that it supports multi-evaluation in time $\mathcal{O}(n \cdot \log^2 n)$. More generally, our algorithm applies to polynomials $\quad \mathbb{H}_3^1[X] \quad := \quad \{\sum_{\ell=0}^{n-1} a_\ell \cdot X^\ell \cdot b_\ell \; : \; n \in \mathbb{N}_0, \; a_\ell, b_\ell \in \mathbb{H}\}$ with coefficients to *both* sides of each monomial X^ℓ. This generalized notion has the advantage of yielding not only an $\mathbb{R}$-vector space but a two-sided $\mathbb{H}$-vector space.

3 Algorithms

3.1 Convolution of Quaternion Sequences

Beginning with the simplest case of $\mathbb{H}_2[X]$:
Let $n \in \mathbb{N}$. Given $a = (a_0, a_1, \dots, a_{n-1}) \in \mathbb{H}^n$ and $b = (b_0, b_1, \dots, b_{m-1}) \in \mathbb{H}^m$, one can compute their convolution according to (5) from 16 real convolutions[2] and 12 additions of real sequences within time $\mathcal{O}(n \cdot \log n)$. Indeed write componentwise

$$a = \mathrm{Re}(a) + i\,\mathrm{Im}_i(a) + j\,\mathrm{Im}_j(a) + k\,\mathrm{Im}_k(a), \quad b = \mathrm{Re}(b) + i\,\mathrm{Im}_i(b) + j\,\mathrm{Im}_j(b) + k\,\mathrm{Im}_k(b)$$

and exploit $\mathbb{R}$-bilinearity of quaternion convolution.

3.2 Ring of Quaternion Mappings

The central point of this subsection is the identification of $\mathbb{H}_1[X]$ with the four-fold Cartesian product of four-variate real polynomials $\prod^4 \mathbb{R}[X_0, X_1, X_2, X_3]$. Formally consider, for $f : \mathbb{H} \to \mathbb{H}$, the quadruple $\tilde{f}$ of four-variate real functions defined by

$$\tilde{f}_0(X_0,..,X_3):=\mathrm{Re}\,(p(X_0+iX_1+jX_2+kX_3)) \quad \tilde{f}_1(X_0,..,X_3):=\mathrm{Im}_i(p(X_0+iX_1+jX_2+kX_3))$$
$$\tilde{f}_2(X_0,..,X_3):=\mathrm{Im}_j(p(X_0+iX_1+jX_2+kX_3)) \quad \tilde{f}_3(X_0,..,X_3):=\mathrm{Im}_k(p(X_0+iX_1+jX_2+kX_3)) \tag{6}$$

and multiplication among such mappings $\tilde{f}, \tilde{g} : \mathbb{R}^4 \to \mathbb{R}^4$ given pointwise by

$$(\tilde{f}_0, \tilde{f}_1, \tilde{f}_2, \tilde{f}_3) \cdot (\tilde{g}_0, \tilde{g}_1, \tilde{g}_2, \tilde{g}_3) \quad :=$$
$$(\tilde{f}_0\tilde{g}_0 - \tilde{f}_1\tilde{g}_1 - \tilde{f}_2\tilde{g}_2 - \tilde{f}_3\tilde{g}_3, \; \tilde{f}_0\tilde{g}_1 + \tilde{f}_1\tilde{g}_0 + \tilde{f}_2\tilde{g}_3 - \tilde{f}_3\tilde{g}_2, \; \tilde{f}_0\tilde{g}_2 + \tilde{f}_2\tilde{g}_0 + \tilde{f}_3\tilde{g}_1 - \tilde{f}_1\tilde{g}_3, \; \tilde{f}_0\tilde{g}_3 + \tilde{f}_3\tilde{g}_0 + \tilde{f}_1\tilde{g}_2 - \tilde{f}_2\tilde{g}_1)$$

In that way, calculations in $\mathbb{H}_1[X]$ can obviously be as well performed in $\prod^4 \mathbb{R}[X_0, .., X_3]$. This allows for application of classical algorithms for multivariate polynomials over commutative fields. But before, we need a notion of *degree* on $\mathbb{H}_1[X]$:

Definition 8. *For a commutative multi-variate polynomial, let* deg *denotes its total degree; e.g.,* $\deg(x^2y^3) = 5$, $\deg(0) = -\infty$. *The **degree** $\deg(q)$ of a quaternion polynomial $q \in \mathbb{H}_1[X]$ is half the total degree of the real four-variate polynomial $\tilde{f}_0^2 + \dots + \tilde{f}_3^2$ with $\tilde{f}_0, \dots, \tilde{f}_3$ according to (6).*

---

[2] In fact, 4 complex convolutions suffice; but asymptotically, that gains nothing.

Rather than the total degree, one might as well have considered the maximum one $\deg(x^2 y^3) := 3$ since, for 4 variables, they differ by at most a constant factor. However we shall later exploit the equality $\deg(p \cdot q) = \deg(p) + \deg(q)$ valid for the first whereas for the latter in general only the *in*equality $\deg(p \cdot q) \leq \deg(p) + \deg(q)$ holds. In fact, this nice property carries over to the degree of quaternion polynomials:

Lemma 9. *The degree* $\deg(p)$ *of* $p \in \mathbb{H}_1[X]$ *is always integral. Furthermore it holds* $\deg(p \cdot q) = \deg(p) + \deg(q)$.

Now recall the following classical results on four-variate polynomials:

Lemma 10. *a) Given (the coefficients of)* $p, q \in \mathbb{C}[X_0, \ldots, X_3]$, *the (coefficients of the) product* $p \cdot q$ *can be computed in time* $\mathcal{O}(n^4 \cdot \log n)$ *where* $n := \deg(p \cdot q) = \deg(p) + \deg(q)$.
  b) Given $p \in \mathbb{C}[X_0, \ldots, X_3]$ *of degree* n, *one can compute within* $\mathcal{O}(n^4 \cdot \log n)$ *steps the coefficients of* $p(T \cdot (X_0, \ldots, X_3)^\dagger + \boldsymbol{y}) \in \mathbb{C}[X_0, \ldots, X_3]$, *that is, perform on* p *an affine variable substitution given by* $T \in \mathbb{C}^{4 \times 4}$ *and* $\boldsymbol{y} \in \mathbb{C}^4$.
  c) A given polynomial $p \in \mathbb{C}[X_0, \ldots, X_3]$ *of degree* $n := \deg(p)$ *can be evaluated on all* n^4 *points of a 4-dimensional complex grid* $G := A_0 \times A_1 \times A_2 \times A_3$ *such that* $A_\ell \subseteq \mathbb{C}, |A_\ell| = n$, *within time* $\mathcal{O}(n^4 \cdot \log^2 n)$.
  d) The same holds for the regular affine image $G' = T \cdot G + \boldsymbol{y}$ *of such a grid, i.e.,*

$$G' = \{T \cdot \boldsymbol{x} + \boldsymbol{y} : \boldsymbol{x} = (x_0, \ldots, x_3)^\dagger \in G\}, \qquad T \in \mathbb{C}^{4 \times 4} \text{ regular}, \quad \boldsymbol{y} \in \mathbb{C}^4 .$$

  e) Let $p \in \mathbb{C}[X_0, \ldots, X_3]$ *be non-zero,* $n \geq \deg(p)$. *Fix arbitrary* $A \subseteq \mathbb{C}$ *of size* $|A| \geq 2n$. *Then, for* $(x_0, \ldots, x_3) \in A^4$ *chosen uniformly at random, the probability of* $p(x_0, \ldots, x_3) = 0$ *is strictly less than* $\frac{1}{2}$.

Proof. a) Reduction to the univariate case by means of KRONECKER's embedding: cf. EQUATION (8.3) on P.62 of [1] for $m := 4$; dealing with the complex field $\mathbb{C}$ rather than an arbitrary ring $\mathcal{R}$ of coefficients, the loglog-factor may be omitted.
  b) Folklore. A proof had to be removed from the final version due to space limitations.
  c) Cf. EQUATION (8.5) and the one below on P.63 of [1] for $m := 4$, $c := n$.
  d) follows from b). It is not known whether multi-evaluation is feasible on *arbitrarily* placed n^4 points within time $\mathcal{O}(n^4 \cdot \text{polylog} \, n)$.
  e) Cf. SUBSECTION 12.1 in [14].

One could of course identify in a similar way complex univariate polynomials $p \in \mathbb{C}[Z]$ with tuples $p_0, p_1 \in \mathbb{R}[X, Y]$ of real bivariate polynomials. However the thus obtained running times of $\mathcal{O}(n^2 \cdot \text{polylog} \, n)$ thus obtained for $\mathbb{C}[Z]$ are strikingly suboptimal, basically because *not every* tuple of real bivariate polynomials corresponds to a complex univariate polynomial. For instance, $z \mapsto \text{Re}(z)$ is well-known not only to be no complex polynomial but to even violate RIEMANN-JACOBY's equations of complex differentiability. Surprisingly for quaternion polynomials, the situation is very different:

Lemma 11. $\text{Re}(X) = \frac{1}{4}(X - iXi - jXj - kXk) \in \mathbb{H}_1[X]$. *More generally, every quadruple of real four-variate polynomials corresponds to a quaternion polynomial.*

The generic quaternion polynomial of degree n thus has $\Theta(n^4)$ free coefficients. Lemmas 10 and 11 together yield

Theorem 12. a) *Multiplication of two quaternion polynomials* $p, q \in \mathbb{H}_1[X]$ *is possible in time* $\mathcal{O}(n^4 \cdot \log n)$ *where* $n := \deg(p \cdot q) = \deg(p) + \deg(q)$.
b) *Multi-evaluation of* p *at* $x_0, \ldots, x_{n-1} \in \mathbb{H}$ *can be done within* $\mathcal{O}(n^4 \cdot \log^2 n)$, $n := \deg(p)$.
c) *Within the same time, multi-evaluation is even feasible at as many as* n^4 *points* x, *provided they lie on a (possibly affinely transformed)* n^4-*grid* G.
The above complexities are optimal up to the (poly-)logarithmic factor.

Theorem 12 presumes the polynomial(s) to be given as (coefficients of four) real four-variate polynomials. But how fast can one convert input in more practical format like (2) or (4) to that form? By means of fast multiplication of *several* polynomials, this can be done efficiently as well:

Theorem 13. a) *The (ordered!) product* $\prod_{\ell=1}^{m} p_\ell$ *of* m *quaternion polynomials* $p_\ell \in \mathbb{H}_1[X]$, *each given as quadruple of real four-variate polynomials, can be computed within* $\mathcal{O}(n^4 \cdot \log n \cdot \log m)$ *where* $n = \sum_\ell \deg(p_\ell)$ *denotes the result's degree.*
b) *An algebraic expression* E *over quaternions, i.e., composed from* $+, -, \cdot$, *constants* $a \in \mathbb{H}$, *and the quaternion variable* X — *but without powers like* X^{99} *nor brackets!* — *can be converted into the quadruple of real four-variate polynomials according to (6) within time* $\mathcal{O}(N^4 \cdot \log^2 N)$ *where* $N = |E|$ *denotes the input string's length.*

The above conversion yields a deterministic $\mathcal{O}(N^4 \cdot \log^2 N)$-test for deciding whether a given quaternion expression like (4) represents the zero polynomial. When satisfied with a *randomized* test, the same can be achieved much faster:

Theorem 13 (continued)
c) *Given* $\varepsilon > 0$ *and an expression* E *of length* $N = |E|$, *composed from* "+", "−", " · ", *constants* $a \in \mathbb{H}$, *the quaternion variable* X, *and possibly brackets* "(", ")"; *then one can test with one-sided error probability at most* ε *whether* E *represents the zero-polynomial within time* $\mathcal{O}(N \cdot \log \frac{1}{\varepsilon})$.

Proof. a) Standard divide-and-conquer w.r.t. m similar to COROLLARY 2.15 in [3].
b) Lacking brackets, the input string E necessarily has the form
$$E \;=\; E_1 \pm E_2 \pm \ldots \pm E_M$$
where E_ℓ describes a product P_ℓ of quaternion constants (degree 0) and the indeterminate X (degree 1). Since obviously $\deg(P_\ell) \leq N_\ell := |E_\ell|$, its real four-variate representation is obtainable within $\mathcal{O}(N_\ell^4 \cdot \log^2 N_\ell)$ steps. Doing so for all $\ell = 1, \ldots, M$ leads to running time $\mathcal{O}(N^4 \cdot \log^2 N)$ as $\sum_\ell N_\ell \leq N$.
W.l.o.g. let $\deg(P_1) \leq \deg(P_2) \leq \ldots \leq \deg(P_M)$. Adding up the just obtained four-variate representations in this increasing order takes additional time
$$\mathcal{O}(N_1^4 + N_2^4 + \ldots + N_M^4) \;\leq\; \mathcal{O}(N^4).$$
c) By virtue of standard amplification it suffices to deal with the case $\varepsilon = \frac{1}{2}$. The algorithm considers any set $A \subseteq \mathbb{R}$ of size $|A| \geq 2N$. It chooses $x_0, x_1, x_2, x_3 \in A$ uniformly and independently at random; and then evaluates the input expression E by substituting $X := x_0 + ix_1 + jx_2 + kx_3$. If the result is zero, the algorithm reports zero, otherwise non-zero.

The running time for evaluation is obviously linear in $|E| = N$. Moreover, only one-sided errors occur. So suppose E represents non-zero $p \in \mathbb{H}_1[X]$. Then obviously $\deg(p) \leq N$ and at least one of the four real four-variate polynomials $\tilde{p}_0, \ldots, \tilde{p}_3$ according to (6) is non-zero as well. By virtue of Lemma 10e), this will be witnessed by $(x_0, \ldots, x_3)$ — i.e., $p(x_0 + ix_1 + jx_2 + kx_3) \neq 0$ — with probability at least $\frac{1}{2}$. $\square$

3.3   Multi-evaluating Two-Sided Polynomials

Consider an expression of the form $p(X) = \sum_{\ell=0}^{n-1} a_\ell X^\ell b_\ell$, $a_\ell, b_\ell \in \mathbb{H}$. Expanding $a_\ell = \mathrm{Re}(a_\ell) + i\,\mathrm{Im}_i(a_\ell) + j\,\mathrm{Im}_j(a_\ell) + k\,\mathrm{Im}_k(a_\ell)$ and similarly for b_ℓ, one obtains, by virtue of distributive laws and since whole $\mathbb{R}$ commutes with X^ℓ, that it suffices to multi-evaluate expressions of the form

$$q(X) \quad = \quad \sum_{\ell=0}^{n-1} \alpha_\ell X^\ell, \qquad \alpha_\ell \in \mathbb{R}\ (!) \tag{7}$$

since $p(X)$ can be obtained from 16 of them, each multiplied both from left and right with some basis element $1, i, j, k$. Now with real α_ℓ, multi-evaluation of (7) is of course trivial on $x_0, \ldots, x_{n-1} \in \mathbb{C}$; but we want x_ℓ to be arbitrary quaternions! Fortunately, the latter can efficiently be reduced to the first.

To this end, consider mappings $\varphi_u : \mathbb{H} \to \mathbb{H}$, $x \mapsto u \cdot x \cdot u^{-1}$ with $u \in \mathbb{H}$ of norm $|u| = 1$. It is well-known [5, pp.214–216] that, identifying $\mathbb{H}$ with $\mathbb{R}^4$, φ_u describes a rotation, i.e., $\varphi_u \in \mathrm{SO}(\mathbb{R}^4)$. Furthermore, restricted to the set

$$\mathrm{Im}\,\mathbb{H} \quad := \quad \{ x \in \mathbb{H} : \mathrm{Re}(x) = 0 \} \quad \cong \quad \mathbb{R}^3$$

of *purely imaginary* quaternions, φ_u exhausts whole $\mathrm{SO}(\mathbb{R}^3)$ as u runs through all unit quaternions; this is called Hamilton's Theorem. Finally, φ_u is an (and in fact, again, the most general) $\mathbb{R}$-algebra automorphism, i.e., satisfies for $\alpha \in \mathbb{R}$ and $x, y \in \mathbb{H}$:

$$\varphi_u(\alpha) = \alpha, \quad \varphi_u(x+y) = \varphi_u(x) + \varphi_u(y), \quad \varphi_u(x \cdot y) = \varphi_u(x) \cdot \varphi_u(y) \ .$$

Lemma 14. *For $v, w \in \mathrm{Im}\,\mathbb{H}$, $|v| = 1 = |w|$, let $u := (v+w)/|v+w|$; then $\varphi_u(v) = w$. In particular for $x \in \mathbb{H} \backslash \mathbb{R}$, $v := \mathrm{Im}(x)/|\,\mathrm{Im}(x)|$, $w := i$, it holds $q(x) = u^{-1} \cdot q(y) \cdot u$ where $y := u \cdot x \cdot u^{-1} \in \mathbb{R} + i\mathbb{R} \cong \mathbb{C}$.*

Our algorithm evaluates $q \in \mathbb{R}[X]$ simultaneously at $x_1, .., x_n \in \mathbb{H}$ as follows:

- For all $x_\ell \in \mathbb{R} + i\mathbb{R}$, let $u_\ell := 1$;
- for each $x_\ell \notin \mathbb{R}$, compute (in constant time) u_ℓ according to Lemma 14.
- Perform in linear time the transformation $y_\ell := u_\ell \cdot x_\ell \cdot u_\ell^{-1}$.
- Use classical techniques to multi-evaluate q at $y_1, \ldots, y_n \in \mathbb{C}$ within $\mathcal{O}(n \cdot \log^2 n)$.
- Re-transform the values $q(y_\ell)$ to $q(x_\ell) = u_\ell^{-1} \cdot q(y_\ell) \cdot u_\ell$.

This proves the claimed running time of $\mathcal{O}(n \cdot \log^2 n)$. $\square$

4   Conclusion

We proposed three generalizations for the notion *'polynomial'* from fields $\mathbb{R}$ and $\mathbb{C}$ to the skew-field $\mathbb{H}$ of quaternions and analyzed their respective properties. For each notion, we then investigated (where applicable) on the algebraic complexity of operations multiplication and multi-evaluation on polynomials in terms of their degree. The upper bounds attained by our respective algorithms match (usually trivial) lower bounds up to polylogarithmic factors.

However since each of the above notions lacks one (e.g., closure under multiplication) or another (e.g., quasi-linear complexity) desirable property, a satisfactory definition for quaternion polynomials is still missing. Here comes another one, generalizing the representation of complex polynomials in terms of their roots:

$$\mathbb{K}_4[X] \quad := \quad \left\{ a_0 \cdot (X - a_1) \cdot (X - a_2) \cdots (X - a_n) : n \in \mathbb{N}_0, a_\ell \in \mathbb{H} \right\} \tag{8}$$

So what is the complexity for multi-evaluation in $\mathbb{H}_4[X]$?

In view of the planar N-body problem, GERASOULIS' major break-through was fast multi-evaluation of complex rational functions

$$\sum_{\ell=1}^{N} (X - a_\ell)^{-1} \tag{9}$$

for given $a_1, \dots, a_N \in \mathbb{C}$ at given $x_1, \dots, x_N \in \mathbb{C}$; cf. also COROLLARY 7 in [13]. Our techniques from Subsection 3.3 yield the same for $x_\ell \in \mathbb{H}$ and $a_\ell \in \mathbb{R}$. Thus the crucial question remains whether (9) also allows multi-evaluation in sub-quadratic time for both a_ℓ and x_ℓ being quaternions. But what is a rational quaternion function, anyway? We do not even know what a quaternion polynomial is! Observe that, lacking commutativity,

$$\frac{1}{X - a} + \frac{1}{X - b} \quad = \quad \frac{1}{X - a} \cdot \frac{1}{X - b} \cdot (X - b) + (X - a) \cdot \frac{1}{X - a} \cdot \frac{1}{X - b}$$

cannot be collected into one single fraction, in spite of the common denominator.

Acknowledgments. The idea to use quaternions for N-Body Simulation was suggested by PETER BÜRGISSER. The author wishes to thank his student, TOMAS BRAJKOVIC, for having chosen him as supervisor. In fact, Sections 2.1 and 3.2 constitute the core of TOMAS' *Staatsexamensarbeit* (high school teacher's thesis).

References

1. BINI, D., AND V. PAN: "Polynomial and Matrix Computations", Birkhäuser (1994).
2. BLÄSER, M., AND P. KIRRINNIS, AND D. LAUER: "On the multiplicative complexity of the inversion and division of Hamiltonian quaternions", pp.191–199 in *Found. Comput. Math.* **2** (2002).
3. BÜRGISSER, P., AND M. CLAUSEN, AND M.A. SHOKROLLAHI: "Algebraic Complexity Theory", Springer (1997).

4. COOLEY, J.W., AND J.W. TUKEY: "An Algorithm for the Machine Calculation of Complex Fourier Series", pp.297–301 in *Math. Comp.* **19** (1965).
5. EBBINGHAUS, H.-D., AND H. HERMES, AND F. HIRZEBRUCH, AND M. KOECHER, AND K. MAINZER, AND J. NEUKIRCH, AND A. PRESTEL, AND R. REMMERT: "Numbers", GTM **123**, Springer (1990).
6. EILENBERG, S. AND I. NIVEN: "The Fundamental Theorem of Algebra for Quaternions", pp.246–248 in *Bull. AMS* **50** (1944).
7. VON ZUR GATHEN, J., AND J. GERHARD: "Modern Computer Algebra", Cambridge Univ. Press (1999).
8. GERASOULIS, A.: "A Fast Algorithm for the Multiplication of Generalized Hilbert Matrices with Vectors", pp.179–188 in *Mathematics of Computation* Vol.**50** No.**181** (1988).
9. HOU RENMIN, AND ZHAO XUQIANG, AND WANG LIANGTAO: "The Double Determinant of Vandermonde's Type over Quaternion Field", pp.1046–1053 in *Applied Mathematics and Mechanics*, English Edition Vol.**20** No.**9** (1999).
10. LAM, T.Y.: "A First Course in Noncommutative Rings", GTM **131**, Springer (1991).
11. PAN, V., AND J.H. REIF, AND S.R. TATE: "The Power of Combining the Techniques of Algebraic and Numerical Computing: Improved Approximate Multipoint Polynomial Evaluation and Improved Multipole Algorithms", pp.703–713 in *Proc. 32th Annual IEEE Symposium on Foundations of Computer Science* (FOCS'1992).
12. ROTA, G.-C.: "Indiscrete Thoughts", Birkhäuser (1997).
13. ZIEGLER, M.: "Fast Relative Approximation of Potential Fields", pp.140–149 in *Proc. 8th Workshop on Algorithms an Data Structures* (WADS2003), Springer LNCS vol.**2748**.
14. ZIPPEL, R.E.: "Effective polynomial computation", Kluwer (1993).

Upper Bounds on the Complexity of Some Galois Theory Problems

(Extended Abstract)*

V. Arvind and Piyush P Kurur

Institute of Mathematical Sciences, C.I.T Campus,
Chennai 600113, India
{arvind,ppk}@imsc.res.in

Abstract. Assuming the generalized Riemann hypothesis, we prove the following complexity bounds: The order of the Galois group of an arbitrary polynomial $f(x) \in \mathbb{Z}[x]$ can be computed in $P^{\#P}$. Furthermore, the order can be approximated by a randomized polynomial-time algorithm with access to an NP oracle. For polynomials f with solvable Galois group we show that the order can be computed exactly by a randomized polynomial-time algorithm with access to an NP oracle. For all polynomials f with abelian Galois group we show that a generator set for the Galois group can be computed in randomized polynomial time.

1 Introduction

A fundamental problem in computational algebraic number theory is to determine the Galois group of a polynomial $f(x) \in \mathbb{Q}[x]$. Formally, in this paper we study the computational complexity of the following problem:

Problem 1. Given a nonzero polynomial $f(x)$ over the rationals $\mathbb{Q}$,

(a) determine the Galois group of f over $\mathbb{Q}$.
(b) determine the order of the Galois group of f over $\mathbb{Q}$.

An *extension* of a field K is a field L that contains K (written L/K). If L/K is a field extension then L is a vector space over K and its dimension, denoted by $[L : K]$ is called its *degree*. If $[L : K]$ is finite then L/K is a *finite* extension. If L/M and M/K are finite extensions then $[L : K] = [L : M].[M : K]$.

Let $K[x]$ denotes the ring of polynomials with indeterminate x and coefficients from the field K. A polynomial $f(x) \in K[x]$ is *irreducible* if it has no nontrivial factor over K. The *splitting field* K_f of a polynomial $f(x) \in K[x]$ is the smallest extension L of K such that f factorizes into linear factors in L. An extension L/K is *normal* if for any irreducible polynomial $f(x) \in K[x]$, f either splits in L or has no root in L. An extension L/K is *separable* if for all

---

* The full version of the paper is available at www.imsc.res.in/~ppk.

T. Ibaraki, N. Katoh, and H. Ono (Eds.): ISAAC 2003, LNCS 2906, pp. 716–725, 2003.
© Springer-Verlag Berlin Heidelberg 2003

irreducible polynomials $f(x) \in K[x]$ there are no multiple roots in L. A normal and separable finite extension L/K is called a *Galois extension*.

An *automorphism* of a field L is a field isomorphism $\sigma : L \to L$. The *Galois group* $Gal\,(L/K)$ of a field extension L/K is the subgroup of the group of automorphisms of L that leaves K fixed: i.e. for every $\sigma \in Gal\,(L/K)$, $\sigma(a) = a$ for all $a \in K$. By the Galois group of a polynomial $f \in K[x]$ we mean $Gal\,(K_f/K)$.

Roots of polynomials over $\mathbb{Q}$ are *algebraic numbers*. The *minimal polynomial* $T \in \mathbb{Q}[x]$ of an algebraic number α is the unique monic polynomial of least degree with α as a root. *Algebraic integers* are roots of monic polynomials in $\mathbb{Z}[x]$. A *number field* is a finite extension of $\mathbb{Q}$. For an algebraic number α, $\mathbb{Q}(\alpha)$ denotes the smallest number field that contains α. If $f(x)$ is the minimal polynomial of α then $\mathbb{Q}(\alpha)$ can be identified with the quotient $\mathbb{Q}[x]/(f(x)\mathbb{Q}[x])$. Every number field K has an element α such that $K = \mathbb{Q}(\alpha)$ (see [7, Theorem 4.6 Chap.V]). Such elements are called *primitive* elements of the field K.

Let $f \in \mathbb{Q}[x]$ with roots $\alpha_1, \alpha_2, \dots, \alpha_n \in \mathbb{Q}_f$. A well known lemma [14] states that $\mathbb{Q}_f$ has a primitive element of the form $\sum_{i=1}^{n} c_i \alpha_i$ for integers c_i. The proof actually yields a probabilistic version which states that $\sum_{i=1}^{n} c_i \alpha_i$ is primitive for most c_i.

Lemma 1. *Let $f \in \mathbb{Q}[x]$ be a degree n polynomial with roots $\alpha_1, \alpha_2, \dots, \alpha_n$. For a random choice of integers $c_1, c_2, \dots, c_n$ such that $size(c_i) \le n^2$ the algebraic integer $\theta = \sum_{i=1}^{n} c_i \alpha_i$ is such that $L = \mathbb{Q}(\theta)$ with probability $1 - \frac{1}{2^{O(n^2)}}$.*

A polynomial $f(x) \in \mathbb{Q}[x]$ is said to be solvable by radicals if the roots of f can be expressed, starting with the coefficients of f, using only field operations and taking r^{th} roots for integer r. Galois showed that a polynomial is solvable by radicals if and only if its Galois group is solvable.

Let L be a number field and O_L be the ring of algebraic integers in L. We can write O_L as $O_L = \{\sum_{i=1}^{N} a_i \omega_i \mid a_i \in \mathbb{Z}\}$ where $\omega_1, \omega_2, \dots, \omega_N$ is its $\mathbb{Z}$-basis. The *discriminant* d_L of the field L is defined as the determinant of the matrix $(Tr(\omega_i \omega_j))_{i,j}$ where $Tr : L \to \mathbb{Q}$ is the trace map. The discriminant d_L is always a nonzero integer. Let T be any polynomial of degree N. Then the discriminant $d(T)$ of the polynomial T is defined as $d(T) = \prod_{i \neq j}(\theta_i - \theta_j)$, where $\theta_1, \theta_2, \dots, \theta_N$ are the N distinct roots of T (i.e. all the conjugates of θ). The following is important property that relates $d(T)$ and d_L.

Proposition 1. [2, Proposition 4.4.4] *Let L be a number field and T be the minimal polynomial of a primitive element θ of L. Then $d_L \mid d(T)$. More precisely, $d(T) = d_L \cdot t^2$, for an integer t.*

Let $size(a)$ denote the length of the binary encoding of an integer a. For a rational $r = p/q$ such that $gcd(p,q) = 1$, let $size(r) = size(p) + size(q)$. A polynomial is encoded as a list of its coefficients. For a polynomial $f(x) = \sum a_i x^i \in \mathbb{Q}[x]$ we define $size(f) = \sum size(a_i)$. Thus, for an algorithm taking a polynomial f as input, the input size is $size(f)$.

For any polynomial $g(x) = a_0 + a_1 x + \dots + a_n x^n$ in $\mathbb{Z}[x]$, let $|g|_2 = \sqrt{\sum a_i^2}$. Applying an inequality [4] which bounds every root η of g by $|g|_2$, we obtain the following.

Theorem 1. *Let $f(x) \in \mathbb{Z}[x]$ be a monic polynomial of degree n with splitting field L. Let $\alpha_1, \alpha_2, \ldots, \alpha_n$ be the roots of f. Consider an element of the form $\theta = \sum c_i \alpha_i$, $c_i \in \mathbb{Z}$, and let T be the minimal polynomial of θ. Then $|d(T)| \leq (2c|f|_2)^{N^2}$, where $c = \max\{|c_i| : 1 \leq i \leq n\}$. As a consequence, $d_L \leq (2^{n^2}|f|_2)^{n!^2}$ and $\log d_L \leq (n+1)!^2.\text{size}(f)$.*

The Galois group of a polynomial $f(x) \in K[x]$ is completely determined by its action on the roots of f in K_f. We assume w.l.o.g throughout this paper that f is square-free. Otherwise, we can replace f by $f/gcd(f.f')$ which is square-free with the same Galois group. Thus, if we label the n distinct zeroes of f, we can consider the Galois group as a subgroup of the symmetric group S_n. Notice that this subgroup is determined only up to conjugacy (as the labeling of the zeroes of f is arbitrary). Since every subgroup of S_n has a generator set of size $n-1$ (c.f. [12] and [9]), we can specify the Galois group in size polynomial in n. By computing the Galois group of a polynomial f we mean finding a small generator set (polynomial in n) for it as a subgroup of S_n.

We now state Landau's result on computing the Galois group of a polynomial f. Its worst case running time is exponential in $\text{size}(f)$.

Theorem 2. [5] *Given a polynomial $f \in F[x]$, where the number field F is given as a vector space over $\mathbb{Q}$, the Galois group G of f over F can be computed in time polynomial in $|G|$ and $\text{size}(f)$.*

The extended abstract is organized as follows: In Sect. 2 we explain the Chebotarev density theorem in a form that is useful to us. In Sect. 3 we give a polynomial time algorithm making a single query to #P to compute the order of the Galois group of a polynomial $f(x) \in \mathbb{Q}$. In Sect. 4 we show that if the polynomial is solvable by radicals the order of its Galois group can be computed by a randomized algorithm with an NP oracle. Finally in Sect. 5 we show that if the Galois group of f is abelian then it can be computed by a randomized polynomial time algorithm. For the definitions of various complexity classes the reader can consult any complexity theory text like [1].

2   Chebotarev Density Theorem

The main tool in the proofs of our complexity results is the Chebotarev density theorem. In this section we explain the theorem statement and also state it in a form that is suitable for our applications.

Let L be a Galois number field and O_L be the ring of algebraic integers in L. Let $n = [L : \mathbb{Q}]$ be the degree of L. For any prime $p \in \mathbb{Q}$ consider the principal ideal pO_L generated by p (which we denote by p). The ideal p factorizes in O_L as $p = \mathfrak{p}_1^e \mathfrak{p}_2^e \ldots \mathfrak{p}_g^e$ for some positive integer e. For each i, $O_L/\mathfrak{p}_i$ is a finite field extension of $\mathbb{F}_p$ with p^f elements for some positive integer f. Furthermore $efg = n$.

The prime p is said to be *ramified* in L if $e > 1$ and *unramified* otherwise. It is a basic fact about number fields that a prime p is ramified in L if and only if p divides the discriminant of L (see [11, Theorem 1, pg. 238]).

Let p be an unramified prime with factorization $p = \mathfrak{p}_1 \mathfrak{p}_2 \ldots \mathfrak{p}_g$ in O_L. Corresponding to the Frobenius automorphism of the finite field $O_L/\mathfrak{p}_i$, there is an element denoted $\left(\dfrac{L/\mathbb{Q}}{\mathfrak{p}_i} \right)$ in the Galois group $G = Gal\,(L/\mathbb{Q})$ known as the Frobenius element of $\mathfrak{p}_i$, for $i = 1, 2, \ldots, g$. Furthermore, it is known that the set

$$\left[\frac{L/\mathbb{Q}}{p} \right] = \left\{ \left(\frac{L/\mathbb{Q}}{\mathfrak{p}} \right) : \mathfrak{p} | p \right\}$$

is a conjugacy class in the Galois group G. For any conjugacy class C of G let $\pi_C(x)$ be the number of unramified primes less that x such that $\left[\dfrac{L/\mathbb{Q}}{p} \right] = C$.
We have the following theorem:

Theorem 3 (Chebotarev's density theorem). *Let $L/\mathbb{Q}$ be a Galois extension and $G = Gal\,(L/\mathbb{Q})$ be its Galois group. Then for every conjugacy class C of G, $\pi_C(x)$ converges to $\dfrac{|C|}{|G|} \cdot \dfrac{x}{\ln x}$ as $x \to \infty$.*

In order to apply the above theorem in a complexity-theoretic context, we need the following effective version due to Lagarias and Odlyzko [3] proved assuming the GRH.

Theorem 4. *Let $L/\mathbb{Q}$ be a Galois extension and $G = Gal\,(L/\mathbb{Q})$ be its Galois group. If the GRH is true then there is an absolute constant x_0 such that for all $x > x_0$:*

$$\left| \pi_C(x) - \frac{|C|}{|G|} \frac{x}{\ln x} \right| \leq \frac{|C|}{|G|} x^{1/2} \ln d_L + x^{1/2} \ln x.|G|.$$

An unramified prime p such that $\left[\dfrac{L/\mathbb{Q}}{p} \right] = \{1\}$ is called a *split prime*. By definition, $\pi_1(x)$ denotes the number of split primes $p \leq x$.

Corollary 1. *Let $G = Gal\,(L/\mathbb{Q})$ for a Galois extension $L/\mathbb{Q}$. If the GRH is true then there is an absolute constant x_0 such that for all $x > x_0$:*

$$\left| \pi_1(x) - \frac{1}{|G|} \frac{x}{\ln x} \right| \leq \frac{1}{|G|} x^{1/2} \ln d_L + x^{1/2} \ln x.|G|.$$

3   Computing the Order of Galois Groups

Let $f(x) \in \mathbb{Z}[x]$ be a monic polynomial of degree n without multiple roots and let L denote the splitting field of f. Suppose $\{\alpha_1, \alpha_2, \ldots, \alpha_n\}$ is the set of roots of f.

As mentioned before, the Galois group $G = Gal\,(L/\mathbb{Q})$ can be seen as a subgroup of S_n. Each $\sigma \in G$, when considered as a permutation in S_n, can be expressed as a product of disjoint cycles. Looking at the lengths of these cycles we get the *cycle pattern* $\langle m_1, m_2, \ldots, m_n \rangle$ of σ, where m_i is the number of cycles of length i, $1 \leq i \leq n$. We have $n = \sum_{i=1}^{n} m_i$.

If p is a prime such that $p \nmid d(f)$, we can factorize $f = g_1 g_2 \ldots g_s$ into its distinct irreducible factors g_i over $\mathbb{F}_p$. Looking at the degrees of these irreducible factors we get the *decomposition pattern* $\langle m_1, m_2, \ldots, m_n \rangle$ of $f(\bmod p)$, where m_i is the number of irreducible factors of degree i.

We now state an interesting fact from Galois theory (see [14, page 198] and [7, Theorem 2.9, Chap. VII]).

Theorem 5. *Let $f(x) \in \mathbb{Z}[x]$ be a monic polynomial of degree n such that $d(f) \neq 0$, and let L denote its splitting field. Let $G = Gal(L/\mathbb{Q})$. Let p be a prime such that $p \nmid d(f)$. Then there is a conjugacy class C of G such that for each $\sigma \in C$ the cycle pattern of σ is the same as the decomposition pattern of f factorized over $\mathbb{F}_p$. Furthermore, if $\{\alpha_1, \alpha_2, \ldots, \alpha_n\}$ are the n roots of f in its splitting field and if $\mathbb{F}_{p^m}$ is the extension of $\mathbb{F}_p$ where $f \pmod p$ splits then there is an ordering of the roots $\{\alpha'_1, \alpha'_2, \ldots, \alpha'_n\}$ of f in $\mathbb{F}_{p^m}$ such that for all indices k and l, $\sigma(\alpha_k) = \alpha_l$ if and only if the Frobenius automorphism $x \mapsto x^p$ of $\mathbb{F}_{p^m}$ maps α'_k to α'_l.*

For any prime p that divides the order of the Galois group there is an element whose order is divisible by p. This can happen only if there is a prime q such that the decomposition pattern of $f \pmod q$ contains only the integers p and 1 (using Theorem 5). Furthermore using the effective Chebotarev density theorem (Theorem 4) we can show that there is a q with size $size(f)^{O(1)}$ satisfying the above property. So to check whether p divides the order of the Galois group we guess such a q. This leads to the following theorem.

Theorem 6. *Assuming GRH, the following problem is in* NP*: Given a prime $p \leq n$, and a monic polynomial $f \in \mathbb{Z}[x]$ with $d(f) \neq 0$ as input, test if p divides the order of the Galois group of f. As a consequence, the set of prime factors of $|Gal(\mathbb{Q}_f/\mathbb{Q})|$ can be computed in* P^{NP}.

Now for the main result of this section.

Theorem 7. *Assuming GRH, the order of the Galois group of a monic polynomial $f \in \mathbb{Z}[x]$ can be computed in* $\mathrm{P}^{\#\mathrm{P}}$.

The algorithm first count the number of split primes (with a certain exponentially small error) less than a suitably large x ($size(x) = size(f)^{O(1)}$) using a single #P query. The order of the Galois group is the nearest integer to $\frac{1}{\pi_1(x)} \frac{x}{\ln x}$ which can be computed in polynomial time.

To the best of our knowledge, this is the first polynomial-space bounded algorithm for the problem. Next we consider the approximate counting problem.

Definition 1. *A randomized algorithm $\mathcal{A}$ is an r-approximation algorithm for a #P function f with error probability $\delta < \frac{1}{2}$ if for all $x \in \{0,1\}^*$:*

$$Prob_y \left[|1 - \frac{\mathcal{A}(x,y)}{f(x)}| \leq r(|x|) \right] \geq 1 - \delta,$$

where y is a uniformly chosen random string used by the algorithm $\mathcal{A}$ on input x.

Stockmeyer [13] showed that for any #P function there is a $n^{-O(1)}$-approximation BPP^{NP} algorithm. We can use Stockmeyer's result to approximate $\pi_1(x)$ within an inverse polynomial error and use this approximation instead. This yields the algorithm in the following theorem.

Theorem 8. *Let $f(x) \in \mathbb{Z}[x]$ be a degree n polynomial, G be its Galois group, and s denote size(f). For any constant $c > 0$ there is a BPP^{NP} algorithm that computes an approximation A of $|G|$ such that*

$$\left(1 - \frac{1}{s^c}\right) A \leq |G| \leq \left(1 + \frac{1}{s^c}\right) A.$$

with probability greater than $\frac{2}{3}$.

We now derive a useful lemma as an immediate consequence of the above result.

Lemma 2. *Let f and g be monic polynomials in $\mathbb{Z}[x]$ with nonzero discriminant. Suppose the splitting field $\mathbb{Q}_g$ of g is contained in $\mathbb{Q}_f$ of f and $[\mathbb{Q}_f : \mathbb{Q}_g]$ is a prime power p^l. There is a BPP^{NP} algorithm that computes $[\mathbb{Q}_f : \mathbb{Q}_g]$ exactly, assuming that $|\text{Gal}\,(\mathbb{Q}_g/\mathbb{Q})|$ is already computed.*

4   Computing the Order of Solvable Galois Groups

In this section we show that if the Galois group G of $f \in \mathbb{Z}[x]$ is solvable then $|G|$ can be computed exactly in BPP^{NP}, assuming GRH. In fact, we show that for solvable Galois groups, finding $|G|$ is polynomial-time reducible to approximating $|G|$.

To begin with we need a test for solvability by radicals. A naive application of Galois' theorem gives an exponential time algorithm (using Theorem. 2). An important breakthrough was achieved by Landau and Miller when they gave a deterministic polynomial time algorithm to check whether a polynomial is solvable by radicals without actually computing the Galois group (see. [6]). We make use of results from [6]. We begin by recalling some definitions.

A group G is said to be *solvable* if there is a *composition series* of G, $G = G_0 \triangleright G_1 \triangleright \ldots \triangleright G_t = 1$ such that G_i/G_{i+1} is a cyclic group of prime order. Throughout this section by composition series we mean such a composition series.

A Galois extension K/F is said to be *solvable* if $\text{Gal}\,(K/F)$ is a solvable group. Let $G = G_0 \triangleright G_1 \triangleright \ldots \triangleright G_t = 1$ be a composition series of G. There is a corresponding tower of fields $F = E_0 \subseteq E_1 \subseteq \ldots \subseteq E_t = K$ such that $\text{Gal}\,(K/E_i) = G_i$. Moreover if K/F is Galois then by the fundamental theorem of Galois, since $G_i \triangleright G_{i+1}$, the extension E_{i+1}/E_i is Galois.

At this point we recall some permutation group theory (c.f. [15]): Let G be a subgroup of S_n acting on a set $\Omega = \{1, 2, \ldots, n\}$ of n elements. G is said to be *transitive* if for every pair of distinct elements $i, j \in \Omega$, there is a $\sigma \in G$ such that

σ maps i to j, written as $i^\sigma = j$. A *block* is a subset $B \subseteq \Omega$ such that for every $\sigma \in G$ either $B^\sigma = B$ or $B^\sigma \cap B = \emptyset$. If G is transitive then under G-action blocks are mapped to blocks, so that starting with a block $B_1 \subseteq \Omega$ we get a *complete block system* $\{B_1, B_2, \dots, B_s\}$ which is a partition of Ω. Notice that singleton sets and Ω are blocks for any permutation group. These are the *trivial* blocks. A transitive group G is *primitive* if it has only trivial blocks. Otherwise it is called *imprimitive*. A *minimal block* of an imprimitive group is a nontrivial block of least cardinality. The corresponding block system is a *minimal block system*.

The following result about solvable primitive permutation groups [10] has been used to show polynomial time bounds for several permutation group algorithms [9].

Theorem 9 (Pálfy's bound). [10] *If $G < S_n$ is a solvable primitive group then $|G| \leq n^{3.25}$.*

Let $f(x) \in \mathbb{Z}[x]$ be a monic irreducible polynomial and let G be the Galois group $\mathrm{Gal}\,(\mathbb{Q}_f/\mathbb{Q})$ which acts transitively on the set of roots $\Omega = \{\alpha_1, \alpha_2, \dots, \alpha_n\}$ of f. Let $\{B_1, B_2, \dots, B_s\}$ be the minimal block system of Ω under the action of G and H be the subgroup of G that setwise stabilizes all the blocks: i.e. elements of H map B_i to B_i for each i. Let $B_1 = \{\alpha_1, \alpha_2, \dots, \alpha_k\}$, where $k = n/s$. Consider the polynomial $p(x) = \prod_{i=1}^{k}(x - \alpha_i) = \sum_{i=0}^{k} \delta_i x^i$.

In [6] it is shown that $p(x) \in \mathbb{Q}(\alpha_1)[x]$ and there is a polynomial time deterministic algorithm to find $p(x)$: the algorithm computes each coefficient δ_i as a polynomial $p_i(\alpha_1)$ with rational coefficients. In polynomial time we can compute a primitive element β_1 of $\mathbb{Q}(\delta_0, \delta_1, \dots, \delta_k)$ [6] so that $\mathbb{Q}(\beta_1) = \mathbb{Q}(\delta_0, \delta_1, \dots, \delta_k)$. Let $g(x) \in \mathbb{Z}[x]$ be the minimal polynomial of β_1. In the following theorem we recall some results from [6], suitably rephrased.

Theorem 10.

1. *The degree of $g(x)$ is s.*
2. *$H = \mathrm{Gal}\,(\mathbb{Q}_f/\mathbb{Q}_g)$ and $\mathrm{Gal}\,(\mathbb{Q}_g/\mathbb{Q}) = G/H$.*
3. *The Galois group $\mathrm{Gal}\,(\mathbb{Q}(B_1)/\mathbb{Q}(\beta_1))$ acts primitively on B_1.*

Let $\mathrm{Gal}\,(\mathbb{Q}(B_1)/\mathbb{Q}(\beta)) = G^{B_1} = G_0 \triangleright G_1 \triangleright \dots \triangleright G_t = 1$ be a composition series of the solvable group G^{B_1} and let $\mathbb{Q}(\beta_1) = K_0 \subseteq K_1 \subseteq \dots \subseteq K_t = \mathbb{Q}(B_1)$ be the corresponding tower of subfields of the extension $\mathbb{Q}(B_1)/\mathbb{Q}(\beta_1)$. Since K_{i+1}/K_i is an extension of prime degree for each i we have the following proposition.

Proposition 2. *For all $0 \leq i < t$ if K' be any field such that $K_i \subseteq K' \subseteq K_{i+1}$ then either $K' = K_i$ or $K' = K_{i+1}$.*

For each field K_j in the above tower, let θ_j be a primitive element, $0 \leq j \leq t$. I.e. $\mathbb{Q}(\theta_j) = K_j$ for each j. Let $h_j(x) \in K_{j-1}[x]$ be the minimal polynomial of θ_j over K_{j-1}. We can consider $h_j(x)$ as $h_j(x, \theta_{j-1})$, a polynomial over $\mathbb{Q}$ in the indeterminate x and the algebraic number θ_{j-1} as parameter. As before let $G = \cup_{i=1}^{s} H\sigma_i$. For each field K_j let K_{ij} be the conjugate field under the action of σ_i. More precisely, let $K_{ij} = K_j^{\sigma_i}$ and $\theta_{ij} = \theta_j^{\sigma_i}$. We have the following proposition which follows from the fact that σ_i is a field isomorphism which maps the extension $\mathbb{Q}(B_1)/\mathbb{Q}(\beta_1)$ to $\mathbb{Q}(B_i)/\mathbb{Q}(\beta_i)$, for each i.

Proposition 3.

1. $K_{i0} \subseteq K_{i1} \subseteq \ldots \subseteq K_{it}$ forms a tower of fields of the extension $\mathbb{Q}(B_i)/\mathbb{Q}(\beta_i)$ corresponding to the composition series of $Gal\,(\mathbb{Q}(B_i)/\mathbb{Q}(\beta_i))$.
2. $Gal\,(K_{it}/K_{ij}) = \sigma_i^{-1}G_j\sigma_i$.
3. $K_{ij} = \mathbb{Q}(\theta_{ij})$, where $\theta_{ij} = \theta_j^{\sigma_i}$.
4. The minimal polynomial of θ_{ij} over the field K_{ij-1} is $h_{ij}(x) = h_j(x, \theta_{ij-1})$.

For each i, let $\overline{h}_i(x)$ denote the minimal polynomial of θ_i over $\mathbb{Q}$ and let n_i be its degree. We have the following lemma:

Lemma 3. Let $n_i = deg(\overline{h}_i)$ then $n_0 = [\mathbb{Q}(\beta_1) : \mathbb{Q}]$ and $n_i = p_i n_{i-1}$, where $[K_i : K_{i-1}] = p_i$ for each i.

Let $E_i = \mathbb{Q}_{\overline{h}_i}$, $0 \leq i \leq t$. Notice that $\mathbb{Q}_f = E_t$ and $\mathbb{Q}_g = E_0$. We have the following theorem:

Theorem 11. Let p_i be the order of G_i/G_{i-1}. For every i there is a l_i such that $Gal\,(E_i/E_{i-1})$ is an abelian group of order $p_i^{l_i}$. Furthermore $Gal\,(E_i/E_{i-1})$ is an elementary abelian p_i-group.

Suppose we know $[\mathbb{Q}_g : \mathbb{Q}]$. Using Lemma 2 we can compute $[\mathbb{Q}_f : \mathbb{Q}]$ by finding $[E_i : \mathbb{Q}]$ for each $1 \leq i \leq t$ starting from $i = 1$. We will find $[\mathbb{Q}_g : \mathbb{Q}]$ recursively. It is also easy to generalize this algorithm for reducible polynomials $f(x) \in \mathbb{Q}[x]$. This gives the following theorem:

Theorem 12. Assuming the GRH, there is a BPP^{NP} procedure that takes as input a monic polynomial $f \in \mathbb{Z}[x]$ such that $d(f) \neq 0$, and computes $|Gal\,(\mathbb{Q}_f/\mathbb{Q})|$ exactly when $Gal\,(\mathbb{Q}_f/\mathbb{Q})$ is solvable.

5   Finding the Galois Group of an Abelian Extension

Let f be a polynomial over $\mathbb{Z}[x]$ such that $Gal\,(\mathbb{Q}_f/\mathbb{Q})$ is abelian. In this section we give a polynomial-time randomized algorithm that computes the Galois group (as a set of generators) with constant success probability.

Suppose $f \in \mathbb{Z}[x]$ is irreducible of degree n with Galois group G. Since G is a transitive subgroup of S_n, if G is abelian then $|G| = n$. Thus, given an irreducible $f \in \mathbb{Z}[x]$, the algorithm of Theorem 2 gives a $(size(f))^{O(1)}$ algorithm for testing if its Galois group is abelian, and if so, finding the group explicitly. On the other hand, when f is reducible with abelian Galois group, no polynomial time algorithm is known for computing the Galois group (c.f. Lenstra [8]). However, for any polynomial f testing if its Galois group is abelian can be done in polynomial time: we only need to test if the Galois group of each irreducible factors of f is abelian.

Let f be a polynomial over $\mathbb{Z}[x]$ such that $Gal\,(\mathbb{Q}_f/\mathbb{Q})$ is abelian. Let $f = f_1 f_2 \ldots f_t$ be its factorization into irreducible factors f_i. Notice that if $Gal\,(\mathbb{Q}_f/\mathbb{Q})$ is abelian then $Gal\,(\mathbb{Q}_{f_i}/\mathbb{Q})$ is abelian for each i. Consequently, each f_i is a primitive polynomial. Let $G = Gal\,(\mathbb{Q}_f/\mathbb{Q})$ and let $G_i = Gal\,(\mathbb{Q}_{f_i}/\mathbb{Q})$ for each i. Notice that $G \le G_1 \times G_2 \times \ldots G_t$.

Let n_i be the degree of f_i. Since each f_i is a primitive polynomial, $|G_i| = n_i$. Let θ_i be any root of f_i, $1 \le i \le t$. Then, $\mathbb{Q}_{f_i} = \mathbb{Q}(\theta_i)$ for each i. Factorizing f_i in $\mathbb{Q}(\theta_i)$, we can express the other roots of f_i as $A_{ij}(\theta_i)$, where $A_{ij}(x)$ are all polynomials of degree at most n_i, $1 \le j \le n_i$. We can efficiently find these polynomials $A_{ij}(x)$ for $1 \le i \le t$, $1 \le j \le n_i$. Thus we can write $f_i(x) = \prod_{j=1}^{n_i}(x - A_{ij}(\theta_i))$, where θ_i is one of the roots of f_i. We have the following lemma:

Lemma 4. *Let θ be any root of f_i and let A_{ij} be polynomials of degree less than $\deg(f_i)$ such that $f_i(x) = \prod_{j=1}^{n_i}(x - A_{ij}(\theta))$. Then for $1 \le j < \deg(f_i)$, we have $A_{ij}(A_{ik}(\theta)) = A_{ik}(A_{ij}(\theta))$. Furthermore, for every $\sigma \in G_i$ there is an index $k, 1 \le k \le n_i$ such that for any root η of $f_i(x)$ we have $\sigma(\eta) = A_{ik}(\eta)$.*

From the above lemma it also follows that for each $i, 1 \le i \le t$, the polynomials A_{ij}, $1 \le j \le n_i$ are independent of the choice of the root θ of f_i because the Galois group is abelian.

Now, let σ_{ij} denote the unique automorphism of $\mathbb{Q}_{f_i}$ that maps θ to $A_{ij}(\theta)$ for every root θ of f_i. Since $G \le G_1 \times G_2 \times \ldots \times G_t$, any element $\sigma \in G$ is a t-tuple $\sigma = \langle \sigma_{1j_1}, \sigma_{2j_2}, \ldots, \sigma_{tj_t} \rangle$, for indices $j_1, j_2, \ldots, j_t$. We will apply the Chebotarev density theorem to determine a generator set for G.

Let q be a prime such that $q \nmid d(f)$ and $\mathbb{F}_{q^m}$ be the extension of $\mathbb{F}_q$ where f splits. Observe that since G is abelian every conjugacy class of G is a singleton set. Let $\pi_g(x)$ denote the number of primes $p \le x$ whose Frobenius corresponds to g. By Theorem 3 $\pi_g(x)$ converges to $\frac{x}{(\ln x)|G|}$. Furthermore using Theorem 4 we can show that for a random prime $p \le x$, the probability that the Frobenius corresponding to p is g lies in the range $\left(\frac{1}{|G|} - \epsilon, \frac{1}{|G|} + \epsilon\right)$, $\epsilon = \frac{1}{x^{O(1)}}$.

Next, fix i and let $\{\alpha_1, \alpha_2, \ldots, \alpha_{n_i}\}$ be the roots of f_i. By Theorem 5, there is an ordering $\{\overline{\alpha}_1, \overline{\alpha}_2, \ldots, \overline{\alpha}_{n_i}\}$ of the roots of f_i in $\mathbb{F}_{q^m}$ such that the Frobenius automorphism $x \mapsto x^q$ maps $\overline{\alpha}_k$ to $\overline{\alpha}_l$ if and only if the element g (the unique Frobenius element corresponding to q) maps α_k to α_l. If the element $g = \langle \sigma_{1j_1}, \sigma_{2j_2}, \ldots, \sigma_{tj_t} \rangle$ we can determine σ_{ij_i} as follows: find the splitting field $\mathbb{F}_{q^k}$ of f_i. Since f_i is a primitive polynomial, $k \le n_i$, thus $\mathbb{F}_{q^k}$ can be found efficiently.[1] Now, factorize f_i in $\mathbb{F}_{q^k}$. Pick any root $\overline{\theta} \in \mathbb{F}_{q^k}$ of f_i. Then $\overline{\theta}^q = A_{ij}(\overline{\theta})$ for exactly one polynomial A_{ij_i}, which can be found by trying all of them. This gives us σ_{ij_i}. Thus, we can determine g as a t-tuple in polynomial time, in a manner independent of the choice of the root $\overline{\theta}$ of f_i in $\mathbb{F}_{q^k}$.

We have the following almost uniform polynomial-time sampling algorithm from the Galois group G: Pick primes $p \nmid d(f)$ less that a suitably large

---

[1] In fact $k|n_i$ because k is the order of the corresponding Frobenius element which is in the Galois group of f_i, and the order of the Galois group is n_i.

x and recover corresponding Frobenius. It can be shown that if we choose $x \geq (n!)^{10}.\text{size}(f)^2$, the algorithm samples $g \in G$ with probability in the range $\left(\frac{1}{|G|} - \frac{1}{x^{1/4}}, \frac{1}{|G|} + \frac{1}{x^{1/4}} \right)$. We require the following lemma to complete the proof

Lemma 5. *Suppose we have a (almost) uniform sampling procedure $\mathcal{A}$ from a subgroup G of S_n. Then for every constant $c > 0$, there is a polynomial-time randomized algorithm with $\mathcal{A}$ as subroutine that outputs a generator set for G with error probability bounded by 2^{-n^c}.*

The above lemma implies the the following theorem.

Theorem 13. *There is a randomized polynomial time algorithm for computing a generator set for the Galois group of a polynomial $f \in \mathbb{Z}[x]$ if it is abelian.*

References

1. J. L. Balcázar, J. Díaz, and J. Gabarró. *Structural Complexity I & II*. ETACS monographs on theoretical computer science. Springer-Verlag, Berlin, 1988 and 1990.
2. H. Cohen. *A Course in Computational Algebraic Number Theory*. Springer-Verlag, Berlin, 1993.
3. J. C. Lagarias and A. M. Odlyzko. Effective versions of the Chebotarev density theorem. In A. Fröhlich, editor, *Algebraic Number Fields*, pages 409–464. Academic Press, London, 1977.
4. E. Landau. Sur quelques théorèmes de M. Petrovitch relatifs aux zéros des fonctions analytiques. *Bulletin de la Société de France*, 33:251–261, 1905.
5. S. Landau. Polynomial time algorithms for galois groups. In J. Fitch, editor, *EUROSAM 84 Proceedings of International Symposium on Symbolic and Algebraic Computation*, volume 174 of *Lecture Notes in Computer Sciences*, pages 225–236. Springer, July 1984.
6. S. Landau and G. L. Miller. Solvability by radicals is in polynomial time. *Journal of Computer and System Sciences*, 30:179–208, 1985.
7. S. Lang. *Algebra*. Addison-Wesley Publishing Company, Inc, third edition, 1999.
8. H. W. Lenstra Jr. Algorithms in algebraic number theory. *Bulletin of the American Mathematical Society*, 26(2):211–244, April 1992.
9. E. M. Luks. Permutation groups and polynomial time computations. *DIMACS Series in Discrete Mathematics and Theoretical Computer Science*, 11:139–175, 1993.
10. P. Pálfy. A polynomial bound for the orders of primitive solvable groups. *Journal of Algebra*, pages 127–137, July 1982.
11. P. Ribenboim. *Classical theory of algebraic numbers*. Universitext. Springer, 1999.
12. C. C. Sims. Computational methods in the study of permutation groups. *Computational problems in Abstract Algebra*, pages 169–183, 1970.
13. L. Stockmeyer. On approximating algorithms for #P. *SIAM Journal of Computing*, 14:849–861, 1985.
14. B. L. van der Waerden. *Algebra*, volume I. Springer-Verlag, seventh edition, 1991.
15. H. Wielandt. *Finite Permutation Groups*. Academic Press, New York, 1964.

Unfolded Modular Multiplication

Wieland Fischer and Jean-Pierre Seifert

Infineon Technologies, Secure Mobile Solutions
D-81609 Munich, GERMANY
{Wieland.Fischer,Jean-Pierre.Seifert}@infineon.com

Abstract. Sedlak's [Sed] modular multiplication algorithm is one of the
first real silicon implementations to speed up the RSA signature generation [RSA] on a smartcard, cf. [DQ]. Although it is nearly unknown
in the scientific literature on cryptographic hardware it received in the
practical smartcard world a considerable amount of interest, cf. [HP1,
HP2,NMR]. The reason why it is so unknown might be given by the fact
that the original publication was extremely hard to read and that Sedlak
didn't explain all the subtle implementation issues. Theoretically, Sedlak's algorithm needs on average $n/3$ steps (i.e., additions/subtractions)
to compute the modular product $(\alpha \cdot \beta \bmod \nu)$ for α, β and ν being n-
bit numbers. The main result of this paper is that Sedlak's algorithm
can be *practically* speeded up by an arbitrary integral factor $i \geq 2$, i.e.,
our new algorithm needs on average $n/(3 \cdot i)$ steps in order to compute
the modular product $(\alpha \cdot \beta \bmod \nu)$. A further contribution of this paper
is the mathematically proper and reader-friendly derivation of Sedlak's
algorithm leading naturally to our main result.

Keywords: Booth recoding, Computer arithmetic, Implementation issues, Sedlak's algorithm, Modular multiplication.

1 Introduction

In this paper we will be concerned with the computation of $(\alpha \cdot \beta \bmod \nu)$ where
$2^{n-1} \leq \nu < 2^n$ and $0 \leq \alpha, \beta < \nu$ for some integer n of the size, e.g., 1024 or 2048.
Our starting point will be the following simple and straightforward textbook al-
gorithm *Modular Multiplication I*, see figure, where β_i denotes $(\beta \operatorname{div} 2^i) \bmod 2$,
the i-th bit of β, i.e., $\beta = (\beta_{n-1}, \dots, \beta_0)_2$ in binary representation.

Neglecting its impracticality for a real silicon realization it is obvious that
this algorithm needs $2n$ steps using also registers of length $2n$. Both of these
algorithm aspects, i.e., speed and register length have been addressed by Sedlak
[Sed]. Sedlak's algorithm improves the multiplication itself by using the classical
Booth algorithm which only needs $n/3$ steps (additions/subtractions), cf. [Bo,
Spa,Mac], and developing a novel reduction concept. This admits also a speed-up
by a factor of 3 on average. Combining both algorithms into one single algorithm
(running in parallel) improves the above algorithm from $2n/3$ to $n/3$ additions
on average. Of course, the additions became a little bit more complicated since
3 operands were used instead of 2, but the additional resources are negligible.

T. Ibaraki, N. Katoh, and H. Ono (Eds.): ISAAC 2003, LNCS 2906, pp. 726–735, 2003.

input: α, β, ν
output: $\gamma := \alpha \cdot \beta \bmod \nu$

$Z := 0$, $C := \alpha$, $N := \nu$
for $i := n - 1$ downto 0 do
  $Z := Z \cdot 2$
  if $\beta_i = 1$ then $Z := Z + C$ endif
  /* now $Z = \alpha \cdot (\beta_{n-1}, \ldots, \beta_i)_2$ */
endfor
/* now $Z = \alpha \cdot \beta, 0 \leq Z < \nu \cdot 2^n$ */
for $i := n - 1$ downto 0 do
  if $Z \geq N \cdot 2^i$ then $Z := Z - N \cdot 2^i$
  endif
  /* now $Z = \alpha \cdot \beta \bmod \nu \cdot 2^i$ */
endfor
return Z

Modular Multiplication I.

---

input: α, β, ν
output: $\gamma := \alpha \cdot \beta \bmod \nu$

$Z := 0$, $C := \alpha$, $N := \nu$
for $i := n - 1$ downto 0 do
  $C := C/2$
  if $\beta_i = 1$ then $Z := Z + C$ endif
  /* $Z = \alpha \cdot (\beta_{n-1}, \ldots, \beta_i)_2 \cdot 2^{-n+i}$ */
endfor
/* $Z = \alpha \cdot \beta \cdot 2^{-n}, 0 \leq Z < N$ */
for $i := n - 1$ downto 0 do
  $Z := Z \cdot 2$
  if $Z \geq N$ then $Z := Z - N$ endif
  /* now $Z = \alpha \cdot \beta \cdot 2^{-i} \bmod \nu$ */
endfor
return Z

Modular Multiplication II.

With this approach also the register length can be bounded by $n + k$, for a few k buffer bits (say $k = 20$ or 32). This is due to the fact that here the reduction and multiplication run in parallel.

Using this presentation of Sedlak's algorithm it is then very easy to derive our main result which shows that Sedlak's algorithm can be practically speeded up by an arbitrary integral factor i, i.e, the new algorithm needs on average only $n/(3 \cdot i)$, $i \geq 2$, steps to compute a modular multiplication. The starting point for our construction will be a variant of the above algorithm. Since only the relative ratio between Z and C is important, the above algorithm works equally with $C := C/2$ instead of $Z := Z \cdot 2$. This idea leads to the algorithm *Modular Multiplication II*. Note that the variables in the algorithm contain *rational numbers* and not just integers!

The paper is organized as follows. Section 2 recapitulates Booth's algorithm. Section 3 gives an introduction to the so called ZDN-reduction. The ZDN-reduction will also be set into an algorithm according to our needs. Section 4 merges the algorithms of 2 and 3, resulting in a variant of the so called (simple) ZDN-multiplication. Section 5 will present the promised speeded up version for the factor $i = 2$. Up to this point the algorithms are only mathematical ones: We are not concerned about finite registers or shifter lengths. This will shortly be discussed in section 6. Also we will address the multiple ZDN-based modular multiplication. Section 7 gives practical results for the algorithms. We are talking about the real average shift values (hence performance) which can be reached in reality. Furthermore, areas of silicon implementations for the different approaches will also be discussed.

2   Multiplication with Booth

To enhance the average shift value 1 (over the multiplier) of the multiplication, shown in the former algorithms, the classical method of Booth [Bo] can be used. This algorithm is described in [Mac,Kor,Spa,Par] and achieves asymptotically an average shift value of 3. It requires variable shifts and the ability to subtract numbers.

The method of Booth is based on representing numbers in the signed-digit notation SD2: Let β be an n-bit integer in binary notation. $\beta = (\beta_{n-1}, \dots, \beta_0)_2$, i.e., $\beta = \sum_{i=0}^{n-1} \beta_i \cdot 2^i$. Then, there exists a representation of β in the form $\beta = \sum_{i=0}^{n} \bar{\beta}_i \cdot 2^i$ (also written as $(\bar{\beta}_n, \dots, \bar{\beta}_0)_{\text{SD2}}$) where $\bar{\beta}_i \in \{-1, 0, 1\}$. Among these representations there is one with a minimal Hamming weight $H(\bar{\beta})$. For these representations one knows about the expectation value: $\mathbb{E}(H(\bar{\beta})) = (n+1)/3$. With the algorithms described in [Kor,Mac,JY] such a representation can be efficiently obtained on-the fly. For the rest of the paper we fix one of those algorithms and use it to construct one of these representations, i.e., we define a map $Booth\colon \beta \longmapsto (\bar{\beta}_n, \dots, \bar{\beta}_0)$. Thus, the multiplication is then given by $\alpha \cdot \beta = \sum_{i=0}^{n} \alpha_i \cdot \bar{\beta}_i \cdot 2^i$, or written in algorithmic form as *Multiplication I*:

input: α, β
output: $\gamma := \alpha \cdot \beta$
$Z := 0,\ C := \alpha,\ m := n+1$
while $m > 0$ **do**
$\quad$ LABooth$(\beta, \&m, \&s, \&v)$
$\quad Z := Z \cdot 2^s$
$\quad Z := Z + v \cdot C$
$\quad$ /* now $Z = \alpha \cdot (\bar{\beta}_n, \dots, \bar{\beta}_m)_{\text{SD2}}$ */
endwhile
return Z

Multiplication I.

input: α, β
output: $\gamma := \alpha \cdot \beta$
$Z := 0,\ C := \alpha,\ m := n+1,\ c := 0$
while $m > 0$ **do**
$\quad$ LABooth$(\beta, \&m, \&s, \&v)$
$\quad C := C \cdot 2^{-s}$
$\quad Z := Z + v \cdot C$
$\quad c := c + s\quad$ /* $= n+1-m$ */
$\quad$ /* $Z \cdot 2^c = \alpha \cdot (\bar{\beta}_n, \dots, \bar{\beta}_m)_{\text{SD2}}$ */
endwhile
return $Z \cdot 2^c$

Multiplication II.

Here, the subroutine LABooth$(\beta, \&m, \&s, \&v)$ provides the shift value s, sign v and current position m in the multiplier. It manipulates the variables m, s and v (denoted by the &-sign) and it is given by the following rule: Let m' be the largest index with $m' < m$ and $\bar{\beta}_{m'} \neq 0$, otherwise if there is none, set $m' := -1$. Then LABooth sets the variables to

$$\begin{cases} s \leftarrow (m - m'),\ v \leftarrow \bar{\beta}_{m'},\ m \leftarrow m', & \text{if } m' \geq 0 \\ s \leftarrow m,\ v \leftarrow 0,\ m \leftarrow 0, & \text{if } m' = -1 \end{cases}$$

— to be read from left to right. During the run of the algorithm the variable m jumps through all indices with $\bar{\beta}_m \neq 0$ including $m = 0$. Note that $\mathbb{E}(H(\bar{\beta})) = (n+1)/3$ implies that $\mathbb{E}(s) = 3$, which means that the above algorithm achieves asymptotically a performance factor of 3 compared to the simple multiplication. Or, one can say one has an average shift value of 3. Due to reasons which become clear later, we will use the above algorithm in the equivalent form of *Multiplication II*. (The variable c was included for later purposes.) Again note, that in this mathematical algorithm, the variables still contain *rational numbers*!

3   The ZDN-Reduction

As we have seen above, the classical variable shift Booth algorithm achieves a speed-up of the factor 3 asymptotically. In other words, at every step, the integer in Z grows by 3 bits on average (in version I it grows to the left and in version II to the right, behind the comma). As we want to interleave the multiplication and the reduction (i.e., simultaneous execution) we need a reduction algorithm which achieves also a reduction by 3 bits on average. This can be accomplished by the so called ZDN algorithm ($2/3N = $ "**Z**wei **D**rittel **N**" in german) which is based on the following Lemma:

Lemma 1. *Let $\nu \in \mathbb{N}$ and ζ a real number with $\zeta \in [-\nu, \nu[$. Furthermore, let $s := s_\zeta \in \mathbb{N}_0 \cup \{\infty\}$ be the unique integer such that $\zeta \cdot 2^s \in [\frac{2}{3}\nu, \frac{4}{3}\nu[$ or $\zeta \cdot 2^s \in [-\frac{4}{3}\nu, -\frac{2}{3}\nu[$. If $\zeta = 0$, we set $s_\zeta := \infty$. Then $(\zeta \cdot 2^s - \text{sign}(\zeta) \cdot \nu) \in [-\frac{\nu}{3}, \frac{\nu}{3}[$.*
If $\zeta: \Omega \longrightarrow [-\frac{\nu}{3}, \frac{\nu}{3}[$ is a uniformly distributed random variable, then the expectation value of s_ζ is given by $\mathbb{E}(s_\zeta) = 3$.

This lemma immediately gives us a method for a fast reduction algorithm. This reduction algorithm enables the computation of a look-ahead shift on-the fly, like the Booth algorithm. We substitute the (somewhat) classical reduction algorithm *Reduction I* by the so called ZDN-reduction *Reduction II*:

input: ζ, ν with $0 \leq \zeta < 2^c \cdot \nu$	input: ζ, ν with $0 \leq \zeta < 2^c \cdot \nu$
output: $\gamma := \zeta \bmod \nu$	output: $\gamma := \zeta \bmod \nu$
$Z := \zeta \cdot 2^{-c}$, $N := \nu$	$Z := \zeta \cdot 2^{-c}$, $N := \nu$
while $c > 0$ **do**	**while** $c > 0$ **do**
$\quad Z := Z \cdot 2$	$\quad$ LARed($Z, N, c, \&s, \&v$)
$\quad$ **if** $Z \geq N$ **then** $Z := Z - N$ **endif**	$\quad Z := Z \cdot 2^s + v \cdot N$
$\quad c := c - 1$	$\quad c := c - s$
$\quad$ /* now $Z \cdot 2^c = (\zeta \bmod \nu \cdot 2^c)$ */	$\quad$ /* now $Z \cdot 2^c \equiv \zeta \pmod{\nu \cdot 2^c}$ */
endwhile	**endwhile**
	if $Z < 0$ **then** $Z := Z + N$
return Z	**return** Z
Reduction I.	*Reduction II.*

Here, the subroutine LARed($\zeta, \nu, \max, \&s, \&v$) (Look Ahead Reduction) is given by: $s \leftarrow \min\{s_\zeta, \max\}$ where s_ζ is determined according to the lemma (max is here given by c) and $v \leftarrow -1$, if $\zeta \geq 0$ and $s = s_\zeta$; $v \leftarrow +1$, if $\zeta < 0$ and $s = s_\zeta$; $v \leftarrow 0$, if $s < s_\zeta$.

4   The Simple ZDN-Based Modular Multiplication

Now, we will combine the two former algorithms *Multiplication II & Reduction II* into one single algorithm. We start with *Modular Multiplication III* (figure not shown here), a simple concatenation of the two algorithms.

However, as we want to merge both loops, the following approach of *Modular Multiplication IV* would be conceivable. But, observe that this algorithm really

input: α, β, ν
 output: $\gamma := \alpha \cdot \beta \bmod \nu$
 	
 $Z := 0, \ C := \alpha, \ N := \nu,$
 $m := n + 1, \ c := 0$
 while $m > 0$ **or** $c > 0$ **do**
 $\quad$ LABooth(β, &m, &s_1, &v_1)
 $\quad C := C \cdot 2^{-s_1}$
 $\quad Z := Z + v_1 \cdot C$
 $\quad c := c + s_1$
 $\quad$ LARed(Z, N, c, &s_2, &v_2)
 $\quad C := C \cdot 2^{s_2}$
 $\quad Z := Z \cdot 2^{s_2} + v_2 \cdot N$
 $\quad c := c - s_2$
 endwhile
 if $Z < 0$ **then** $Z := Z + N$ **endif**
 return Z
 	
 Modular Multiplication IV.

input: α, β, ν
 output: $\gamma := \alpha \cdot \beta \bmod \nu$
 	
 $Z := 0, \ C := \alpha, \ N := \nu,$
 $m := n + 1, \ c := 0$
 while $m > 0$ **or** $c > 0$ **do**
 $\quad$ LARed(Z, N, c, &s_Z, &v_N)
 $\quad$ LABooth(β, &m, &s_β, &v_C)
 $\quad s_C := s_Z - s_\beta$
 $\quad C := C \cdot 2^{s_C}$
 $\quad Z := Z \cdot 2^{s_Z} + v_C \cdot C + v_N \cdot N$
 $\quad c := c - s_C$
 endwhile
 if $Z < 0$ **then** $Z := Z + N$ **endif**
 return Z
 	
 Modular Multiplication V.

differs from the above one: In *III* the reduction is applied to the full product $\alpha \cdot \beta$ while in *IV* the single reduction steps are applied to the intermediary products (which are already reduced a little bit by the former reduction steps).

For a later hardware realization of the algorithm it is much better to merge the analysis algorithms (LARed and LABooth) as well as the calculation part. This gives us the final algorithm *Modular Multiplication V*. We also change the notation of the parameters to the obvious ones ($s_Z := s_2$, $s_\beta := s_1$).

We would like to point out that this modification also is a change in the algorithm which slows down the reduction. This is due to the fact that in LARed max $= c$ is used instead of $c + s_1$ as originally and we use the former value of Z instead of the actual one. However, this performance loss is definitely irrelevant, since in most cases the value max will not be surpassed.

The big advantage of this version is given by the following fact: One can now substitute the two single additions/subtractions $Z := Z + v_C \cdot C$ and $Z := Z \cdot 2^s + v_N \cdot N$ by one single 3-operand addition $Z := Z \cdot 2^s + v_C \cdot C + v_N \cdot N$. In the case of our architecture this extra-overhead is also nearly negligible. All in all, this results in a nearly doubled performance, since the two arithmetic operations which need at least 2 clock cycles are substituted by a one-clock-cycle operation.

Remarks on behavior of the algorithm: The algorithm has an asymptotically average shift value of 3, meaning that the number of loops is $(n + 1)/3$. This would be obvious for the single LABooth, as $\mathbb{E}(s_\beta) = 3$. However, LARed undergoes the technical constraint max $= c$. This especially means that the reduction is slowed down in the beginning, i.e., one cannot any longer assume that $\mathbb{E}(s_Z) = 3$ holds in general. But we still can say $\mathbb{E}(s_Z) \to 3$ for $n \to \infty$, as we will show in the full version of the paper.

5   Modular Multiplication: The Doubling Approach

The development of the last algorithm was driven by the fact that it is much more efficient (in terms of speed) to merge two single 2-operand additions into one single 3-operand addition. This was accomplished by a slightly more complicated loop control structure.

Of course, this idea can be continued in a natural (naive) fashion. Simply, merge two successive loop-iterations of *Modular Multiplication V* into one single loop-iteration. Although this will increase again the loop control structure, we want to start with this naive approach and then refine it gradually to a practical algorithm during several steps. Firstly, in *Loop I* (not shown here) we simply stick together two successive loop-iterations. For the following we use upper indices which are not exponents! The parts of the first resp. second loop are denoted with the upper indices 1 resp. 2. Although the second LABooth can be directly

$$
\begin{aligned}
&\text{LARed}(Z, N, c, \&s_Z^1, \&v_N^1)\\
&\text{LABooth}(\beta, \&m, \&s_\beta^1, \&v_C^1)\\
&\text{LARed}(Z \cdot 2^{s_Z^1} + v_C^1 \cdot C + v_N^1 \cdot N,\\
&\qquad N, c - s_Z^1 + s_\beta^1, \&s_Z^2, \&v_N^2)\\
&\text{LABooth}(\beta, \&m, \&s_\beta^1, \&v_C^1)\\
&s_C^1 := s_Z^1 - s_\beta^1\\
&C := C \cdot 2^{s_C^1}\\
&Z := Z \cdot 2^{s_Z^1} + v_C^1 \cdot C + v_N^1 \cdot N\\
&c := c - s_C^1\\
&s_C^2 := s_Z^2 - s_\beta^2\\
&C := C \cdot 2^{s_C^2}\\
&Z := Z \cdot 2^{s_Z^2} + v_C^2 \cdot C + v_N^2 \cdot N\\
&c := c - s_C^2
\end{aligned}
$$

Loop II.

input: α, β, ν
output: $\gamma := \alpha \cdot \beta \bmod \nu$
$Z := 0$, $C := \alpha$, $N := \nu$,
$m := n + 1$, $c := 0$
while $m > 0$ **or** $c > 0$ **do**
    $\text{LARed}(Z, N, c, \&s_Z, \&v_N^1)$
    $\text{LARed}(Z \cdot 2^{s_Z} + v_N^1 \cdot N, N,$
        $c - s_Z, \&s_N, \&v_N^2)$
    $\text{LABooth}(\beta, \&m, \&s_\beta^1, \&v_C^1)$
    $\text{LABooth}(\beta, \&m, \&s_\beta^2, \&v_C^2)$
    $s_C^1 := s_Z - s_\beta^1$
    $s_C^2 := -s_\beta^2$
    $c := c - s_C^1 - s_C^2$
    $C := C \cdot 2^{s_C^1 + s_C^2}$
    $Z := Z \cdot 2^{s_Z} + v_C^1 \cdot (C \cdot 2^{-s_C^2})$
        $+ v_N^1 \cdot N + v_C^2 \cdot C + v_N^2 \cdot (N \cdot 2^{-s_N})$
endwhile
if $Z < 0$ **then** $Z := Z + N$ **endif**
return Z

Modular Multiplication VI.

executed after the first LABooth (remember that it is independent of anything else) the situation with the second LARed is not so easy. Indeed, the second LARed depends on the result Z which is influenced by the first LARed. So, we have to do some pre-computation! This is shown in the first parameter of the second LARed in *Loop II*.

Starting to make things easier, the second LARed will not receive $Z \cdot 2^{s_Z^1} + v_C^1 \cdot C + v_N^1 \cdot N$ as input, but simply the approximation $Z \cdot 2^{s_Z^1} + v_N^1 \cdot N$. Here we assume, that the influence of C will be irrelevant in most cases. In some rare cases (when c is very small) a "wrong" reduction value can be delivered. However, the reduction value is not really wrong but only sub-optimal in terms of reduction speed. On the other side, we save the "shifting" step of Z by s_Z^2 for the next loop. This yields *Modular Multiplication VI*. (Remember that the variables contain rational numbers!)

Asymptotically this algorithm needs $(n+1)/6$ loop cycles in theory. This can be seen similarly to the last paragraph and will be explained in a full version of the paper. Clearly, the "small" side computation $Z \cdot 2^{s_Z} + v_N^1 \cdot N$ needs to be done only on a small fraction of the leading register-bits. This is due to the fact that LABooth($Z, N, \dots$) and LABooth($Z \cdot 2^t, N \cdot 2^t, \dots$) return the same values s and v.

6   Implementing the ZDN-Based Modular Multiplications

In the full version of the paper (which is available from the authors) we will discuss the implementation of the above algorithms in a computer architecture. Here we will only give a short overview of the possibilities and problems arising at this task. First, we will summarize some of the specific properties of the algorithms which are determining the architecture:
(i) Z takes positive and negative values, i.e., $Z \in [-N, N]$ in steps of 2^{-k}— for some k. (ii) C will be divided/multiplied by powers of 2. (iii) Z will only be multiplied by powers of 2. (iv) N doesn't change at all. (v) There is a 3(5)-operand addition. (vi) The multiplier β affects the computation only through the values s_β and v_C.

These properties are mirrored by the following rough architecture:
There is one *calculation unit* and one *control unit*. (i) The calculation unit consists of 3 registers N, C and Z of length $rl := n + 1 + k$ for some k (say, $k = 32$). There is a virtual comma at the bit-position k such that the interval $[-2^n, 2^n[$ is realized in steps of 2^{-k} (in two's complement representation). (ii) The register C can be shifted by the values $-ShL, \dots, +ShL$. (iii) There is a shifter which latches Z into the adder by shift values of $s_Z \in \{0, \dots, ShL\}$. (iv) The register N has no additional features. (v) There is a realization of the 3(5)-operand adder. In the latter case an additional shifter, which latches N into the 5-operand-adder a second time by a (down-)shift value of $s_N \in \{0, \dots, ShL_N\}$. (vi) The control unit holds information about the multiplier β and Z and also delivers the control signals s_Z, s_C, v_C, v_N resp. $s_Z, s_C^1, v_C^1, v_N^1, s_C^2, v_C^2, s_N, v_N^2$ for the adder.

Based on this architecture we will present the modular multiplication algorithms, *Modular Multiplication VII* resp. *Modular Multiplication IX*, which are the architectural realizations of the algorithms *Modular Multiplication V* resp. *Modular Multiplication VI*. Here some refinements are necessary since in our architecture we have to obey certain constraints: Finite register length. Finite shifter length. The two's complement representation of numbers in Z, i.e., a number that erroneously was shifted to far could be interpreted as a totally different number. Of course, these constraints are slowing down the multiplication, cf. section 7.

Another problem arises by the observation that the plausibility chain forces LARed to use the result of the previously computed 3(5)-operand addition. So, for at least one clock cycle, the adder has to pause while LARed is preparing the new control values. If the adder is so fast that it also works in one clock cycle (like in our design) it only works 50% of the time, while waiting the other half—wasting resources.

However, the dependence of LARed from the outcome Z of the last addition can be avoided when a good approximation of Z can be provided a little bit earlier: When the "big" addition $Z := Z << s_Z + v_C \cdot C + v_N \cdot N$ starts, we start a second addition, namely $\widetilde{Z} := Z << s_Z + v_N \cdot N$ and this only on a few top bits. This addition can be executed much faster and in the remaining time, until the big addition is done, LARed can compute the next control values with $\widetilde{Z}$ instead of Z. This approximation can be used, since we assume that c has become large enough, a few steps after starting the multiplication algorithm. This leads to a fairly good description of a real existing hardware implementation of the ZDN-multiplication: *Modular Multiplication VIII*. Similarly, for the double ZDN-modular multiplication, we can do the same which we will describe in *Modular Multiplication X*.

The multiple ZDN-based modular multiplication: Instead of unfolding the loop of the *Modular Multiplication V* just two times (as done in section 5) one can do this i times, gaining a performance of the factor i compared to the simple one. Of course the generation of the increasing number of control signals will become more and more complicated. So this strategy only makes sense for very long registers and it is only practicable for a factor of $i \leq 3$.

7   Practical Results

Average shift values: As all theoretically derived results are only valid for $n \to \infty$ and unlimited shifters, it is interesting to consider real practical results. However, our algorithms are a mixture between multiplication and reduction, where the reduction always runs a little bit behind the multiplication: One can multiply in advance, but one cannot reduce in advance! Thus, it is difficult to give *average shift values* for the algorithms. Both algorithms have their individual shift values. Although they could be estimated taking into account a given shifter length, their interplay is hard to estimate.

Therefore, we define the *average shift value* as the quotient of $n + 1$ and the number of loops, i.e., the number of all necessary additions. From software simulations we obtained shift values shown in the following table. These data

n	ShL	MM V	MM VII	MM VIII
512	∞	2.84		
1024	∞	2.90		
2048	∞	2.92		
1024	3		2.31	2.22
	4		2.62	2.54
	5		2.77	2.71
	6		2.83	2.78
	7		2.85	2.81

n	ShL	ShL_N	MM VI	MM IX	MM X
512	∞	∞	5.59		
1024	∞	∞	5.71		
2048	∞	∞	5.76		
1024	5	3		4.44	4.35
	6	4		4.98	4.90
	7	5		5.32	5.24
	8	5		5.49	5.37
	9	5		5.56	5.40

Average shift values of Simple ZDN.   *Average shift values of Double ZDN.*

(and some, not shown here) tell us that the average shift value does not depend noteworthy on the size of the k buffer bits, as long as $k \geq 20$. It also comes closer to the theoretical ones the longer the registers and shifters are.

Silicon realization: For the development of a new co-processor, capable of handling 2048 bit RSA, a study was done in order to compare two designs:

1. Realization of the simple ($i = 1$) ZDN-algorithm *Modular Multiplication VIII* with $n = 2048$.
2. Realization of the triple ($i = 3$) ZDN based modular multiplication, for $n = 1024$ with some additional feature described in [FS], called *MultModDiv*.

Using the method described in [FS] one needs 6 modular multiplications of length 1024 bit in order to emulate one modular multiplication of length 2048 bit. Since in our architectures the complexity of a modular multiplication is linear in the bit length of the multiplier and because the algorithm in 2.) is 3 times as fast as the one in 1.), the performance (for RSA 2048) of these two architectures is comparable. The design 2.) has the advantage that here RSA for 1024 bit length is three times as fast as in design 1). On the other hand 2.) is more complex, both in the implementation of the hardware as well as in the implementation of the necessary software.

Interestingly it turned out that both designs cost approximately the same silicon area: The design 2.) needs a very sophisticated 7-operand-adder with more shifters than the 3-operand-adder used in 1). However in 2.) only an adder of length 1024 bits has to be realized! All in all both adders have about the same size. In both cases, the control structures are negligible compared to the adders.

Finally, the design 1.) was realized as a co-processor for chip card applications, which is commercially available. In a quarter micron technology the silicon area is 2.8 mm^2. This area includes the following additional features: The actual bit length of the registers are even 2304. The lengths of the shifters of Z and C are not equal, namely they are [0,5] and [-3, 3] respectively. The arithmetic part (adder) is built in dual rail with pre-charge logic, for security reasons. A double control part is included in order to being able to compute two multiplications in parallel (which is possible since the adder is dividable in two adders of half size). Abandoning the last two features we can save more area. Since this was not done, we estimate the achievable size by at most 1.8–2.0 mm^2.

References

[Bo]   A.D. Booth, "A signed binary multiplication technique", *Q. J. Mech. Appl. Math* **4**(2):236–240, 1951.

[DQ]   J.-F. Dhem, J.-J. Quisquater, "Recent results on modular multiplication for smart cards", *Proc. of CARDIS '98* Springer LNCS vol. 1820, pp. 336–357, 1998.

[FS]   W. Fischer, J.-P. Seifert, "Increasing the bitlength of a crypto-coprocessor", *Proc. of CHES '02*, Springer LNCS, vol. 2523, pp. 71–81, 2002.

[HP1]   H. Handschuh, P. Pailler, "Smart Card Crypto-Coprocessors for Public-Key Cryptography", *CryptoBytes* **4**(1):6–11, 1998.

[HP2]   H. Handschuh, P. Pailler, "Smart Card Crypto-Coprocessors for Public-Key Cryptography", *Proc. of CARDIS '98* Springer LNCS vol. 1820, pp. 372–380, 1998.

[JY]   M. Joye, S.-M. Yen, "Optimal left-to-right binary signed-digit exponent recoding", *IEEE Transactions on Computers* **49**(7): 740–748, 2000.

[Kor]   I. Koren, *Computer Arithmetic Algorithms*, Brookside Court Publishers, Amherst MA, 1998.

[Mac]   O. L. MacSorley, "High-speed arithmetic in binary computers", *Proc. IRE*, **49**:67–91, 1961.

[NMR]   D. Naccache, D. M'Raihi, "Arithmetic co-processors for public-key cryptography: The state of the art", *IEEE Micro*, pp. 14–24, 1996.

[Par]   B. Parhami, *Computer Arithmetic*, Oxford University Press, New York, 2000.

[Spa]   O. Spaniol, *Arithmetik in Rechenanlagen*, B. G. Teubner, Stuttgart, 1976.

[RSA]   R. Rivest, A. Shamir, L. Adleman, "A method for obtaining digital signatures and public-key cryptosystems", *Comm. of the ACM* **21**:120–126, 1978.

[Sed]   H. Sedlak, "The RSA cryptographic Processor: The first High Speed One-Chip Solution", *Proc. of EUROCRYPT '87*, Springer LNCS, vol. 293, pp. 95–105, 198.

[WQ]   D. de Waleffe, J.-J. Quisquater, "CORSAIR, a smart card for public-key cryptosystems", *Proc. of CRYPTO '90*, Springer LNCS, vol. 537, pp. 503–513, 1990.

[Wa]   C. Walter, "Techniques for the Hardware Implementation of Modular Multiplication", *Proc. of 2nd IMACS Internat. Conf. on Circuits, Systems and Computers*, vol. **2**, pp. 945–949, 1998.

Gauss Period, Sparse Polynomial, Redundant Basis, and Efficient Exponentiation for a Class of Finite Fields with Small Characteristic

Soonhak Kwon[1], Chang Hoon Kim[2], and Chun Pyo Hong[2]

[1] Inst. of Basic Science and Dept. of Mathematics, Sungkyunkwan University,
Suwon 440-746, Korea
shkwon@math.skku.ac.kr
[2] Dept. of Computer and Information Engineering, Daegu University,
Kyungsan 712-714, Korea
chkim@dsp.taegu.ac.kr, cphong@daegu.ac.kr

Abstract. We present an efficient exponentiation algorithm in a finite field $GF(q^n)$ using a Gauss period of type $(n, 1)$. Though the Gauss period α of type $(n, 1)$ in $GF(q^n)$ is never primitive, a computational evidence says that there always exists a sparse polynomial (especially, a trinomial) of α which is a primitive element in $GF(q^n)$. Our idea is easily generalized to the field determined by a root of unity over $GF(q)$ with redundant basis technique. Consequently, we find primitive elements which yield a fast exponentiation algorithm for many finite fields $GF(q^n)$, where a Gauss period of type (n, k) exists only for larger values of k or the existing Gauss period is not primitive and has large index in the multiplicative group $GF(q^n)^\times$.

Keywords: Finite field, Gauss period, exponentiation, root of unity, trinomial, redundant basis.

1 Introduction

Fast exponentiation in finite fields is very important in many cryptographic applications such as Diffie-Hellman key exchange and pseudo random bit generators. Though exponentiation is the most complex arithmetic operation, in some situations, one can devise an efficient exponentiation algorithm since a fixed (primitive) element is raised to many different powers.

Let $GF(q^n)$ be a finite field with q^n element with q a power of a prime and let $g \in GF(q^n)$ be a primitive element (or an element of high multiplicative order). Roughly speaking, the computation of g^s for arbitrary values of s is studied from two different directions. One is the use of precomputation with vector addition chains such as BGMW method [1] and its improvements by Lim and Lee [6] and also by Rooij [7].

The other approach is suggested by Gao et al. [4,5] and it uses a special primitive element called a Gauss period which generates a normal basis for $GF(q^n)$

T. Ibaraki, N. Katoh, and H. Ono (Eds.): ISAAC 2003, LNCS 2906, pp. 736–745, 2003.

over $GF(q)$. The BGMW method and its improvements are applicable to arbitrary finite field $GF(q^n)$ and very flexible. On the other hand, an ideal version of BGMW method requires a memory of order $O(n \log q / \log(n \log q))$ values in $GF(q^n)$ and multiplications of order $O(\log(n \log q))$ which amounts to an order of $O(n^2 \log^2 q \log(n \log q))$ bit additions. An algorithm proposed by Gao et al. is not applicable to all finite fields. However, it does not need a precomputation and the complexity of the algorithm is $O(kqn^2)$ additions. Therefore if q is small and if there is a Gauss period of high order of type (n, k) for a small value of $k \geq 2$, then the method of Gao et al. outperforms the precomputation methods.

In this paper, we will give an algorithm for efficient exponentiation in the field determined by a Gauss period of type $(n, 1)$ over $GF(q)$. This is possible since we may successfully find a primitive element which is a trinomial of the type $(n, 1)$ Gauss period for most of the cases. By extending our idea to other finite fields with redundant basis technique, we find primitive elements which yield a simple exponentiation algorithm in $GF(q^n)$, where a Gauss period of type (n, k) exists only for larger values of k or the existing Gauss period is not primitive and has large index in the multiplicative group $GF(q^n)^\times$.

2   Gauss Periods of Type (n, k) in $GF(q^n)$

Let us briefly review the theory of Gauss periods and the method of Gao et al.. Let n, k be positive integers such that $p = nk + 1$ is a prime not dividing q. Let $K = \langle \tau \rangle$ be a unique subgroup of order k in $GF(p)^\times$. Let $ord_p q$ be the order of q modulo p and assume $gcd(nk/ord_p q, n) = 1$. Let β be a primitive pth root of unity in $GF(q^{nk})$. Then the the following element

$$\alpha = \sum_{j=0}^{k-1} \beta^{\tau^j} \tag{1}$$

is called a Gauss period of type (n, k) over $GF(q)$. It is well known that α is a normal element in $GF(q^n)$. That is, letting $\alpha_i = \alpha^{q^i}$ for $0 \leq i \leq n - 1$, $\{\alpha_0, \alpha_1, \alpha_2, \cdots, \alpha_{n-1}\}$ is a basis for $GF(q^n)$ over $GF(q)$.

Since $K = \langle \tau \rangle$ is a subgroup of order k in $GF(p)^\times$, the quotient group $GF(p)^\times / K$ is a cyclic group of order n and the generator of the group is qK. Therefore we have a coset decomposition of $GF(p)^\times$ as a disjoint union,

$$GF(p)^\times = K_0 \cup K_1 \cup K_2 \cdots \cup K_{n-1}, \tag{2}$$

where $K_i = q^i K, 0 \leq i \leq n - 1$. Note that any element in $GF(p)^\times$ is uniquely written as $\tau^s q^t$ for some $0 \leq s \leq k - 1$ and $0 \leq t \leq n - 1$.

For each $0 \leq i \leq n - 1$, we have

$$\alpha \alpha_i = \sum_{s=0}^{k-1} \beta^{\tau^s} \sum_{t=0}^{k-1} \beta^{\tau^t q^i} = \sum_{s=0}^{k-1} \sum_{t=0}^{k-1} \beta^{\tau^s (1 + \tau^{t-s} q^i)} = \sum_{s=0}^{k-1} \sum_{t=0}^{k-1} \beta^{\tau^s (1 + \tau^t q^i)}. \tag{3}$$

There is unique $0 \leq u \leq k-1$ and $0 \leq v \leq n-1$ such that $1+\tau^u q^v = 0 \in GF(p)$. If $t \neq u$ or $i \neq v$, then we have $1 + \tau^t q^i \in K_{\sigma(t,i)}$ for some $0 \leq \sigma(t,i) \leq n-1$ depending on t and i. Thus we may write $1 + \tau^t q^i = \tau^{t'} q^{\sigma(t,i)}$ for some t'. Now when $i \neq v$,

$$\alpha\alpha_i = \sum_{s=0}^{k-1}\sum_{t=0}^{k-1} \beta^{\tau^s(1+\tau^t q^i)} = \sum_{s=0}^{k-1}\sum_{t=0}^{k-1} \beta^{\tau^s(\tau^{t'} q^{\sigma(t,i)})} = \sum_{t=0}^{k-1} \alpha^{q^{\sigma(t,i)}} = \sum_{t=0}^{k-1} \alpha_{\sigma(t,i)}. \tag{4}$$

Also when $i = v$,

$$\alpha\alpha_v = \sum_{t \neq u}\sum_{s=0}^{k-1} \beta^{\tau^s(\tau^{t'} q^{\sigma(t,v)})} + \sum_{s=0}^{k-1} \beta^{\tau^s(1+\tau^u q^v)} = \sum_{t \neq u} \alpha_{\sigma(t,v)} + k. \tag{5}$$

Therefore $\alpha\alpha_i$ is computed by the sum of at most k basis elements in $\{\alpha_0, \alpha_1, \cdots, \alpha_{n-1}\}$ for $i \neq v$ and $\alpha\alpha_v$ is computed by the sum of at most $k-1$ basis elements and the constant term $k \in GF(q)$. Using these ideas, Gao et al. [4] showed the following.

Theorem 1. *Let α be a Gauss period of type (n, k) over $GF(q)$, with k and q bounded. For any $0 \leq r < q^n$, α^r can be computed in $O(n^2)$ additions in $GF(q)$.*

Sketch of Proof. Write $r = \sum_{j=0}^{n-1} r_j q^j$ with $0 \leq r_j < q$. Then the following algorithm gives an output α^r.

Table 1. An exponentiation algorithm in [4]

Input: $r = \sum_{j=0}^{n-1} r_j q^j$, Output: $\alpha^r = \prod_{0 \leq i \leq n-1} \alpha_i^{r_i}$
$A \leftarrow 1$
for $(i = 0$ to $n - 1$; $i++)$
  for $(j = 1$ to r_i ; $j++)$
    $A \leftarrow A\alpha_i$
  end for
end for

Assuming that qth Frobenius map $\alpha \rightarrow \alpha^q$ is almost free, $A\alpha_i$ is computed by at most $(k-1)(n+1)$ additions in $GF(q)$ in a redundant basis $\{\alpha_0, \alpha_1, \cdots, \alpha_{n-1}, 1\}$. For each i, the inner loop $A \leftarrow A\alpha_i$ runs r_i times. Therefore the total number of multiplications $A \leftarrow A\alpha_i$ is $\sum_{i=0}^{n-1} r_i \leq (q - 1)n$. Since $A\alpha_i$ is computed by $(k-1)(n+1)$ additions, one can compute α^r by $(k-1)(q-1)n(n+1)$ additions in $GF(q)$ in a redundant basis, whose complexity is $O((k - 1)(q - 1)n^2)$. $\square$

Various computational results imply that the Gauss period α of type (n, k), $k \geq 2$, over $GF(q)$ is very often primitive, and even in the cases that α is not primitive, it usually has a very high multiplicative order. For example, it is known [4] that, among the 177 values of $n \leq 1000$ for which a Gauss period α of type $(n, 2)$ over $GF(2)$ exists, α is a primitive element for 146 values of n. In

[4], it is also shown that for approximately 1050 values of $2 \leq n \leq 1200$, there is a primitive Gauss period of type (n, k) for some k, and in many cases, one can choose $k < 20$. A theorem supporting this experimental evidence is obtained by Gathen and Shparlinski [13], where it is shown that a Gauss period of type $(n, 2)$ in $GF(q^n)$ has order at least $2^{\sqrt{2n}-2}$ for infinitely many n. On the other hand, Feisel et al. [10] extended the notion of Gauss periods to obtain general Gauss periods which, in many cases, have low computational cost in multiplication than the usual Gauss periods. Also, Kwon et al. [8] found a hardware architecture for a fast exponentiation using Gauss periods technique.

3   Efficient Exponentiation in $GF(q^n)$ Using Primitive Elements Which Are Sparse Polynomials of Roots of Unity

3.1   Gauss Periods of Type $(n, 1)$ over $GF(q)$

For a fast exponentiation, one has to choose a Gauss period of type (n, k) for small k. Therefore if a given finite field $GF(q^n)$ has a Gauss period of type (n, k) only for large k or if the field has no Gauss period at all, one can no longer use the algorithm in Table 1 for an efficient exponentiation. Moreover in many situations, we want to have a primitive element, not just an element of high order.

Though the Gauss periods are very often primitive, there do exist non-primitive Gauss periods and, in some cases, they have very large indices in given finite fields. Therefore, it is worthwhile to find an alternative element in such cases. That is, we want to find an element which is primitive and gives a low complexity exponentiation algorithm.

A Gauss period α of type $(n, 1)$ is a primitive pth root of unity in $GF(q^n)$, where $n + 1 = p$ is a prime and q is a primitive root (mod p). α is not a primitive element in $GF(q^n)$ and has very low order $n + 1 \ll q^n - 1$. However, our computational evidence, in Table 4 and 5, says that a suitably chosen trinomial $\gamma = 1 \pm \alpha^s \pm \alpha^t$ of α is always a primitive element in $GF(q^n)$. Using this idea, one can easily realize efficient exponentiation as follows. Let $\gamma = 1 \pm \alpha^s \pm \alpha^t$ be a fixed primitive element in $GF(q^n)$ where α is a Gauss period of type $(n, 1)$. Then we have the following algorithm which computes γ^r using the redundant basis $\{1, \alpha, \alpha^2, \cdots, \alpha^n\}$.

Table 2. Exponentiation using a primitive element, $\gamma = 1 \pm \alpha^s \pm \alpha^t$, where α is a Gauss period of type $(n, 1)$ over $GF(q)$

Input: $r = \sum_{j=0}^{n-1} r_j q^j$,   Output: γ^r
$A \leftarrow 1$
for $(i = n - 1$ to 0 ; $i - -)$
    $A \leftarrow A^q \gamma^{r_i}$
end for

Above algorithm is applicable for both software and hardware purposes. For efficient exponentiation, one needs to choose q small such as $q = 2, 3, 5$. The operation $A \leftarrow A^q$ is (almost) free in our basis because $\{1, \alpha, \alpha^2, \cdots, \alpha^n\} = \{1, \alpha, \alpha^q, \alpha^{q^2}, \cdots, \alpha^{q^{n-1}}\}$. Now letting $A = \sum_{i=0}^n a_i \alpha^i$, we get

$$
\begin{aligned}
A\gamma = A \pm A\alpha^s \pm A\alpha^t &= \sum_{i=0}^n a_i \alpha^i \pm \sum_{i=0}^n a_i \alpha^{i+s} \pm \sum_{i=0}^n a_i \alpha^{i+t} \\
&= \sum_{i=0}^n a_i \alpha^i \pm \sum_{i=0}^n a_{i-s} \alpha^i \pm \sum_{i=0}^n a_{i-t} \alpha^i = \sum_{i=0}^n (a_i \pm a_{i-s} \pm a_{i-t})\alpha^i,
\end{aligned}
\tag{6}
$$

where the coefficients a_i, a_j are understood as $a_i = a_j$ if $i \equiv j \pmod{n+1}$ since $\alpha^{n+1} = 1$. Therefore the computation $A \leftarrow A\gamma$ needs 2 additions for each coefficient of α^i ($0 \le i \le n$) and the total number of $GF(q)$-additions needed to compute $A \leftarrow A^q \gamma^{r_i}$ is at most $2(n+1)r_i$. Consequently the total number of additions in $GF(q)$ to compute γ^r is at most $2(n+1)\sum_{i=0}^{n-1} r_i \le 2(q-1)n(n+1)$. Notice that one needs at most $(k-1)(q-1)n(n+1)$ additions in $GF(q)$ using the Gauss period of type (n, k) in Table 1. Thus the complexity of our algorithm is same to the algorithm using type $(n, 3)$ Gauss period, and has lower complexity than the algorithm using type (n, k) Gauss period when $k > 3$.

3.2   Primitive Elements Which Are Sparse Polynomials of Roots of Unity and Redundant Basis

Let α be a primitive mth root of unity over $GF(q)$ where m and q are relatively prime. By adjoining α to the field $GF(q)$, we get the extension field $GF(q^n)$ where n is the order of $q \pmod{m}$, i.e. n is the least positive integer satisfying $q^n \equiv 1 \pmod{m}$. If m is not so large compared with n, as the case of type $(n, 1)$ Gauss period, one may use the redundant basis $\{1, \alpha, \alpha^2, \cdots, \alpha^{m-1}\}$ and still get an efficient exponentiation algorithm. This is possible since we can always find a primitive element of the form $1 + c_s \alpha^s + c_t \alpha^t$ with $c_s, c_t \in GF(q)$. Let us briefly explain how this can be done in computational point of view.

The number of primitive elements in $GF(q^n)$ is $\phi(q^n - 1)$, where $\phi(x)$ is Euler's *phi*-function. Thus, the probability for a randomly chosen element $\alpha \in GF(q^n)^\times$ to be a primitive element is

$$
\phi(q^n - 1)/(q^n - 1) = \prod_{r | q^n - 1} \left(1 - \frac{1}{r}\right),
\tag{7}
$$

where the product runs through all primes r dividing $q^n - 1$. As long as $q^n - 1$ is not a product of many small prime factors, which is a necessary condition to avoid the Pohlig-Hellman attack for discrete logarithm problem, the probability is not so small. In fact, the following formula for average value of the probability is well known [2],

$$
\sum_{n=1}^N \phi(n)/n = \frac{6}{\pi^2} N + O(\log N).
\tag{8}
$$

Of course, our choice of α is not at all random. Though α is not a primitive element, we may ask a natural question whether there exists a primitive element which is a sparse polynomial of α, for example, a binomial of the form $\alpha^s \pm \alpha^t$. However it turns out that they are seldom primitive, especially when n is even. To show this,

Lemma 1. *Let q and m be a prime with $\gcd(m,q) = 1$. Let $\alpha \in GF(q^n)$ be a primitive mth root of unity, where n is the least positive integer satisfying $q^n \equiv 1 \pmod{m}$. Suppose that n is even. Then a binomial of α, $\alpha^s \pm \alpha^t$ is never primitive when $m < q^{n/2} + 1$.*

Proof. Since the order of $q \pmod m$ is n and m is prime, we have $q^{n/2} \equiv -1 \pmod m$. Thus,

$$(\alpha^s \pm \alpha^t)^{q^{n/2}} = \alpha^{-s} \pm \alpha^{-t} = \frac{\alpha^t \pm \alpha^s}{\alpha^{s+t}},$$

which implies,

$$(\alpha^s \pm \alpha^t)^{(q^{n/2}-1)m} = \alpha^{\pm(s+t)m} = 1.$$

$\square$

When the characteristic q of the field $GF(q^n)$ is 2 or 3 and when α is a Gauss period of type $(n,1)$ over $GF(q)$, any binomial is of the form $\alpha^s \pm \alpha^t$ for some s, t and it is never primitive when $n+1 < q^{n/2} + 1$, i.e. when $n > 4$ if $q = 2$ and when $n > 1$ if $q = 3$. This result corresponds to the computation table of ours of the primitive elements for the cases $q = 2, 3$. However, it should be noticed that a binomial of α can be a primitive element when n is odd or when m is composite which happens in Table 4.

For trinomials of the form, $1 + c_s\alpha^s + c_t\alpha^t$ with $c_s, c_t \in GF(q)$, we could not use the same technique as proving that $\alpha^s \pm \alpha^t$ is of low order. In fact we found that, for all $n \le 550$, $1 \pm \alpha \pm \alpha^s$ in $GF(q^n)$ ($q = 2, 3$) with α a type $(n, 1)$ Gauss period, is always a primitive element for some s. Now let us explain, with redundant basis technique, how one can realize an efficient exponentiation using a primitive element of the form $1 + c_s\alpha^s + c_t\alpha^t$ in $GF(q^n)$, where α is a primitive mth root of unity in $GF(q^n)$ with $\mathrm{ord}_m q = n$.

Table 3. Exponentiation using $\gamma = 1 + c_s\alpha^s + c_t\alpha^t$ with redundant basis technique

---

Input: $r = \sum_{j=0}^{n-1} r_j q^j$
Output: $A = \gamma^r$ with respect to the polynomial basis $\{1, \alpha, \alpha^2, \cdots, \alpha^{n-1}\}$
$A \leftarrow 1$ with respect to the redundant basis $\{1, \alpha, \alpha^2, \cdots, \alpha^{m-1}\}$
for $(i = n - 1$ to 0 ; $i - -)$
    $A \leftarrow A^q \gamma^{r_i}$
end for
Express A with respect to the polynomial basis $\{1, \alpha, \alpha^2, \cdots, \alpha^{n-1}\}$

The complexity of above algorithm depends on two different steps, one is the complexity of the for-loop and the other is the complexity of the basis reduction step. Let us consider the complexity of the first step.

Lemma 2. *The operation $A \leftarrow A^q$ is (almost) free in our redundant basis $\{1, \alpha, \alpha^2, \cdots, \alpha^{m-1}\}$.*

Proof. Enough to show that the Frobenius map $\alpha^i \to \alpha^{iq}$ results in the permutation of basis elements, $\{1, \alpha^q, \alpha^{2q}, \cdots, \alpha^{(m-1)q}\} = \{1, \alpha, \alpha^2, \cdots, \alpha^{m-1}\}$. Since q is relative prime to m, it clear that $\{0, 1, 2, \cdots, m-1\}$ and $\{0, 1q, 2q, \cdots, (m-1)q\}$ are the same residue system (mod m). □

Now letting $A = \sum_{i=0}^{m-1} a_i \alpha^i$, we get

$$A\gamma = A + c_s A\alpha^s + c_t A\alpha^t = \sum_{i=0}^{m-1} a_i \alpha^i + c_s \sum_{i=0}^{m-1} a_{i-s}\alpha^i + c_t \sum_{i=0}^{m-1} a_{i-t}\alpha^i$$

$$= \sum_{i=0}^{m-1} (a_i + c_s a_{i-s} + c_t a_{i-t})\alpha^i, \tag{9}$$

where the coefficients a_i, a_j are understood as $a_i = a_j$ if $i \equiv j$ (mod m) since $\alpha^m = 1$. Assuming $q = 2$ or 3, the computation $A \leftarrow A\gamma$ needs 2 additions for each coefficient of α^i ($0 \le i \le m-1$) and the total number of $GF(q)$-additions needed to compute $A \leftarrow A^q \gamma^{r_i}$ is at most $2mr_i$. Consequently the total number of additions in $GF(q)$ at the end of the for-loop is at most $2m \sum_{i=0}^{n-1} r_i \le 2(q-1)mn$.

The complexity of the basis reduction step can be calculated as follows. Let $A = \sum_{i=0}^{m-1} a_i \alpha^i$ be the result of γ^r when the for-loop is finished. Let $u = \lfloor m/n \rfloor$ and write A as

$$A = \sum_{i=0}^{n-1} a_i \alpha^i + \alpha^n \sum_{i=0}^{n-1} a_{n+i}\alpha^i + \alpha^{2n} \sum_{i=0}^{n-1} a_{2n+i}\alpha^i + \cdots + \alpha^{un} \sum_{i=0}^{n-1} a_{un+i}\alpha^i. \tag{10}$$

Now $\alpha^n \sum_{i=0}^{n-1} a_{n+i}\alpha^i$ is computed by repeated multiplication and reduction and this can be done with at most n^2 additions in $GF(q)$. (This depends on the hamming weight of the irreducible polynomial of α over $GF(q)$.) Notice that no multiplication in $GF(q)$ is involved in these operations when $q = 2, 3$. In a similar way, $\alpha^{2n} \sum_{i=0}^{n-1} a_{2n+i}\alpha^i$ is computed by at most $2n^2$ additions in $GF(q)$, and $\alpha^{un} \sum_{i=0}^{n-1} a_{un+i}\alpha^i$ is computed by at most un^2 additions in $GF(q)$. Therefore, the total number of additions needed to complete the reduction step is at most $\frac{u(u+1)}{2}n^2 + un$.

Since we needed at most $2(q-1)mn \le 2(q-1)(u+1)n^2$ additions in the first step, the total number of additions to complete the algorithm in Table 3 is bounded by $\frac{u(u+1)}{2}n^2 + un + 2(q-1)(u+1)n^2$ which is of $O(\frac{(u+1)(u+4q-4)}{2}n^2)$. Recall that the total number of additions to complete the algorithm of Gao et al. in Table 1 is at most $(k-1)(q-1)n(n+1)$ which is of $O((k-1)(q-1)n^2)$. Thus for small values of $u = 0, 1, 2$, our algorithm has a comparable or lower complexity than the Gauss periods method. For example, when $u = 0$, our algorithm has a comparable or lower complexity than the method of Gauss periods of type (n, k) if $k \ge 3$. This is the case of type $(n, 1)$ Gauss periods with AOP basis which was already explained in section 3.1. When $u = 1$, our method has a lower complexity if $k \geq 6$. When $u = 2$ and $q = 2$, our algorithm has a comparable or lower computational cost if $k \geq 10$. When $u = 2$ and $q = 3$, our algorithm is better if $k \geq 9$. One of the novel features of our method is that we always use a primitive element for our exponentiation algorithm, whereas the Gauss periods may not be primitive in some situations. Of course, our method uses more memory than the Gauss periods method. However, both our method and the method of Gao et al. require negligible amount of memory compared with precomputation methods in [1,6,7].

4   Computational Results and Comparisons

For a binary field $GF(2^n)$, we tried all $100 \leq n \leq 550$ to find the least m satisfying $ord_m 2 = n$. We collected, in Table 4, all such n and m if $m < 3n$, i.e. if $u = \lfloor m/n \rfloor \leq 2$. For $GF(3^n)$, we collected all $n \leq 550$, in Table 5, for which the Gauss period of type $(n, 1)$ exists.

Table 4. Comparison of Gauss periods in Gao et al. [4] with our primitive elements in $GF(2^n)$ for $100 \leq n \leq 550$

	[4]	ours		[4]	ours		[4]	ours		[4]	ours
n	(k,e)	(m,s)	n	(k,e)	(m,s)	n	(k,e)	(m,s)	n	(k,e)	(m,s)
100	(7,3)	(101,7)	214	(3,3)	(643,3)	342	(6,7)	(361,4)	464	NE	(929,3)
102	(6,1)	(307,7)	220	(3,1)	(575,0)	346	(10,1)	(347,7)	466	(6,3)	(467,3)
106	(10,1)	(107,3)	224	NE	(449,5)	348	(5,1)	(349,6)	468	(21,1)	(1007,0)
110	(6,1)	(253,6)	226	(13,1)	(227,3)	350	(2,3)	(1051,4)	476	(5,3)	(1195,3)
116	(3,1)	(295,5)	230	(2,1)	(517,0)	356	(3,1)	(895,3)	478	(7,1)	(1437,0)
119	(2,1)	(239,0)	231	(2,1)	(463,0)	358	(10,3)	(1077,5)	483	(2,1)	(967,0)
130	(9,3)	(131,3)	238	(7,3)	(717,0)	359	(2,1)	(719,0)	486	(10,5103)	(729,3)
131	(2,1)	(263,0)	239	(2,1)	(479,0)	364	(3,1)	(1093,3)	488	NE	(977,3)
132	(5,23)	(299,4)	243	(2,1)	(487,0)	366	(22,9)	(1101,4)	490	(18,3)	(491,7)
135	(2,1)	(271,0)	244	(3,5)	(733,4)	371	(2,1)	(743,0)	491	(2,1)	(983,0)
136	NE	(289,3)	246	(11,1)	(581,0)	372	(3,3)	(373,6)	492	(13,5)	(1079,5)
138	(6,3)	(139,4)	251	(2,1)	(503,0)	375	(2,1)	(751,0)	495	(2,1)	(991,0)
140	(3,1)	(319,0)	252	(3,15)	(551,0)	378	(2,3)	(379,3)	498	(9,7)	(1503,0)
147	(6,1)	(343,0)	253	(10,1)	(529,0)	380	(5,3)	(761,3)	500	(11,3)	(625,7)
148	(15,3)	(149,5)	260	(5,1)	(521,7)	382	(6,1)	(1149,0)	502	(10,3)	(1509,0)
155	(2,1)	(311,0)	262	(3,1)	(789,0)	384	NE	(769,7)	504	NE	(1009,7)
156	(13,5)	(169,3)	268	(7,1)	(269,8)	388	(15,1)	(389,7)	508	(7,1)	(509,3)
162	(10,19)	(163,3)	270	(2,7)	(811,4)	390	(3,1)	(869,0)	510	(3,3)	(1133,0)
164	(5,1)	(415,0)	276	(3,3)	(611,4)	396	(11,135)	(851,3)	515	(2,1)	(1031,0)
166	(3,1)	(499,3)	284	(3,3)	(569,3)	404	(3,3)	(809,5)	516	(3,1)	(1211,6)
172	(9,1)	(173,3)	290	(5,3)	(649,4)	410	(2,11)	(913,4)	519	(2,1)	(1039,0)
174	(2,3)	(413,0)	292	(3,5)	(293,3)	411	(2,1)	(823,0)	522	(14,1)	(523,3)
178	(6,1)	(179,3)	299	(2,1)	(599,0)	414	(2,3)	(893,0)	524	(5,5)	(1315,4)
179	(2,1)	(359,0)	300	(19,17173)	(707,4)	418	(21,3)	(419,5)	526	(3,1)	(1579,3)
180	(3,1)	(181,5)	303	(2,1)	(607,0)	419	(2,1)	(839,0)	530	(2,1)	(1177,3)
183	(2,1)	(367,0)	308	(15,5)	(667,7)	420	(11,143)	(421,8)	531	(2,1)	(1063,0)
190	(10,93)	(573,0)	310	(6,3)	(933,0)	428	(5,15)	(857,4)	532	(3,3)	(1597,6)
191	(2,1)	(383,0)	316	(7,1)	(317,7)	431	(2,1)	(863,0)	534	(7,1)	(1253,0)
196	(7,15)	(197,9)	318	(11,1)	(749,0)	442	(21,3)	(443,3)	540	(3,1)	(541,7)
198	(22,67)	(437,0)	323	(2,1)	(647,0)	443	(2,1)	(887,0)	542	(3,3)	(1627,3)
200	NE	(401,3)	324	(5,1)	(815,3)	444	(5,1)	(1043,4)	543	(2,1)	(1087,0)
204	(3,1)	(409,6)	330	(2,1)	(737,4)	452	(11,1)	(1135,0)	546	(17,1)	(547,3)
210	(2,1)	(211,3)	332	(3,5)	(835,0)	460	(3,75)	(461,7)			
212	(5,15)	(535,0)	340	(3,1)	(1021,7)	462	(10,3)	(1389,6)			

Explanation of Table 4: For each n, in the entries of the column of (k, e), k means the least k for which the Gauss period of type (n, k) exists and e is the corresponding index $e = (2^n - 1)/(\text{order of the Gauss period})$. Also in entries of the column of (m, s), m denotes the least m for which $ord_m 2 = n$ and s implies the existence of a primitive element of the form $1 + \alpha + \alpha^s$, $s > 0$ ($1 + \alpha$ if $s = 0$), where α is a primitive mth root of unity over $GF(2)$. NE means that the corresponding Gauss period does not exist. When there is a primitive element of the form $1 + \alpha$ in $GF(2^n)$, the number of additions in $GF(2)$ is reduced to $O(\frac{(u+1)(u+2q-2)}{2}n^2)$ since, in the for-loop of Table 3, $A \leftarrow A^q \gamma$ needs just one addition for each coefficient of α^i. The bolded letters in the column of n in Table 4 means that our method has a comparable or lower computational complexity than the method of Gauss periods. For example, when $n = 500$, the Gauss period of type $(500, 11)$ exists in $GF(2^{500})$ and there is no Gauss period of type $(500, k)$ for $k < 11$. In this case, our method says that a primitive 625th root of unity α over $GF(2)$ generates $GF(2^{500})$ and the irreducible polynomial $f(x)$ of α over $GF(2)$ is $f(x) = x^{500} + x^{375} + x^{250} + x^{125} + 1$. We also find that $1 + \alpha + \alpha^7$ is a primitive element in $GF(2^{500})$. Therefore an efficient exponentiation is realized using $1 + \alpha + \alpha^7$ rather than using the Gauss period. Moreover the Gauss period is not a primitive element in this case. A more spectacular example is the Gauss period of type $(n, k) = (300, 17173)$ where the index is 17173, which is unsuitable for an element to be exponentiated. However, our method always gives a primitive element, which is either $1 + \alpha$ or $1 + \alpha + \alpha^s$. One thing to be noticed is that for a composite m, there may exist more than one irreducible polynomial of degree n whose zeros are primitive mth roots of unity. In that case, the corresponding primitive elements $1 + \alpha + \alpha^s$ may have different s. All these computations can be done by using MAPLE.

Table 5. List of $n \leq 550$ for which a type $(n, 1)$ Gauss period α exists and the corresponding primitive elements in $GF(3^n)$

n	primitive element	n	primitive element	n	primitive element	n	primitive element
4	$1 + \alpha - \alpha^2$	100	$1 + \alpha - \alpha^3$	210	$1 + \alpha - \alpha^4$	352	$1 + \alpha + \alpha^5$
6	$1 - \alpha - \alpha^2$	112	$1 - \alpha + \alpha^5$	222	$1 + \alpha + \alpha^3$	378	$1 - \alpha + \alpha^3$
16	$1 + \alpha - \alpha^3$	126	$1 + \alpha + \alpha^3$	232	$1 + \alpha + \alpha^3$	388	$1 - \alpha - \alpha^2$
18	$1 - \alpha + \alpha^3$	136	$1 - \alpha + \alpha^3$	256	$1 + \alpha - \alpha^3$	400	$1 + \alpha - \alpha^3$
28	$1 - \alpha - \alpha^2$	138	$1 + \alpha - \alpha^4$	268	$1 - \alpha - \alpha^2$	448	$1 - \alpha + \alpha^3$
30	$1 + \alpha + \alpha^3$	148	$1 - \alpha - \alpha^2$	280	$1 + \alpha - \alpha^3$	460	$1 - \alpha - \alpha^6$
42	$1 + \alpha - \alpha^3$	162	$1 + \alpha - \alpha^3$	282	$1 + \alpha - \alpha^3$	462	$1 + \alpha - \alpha^3$
52	$1 - \alpha - \alpha^2$	172	$1 - \alpha - \alpha^2$	292	$1 - \alpha - \alpha^2$	486	$1 - \alpha - \alpha^2$
78	$1 - \alpha - \alpha^2$	196	$1 - \alpha - \alpha^2$	316	$1 - \alpha + \alpha^3$	508	$1 - \alpha - \alpha^2$
88	$1 + \alpha + \alpha^3$	198	$1 + \alpha + \alpha^4$	330	$1 + \alpha + \alpha^4$	520	$1 + \alpha + \alpha^4$

In [10], Feisel et al. significantly improved the lower bound of k for the Gauss periods in $GF(q^n)$ using the notion of square-free Gauss periods and general Gauss periods. Since the primitivity of those elements are not discussed in [10], we omit the comparison with our results in Table 4,5. Moreover in the case of general Gauss periods (not the square-free Gauss periods), the complexity of exponentiation should be explained in detail. A table of general Gauss periods in $GF(3^n)$ is given in [10]. In the table, 128 values of $n \leq 400$ are given for which a general Gauss period of type (n, k) exists with an improved lower bound of k. It should be mentioned that not a single n in our list of Table 5 is contained in the table of [10]. Thus our result can be used for efficient exponentiation in new finite field $GF(3^n)$, where the Gauss period of type (n, k), $k \geq 2$, does not exist or may not be used properly because of large k or large index.

5   Conclusions

We proposed an efficient exponentiation algorithm in $GF(q^n)$ using the idea of primitive roots, Gauss periods of type $(n, 1)$, sparse polynomials, and redundant basis technique. We generated primitive elements which are trinomials or binomials of primitive roots over $GF(q)$ and showed these elements yield a low complexity exponentiation algorithm. A computational result implies that our method significantly improves the method using Gauss periods of type (n, k), $k \geq 2$, for a finite field $GF(q^n)$ with small characteristic.

Acknowledgements. This work was supported by grant No. R05-2003-000-11325-0 from the Basic Research Program of the Korea Science & Engineering Foundation.

References

1. E.F. Brickell, D.M. Gordon, K.S. McCurley, and D.B. Wilson, "Fast exponentiation with precomputation," *Eurocrypt 92, LNCS*, vol. 658, pp. 200–207, 1992.
2. G. Tenenbaum, "*Introduction to analytic and probabilistic number theory*," Cambridge Univ. Press, 1995.
3. S. Gao, J. von zur Gathen, and D. Panario, "Gauss periods and fast exponentiation in finite fields," *Latin 95, LNCS*, vol. 911, pp. 311–322, 1995.
4. S. Gao, J. von zur Gathen, and D. Panario, "Orders and cryptographical applications," *Math. Comp.*, vol. 67, pp. 343–352, 1998.
5. S. Gao and S. Vanstone, "On orders of optimal normal basis generators," *Math. Comp.*, vol. 64, pp. 1227–1233, 1995.
6. C.H. Lim and P.J. Lee, "More flexible exponentiation with precomputation," *Crypto 94, LNCS*, vol. 839, pp. 95–107, 1994.
7. P. de Rooij, "Efficient exponentiation using precomputation and vector addition chains," *Eurocrypt 94, LNCS*, vol. 950, pp. 389–399, 1994.
8. S. Kwon, C.H. Kim, and C.P. Hong, "Efficient exponentiation for a class of finite fields $GF(2^n)$ determined by Gauss periods" *CHES 03, LNCS*, To appear, 2003.
9. A.J. Menezes, I.F. Blake, S. Gao, R.C. Mullin, S.A. Vanstone, and T. Yaghoobian, *Applications of finite fields*, Kluwer Academic Publisher, 1993.
10. S. Feisel, J. von zur Gathen, M. Shokrollahi, "Normal bases via general Gauss periods," *Math. Comp.*, vol. 68, pp. 271–290, 1999.
11. J. von zur Gathen and I. Shparlinski, "Constructing elements of large order in finite fields," *AAECC 99, LNCS*, vol. 1719, pp. 404–409, 1997.
12. J. von zur Gathen and M.J. Nöcker, "Exponentiation in finite fields: Theory and Practice," *AAECC 97, LNCS*, vol. 1255, pp. 88–133, 1997.
13. J. von zur Gathen and I. Shparlinski, "Orders of Gauss periods in finite fields," *ISAAC 95, LNCS*, vol. 1004, pp. 208–215, 1995.

Author Index